D1052717

Geigy
Scientific
Tables

Geigy Scientific Tables

Volume 1

Units of Measurement, Body Fluids,
Composition of the Body, Nutrition

Edited by C. Lentner

Eighth, revised and enlarged edition
Published by CIBA-GEIGY

ISBN 0-914168-50-9
Library of Congress Catalogue No. 81 - 70045

Editor: Cornelius Lentner
Associate editors: Charlotte Lentner and
Anthony Wink
International Medical and Pharmaceutical
Information, Ciba-Geigy Limited, Basle

American edition published by Medical
Education Division, Ciba-Geigy Corporation,
West Caldwell, New Jersey 07006

International edition published by
Ciba-Geigy Limited, Basle, Switzerland

By way of explanation

This completely revised and expanded 8th edition of the *Geigy Scientific Tables* represents the continuation of a work that has stood the test of time. Its aim is to provide scientists and, in particular, doctors with a concise compendium of scientific data backed by literature references and thus to spare them much laborious searching.

The vast increase in the amount of subject matter to be included has meant that the *Geigy Scientific Tables* have had to be steadily extended, with the result that they are becoming too voluminous to be published in a single book. Dividing the book up into several separate volumes has made it possible to incorporate a number of additional chapters and has also helped to ensure that the data on the various branches of knowledge are more up-to-date than they could have been in a single-volume work. The other volumes are in preparation.

CIBA-GEIGY Limited, Basle

Foreword

An improvement in the 8th edition of the *Geigy Scientific Tables,* as compared with the 7th edition, consists in the unreserved use made of the International System of Units. The 'Système International d'Unités' (SI) is a version of the metric system extended to seven officially defined base units: meter, kilogram, second, ampere, kelvin, mole, and candela. The International Union of Pure and Applied Chemistry (IUPAC) and the International Federation of Clinical Chemistry (IFCC) recommend that concentrations of substances whose chemical structure is sufficiently accurately known should be given using the unit mole, i.e. in terms of amount of substance concentration, substance (mole) ratio and molality[1]; it should, however, be noted that the use of the unit kilogram is fully compatible with the International System of Units[2].

In the chapter 'Units of Measurement' due account has been taken of the resolutions passed by the General Conferences on Weights and Measures up to and including the 16th Conference (1979). The values given for physical constants reflect the recommendations of the Committee on Data for Science and Technology (1973).

The chapters on the composition of body fluids contain data from the literature published up to 1980. The composition of blood, as well as hematological data, will be described in one of the subsequent volumes of the *Geigy Scientific Tables.* In this volume, for the first time, data on the composition of aqueous humor, tears and amniotic fluid are incorporated. Concerning the excretion of hormones in the urine, the reader is referred to the chapter 'Endocrinology' to be included in a subsequent volume of the *Geigy Scientific Tables.* In all these chapters, both amount of substance concentration and mass concentration have been indicated wherever space permitted. In addition, the data expressed in SI units figure side by side with data expressed in conventional units of measurement. In the guidelines on food intake, due regard has been paid first and foremost to the recommendations of the FAO/WHO and of the Food and Nutrition Board, USA, and these guidelines have been supplemented by recent views on trace element requirements. The tables dealing with the composition of foodstuffs have been carefully revised and expanded by including data on zinc content, iodine content, and the content of individual fatty acids and carbohydrates.

We are sure that our readers will join us in expressing gratitude to all those who have offered us their help and advice in compiling this volume of the *Geigy Scientific Tables.* A special vote of thanks must go to the late Prof. U. STILLE (Braunschweig), to whose tremendous efforts we owe the chapter 'Units of Measurement', as well as to Dr. D.T. GOLDMAN of the National Bureau of Standards in Washington, USA, who supervised the English version of this chapter. We are also indebted to all those readers who have sent us proposals for improvements or have drawn our attention to printing errors. We shall continue in the future to take account, wherever possible, of any suggestions our readers care to send us.

Basle, October 1981   *The Editors*

[1] Quantities and Units in Clinical Chemistry, Recommendation 1973, *Pure appl. Chem.,* **37**, 519 (1974). DYBKAER, R., Approved Recommendation (1978): Quantities and Units in Clinical Chemistry, *Clin. chim. Acta,* **96**, 157 (1979).
[2] LOWE, D.A., *A Guide to the International Recommendations on Names and Symbols for Quantities and on Units of Measurement,* WHO, Geneva, 1975.

Acknowledgments

The publishers and editors are indebted to the following for their contributions and assistance in compiling this volume of the Geigy Scientific Tables:

Prof. G. BECKER
Physikalisch-Technische Bundesanstalt
D–3300 Braunschweig, Federal Republic of Germany
Prof. P. DÄMMIG
Physikalisch-Technische Bundesanstalt
D–3300 Braunschweig, Federal Republic of Germany
Prof. J. W. T. DICKERSON
Department of Human Nutrition
University of Surrey
Guildford, Surrey GU1 1AA, UK
Dr. D. T. GOLDMAN
United States Department of Commerce
National Bureau of Standards
Washington, D.C. 20234, USA
Prof. H. GREILING
Klinisch-Chemisches Zentrallaboratorium
Rheinisch-Westfälische Technische Hochschule
D–5100 Aachen, Federal Republic of Germany
J. HOPPE-BLANK
Physikalisch-Technische Bundesanstalt
D–3300 Braunschweig, Federal Republic of Germany
Prof. F. E. HYTTEN
Clinical Research Centre
Division of Perinatal Medicine
Harrow, Middlesex HA1 3UJ, UK
Prof. H.-H. KIRCHNER
Physikalisch-Technische Bundesanstalt
D–3300 Braunschweig, Federal Republic of Germany
Dr. T. LIND
MRC Human Reproduction Group
Princess Mary Maternity Hospital
Newcastle upon Tyne, NE2 3BD, UK
Prof. D. P. MERTZ
Kurklinik am Park
D–4934 Horn-Bad Meinberg, Federal Republic of Germany
Prof. H. REICH
Physikalisch-Technische Bundesanstalt
D–3300 Braunschweig, Federal Republic of Germany
Dr. H. P. RIEDER
Liquor- und Eiweisslabor des Kantonsspitals
CH–4031 Basle, Switzerland
Prof. U. STILLE
Physikalisch-Technische Bundesanstalt
D–3300 Braunschweig, Federal Republic of Germany
Prof. H.-M. WEISS
Physikalisch-Technische Bundesanstalt
D–3300 Braunschweig, Federal Republic of Germany
Prof. ELSIE M. WIDDOWSON
University of Cambridge Clinical School
Department of Medicine
Cambridge CB2 2QQ, UK

The publishers and editors wish to thank the following scientific bodies, journals and publishing houses for permission to reproduce data or illustrations:

Acta Paediatrica Scandinavica, Stockholm (pages 122, 230)
Acta Physiologica Scandinavica, Stockholm (page 126)
American Fertility and Sterility, Rochester, Minn. (pages 185, 194)
American Institute of Nutrition, Bethesda, Md. (page 71)
American Journal of Medicine, New York (pages 97, 123)
American Medical Association, Chicago, Ill. (pages 63, 127)
Archives of Oral Biology, Pergamon Press, Oxford (pages 114, 115, 117)
J. F. Bergmann-Verlag, Munich (pages 55, 102, 119)
British Journal of Hospital Medicine, London (page 197)
British Journal of Obstetrics and Gynaecology, London (pages 197, 198)
British Medical Association, London (pages 64, 147, 148, 206)
Clinica Chimica Acta, Amsterdam (pages 99, 100, 208)
Clinical Chemistry, Winston-Salem, N. C. (page 57)
W. J. Dornan Inc., Collingdale, Pa. (page 104)
European Journal of Clinical Investigation, Edinburgh (pages 109, 110)
Harvard University Press, Cambridge, Mass. (page 104)
Heinemann Limited, London (page 228)
The Journal of Clinical Investigation, St. Louis, Miss. (pages 57, 58, 145)
S. Karger AG, Publishers, Basle (pages 115, 117, 118)
The Lancet, London (pages 65, 104, 131, 148, 202)
J. B. Lippincott Company, Philadelphia, Pa. (pages 59, 211)
Mayo Clinic Proceedings, Rochester, Minn. (page 161)
Methuen Co. Limited, London (page 195)
The C. V. Mosby Company, St. Louis, Miss. (pages 77, 202, 207, 210)
Nature, London (page 127)
Pediatric Research, Washington, D. C. (page 218)
Plenum Publishing Corporation, New York (page 136)
Quarterly Journal of Medicine, London (page 64)
W. B. Saunders Company, Philadelphia, Pa. (page 150)
Schwabe & Co., Publishers, Basle (pages 110, 171)
Society for Experimental Biology and Medicine, New York (page 79)
Springer-Verlag, Berlin, Heidelberg, New York (pages 103, 104, 109, 110, 150, 187)
Georg Thieme Verlag, Stuttgart (pages 83, 106)
Wiener medizinische Akademie, Publishers, Vienna (page 110)
Williams & Wilkins Co., Baltimore, Md. (pages 96, 113, 126, 136, 139)
Year Book Medical Publishers, Chicago, Ill. (page 144)

Contents

Notes for the guidance of users

As a rule, all symbols, abbreviations, etc. used are defined or explained at the place where they occur. Zero values are indicated throughout by the figure 0.

In numerical expressions a point over the last figure or figures indicates a recurring figure, e. g.:

$1.\dot{6} = 1.666\,666...$

$1.652\dot{7}\dot{8} = 1.652\,78\,278\,278...$

Where necessary, exact values have been distinguished from rounded-off values by printing the last figure in bold-face type. Thus, 1.125 7 is the rounded-off value of, say, 1.125 7(35 486...), whereas 1.125 **7** is an exact number. This notation is also used for the arbitrarily defined values of constants.

In the sections dealing with body fluids a 95% range for the values given is included only in cases where it has been ascertained by means of distribution-free procedures or where it has been calculated as a mean value $\pm 2s$ on the basis of a sufficiently large sample and in the presence of a normal distribution.

The biochemical nomenclature employed conforms largely to the recommendations of the International Union for Pure and Applied Chemistry (IUPAC) and of the International Union of Biochemistry (IUB)[1]; the enzyme nomenclature is based on the recommendations of the Enzyme Commission (EC) of the IUB[2].

The abbreviations used in the literature references are those recommended by UNESCO (*World Medical Periodicals*, 1961 and 1968)[3].

Statistical symbols

N	Size of sample	s_r	Relative standard deviation
$\bar{x}$	Mean value	V	Coefficient of variability
s	Standard deviation	r	Correlation coefficient
$s_{\bar{x}}$	Standard deviation of the mean		

Greek alphabet

Greek character				Greek name	Roman equivalent	
Upright		Italics				
A	α	*A*	*α*	alpha	A	a
B	β	*B*	*β*	beta	B	b
Γ	γ	*Γ*	*γ*	gamma	G	g
Δ	δ	*Δ*	*δ*	delta	D	d
E	ε,ϵ	*E*	*ε,ϵ*	epsilon	Ĕ	ĕ
Z	ζ	*Z*	*ζ*	zeta	Z	z
H	η	*H*	*η*	eta	Ē	ē
Θ	ϑ,θ	*Θ*	*ϑ,θ*	theta	Th	th
I	ι	*I*	*ι*	iota	I	i
K	ϰ,κ	*K*	*ϰ,κ*	kappa	K	k
Λ	λ	*Λ*	*λ*	lambda	L	l
M	μ	*M*	*μ*	mu	M	m
N	ν	*N*	*ν*	nu	N	n
Ξ	ξ	*Ξ*	*ξ*	xi	X	x
O	o	*O*	*o*	omicron	Ŏ	ŏ
Π	π,ϖ	*Π*	*π,ϖ*	pi	P	p
P	ϱ	*P*	*ϱ*	rho	R	r
Σ	σ,ς	*Σ*	*σ,ς*	sigma	S	s
T	τ	*T*	*τ*	tau	T	t
Υ	υ	*Υ*	*υ*	upsilon	Y	y
Φ	φ,ϕ	*Φ*	*φ,ϕ*	phi	Ph	ph
X	χ	*X*	*χ*	chi	Ch	ch
Ψ	ψ	*Ψ*	*ψ*	psi	Ps	ps
Ω	ω	*Ω*	*ω*	omega	Ō	ō

References

[1] *Collected Tentative Rules and Recommendations of the Commission on Biochemical Nomenclature IUPAC-IUB and Related Documents*, 2nd ed., American Society of Biological Chemists, Bethesda (Md.), 1975.

[2] *Enzyme Nomenclature*, Recommendations (1972) of the International Union of Pure and Applied Chemistry and the International Union of Biochemistry, Elsevier, Amsterdam, 1978.

[3] CLEGG, H. A. (Ed.), *World Medical Periodicals*, 3rd ed., World Medical Association, New York, 1961, and WARE, M. (Ed.), supplement to the 3rd edition, New York, 1968.

In this chapter, the units of measurement are dealt with under the headings of the quantities they express. In each case, the first unit given is the *coherent unit of the International System of Units* (SI) *of the Metric Convention*. This is followed by the corresponding coherent units of the Anglo-Saxon foot-pound-second system (*ft-lb-s system*), then by other units not coherent with these two systems but used either in conjunction with the coherent units or in association with them in particular fields of science and technology. The information is supplemented by the *multiples and submultiples* of the units in common usage.

The International System of Units (SI)

The International System of Units is the modern version of the metric system extended to seven base units. The 9th General Conference on Weights and Measures (1948)[1] decided to establish a 'practical system of units' for unifying techniques of measurement used in industry and commerce as well as in research and education, and capable of being adopted by all states signatory to the Metric Convention of May 20, 1875[2].

Base SI units

The 10th General Conference on Weights and Measures (1954, Resolution 6)[3] and the 14th General Conference on Weights and Measures (1971, Resolution 3)[4] agreed on seven base units for seven basic quantities as the foundation of this system of units. The seven base units, listed below, are regarded as independent of one another in respect of dimension.

For length	meter (m)
For mass....................................	kilogram (kg)
For time	second (s)
For electric current intensity	ampere (A)
For thermodynamic temperature.............	kelvin (K)
For amount of substance	mole (mol)
For luminous intensity	candela (cd)

The definitions of the base SI units agreed upon by the General Conferences on Weights and Measures are given in the text on pages 9–28 under the corresponding basic quantities.

Derived SI units

The 11th General Conference on Weights and Measures (1960, Resolution 12)[5], after agreeing on the name *International System of Units* (*Système International d'Unités*) with the international symbol SI, listed examples of coherent derived SI units formed by combination of powers of base SI units using selected algebraic relationships linking the corresponding quantities. There are special names for some of the derived SI units that in turn may be used for forming further derived SI units in accordance with the same rules. Later General Conferences supplemented the list of derived SI units with other examples.

Derived SI units can thus often be expressed in several different ways – for example, the SI unit of energy as the meter squared kilogram per second squared ($m^2 kg s^{-2}$) or as the Joule (J), the Newton meter (N m) or the volt ampere second (V A s). In principle, all names are equivalent and denote one and the same unit, and the user is free to choose any of the names for a particular purpose.

Supplementary units

The General Conference on Weights and Measures came to no decision as to whether the SI unit of the plane angle, the radian (rad), and the SI unit of the solid angle, the steradian (sr), should be regarded as base or derived units. For this reason, both units were designated as *supplementary units*[5] of the International System of Units. The user is thus free to decide whether and in what circumstances he should regard them as base or derived units. In this chapter they will be looked upon as derived units for the reason that the corresponding quantities (plane angle, solid angle) are also defined as derived quantities of dimension 1.

Coherent systems of units

The base SI units, the derived SI units, and the supplementary units together form a coherent *system of units* in which the derived units obtained from the base units are expressed in algebraic form by making use of the signs for multiplication and division and of powers.

The International Bureau of Weights and Measures has published a comprehensive document[6] that describes the origins of the International System of Units, based on decisions of the General Conference on Weights and Measures and the International Committee for Weights and Measures, the practical application of the System, and the methods by which the most important units are realized at the principal national metrological institutes.

Decimal multiples and submultiples of SI units

For the purpose of creating a limited series of decimal multiples and submultiples of SI units, several General Conferences on Weights and Measures, the 11th (1960, Resolution 12)[5], the 12th (1964, Resolution 8)[7], and the 15th (1975, Resolution 10)[8], adopted the following SI prefixes and symbols:

exa (E).............	for 10^{18}	deci (d)...........	for 10^{-1}
peta (P)	for 10^{15}	centi (c)	for 10^{-2}
tera (T)	for 10^{12}	milli (m)	for 10^{-3}
giga (G)............	for 10^{9}	micro (μ)	for 10^{-6}
mega (M)	for 10^{6}	nano (n)..........	for 10^{-9}
kilo (k).............	for 10^{3}	pico (p)	for 10^{-12}
hecto (h)	for 10^{2}	femto (f)	for 10^{-15}
deca (da)..........	for 10^{1}	atto (a)...........	for 10^{-18}

When it is necessary to distinguish between the coherent totality of the SI units and the decimal multiples and submultiples bearing the SI prefixes, the latter units are referred to simply as decimal multiples and submultiples of SI units[6].

The SI prefixes can of course also be used for forming the corresponding decimal multiples and submultiples of units not belonging to the coherent system of SI units.

The ft-lb-s system

Of the Anglo-Saxon systems of coherent units used in mechanics, the commonest is that founded on the base units *foot* (ft) for length, *pound* (lb) for mass, and *second* (s) for time. The foot is one-third of the unit yard (yd). A coherent derived unit in this system with a special designation is the poundal (pdl), the unit of force.

Other units

These include all the units described in the chapter 'Units of Measurement' on pages 9–28 and not belonging either to the International System of Units or to the ft-lb-s system.

The mechanical units of the earlier centimeter-gram-second (CGS) system are now without exception decimal multiples or submultiples of SI units bearing SI prefixes. If they have special names, these are given under the heading 'Other units'. Examples are the unit of force dyne (dyn), the unit of energy erg (erg), the unit of dynamic viscosity poise (P), and the unit of kinematic viscosity stokes (St).

For the 'electrostatic' and 'electromagnetic' CGS units (those with their own names are: Gilbert, Oersted, Maxwell, Gauss) see pages 27 and 28.

Insofar as Anglo-Saxon units not belonging to the ft-lb-s system are included, these are also given under the heading 'Other units'.

For the luminance units stilb, apostilb, lambert and foot lambert, as well as the illuminance units phot and foot candle, see footnotes ◊ and §, page 39.

References

[1] Conférence Générale des Poids et Mesures, *Comptes rendus des séances de la 9ᵉ Conférence Générale des Poids et Mesures, Paris 1948*, Gauthier-Villars, Paris, 1949, page 64.

[2] *Convention du mètre signée à Paris le 20 mai 1875 et de son règlement annexé, portant modification de la Convention Internationale signée à Sèvres le 6 octobre 1921*, Gauthier-Villars, Paris, 1950.

[3] Conférence Générale des Poids et Mesures, *Comptes rendus des séances de la 10ᵉ Conférence Générale des Poids et Mesures, Paris 1954*, Gauthier-Villars, Paris, 1955, page 80.

[4] Conférence Générale des Poids et Mesures, *Comptes rendus des séances de la 14ᵉ Conférence Générale des Poids et Mesures, Paris 1971*, Bureau International des Poids et Mesures, Sèvres, 1972, pages 59 and 78.

---

*The chapters 'Units of Measurement' and 'Physical Constants' (pages 9–51) have been compiled in collaboration with G. Becker, P. Dämmig, J. Hoppe-Blank, H.-H. Kirchner, H. Reich, the late U. Stille, and H.-M. Weiss, Braunschweig.

[5] Conférence Générale des Poids et Mesures, *Comptes rendus des séances de la 11ᵉ Conférence Générale des Poids et Mesures, Paris 1960,* Gauthier-Villars, Paris, 1961, pages 68 and 87.
[6] Bureau International des Poids et Mesures, *Le Système International d'Unités (SI),* 3rd ed., Bureau International des Poids et Mesures, Sèvres, 1977.
[7] Conférence Générale des Poids et Mesures, *Comptes rendus des séances de la 12ᵉ Conférence Générale des Poids et Mesures, Paris 1964,* Gauthier-Villars, Paris, 1964, pages 74 and 94.
[8] Conférence Générale des Poids et Mesures, *Comptes rendus des séances de la 15ᵉ Conférence Générale des Poids et Mesures, Paris 1975,* Bureau International des Poids et Mesures, Sèvres, 1976, page 106. For a general review see: KLEIN, H. A., *The World of Measurements,* Simon & Schuster, New York, 1974; PAGE and VIGOUREUX (Eds.), *The International Bureau of Weights and Measures,* National Bureau of Standards, Special Publication 420, Washington, 1975; National Bureau of Standards, *Units and Systems of Weight and Measures: Their Origin, Development, and Present Status,* LC 1035, Washington, 1976; JUDSON, L. V., *Weights and Measures Standards of the United States: a Brief History,* National Bureau of Standards, Special Publication 447 [updated], Washington, 1976.

Length (l)

Dimension: L

Base SI unit: meter (m)

Unit in the ft-lb-s system: foot (ft) $= 0.3048$ m

Base SI unit of length

The base SI unit of length is the *meter* (m) (see page 9). This was newly defined in 1960[1] as a multiple of the vacuum wavelength $\lambda(^{86}\mathrm{Kr})$ of the orange-red spectral line of the atom of krypton-86 as follows: The meter is the length equal to 1650763.73 wavelengths in vacuum of the radiation corresponding to the transition between the levels $2p_{10}$ and $5d_5$ of the krypton-86 atom. The meter is therefore based on a natural quantity, namely the energy difference between two electron levels of an unperturbed atom. For the history of the meter as a unit see reference[2]. The defined relationship is:

$$1 \text{ meter} = 1.65076373 \times 10^6 \; \lambda(^{86}\mathrm{Kr})$$
$$\lambda(^{86}\mathrm{Kr}) = 6.05780211 \times 10^{-7} \text{ meters}$$

Secondary standards[3]

Vacuum wavelengths of the krypton nuclide ^{86}Kr
$2p_9\text{--}5d_4'$: 6.4580720×10^{-7} m
$2p_8\text{--}5d_4'$: 6.4228006×10^{-7} m
$1s_3\text{--}3p_{10}$: 5.6511286×10^{-7} m
$1s_4\text{--}3p_8$: 4.5036162×10^{-7} m

Vacuum wavelengths of the mercury nuclide ^{198}Hg
$6^1P_1\text{--}6^1D_2$: 5.7922683×10^{-7} m
$6^1P_1\text{--}6^3D_2$: 5.7711983×10^{-7} m
$6^3P_2\text{--}7^3S_1$: 5.4622705×10^{-7} m
$6^3P_1\text{--}7^3S_1$: 4.3595624×10^{-7} m

Vacuum wavelengths of the cadmium nuclide ^{114}Cd
$5^1P_1\text{--}6^1D_2$: 6.4402480×10^{-7} m
$5^3P_2\text{--}6^3S_1$: 5.0872379×10^{-7} m
$5^3P_1\text{--}6^3S_1$: 4.8012521×10^{-7} m
$5^3P_0\text{--}6^3S_1$: 4.6794581×10^{-7} m

Vacuum wavelengths of absorption-stabilized lasers[4]
CH_4, P(7), band ν_3:
$\quad \lambda = 3392231.40 \times 10^{-12}$ m
$^{127}I_2$, R(127), band 11-5, component i:
$\quad \lambda = 632991.399 \times 10^{-12}$ m

Or another component of $^{127}I_2$ or $^{129}I_2$, for example $^{129}I_2$, R(127), band 11-5, component B:
$\quad \lambda = 632990.078 \times 10^{-12}$ m

The relative uncertainty of the above three wavelength values due to the uncertainty inherent in the definition of the unit meter is estimated by the Comité Consultatif pour la Définition de Mètre (CCDM) at $\pm 4 \times 10^{-9}$*.

---

*The frequency of CH_4, P(7), band ν_3 laser radiation has been determined as $\nu = 88376181627$ kHz, with a relative uncertainty of $\pm 6 \times 10^{-10}$. From the λ and ν of this laser radiation, the CCDM derives the velocity of light in vacuo $c = 299792458$ m s^{-1}, with a relative uncertainty of $\pm 4 \times 10^{-9}$.

Conversion of decimal multiples and submultiples of the meter

			nm	µm	mm	cm	dm	m	km
nanometer* ...	1 nm	=	1	10^{-3}	10^{-6}	10^{-7}	10^{-8}	10^{-9}	10^{-12}
micrometer* ..	1 µm	=	10^3	1	10^{-3}	10^{-4}	10^{-5}	10^{-6}	10^{-9}
millimeter	1 mm	=	10^6	10^3	1	10^{-1}	10^{-2}	10^{-3}	10^{-6}
centimeter	1 cm	=	10^7	10^4	10	1	10^{-1}	10^{-2}	10^{-5}
decimeter.....	1 dm	=	10^8	10^5	10^2	10	1	10^{-1}	10^{-4}
meter	1 m	=	10^9	10^6	10^3	10^2	10	1	10^{-3}
decameter	1 dam	=	10^{10}	10^7	10^4	10^3	10^2	10	10^{-2}
hectometer ...	1 hm	=	10^{11}	10^8	10^5	10^4	10^3	10^2	10^{-1}
kilometer.....	1 km	=	10^{12}	10^9	10^6	10^5	10^4	10^3	1

*The names millimicron (mµ) for nanometer (nm) and micron (µ) for micrometer (µm) should no longer be used (Resolution 7 of the 13th General Conference on Weights and Measures, 1967).

Anglo-Saxon units of length

The primary standard of length in the Anglo-Saxon systems of units is the *yard* (yd), although the unit *foot* (1 ft $= 1/3$ yd) is used as coherent unit of length in the ft-lb-s system. Since 1959 the yard has been defined in terms of the meter by relation[5]

$$1 \text{ yard} = 0.9144 \text{ m} = 1.5094583_5 \times 10^6 \; \lambda(^{86}\mathrm{Kr})$$

This newly defined 'unified' yard lies between the former imperial yard of the United Kingdom[6] and the former US yard[7]:

$$1 \text{ imperial yard} = 0.91439841 \text{ m} < 1 \text{ unified yard} < 1 \text{ US yard}$$
$$= (36/39.37) \text{ m} = 0.91440183 \text{ m}$$

An exception is the US Survey foot used by the US Coast and Geodetic Survey and defined as

$$1 \text{ US Survey foot} = \frac{1200}{3937} \text{ m} \; (= 3.04800609 \times 10^{-1} \text{ m}).$$

Conversion of Anglo-Saxon units of length

			yd	ft	m
mil	1 mil	=	1/36000	1/12000	2.54×10^{-5}
point (printer's) (US)* .	1 point	=	–	–	3.515×10^{-4}
line (button) (US).....	1 line	=	1/1440	1/480	6.35×10^{-4}
inch	1 in	=	1/36	1/12	2.54×10^{-2}
hand...............	1 hand	=	1/9	1/3	1.016×10^{-1}
link................	1 li◊	=	22/100	66/100	2.01168×10^{-1}
span (US)	1 span	=	1/4	3/4	2.286×10^{-1}
foot................	1 ft	=	1/3	1	3.048×10^{-1}
yard	1 yd	=	1	3	9.144×10^{-1}
fathom	1 fath◊	=	2	6	1.8288
rod (pole, perch)......	1 rd◊	=	11/2	33/2	5.0292
chain	1 ch◊	=	22	66	2.01168×10
furlong.............	1 fur.◊	=	220	660	2.01168×10^2
(statute) mile........	1 mile§	=	1760	5280	1.609344×10^3

*Definition: 1 point (printer's) (US) $= 0.013837$ in.
◊This symbol is used in the US only.
§US symbol: mi.

Other units

Nautical units of length

The *nautical mile* is defined as the length of the mean minute of arc on the meridian of the earth (mean minute of latitude). When the values of the terrestrial polar and equatorial radii derived from the international terrestrial geoid[8] are used

$$1 \text{ nautical mile} = \frac{\text{quadrant of meridian } Q_\delta^{\mathrm{Me}}}{90 \times 60} = 1852.276 \text{ m}$$

In 1929 the International Hydrographic Conference in Monaco proposed the following international unified definition[9]:

$$1 \text{ international nautical mile} = 1852 \text{ m}$$

This value was accepted by all maritime nations (by USA in 1954[10]) with the exception of the United Kingdom, where the nautical mile is based on the knot.

The definition of the British unit *nautical mile* (n mile) is based on the *admiralty knot*[11]

$$1 \text{ admiralty knot} = \frac{1 \text{ nautical mile}}{1 \text{ hour}}$$
$$= 6080 \text{ imperial feet per hour}$$

whence

1 imperial nautical mile = 1853.181 m

Astronomical units of length

In astronomy the unit of length is the *astronomical unit* (AU). This is based on a definition requiring some preliminary explanation. With the ephemeris day (d) of 86400 ephemeris seconds (s) as time unit and the mass of the sun ($\mathfrak{M}_\odot$) as mass unit the undisturbed elliptical ('Kepler') path of a planet is characterized by

n the sideral mean daily motion (angular velocity) in rad/d
$\bar{m}$ the mass in $\mathfrak{M}_\odot$
a the semi-major axis in AU
k the Gauss gravitational constant in
$(AU)^{3/2} \text{ rad d}^{-1} \mathfrak{M}_\odot^{-1/2}$

The AU is then defined as that unit in which the quantity a is measured in Kepler's Third Law $n^2 a^3 = k^2 (1 + \bar{m})$ (as equation between numerical values) with the conventionally agreed numerical value $k = na^{3/2} = 0.01720209895$ for the Gauss gravitational constant, measured in $(AU)^{3/2} \text{ rad d}^{-1} \mathfrak{M}_\odot^{-1/2}$. The AU is thus a derived unit determined by the units chosen for time and mass and the fixed value of the Gauss constant k. It can be described as the radius of the circular path round the sun followed by a body of negligible mass in the time $P_0 = (2\pi/k) \text{ d} = 365.2569185... \text{ d}$, i.e., with the uniform angular velocity $360°/P_0 = k \, 180°/(\pi \text{ d}) = 0.9856076142...°/\text{d}[12]$. The AU can be taken as nearly equal to the semi-major axis of the earth's path (establishing this agreement was the reason for Gauss's measurement of k). When the disturbing effects of the other planets are taken into account the value is 1.0000002 AU.

It is still necessary to express the AU as a multiple A of 1 m or some other reference length. The former is obtained directly from radar measurements (up to now mainly of the planet Venus, whose distance is known from the ephemerides); determination of the solar parallax $\pi_\odot$ measures the relationship of the AU to the equatorial radius a_e of the earth. The 'IAU System of Astronomical Constants' was laid down by the 16th General Assembly of the International Astronomical Union in 1976[12] by assigning conventionally agreed values to the 'defining' and the 'primary' constants. In this system

$1 \text{ AU} = 1 A \text{ m} = 1.49597870 \times 10^{11} \text{ m}$
$\pi_\odot = \text{arc sin } (a_e/A \text{ m}) = 8.794148''$, with $a_e = 6378140 \text{ m}$

Since radar measurements are measurements of time differences the time τ_A taken by light to travel 1 AU is also given; in the same system it is

$\tau_A = (A \text{ m})/c = 499.004782 \text{ s}$, with $c = 299792458 \text{ m s}^{-1}$ [12]

In stellar astronomy the distances involved are far greater than those of the solar system ($> 2 \times 10^5$ AU), and more appropriate length units have been introduced, namely the parsec, light year and distance modulus.

The *parsec* (pc) is defined as that distance at which 1 AU subtends an angle p of 1''. The angle p (measured in seconds of arc) is known as the annual parallax of the object, so that the parsec so defined is the distance of a fixed star with parallax $p = 1''$ (whence parsec from parallax and second). Since $p < 0.8''$ for all stellar parallaxes, parallax and distance are related as follows:

$\pi \, r \, p/648000'' = 1 \text{ AU}$
whence $r = 648000''/(\pi p) \text{ AU}$
and $r = 1/p \text{ pc by definition}$

It follows that $1 \text{ pc} = 648000/\pi \text{ AU} = 206264.8062 \text{ AU}$
and $1 \text{ pc} = 648000/\pi A \text{ m} = 3.085677567 \times 10^{13} \text{ km}$

The larger units usually employed are

$1 \text{ kpc} = 10^3 \text{ pc}; \ 1 \text{ Mpc} = 10^6 \text{ pc}$

The *light year* (l.y.) is the distance traveled by light in one tropical year. When the values of the IAU System of Astronomical Constants[12] for the velocity of light and the number of ephemeris seconds in 1 tropical year are used

$1 \text{ l.y.} = 299792458 \text{ m s}^{-1} \times 31556925.9747 \text{ s}$
$= 9.460528405 \times 10^{12} \text{ km}$

For objects whose parallax cannot be (more or less) directly measured, the *distance modulus* is used as indirect measure of distance. If m is the apparent (i.e., measured) brightness in magnitudes (^{m} or mag.) of an object at distance r pc, M its absolute brightness at the standard distance of 10 pc, then the distance modulus can be expressed as the quantity $m - M$. According to the $1/r^2$ law which governs the propagation of light in an absorption-free space

$$m - M = 5 \log_{10} (r/\text{pc}) - 5 = -5 - 5 \log_{10} (\text{p}/'')$$

For $m - M = -5^m, \ 0^m, +5^m, +10^m, \ldots +25^m$ the corresponding distances are $r = 1, 10, 100, 1000, \ldots 10^6$ pc.
If M can be determined from the physical structure of the object, r or p can be obtained from

$$\log_{10} (r/\text{pc}) = 0.2 (m - M + 5) = -\log_{10} (\text{p}/'')$$

Conversion of astronomical units of length[*]

	AU	pc	l.y.
astronomical unit...1 AU =	1	4.848137×10^{-6}	1.581285×10^{-5}
parsec ....1 pc =	2.062648×10^5	1	3.261633
light year..1 l.y. =	6.323973×10^4	3.065948×10^{-1}	1

* Based on the values of the solar parallax and terrestrial equatorial radius adopted by the International Astronomical Union in 1976[12].

Spectrometric units of length

X-unit

The customary *wavelength unit in x-ray spectrometry* is the x-unit (XU), related by Siegbahn[15] to the lattice constant of calcite, i.e., the interval $d_{211}^{18°}$ (CaCO$_3$) between the (211) levels of the crystal at 18°C, and defined as

$$1 \text{ XU} = [1/3029,45 \, d_{211}^{18°} (\text{CaCO}_3)]$$

The very great accuracy necessary in x-ray wavelength measurements (relative uncertainty $\approx 10^{-6}$) is no longer met by Siegbahn's definition of the x-unit since the natural imperfections of the calcite crystal (impurities, lattice defects, mosaic- or superstructure, surface effects, etc.) render it an unsatisfactory primary standard.

Today no value for the conversion factor A between x-unit and meter ($\Lambda = 1 \text{ XU}/10^{-13} \text{ m} = 1 \text{ XU}/1 \text{ mÅ [for Å see below]}$) can be given with the degree of certainty called for in x-ray spectrometry and lattice-constant measurements (e.g., $s < 10^{-6}$)*.
Measurements 'in XU' have for many years been based on tabulated wavelengths of x-ray lines in XU[16,17], namely in the 'long-wave' region on $\lambda(\text{CuK}\alpha_1) = 1537.396$ XU (or 1537.40 XU), in the 'short-wave' region on $\lambda(\text{MoK}\alpha_1) = 707.831$ XU.
In 1965, Bearden[18] suggested that Siegbahn's definition of the XU should be replaced by a new scale of x-ray wavelengths whose unit should be denoted provisionally by 'Å' and defined by assigning an exact value of the wavelength of the peak of the WKα_1 line, namely $\lambda(\text{WK}\alpha_1) = 0.2090100$ Å. This defining value had been derived by Bearden in 1964 from the value of $\lambda(\text{WK}\alpha_1) = 208.5770$ XU $= 208.5770 \times \Lambda$ mÅ and his 'experimentally' determined value $\Lambda = 1.002076$ based on the 'working standard' wavelength $\lambda(\text{MoK}\alpha_1)$; this means that the new x-ray wavelength unit also satisfies the relationship $1 \text{ mÅ} = (1.002076 \pm 5 \times 10^{-6})^{-1}$ XU. According to Bearden, 1 Å is identical with 1 Å (within a relative probable error of $\pm 5 \times 10^{-6}$).
Subsequently Bearden, in conjunction with six collaborators, prepared a new table of some 2700 wavelengths of x-ray fluorescence lines of the K-, L-, M-, N- and O-series (given as maximum of the line profile) and x-ray absorption edges in his proposed Å unit; this table was published in 1964 by the U.S. Atomic Energy Commission[19]; the wavelengths in XU, based on $\lambda(\text{WK}\alpha_1) = 208.5770$ XU, are given in the appendix to this publication (Evaluation of Wavelength Data).
In 1967, Bearden[20] published his wavelength tables in *Reviews of Modern Physics* with the following differences compared with

* Some authorities still use the value 1 XU = (1.00202 ± 0.00003) mÅ agreed on in 1947 between Siegbahn, the X-Ray Analysis Group of the Institute of Physics (UK) and the American Society for X-Ray and Electron Diffraction[14,15].

the earlier USAEC publication[19] mentioned above: 1. The new x-ray wavelength unit defined by the value $\lambda(WK\alpha_1) = 0.2090100$ is given the symbol Å* [1 Å* = $(1 \pm 5 \times 10^{-6})$Å]. 2. As 'working standard' the wavelength $\lambda(CuK\alpha_1) = 1537.400$ XU is given, with a resulting experimental Λ value of 1.002056. 3. The wavelengths are given in Å* only (the appendix with values in XU is omitted). 4. The wavelengths of the 4 secondary standard lines are given in Å* only: $\lambda(AgK\alpha_1) = 0.5594075$ Å*, $\lambda(MoK\alpha_1) = 0.709300$ Å*, $\lambda(CuK\alpha_1) = 1.540562$ Å*, $\lambda(CrK\alpha_2) = 2.393606$ Å* [relative probable error compared to the primary standard wavelength $\lambda(WK\alpha_1) = 0.2090100$ Å*: $\pm 1.1 - 1.3 \times 10^{-6}$].

Between 1969 and 1973, the Task Group on Fundamental Constants of the Committee on Data for Science and Technology (CODATA) of the International Council of Scientific Unions (ICSU) made a close study of the experimental and theoretical data used as basis for evaluation of the fundamental physical constants. Using these data, COHEN and TAYLOR[21] in 1973 made a new analysis of all the information available in this field. After a careful statistical study of the existing discrepancies, they put forward a new set of 'best' values for the fundamental physical constants to replace the old 1963 values. The primary data used also contained values expressed in x-units, for x-ray wavelengths and crystal lattice constants (for instance for determination of 'standard' x-ray wavelengths with the aid of plane and concave lattices or directly expressed in krypton wavelengths, or for evaluation of the shortwave limit of the continuous x-ray spectrum, the Avogadro constant, and of the Compton wavelength of the electron).

This set of values, accepted by CODATA[22] in August 1973 and recommended for general use, contains the following values for the conversion factors Λ and Λ*:

- based on the wavelength of the profile maximum of the CuKα_1 line

$\lambda(CuK\alpha_1)$ = 1537.400 XU
Λ = 1 XU/1 mÅ = 1.0020722 ($s = 5.4 \times 10^{-6}$)

- based on the wavelength of the profile maximum of the WKα_1 line

$\lambda(WK\alpha_1) = 0.2090100$ Å*
Λ* = 1 Å*/1 Å = 1.0000205 ($s = 5.6 \times 10^{-6}$)

The ångström

The ångström (Å) is widely used as a *unit of length in atomic and molecular spectrometry,* especially in the visible and ultraviolet spectral range. Following the new definition of the meter by the 11th General Conference on Weights and Measures[1] in 1960, the International Astronomical Union in 1961 replaced its 1907 definition[23] of the ångström based on the wavelength of cadmium as primary standard by the relationship[24]

1 ångström = 10^{-10} meter

Ångström is thus now no more than a special name for 10^{-10} m.

References

[1] Conférence Générale des Poids et Mesures, *Comptes rendus des séances de la 11ᵉ Conférence Générale des Poids et Mesures, Paris 1960,* Gauthier-Villars, Paris, 1961, pages 51 and 85.
[2] For example, BARRELL, H., *Contemp. Phys.,* **3,** 415 (1961/62); STILLE, U., *Z. angew. Phys.,* **11,** 316 (1959); STILLE, U., *Messen und Rechnen in der Physik,* 2nd ed., Vieweg, Braunschweig, 1961; ENGELHARD and VIEWEG, *Z. angew. Phys.,* **13,** 580 (1961); CLUSIUS, K., *Experientia (Basel),* **19,** 169 (1963); DE BOER, J., in PAGE and VIGOUREUX (Eds.), *The International Bureau of Weights and Measures, 1275–1975,* National Bureau of Standards, Special Publication 420, Washington, 1975, page 1.
[3] Comité International des Poids et Mesures, *Procès-verbaux des séances,* **31,** 26 (1963).
[4] Comité International des Poids et Mesures, *Comité Consultatif pour la Définition du Mètre, 5ᵉ session, 1973,* Sèvres, 1974, page M23.
[5] National Bureau of Standards, *Nat. Bur. Stand., Techn. News Bull.,* **43,** 1 (1959); National Physical Laboratory, *Nature,* **183,** 80 (1959); HOWLETT, L. E., for National Research Council, *Canad. J. Phys.,* **37,** 84 (1959); United States of America, *U.S. Federal Register,* Document 59-5442, filed June 30, 1959; Great Britain, *Weights and Measures Act, 1963:* 11 Eliz. 2, Ch. 31, HMSO, London, 1963.
[6] Great Britain, *Weights and Measures Act, 1878:* 41 and 42 Vict., Ch. 49, HMSO, London; National Physical Laboratory, *Units and Standards of Measurement Employed at the National Physical Laboratory,* Part I: Length, Mass, Time, etc., 1st ed., HMSO, London, 1951, page 4, and 3rd ed., HMSO, London, 1962, page 3; British Standards Institution, *Conversion Factors and Tables,* B.S. 350: Part 1, 1959, page 9.
[7] United States of America, *U.S. Code of Federal Regulations,* 1946, Title 15, Ch. 6: Metric System, Sec. 204 – Metric System Authorized (1866), Sec. 205 – Authorized Tables (1866), Revised Statutes, Sec. 3570; U.S. Coast and Geodetic Survey, Treasury Department, Bulletin No. 26, *Fundamental Standards*

of Length and Mass, approved for publication April 5, 1893 (Mendenhall Order); U.S. Coast and Geodetic Survey, Treasury Department, *Report for 1893,* Appendix No. 6 (1894); JUDSON, L. V., *Weights and Measures Standards of the United States, A Brief History,* National Bureau of Standards, Miscellaneous Publication No. 247, U.S. Government Printing Office, Washington, 1963; American National Standards Institute, *Metric Practice Guide,* ANSI Z 210.1 – 1973.
[8] International Union of Geodesy and Geophysics, *Bull. géod. int.,* **1925,** 157, 540 and 552.
[9] Bureau des Longitudes, *Annuaire pour l'an 1966,* Gauthier-Villars, Paris, 1965, page 441.
[10] National Bureau of Standards, *Nat. Bur. Stand., Techn. News Bull.,* **38,** 122 (1954).
[11] WATERS, D. W., *The Art of Navigation in England in Elizabethan and Early Stuart Times,* Hollis and Carter, London, 1958, Ch. 5.
[12] International Astronomical Union, *Trans. int. astron. Un.,* **XVIII,** 58 (1977).
[13] SIEGBAHN, M., *Ann. Phys.,* 4th series, **59,** 56 (1919); *Ark. Mat. Astron. Fys.,* **14,** No. 9 (1920); SIEGBAHN, M., *Spektroskopie der Röntgenstrahlen,* 2nd ed., Springer, Berlin, 1931, page 42.
[14] For example, BRAGG, W. L., *J. sci. Instrum.,* **24,** 27 (1947); *Acta Cryst.,* **1,** 46, (1948); WOOD, E. A., *Phys. Rev.,* 2nd series, **72,** 436 (1947).
[15] For example, in International Union of Crystallography, *International Tables for X-ray Crystallography,* volume III, Physical and Chemical Tables, Kynoch Press, Birmingham, 1962, pages 41 and 59.
[16] CAUCHOIS and HULUBEI, *Constantes sélectionnées, longeurs d'onde des émissions X et des discontinuités d'absorption X,* Hermann, Paris, 1947.
[17] SANDSTROM, A. E., in FLÜGGE, S. (Ed.), *Handbuch der Physik,* volume 30, Springer, Berlin, 1957, page 78.
[18] BEARDEN, J. A., *Phys. Rev.,* 2nd series, **137B,** 455 (1965); DESLATTES et al., *Metrologia,* **2,** 104 (1966).
[19] BEARDEN, J. A., *X-Ray Wavelengths,* U.S. Atomic Energy Commission, Division of Technical Information Extension, NYO-10586, Oak Ridge (Tenn.), 1964.
[20] BEARDEN, J. A., *Rev. mod. Phys.,* **39,** 78 (1967).
[21] COHEN and TAYLOR, *J. phys. chem. Ref. Data,* **2,** 663 (1973).
[22] Committee on Data for Science and Technology (CODATA) of the International Council of Scientific Unions (ICSU), *Recommended Consistent Values of the Fundamental Physical Constants, 1973,* CODATA Bulletin No. 11 (Frankfurt, 1973).
[23] International Union for Co-operation in Solar Research, *Trans. int. Un. Coop. Sol. Res.,* **2,** 20 (1908).
[24] International Astronomical Union, *Trans. int. astron. Un.,* **XIB,** 88 (1962).

Area* (*A* or *S*)

Dimension: L^2

SI unit: square meter (m²)

Unit in the ft-lb-s system: square foot (ft²) = 9.290304×10^{-2} m²

Conversion of decimal multiples and submultiples of the SI unit

	µm²	mm²	cm²	dm²	m²	km²
square micrometer . 1 µm² =	1	10^{-6}	10^{-8}	10^{-10}	10^{-12}	10^{-18}
square millimeter . 1 mm² =	10^6	1	10^{-2}	10^{-4}	10^{-6}	10^{-12}
square centimeter . . 1 cm² =	10^8	10^2	1	10^{-2}	10^{-4}	10^{-10}
square decimeter . . 1 dm² =	10^{10}	10^4	10^2	1	10^{-2}	10^{-8}
square meter . . . . . . 1 m² =	10^{12}	10^6	10^4	10^2	1	10^{-6}
square decameter . . 1 dam² =	10^{14}	10^8	10^6	10^4	10^2	10^{-4}
square hectometer . 1 hm² =	10^{16}	10^{10}	10^8	10^6	10^4	10^{-2}
square kilometer . . . 1 km² =	10^{18}	10^{12}	10^{10}	10^8	10^6	1

Other units

The *barn* (b) is a special area unit for expressing effective cross sections in nuclear physics. At its 10th General Meeting in 1960[1], the International Union for Pure and Applied Physics (IUPAP) recommended use of the name barn for 10^{-24} cm²:

1 b = 10^{-24} cm² = 10^{-28} m²

The units *are* (a) and *hectare* (ha) are special units for expressing land areas. These units were accepted in 1879 by the International Committee for Weights and Measures[2] and are now in the category of units to be used temporarily with SI (Comité International des Poids et Mesures, 1969)[3].

1 a = 1 dam² = 10^2 m²
1 ha = 1 hm² = 10^4 m²

---

*For the length units on which the area units are based, see the section 'Length' (page 10).

Conversion of Anglo-Saxon area units

		yd²	ft²	m²
circular mil◊	1 circular mil =	$\pi/5184 \times 10^6$	$\pi/576 \times 10^6$	$1.6129\pi \times 10^{-10}$
square inch .	1 in² =	1/1296	1/144	6.4516×10^{-4}
circular inch	1 circular inch =	$\pi/5184$	$\pi/576$	$1.6129\pi \times 10^{-4}$
square link .	1 li²† =	$484/10^4$	$4356/10^4$	4.04686×10^{-2}
square foot .	1 ft² =	1/9	1	9.290304×10^{-2}
square yard .	1 yd² =	1	9	8.3612736×10^{-1}
square rod . .	1 rd²† =	121/4	1089/4	2.52929×10
(square pole, square perch)				
square chain .	1 ch²† =	484	4356	4.04686×10^2
rood (UK) . .	1 rood =	1210	10890	1.01171×10^3
acre	1 acre =	4840	43560	4.04686×10^3
square mile .	1 mile²§ =	3097600	27878400	2.58999×10^6

◊ The circular mil is defined as the area of a circle 0.001 inch in diameter: 1 circular mil = 10^{-6} circular inch = $(\pi/4) \times 10^{-6}$ in².
† This symbol is used only in the US.
§ In the US: mi².

References

[1] International Union of Pure and Applied Physics (IUPAP), *Report of the 10th General Assembly, Ottawa, 1960,* pages 7 and 24; International Union of Pure and Applied Physics, *Symbols, Units and Nomenclature in Physics,* Document U.I.P. 11 (S.U.N. 65-3), 1965, page 25.
[2] Comité International des Poids et Mesures, *Procès-verbaux des séances de 1879,* Gauthier-Villars, Paris, 1880, page 41.
[3] Comité International des Poids et Mesures, *Comité Consultatif des Unités, 2ᵉ session, 1969,* Bureau International des Poids et Mesures, Sèvres, 1970, U 17.

Volume* (V)

Dimension: L^3

SI unit: cubic meter (m³)

Unit in the ft-lb-s system: cubic foot (ft³) = $2.8316846592 \times 10^{-2}$ m³

Conversion of decimal multiples and submultiples of the SI unit

		nm³	μm³	mm³	cm³	dm³ = L	m³
cubic nanometer	1 nm³ =	1	10^{-9}	10^{-18}	10^{-21}	10^{-24}	10^{-27}
cubic micrometer	1 μm³ =	10^9	1	10^{-9}	10^{-12}	10^{-15}	10^{-18}
cubic millimeter	1 mm³ =	10^{18}	10^9	1	10^{-3}	10^{-6}	10^{-9}
cubic centimeter	1 cm³ =	10^{21}	10^{12}	10^3	1	10^{-3}	10^{-6}
cubic decimeter	1 dm³ =	10^{24}	10^{15}	10^6	10^3	1	10^{-3}
liter.	1 L =						
cubic meter	1 m³ =	10^{27}	10^{18}	10^9	10^6	10^3	1
cubic kilometer	1 km³ =	10^{36}	10^{27}	10^{18}	10^{15}	10^{12}	10^9

Other units and special names for units

Up to 1964, the liter (l, L)◊ was defined as the volume of 1 kg of pure, air-free water at its maximum density (≈ 3.98 °C) under normal atmospheric pressure (101325 Pa)[1]. In 1950, the International Committee for Weights and Measures[2] gave 1 L = 1.000028 dm³ ($s = 3 \times 10^{-6}$) as the best conversion factor between the liter so defined and the cubic decimeter.

In 1964, the 12th General Conference on Weights and Measures[3] abolished the old liter definition of the 3rd General Conference in 1901 and agreed that the name 'liter' should be used as synonym for cubic decimeter with the express recommendation that the results of very precise volume determinations should be given not in liters but in the SI unit cubic meter or its decimal multiples or submultiples:

$$1 \text{ L} = 1 \text{ dm}^3 = 10^{-3} \text{ m}^3$$

*For the length units on which the volume units are based, see the section 'Length' (page 10).
◊ In 1979[10], the General Conference on Weights and Measures accepted the additional symbol 'L' for the liter.

Conversion of decimal multiples and submultiples of the SI unit

		μL	mL	L	m³
microliter (= 1 mm³).	1 μL =	1	10^{-3}	10^{-6}	10^{-9}
milliliter (= 1 cm³)	1 mL =	10^3	1	10^{-3}	10^{-6}
deciliter (= 0.1 dm³)	1 dL =	10^5	10^2	10^{-1}	10^{-4}
liter (= 1 dm³)	1 L =	10^6	10^3	1	10^{-3}
hectoliter (= 0.1 m³)	1 hL =	10^8	10^5	10^2	10^{-1}

The *stere* (st) is a name still commonly used in forestry and the lumber industry for the cubic meter of stacked wood including air gaps. The stere was accepted by the International Committee for Weights and Measures in 1879[4], its symbol 'st' by the 9th General Conference on Weights and Measures[5]:

$$1 \text{ st} = 1 \text{ m}^3$$

Anglo-Saxon units of volume[6]

In the United Kingdom the *commercial* units of volume both for fluids and dry substances are the *gallon* (gal) and units derived from it. The gallon is the volume of a quantity of water of a specified mass when weighed under the conditions laid down[7]; this definition results in the following relationships:

$$1 \text{ gal(UK)} = 277.42 \text{ in}^3 = 4.54609 \text{ dm}^3$$

In the United States the *gallon* (gal) and the units of volume derived from it are legal measures only for fluids. The gallon is there defined[8, 9] as

$$1 \text{ gal(US)} = 231 \text{ in}^3 = 3.785411784 \text{ dm}^3$$

whence the relationships

$$1 \text{ gal(US)} = 0.832674 \text{ gal(UK)}$$
$$1 \text{ gal(UK)} = 1.200950 \text{ gal(US)}$$

In the United States the units of volume for dry substances are the *bushel* (bu) and units derived from it. The bushel (bu) is defined[8, 9] as follows:

$$1 \text{ bu(US)} = 2150.42 \text{ in}^3 = 35.23907016688 \text{ dm}^3$$

This unit is related to the bushel used in the United Kingdom, defined as 1 bu(UK) = 8 gal(UK), as follows:

$$1 \text{ bu(US)} = 0.968939 \text{ bu(UK)}$$
$$1 \text{ bu(UK)} = 1.032057 \text{ bu(US)}$$

Conversion of Anglo-Saxon units of volume

		yd³	ft³	m³
cubic inch	1 in³ =	1/46656	1/1728	1.6387064×10^{-5}
board foot (timber) . . .	1 fbm =	1/324	1/12	2.35974×10^{-3}
cubic foot	1 ft³ =	1/27	1	2.83168×10^{-2}
cubic yard	1 yd³ =	1	27	7.64555×10^{-1}
cord (timber).	1 cd =	128/27	128	3.62456

Conversion of United Kingdom units of volume (UK units)

		gal	in³	L = dm³
minim	1 min =	1/76800	3.61223×10^{-3}	5.91939×10^{-5}
fluid drachm . . .	1 fl dr =	1/1280	2.16734×10^{-1}	3.55163×10^{-3}
(= 60 min)				
fluid ounce	1 fl oz =	1/160	1.73387	2.84131×10^{-2}
(= 480 min)				
gill	1 gill =	1/32	8.66936	1.42065×10^{-1}
pint.	1 pint =	1/8	3.46774×10	5.68261×10^{-1}
quart	1 quart =	1/4	6.93549×10	1.13652
gallon.	1 gal =	1	2.77420×10^2	4.54609
peck	1 peck =	2	5.54839×10^2	9.09218
bushel	1 bushel =	8	2.21935×10^3	3.63687×10
cran	1 cran =	37.5	1.04033×10^4	1.70479×10^2
quarter (volume)	1 quarter =	64	1.77549×10^4	2.90950×10^2
chaldron	1 chaldron =	288	7.98968×10^4	1.30927×10^3

Conversion of United States units of volume (US units)

For fluids

		gal	in³	L = dm³
minim .... 1 min	=	1/61 440	$3.759\,77 \times 10^{-3}$	$6.161\,15 \times 10^{-5}$
fluid dram .... 1 fl dr	=	1/1024	$2.255\,86 \times 10^{-1}$	$3.696\,69 \times 10^{-3}$
fluid ounce .... 1 fl oz	=	1/128	1.804 69	$2.957\,35 \times 10^{-2}$
gill .... 1 gi	=	1/32	7.218 75	$1.182\,94 \times 10^{-1}$
liquid pint .... 1 liq pt	=	1/8	2.8875×10	$4.731\,75 \times 10^{-1}$
liquid quart ...... 1 liq qt	=	1/4	5.775×10	$9.463\,53 \times 10^{-1}$
gallon .... 1 gal	=	1	2.31×10^2	3.785 41
1 barrel (petroleum)[8,9]	=	42	9.702×10^3	$1.589\,87 \times 10^2$

For dry substances

		bu	in³	L = dm³
dry pint .... 1 dry pt	=	1/64	$3.360\,03 \times 10$	$5.506\,10 \times 10^{-1}$
dry quart .... 1 dry qt	=	1/32	$6.720\,06 \times 10$	1.101 22
peck .... 1 pk	=	1/4	$5.376\,05 \times 10^2$	8.809 77
bushel* .... 1 bu	=	1	$2.150\,42 \times 10^3$	$3.523\,91 \times 10$
barrel[○] ..... 1 bbl	=	105/32[†]	7.056×10^3	$1.156\,27 \times 10^2$

* So-called 'stricken' or 'struck' bushel. There is also a 'heaped bushel' of 2747.715 in³ ≈ 45.027 L for apples, and a 'heaped bushel' = 1¼ striken bushel ≈ 44.049 L[8,9].
[○] For fruits and other products except cranberries, this barrel = 7056 in³. For cranberries, the barrel = 5826 in³ ≈ 95.471 L[7,8].
[†] This fraction is approximate. Exact conversion on the basis of the cubic inch definitions of bushel and barrel gives 1 bbl = (7056/2150.42) bu.

References

[1] Conférence Générale des Poids et Mesures, *Comptes rendus des séances de la 3ᵉ Conférence Générale des Poids et Mesures, Paris 1901*, Gauthier-Villars, Paris, 1901, page 38.
[2] Comité International des Poids et Mesures, *Procès-verbaux des séances*, **22**, 77 and 94 (1950).
[3] Conférence Générale des Poids et Mesures, *Comptes rendus des séances de la 12ᵉ Conférence Générale des Poids et Mesures, Paris 1964*, Gauthier-Villars, Paris, 1964, page 93.
[4] Comité International des Poids et Mesures, *Procès-verbaux des séances de 1879*, Gauthier-Villars, Paris, 1880, page 41.
[5] Conférence Générale des Poids et Mesures, *Comptes rendus des séances de la 9ᵉ Conférence Générale des Poids et Mesures, Paris 1948*, Gauthier-Villars, Paris, 1949, page 70.
[6] SKINNER, F. G., *Weights and Measures: Their Ancient Origins and Their Development in Great Britain up to AD 1855*, HMSO, London, 1967; KAYE and LABY, *Tables of Physical and Chemical Constants and some Mathematical Functions*, 13th ed., Longmans, London, 1966; STILLE, U., *Messen und Rechnen in der Physik*, 2nd ed., Vieweg, Braunschweig, 1961.
[7] Great Britain, *Weights and Measures Act, 1963*: 11 Eliz.2, Ch.31, HMSO, London, 1963; *Weights and Measures Act, 1878*: 41 and 42 Vict., Ch.49, HMSO, London; National Physical Laboratory, *Units and Standards of Measurement Employed at the National Physical Laboratory*, Part 1: Length, Mass, Time, etc., 1st ed., HMSO, London, 1951, page 4, and 3rd ed., HMSO, London, 1962, page 3; British Standards Institution, *Conversion Factors and Tables*, B.S.350: Part 1, 1959, page 14.
[8] United States of America, *U.S. Code of Federal Regulations*, 1946, Title 15, Ch.6: Metric System, Sec.204 – Metric System Authorized (1866), Sec.205 – Authorized Tables (1866), Revised Statutes, Sec.3570; U.S. Coast and Geodetic Survey, Treasury Department, Bulletin No.26, *Fundamental Standards of Length and Mass*, approved for publication April 5, 1893 (Mendenhall Order); U.S. Coast and Geodetic Survey, Treasury Department, *Report for 1893*, Appendix No.6 (1894); JUDSON, L. V., *Weights and Measures Standards of the United States, A Brief History*, National Bureau of Standards, Miscellaneous Publication No.247, U.S. Government Printing Office, Washington, 1963.
[9] JUDSON, L. V., *Units of Weight and Measure (United States Customary and Metric), Definitions and Tables of Equivalents*, National Bureau of Standards, Miscellaneous Publication No.233, U.S. Government Printing Office, Washington, 1960; American National Standards Institute, *Metric Practice Guide*, ANSI Z 210.1–1973.
[10] Conférence Générale des Poids et Mesures, *Comptes rendus de la 16ᵉ Conférence Générale des Poids et Mesures, Paris 1979*, Bureau International des Poids et Mesures, Sèvres 1979, page 101.

Mass (*m*)

Dimension: M

Base SI unit: kilogram (kg)

Unit in the ft-lb-s system: pound (lb) = 0.453 592 37 kg

Base SI unit of mass

The base SI unit of mass[1] is the *kilogram* (kg) (see page 9). Its realization is the international kilogram prototype, a platinum–iridium cylinder kept in the International Bureau of Weights and Measures in Sèvres (France).

Conversion of decimal multiples and submultiples of the kilogram

		ag	fg	pg	ng	µg	mg	g	kg
attogram ...... 1 ag	=	1	10^{-3}	10^{-6}	10^{-9}	10^{-12}	10^{-15}	10^{-18}	10^{-21}
femtogram..... 1 fg	=	10^3	1	10^{-3}	10^{-6}	10^{-9}	10^{-12}	10^{-15}	10^{-18}
picogram ..... 1 pg	=	10^6	10^3	1	10^{-3}	10^{-6}	10^{-9}	10^{-12}	10^{-15}
nanogram ..... 1 ng	=	10^9	10^6	10^3	1	10^{-3}	10^{-6}	10^{-9}	10^{-12}
microgram*.... 1 µg	=	10^{12}	10^9	10^6	10^3	1	10^{-3}	10^{-6}	10^{-9}
milligram...... 1 mg	=	10^{15}	10^{12}	10^9	10^6	10^3	1	10^{-3}	10^{-6}
gram .... 1 g	=	10^{18}	10^{15}	10^{12}	10^9	10^6	10^3	1	10^{-3}
kilogram ...... 1 kg	=	10^{21}	10^{18}	10^{15}	10^{12}	10^9	10^6	10^3	1
megagram ..... 1 Mg metric ton ..... 1 t (tonne)	= }	10^{24}	10^{21}	10^{18}	10^{15}	10^{12}	10^9	10^6	10^3

* Formerly also known as the gamma (*γ*), a name that should no longer be used.

Other units and special names for units

Tonne (metric ton) (t) is a special name for the megagram (Mg); the symbol for this unit term was approved in Resolution 7 of the 9th General Conference on Weights and Measures (1948)[2].

1 t = 1 Mg = 10^3 kg

Conversion of decimal multiples and submultiples of the tonne

		dt	t	kt	Mt	kg
decitonne................1 dt	=	1	10^{-1}	10^{-4}	10^{-7}	10^2
tonne ....1 t	=	10	1	10^{-3}	10^{-6}	10^3
kilotonne................1 kt	=	10^4	10^3	1	10^{-3}	10^6
megatonne ....1 MT	=	10^7	10^6	10^3	1	10^9

The *metric carat* is a unit of mass recommended by the 4th General Conference on Weights and Measures (1907)[3] on account of the many individual carat units then in use for trading in diamonds, genuine pearls, and precious stones; no international symbol has been established for this unit.

1 metric carat = 200 mg = 0.2 g = 2×10^{-4} kg

The *atomic mass unit* (u) is closely related to the mole, the unit of amount of substance (see page 45). Both units are defined by the same primary standard, the carbon nuclide ^{12}C: 1 atomic mass unit is equal to $^{1}/_{12}$ the mass of the ^{12}C nuclide. In the scale of relative atomic masses (see page 45) the ^{12}C nuclide is the reference nuclide, with the relative atomic mass 12 and the atomic mass 12 u defining this scale. The relationship of the atomic mass unit to the base SI unit is established by the experimentally determined value of the Avogadro constant. In accordance with the currently accepted values of the fundamental physical constants[4] (see page 47) the conversion relationship is

1 u = $1.660\,5655 \times 10^{-27}$ kg ($s = 8.6 \times 10^{-33}$ kg)

Anglo-Saxon units of mass

In the Anglo-Saxon countries, in addition to the metric units employed in scientific work, three groups of mass units are in simultaneous use: the *avoirdupois* units of commerce and industry, the *troy* units for precious metals and coins, and the *apothecaries'* units. Common to all three groups is the grain (gr), defined as the 7000th part of the avoirdupois pound (lb avdp or lb av).

The avoirdupois pound has for some years been related to the kilogram by a precise numerical factor[5]

1 lb = 0.453 592 37 kg

This new 'unified' pound, sometimes called the international pound, is divisible by 7; it is somewhat larger than the former imperial pound of the United Kingdom[6] and somewhat smaller than the earlier avoirdupois pound of the United States[7]:

1 imperial pound = 0.453592338 kg < 1 unified pound
< U.S. pound avoirdupois = 0.4535924277 kg

In the United Kingdom the pound troy (lb t) is no longer a statutory unit; however, a number of its subsidiary units still have legal standing for precious metals. In the United States, on the other hand, the pound troy (lb t [US]) is the statutory unit for coins:

1 U.S. pound troy [lb t (US)]
= 5760/7000 US pound avoirdupois [lb avdp(US)]

Conversion of Anglo-Saxon units of mass

Avoirdupois units

		gr	lb	kg
grain (US, UK)...1 gr	=	1	1/7000	6.479891×10^{-5}
dram (US, UK)...1 dr	=	875/32	1/256	1.77185×10^{-3}
ounce (US, UK)..1 oz	=	875/2	1/16	2.83495×10^{-2}
pound (US, UK)..1 lb	=	7×10^3	1	4.5359237×10^{-1}
stone (UK)......1 stone	=	9.8×10^4	14	6.35029
quarter (UK).....1 qr	=	1.96×10^5	28	1.27006×10
cental (UK)......1 cental	=			
short hundred-weight (US)....1 sh cwt	= }	7×10^5	100	4.53592×10
hundredweight (UK).........1 cwt	=			
1 long hundred-weight (UK)....	= }	7.84×10^5	112	5.08023×10
(short) ton (US)..1 sh tn	=	1.4×10^7	2000	9.07185×10^2
ton (UK).......1 ton	=			
long ton (US)....1 long ton	= }	1.568×10^7	2240	1.01605×10^3

Troy units

		gr	lb	g
pennyweight.........1 dwt	=	24	3/875	1.55517
ounce troy...........1 oz t*	=	480	12/175	3.11035×10
pound troy (US).......1 lb t	=	5760	144/175	3.73242×10^2

* In the United Kingdom: oz tr.

Apothecaries' units

		gr	lb	g
apothecaries' scruple (US)... scruple (UK)..............	}1 s ap* =	20	1/350	1.29598
apothecaries' dram (US)..... drachm (UK)	}1 dr ap* =	60	3/350	3.88793
apothecaries' ounce (US, UK)	1 oz ap* =	480	12/175	3.11035×10
apothecaries' pound (US)....	1 lb ap* =	5760	144/175	3.73242×10^2

* In the United Kingdom: apoth instead of ap.

References

[1] Conférence Générale des Poids et Mesures, *Comptes rendus des séances de la 3e Conférence Générale des Poids et Mesures, Paris 1901*, Gauthier-Villars, Paris, 1902, pages 62 and 68.
[2] Conférence Générale des Poids et Mesures, *Comptes rendus des séances de la 9e Conférence Générale des Poids et Mesures, Paris 1948*, Gauthier-Villars, Paris, 1949, page 70.
[3] Conférence Générale des Poids et Mesures, *Comptes rendus des séances de la 4e Conférence Générale des Poids et Mesures, Paris 1907*, Gauthier-Villars, Paris, 1907, page 89.
[4] Committee on Data for Science and Technology (CODATA) of the International Council of Scientific Unions (ICSU), *Recommended Consistent Values of the Fundamental Physical Constants, 1973*, CODATA Bulletin, No. 11 (December 1973).
[5] National Bureau of Standards, *Nat. Bur. Stand., Techn. News Bull.*, **43**, 1 (1959); National Physical Laboratory, *Nature*, **183**, 80 (1959); Howlett, L. E., for National Research Council, *Canad. J. Phys.*, **37**, 84 (1959); United States of America, *U.S. Federal Register*, Document 59–5442, filed June 30, 1959; Great Britain, *Weights and Measures Act, 1963*: 11 Eliz.2, Ch.31, HMSO, London, 1963.
[6] Great Britain, *Weights and Measures Act, 1878*: 41 and 42 Vict., Ch.49, HMSO, London; National Physical Laboratory, *Units and Standards of Measurement Employed at the National Physical Laboratory*, Part 1: Length,

Mass, Time, etc., 3rd ed., HMSO, London, 1962, page 3; British Standards Institution, *Conversion Factors and Tables*, B.S.350: Part 1, 1959, page 9.
[7] United States of America, *U.S. Code of Federal Regulations*, 1946, Title 15, Ch.6: Metric System, Sec. 204 – Metric System Authorized (1866), Sec. 205 – Authorized Tables (1866), Revised Statutes, Sec. 3570; U.S. Coast and Geodetic Survey, Treasury Department, Bulletin No. 26, *Fundamental Standards of Length and Mass*, approved for publication April 5, 1893 (Mendenhall Order); U.S. Coast and Geodetic Survey, Treasury Department, *Report for 1893*, Appendix No.6 (1894); Judson, L. V., *Weights and Measures Standards of the United States, A Brief History*, National Bureau of Standards, Miscellaneous Publication No.247, U.S. Government Printing Office, Washington, 1963; Judson, L. V., *Units of Weight and Measure (United States Customary and Metric), Definitions and Tables of Equivalents*, National Bureau of Standards, Miscellaneous Publication No.233, U.S. Government Printing Office, Washington, 1960; American National Standards Institute, *Metric Practice Guide*, ANSI Z 210.1–1973, page 25.

Time (t)

Dimension: T

Base unit of time in all systems of measurement: second (s)

Time scales can be derived from all periodic natural phenomena (revolutions of the planets and moon, axial rotation of the earth, transitions in atoms and molecules). The base unit of time in the International System of Units (page 9) is the second, derived from the period of oscillation of the cesium atom. The highly uniform scale of 'atomic time' is established by atomic clocks. In everyday life, time is regulated partly by atomic time and partly by a time scale derived from the axial rotation of the earth. For historical information on the definition of the second, and for the fundamentals of the atomic clock, see the reference[1].

Time units derived from the earth's rotation • Universal Time

The *apparent solar day* is the time interval between two successive passages of the sun through the meridian of the observer. Owing to the inclination of the ecliptic and the fact that the earth moves around the sun not in a circular but in an elliptical path, the apparent solar day differs from the *mean solar day* (d_m) by a varying amount (up to about 30 seconds). The mean solar day is derived from the movement of a '*mean sun*' assumed to move with uniform velocity along the celestial equator in such a way that its passage through the vernal equinox (one of the intersections of the celestial equator and the ecliptic) coincides with that of the true sun. The difference between 'apparent' and 'mean' time, known as the equation of time, varies in the course of the year between about +15 and −16 minutes. The mean solar day is the time elapsing between successive passages of the mean sun through the meridian of the observer. These passages define the time 12 noon of mean solar time (mean local time).

The mean solar day (d_m) is divided into 24 hours, each of 60 minutes, and each of the latter into 60 seconds. These units should not be confused with the SI units day (d), hour (h), minute (min) and second (s). The second of mean solar time is also the time unit of a special mean solar time known as *Universal Time*.

In practice, the length of the mean solar day and hence of the second of Universal Time is obtained from the stellar day (d*), the time elapsing between two successive passages of the vernal equinox through the meridian of the observer. Since the position of the vernal equinox as a result of the *general precession* of the earth, the stellar day is about 9 ms shorter than the time taken by the earth to complete a 360° rotation relative to the fixed stars. The relationship between d_m and d* is

$$d_m = d* (1 + 1/n),$$

where n is the number of mean solar days in the tropical year.

The stellar day (d*) is divided into 24 stellar hours (h*), each of 60 stellar minutes (min*), and each of the latter into 60 stellar seconds (s*).

On the *Universal Time* scale (UT) the time 12 noon UT is defined by the passages of the mean sun through the zero meridian (Greenwich). Statutory local time scales in use in particular countries are *zonal time* scales (15° difference in longitude ≙ 1 h), for example Central European Time (CET) = Universal Time + 1 h. Coordinated Universal Time (UTC, page 17) has, however, *de facto* taken over the function of Universal Time as the basis of zonal times. For the differences between the various local times, see the yearbooks issued by the Bureau des Longitudes[2].

Times on a particular time scale are often symbolized by the superscripts h, m (instead of min) and s, for example $2^h25^m3^s$ CET.

Time designations in UT are indicated by the letter 'T', for example 1ʰ25ᵐ3ˢ T.

Variations in the polar altitude of the earth and the seasonal variations in the earth's rotation (the latter in a pattern remaining roughly constant from year to year) result in changes in the length of the mean solar day that can be calculated. This has made it possible to define a more uniform scale of Universal Time known as UT 2. Up to 1956 the second of UT 2 was in use for very precise time measurements, but this practice has since been abandoned because the gradual slowing of the earth's rotational speed causes the second of UT 2 to increase by about 2×10^{-10} s per year. Moreover, irregular variations in the earth's rotation may result in fairly rapid changes in the UT second of, for instance, 10^{-8} s during the course of the year.

Multiples of the mean solar day and the second of Universal Time obtained with defined numerical factors prior to the introduction of Coordinated Universal Time are:

Calendar ordinary year = 365 mean solar days = 31 536 000 UT seconds

Calendar leap year = 366 mean solar days = 31 622 400 UT seconds

Mean Julian year (a_{jul}) = (3 calendar ordinary years + 1 calendar leap year)/4 = 365.25 mean solar days = 31 557 600 UT seconds

Mean Gregorian year (a_{greg}) = (400 a_{jul} − 3 d)/400 = 365.2425 mean solar days = 31 556 952 UT seconds

The definitions of the mean Julian and Gregorian years are chosen in such a way that their lengths approximate to that of the tropical year (ca. 365.2422 mean solar days). This figure is not constant but varies not only as a result of changes in the earth's rotation but also because the length of the tropical year itself is variable.

The zero point of the Universal Time scale is January 1 of the year 1 B.C. at 0ʰ UT, so that the number of the year indicates the number of complete calendar years that have since elapsed. It should be noted that only one calendar year separates 1 B.C. 0ʰ UT and 1 A.D. 0ʰ UT.

Up to 1581 each year exactly divisible by 4 was a leap year, as were the years 1, 5, 9, etc. B.C. This constituted the so-called Julian Calendar, introduced by JULIUS CAESAR in 45 B.C. Owing to the fact that the Julian year is some 11 minutes longer than the tropical year (based on the earth's orbital motion) the Julian Calendar showed earlier and earlier dates for natural events like the seasons. The growing discrepancy was finally rectified by the calendar reform introduced by Pope GREGORY XIII's bull of February 24 1582. Under this reform, 10 days were to be dropped from the calendar of the year 1582, October 5–14 inclusive, in order to restore the vernal equinox to March 21. France adopted the reform the same year, dropping the days from December 10 to 19 1582. In England, the Gregorian Calendar was not adopted until 1752, when 11 days, September 3–13, had to be dropped. In order to keep the Gregorian Calendar in step with the tropical years, the reform also laid down that three out of every four century years were to be ordinary years instead of leap years, i.e., that only those century years divisible by 400 were to be leap years. The mean Gregorian year is therefore 0.4 min longer than the tropical year.

Units of time derived from the orbital movement of the earth • Ephemeris Time

The following time intervals are derived from the revolution of the earth around the sun:

The *sidereal year* (a_{sid}) is the time taken by the earth to complete one 360° revolution around the sun, as related to the system of fixed stars. Since it cannot be measured directly the sidereal year is not used in time measurements.

The *anomalistic year* (a_{anom}) is the time elapsing between two successive passages of the earth through the perihelion.

The *astronomical year* (a_{astr}), also known as Bessel's year or annus fictus, is the time during which the right ascension of the (fictitious) mean sun increases by 360°; it differs only slightly from the tropical year.

The *tropical year* (a_{trop}), of great importance in time measurements, is the time elapsing between two successive passages of the

Conversion of time units and time scale measures

			s	min	h	d	In the conversion, s, min, h and d are:
SI unit and multiples	second	1 s =	1	1.6×10^{-2}	2.7×10^{-4}	1.15740×10^{-5}	the SI unit and its multiples
	minute	1 min =	6×10	1	1.6×10^{-2}	6.94×10^{-4}	
	hour	1 h =	3.6×10^3	6×10	1	4.16×10^{-2}	
	day	1 d =	8.64×10^4	1.44×10^3	2.4×10	1	
Scale measure of Coordinated Universal Time (UTC)	second	1 s =	1	1.6×10^{-2}	2.7×10^{-4}	1.15740×10^{-5}	the SI unit and its multiples
	minute◊	1 min =	6×10	1	1.6×10^{-2}	6.94×10^{-4}	
	hour◊	1 h =	3.6×10^3	6×10	1	4.16×10^{-2}	
	calendar day◊	1 d =	8.64×10^4	1.44×10^3	2.4×10	1	
	calendar year:						
	normal year◊	1 a_{365} =	3.1536×10^7	5.256×10^5	8.76×10^3	3.65×10^2	
	leap year◊	1 a_{366} =	3.16224×10^7	5.2704×10^5	8.784×10^3	3.66×10^2	
Scale measure of Sidereal Time⁹	sidereal second	1 s* =	$9.97269566 \times 10^{-1}$	$1.66211594 \times 10^{-2}$	$2.77019324 \times 10^{-4}$	$1.15424718 \times 10^{-5}$	the scale measures of mean solar time†
	sidereal minute	1 min* =	5.98361740×10	$9.97269566 \times 10^{-1}$	$1.66211594 \times 10^{-2}$	$6.92548310 \times 10^{-4}$	
	sidereal hour	1 h* =	3.59017044×10^3	5.98361740×10	$9.97269566 \times 10^{-1}$	$4.15528986 \times 10^{-2}$	
	sidereal day	1 d* =	8.61640905×10^4	1.43606818×10^3	2.39344696×10	$9.97269566 \times 10^{-1}$	

◊ The conversion factors for these scale measures are valid for the case where there are no leap seconds. In cases where a second has been added, the scale measures are increased by one second.

† There are no fixed relationships between the scale measures of mean solar time and the SI unit of time.

Duration of the year according to various definitions◊

			s	min	h	d	s, min, h and d are:
Years defined on the basis of the earth's rotation	mean Julian year	1 a_{jul} =	3.15576×10^7	5.2596×10^5	8.766×10^3	3.6525×10^2	scale measures of mean solar time†
	mean Gregorian year	1 a_{greg} =	3.1556952×10^7	5.259492×10^5	8.76582×10^3	3.652425×10^2	
Years defined on the basis of the earth's revolution at time 1900.0⁹	sidereal year	1 a_{sid} =	3.15581497×10^7	5.25969162×10^5	8.76615271×10^3	3.65256362×10^2	ephemeris second (≃ SI unit) and its multiples
	tropical year	1 a_{trop} =	3.15569260×10^7	5.25948766×10^5	8.76581277×10^3	3.65242199×10^2	
	anomalous year	1 a_{anom} =	3.15584330×10^7	5.25973883×10^5	8.76623139×10^3	3.65259641×10^2	

◊ For calendar years see the preceding table.

† There are no fixed relationships between the scale measures of mean solar time and the SI unit of time.

true sun through the mean vernal equinox. Owing to the general precession of the earth the vernal equinox moves once round the ecliptic in about 26000 years. In addition to this movement, the vernal equinox is subject to a slight 'secular' acceleration as well as to periodic fluctuations. The fictitious *mean* vernal equinox is not subject to these periodic fluctuations. As a result of the general precession of the earth the tropical year is 20.4 min shorter than the sidereal year, and because of the secular acceleration of the vernal equinox each tropical year is about 5.3 ms shorter than the preceding one. The tropical year remains in phase with the seasons of the earth.

In order to construct calendars the approximate tropical year up to 1581 was calculated from the mean Julian year based on the mean solar day (a_{trop} is 11.2 min shorter) and for 1583 and subsequently from the mean Gregorian year likewise based on the mean solar day (a_{trop} is 0.4 min shorter). The tropical year is 25.1 min shorter than the anomalistic year.

The tropical year at a particular epoch is equal to $360°/(dL/dt)$, where L is the mean longitude of the sun, or angle subtended at the earth by the positions of the mean sun and the mean vernal equinox at that epoch. Owing to the secular acceleration of the vernal equinox the angular velocity dL/dt is a function of time. Of special importance is the length of the tropical year at the epoch 1900, January 0, 12 noon Ephemeris Time, which is December 31 1899, 12 noon plus ca. 4.5^s Universal Time. At this time the mean longitude of the sun was $279° \, 41' \, 48.04''$. The ephemeris second is derived from the length of the tropical year at this particular time.

Because of the fluctuations in the length of the second of Universal Time due to the rotational irregularities of the earth the International Committee for Weights and Measures[3] in 1956 defined the second as basic unit of the International System of Units (SI units) for use in time and frequency measurements in science and technology as the 31556925.9747th part of the tropical year at the epoch 1900, January 0, 12 noon Ephemeris Time (ratified in 1960 by the 11th General Conference on Weights and Measures[4]). This fraction was so chosen that the length of the second defined in this way *(ephemeris second)* is identical with the mean second of Universal Time between 1680 and 1895. Measurements of the longitude L of the sun made during this period and related to Universal Time (comparison of the axial and orbital movements of the earth) have been evaluated by NEWCOMB. In 1967 the ephemeris second was replaced as base unit in the International System of Units by the atomic second.

For astronomical use the ephemeris second has formed the basis of the very uniform *Ephemeris Time* scale. At the beginning of this century, times on the Ephemeris Time and Universal Time scales still almost coincided, whereas by 1977 they differed by about 48 s as a result of the slowing of the earth's rotation in the period of about 200 years since the time on which the ephemeris second is based. In 1979 the second of Universal Time was about 3.5×10^{-8} s longer than the ephemeris second.

Since the mean longitude L of the sun cannot be measured with sufficient accuracy Ephemeris Time is determined from the motion of the moon. This is possible since lunar theory has now developed to the point where the variable relationship between the moon's orbital and the earth's axial rotational frequencies is known.

Comparison of Ephemeris Time with Atomic Time commenced in 1955 and led up to the present definition of the second (see below) based on the period of the hyperfine structure transition frequency of the atom of cesium-133.

Multiples of the ephemeris second are analogous to those of the second of Universal Time, e.g., ephemeris day = 86400 ephemeris seconds. Occasionally the older designation *mean day* (not to be confused with the mean solar day) is used for ephemeris day. It is also sometimes stated that the mean day equals 86400 seconds of the mean solar day (i.e., seconds of Universal Time) at the time 1900.0. This is, however, incorrect. The mean day is NEWCOMB's calculated mean value of the mean solar day during the period 1680–1895.

Units of time derived from atomic transitions • Atomic Time

Atomic Time is based on the frequencies corresponding to hyperfine structure transitions in the atoms of the cesium, hydrogen and thallium nuclides ^{133}Cs, ^{1}H and ^{205}Tl; in the classical interpretation such transitions are due to the precession of the electrons of the outer shell (photoelectrons) in the magnetic field of the nucleus. The hydrogen frequency is measured in a *hydrogen maser* and the cesium and thallium frequencies in an *atomic beam resonance apparatus*. To obtain time intervals and time scales the periods of the atomic frequencies must be counted continuously. A

typical instrument for this purpose is variously known as a cesium beam apparatus, cesium atomic clock or cesium time and frequency standard.

Since the ephemeris second can be determined only with an uncertainty of several times 10^{-9} s, the 13th General Conference on Weights and Measures[5] in 1967 redefined the base SI unit second *(atomic second)* as the duration of 9192631770 periods of the radiation corresponding to the transition between the hyperfine structure levels in the ground state of the ^{133}Cs nuclide. The number specified in this definition is so chosen that the atomic second coincides as closely as possible with the ephemeris second.

In the best of present day primary cesium time and frequency standards, after allowance has been made for all known perturbations, the emitted frequency deviates from the frequency of the unperturbed atomic transitions by a factor of the order of 10^{-13} only[6]. This corresponds to a time difference between two atomic clocks of 1 s in 300000 years. The base SI unit, the second, can therefore be determined with an uncertainty of about 10^{-13} s.

In 1971, the 14th General Conference on Weights and Measures[7] approved the definition of the International Atomic Time Scale (TAI [Temps Atomique International]) proposed in 1970 by the International Committee for Weights and Measures. This definition was derived by weighted averaging of the time scales from the atomic clocks of various institutes and is intended for scientific usage. The starting point of TAI (January 1, 1958, 0^h TAI) coincides with January 1, 1958, 0^h UT2. TAI is not broadcast by time signals.

Other units

Multiples of the base SI unit, the second (see table, page 16):

minute (min)	1 min = 60 s
hour (h)	1 h = 3600 s
day (d)	1 d = 86400 s

Coordinated Universal Time

Since the beginning of 1972 the only time signals broadcast have been those based on the combination of atomic and universal time developed by the Comité Consultatif International des Radiocommunications (CCIR)[8] and given the name Coordinated Universal Time (UTC). This has as its scale measure, the TAI second, and can deviate from UT 1 by up to 0.9 s. UTC differs from TAI by many seconds (by mid-1974, for example, TAI was about 13 s ahead). To ensure approximate coincidence of UTC with UT 1, a leap second is added as necessary in UTC at the end of a UTC calendar quarter-year (preferably the end of December and the end of June). With the present rotational velocity of the earth, one or two such leap seconds must be added each calendar year. This means that from time to time there is a leap minute of 61 s, a scale hour of 3601 s, and a calendar day of 86401 s. In the same way, with an increase in the rotational velocity of the earth it is occasionally necessary to subtract a second from UTC. A second is simultaneously added to or subtracted from, all zone times based on UTC; in the CET zone, such a second is always the last second of the first hour starting a quarter-year. On account of these added or subtracted seconds, the number of seconds in the calendar year is no longer constant.

The General Conference on Weights and Measurements[10] has recommended the general use of UTC (as basis of zonal times).

References

[1] STILLE, U., *Messen und Rechnen in der Physik*, 2nd ed., Vieweg, Braunschweig, 1961; BECKER, G., *PTB-Mitteilungen*, **76**, 315 and 415 (1966); BECKER, G., *Naturwiss.*, **54**, 330 (1967); JESPERSEN and FITZ-RANDOLPH, *From Sundials to Atomic Clocks: Understanding Time and Frequency*, National Bureau of Standards, Monograph 155, Washington, 1977.

[2] Bureau des Longitudes, *Annuaire pour l'an 1967*, Gauthier-Villars, Paris, 1967, page 270.

[3] Comité International des Poids et Mesures, *Procès-verbaux des séances*, **25**, 77 (1957).

[4] Conférence Générale des Poids et Mesures, *Comptes rendus des séances de la 11e Conférence Générale des Poids et Mesures, Paris 1960*, Gauthier-Villars, Paris, 1961, page 86.

[5] Conférence Générale des Poids et Mesures, *Comptes rendus des séances de la 13e Conférence Générale des Poids et Mesures, Paris 1967/68*, Gauthier-Villars, Paris, 1968, page 103.

[6] HELLWIG, H., *Radio Science*, **14**, 541 (1979).

[7] Conférence Générale des Poids et Mesures, *Comptes rendus des séances de la 14e Conférence Générale des Poids et Mesures, Paris 1971*, Bureau International des Poids et Mesures, Sèvres, 1972, page 77.

[8] Comité Consultatif International des Radiocommunications (CCIR), *XIIIe Assemblée générale, Genève 1974*, Union Internationale des Télécommunications (UIT), Recommandation 7/460.

[9] Values from or calculated from data of the Bureau des Longitudes, *Annuaire pour l'an 1966*, Gauthier-Villars, Paris, 1965, pages 213, 251, 252.
[10] Conférence Générale des Poids et Mesures, *Comptes rendus des séances de la 15ᵉ Conférence Générale des Poids et Mesures, Paris 1975*, Bureau International des Poids et Mesures, Sèvres, 1976, page 104.

Plane angle (α, β, γ, ϑ, φ etc.)

Dimension: L^0

SI unit: radian (rad)

The plane angle φ between two straight lines a and b intersecting at the point M is defined as the ratio of the arc s of a circle (the center of which is point M) to the radius r of the circle:

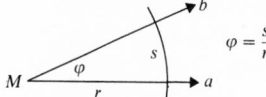

$$\varphi = \frac{s}{r}$$

In this definition, the plane angle is a quantity of dimension 1. The angle is positive if line b follows line a in a positive, i.e., counterclockwise, direction of rotation.

SI unit of plane angle

The *radian* (rad) is defined as the plane angle which, as the central angle of a circle of radius $r = 1$ m, cuts an arc $s = 1$ m out of the circumference:

$$1 \text{ rad} = \frac{1 \text{ m}}{1 \text{ m}}$$

In certain cases the radian can be replaced by the number 1.

Other units

The *degree* (°) is defined as the plane angle which, as the central angle of a circle, cuts out one 360th part of the circumference.

$$1° = \frac{\pi}{180} \text{ rad} = 0.01745329 \text{ rad}$$

The degree is divided sexagesimally into 60 minutes ('), each of which is subdivided into 60 seconds (″).

$$1' = \frac{1°}{60}; \quad 1'' = \frac{1'}{60} = \frac{1°}{3600}$$

Degrees, minutes and seconds can also be expressed in the form of decimal fractions; the unit symbol is then placed directly after the last digit of the fraction.
The *gon* (gon) or *new degree* (ᵍ) is defined as the plane angle which, as the central angle of a circle, cuts out one 400th part of the circumference.

$$1 \text{ gon} = 1^\text{g} = \frac{\pi}{200} \text{ rad} = 0.01570796 \text{ rad}$$

Decimal parts of the angle unit gon can be formed by prefixes; for example:

decigon (dgon)	1 dgon $= 10^{-1}$ gon
centigon (cgon)	1 cgon $= 10^{-2}$ gon
milligon (mgon)	1 mgon $= 10^{-3}$ gon
microgon (μgon)	1 μgon $= 10^{-6}$ gon

Conversion of plane angles

		°	gon	rad
degree . . . . . 1°	=	1	1.1̇	1.745329×10^{-2}
minute . . . . . 1'	=	1.6×10^{-2}	$1.8\dot{5}1 \times 10^{-2}$	2.908882×10^{-4}
second . . . . . 1″	=	$2.\dot{7} \times 10^{-4}$	3.08642×10^{-4}	4.848137×10^{-6}
gon . . . . 1 gon =	}	9×10^{-1}	1	1.570796×10^{-2}
new degree . 1ᵍ	=			
new minute . 1ᶜ	=	9×10^{-3}	10^{-2}	1.570796×10^{-4}
new second . 1ᶜᶜ	=	9×10^{-5}	10^{-4}	1.570796×10^{-6}
radian . . . . . 1 rad =		5.729578×10	6.366198×10	1
right angle . . 1ᴸ	=	9×10	10^2	1.570796
perigon	=	3.6×10^2	4×10^2	6.283185

The following subdivisions of the angle unit new degree are in use:

new minute (ᶜ)	1ᶜ $= 0.01^\text{g}$
new second (ᶜᶜ)	1ᶜᶜ $= 0.0001^\text{g}$

The *perigon* is defined as the plane angle formed when the line b coincides with line a after a complete rotation around point M. There is no international symbol for this unit.

$$1 \text{ perigon} = 2\pi \text{ rad}$$

The right angle ($\llcorner$) is equal to one-quarter of the perigon.

$$1^\llcorner = \frac{1}{4} \text{ perigon} = \frac{\pi}{2} \text{ rad}$$

Solid angle (Ω)

Dimension: L^0

SI unit: steradian (sr)

The solid angle Ω is defined as the ratio of the area F of the surface of a sphere cut out by a cone whose apex coincides with the center M of the sphere to the square of the radius r of the sphere.

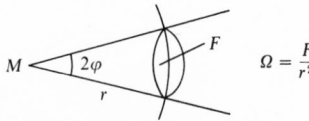

$$\Omega = \frac{F}{r^2}$$

In this definition, the solid angle is a quantity of dimension 1.

SI unit of solid angle

The steradian (sr) is defined as the solid angle subtended at the center of a sphere of radius $r = 1$ m by a cap of area $F = 1$ m² on the sphere's surface:

$$1 \text{ sr} = \frac{1 \text{ m}^2}{1 \text{ m}^2}$$

In certain cases the steradian can be replaced by the number 1.

Other units

Earlier units of solid angle also in use were the squares of the degree and gon units of plane angle (see under 'Plane angle' above) with the names *square degree* [symbol: (°)² or □°] and *square gon* [symbol: (ᵍ)²].

$$1 \, (°)^2 = 1 \, \square° = (\pi/180)^2 \text{ sr} = 3.046174 \times 10^{-4} \text{ sr}$$
$$1 \text{ gon}^2 = 1 \, (^\text{g})^2 = (\pi/200)^2 \text{ sr} = 2.467401 \times 10^{-4} \text{ sr}$$

Frequency (f, ν)

Dimension: T^{-1}

SI unit: hertz (Hz)

The hertz (Hz) is defined as the frequency f of a periodic process with the period $T = 1$ s.

$$1 \text{ HZ} = 1 \text{ s}^{-1}$$

The following decimal multiples of the hertz are in use:

kilohertz (kHz)	1 kHz $= 10^3$ Hz
megahertz (MHz)	1 MHz $= 10^6$ Hz
gigahertz (GHz)	1 GHz $= 10^9$ Hz
terahertz (THz)	1 THz $= 10^{12}$ Hz

Special name for the frequency unit

In Anglo-Saxon countries the frequency unit is sometimes still known as the *cycle per second* (c/s or cps) (1 c/s = 1 Hz).

Angular frequency (ω)

The SI unit of angular frequency (pulsatance) $\omega = 2\pi f$ is the reciprocal second (s⁻¹). The thousand multiple of the reciprocal second is the reciprocal millisecond (ms⁻¹ 1): Λ ms⁻¹ $= 10^{-3}$ s⁻¹. Angular frequency should not be given in terms of the frequency unit hertz.

Frequency of rotation (n)

Dimension: T^{-1}

SI unit: reciprocal second (s^{-1})

Other units

Reciprocal minute (min^{-1}): $1 \, min^{-1} = \dfrac{1}{60} \, s^{-1}$.

In *mechanical engineering,* the reciprocal value of a periodic duration is given in the following units, where the word *revolution* designates not an angle but the number of revolutions of a machine part completed in a given period of time:

revolutions per second (rps)
1 rps = $1 \, s^{-1}$

revolutions per minute (rpm)
1 rpm = $1.6 \times 10^{-2} \, s^{-1}$

revolutions per hour (rph)
1 rph = $2.7 \times 10^{-4} \, s^{-1}$

revolutions per day (rpd)
1 rpd = $1.15740 \times 10^{-5} \, s^{-1}$

Temperature

Dimension: $\ominus$

Basic SI unit: kelvin (K)

Unit in the extended ft-lb-s system:
degree Rankine (°R) = 5/9 K

Special units
- for the kelvin when the temperature is given in Celsius:

degree Celsius (°C)
1 °C = 1 K

- for the unit degree Rankine when the temperature is given in Fahrenheit:

degree Fahrenheit (°F)
1 °F = 1 °R

The concepts *temperature* and *heat* (quantity of heat) are rigorously differentiated in physics. The same quantity of heat can be distributed over a larger or smaller amount of the same material, which will have a lower temperature in the former case than in the latter.

Heat is a form of energy (see 'Energy, Work, Amount of heat', page 24), while the temperature of a body is a measure of the average kinetic energy per degree of freedom of the constituent molecules. Since it is related to the average movement of the latter, the concept of 'temperature' can be applied only to bodies consisting of a large number of molecules. This simple relationship no longer applies at very low temperatures.

Thermodynamic temperature (T) and temperature scales

The only term for temperature that allows clear and consistent expression of all the states, processes and laws of thermodynamics is the *thermodynamic temperature T,* whether this is introduced by way of relationships between quantities of classical thermodynamics (for instance, the amounts of heat and work in a Carnot cycle or the behavior of ideal gases) or statistically defined (either kinetically, starting from the energy distribution of the molecules of a system or from the characteristic parameter $\Theta = k \, T$ of the Gibbs canonical distribution in statistical mechanics)[1]. In a Carnot cycle operating between two temperatures T_1 and $T_2 < T_1$ the amounts of heat Q_1 and Q_2 absorbed or liberated are proportional to the corresponding temperatures: $Q_1/Q_2 = T_1/T_2$. According to the Second Law of Thermodynamics the thermodynamic temperature T has a lowest value below which it cannot fall and which can be given the value zero: the 'absolute zero' of thermodynamics. In a Carnot cycle operating between a finite temperature T_1 and the absolute zero (a special case in physics) the efficiency (η = work done, ΔA, divided by the amount of heat removed, ΔQ) attains the value 1.

International System of Units

The base SI unit of thermodynamic temperature is the kelvin (K), defined[2-4] as the fraction 1/273.16 of the thermodynamic temperature T_{tr} of the triple point of water (the point at which the solid, liquid and gaseous phases of pure water are in equilibrium). The same unit and symbol are also used to express an interval or difference of temperature[3].

This definition is also the basis of the thermodynamic *Kelvin temperature scale*[5], starting at the absolute zero $T = 0$ K, introduced by Lord KELVIN in 1848; as a linear scale this can be constructed from any variable quantity bearing a linear relationship to the thermodynamic temperature T. Such a simple relationship relates the energy of ideal gases to a function of temperature expressed by the equation of state $T = p \, V_m/R$ (where p = gas pressure, V_m = molar volume of an ideal gas, R = molar constant (see 'Amount of substance', page 45, and 'Fundamental Physical Constants', page 47) and can be determined experimentally by means of a gas thermometer.

Anglo-Saxon unit

The Anglo-Saxon unit of thermodynamic temperature is the degree Rankine (°R), defined as 5/9 of the kelvin[6]. The thermodynamic Rankine scale starts at the absolute zero $T = 0$ °R, and can likewise be realized by gas thermometry.
When expressing temperature interval $\Delta T = T_1 - T_2$ the degree Rankine is usually written degR.

Celsius temperature (t) and Celsius temperature scale

The *Celsius temperature* (t) assigned to a system is defined as the difference between the corresponding thermodynamic temperature T of the system and a special thermodynamic temperature T_0 the value of which has no special physical significance but is arbitrarily chosen and conventionally fixed[3,5,6]: $t = T - T_0$. The zero point defining Celsius temperature is the temperature $T_0 = $ 273.15 K lying 0.01 K below the triple point of water.
To express Celsius temperatures the base SI unit kelvin is designated simply degree Celsius (°C). The same unit designation and symbol are also used for expressing Celsius temperature intervals or Celsius temperature differences.
The thermodynamic *Celsius scale*[5] is therefore subdivided into the same intervals as the thermodynamic Kelvin scale but has a zero point displaced by 273.15 K. The Celsius temperature $t_0 = $ **0** °C expresses the same temperature as the thermodynamic temperature $T_0 = 273.15$ K.

Fahrenheit temperature (ϑ) and Fahrenheit temperature scale

In English-speaking countries Fahrenheit temperature (ϑ) also continues in use for the time being. The Fahrenheit temperature assigned to a system is defined as the difference between the corresponding thermodynamic temperature T of the system and a special temperature $T_{0,F}$ established by convention and without special physical significance[6]: $\vartheta = T - T_{0,F}$. The zero point defining Fahrenheit temperature is the temperature $T_{0,F} = 459.67$ °R lying 32.018 °R below the triple point of water.
To express Fahrenheit temperatures the degree Rankine is designated simply degree Fahrenheit (°F). The same unit designation and symbol are also used for expressing Fahrenheit temperature intervals. For expressing a Fahrenheit temperature difference $\Delta \vartheta = \vartheta_1 - \vartheta_2$ the degree Fahrenheit is usually written degF. The thermodynamic *Fahrenheit scale*[6] is therefore subdivided into the same intervals as the thermodynamic Rankine scale but has a zero point displaced by 459.67 degR. The Fahrenheit temperature $\vartheta_0 = $ **0** °F expresses the same temperature as the thermodynamic temperature $T_{0,F} = 459.67$ °R.

Fundamental points and temperature conversions

Up to 1954 the thermodynamic scales were based on the interval between the melting point of ice (ice point) and the condensing point of steam (steam point), two fixed points assigned the values 273.15 K and 373.15 K. The new definition of the scale[2] by the triple point of water $T_{tr} = 273.16$ K and the absolute zero of thermodynamics $T = 0$ K means that the temperatures of the ice and steam point are now values that must be determined experimentally.

Fundamental points of thermodynamic temperature scales

	Temperature value at	
	absolute zero	triple point of water*
kelvin (K)	0	273.16
degree Celsius (°C)	−273.15	0.01
degree Rankine (°R)	0	491.688
degree Fahrenheit (°F)	−459.67	32.018

* Temperature at which the solid, liquid and gaseous phases of water are in equilibrium.

Conversions

– between temperature units and unit designations of temperature:

$$1\,°R = 1\,°F = \frac{5}{9}K = \frac{5}{9}°C$$

$$1\,K = 1\,°C = \frac{9}{5}°R = \frac{9}{5}°F$$

– of numerical values on the four thermodynamic temperature scales ($T = T_K K = T_R\,°R$; $t = t_c\,°C$; $\vartheta = \vartheta_F\,°F$):

$$T_K = \frac{5}{9}T_R = t_c + 273.15 = \frac{5}{9}(\vartheta_F + 459.67)$$

$$T_R = \frac{9}{5}T_K = \vartheta_F + 459.67 = \frac{9}{5}t_c + 491.67$$

$$t_c = T_K - 273.15 = \frac{5}{9}(T_R - 491.67) = \frac{5}{9}(\vartheta_F - 32)$$

$$\vartheta_F = T_R - 459.67 = \frac{9}{5}T_K - 459.67 = \frac{9}{5}t_c + 32$$

International Practical Temperature Scale of 1968 (IPTS-68)

The IPTS-68 was adopted by the International Committee for Weights and Measures[5,7,10] in 1968 under the powers conferred on it by Resolution 8 of the 13th General Conference on Weights and Measures[3] in 1967.

The IPTS-68 is based on the assigned values of the temperatures (column 2 of the table below) of a number of reproducible equilibrium states (defining fixed points; column 1 of the table) and on standard instruments calibrated at these temperatures. Interpolation between the fixed point temperatures is effected by means of formulas establishing the relationship between the readings of the standard instruments and the temperature values.

The *International Practical Kelvin Temperature* (T_{68}) and the *International Practical Celsius Temperature* (t_{68}) measured in the

Defining fixed points of the IPTS-68*

Defining fixed points	Assigned value	
	T_{68} in K	t_{68} in °C
Triple point of equilibrium hydrogen	13.81	−259.34
Equilibrium between liquid and vapor phase of equilibrium hydrogen at 33330.6 Pa (= 25/76 atm)◊	17.042	−256.108
Boiling point of equilibrium hydrogen◊	20.28	−252.87
Boiling point of neon◊	27.102	−246.048
Triple point of oxygen	54.361	−218.789
Triple point of argon	83.798	−189.352
Dew point of oxygen◊	90.188	−182.962
Triple point of water	273.16	0.01
Boiling point of water	373.15	100
Freezing point of tin	505.1181	231.9681
Freezing point of zinc	692.73	419.58
Freezing point of silver	1235.08	961.93
Freezing point of gold	1337.58	1064.43

* Except for the triple points and one equilibrium hydrogen point (17.042 K), the assigned temperatures are for equilibrium states at a pressure $p_0 = 101325$ Pa (= 1 atm). In those cases where differing isotopic abundances could significantly affect the fixed point temperature, specified abundances must be used.
◊ Fractionation of isotopes or impurities dictates the use of the boiling points of hydrogen and neon (negligibly small boiling fraction) and of the dew point of oxygen (negligibly small liquefying fraction).

IPTS-68 are defined by different relations in several adjacent temperature ranges. This may lead to discontinuities in the higher derivatives of T_{68} and t_{68}.

The unit of the International Practical Kelvin Temperature T_{68} is the base SI unit Kelvin (K). The International Practical Celsius Temperature t_{68} is specified in degrees Celsius (°C). The relationship $t_{68} = T_{68} - T_0$, where $T_0 = 273.15$ K, is also valid for the (empirical) temperature values T_{68} and t_{68}.

The defining fixed points are obtained by realizing equilibrium states between the phases of pure substances. The following standard instruments and interpolation equations are used: in the range 13.81 K $< T_{68} <$ 630.74 K (freezing point of antimony as secondary reference point), the platinum resistance thermometer; in the range 630.74 K $< T_{68} <$ 1337.58 K (freezing point of gold as a defining fixed point), the platinum 10% rhodium/platinum thermocouple; above 1337.58 K, the Planck radiation law given in spectral densities $L_{e\lambda}$ (see page 38), with 1337.58 K as the reference temperature and the value 0.014388 meter kelvin for the second radiation constant c_2 (see page 48).

The IPTS-68 has been constructed in such a way that any temperature T_{68} measured on it is a close approximation to the numerically corresponding thermodynamic temperature T: $T_{68} = T + \Delta T_{68} \approx T$, and analogous by $t_{68} = t + \Delta t_{68} \approx t$. Estimated values for the deviations $\Delta T_{68} = \Delta t_{68}$ are published from time to time by the Comité Consultatif de Thermométrie. At the triple point of water, the temperatures T and T_{68} are by definition identical.

The above table of defining fixed points takes into account the changes announced in the *Amended Edition, 1975,* of the IPTS-68, adopted in 1975 by the 15th General Conference on Weights and Measures[10].

Practical temperature scales for use at low temperatures

The temperatures in the range 0.2 K to 5.2 K were derived from the measured vapor pressures of ⁴He and ³He. The upper limits of application were given by the critical points of these gases (5.2 K for ⁴He and 3.3 K for ³He). The lower limits corresponded to the temperatures at which the vapor pressures of the gases were too low for practical measurement. The '⁴He scale of 1958'[8] and the '³He scale of 1962'[9] were recommended scales on which (empirical) temperatures T_{58} or T_{62} were given.

The '⁴He scale of 1958' recommended in 1958 by the International Committee for Weights and Measures was defined by a table showing the temperature dependence of the vapor pressure of ⁴He. The '³He scale of 1962' recommended in 1962 by the International Committee for Weights and Measures was defined by an equation for the temperature dependence of the vapor pressure of ³He.

The Comité Consultatif de Thermométrie is to recommend new scales for the low temperature range; these will be published in the journal *Metrologia*.

References

[1] For example, DE BOER, J., *Metrologia*, **1**, 158 (1965).
[2] Conférence Générale des Poids et Mesures, *Comptes rendus des séances de la 10ᵉ Conférale Générale des Poids et Mesures, Paris 1954,* Gauthier-Villars, Paris 1955, page 79.
[3] Conférence Générale des Poids et Mesures, *Comptes rendus des séances de la 13ᵉ Conférence Générale des Poids et Mesures, Paris 1967/1968,* Bureau International des Poids et Mesures, Sèvres, 1969, pages 18, 19, 60, 63, 70, 104, 105, and A1.
[4] Bureau International des Poids et Mesures, *Le Système International d'Unités (SI),* 2nd ed., Bureau International des Poids et Mesures, Sèvres, 1973, page 7.
[5] Comité Consultatif de Thermométrie, The International Practical Temperature Scale of 1968, Amended Edition of 1975, *Metrologia*, **12**, 7 (1976).
[6] International Organization for Standardization (ISO), *Quantities and Units of Heat,* Draft International Standard ISO/DIS 31/IV, 1975; British Standards Institution, *Conversion Factors and Tables,* B.S.350: Part 1, 1959, page 26.
[7] Comité International des Poids et Mesures, *Comité Consultatif de Thermométrie, 8ᵉ session, 1967,* Bureau International des Poids et Mesures, Sèvres, 1969, page A1 (see also *Metrologia*, **1**, 35 [1969]; National Physical Laboratory, *The International Practical Temperature Scale of 1968,* HMSO, London, 1969; BARBER, C.R., *Nature*, **222**, 929 [1969]).
[8] Comité International des Poids et Mesures (Comité Consultatif de Thermométrie, 5ᵉ session, 1958), *Procès-verbaux des séances,* **26-A**, 73, T192 (1959); *Nat. Bur. Stand. J. Res.*, **64A**, 1 (1960).
[9] Comité International des Poids et Mesures, *Procès-verbaux des séances,* **30**, 25, 124 (1962); SYDORIAK et al., in *Comité Consultatif de Thermométrie, 6ᵉ session, 1962,* page 183; *Nat. Bur. Stand. J. Res.*, **68A**, 547, 559, 567, 579 (1964).
[10] Conférence Générale des Poids et Mesures, *Comptes rendus des séances de la 15ᵉ Conférence Générale des Poids et Mesures, Paris 1975,* Bureau International des Poids et Mesures, Sèvres, 1976, page 105 and Appendix 2.

Density (ϱ)

Dimension: $L^{-3} M$

SI unit: kilogram per cubic meter ($kg\ m^{-3}$)

Unit in ft-lb-s system: pound per cubic foot ($lb\ ft^{-3}$) = $1.60184634 \times 10\ kg\ m^{-3}$

The *density* (ϱ) of a substance is the ratio of its mass m to its volume V:

$$\varrho = \frac{m}{V}$$

Since the density of a substance depends on its state, the latter should generally be specified (temperature, pressure, humidity, etc.).

The *standard density* (ϱ_n) of a substance is its density under standard physical conditions ($t_n = 0\,°C$; $p_n = 101325\ Pa = 1.01325\ bar$). Important density constants are

- standard density of dry air free of carbon dioxide[1] ($0\,°C$; $101325\ Pa$):

$\varrho_n(air) = 1.2928 \times 10^{-3}\ kg\ dm^{-3}$

- standard density of mercury[2] ($0\,°C$; $101325\ Pa$):

$\varrho_n(Hg) = 13.59508\ kg\ dm^{-3}$

- maximum density of water[3] ($\approx 3.98\,°C$; $101325\ Pa$; air-free):

$\varrho_{max}(H_2O) = 0.999972\ kg\ dm^{-3}$ ($s = 3 \times 10^{-6}\ kg\ dm^{-3}$)

The *relative density* or *density number* (d) of a substance is the ratio of its density to the density of a reference substance under conditions which must be stated for both. This is a quantity of dimension 1. The earlier term 'specific gravity' should no longer be used. The usual reference density for liquids and solids is the maximum density of water [$\varrho_{max}(H_2O)$], for gases the standard density of air [$\varrho_n(air)$], as shown in the following example:

Density of mercury relative to water:

$d(Hg) = \varrho_n(Hg)/\varrho_{max}(H_2O) = 13.59546$

Since two temperatures are involved in the specification of a relative density (the ratio of two densities) that for example of a solid or liquid substance A at $20\,°C$ with respect to the maximum density of water is given by the ratio

$\dfrac{\text{density of the substance A at } 20\,°C}{\text{density of water at } 4\,°C}$, with the symbol d_4^{20}.

The quantity *specific weight* (γ) is still occasionally used. It is the product of the density (ϱ) of a substance and the local acceleration due to gravity (g_{loc}) : $\gamma = \varrho\ g_{loc}$. Specific weight therefore depends not only on thermodynamic variables but also on the local acceleration due to gravity, so that unlike density it is *not* a characteristic property of a substance. The usual unit of specific weight is the newton per cubic decimeter ($N\ dm^{-3}$).

Conversion of Anglo-Saxon units of density

		lb ft^{-3}	kg m^{-3}
pound per cubic foot .... 1 lb ft^{-3} =	1	1.60185 × 10
pound per gallon (US)........ 1 lb gal^{-1} =	1728/231	1.19826 × 10^2
pound per gallon (UK) .... 1 lb gal^{-1} =	6.22883	9.97764 × 10

References

[1] OTTO and THOMAS, in HAUSEN, H. (Ed.), *Landolt-Börnstein, Physikalisch-chemische Tabellen*, 6th ed., volume IV, part 4/a, Springer, Berlin, 1967, page 174; DIN, F., *Thermodynamic Functions of Gases*, volume 2, Butterworth, London, 1956, page 39.

[2] COOK and STONE, *Phil. Trans. Roy. Soc.*, 250A, 279 (1957); COOK, A. H., *Phil. Trans. Roy. Soc.*, 254A, 125 (1961); BEATTIE et al., *Proc. Amer. Acad. Arts Sci.*, 74, 371 (1940/42).

[3] Comité International des Poids et Mesures, *Procès-verbaux des séances*, 22, 77 (1950); STILLE, U., *Messen und Rechnen in der Physik*, 2nd ed., Vieweg, Braunschweig, 1961, page 286.

Linear velocity ($v = ds/dt$; s: distance)

Dimension: $L\ T^{-1}$

SI unit: meter per second ($m\ s^{-1}$)

Unit in ft-lb-s system: foot per second ($ft\ s^{-1}$) = $0.3048\ m\ s^{-1}$

Other units

Conversion of Anglo-Saxon units of linear velocity

		ft s^{-1}	km h^{-1}	m s^{-1}
foot per minute ..... 1 ft min^{-1} =	1.6 × 10^{-2}	1.8288 × 10^{-2}	5.08 × 10^{-3}
foot per second ..... 1 ft s^{-1} =	1	1.09728	3.048 × 10^{-1}
(statute) mile per hour .... 1 mile* h^{-1} =	1.46	1.609344	4.4704 × 10^{-1}
*Symbol in the US: mi.				

Conversion of metric units of density

		mg mm^{-3} g cm^{-3} kg dm^{-3}	mg cm^{-3} g dm^{-3} kg m^{-3}
microgram per cubic centimeter ....1 µg cm^{-3} = or milliliter ....1 µg mL^{-1} = milligram per cubic decimeter ....1 mg dm^{-3} = or liter ....1 mg L^{-1} =		10^{-6}	10^{-3}
milligram per cubic centimeter ....1 mg cm^{-3} = or milliliter ....1 mg mL^{-1} = gram per cubic decimeter ....1 g dm^{-3} = or liter ....1 g L^{-1} = kilogram per cubic meter ....1 kg m^{-3} =		10^{-3}	1
picogram per cubic micrometer ....1 pg µm^{-3} = milligram per cubic millimeter ....1 mg mm^{-3} = or microliter ....1 mg µL^{-1} = gram per cubic centimeter ....1 g cm^{-3} = or milliliter ....1 g mL^{-1} = kilogram per cubic decimeter ....1 kg dm^{-3} = or liter ....1 kg L^{-1} =		1	10^3

Conversion of metric units of linear velocity

		m min^{-1}	km h^{-1}	m s^{-1}
centimeter per second ... 1 cm s^{-1} =	6 × 10^{-1}	3.6 × 10^{-2}	10^{-2}
meter per minute .... 1 m min^{-1} =	1	6 × 10^{-2}	1.6 × 10^{-2}
kilometer per hour ...... 1 km h^{-1} =	1.6 × 10	1	2.7 × 10^{-1}
meter per second .... 1 m s^{-1} =	6 × 10	3.6	1
kilometer per second .... 1 km s^{-1} =	6 × 10^4	3.6 × 10^3	10^3

Conversion of nautical units of linear velocity

		km h^{-1}	m s^{-1}
knot .... 1 kn = (= international sea mile per hour)	1.852	5.14 × 10^{-1}
knot (UK) .... 1 kn (UK) = (= nautical mile per hour)	1.853181	5.147724 × 10^{-1}

Angular velocity ($\omega = d\varrho/dt$)

Dimension: $L^0\,T^{-1}$

SI unit: radian per second (rad s^{-1})

Other units

Conversion of units of angular velocity

	°s^{-1}	gon s^{-1}	rad s^{-1}
radian per minute .. 1 rad min^{-1} =	9.54930×10^{-1}	1.06103	$1.\dot{6} \times 10^{-2}$
degree per second .. 1° s^{-1} =	1	$1.\dot{1}$	1.74533×10^{-2}
degree per minute .. 1° min^{-1} =	$1.\dot{6} \times 10^{-2}$	$1.8\dot{5}\dot{1} \times 10^{-2}$	2.90888×10^{-4}
gon per second .. 1 gon s^{-1} =	9×10^{-1}	1	1.57080×10^{-2}
gon per minute .. 1 gon min^{-1} =	1.5×10^{-2}	$1.\dot{6} \times 10^{-2}$	2.61799×10^{-4}
radian per second .. 1 rad s^{-1} =	5.72958×10	6.36620×10	1

Acceleration ($a = dv/dt$)

Dimension: $L^0\,T^{-2}$

SI unit: meter per second squared (m s^{-2})

Unit in ft-lb-s system: foot per second squared (ft s^{-2}) = 0.3048 m s^{-2}

Other units

Conversion of metric units of acceleration

	cm s^{-2} = Gal	km h^{-1} s^{-1}	m s^{-2}
centimeter per second squared .... 1 cm s^{-2} =	1	3.6×10^{-2}	10^{-2}
Gal*.............. 1 Gal =			
kilometer per hour per second........ 1 km h^{-1} s^{-1} =	$2.\dot{7} \times 10$	1	$2.\dot{7} \times 10^{-1}$
meter per second squared .... 1 m s^{-2} =	10^2	3.6	1

*The name Gal is used only for the unit of acceleration due to gravity (see below and page 51).

Conversion of Anglo-Saxon units of acceleration

	ft s^{-2}	mile h^{-1} s^{-1}	m s^{-2}
foot per second squared ... 1 ft s^{-2} =	1	$6.8\dot{1} \times 10^{-1}$	3.048×10^{-1}
mile per hour per second........ 1 mile* h^{-1} s^{-1} =	1.46	1	4.4704×10^{-1}

*(statute) mile, symbol in US: mi.

Acceleration due to gravity (g_n)

The internationally accepted value[1] of the acceleration due to gravity is

$$g_n = 9.80665 \text{ m s}^{-2} = 980.665 \text{ Gal} \approx 32.17405 \text{ ft s}^{-2}$$

Reference

[1] Conférence Générale des Poids et Mesures, *Comptes rendus des séances de la 3e Conférence Générale des Poids et Mesures, Paris 1901,* Gauthier-Villars, Paris, 1901, page 70.

Angular acceleration ($\alpha = d\omega/dt = d^2\varrho/dt^2$)

Dimension: $L^0\,T^{-2}$

SI unit: radian per second squared (rad s^{-2})

Other units

Conversion of units of angular acceleration

	° s^{-2}	gon s^{-2}	rad s^{-2}
degree per second squared ...... 1° s^{-2} =	1	$1.\dot{1}$	1.74533×10^{-2}
gon per second squared ....1 gon s^{-2} =	9×10^{-1}	1	1.57080×10^{-2}
radian per second squared ....1 rad s^{-2} =	5.72958×10	6.36620×10	1

Force (F)

Dimension: L M T^{-2}

SI unit: newton (N)

Unit in ft-lb-s system: poundal (pdl) = 0.138 254 954 376 N

SI unit of force

The newton (N) is defined as the force that confers an acceleration of 1 m s^{-2} on a mass of 1 kg:

$$1 \text{ N} = 1 \text{ m kg s}^{-2}$$

ft-lb-s unit of force

The poundal (pdl) is defined as the force that imparts an acceleration of 1 ft s^{-2} on a mass of 1 lb:

$$1 \text{ pdl} = 1 \text{ ft lb s}^{-2}$$

Other units

The dyne (dyn) was the unit of force in the CGS system:

$$1 \text{ dyn} = 1 \text{ cm g s}^{-2} = 10^{-5} \text{ N}$$

In technology, *noncoherent* 'technical' units of force are still in use in which the mass unit is multiplied not by the coherent unit of acceleration but by the standard acceleration due to gravity g_n (see left-hand column). The 'technical' units of force are in themselves superfluous and are steadily being replaced by the SI unit newton (N) and its multiples and submultiples.

Conversion of noncoherent units of force

	pdl	N
pond* [$g_n \times (1$ g)] ....1 p =	7.09316×10^{-2}	9.80665×10^{-3}
gram-force [$g_n \times (1$ g)] ...1 gf =		
pound-force [$g_n \times (1$ lb)] . 1 lbf =	3.21740×10	4.44822
kilopond* [$g_n \times (1$ kg)] ....1 kp =	7.09316×10	9.80665
kilogram-force [$g_n \times (1$ kg)] ....1 kgf =		
ton-force (UK) [$g_n \times (1$ ton)] ....1 tonf =	7.20699×10^4	9.96402×10^3
long ton-force (US) [$g_n \times (1$ ton)] ....1 tonf =		

*In Switzerland, the terms gram-force (gf) and kilogram-force (kgf) are usually employed.

Weight-force

In German-speaking countries, in order to avoid the ambiguity in the meaning of the German word for 'weight' used for both mass m and force $G = m\,g$ (where g is the local acceleration due to gravity), it has been suggested[1] that the term should be avoided and replaced by the expressions 'mass' and 'weight-force' as appropriate. Thus a body whose mass on the balance is $m = 65$ kg at a locality where the acceleration due to gravity $g_{PTB} = 9.812523$ m s^{-2} exerts a weight-force $G = m\,g_{PTB} = 637.814$ N (the standard weight-force $m\,g_n = 637.432$ N) (PTB: Physikalisch-Technische Bundesanstalt Braunschweig).

In English-speaking countries the term 'weight-force' does not exist. Hence, to resolve the ambiguity in the meaning of the word 'weight', it is important to differentiate between whether mass or force is meant by using SI units properly; i.e., by using kilograms when mass is intended and newtons where force is intended.

Reference

[1] Deutscher Normenausschuss, *Masse, Gewicht, Gewichtskraft, Fallbeschleunigung (Begriffe)* DIN 1305, June 1968, Beuth, Berlin, 1968.

Pressure (p) (= force per unit area)

Dimension: L^{-1} M T^{-2}

SI unit: Pascal (Pa)

Unit in ft-lb-s system: poundal per square foot (pdl ft^{-2}) = 1.488163944 Pa

SI unit of pressure

The pascal (Pa) is defined as the pressure, acting uniformly on an area, which exerts a force of 1 N vertically on 1 m^2 of the area. The name pascal was approved by the 14th General Conference on Weights and Measures, 1971[1]:
$$1\,\text{Pa} = 1\,\text{N m}^{-2} = 1\,\text{m}^{-1}\,\text{kg s}^{-2}$$

ft-lb-s unit of pressure

The poundal per square foot (pdl ft^{-2}) is the ratio of the force unit poundal (pdl) to the area unit square foot (ft^{-2}):
$$1\,\text{pdl ft}^{-2} = 1\,\text{ft}^{-1}\,\text{lb s}^{-2}$$

Other units

(a) The *bar* (bar) is the special name for a pressure unit 10^5 times greater than the pascal:
$$1\,\text{bar} = 10^5\,\text{Pa}$$

The *millibar* (mbar) has been the internationally accepted unit of pressure in meteorology since 1955[2]:
$$1\,\text{mbar} = 10^{-3}\,\text{bar} = 10^2\,\text{Pa}$$

The symbol mb, often wrongly used for the millibar, is assigned to the millibarn (mb) (see page 12). The microbar (μbar) is mainly used for sound pressure measurements in acoustics:
$$1\,\mu\text{bar} = 10^{-6}\,\text{bar} = 10^{-1}\,\text{Pa}$$

Conversion of metric units of pressure

			μbar	Pa = N m^{-2}	mbar	bar
microbar	1 μbar	=	1	10^{-1}	10^{-3}	10^{-6}
pascal	1 Pa	=	} 10	1	10^{-2}	10^{-5}
newton per square meter .	1 N m^{-2} =					
millibar	1 mbar	=	10^3	10^2	1	10^{-3}
bar	1 bar	=	10^6	10^5	10^3	1

(b) The *noncoherent technical units of pressure* are defined as ratios of a technical unit of force (see page 22) to a unit of area:

1 kilopond per square meter (kp m^{-2}) = 9.80665 Pa
1 kilopond per square centimeter (kp cm^{-2}) =} 98066.5 Pa
1 technical atmosphere (at) =

(c) *Noncoherent special units of pressure:*

The *physical atmosphere* (atm) was defined[3] in connection with the International Practical Temperature Scale of 1948 (IPTS-48) by the relation
$$1\,\text{atm} = 101325\,\text{Pa}$$

The *torr* (torr) is defined by the relation
$$1\,\text{torr} = \frac{1}{760}\,\text{atm} = 133.322368\,\text{Pa}$$

The *conventional millimeter of water* (mmH$_2$O) is defined as the pressure exerted by a column of liquid 1 mm in height with a density of 1 g cm^{-3} under the standard acceleration due to gravity g_n:
$$1\,\text{mmH}_2\text{O} = 0.1\,\text{cm} \times 1\,\text{g cm}^{-3} \times 980.665\,\text{cm s}^{-2} = 9.80665\,\text{Pa}$$

In practice this definition is realized by a column of water 1 mm in height at 4 °C at standard pressure (101325 Pa).

The *conventional millimeter of mercury* (mmHg) is defined in accordance with the International Barometric Conventions of the World Meteorological Organization[2] as the pressure exerted by a column of liquid 1 mm in height with a density of 13.5951 g cm^{-3} under the standard acceleration due to gravity g_n:
$$1\,\text{mmHg} = 0.1\,\text{cm} \times 13.5951\,\text{g cm}^{-3} \times 980.665\,\text{cm s}^{-2}$$
$$= 133.322387\,\text{Pa}$$
$$= 1.00000014\,\text{torr}$$

In practice this definition is realized by a column of mercury 1 mm in height at 0 °C at standard pressure (101325 Pa). The torr is preferred to the mmHg since unlike the latter it is independent of material constants.

The noncoherent *Anglo-Saxon* units of pressure, namely the *conventional inch of water* (inH$_2$O), the *conventional foot of water* (ftH$_2$O) and the *conventional inch of mercury* (inHg), are defined by the formulas given for the conventional millimeter of water and conventional millimeter of mercury with the metric unit of length (0.1 cm) replaced by 1 inch or 1 foot.

Standard pressure (p_n)

Standard pressure in both physics and meteorology is
$$p_n = 101325\,\text{Pa} = 1\,\text{atm} = 760\,\text{torr}$$

It is approximately equal to the mean atmospheric pressure at sea level under the standard acceleration due to gravity.

References

[1] Conférence Générale des Poids et Mesures, *Comptes rendus des séances de la 14e Conférence Générale des Poids et Mesures, Paris 1971*, Bureau International des Poids et Mesures, Sèvres, 1972, page 78.
[2] World Meteorological Organization, *International Barometric Conventions, Toronto 1953*, Recommendation II-2; British Standards Institution, *Barometer Conventions and Tables*, B.S.2520, 1954; STILLE, U., *Messen und Rechnen in der Physik*, 2nd ed., Vieweg, Braunschweig, 1961, page 356.
[3] Conférence Générale des Poids et Mesures, *Comptes rendus des séances de la 9e Conférence Générale des Poids et Mesures, Paris 1948*, Gauthier-Villars, Paris, 1949, pages 57 and 89; *Comptes rendus des séances de la 10e Conférence Générale des Poids et Mesures, Paris 1954*, Gauthier-Villars, Paris, 1955, page 79.

Conversion of noncoherent units of pressure

			atm	pdl ft^{-2}	Pa
conventional millimeter of water	1 mm H$_2$O	=	} 9.67841 × 10^{-5}	6.58976	9.80665
kilopond° per square meter	1 kp m^{-2}	=			
pound-force per square foot	1 lbf ft^{-2}	=	4.72541 × 10^{-4}	3.21740 × 10	4.78803 × 10
torr	1 torr	=	1.31579 × 10^{-3}	8.95885 × 10	1.33322 × 10^2
conventional inch of water	1 inH$_2$O	=	2.45832 × 10^{-3}	1.67380 × 10^2	2.49089 × 10^2
conventional foot of water	1 ftH$_2$O	=	2.94998 × 10^{-2}	2.00856 × 10^3	2.98907 × 10^3
conventional inch of mercury	1 inHg	=	3.34211 × 10^{-2}	2.27555 × 10^3	3.38639 × 10^3
pound-force per square inch	1 lbf in^{-2}	=	6.80460 × 10^{-2}	4.63306 × 10^3	6.89476 × 10^3
technical atmosphere	1 at	=	9.67841 × 10^{-1}	6.58976 × 10^4	9.80665 × 10^4
physical atmosphere	1 atm	=	1	6.80873 × 10^4	1.01325 × 10^5
ton-force per square foot	1 tonf ft^{-2}	=	1.05849	7.20699 × 10^4	1.07252 × 10^5

° The term kilogram-force (kgf) is customary in Switzerland.

Energy, Work, Amount of Heat

Dimension: $L^2 M T^{-2}$

SI unit: joule (J)

Unit in ft-lb-s system: foot poundal (ft pdl) = $4.21401101 \times 10^{-2}$ J

Symbols

Energy	$E\,(W)$
Potential energy	E_p, V, Φ
Kinetic energy	E_k, K, T
Work	$W\,(A)$
Amount of heat	Q
Radiant energy	$Q, W\,(U, Q_e)$ (see also page 37)

Energy, work, and *amount of heat* are physical quantities of the same dimension and should therefore be measured in a common unit. This unification was made possible by the introduction of the International System of Units (SI).

Coherent units of energy

The joule is defined as the work performed when the point of application of a force of 1 N is moved 1 m in the direction of the force. When the special names for other derived SI units are used, the joule can also be expressed as the watt second (W s) or newton meter (N m):

$$1\,J = 1\,W\,s = 1\,N\,m = 1\,m^2\,kg\,s^{-2}$$

The foot poundal is the work performed when the point of application of a force of 1 pdl is moved 1 ft in the direction of the force:

$$1\,ft\,pdl = 1\,ft^2\,lb\,s^{-2}$$

Other units of energy

The *erg* (erg) was the unit of energy in the CGS system.

$$1\,erg = 1\,cm^2\,g\,s^{-2} = 10^{-7}\,J$$

Although the noncoherent, so-called 'mechanical', 'electrical' and 'caloric' units still in use will eventually be of mere historical interest, they are described below to facilitate the transition.

The transition process is also affecting the use of the 'calorie', a unit whose use is deeply rooted in technical and general terminology, in particular in expressing the physiological energy values of foodstuffs (see 'Energy Expenditure', page 228, 'Nutritional Standards', page 232, and 'Foods', pages 241–246). In this book, such values are given in joules as well as 'calories'. Where 'caloric' units are still used, they should be limited to cases where conversion into joules[1] is straightforward.

The unit *foot pound-force* (ft lbf) = 1.35582 J (for lbf, see page 22).

The unit *thermochemical calorie* (cal$_{thermochem}$) was newly defined in 1948[2–4]: $1\,cal_{thermochem} = 4.184$ J.

The *15° calorie* (cal$_{15}$), also known as the *gram-calorie,* is defined as the amount of heat required to raise the temperature of 1 g of water from 14.5 °C to 15.5 °C at a pressure of 101325 Pa: $1\,cal_{15} = 4.1855$ J. The values of the specific heat capacity of water between 0 and 100 °C agreed upon in 1950 by the International Committee for Weights and Measures[5] are given in joules and 15° calories (with a relative uncertainty of $\approx 0.1\%$) on page 51.

The *International Steam Table calorie* (cal$_{IT}$) was redefined in 1956 by the 5th International Steam Table Conference[2,3,6]: $1\,cal_{IT} = 4.1868$ J.

The unit *kilopond meter* (kp m) = 9.80665 J (for kp, see page 22).

The *liter atmosphere* (L atm) = $1\,dm^3 \times 101325\,Pa = 1.01325 \times 10^2$ J (for L, see page 13; for atm, see page 23).

Conversion of noncoherent units of energy

			kW h	ft pdl	J
foot pound-force	1 ft lbf	=	3.76616×10^{-7}	3.21740×10	1.35582
thermochemical calorie	1 cal$_{thermochem}$	=	1.162×10^{-6}	9.92878×10	4.184
15° calorie	1 cal$_{15}$	=	1.1626×10^{-6}	9.93234×10	4.1855
International Steam Table calorie	1 cal$_{IT}$	=	1.163×10^{-6}	9.93543×10	4.1868
kilopond meter*	1 kp m	=	2.72407×10^{-6}	2.32715×10^2	9.80665
liter atmosphere	1 L atm	=	2.81458×10^{-5}	2.40448×10^3	1.01325×10^2
British thermal unit	1 Btu	=	2.93071×10^{-4}	2.50569×10^4	1.05506×10^3
horsepower-hour	1 hp h	=	7.45700×10^{-1}	6.37046×10^7	2.68452×10^6
metric horsepower-hour	1 ch h or PS h	=	7.3549875×10^{-1}	6.28331×10^7	2.64780×10^6
kilowatt hour	1 kW h	=	1	8.54293×10^7	3.6×10^6
therm	1 therm	=	2.93071×10	2.50369×10^9	1.05506×10^8

* Also known as 'kilogram-force meter' (kgf m).

Conversion of units of energy used in atomic physics[2,7]

			kg	J	u	Ry
kilogram [$\triangleq E(kg)$]	1 kg	=	1	8.9876×10^{16}	6.0220×10^{26}	4.1229×10^{34}
joule	1 J	=	1.1127×10^{-17}	1	6.7004×10^9	4.5874×10^{17}
atomic mass unit [$\triangleq E(u)$]	1 u	=	1.6606×10^{-27}	1.4924×10^{-10}	1	6.8464×10^7
rydberg	1 Ry	=	2.4255×10^{-35}	2.1799×10^{-18}	1.4606×10^{-8}	1
electron volt	1 eV	=	1.7827×10^{-36}	1.6022×10^{-19}	1.0735×10^{-9}	7.3498×10^{-2}
kelvin [$\triangleq E(K)$]	1 K	=	1.5362×10^{-40}	1.3807×10^{-23}	9.2510×10^{-14}	6.3336×10^{-6}
meter to the power minus one [$\triangleq E(m^{-1})$]	1 m^{-1}	=	2.2103×10^{-42}	1.9865×10^{-25}	1.3310×10^{-15}	9.1127×10^{-8}
second to the power minus one [$\triangleq E(s^{-1})$]	1 s^{-1}	=	7.3726×10^{-51}	6.6262×10^{-34}	4.4398×10^{-24}	3.0397×10^{-16}

			eV	K	m^{-1}	s^{-1}
kilogram [$\triangleq E(kg)$]	1 kg	=	5.6095×10^{35}	6.5096×10^{39}	4.5244×10^{41}	1.3564×10^{50}
joule	1 J	=	6.2415×10^{18}	7.2429×10^{22}	5.0340×10^{24}	1.5092×10^{33}
atomic mass unit [$\triangleq E(u)$]	1 u	=	9.3150×10^8	1.0810×10^{13}	7.5130×10^{14}	2.2523×10^{23}
rydberg	1 Ry	=	1.3606×10	1.5789×10^5	1.0974×10^7	3.2898×10^{15}
electron volt	1 eV	=	1	1.1604×10^4	8.0655×10^5	2.4180×10^{14}
kelvin [$\triangleq E(K)$]	1 K	=	8.6173×10^{-5}	1	6.9503×10	2.0836×10^{10}
meter to the power minus one [$\triangleq E(m^{-1})$]	1 m^{-1}	=	1.2399×10^{-6}	1.4388×10^{-2}	1	2.9979×10^8
second to the power minus one [$\triangleq E(s^{-1})$]	1 s^{-1}	=	4.1357×10^{-15}	4.7993×10^{-11}	3.3356×10^{-9}	1

The *British thermal unit* (B.t.u.$_{IT}$; Btu), like the International Steam Table calorie, was redefined in 1956[2, 3, 6]:

$$1 \text{ Btu} = 4.1868 \frac{\text{degF}}{\text{K}} \times \frac{\text{lb}}{\text{g}} \text{ J} = 2.326 \frac{\text{lb}}{\text{g}} \text{ J} = 1.05506 \times 10^3 \text{ J}$$

The *horsepower-hour* (hp h) = hp × h = 2.68452×10^6 J (for hp, see under 'Power' below).

The *metric horsepower-hour* (French ch h, German PS h) = ch (or PS) × h = 2.64780×10^6 J (for ch and PS, see under 'Power' below).

The *kilowatt hour* (kW h) = kW × h = 3.6×10^6 J (for W, see the section 'Power').

The unit *therm* (therm) = 10^5 Btu = 1.05506×10^8 J.

Units of energy and energy equivalents in atomic and nuclear physics

The units of energy used in atomic and nuclear physics contain one or more fundamental physical constants as factors, namely the velocity of light in vacuum c, elementary charge e, Planck constant h, Avogadro constant N_A, Boltzmann constant k, and Rydberg constant R_∞. These constants are used to define the energy units rydberg (Ry) and electron volt (eV) as well as the following energy equivalents (treated as energy units because they are proportional to energy): kilogram [kg $\sim E$(kg)], atomic mass unit [u $\sim E$(u)], meter to the power minus one [m$^{-1} \sim E$(m^{-1})], kelvin [K $\sim E$(K)], and second to the power minus one [s$^{-1} \sim E$(s^{-1})]. The relationships of these energy units to the energy unit joule (J) used in macrophysics depend numerically on the results of determinations of the fundamental constants. The consistent set of values of the latter recommended by CODATA[7] in 1973 and used for the conversion table of the energy units of atomic physics (see above) is to be found on pages 47–49.

References

[1] Conférence Générale des Poids et Mesures, *Comptes rendus des séances de la 9ᵉ Conférence Générale des Poids et Mesures, Paris 1948*, Gauthier-Villars, Paris, 1949, pages 54 and 63.
[2] STILLE, U., *Messen und Rechnen in der Physik*, 2nd ed., Vieweg, Braunschweig, 1961.
[3] International Organization for Standardization (ISO), *Quantities and Units of Mechanics*, ISO/DIS 31/III, 1975.
[4] ROSSINI, F. D., *Nat. Bur. Stand. J. Res.*, **6**, 1 (1931); WAGMAN et al., *Nat. Bur. Stand. J. Res.*, **34**, 143 (1945).
[5] Comité International des Poids et Mesures, *Procès-verbaux des séances*, **22**, 79 (1950).
[6] SCHMIDT, E., *Brennstoff, Wärme, Kraft*, **9**, 432 (1957).
[7] Committee on Data for Science and Technology (CODATA) of the International Council of Scientific Unions (ICSU), *Recommended Consistent Values of the Fundamental Physical Constants, 1973*, CODATA Bulletin, No. 11 (Frankfurt, 1973).

Power (P)
(= energy/time = force × velocity)

Dimension: L^2 M T^{-3}

SI unit: watt (W)

Unit in ft-lb-s system: foot poundal per second (ft pdl s^{-1}) = $4.21401101 \times 10^{-2}$ W

Coherent power units

The watt is the power required to transform 1 J of energy in the time of 1 s. When the special names for other derived SI units are used, the watt can also be expressed as the joule per second (J s^{-1}) or newton meter per second (N m s^{-1}):

$$1 \text{ W} = 1 \text{ J s}^{-1} = 1 \text{ N m s}^{-1} = 1 \text{ m}^2 \text{ kg s}^{-3}$$

The foot poundal per second is the power required to transform 1 ft pdl of energy in the time of 1 s:

$$1 \text{ ft pdl s}^{-1} = 1 \text{ ft}^2 \text{ lb s}^{-3}$$

Other units of power

Conversion of noncoherent units of power

For conversion of power units based on the second (for example cal$_{IT}$ s^{-1}) to ft pdl s^{-1} or to watt (= J s^{-1}) use should be made of the factors for energy units given on pages 24 and 25.

Conversion of noncoherent units of power

	ft pdl s^{-1}	W (= J s^{-1})
International Steam Table calorie per hour............ 1 cal$_{IT}$ h^{-1} =	2.75984×10^{-2}	1.163×10^{-3}
British thermal unit per hour............ 1 Btu h^{-1} =	6.95468	2.93071×10^{-1}
horsepower* .... 1 hp =	1.76957×10^4	7.45700×10^2
metric horsepower⁰ .... 1 ch or PS =	1.74537×10^4	7.3549875×10^2

* 1 hp = 550 ft lbf s^{-1}.
⁰ 1 ch or PS = 75 m kp s^{-1} = 75 × 9.80665 m N s^{-1}.

Action (= energy × time)

Dimension: L^2 M T^{-1}

SI unit: joule second (J s)

Unit in ft-lb-s system: foot poundal second (ft pdl s) = $4.21401101 \times 10^{-2}$ J s

The derived SI unit of action is the product m² kg s^{-1} formed from base SI units. When the special names for other derived SI units are used, this unit can also be expressed as the joule second (J s) or newton meter second (N m s):

$$1 \text{ J s} = 1 \text{ N m s} = 1 \text{ m}^2 \text{ kg s}^{-1}$$

The foot poundal second is the following product formed from base ft-lb-s units:

$$1 \text{ ft pdl s} = 1 \text{ ft}^2 \text{ lb s}^{-1}$$

Entropy (S)

Dimension: L^2 M T^{-2} Θ^{-1}

SI unit: joule per kelvin (J K^{-1})

Unit in extended ft-lb-s system: foot poundal per degree Rankine (ft pdl °R^{-1}) = $7.58521982 \times 10^{-2}$ J K^{-1}

Units of specific entropy

Entropy related to mass is *specific entropy* (s), with the dimension: L^2 T^{-2} Θ^{-1}.
The SI unit of specific entropy is the joule per kilogram per kelvin (J kg^{-1} K^{-1}). Noncoherent units of specific entropy are:

calorie per gram per kelvin (cal$_{IT}$ g^{-1} K^{-1}):
$$1 \text{ cal}_{IT} \text{ g}^{-1} \text{ K}^{-1} = 4.1868 \times 10^3 \text{ J kg}^{-1} \text{ K}^{-1}$$

thermochemical calorie per gram per kelvin (cal$_{thermochem}$ g^{-1} K^{-1}):
$$1 \text{ cal}_{thermochem} \text{ g}^{-1} \text{ K}^{-1} = 4.184 \times 10^3 \text{ J kg}^{-1} \text{ K}^{-1}$$

British thermal unit per pound per degree Rankine (Btu lb^{-1} °R^{-1}):
$$1 \text{ Btu lb}^{-1} \text{ °R}^{-1} = 4.1868 \times 10^3 \text{ J kg}^{-1} \text{ K}^{-1}$$

Dynamic viscosity (η)

Dimension: L^{-1} M T^{-1}

SI unit: pascal second (Pa s)

Unit in ft-lb-s system: poundal second per square foot (pdl s ft^{-2}) = 1.488163944 Pa s

Dynamic viscosity (η) is the property of a fluid (in the main a liquid or gas) of offering resistance ('internal friction') to the non-accelerated displacement of two adjacent layers.

The reciprocal of dynamic viscosity is known as the *fluidity* and is given the symbol φ:

$$\varphi = \frac{1}{\eta}$$

The poise (P) was the unit of dynamic viscosity in the CGS system:

$1\,P = 1\,\text{cm}^{-1}\,\text{g}\,\text{s}^{-1} = 10^{-1}\,\text{Pa s}$

Kinematic viscosity (ν)

Dimension: $L^2\,T^{-1}$

SI unit: square meter per second ($\text{m}^2\,\text{s}^{-1}$)

Unit in ft-lb-s system: square foot per second ($\text{ft}^2\,\text{s}^{-1}$) = $9.290304 \times 10^{-2}\,\text{m}^2\,\text{s}^{-1}$

MAXWELL's *kinematic viscosity* (ν) is the ratio of the dynamic viscosity η and the density ϱ:

$$\nu = \frac{\eta}{\varrho}$$

The stokes (St) was the unit of kinematic viscosity in the CGS system:

$1\,\text{St} = 1\,\text{cm}^2\,\text{s}^{-1} = 10^{-4}\,\text{m}^2\,\text{s}^{-1}$

Viscosity of solutions

Relative viscosity η_r

The ratio of the viscosity of a solution (η) and the viscosity of the solvent (η_0) is known as the *viscosity ratio:*

$$\eta_r = \frac{\eta}{\eta_0}$$

This quantity has no dimension.

Viscosity increment

The ratio $(\eta - \eta_0)/\eta_0 = \eta_r - 1$ is known as the *viscosity increment*.
This quantity has no dimension.

Concentration-based viscosity increment J

The *concentration-based viscosity increment J* is the viscosity increment related to the concentration ϱ_i of the solute in the solution:

$$J = \frac{1}{\varrho_i} \times \frac{\eta - \eta_0}{\eta_0}$$

It is also known as the *Staudinger function*.
The SI unit of concentration-based viscosity increment is the cubic meter per kilogram ($\text{m}^3\,\text{kg}^{-1}$).
The coherent unit in the ft-lb-s system is the cubic foot per pound ($\text{ft}^3\,\text{lb}^{-1}$) = $6.2427 9606 \times 10^{-2}\,\text{m}^3\,\text{kg}^{-1}$.

Viscosity number I_s

The ratio of the viscosity increment $(\eta - \eta_0)/\eta_0$ and the mass w_i of the solute in the solution is dimensionless and therefore known as the *viscosity number I_s*:

$$I_s = \frac{1}{w_i} \times \frac{\eta - \eta_0}{\eta_0}$$

Staudinger Index J_0

As the concentration ϱ_i of the solute in the solution and the shear stress τ fall, the Staudinger function (see above) approaches the limiting value:

$$J_0 = \lim_{\substack{\varrho_i \to 0 \\ \tau \to 0}} \left(\frac{1}{\varrho_i} \times \frac{\eta - \eta_0}{\eta_0} \right)$$

This limiting value is known as the *Staudinger Index*. Its SI unit is the cubic meter per kilogram ($\text{m}^3\,\text{kg}^{-1}$). The coherent unit in the ft-lb-s system is the cubic foot per pound ($\text{ft}^3\,\text{lb}^{-1}$) = $6.2427 9606 \times 10^{-2}\,\text{m}^3\,\text{kg}^{-1}$.

Limiting viscosity number I_0

As the mass w_i of the solute in the solution and the shear stress τ fall, the viscosity number (see above) approaches the limiting value:

$$I_0 = \lim_{\substack{w_i \to 0 \\ \tau \to 0}} \left(\frac{1}{w_i} \times \frac{\eta - \eta_0}{\eta_0} \right),$$

known as the *limiting viscosity number* (*intrinsic viscosity*).
This quantity has no dimension.

Surface tension (σ)

Dimension: $M\,T^{-2}$

SI unit: newton per meter ($\text{N}\,\text{m}^{-1}$)

Unit in the ft-lb-s system: poundal per foot ($\text{pdl}\,\text{ft}^{-1}$) = $0.45359237\,\text{N}\,\text{m}^{-1}$

The derived SI unit of surface tension is the product $\text{kg}\,\text{s}^{-2}$ formed from base SI units. When the special names for other derived SI units are used, it can be expressed as newton per meter ($\text{N}\,\text{m}^{-1}$) or joule per square meter ($\text{J}\,\text{m}^{-2}$):

$1\,\text{N}\,\text{m}^{-1} = 1\,\text{J}\,\text{m}^{-2} = 1\,\text{kg}\,\text{s}^{-2}$

The poundal per foot is the following product of base ft-lb-s units:

$1\,\text{pdl}\,\text{ft}^{-1} = 1\,\text{lb}\,\text{s}^{-2}$

Thermal conductivity (λ)

Dimension: $L\,M\,T^{-3}\,\Theta^{-1}$

SI unit: watt per meter per kelvin ($\text{W}\,\text{m}^{-1}\,\text{K}^{-1}$)

Unit in extended ft-lb-s system: poundal per second per degree Rankine ($\text{pdl}\,\text{s}^{-1}\,°\text{R}^{-1}$) = $0.248858918\,\text{W}\,\text{m}^{-1}\,\text{K}^{-1}$

The derived SI unit of thermal conductivity is the product formed from base units m kg $\text{s}^{-3}\,\text{K}^{-1}$. When the special name watt for the SI unit of power is used, it can also be expressed as watt per meter per kelvin ($\text{W}\,\text{m}^{-1}\,\text{K}^{-1}$):

$1\,\text{W}\,\text{m}^{-1}\,\text{K}^{-1} = 1\,\text{m}\,\text{kg}\,\text{s}^{-3}\,\text{K}^{-1}$

The poundal per second degree Rankine is the following product of base units in the extended ft-lb-s system:

$1\,\text{pdl}\,\text{s}^{-1}\,°\text{R}^{-1} = 1\,\text{ft}\,\text{lb}\,\text{s}^{-3}\,°\text{R}^{-1}$

Conversion of noncoherent units of thermal conductivity
($1\,\text{cal}_{IT} = 4.1868\,\text{J};\ 1\,\text{cal}_{thermochem} = 4.184\,\text{J};\ 1\,\text{Btu} = 1.055056 \times 10^3\,\text{J}$)

			$\text{cal}_{IT}\,\text{s}^{-1}\,\text{cm}^{-1}\,\text{K}^{-1}$	$\text{Btu}\,\text{s}^{-1}\,\text{ft}^{-1}\,°\text{R}^{-1}$	$\text{W}\,\text{m}^{-1}\,\text{K}^{-1}$
British thermal unit inch per hour square foot degree Rankin	1 Btu in $\text{h}^{-1}\,\text{ft}^{-2}\,°\text{R}^{-1}$	=	3.44482×10^{-4}	2.31481×10^{-5}	1.44228×10^{-1}
kilocalorie per hour, meter and kelvin	1 $\text{kcal}_{IT}\,\text{h}^{-1}\,\text{m}^{-1}\,\text{K}^{-1}$	=	2.7×10^{-3}	1.86658×10^{-4}	1.163
British thermal unit per hour foot degree Rankine	1 Btu $\text{h}^{-1}\,\text{ft}^{-1}\,°\text{R}^{-1}$	=	4.13379×10^{-3}	2.7×10^{-4}	1.73073
thermochemical calorie per second centimeter kelvin	1 $\text{cal}_{thermochem}\,\text{s}^{-1}\,\text{cm}^{-1}\,\text{K}^{-1}$ =		0.99933	6.71520×10^{-2}	4.184×10^2
calorie per second, centimeter and kelvin	1 $\text{cal}_{IT}\,\text{s}^{-1}\,\text{cm}^{-1}\,\text{K}^{-1}$	=	1	6.71969×10^{-2}	4.1868×10^2
British thermal unit per second foot degree Rankine	1 Btu $\text{s}^{-1}\,\text{ft}^{-1}\,°\text{R}^{-1}$	=	1.48816×10	1	6.23064×10^3

(Surface) coefficient of heat transfer (α)
(Over-all) coefficient of heat transfer (K)

Dimension: $M\,T^{-3}\,\Theta^{-1}$

SI unit: watt per square meter per kelvin ($W\,m^{-2}\,K^{-1}$)

Unit in extended ft-lb-s system: poundal per second foot degree Rankine (pdl $s^{-1}\,ft^{-1}\,°R$) $= 0.816466266\ W\,m^{-2}\,K^{-1}$

Conversion of noncoherent units of the heat transfer coefficients
($1\ cal_{IT} = 4.1868\ J$; $1\ cal_{thermochem} = 4.184\ J$; $1\ Btu = 1.055056 \times 10^3\ J$)

The derived SI unit of the heat transfer coefficients is the product formed from base SI units $kg\,s^{-3}\,K^{-1}$. When the special name watt for the SI power unit is used, it can also be expressed as watt per square meter per kelvin ($W\,m^{-2}\,K^{-1}$):

$$1\ W\,m^{-2}\,K^{-1} = 1\ kg\,s^{-3}\,K^{-1}$$

The poundal per second foot degree Rankine is the following product of base units in the extended ft-lb-s system:

$$1\ pdl\ s^{-1}\,ft^{-1}\,°R^{-1} = 1\ lb\,s^{-3}\,°R^{-1}$$

		$cal_{IT}\ s^{-1}\,cm^{-2}\,K^{-1}$	$Btu\ s^{-1}\,ft^{-2}\,°R^{-1}$	$W\,m^{-2}\,K^{-1}$
kilocalorie per hour, square meter and kelvin	$1\ kcal_{IT}\ h^{-1}\,m^{-2}\,K^{-1} =$	$2.\overline{7} \times 10^{-5}$	5.68934×10^{-5}	1.163
British thermal unit per hour square foot degree Rankine	$1\ Btu\ h^{-1}\,ft^{-2}\,°R^{-1} =$	1.35623×10^{-4}	$2.\overline{7} \times 10^{-4}$	5.67826
British thermal unit per second square foot degree Rankine	$1\ Btu\ s^{-1}\,ft^{-2}\,°R^{-1} =$	4.88243×10^{-1}	1	2.04418×10^{4}
thermochemical calorie per second square centimeter kelvin	$1\ cal_{thermochem}\ s^{-1}\,cm^{-2}\,K^{-1} =$	0.99933	2.04679	4.184×10^{4}
calorie per second, square centimeter and kelvin	$1\ cal_{IT}\ s^{-1}\,cm^{-2}\,K^{-1} =$	1	2.04816	4.1868×10^{4}

Electrical and magnetic units

International System of Units (SI units)

The base electrical unit is that of electric current, the ampere (A), defined[1] as that constant current which, if maintained in two straight parallel conductors of infinite length, of negligible circular cross-section, and placed 1 m apart in vacuum, would produce between these conductors a force equal to 2×10^{-7} N per 1 m of length.

This theoretical definition is realized experimentally in so-called 'absolute ampere measurements' by determining the force between arrangements of conductors carrying current. The ampere is 'maintained' in various national institutes as the ratio volt/ohm in the form of standard cells and resistors. In scalar terms the law of force valid for the length l of the pair of conductors a distance d apart and carrying electric currents of intensity I_1 and I_2 is given by $F/l = \mu_0 I_1 I_2/(2\pi d)$; inserting the data contained in the definition of the ampere gives for the magnetic field constant $\mu_0 = 4\pi \times 10^{-7}\ N/A^2$, i.e., the relation[2] $1\ A = (4\pi \times 10^{-7}\ N/\mu_0)^{1/2}$ is equivalent to the definition given for the ampere by the General Conference on Weights and Measures[1].

Electrodynamics is now generally described by means of the field theory (as recommended by the IUPAP[3], IEC[4], ISO[5], etc.). In so doing it is customary to use a four-dimensional system of quantities (general symbol X), for example length, mass, time, intensity of electric current as four base quantities, dimensional system LMTI. The equations with four base quantities involve explicitly two field constants, the electric field constant ε_0 and the magnetic field constant μ_0, linked by the velocity of light in vacuum c ($c = 2.99792458 \times 10^8\ m\,s^{-1} = \xi\ cm\,s^{-1}$):

$$\mu_0 = 4\pi \times 10^{-7}\ H\,m^{-1} = 1.256637 \ldots \times 10^{-6}\ H\,m^{-1}$$
$$\varepsilon_0 = 1/(\mu_0\,c^2) = 8.85418782 \times 10^{-12}\ F\,m^{-1}\ (s_r = 8 \times 10^{-9})$$

This system has now largely displaced the three-dimensional systems derived from three base quantities (e.g., length, mass, time; dimensional system LMT) used almost exclusively in the 19th century. The latter can be subdivided into 'electrical' and 'magnetic' variants, namely those with an 'electromagnetic' (general symbol X_m) and an 'electrostatic' (general symbol X_e) three-dimensional definition of quantities. These variants, and the four-dimensional system, use different dimensions. ε_0 and μ_0 do not appear in the equations of the three-dimensional systems, where only c appears.

A coherent system of units appropriate to the four-dimensional system X is the International System of Units (SI) or, more precisely, the sub-system (MKSA system) derived from the SI units m, kg, s, A. A coherent system of units appropriate to the three-dimensional quantities is the CGS system, with the 'electromagnetic' CGS units (emu) for the quantities X_m with electromagnetic definitions and the 'electrostatic' CGS units (esu) for the quantities X_e with electrostatic definitions as its two subsystems.

Apart from the dimensional difference between the three- and four-dimensional systems there is also the alternative between geometrically 'rationalized' and 'nonrationalized' versions. The conversion factors in the table on page 28 are based on *rationalized* versions of the *four-dimensional quantities* X and on *nonrationalized* versions of the *three-dimensional quantities* X_m and X_e.

The dimensional difference between the SI units and the emu and esu implies that they are interconvertible simply by the use of *numerical factors* (b or b'); a possible means of expressing the relationship between the two for a particular electrical or magnetic quantity is: $1\ SI\ unit = b^{-1}\ (X/X_m)\ emu = b'^{-1}\ (X/X_e)\ esu$. (On the quotients X/X_m and X/X_e and the formulas defining the three- and four-dimensional quantities see for example STILLE[2].) For this reason the table on page 28 lists all the conversion factors of practical interest relating the *numerical values* of the nonrationalized three-dimensional quantities X_m and X_e, measured in their emu and esu respectively, to the *numerical value* of the corresponding rationalized four-dimensional quantity X measured in its SI unit:

$$\frac{X}{SI\ unit} = b\,\frac{X_m}{emu} = b'\,\frac{X_e}{esu}$$

References

[1] Conférence Générale des Poids et Mesures, *Comptes rendus des séances de la 9ᵉ Conférence Générale des Poids et Mesures, Paris 1948*, Gauthier-Villars, Paris, 1949, page 49.
[2] STILLE, U., *Messen und Rechnen in der Physik*, 2nd ed., Vieweg, Braunschweig, 1961 (also in EBERT, H. [Ed.], *Physikalisches Taschenbuch*, 4th ed., Vieweg, Braunschweig, 1967, section 111.2, page 6).
[3] International Union of Pure and Applied Physics (IUPAP), *Symbols, Units and Nomenclature in Physics*, Document U.I.P. 11 (S.U.N. 65-3) 1965 (German edition: *Symbole, Einheiten und Nomenklatur in der Physik*, Vieweg, Braunschweig, 1966).
[4] International Electrotechnical Commission (IEC), *Letter Symbols to be Used in Electrical Technology*, Publication 27-1, 5th ed., Geneva, 1971.
[5] International Organization for Standardization (ISO), *Quantities and Units of Electricity and Magnetism*, Draft International Standard ISO/DIS 31/V, 1978.

Electrical and magnetic units

Numerical value of X in SI unit $= b \times$ numerical value of X_m in emu $= b' \times$ numerical value of X_e in esu

Quantity (symbol)	Dimension	International System of Units (SI)		CGS system			
		SI unit ($X = 1$)		electromagnetic (X_m/emE)		electrostatic (X_e/esE)	
		Name	Symbol	emE	$b^\diamond$	esE	$b'^\diamond$
Electric potential difference (U)	L^2 M T^{-3} I^{-1}	volt	V	$cm^{3/2}\,g^{1/2}\,s^{-2}$	10^{-8}	$cm^{1/2}\,g^{1/2}\,s^{-1}$	$\zeta \times 10^{-8}$
Electric current (I)	I	ampere	A	$cm^{1/2}\,g^{1/2}\,s^{-1}$	10	$cm^{3/2}\,g^{1/2}\,s^{-2}$	$10/\zeta$
Electric current density ($\boldsymbol{J}$ or $\boldsymbol{S}$)	L^{-2} I	ampere/ square meter	A m^{-2}	$cm^{-3/2}\,g^{1/2}\,s^{-1}$	10^5	$cm^{-1/2}\,g^{1/2}\,s^{-2}$	$10^5/\zeta$
Electric linear current density (A or α)	L^{-1} I	ampere/meter	A m^{-1}	$cm^{-1/2}\,g^{1/2}\,s^{-1}$	10^3	$cm^{1/2}\,g^{1/2}\,s^{-2}$	$10^3/\zeta$
Electric field strength ($\boldsymbol{E}$)	L M T^{-3} I^{-1}	volt/meter	V m^{-1}	$cm^{1/2}\,g^{1/2}\,s^{-2}$	10^{-6}	$cm^{-1/2}\,g^{1/2}\,s^{-1}$	$\zeta \times 10^{-6}$
Electric flux density, displacement ($\boldsymbol{D}$)	L^{-2} T I	coulomb/ square meter	C m^{-2}	$cm^{-3/2}\,g^{1/2}$	$10^5/(4\pi)$	$cm^{-1/2}\,g^{1/2}\,s^{-1}$	$10^5/(4\pi\zeta)$
Electric (displacement) flux (Ψ)	T I	coulomb	C ($=$ A s)	$cm^{1/2}\,g^{1/2}$	$10/(4\pi)$	$cm^{3/2}\,g^{1/2}\,s^{-1}$	$10/(4\pi\zeta)$
Electric polarization ($\boldsymbol{P}$)	L^{-2} T I	coulomb/ square meter	C m^{-2}	$cm^{-3/2}\,g^{1/2}$	10^5	$cm^{-1/2}\,g^{1/2}\,s^{-1}$	$10^5/\zeta$
Electric dipole moment ($\boldsymbol{p}$)	L T I	coulomb $\times$ meter	C m	$cm^{3/2}\,g^{1/2}$	10^{-1}	$cm^{5/2}\,g^{1/2}\,s^{-1}$	$10^{-1}/\zeta$
Electric polarizability (α_e)	M^{-1} T^4 I^2	farad $\times$ square meter	F m^2	$cm\,s^2$	10^5	cm^3	$10^5/\zeta^2$
Electric susceptibility (χ_e or χ)	L^0 M^0 T^0 I^0	1	1	1	4π	1	4π
Electric susceptibility (χ_e or χ)	T I	coulomb	C ($=$ A s)	$cm^{1/2}\,g^{1/2}$	10	$cm^{3/2}\,g^{1/2}\,s^{-1}$	$10/\zeta$
Volume density of electric charge, charge density (ϱ or η)	L^{-3} T I	coulomb/ cubic meter	C m^{-3}	$cm^{-5/2}\,g^{1/2}$	10^7	$cm^{-3/2}\,g^{1/2}\,s^{-1}$	$10^7/\zeta$
Surface density of electric charge (σ)	L^{-2} T I	coulomb/ square meter	C m^{-2}	$cm^{-3/2}\,g^{1/2}$	10^5	$cm^{-1/2}\,g^{1/2}\,s^{-1}$	$10^5/\zeta$
Capacitance (C)	L^{-2} M^{-1} T^4 I^2	farad	F ($=$ A s V^{-1})	$cm^{-1}\,s^2$	10^9	cm	$10^9/\zeta^2$
Electric resistance (R) (to direct current)	L^2 M T^{-3} I^{-2}	ohm	Ω ($=$ V A^{-1})	$cm\,s^{-1}$	10^{-9}	$cm^{-1}\,s$	$\zeta^2 \times 10^{-9}$
Electric conductance (G) (to direct current)	L^{-2} M^{-1} T^3 I^2	siemens	S ($=$ A V^{-1})	$cm^{-1}\,s$	10^9	$cm\,s^{-1}$	$10^9/\zeta^2$
Electric resistivity (ϱ)	L^3 M T^{-3} I^{-2}	ohm $\times$ meter	Ω m	$cm^2\,s^{-1}$	10^{-11}	s	$\zeta^2 \times 10^{-11}$
Electric conductivity (γ or σ)	L^{-3} M^{-1} T^3 I^2	siemens/ meter	S m^{-1}	$cm^{-2}\,s$	10^{11}	s^{-1}	$10^{11}/\zeta^2$
Magnetic potential difference (V)	I	ampere	A	$cm^{1/2}\,g^{1/2}\,s^{-1}$ (Gilbert, Gb)	$10/(4\pi)$	$cm^{3/2}\,g^{1/2}\,s^{-2}$	$10/(4\pi\zeta)$
Magnetic field strength ($\boldsymbol{H}$)	L^{-1} I	ampere/meter	A m^{-1}	$cm^{-1/2}\,g^{1/2}\,s^{-1}$ (Oersted, Oe)*	$10^3/(4\pi)$	$cm^{1/2}\,g^{1/2}\,s^{-2}$	$10^3/(4\pi\zeta)$
Magnetic vector potential ($\boldsymbol{A}$)	L M T^{-2} I^{-1}	weber/meter	Wb m^{-1}	$cm^{1/2}\,g^{1/2}\,s^{-1}$	10^{-6}	$cm^{-1/2}\,g^{1/2}$	$\zeta \times 10^{-6}$
Magnetic flux density ($\boldsymbol{B}$) (magnetic induction)	M T^{-2} I^{-1}	tesla	T ($=$ Wb m^{-2})	$cm^{-1/2}\,g^{1/2}\,s^{-1}$ (Gauss, Gs)*	10^{-4}	$cm^{-3/2}\,g^{1/2}$	$\zeta \times 10^{-4}$
Magnetic flux (Φ)	L^2 M T^{-2} I^{-1}	weber	Wb ($=$ V s)	$cm^{3/2}\,g^{1/2}\,s^{-1}$ (Maxwell, Mx)	10^{-8}	$cm^{1/2}\,g^{1/2}$	$\zeta \times 10^{-8}$
Magnetization ($\boldsymbol{M}$ or $\boldsymbol{H}_\mathrm{i}$)	L^{-1} I	ampere/meter	A m^{-1}	$cm^{-1/2}\,g^{1/2}\,s^{-1}$	10^3	$cm^{1/2}\,g^{1/2}\,s^{-2}$	$10^3/\zeta$
(Electro)magnetic moment ($\boldsymbol{m}$)	L^2 I	ampere $\times$ square meter	A m^2	$cm^{5/2}\,g^{1/2}\,s^{-1}$	10^{-3}	$cm^{7/2}\,g^{1/2}\,s^{-2}$	$10^{-3}/\zeta$
Magnetic susceptibility (χ_m or κ)	L^0 M^0 T^0 I^0	1	1	1	4π	1	4π
Magnetic polarization ($\boldsymbol{J}$ or $\boldsymbol{B}_\mathrm{i}$)	M T^{-2} I^{-1}	tesla	T ($=$ Wb m^{-2})	$cm^{-1/2}\,g^{1/2}\,s^{-1}$	$4\pi \times 10^{-4}$	$cm^{-3/2}\,g^{1/2}$	$4\pi\zeta \times 10^{-4}$
Magnetic dipole moment ($\boldsymbol{j}$)	L^3 M T^{-2} I^{-1}	weber $\times$ meter	Wb m	$cm^{5/2}\,g^{1/2}\,s^{-1}$	$4\pi \times 10^{-10}$	$cm^{3/2}\,g^{1/2}$	$4\pi\zeta \times 10^{-10}$
(Coulomb's) magnetic pole strength (m)	L^2 M T^{-2} I^{-1}	weber	Wb ($=$ V s)	$cm^{3/2}\,g^{1/2}\,s^{-1}$	$4\pi \times 10^{-8}$	$cm^{1/2}\,g^{1/2}$	$4\pi\zeta \times 10^{-8}$
Self inductance (L)	L^2 M T^{-2} I^{-2}	henry	H ($=$ V s A^{-1})	cm	10^{-9}	$cm^{-1}\,s^2$	$\zeta^2 \times 10^{-9}$
Permeance (Λ)	L^2 M T^{-2} I^{-2}	henry	H ($=$ V s A^{-1})	cm	$4\pi \times 10^{-9}$	$cm^{-1}\,s^2$	$4\pi\zeta^2 \times 10^{-9}$
De-electrification or demagnetization factor (N)	L^0 M^0 T^0 I^0	1	1	1	$1/(4\pi)$	1	$1/(4\pi)$
Electric or magnetic force ($\boldsymbol{F}$)[†]	L M T^{-2}	newton	N ($=$ J m^{-1})	$cm\,g\,s^{-2} =$ dyn	10^{-5}	$cm\,g\,s^{-2} =$ dyn	10^{-5}
Electric or magnetic energy (W)[†]	L^2 M T^{-2}	joule	J ($=$ V A s)	$cm^2\,g\,s^{-2} =$ erg	10^{-7}	$cm^2\,g\,s^{-2} =$ erg	10^{-7}
Electric or magnetic energy density (w)[†]	L^{-1} M T^{-2}	joule/ cubic meter	J m^{-3}	$cm^{-1}\,g\,s^{-2}$	10^{-1}	$cm^{-1}\,g\,s^{-2}$	10^{-1}
Electric or magnetic power (P)[†]	L^2 M T^{-3}	watt	W ($=$ V A)	$cm^2\,g\,s^{-3}$	10^{-7}	$cm^2\,g\,s^{-3}$	10^{-7}
Poynting vector ($\boldsymbol{S}$) (surface density of power in an electromagnetic wave)	M T^{-3}	watt/ square meter	W m^{-2}	$g\,s^{-3}$	10^{-3}	$g\,s^{-3}$	10^{-3}

$\diamond$ $\zeta = 2.99792458 \times 10^{10}$ $1/4\pi = 7.957747 \times 10^{-2}$
$1/\zeta = 3.335641 \times 10^{-11}$ $4\pi\,\zeta = 3.767303 \times 10^{11}$
$\zeta^2 = 8.987552 \times 10^{20}$ $1/4\pi\,\zeta = 2.654419 \times 10^{-12}$
$1/\zeta^2 = 1.112650 \times 10^{-21}$ $4\pi\,\zeta^2 = 1.129409 \times 10^{22}$
$4\pi = 1.256637 \times 10$ $1/4\pi\,\zeta^2 = 8.854188 \times 10^{-23}$

*The names oersted and gauss are often interchanged.
[†] See also under 'Force', 'Energy' and 'Power', pages 22–25.

Radioactivity

Basic concepts

The term *nuclide* indicates a species of atoms having specified numbers of protons and neutrons in its nucleus. Nuclides of one and the same chemical element, i.e., nuclides with the same number of protons and differing only in the number of neutrons, are known as *isotopes* of the element concerned. In some nuclides various energy states of the nucleus with finite lifetimes are possible. These states are called *isomers* of the nuclide. Isomeric *nuclides* have the same numbers of protons and neutrons and differ only in their energy content and thus their lifetime.

The nature of a nuclide is indicated unambiguously by the chemical symbol of the element and the number of nucleons (sum of the protons and neutrons = mass number) shown as an upper index to the left of the element symbol (e.g., ^{12}C, ^{32}P). Additionally, the number of protons (atomic number) can be given as a lower index on the left. Isomers in an excited, metastable state are indicated by a right upper index 'm' (e.g., $^{99}Tc^{m}$).

Radioactivity and law of disintegration

Radioactivity is the property of certain nuclides of spontaneously emitting either particles or gamma rays from the nucleus (nuclear radiation) or x rays from the shell after capture of an electron from the shell by the nucleus (characteristic x radiation). Except for isomeric transitions, this process always results in a change in the nature of the nuclide (radioactive transformation or radioactive disintegration). Nuclides possessing this property are known as radionuclides.

It is impossible to predict the time when an individual atom will disintegrate; the occurrence of disintegrations is statistically distributed, i.e., it is a stochastic process. For a large number of atoms of the same radionuclide or isomer disintegration is governed by the empirical law stating that the number dN of atoms disintegrating in the time dt is at all times proportional to the number N of atoms not yet disintegrated. The proportionality factor is known as the *decay constant* λ; this is a characteristic constant of the nuclide concerned:

$$- \, dN = \lambda \, N \, dt$$

If at time zero N_0 atoms of an isolated radionuclide are present, the number N_t of atoms not yet disintegrated at any time t is given by

$$N_t = N_0 \, e^{-\lambda t}$$

In equal time intervals the number of radioactive atoms decreases by the same proportion; the time interval during which the number decreases by half is known as the *half-life* ($T_{1/2}$):

$$T_{1/2} = \frac{\ln 2}{\lambda} = \frac{0.693}{\lambda}$$

The reciprocal of the decay constant λ has the dimension of time and is known as the *mean lifetime* τ. τ is the time during which the number of atoms of a radionuclide falls to the fraction $1/e$ ($\approx 37\%$) of its original value.

Activity

The quantity $- \, (dN/dt) = \lambda N$, i.e., the number of radioactive transformations taking place in a sample during the time dt divided by this time interval, is called the *activity A*. It is a measure of the 'strength' of the radioactive sample.

The unit of activity in the International System of Units is the reciprocal of the base SI unit, the second. The special name, becquerel (Bq), was adopted for the SI unit of activity by the 15th General Conference on Weights and Measures (1975, Resolution 8)[1]:

$$1 \, \text{Bq} = 1 \, \text{s}^{-1}$$

The special unit of activity, curie (Ci), may be used temporarily[2]:

$$1 \, \text{Ci} = 3.7 \times 10^{10} \, \text{Bq} = 37 \, \text{GBq}$$

In addition to the activity, the radionuclide and the time when the activity was measured must be specified when giving activity data. In radioactive decay series, where radioactive equilibrium has been reached, usually only the activity of the parent nuclide need be specified; thus in $^{90}Sr + {}^{90}Y$ preparations, for example, only the activity of the ^{90}Sr is given.

Specific activity

The *specific activity a of a radioactive material* (for instance a radioactive solution) is the activity A of the radionuclide contained in it divided by the mass m of the material:

$$a = \frac{A}{m}$$

The SI unit of specific activity is the becquerel per kilogram (Bq kg^{-1}). The special unit still authorized for the time being is the curie per gram (Ci g^{-1}):

$$1 \, \text{Ci g}^{-1} = 3.7 \times 10^{13} \, \text{Bq kg}^{-1}$$

The *specific activity of a radionuclide* a_N is obtained by dividing the activity $A = \lambda N$ of the radionuclide by the mass of N of its atoms. This quantity is a characteristic constant of the radionuclide expressing the maximum specific activity attainable (i.e., in the carrier-free state):

$$a_N = \frac{\lambda \, N_A}{M} = 1.63 \times 10^{13} \frac{\lambda}{A_r} \, \text{Ci g}^{-1} = 6.02 \times 10^{26} \frac{\lambda}{A_r} \, \text{Bq kg}^{-1}$$

where N_A is the Avogadro constant, M the molar mass in gram per mole (see page 45) of the radionuclide, A_r its relative atomic mass (see page 45) and λ the value of its decay constant in s^{-1}. Some examples are given in Table 1.

Table 1
Reciprocals of the specific activities of some radionuclides[3]

Radionuclide	$T_{1/2}$	1/a_N	
		µg Ci^{-1}	µg GBq^{-1}
^{24}Na	15.0 h	0.115	0.003 11
^{131}I	8.02 d	8.05	0.218
^{32}P	14.3 d	3.51	0.0948
^{45}Ca	163 d	56.2	1.52
^{14}C	5730 a	2.24×10^5	6.07×10^3

Activity concentration

The *activity concentration* of a radioactive material (liquid or gaseous, at a given temperature and pressure) is the ratio of the activity of the contained radionuclide to the volume of the material.

The SI unit of activity concentration is the becquerel per cubic meter (Bq m^{-3}). The special unit still authorized for the time being is the curie per liter (Ci L^{-1}):

$$1 \, \text{Ci L}^{-1} = 3.7 \times 10^{13} \, \text{Bq m}^{-3}$$

Radiation dosimetry

1. Introduction

There is now a considerable measure of agreement on the definition of radiological quantities and units as well as on the transition to the International System of Units (SI). This is reflected in the recommendations made by the International Commission on Radiation Units and Measurements (ICRU Report 33, 1980[4]) and in the 1975 and 1979[1] resolutions of the General Conference on Weights and Measures, which is responsible for the 'international unification and development of the metric system'.

The special units hitherto used for the following radiological quantities are not coherent* with the units of the International System and are therefore listed as still authorized for the time being:

The unit 'curie' for the activity of a radiological substance.
The unit 'roentgen' for ion dose and exposure.
The unit 'rad' for absorbed dose.
The unit 'rem' for dose equivalent.

A directive of the Council of the European Communities[2] obliges the Member States to use the SI units instead of the curie, roentgen, rad and rem as of October 1, 1981 at the latest. Further

---

* A 'coherent system of units' is one in which all derived units can be obtained from a selected set of base units (by multiplication or division of the base units) without the introduction of numerical factors. Four of the seven base units of the International System are relevant to units used in radiology: the meter (m), the kilogram (kg), the second (s), and the ampere (A).

use of the old units is permitted until December 31, 1985 at the latest.

So far only partly clarified is the problem of which of the various quantities should primarily be used in practice, i.e., in the calibration of measuring instruments. What is certain is that the transition to the International System of Units will cause 'exposure' to lose the preeminent position it has held for 50 years as the dosage quantity for photon radiation. The reason for this is that the conversion factor to other necessary quantities is an awkward one in the International System. 'Exposure' will probably be replaced:

in radiotherapy by the 'absorbed dose in water under specified conditions' (see REICH[5]);

in radiation protection by a special quantity still to be decided upon and of the nature of the 'dose equivalent in standard tissue' (ICRU Reports 33[4] and 25[16], see under 9).

In deciding upon quantities for radiation protection, it has to be borne in mind that in recent decades the types of radiation and the radiation energy ranges in common use have increased in number.

Of special importance are:

Photon radiation between 5 keV and 25 MeV
Electron radiation between 80 keV and 25 MeV
Neutron radiation between 0.025 eV (thermal) and 14 MeV

This situation, coupled with need for directional dependence of the response of appropriately calibrated radiation protection dosimeters, makes it difficult to decide upon a quantity that permits correct addition of all the fractional doses contributed by the various radiation components.

The following text is limited to a description of the basic concepts of dosimetry in which, because of their widespread use, photon and electron radiation as used in therapy occupies the most important place. As far as methods of measurement are concerned, only ionization chamber techniques will be discussed. Neutron radiation is relegated to a minor place since neutron dosimetry lies beyond the scope of this presentation.

In the literature on dosimetry, the four-volume work on radiation dosimetry edited by ATTIX, ROESCH and TOCHILIN[6] as well as the book on dosimetry and radiation protection edited by JAEGER and HÜBNER[7] are still authoritative. The efforts of ICRU concerning the standardization of dosimetric methods has resulted in ICRU Reports 14[8], 17[9], and 23[10], for different photon energy ranges, Report 21[11] for electron beams, and Reports 13[12] and 26[13] for neutrons. Report 18[14] deals with high-activity gamma-ray sources for teletherapy and industrial radiography, Report 20[15] with measurement instruments for radiation protection and their calibration, and Report 25[16] with the conceptual basis for the determination of the dose equivalent. Six further Reports (Nos. 27 to 32) edited in 1978 and 1979 deal with special problems of applied dosimetry and are not quoted in detail here. A recommendation of the International Electrotechnical Commission (IEC)[17] sets forth in detail the requirements for therapy level dosimeters with ionization chambers. A series of standards of the DIN (Deutsches Institut für Normung), written in German, may also be mentioned: Dose Measuring Procedures in Radiological Technique (6800)[18], Neutron Dosimetry (6802)[19], Clinical Dosimetry (6809)[20], Concepts and Definitions in the Field of Radiological Technique (6814)[21], Therapy Level Dosimeters with Ionization Chambers for X-Ray, Gamma, and Electron Radiation (6817)[22], and Radiation Protection Dosimeters (6818)[23]. Basic physical data for dosimetry, still valid, are presented in ICRU Report 10b, 1964[24], while calibration procedures for use in hospitals are described in a book of MASSEY of the IAEA Technical Reports Series 1970[25].

2. Basic concepts of dosimetry

The effects of radiation on matter are produced by the energy imparted by the radiation and correspondingly absorbed by the irradiated material. For ionizing radiation, this energy transfer or conversion occurs in several steps[26] before manifesting itself biologically. The energy imparted to matter appears in the form of excitation, ionization or changes in the binding energy of the atoms. It is defined by

$$\varepsilon = R_{\text{in}} - R_{\text{out}} + \Sigma Q$$

where

ε is the energy imparted to matter in a volume by ionizing radiation;

R_{in} is the radiant energy incident on the volume, i.e., the sum of the energies (excluding rest energies) of all charged and uncharged ionizing particles entering the volume;

R_{out} is the radiant energy emerging from the volume, i.e., the sum of the energies (excluding rest energies) of all charged and uncharged ionizing particles leaving the volume;

ΣQ is the sum of all changes (decreases: positive sign, increases: negative sign) of the rest mass energy of nuclei and elementary particles in any nuclear transformations occurring in the volume.

If, for example, an electron pair (electron and positron) is produced by absorption of a photon in the volume, an endothermic process occurs in which $\Sigma Q = -2 m_e c^2$ (m_e = rest mass of the electron; c = velocity of light).

The *absorbed dose* is defined with the aid of the energy ε imparted to the mass m of the material. The basic function of dosimetry is to determine the absorbed dose; in the modern view it is the most suitable reference quantity for the chemical, biological and medical changes observed. The absorbed dose results from interactions between the radiation and the material; these in turn depend on the type, (particle) fluence and spectral distribution of the radiant energy as well as on the atomic composition of the material. The Swiss physician and physicist CHRISTEN[27] was the first to define a 'physical dose', namely as dE/dV, where dE is the radiation energy absorbed by the material within the volume dV. The term 'dose' without a modifying adjective is ambiguous since in addition to absorbed dose other quantities such as *ion dose* and *dose equivalent* are also used in dosimetry.

Radiation fields and dose rate fields are often markedly inhomogeneous in space and time, for example fields produced by pulsed electron beams from accelerators or the local dose rate distribution at interfaces between soft tissue and bones. The corresponding definitions must therefore be based on such small masses or such short time intervals that a further reduction has no effect on the quotients concerned. In the limit as the mass or the time approach zero, this procedure yields values for the differential quotients. However, since radiation and its interaction with material are of a discrete nature, there is a limit beyond which the mass element cannot be reduced. The energy ε imparted to a material of finite mass m (a biological cell, for example) is subject to random fluctuations whose amplitude varies inversely with the size of the mass element. The *specific energy* ε/m is a stochastic quantity that can differ greatly from the nonstochastic absorbed dose D (see 5.1 below). The differential quotients defined below must therefore be regarded as *expectation values* or *mean values* of the quantities concerned at a point in the material.

3. Radiation field quantities

3.1 General

A *radiation field* is a region, in vacuum or in a material, traversed by radiation. Ionizing radiation consists of *charged particles* (e.g., electrons, protons, etc.) or *uncharged particles* (e.g., photons or neutrons) capable of causing ionization through primary or secondary processes.

In this section definitions of important radiation quantities will be given for particles (sections 3.2–3.6) and for particle energies (sections 3.7–3.11). Beginning with third order differential radiation field quantities (3.2 and 3.7) integration over the solid angle yields the second-order differential quantities given in 3.3 and 3.8. Further integration over time or area yields fluence (3.4 and 3.9) or flux (3.5 and 3.10), respectively. All these quantities are obtainable by integration of their *spectral distributions*. By spectral distribution, for example of the particle fluence Φ (see 3.4), is understood its derivative with respect to the particle energy E:

Spectral particle fluence $\Phi_E = d\Phi(E)/dE$.

The sum distribution $\Phi(E)$ is that part of the fluence Φ due to particles of energies between zero and E. The integral of the differential distribution of Φ_E over all particle energies from zero to infinity is the

particle fluence $\Phi = \Phi(\infty) = \int_0^\infty \Phi_E(E)\, dE$

3.2 *Particle radiance* $p = d^3N/(da\, dt\, d\Omega)$; unit: $\text{m}^{-2}\,\text{s}^{-1}\,\text{sr}^{-1}$

where d^3N is the number of particles incident on (or emitted from) a sphere of cross-sectional area da in the time interval dt within the solid angle $d\Omega$. The area da must be perpendicular to the direction of each particle, a condition best satisfied by a sphere.

3.3 (*Particle*) *fluence rate or particle flux* (*surface*) *density*

$\varphi = \int_\Omega p\, d\Omega = d^2N/(da\, dt)$; unit: $\text{m}^{-2}\,\text{s}^{-1}$

Note: The first term is preferred by ICRU. It is derived from the (particle) fluence, which is the integral of φ over the time t (see

3.4). The second term is a somewhat better description of the physical meaning; its disadvantage is that the word 'density' has several connotations.

3.4 (Particle) fluence* $\Phi = \int_t \varphi \, dt = dN/da$; unit: m^{-2}

3.5 (Particle) flux $\dot{N} = dN/dt$; unit: s^{-1}

where dN is the increment of the number of particles in the time dt. Note that $\dot{N}$ cannot be derived in a simple way from φ by integration over the area a since da is not fixed in space (see 3.2).

3.6 Particle number N; unit: 1

This is the number of particles emitted, transferred, or received.

3.7 Energy radiance $r = d^3R/(da \, dt \, d\Omega)$; unit: $W \, m^{-2} \, sr^{-1}$

where d^3R is the sum of the energies of all ionizing particles (excluding rest energies) incident on or emerging from a sphere of cross-sectional area da in the time interval dt within the solid angle $d\Omega$.

3.8 Energy fluence rate $\psi = \int_\Omega r \, d\Omega = d^2R/(da \, dt)$; unit: $W \, m^{-2}$

Note: Another name for this quantity (see 3.3) is *energy flux (surface) density*.

3.9 Energy fluence $\Psi = \int_t \psi \, dt = dR/da$; unit: $J \, m^{-2}$

3.10 Energy flux $\dot{R} = dR/dt$; unit: W

where dR is the increment of radiant energy in the time interval dt. $\dot{R}$ is also called 'radiant flux' or 'radiant power' and is described as 'power emitted, transferred or received in the form of radiation'.

3.11 Radiant energy R; unit: J

This is the sum of the energies of ionizing particles (excluding rest energies) emitted, transferred or received.

4. Interactions

4.1 When uncharged particles (photons or neutrons) interact with atoms or molecules, part of their energy is transferred to charged particles displaced from the atoms or molecules. The interaction of photons produces mostly secondary electrons by the photoelectric effect, by the Compton effect, or by pair production.

The *mass-energy transfer coefficient*, μ_{tr}/ϱ, of a material for uncharged ionizing particles is the quotient of $dE_{tr}/E \, N$ by $\varrho \, dl$, where E is the energy of each particle (excluding rest energy), N is the number of particles, and $dE_{tr}/E \, N$ is the fraction of incident particle energy that is transferred to kinetic energy of charged particles by interactions in traversing a distance dl in the material of density ϱ:

$$\mu_{tr}/\varrho = (dE_{tr}/E \, N) \times (1/\varrho \, dl); \text{ unit: } m^2 \, kg^{-1}$$

4.2 Most of the energy of the secondary charged particles is locally converted into ionization and excitation, while a small portion of it (in particular in the case of secondary electrons) escapes from the material in the form of bremsstrahlung.

Mass-energy absorption coefficient:

$$\mu_{en}/\varrho = (\mu_{tr}/\varrho) \times (1 - g); \text{ unit: } m^2 \, kg^{-1}$$

where g is the fraction of energy of the secondary charged particles (electrons) lost as bremsstrahlung in the material which is indicated below by the subscripts 'a' for air and 'w' for water. In air for photons, $g_a \approx 0.004$ at 1.3 MeV and is negligible at lower photon energies.

The factors μ_{en}/ϱ and μ_{tr}/ϱ can differ appreciably when the kinetic energies of the secondary electrons are comparable to or larger than their rest-mass energy (0.511 MeV), particularly for interactions in materials of high atomic number.

4.3 When charged particles interact with atoms, a portion of their kinetic energy is lost in individual collisions by (a) excitation and ionization of the atoms or molecules, and (b) the emission of x rays.

The *total mass stopping power* S/ϱ of a material for charged particles is the ratio of dE to $\varrho \, dl$, where dE is the energy lost by a charged particle in traversing a distance dl in a material of density ϱ:

$$S/\varrho = (1/\varrho) \times (dE/dl); \text{ unit: } J \, m^2 \, kg^{-1}$$

---

* This quantity is the same as the quantity $n \, v \, t$ commonly used in neutron physics, where n is the (volume) density of neutrons, v their velocity, and t the time.

E may be expressed in eV and hence S/ϱ in the units $eV \, m^2 \, kg^{-1}$. S is called the *total linear stopping power*.

5. Dose quantities and units

5.1 Absorbed dose and absorbed dose rates

The quantities absorbed dose and absorbed dose rate are applicable to any kind of radiation and energy range.

5.1.1 The *absorbed dose D* is the ratio of $d\bar{\varepsilon}$ to dm, where $d\bar{\varepsilon}$ is the mean energy imparted to a material of mass dm by ionizing radiation:

$$D = d\bar{\varepsilon}/dm; \text{ unit: } J \, kg^{-1}$$

The special name for the unit of absorbed dose is the gray (Gy):

$$1 \, Gy = 1 \, J \, kg^{-1}$$

The special unit of absorbed dose, the rad (rd), may be used temporarily:

$$1 \, rd = 10^{-2} \, J \, kg^{-1}$$

The expression 'integral absorbed dose' still in common use thus simply means the amount of energy imparted to matter:

$$\varepsilon = \int D \, dm$$

(see chapter 2).

The stochastic quantity

specific energy, $z = \varepsilon/m$

is related to the nonstochastic quantity D by its mean value $\bar{z}$. The absorbed dose D is equal to the limiting value of $\bar{z}$ as the mass m approaches zero:

$$D = \lim_{m \to 0} \bar{z}$$

The mean absorbed dose in a volume is equal to the mean specific energy $\bar{z}$ in that volume.

5.1.2 The *absorbed dose rate $\dot{D}$* is the ratio of dD to dt, where dD is the increment of absorbed dose in the time dt:

$$\dot{D} = dD/dt; \text{ unit: } J \, kg^{-1} \, s^{-1} \text{ or } Gy \, s^{-1}$$

Also in common use are the units $Gy \, min^{-1}$ and $Gy \, h^{-1}$.

The special unit of absorbed dose, the rad (rd), may be used temporarily:

$$1 \, rd \, s^{-1} = 10^{-2} \, Gy \, s^{-1}$$
$$1 \, rd \, min^{-1} = 10^{-2} \, Gy \, min^{-1} = 1.667 \times 10^{-4} \, Gy \, s^{-1}$$
$$1 \, rd \, h^{-1} = 10^{-2} \, Gy \, h^{-1} = 2.778 \times 10^{-6} \, Gy \, s^{-1}$$

The direct measurement of absorbed dose or absorbed dose rate is possible only by means of calorimetry in phantoms and requires a great effort. In practical dosimetry indirect methods are used, particularly those based on ionization measurements in air, in which the absorbed dose is obtained by calculation.

5.2 Ion dose and ion dose rate

The quantity 'ion dose' (appearing in the appropriate German DIN Standard[21]) is not included in ICRU recommendations, although it is useful in dealing with problems of dosimetry when ionization chambers are used. The 'ion dose' is applicable to all kinds of radiation except neutrons and to all energy ranges. It refers to small volumes filled with air and surrounded by arbitrary materials.

5.2.1 The *ion dose J* is the ratio of dQ to dm_a, where dQ is the charge of the ions of one sign generated directly or indirectly by ionizing radiation in a mass dm_a of air:

$$J = dQ/dm_a; \text{ unit: } C \, kg^{-1}$$

The special unit of ion dose, the roentgen (R), may be used temporarily:

$$1 \, R = 2.58 \times 10^{-4} \, C \, kg^{-1} \text{ (exactly)}$$

5.2.2 The *ion dose rate $\dot{J}$* is the ratio of dJ to dt, where dJ is the increment of ion dose in the time interval dt:

$$\dot{J} = dJ/dt; \text{ unit: } C \, kg^{-1} \, s^{-1}$$

The special unit, the roentgen (R), may be used temporarily:

$$1 \, R \, s^{-1} = 2.58 \times 10^{-4} \, C \, kg^{-1} \, s^{-1} \text{ (exactly)}$$

The time units min and h are also in common use.

5.2.3 The *cavity ion dose J_c[21]* is the ion dose under the 'Bragg-Gray conditions' described under 6.2.2. The cavity ion dose is applicable to high-energy photon radiation and electron radiation.

5.3 Exposure and exposure rate

These quantities refer to photon radiation only, and are applicable in practice to energies up to about 3 MeV, due to difficulties in measurement above this energy.

5.3.1 The *exposure X* is the quotient of dQ by dm_a, where the value of dQ is the absolute value of the total charge of the ions of one sign generated in air when all the electrons (negatrons and positrons) liberated by photons in air of mass dm_a are completely stopped in air. The charge dQ does not include the ionization due to absorption of the bremsstrahlung emitted by the electrons:

$$X = dQ/dm_a; \text{ unit: C kg}^{-1}$$

The special unit of exposure, the roentgen (R), may be used temporarily:

$$1 \text{ R} = 2.58 \times 10^{-4} \text{ C kg}^{-1} \text{ (exactly)}$$

It may be convenient to refer to a value of exposure at a point inside a material different from air. For this case, as dm_a approaches zero, the secondary electrons, because of their finite range, are no longer stopped in air. Nevertheless, the value of the 'exposure at a point inside a material' different from air will be that which would be determined for a small quantity of air placed at the point of interest under the assumption that dQ is produced in air only.

The measurement of exposure requires that certain experimental conditions be met (see 6.2.1).

5.3.2 *Exposure rate* $\dot{X} = dX/dt$; unit: $\text{C kg}^{-1} \text{s}^{-1}$ (see under 5.2.2).

5.4 Kerma and kerma rate

The term kerma is the acronym for *k*inetic *e*nergy *r*eleased in *ma*terial[24]. The kerma may be applied to indirectly ionizing (uncharged) particles (photons, neutrons) and, in the case of photons, to energies up to about 3 MeV above which present techniques make measurements difficult to perform. Note the similarity between the definitions of kerma and exposure.

5.4.1 The *kerma K* is the quotient of dE_{tr} by dm, where dE_{tr} is the sum of the initial kinetic energies of all the charged ionizing particles liberated by uncharged ionizing particles in a material of mass dm:

$$K = dE_{tr}/dm; \text{ unit: J kg}^{-1} \text{ or Gy (temporarily rd)}$$

By definition, dE_{tr} (in contrast to dQ with the exposure) includes the energy lost by secondary electrons as bremsstrahlung (the subscript 'tr' refers to the energy *tr*ansfer).

As in the case of exposure inside a medium, it is possible to define, for example, 'air kerma at a point inside a water phantom'. This means that the kerma that would be obtained if a small quantity of air were placed at the point of interest in the phantom.

The relation between air kerma and exposure is

$$K_a = (\bar{W}/e) X (1 - g_a)^{-1}$$

where $\bar{W}$ is the mean energy expended in air per ion formed, e the elementary charge (see 6.3) and g_a as defined above (4.2).

The measurement of kerma requires that certain experimental conditions be met (see 6.2.1).

5.4.2 *Kerma rate* $\dot{K} = dK/dt$; unit: $\text{J kg}^{-1} \text{s}^{-1}$ or Gy s^{-1}

6. Conversion of exposure readings to absorbed dose in matter

As long as all photon dosimeters used in radiotherapy and biology (and most instruments used in radiation protection) continue to be calibrated in terms of exposure, their readings must be converted to obtain the *absorbed dose* in a material. This chapter describes a number of rules for this purpose. When the SI units have been introduced in radiology in the next few years (see under 1), national laboratories will be able to supply data on the 'absorbed dose in water' under specified conditions directly, thus obviating much calculation.

6.1 General implications

Ionization chamber dosimeters are usually calibrated to show the value of exposure at the point of interest in air that would apply at this point if there were no chamber. The calibration factor (i.e., the factor by which the instrument reading is multiplied to yield the value of the measured quantity) includes a correction for the change in the photon fluence at the point of interest when the chamber is inserted into the measurement position. Under different conditions, for instance in a phantom, a correction factor must

be applied, when the air calibration factor is used (k_a or k_c, see Tables 4 and 6). The correction factor for in-phantom measurements varies from 0.97 to 1.01 for thimble chambers up to 0.6 mL in volume and for x-ray generating voltages between 0.1 and 2.0 MV; for thin-window chambers it is up to 1.2 at about 0.1 MV. When this factor is unknown, the true value of the absorbed dose remains uncertain.

In general, the response of a dosimeter (the ratio of the indicated value to the actual value of the quantity) is a function of the energy and direction of the incident radiation. For a given primary beam these two parameters vary in a phantom. They depend on the depth, the irradiation field size and on the source–phantom distance. If the factors for in-phantom calibration are to be reproducible, certain reference conditions must be stipulated. An example taken from several sources but not yet internationally accepted is given in Table 2.

6.2 Ion doses under special conditions

The conditions under which the absorbed dose produced in a material can be calculated from the measured ion dose are of two main types. The first type, represented by the condition of *secondary-electron equilibrium* (SEE), applies to photon radiation with energy up to a few MeV; the second, consisting of the Bragg-Gray conditions, applies to high-energy photon and electron radiations.

6.2.1 *Secondary-electron equilibrium* for photon radiation exists if the energies, number and direction of the secondary electrons are constant throughout the volume of interest. This is equivalent to saying that the spectral distribution of electron radiance does not vary within the volume. In particular, it follows that the sums of the energies (excluding rest energies) of the electrons entering and leaving the volume are equal.

For the purpose of performing measurements, the following three points are important:

1. The ion dose measured at a point in air where SEE exists is equal to the *exposure* at that point. In other words, exposure measurement to determine the ion dose requires the closest possible approximation to the SEE situation.

2. An approximation to SEE can be obtained at any point in a photon radiation field up to a certain energy level (in air or a phantom) by placing a small *ionization chamber with air-equivalent walls* (of graphite, for example) at that point. The walls must be of a thickness at least equal to the range of the secondary electrons. Such a chamber is referred to below as an *equilibrium chamber*.

3. With increasing photon energy the range of the secondary electrons increases, so that the chamber walls must be thickened, e.g., by the use of build-up caps, which in turn increase the disturbing effect of the chamber on the radiation field. A practical limit is reached when the electron range R is no longer small compared with $1/\mu$ for photons, where μ is the linear attenuation coefficient for photon radiation in the wall material. This occurs at photon energies of about 3 MeV.

6.2.2 If a cavity in a material m is filled with material a (air, for example) the *Bragg-Gray conditions* for photon and electron radiation are fulfilled when:

(a) the spectral radiance (see under 3.1 and 3.2) of the first-generation electrons is not changed by filling the cavity with the material a;

(b) the fraction of energy imparted to the material a by secondary electrons liberated within this material is small compared with the total energy imparted to material a;

(c) the fluence rate of the electrons of all generations is uniform throughout the cavity material a.

Conditions (a) and (b) are realized approximately when the linear dimensions of the cavity in the direction of the beam are small compared with $1/\mu$ (μ: linear attenuation coefficient for photon radiation in material a) and small compared with the mean range of the primary or secondary electrons in the material a; i.e., the primary or secondary electron or photon energy must be sufficiently high. The walls of such a cavity ionization chamber must also be thin compared with the mean range of the electrons, or the wall material must have approximately the same mass-energy absorption coefficient μ_{en}/ϱ and mass-electron stopping power S/ϱ as the surrounding material m. This means that a chamber designed for use in a water phantom under Bragg-Gray conditions should have water-equivalent walls.

To reduce the boundary effect between the wall material and the air in the chamber due to low-energy delta electrons, the walls must be lined on the inside with graphite about 1 μm thick; if this

Table 2 *Typical reference conditions for therapy level dosimeters calibrated in terms of absorbed dose to water in a water phantom (cf. under 6.1; international standards are in preparation, some figures may be changed slightly; SSD: source to phantom surface distance)*

Type of radiation	Type of chamber	(Maximum) energy of radiation	Field size at surface in cm × cm	SSD in cm	Reference depth in cm
Photons	Thin-window..................................	10 keV – 100 keV	5 × 5	30	0.007
	Thimble.......................................	50 keV – 150 keV	10 × 10	75	2
	Thimble.......................................	>150 keV – 10 MeV	10 × 10	100	5
	Thimble.......................................	>10 Mev – 25 MeV	10 × 10	100	10
	Thimble.......................................	>25 MeV – 50 MeV	10 × 10	100	10
Beta rays	Thin-window..................................		*	20	0.007
Electrons	Flat chamber..................................	1 MeV – 2 MeV	10 × 10	100	0.2
		>2 MeV – 5 MeV	10 × 10	100	0.5
		>5 MeV – 10 MeV	10 × 10	100	1.0
		>10 MeV – 20 MeV	10 × 10	100	2.0
		>20 MeV – 35 MeV	10 × 10	100	3.0
		>35 MeV – 50 MeV	10 × 10	100	4.0

* Special conditions, e.g. according to ISO/DP 6980, 1980, International Organization for Standardization, Paris.

is not done, the mean cavity ion dose will be dependent on the magnitude of the measuring volume [requirement (c) above].

For photon radiation of energy exceeding 200 keV (with thimble chambers, exceeding 1 MeV) as well as for electron radiation at all energies, satisfactory approximation to Bragg-Gray conditions is obtainable with special flat cylindrical chambers ('pill-box' type). The chambers are known as 'cavity chambers', 'Bragg-Gray chambers' or 'electron chambers', and the ion dose generated is called the 'cavity ion dose J_c' (see under 5.2.3). For photon radia-

tion the same chamber can often be used both as an equilibrium chamber at low energies and as a Bragg-Gray chamber at high energies. In the overlapping region between 1 MeV and 3 MeV, special care must be taken in the choice of the proper corrections.

6.3 Conversions of readings into absorbed dose using equilibrium chambers

When an exposure meter with an equilibrium chamber is positioned at the point of interest in a phantom of material m and irradiated with x or gamma rays of energies less than about 3 MeV, then from the indicated value

$$X_{ind} = M N$$

Table 3 *Conversion factor f for calculating the absorbed dose D_m in mGy for various surrounding materials from the exposure X in R for x rays and gamma rays*

X rays Tube voltage in kV	Fixed filter in mm	Additional filter in mm	Half-value thickness in mm	Muscle	Bone	Fatty tissue	Water
				Conversion factor f in mGy R^{-1}			
10	1.5 Be	–	0.03 Al	9.15	30.97	4.11	9.13
15	1.5 Be	0.05 Al	0.07 Al	9.16	33.25	4.04	9.08
20	1.5 Be	0.15 Al	0.11 Al	9.16	35.24	3.98	9.02
30	1.5 Be	0.30 Al	0.22 Al	9.15	37.14	3.94	8.96
40	1.5 Be	0.50 Al	0.44 Al	9.14	38.62	3.95	8.90
50	1.5 Be	1.0 Al	0.94 Al	9.14	39.89	4.04	8.85
50	4.0 Al	–	2.2 Al	9.14	40.35	4.25	8.81
70	4.0 Al	–	2.8 Al	9.17	38.65	4.64	8.85
100	4.0 Al	0.5 Al	4.4 Al	9.20	35.97	5.11	8.92
120	4.0 Al	0.5 Al	0.28 Cu	9.28	30.92	6.11	9.05
140	4.0 Al	2.0 Al	0.50 Cu	9.34	26.88	6.84	9.16
150	4.0 Al	0.5 Cu	0.85 Cu	9.40	21.93	7.69	9.29
200	4.0 Al	1.0 Cu	1.65 Cu	9.48	16.32	8.60	9.45
250	4.0 Al	1.6 Cu	2.5 Cu	9.52	13.40	9.06	9.54
280	4.0 Al	3.0 Cu	3.4 Cu	9.54	11.42	9.37	9.60
Gamma rays Nuclide							
^{137}Cs	–	–	–	9.6	9.2	9.7	9.7
^{60}Co	–	–	–	9.6	9.2	9.7	9.7

The f values depend upon the energy of the radiation and refer to values in air (see 6.3). The effect on the f values of the variation of energy of the radiation with tissue depth (see[24,25]) can be taken into account by starting from the HVT values in the fourth column.
In determining the dose for soft tissue embedded in bone from the exposure, the factor f should be obtained by interpolation between the values for muscle and bone; the value of f depends on the distance between the point for which the dose is to be ascertained and the bone substance.
The above values have been taken from DIN 6800, part 2, 1980[18]; see also ICRU Report 10b, 1964[24].

(where M is the reading of the meter corrected for air density and N the calibration factor for exposure in air for the radiation quality in question) the absorbed dose D_m in the material is

$$D_m = f X_{ind} k_a$$

The conversion factor f is given by

$$f = \frac{\overline{W}}{e} \times \frac{(\overline{\mu}_{en}/\varrho)_m}{(\overline{\mu}_{en}/\varrho)_a}$$

where $\overline{W}/e = 33.7$ V $= 0.87$ rd R$^{-1} = 0.0087$ Gy R^{-1} is the mean energy required to generate an ion pair in air, divided by the elementary charge, and $\overline{\mu}_{en}/\varrho$ is the mean mass-energy absorption coefficient (see under 4.2) averaged over the photon spectrum in the material (subscript 'm') or in air (subscript 'a'). Values of the conversion factor f for muscle, bone, fatty tissue and water are given in Table 3.

The correction factor k_a (Table 4) which, unlike f, relates to the chamber type, has been discussed briefly under 6.1. The product $k_a X_{ind}$ is the true value of the exposure X at the point of interest and is suitable for determining D_m to a good approximation. For an exact determination of D_m (with an uncertainty of the order of 1%) additional corrections must be made[10,18,28].

6.4 Conversion of readings into absorbed dose using Bragg-Gray chambers

The absorbed dose D_m at a point in a phantom of material m produced by high-energy x or gamma radiation (> 1 MeV) or by electrons is derived from the indicated value

$$X_{ind} = M N_{Co}$$

of an exposure meter used with a Bragg-Gray chamber without build-up cap (where N_{Co} is the calibration factor for exposure in air for ^{60}Co gamma radiation *with* build-up cap if provided) by the equation

$$D_m = g X_{ind} k_c$$

The product $X_{ind} k_c$ is the 'true' ion dose within the chamber provided the Bragg-Gray conditions are fulfilled. It represents the

Table 4 *Calibration correction factor k_a for thimble chambers* (see under 6.3). The table includes data from DIN 6800, part 2[18]. Estimated maximum systematic deviation $\pm 2\%$

Radiation quality				Correction factor k_a
X rays Tube voltage in kV	Added filter in mm	Intrinsic filter in mm Al	Half-value thickness in mm Cu	
60	–	1.8	0.057	0.99
80	–	1.8	0.081	1.00
100	0.2 Cu	2.7	0.30	1.01
150	0.5 Cu	2.7	0.87	1.01
200	1.2 Cu	2.7	1.75	1.00
250	1.5 Cu	2.7	2.45	1.00
300	3.5 Pb 5.0 Cu 2.0 Al	2.7	6.0	1.00
Gamma rays Nuclide				
^{137}Cs	–	–	–	0.97
^{60}Co	–	–	–	0.98

Table 5 *Conversion factor g for calculating the absorbed dose D_m in mGy for various surrounding materials from the cavity ion dose $J_c = X_{ind} k_c$ in R for ultra-hard x rays and electron radiation*

Type of radiation	Conversion factor g			
	Muscle	Bone	Fatty tissue	Water
	in mGy R^{-1}			
Ultra-hard x rays Generating voltage in MV				
5	9.9	9.2	10.2	10.0
10	9.7	9.1	9.9	9.8
20	9.5	8.9	9.8	9.6
30	9.4	8.8	9.7	9.5
40	9.3	8.7	9.6	9.4
Electron radiation Mean kinetic energy in MeV				
1.0	9.7	9.1	9.9	9.8
2.0	9.5	8.9	9.6	9.6
5.0	9.1	8.5	9.2	9.2
10.0	8.7	8.2	8.8	8.8
15.0	8.5	8.1	8.6	8.6
20.0	8.3	7.9	8.4	8.4
30.0	8.1	7.8	8.2	8.2
40.0	8.0	7.7	8.1	8.1
50.0	8.0	7.6	8.1	8.0

For ultra-hard x rays the conversion factor g is strictly valid only for depths greater than that of the maximum dose. In calculating g, averaging over the electron spectra at these depths was included (see 6.4). In electron radiation, it is the mean energy available at the point of measurement rather than the initial energy (at the exit of the accelerator) that is decisive (see under 6.4).
For soft tissue embedded in the bone substance, the valid factor g is that for soft tissue, since the effect of the bone is already allowed for in measuring the cavity ion dose.

Table 6 *Calibration correction factor k_c for thimble chambers* (see under 6.4) *valid for ultra-hard x rays* (maximum energy 5–45 MeV) *and electron radiation* (mean energy at point of measurement 5 to 45 MeV). Values taken from DIN 6800, part 2[18]. Estimated maximum systematic deviation $\pm 2\%$

Chamber wall	k_c
Graphite...	0.98
Plexiglass	0.95

cavity ion dose J_c (see under 6.2.2). The conversion factor g for the corresponding (primary or secondary) electron spectrum is given by

$$g = \frac{\overline{W}}{e} \times \frac{(\overline{S}/\varrho)_m}{(\overline{S}/\varrho)_a}$$

where $\overline{S}/\varrho$ is the mass stopping power (see under 4.3) averaged over the electron spectrum in the material (subscript 'm') or in air (subscript 'a'). Values of g for muscle, bone, fatty tissue and water are given in Table 5. The relevant *electron radiation* energy is not the initial energy E_0 but the mean energy $\overline{E}$ at the depth z of interest within the phantom given by the equation[7, 11]

$$\overline{E} = E_0 (1 - z/R_p)$$

where the practical range R_p of the electrons in cm in water up to $E_0 = 35$ MeV is given by

$$\varrho R_p = 0.512 E_0 - 0.246$$

(ϱ: density of water in g cm^{-3}; E_0 in MeV). Values of the correction factor k_c are given in Table 6. In the dosimetric literature the product $g k_c$ *for water* is often called C_λ for photons and C_E for electrons[8, 11].

7. Radiation field quantities, absorbed dose and kerma

7.1 In the case of secondary-electron equilibrium *for photon radiation* (see under 6.2.1), the relationship between photon energy fluence Ψ_{ph} or photon particle fluence Φ_{ph} and the *absorbed dose* D_m for monoenergetic photons of energy E at the point of interest in material m may be written as

$$D_m = (\mu_{en}/\varrho)_m \Psi_{ph} = (\mu_{en}/\varrho)_m E \Phi_{ph}$$

where $(\mu_{en}/\varrho)_m$ is the mass-energy absorption coefficient (see under 4.2) of the material m for the photon energy concerned.

7.2 The corresponding relationship with the *kerma* K_m is

$$K_m = (\mu_{tr}/\varrho)_m \Psi_{ph} = (\mu_{tr}/\varrho)_m E \Phi_{ph}$$

where $(\mu_{tr}/\varrho)_m$ is the mass-energy transfer coefficient (see under 4.1). Thus for photon energies up to about 0.7 MeV, where the difference between μ_{en}/ϱ and μ_{tr}/ϱ is negligible for material of low atomic number Z, the absorbed dose D_m under equilibrium conditions and the kerma K_m are equal.

7.3 *For monoenergetic electrons*, the relationship between particle fluence Φ_e and absorbed dose D_m under Bragg-Gray conditions (see under 6.2.2) at the point of interest in a material m may be written

$$D_m = (S/\varrho)_m \Phi_e$$

where $(S/\varrho)_m$ is the mass-energy stopping power for the electrons in m.
Since all interaction coefficients are energy-dependent, mean values must be used in dealing with particle spectra.

8. Relative biological effectiveness (RBE)

Radiobiological studies have shown that different kinds of ionizing radiation can produce biological effects of different intensity even when the absorbed dose in the biological material being irradiated, and all other conditions, are the same. The absorbed dose is therefore still not an adequate physical quantity from which all the biological effects can be deduced. This has led to the introduction of the concept of relative biological effectiveness (RBE), with the dimensionless RBE factor ξ defined as

$$\xi = D_0/D$$

where D is the absorbed dose of the radiation under consideration that produces a particular biological effect, and D_0 the absorbed dose of a reference radiation (at present hard filtered 200 kV x rays) that produces the same effect under otherwise identical conditions. The RBE factor is not a constant for a particular kind of radiation since different values are obtained depending on the nature of the irradiation reaction being observed, on the kind of biological system under study, on the stage of development of the object being irradiated, and on the distribution of the absorbed dose in space and time[29]. Since the RBE factor as such is unsuitable for use in the field of radiation protection, the term RBE should be reserved for radiobiology only.

9. Dose equivalent and quality factor

In radiation protection the place of the RBE factor ξ is taken by the quality factor Q, and that of the absorbed dose of the reference radiation – which is not used in radiation protection – by the dose equivalent H (see [4]). The dose equivalent H is the product of D, Q and N:

$$H = DQN$$

where D is the absorbed dose, Q the quality factor, and N the product of all other modifying factors. Q and N are dimensionless; $N = 1$ in external radiation, to which the following discussion will be restricted.

The concept of dose equivalent is intended for use in radiation protection. The quality factor Q is chosen to encompass appropriate RBE values, but to be independent of the organ or tissue or of the biological endpoint under consideration. It is also chosen to be a smooth function of the collision stopping power of the charged particles. It should be noted that the values of Q currently used are only for routine radiation protection applications and should not be used in assessing the effects of high-level accidental exposures.

Values of Q for various types of radiation and different energies are frequently based upon the extrapolation of experimental information which is subject to possibly different evaluations. International agreement on a consistent set of recommended values under the auspices of the International Commission on Radiation Protection (ICRP)[30, 31] gives the values of Q given in Table 7 for different values of the linear energy transfer L_w in water of the radiation particles along their tracks (L_w is numerically equal to the collision stopping power).

For electrons and x rays of all energies

$$L_w < 3.5 \text{ keV } \mu m^{-1}, Q = 1$$

If a number of different radiations are present simultaneously, the total dose equivalent is the sum of the dose equivalents of the individual radiations:

$$H = \Sigma H_i = \Sigma D_i Q_i$$

The SI unit of dose equivalent is the joule per kilogram ($J \, kg^{-1}$). The SI unit for absorbed dose is also the joule per kilogram. In view of the importance of the dose equivalent for human health and to avoid misunderstandings as to the quantities being referred to, the name sievert (Sv) has been proposed as the special name for the SI unit of dose equivalent. This proposal was agreed to by the General Conference on Weights and Measures in 1979[1]. The special unit rem, which may be used temporarily, is related to the sievert as follows:

$$1 \text{ rem} = 10^{-2} \text{ Sv} = 10^{-2} \text{ J kg}^{-1}$$

The sievert is to be used only for the quantity dose equivalent.

In future, radiation protection dosimeters will be calibrated in terms of dose equivalent in Sv, but the detailed specification of this quantity is still under consideration of an ICRU report committee. In order to enable instrument manufacturers and users to perform the change from old units to SI units without delay, an interim solution for photon radiation has recently been proposed by REICH and BENGTSSON[32]. These authors introduce the 'photon dose equivalent' which is derived from exposure by the equation

$$H_x = Q f_0 X$$

where (for photons) $Q = 1 \text{ Sv Gy}^{-1}$ and $f_0 = 0.01 \text{ Gy R}^{-1}$. Since in old units $Q f_0 = 1 \text{ rem R}^{-1}$, the proposal means that for the time being the practice of the last twenty years for determining dose equivalent is pursued. The use of H_x as an interim solution is officially approved in the Federal Republic of Germany.

10. Exposure rate constant and kerma rate constants

The exposure rate constant was invented to characterize the photon radiation output of radioactive sources in terms of the exposure rate produced at a certain distance. In many practical applications this is preferable to the characterization by the activity. Main fields of use of the exposure rate constant are the assessment of packaging for the transport of radioactive sources, the application of gamma-ray sources in intracavitary and interstitial radiotherapy, and the determination of the equivalent activity (GUIHO and HILLION[34]) of sources used for external irradiation, as for instance in ^{60}Co teletherapy.

The *exposure rate constant* $\Gamma_{\delta,\dot{x}}$ of a radioactive nuclide emitting photons is the quotient of $\dot{X}_\delta l^2$ by A, where $\dot{X}_\delta$ is the exposure rate at a distance l due to all photons of energy greater than δ, emitted from a point source of this nuclide with activity A:

$$\Gamma_{\delta,\dot{x}} = \dot{X}_\delta l^2 / A; \text{ old unit: R } m^2 h^{-1} Ci^{-1}$$

The choice of the energy limit δ depends upon the application. Its value is given in keV. $\Gamma_{50,\dot{x}}$ therefore is the exposure rate con-

stant of a radionuclide when all photons with energies greater than 50 keV are taken into account.

For radionuclides with short-lived decay products, the exposure rate constant is given for the state of radioactive equilibrium. The quantity $\dot{X}_\delta$ is then the exposure rate due to the emitted photon radiation of all members of the series, A the activity of the parent nuclide. $\dot{X}_\delta$ refers to a small airfilled volume 'in free space', i.e., for measurements in air or in another medium, absorption of photons between the source and the point of measurement must be taken into account.

With exposure falling into disuse (see under 1) three other types of rate constants may come into use: The *air kerma-rate constant* being proposed by ICRU[4], the *water kerma-rate constant* being appropriate for quantities in terms of which dosimeters are calibrated in the future[33], and the *dose equivalent-rate constant* for radiation protection purposes. Numerical values for some nuclides for the exposure and kerma rate constants are given in Table 8.

Table 7 *Values of the quality factor Q as a function of the linear energy transfer L_w of charged particles in water. Intermediate values can be obtained by interpolation*[31]

	Q
≤ 3.5 keV μm^{-1}	1
7.0 keV μm^{-1}	2
23 keV μm^{-1}	5
53 keV μm^{-1}	10
≥ 175 keV μm^{-1}	20

Table 8 *Exposure rate constant $\Gamma_{\delta,\dot{x}}$, air kerma-rate constant $\Gamma_{\delta,\dot{K}_a}$, and water kerma-rate constant $\Gamma_{\delta,\dot{K}_w}$, for some radio-nuclides* (derived from GUIHO and HILLION, 1974[34]; 2nd and 3rd row values taken from NCRP Report 58, 1978[3]; $\Gamma_{\delta,\dot{K}_w}$ calculated using tables of HUBBELL[35]). The degree of uncertainty of the rate constants is of the order of $\pm 2\%$

Nuclide	Most important gamma energies in keV	Emission probability in %	δ in keV	$\Gamma_{\delta,\dot{x}}$ in $\frac{R \, m^2}{h \, Ci}$	$\Gamma_{\delta,\dot{K}_a}$ in $\frac{mGy \, m^2}{h \, GBq}$	$\Gamma_{\delta,\dot{K}_w}$ in $\frac{mGy \, m^2}{h \, GBq}$
^{24}Na	1368.5	100	2	1.87	0.439	0.488
	2754.1	100				
^{42}K	1524.7	17.9	4	0.138	0.0324	0.0361
^{59}Fe	1099.2	56.1	7	0.625	0.147	0.163
	1291.6	43.6				
^{60}Co	1173.2	99.9	9	1.308	0.307	0.342
	1332.5	100				
^{64}Cu	7.6	16.5	2	(0.248)	(0.0583)	(0.0629)
	511	37	9	0.113	0.0266	0.0295
	1345.9	0.49				
^{125}I	27.4	114	6	0.143	0.0336	0.0339
	31.0	25.8				
	35.5	6.7				
^{131}I	284.3	6.1	6	0.221	0.0519	0.0578
	364.5	81.2				
	637.0	7.3				
^{137}Cs $+^{137}$Ba^m	32.9	7.4	6	0.33	0.0776	0.0862
	661.6	89.9				
^{192}Ir	~302	59	12	0.472	0.111	0.123
	316.5	82.8				
	468.1	47.8				
^{198}Au	411.8	95.5	10	0.244	0.0573	0.0638
^{226}Ra	186.0...			0.826*	0.194*	0.216*
	2447.7					

* By convention, the constant Γ_δ for ^{226}Ra is specified for filtration with 0.5 mm of platinum.

Air kerma-rate constant

$$\Gamma_{\delta,\dot{K}_a} = \dot{K}_{a,\delta} l^2/A \approx (\overline{W}/e)\Gamma_{\delta,\dot{X}}$$

unit: $\text{Gy m}^2 \text{ h}^{-1} \text{ Bq}^{-1} = 10^{12} \text{ mGy m}^2 \text{ h}^{-1} \text{ GBq}^{-1}$

(The unit of hour, h, is in use with the International System, but not an SI unit; therefore the unit of the air kerma-rate constant is not part of a coherent system, see under 1, foot-note.) The approximation given is obtained by neglecting the factor $(1 - g_a)^{-1}$ on the right-hand side of the equation (see under 5.4.1). When the conversion factor $\overline{W}/e = 0.0087$ Gy/C (see under 6.3) is expanded to include the units, in terms of which the two rate constants are usually given, its value is

$$\frac{\overline{W}}{e} = \frac{0.0087}{3.7 \times 10^{10}} \frac{\text{Gy m}^2 \text{ h}^{-1} \text{ Bq}^{-1}}{\text{R m}^2 \text{ h}^{-1} \text{ Ci}^{-1}} = 0.235 \text{ mGy Ci}/(\text{R GBq})$$

Water kerma-rate constant

$$\Gamma_{\delta,\dot{K}_w} = \dot{K}_{w,\delta} l^2/A \approx f_w \Gamma_{\delta,\dot{X}}$$

unit: $\text{Gy m}^2 \text{ h}^{-1} \text{ Bq}^{-1} = 10^{12} \text{ mGy m}^2 \text{ h}^{-1} \text{ GBq}^{-1}$

The conversion factor f_w refers to water and depends slightly on the photon energy, see under 6.3 and Table 3; a typical value is

$$f_w(^{60}\text{Co}) = 0.0097 \text{ Gy/R} = 0.262 \text{ mGy Ci}/(\text{R GBq})$$

The water kerma in air K_w (REICH and TRIER[33]) is connected with the exposure by the equation

$$K_w(1 - g_w) = f_w X$$

(For g_w see under 4.2.) The water kerma is defined in any surrounding medium and was chosen because of its close relation to the quantity absorbed dose D_w in water, in terms of which instruments for radiotherapy will be calibrated in the future. (The difference between K_w and D_w in regions of transient equilibrium is smaller than 1% in the energy range of interest and can be neglected in most cases.) When an instrument calibrated in terms of D_w in water is used for measurements in air, a correction factor similar to the inverse of the factor k_a (see Table 4) may be applied to obtain K_w in air. Thus the water kerma-rate constant can be used in future in connection with therapy level dosimeters in the same way as hitherto the exposure rate constant.

(Photon) dose equivalent rate constant

$$\Gamma_{\delta,\dot{H}} = \dot{H}_\delta l^2/A = Q f_0 \Gamma_{\delta,\dot{X}}$$

unit: $\text{Sv m}^2 \text{ h}^{-1} \text{ Bq}^{-1} = 10^{12} \text{ mSv m}^2 \text{ h}^{-1} \text{ GBq}^{-1}$

With $Q = 1 \text{ Sv Gy}^{-1}$ for photons and with $f_0 = 0.01 \text{ Gy R}^{-1}$ (as proposed for an interim solution under 9) the conversion factor is

$$Q f_0 = 0.270 \text{ mSv Ci R}^{-1} \text{GBq}^{-1}$$

This is sufficiently close, for instance, to the value of $f_w(^{60}\text{Co})$ to allow – for the purpose of radiation protection – the replacement of $\Gamma_{\delta,\dot{H}}$ by $\Gamma_{\delta,\dot{K}_w}$, i.e., taking values for the latter constant from tables such as Table 8 and replacing in the composite unit the Gy by Sv. Another specification of the dose equivalent at a later time may lead to the replacement of f_0 by another factor.

References

[1] Conférence Générale des Poids et Mesures, *Comptes rendus des séances de la 15e Conférence Générale des Poids et Mesures, Paris 1975*, Bureau International des Poids et Mesures, Sèvres, 1976, page 105; Conférence Générale des Poids et Mesures, *Comptes rendus des séances de la 16e Conférence Générale des Poids et Mesures, Paris 1979*, Bureau International des Poids et Mesures, Sèvres, 1980, page 100.

[2] Council Directive on the approximation of the laws of the Member States relating to units of measurement and repealing Council Directive 71/354/EEC (80/181/EEC), *Off. J. Eur. Comm.*, **23**, L39, page 40, February 15, 1980 (Office for Official Publications of the EC, Luxembourg).

[3] QUIMBY et al., *Radioactive Isotopes in Clinical Practice*, Lea & Febiger, Philadelphia, 1958; National Council on Radiation Protection and Measurements (NCRP), *A Handbook of Radioactivity Measurements Procedures*, NCRP Report No. 58, 1978.

[4] International Commission on Radiation Units and Measurements (ICRU), *Radiation Quantities and Units*, ICRU Report 33, 1980.

[5] REICH, H., *Phys. Med. Biol.*, **24**, 895 (1979).

[6] ATTIX et al., *Radiation Dosimetry;* part I: *Fundamentals* (1968); part II: *Instrumentation* (1966); part III: *Sources, Fields, Measurements, and Applications* (1969); suppl. 1: *Topics in Radiation Dosimetry* (1972), Academic Press, New York.

[7] JAEGER and HÜBNER, *Dosimetrie und Strahlenschutz, Physikalisch-technische Daten und Methoden für die Praxis*, Thieme, Stuttgart, 1974.

[8] International Commission on Radiation Units and Measurements (ICRU), *Radiation Dosimetry: X Rays and Gamma Rays with Maximum Photon Energies between 0.6 and 50 MeV*, ICRU Report 14, 1969.

[9] International Commission on Radiation Units and Measurements (ICRU), *Radiation Dosimetry: X Rays Generated at Potentials of 5 to 150 kV*, ICRU Report 17, 1970.

[10] International Commission on Radiation Units and Measurements (ICRU), *Measurements of Absorbed Dose in a Phantom Irradiated by a Single Beam of X or Gamma Rays*, ICRU Report 23, 1973.

[11] International Commission on Radiation Units and Measurements (ICRU), *Radiation Dosimetry: Electrons with Initial Energies between 1 and 50 MeV*, ICRU Report 21, 1972.

[12] International Commission on Radiation Units and Measurements (ICRU), *Neutron Fluence, Neutron Spectra and Kerma*, ICRU Report 13, 1969.

[13] International Commission on Radiation Units and Measurements (ICRU), *Neutron Dosimetry for Biology and Medicine*, ICRU Report 26, 1977.

[14] International Commission on Radiation Units and Measurements (ICRU), *Specification of High Activity Gamma-Ray Sources*, ICRU Report 18, 1970.

[15] International Commission on Radiation Units and Measurements (ICRU), *Radiation Protection Instrumentation and its Application*, ICRU Report 20, 1971.

[16] International Commission on Radiation Units and Measurements (ICRU), *Conceptual Basis for the Determination of Dose Equivalent*, ICRU Report 25, 1976.

[17] International Electrotechnical Commission (IEC), *Dosimeters with Ionization Chambers as Used in Radiotherapy*, IEC Draft Standard, Document 62C (Central Office) 12, Geneva, 1979.

[18] Deutsches Institut für Normung (DIN), *Dosismeßverfahren in der radiologischen Technik*, DIN 6800: part 1: *Allgemeines zur Dosimetrie von Photonen- und Elektronenstrahlung nach der Sondenmethode;* part 2: *Ionisationsdosimetrie;* part 3: *Eisensulfatdosimetrie;* part 4: *Filmdosimetrie;* part 5: *Radiothermoluminiszenz-Dosimetrie;* part 6: *Radiophotoluminiszenz-Dosimetrie* (all parts: 1980), Beuth, Berlin.

[19] Deutsches Institut für Normung (DIN), *Neutronendosimetrie*, DIN 6802: part 1: *Begriffe und Benennungen* (1978); part 2: *Berechnungsgrundlagen* (1978), Beuth, Berlin.

[20] Deutsches Institut für Normung (DIN), *Klinische Dosimetrie*, DIN 6809: part 1: *Therapeutische Anwendung gebündelter Röntgen-, Gamma- und Elektronenstrahlung* (1976); part 2: *Interstitielle und Kontaktbestrahlung mit umschlossenen gamma- und betastrahlenden radioaktiven Stoffen* (1978), Beuth, Berlin.

[21] Deutsches Institut für Normung (DIN), *Begriffe und Benennungen in der radiologischen Technik*, DIN 6814: part 2: *Strahlenphysik* (1980); part 3: *Dosisgrößen und Dosiseinheiten* (draft 1979); part 4: *Radioaktivität* (1980); part 5: *Strahlenschutz* (draft 1980), Beuth, Berlin.

[22] Deutsches Institut für Normung (DIN), *Therapiedosimeter mit Ionisationskammern für Röntgen-, Gamma- und Elektronenstrahlung*, DIN 6817, draft 1980, Beuth, Berlin.

[23] Deutsches Institut für Normung (DIN), *Strahlenschutzdosimeter (für Gamma- und Röntgenstrahlen)*, DIN 6818; part 1: *Allgemeine Regeln* (1976); part 2: *Direkt ablesbare Ionisationskammer-Stabdosimeter* (1979); part 3: *Nicht direkt ablesbare Ionisationskammer-Stabdosimeter* (1979); part 4: *Tragbare Ionisationskammerdosimeter* (1979); part 5: *Zählrohr-Dosisleistungsmesser* (1979), Beuth, Berlin.

[24] International Commission on Radiation Units and Measurements (ICRU), *Physical Aspects of Irradiation*, ICRU Report 10b, 1964.

[25] MASSEY, J. B., *Manual of Dosimetry in Radiotherapy*, IAEA Techn. Rep. Ser. No. 110, Vienna, 1970.

[26] BACQ and ALEXANDER, *Fundamentals of Radiobiology*, 2nd ed., Pergamon Press, Oxford, 1966; STREFFER, C., *Strahlen-Biochemie*, Heidelberger Taschenbücher No. 59/60, Springer, Heidelberg, 1969.

[27] CHRISTEN, T., *Fortschr. Röntgenstr.*, Ergänzungsband **18** (1913).

[28] Nordic Association of Clinical Physics (NACP), Procedures in External Radiation Therapy Dosimetry with Electron and Photon Beams with Maximum Energies between 1 and 50 MeV, *Acta radiol. Oncology*, **19**, 55 (1980).

[29] Relative Biological Effectiveness Committee, *Hlth Phys.*, **9**, 357 (1963).

[30] International Commission on Radiological Protection (ICRP), *Protection against Ionizing Radiation from External Sources*, ICRP Publication 15, Pergamon Press, Oxford, 1970.

[31] International Commission on Radiological Protection (ICRP), *Recommendations of the International Commission on Radiological Protection*, ICRP Publication 26, Pergamon Press, Oxford, 1977; revised on The 1978 Stockholm Meeting of the International Commission on Radiological Protection, *Acta radiol. Oncology*, **18**, 77 (1979).

[32] REICH and BENGTSSON, *Hlth Phys.*, 1981 in press.

[33] REICH and TRIER, Proc. Symp. Paris, IAEA-SM-249/58, October 1980.

[34] GUIHO and HILLION, *J. appl. Radiat. Isot.*, **25**, 105 (1974).

[35] HUBBELL, J. H., *Rad. Res.*, **70**, 58 (1977).

Quantity* and definition	SI unit	
	Name	Symbol
Radiometry (electromagnetic radiation)		
The **radiant energy** W, or **quantity of radiation** Q_e, is the energy emitted, transferred or received as radiation$^\diamond$.	joule	J
The **radiant energy density** w is the radiant energy in an element of volume dV, divided by the volume of that element: $w = dW/dV$	joule per cubic meter	J m^{-3}
The **radiant flux** Φ_e, or **radiant power** P, is the time derivative of the radiant energy: $\Phi_e = P = dW/dt$	watt	W
The **spectral concentration of radiant flux**† $\Phi_{e\lambda}$ is the radiant flux over an infinitesimal interval $d\lambda$ containing a given wavelength λ, divided by that interval, i.e., the radiant flux contribution $d\Phi_e$ of the wavelength interval $d\lambda$ concerned, divided by that interval: $d\Phi_e = \Phi_{e\lambda}\, d\lambda$, or $\Phi_e = \int \Phi_{e\lambda}\, d\lambda$ $\Phi_{e\lambda}$ is often given in watt per nanometer ($1\ \text{W nm}^{-1} = 10^9\ \text{W m}^{-1}$).	watt per meter	W m^{-1}
The **radiant intensity** I_e (of a source in a given direction) is the radiant flux emitted by the source within an element of solid angle $d\Omega$ around the given direction, divided by that element of solid angle: $\Phi_e = \int I_e\, d\Omega$	watt per steradian	W sr^{-1}
The **radiance** L_e (in a given direction, at a point of a radiating surface or at a point of the path of a beam) is the radiant flux leaving, incident upon or traversing an element of area dA including the point and propagated in the given direction ε within an element of solid angle $d\Omega$, divided by the product of the element of solid angle traversed and the orthogonal projection of the element of area on a plane perpendicular to the direction of radiation: $\Phi_e = \int I_e\, d\Omega = \iint L_e \cos\varepsilon\, dA\, d\Omega$	watt per steradian per square meter	W sr^{-1} m^{-2}
The **radiant exitance** M_e (at a point of a surface) is the radiant flux emitted by an element of area dA containing the point, divided by the area of that element: $\Phi_e = \int M_e\, dA$	watt per square meter	W m^{-2}
The **irradiance**§ E_e (at a point of a surface) is the radiant flux incident on an element of area dA containing the point, divided by the area of that element: $\Phi_e = \int E_e\, dA$	watt per square meter	W m^{-2}
The **radiant exposure**** H_e (at a point of a surface) is the radiant energy per unit area incident at the point, i.e., the time integral of the irradiance at that point: $H_e = dQ_e/dA = \int E_e\, dt$	joule per square meter	J m^{-2}
The (hemispherical) **emissivity** ε (of a thermal radiator) is the ratio of the radiant exitance of the radiator to that of a black body at the same temperature$^{\diamond\diamond}$: $\varepsilon = M_e/M_{e,s}$	unity	1
The (hemispherical) **spectral emissivity** $\varepsilon(\lambda)$ (of a thermal radiator) is the ratio of the spectral concentration of radiant exitance of the radiator to that of a black body at the same temperature††: $\varepsilon(\lambda) = M_{e\lambda}/M_{e\lambda,s}$	unity	1

* Where there is no risk of confusion between *radiant* quantities and the corresponding *photometric* quantities (i.e., the photometrically evaluated radiant quantities), or where the discussion concerns exclusively one of the two kinds of quantities, the subscripts 'e' (energy) for radiant quantities and 'v' (visual) for photometric quantities are omitted.

$^\diamond$ In UV therapy and photobiology, the quantity of radiation received is also termed the *integral dose* (International Committee on Photobiology, 1954).

† $\Phi_{e\lambda}$ is one of the quantities expressing 'spectral concentration' with respect to wavelength. As the subscript λ indicates, the quantity has the dimension of a differential quotient with respect to wavelength.

Quantities expressing 'spectral concentration' with respect to frequency or wave number have analogous definitions and symbols, with the subscript λ replaced by ν or σ.

Quantities expressing 'spectral concentration' are also referred to as distribution functions, e.g., distribution function with respect to wavelength, distribution function with respect to frequency.

Where there is no risk of confusion with so-called 'spectral' quantities – for example $\varepsilon(\lambda)$, $K(\lambda)$, $V(\lambda)$, $\varrho(\lambda)$, $\alpha(\lambda)$, $\tau(\lambda)$ – which though functions of wavelength are not spectral distribution functions in the sense of differential quotients with respect to wavelength, the 'spectral concentration of a quantity X' (i.e., $X_\lambda = dX/d\lambda$) may be given the short designation 'spectral quantity X'. Thus the 'spectral concentration of radiant flux' ($\Phi_{e\lambda}$) may be abbreviated to 'spectral radiant flux'.

§ In UV therapy and photobiology, this quantity is termed the *dose rate* (International Committee on Photobiology, 1954).

** In UV therapy and photobiology, this quantity is termed the *dose* (International Committee on Photobiology, 1954).

$^{\diamond\diamond}$ Unpolarized radiant exitance of a black body in a vacuum at temperature T:
$$M_{e,s} = \sigma T^4$$
For the Stefan-Boltzmann constant σ, see page 48.

†† Planck's formula (unpolarized spectral concentration of radiant exitance of a black body in a vacuum at temperature T):
$$M_{e\lambda,s} = c_1 \lambda^{-5} (e^{c_2/\lambda T} - 1)^{-1}$$
For the first and second Planck constants $c_1 = 2\pi h c^2$ and $c_2 = hc/k$, see page 48.

Quantity (see footnote *, page 37) and definition	SI unit	
	Name	Symbol
The **directional emissivity** $\varepsilon(\vartheta, \varphi)$ (of a thermal radiator) is the ratio of the radiance of the radiator in a given direction ϑ, φ to that of a black body at the same temperature: $\varepsilon(\vartheta, \varphi) = L_e/L_{e,s} = \int L_{e\lambda} \, d\lambda / \int L_{e\lambda, s} \, d\lambda$	unity	1
The **spectral directional emissivity** $\varepsilon(\lambda; \vartheta, \varphi)$ (of a thermal radiator) is the ratio of the spectral concentration of the radiance of the radiator in a given direction ϑ, φ to that of a black body at the same temperature: $\varepsilon(\lambda; \vartheta, \varphi) = L_{e\lambda}/L_{e\lambda, s} < 1$	unity	1

Photometry

Quantity	Name	Symbol
The **luminous flux** Φ_v is the radiant flux evaluated photometrically, i.e., by evaluating the radiation according to its action upon a selective receptor. Spectral function for evaluating the spectral concentration of radiant flux $\Phi_{v\lambda}$ is either the spectral luminous efficacy $K(\lambda)$ or the spectral luminous efficiency $V(\lambda)$: $\Phi_v = \int K(\lambda) \, \Phi_{e\lambda} \, d\lambda = K_m \int V(\lambda) \, \Phi_{e\lambda} \, d\lambda$	lumen	$\mathrm{lm} = \mathrm{cd} \; \mathrm{sr}$
The **spectral concentration**$^\Diamond$ **of luminous flux** $\Phi_{v\lambda}$ (of radiation) is the luminous flux over an infinitesimal interval $d\lambda$ containing a given wavelength λ, divided by that interval, i.e., the luminous flux contribution $d\Phi_v$ of the wavelength interval $d\lambda$ concerned, divided by that interval: $d\Phi_v = \Phi_{v\lambda} \, d\lambda$, or $\Phi_v = \int \Phi_{v\lambda} \, d\lambda$ $\Phi_{v\lambda}$ is often given in lumen per nanometer ($1 \; \mathrm{lm} \; \mathrm{nm}^{-1} = 10^9 \; \mathrm{lm} \; \mathrm{m}^{-1}$).	lumen per meter	$\mathrm{lm} \; \mathrm{m}^{-1}$
The **luminous efficacy** K (of a complex radiation) is the luminous flux of this radiation, divided by the corresponding radiant flux: $K = \Phi_v/\Phi_e$	lumen per watt	$\mathrm{lm} \; \mathrm{W}^{-1}$
The **spectral luminous efficacy** $K(\lambda)$ (of a monochromatic radiation of wavelength λ), i.e., the luminous efficacy of that source of wavelength λ is the ratio of the spectral concentration of luminous flux of that wavelength to the spectral concentration of radiant flux of that wavelength: $K(\lambda) = \Phi_{v\lambda}/\Phi_{e\lambda}$ Its maximum value $K_m = K(555 \; \mathrm{nm})$ is of approximately $683 \; \mathrm{lm} \; \mathrm{W}^{-1}$ (at $T_{Pt} = 2042$ K) for the 'CIE standard photometric observer', in photopic vision†.	lumen per watt	$\mathrm{lm} \; \mathrm{W}^{-1}$
The **spectral luminous efficiency** $V(\lambda)$ (of a monochromatic radiation of wavelength λ) is the ratio of the radiant flux at wavelength λ_m to the radiant flux at wavelength λ such that both radiations produce equally intense luminous sensations under specified photometric conditions and λ_m is chosen so that the maximum value of this ratio is equal to 1, i.e., $V(\lambda)$ is the ratio of the spectral luminous efficacy $K(\lambda)$ at the wavelength λ to the maximum value K_m of the spectral luminous efficacy: $V(\lambda) = (\Phi_{e\lambda m}/\Phi_{e\lambda}) \, (\Phi_{v\lambda}/\Phi_{v\lambda m}) \rightarrow (\Phi_{e\lambda m}/\Phi_{e\lambda})$ provided $\Phi_{v\lambda m} = \Phi_{v\lambda}$, or $V(\lambda) = K(\lambda)/K_m$ §	unity	1

$^\Diamond$ See page 37, footnote †.
† The luminance of a black body† is

$$L_{v, s} = (K_m \, c_1/\pi \, n_a^2) \int_0^\infty \lambda_a^{-5} \, V(\lambda) \, (e^{c_2/n_a\lambda_a T} - 1)^{-1} \, d\lambda$$

where λ_a is the wavelength in the medium of refractive index n_a in which the radiation is propagated and $L_{v, s}$ is being determined. In accordance with the earlier definition of the candela[7], abrogated in 1979, the luminance of a black body at the temperature T_{Pt} of solidifying platinum is $L_{v, s}(T_{Pt}) = M_{v, s}(T_{Pt})/\pi = 6 \times 10^5 \, \mathrm{cd} \, \mathrm{m}^{-2}$. Using the c_1 and c_2 values of the consistent set of values for the fundamental constants of physics recommended by CODATA[2] in 1973 (see page 48), the $V(\lambda)$ values fixed by the CIE in 1971[3] and adopted by the International Committee for Weights and Measures in 1972[4], and the temperature $T_{68, Pt} = 2042$ K of solidifying platinum[5] (as secondary fixed point in the 1975 enlarged edition of the IPTS-68, the following values are obtained for the maximum spectral luminous efficacy: $K_m = 684.6 \, \mathrm{lm} \, \mathrm{W}^{-1}$ when the black body radiation is propagated in vacuum ($n_a = 1$), and $K_m = 682.7 \, \mathrm{lm} \, \mathrm{W}^{-1}$ in spectroscopic standard air ($n_a = 1.00028$). With the aim of simplifying the presentation of photometric normal values and improving their accuracy, the General Conference on

Weights and Measures in 1979[8] adopted a new definition of the candela which does not involve a black body (see under luminous intensity, page 39). The candela so defined is applicable as basic unit for both photopic and scotopic quantities as well as for quantities still to be defined in the mesopic range.

§ $V(\lambda)$ for photopic (day) vision, i.e., vision by the normal eye when adapted to luminances 10 cd or more, regarded mainly as a function of the retinal cones; $V'(\lambda)$ for scotopic (night) vision, the vision of the normal eye when adapted to luminances of less than 0.1 cd m^{-2}. Between these two luminance ranges lies that of mesopic vision (example: the vision of night drivers is mainly in the mesopic range).
In 1971, the CIE[3] adopted a table of values for $V(\lambda)$ and $V'(\lambda)$ in the interval from 360–830 nm; the values given in the *Internationales Wörterbuch der Lichttechnik*[6] (1970), after rounding off, agree with these. The International Committee for Weights and Measures in 1972[4] recommended the use of the new values for $V(\lambda)$ – in the range from 360–830 nm – and reprinted the CIE's $V(\lambda)$ table.
The following values for $V(\lambda)$ and $V'(\lambda)$ in the interval from 380–780 nm (range of visual effectiveness of visible radiation, V_s) are taken from the *Internationales Wörterbuch der Lichttechnik*:

λ in nm	Day vision $V(\lambda)$	Night vision $V'(\lambda)$	λ in nm	Day vision $V(\lambda)$	Night vision $V'(\lambda)$	λ in nm	Day vision $V(\lambda)$	Night vision $V'(\lambda)$	λ in nm	Day vision $V(\lambda)$	Night vision $V'(\lambda)$	λ in nm	Day vision $V(\lambda)$	Night vision $V'(\lambda)$	λ in nm	Day vision $V(\lambda)$	Night vision $V'(\lambda)$
380	0.0000	0.000589	450	0.038	0.455	520	0.710	0.935	590	0.757	0.0655	660	0.061	0.0003129	730	0.00052	0.000002546
390	0.0001	0.002209	460	0.060	0.567	530	0.862	0.811	600	0.631	0.03315	670	0.032	0.0001480	740	0.00025	0.000001379
400	0.0004	0.00929	470	0.091	0.676	540	0.954	0.650	610	0.503	0.01593	680	0.017	0.0000715	750	0.00012	0.000000760
410	0.0012	0.03484	480	0.139	0.793	550	0.995	0.481	620	0.381	0.00737	690	0.0082	0.00003533	760	0.00006	0.000000425
420	0.0040	0.0966	490	0.208	0.904	560	0.995	0.3288	630	0.265	0.003335	700	0.0041	0.00001780	770	0.00003	0.000000241
430	0.0116	0.1998	500	0.323	0.982	570	0.952	0.2076	640	0.175	0.001497	710	0.0021	0.00000914	780	0.000015	0.000000139
440	0.023	0.3281	510	0.503	0.997	580	0.870	0.1212	650	0.107	0.000677	720	0.00105	0.00000478			

Quantity (see footnote *, page 37) and definition	SI unit	
	Name	Symbol
The **quantity of light** Q_v is the time integral of the luminous flux: $Q_v = \int \Phi_v \, dt$ Q_v is often expressed in lumen hour (1 lm h = 3600 lm s).	lumen second	lm s = cd sr s
The **luminous intensity** I_v (of a light source in a given direction) is the luminous flux emitted by the source within an element of solid angle $d\Omega$ around the given direction, divided by that element of solid angle: $\Phi_v = \int I_v \, d\Omega$ The *candela*, since 1954 the base SI unit of luminous intensity, is newly defined[8] as the luminous intensity of a source emitting monochromatic radiation of frequency 540×10^{12} hertz in a given direction and with an intensity of $1/683$ watt per steradian in this direction.	candela	cd
The **luminance** L_v (in a given direction, at a point of an illuminating or illuminated surface, or at a point of the path of a beam) is the luminous flux leaving, incident upon or traversing an element of area dA including the point and propagated in the given direction ε within an element of solid angle $d\Omega$, divided by the product of the element of solid angle illuminated and the orthogonal projection of the element of area on a plane perpendicular to the direction of radiation: $\Phi_v = \int I_v \, d\Omega = \iint L_v \cos\varepsilon \, dA \, d\Omega$	candela per square meter	cd m^{-2}
The **luminous exitance**[†] M_v (at a point of a surface) is the luminous flux emitted by an element of area dA containing the point, divided by the area of that element: $\Phi_v = \int M_v \, dA$	lux	lx = lm m^{-2} = cd sr m^{-2}
The **illuminance** E_v (at a point of a surface) is the luminous flux incident on an element of area dA containing the point, divided by the area of that element: $\Phi_v = \int E_v \, dA$	lux[§]	lx = lm m^{-2} = cd sr m^{-2}
The **luminous exposure** H_v (at a point of a surface) is the luminous energy per unit area incident at the point, i.e., the time integral of the illuminance at that point: $H_v = dQ_v/dA = \int E_v \, dt$	lux second	lx s = cd sr m^{-2} s
The **luminous efficacy** η_v (of a light source) is the emitted luminous flux Φ_v divided by the power consumed P_{abs}: $\eta_v = \Phi_v/P_{abs}$	lumen per watt	lm W^{-1}
The **luminous efficiency** V (of a complex radiation) is the radiant flux weighed according to $V(\lambda)$, divided by the corresponding radiant flux itself: $V = \int_0^\infty \Phi_{e\lambda} V(\lambda) \, d\lambda / \int_0^\infty \Phi_{e\lambda} \, d\lambda = K/K_m$	unity	1
The **luminous efficiency of visible radiation** V_s is the luminous efficiency limited to the visible range of radiation – wavelength range of 380 nm to 780 nm: $V_s = \int_{380\,nm}^{780\,nm} \Phi_{e\lambda} V(\lambda) \, d\lambda / \int_{380\,nm}^{780\,nm} \Phi_{e\lambda} \, d\lambda$	unity	1
The **spectral reflectance** $\varrho(\lambda)$ is the spectral concentration of the reflected radiant flux (or luminous flux), divided by the spectral concentration of the incident radiant flux (or luminous flux): $\varrho(\lambda) = \Phi_{\lambda r}/\Phi_\lambda$	unity	1
The **spectral absorptance** $\alpha(\lambda)$ is the spectral concentration of the absorbed radiant flux (or luminous flux), divided by the spectral concentration of the incident radiant flux (or luminous flux): $\alpha(\lambda) = \Phi_{\lambda a}/\Phi_\lambda$**	unity	1
The **spectral transmittance** $\tau(\lambda)$ is the spectral concentration of the transmitted radiant flux (or luminous flux), divided by the spectral concentration of the incident radiant flux (or luminous flux): $\tau(\lambda) = \Phi_{\lambda tr}/\Phi_\lambda$	unity	1

° The unit candela per square centimeter (1 cd cm^{-2} = 10^4 cd m^{-2}) was formerly also known as the stilb (sb). Other luminance units occasionally used are the apostilb [1 asb = $(1/10^4\pi)$sb], the lambert [1 L = $(10^4/\pi)$cd m^{-2}] and the foot lambert (1 ftL = π^{-1} cd ft^{-2}; for ft² see page 13).

† The (unpolarized) luminous exitance of a black body at the temperature T_{Pt} of freezing platinum

$$M_{v,s}(T_{Pt}) = \int_0^\infty M_{e\lambda,s}(T_{Pt}) K(\lambda) \, d\lambda$$

(for $M_{e\lambda,s}$ see footnote ††, page 37)

is given by the relationship $\Phi_v = \int I_v \, d\Omega = \int M_v \, dA$ together with the definition of the candela, as follows:

$$M_{v,s}(T_{Pt}) = K_{max} c_1 \int_0^\infty V(\lambda) \lambda^{-5} (e^{c_2/\lambda T_{Pt}} - 1)^{-1} d\lambda = 6\pi \times 10^{-5} \text{ lx}$$

§ When used for illuminance the unit lumen per square centimeter (1 lm cm^{-2} = 10^{-4} lm m^{-2}) was formerly also known as the phot (phot). Another unit of illuminance occasionally used is the foot candle or lumen per square foot (1 fc = 1 lm ft^{-2}; for ft² see page 13).

** For a thermal radiator emitting or absorbing in any direction (ϑ, φ): $\alpha(\lambda; \vartheta, \varphi) = \varepsilon(\lambda; \vartheta, \varphi) = L_{e\lambda}/L_{e\lambda,s} < 1$

Quantity (see footnote*, page 37) and definition	SI unit	
	Name	Symbol
The **reflectance** ϱ, **absorptance** α, and **transmittance** τ, are the respective ratios of the reflected, absorbed and transmitted radiant flux (or luminous flux) Φ_r, Φ_a and Φ_{tr} to the incident radiant flux (or luminous flux) Φ. The following relationships$^\diamond$ hold for the quantities ϱ, α, τ and $\varrho(\lambda)$, $\alpha(\lambda)$, $\tau(\lambda)$: $$\varrho = \int \Phi_\lambda\, \varrho(\lambda)\, d\lambda / \int \Phi_\lambda\, d\lambda = \Phi_r/\Phi$$ $$\alpha = \int \Phi_\lambda\, \alpha(\lambda)\, d\lambda / \int \Phi_\lambda\, d\lambda = \Phi_a/\Phi$$ $$\tau = \int \Phi_\lambda\, \tau(\lambda)\, d\lambda / \int \Phi_\lambda\, d\lambda = \Phi_{tr}/\Phi$$ $$\Phi = \Phi_r + \Phi_a + \Phi_{tr}$$ $$\varrho + \alpha + \tau = \varrho(\lambda) + \alpha(\lambda) + \tau(\lambda) = 1$$	unity	1

$^\diamond$ In general, the values of the reflectance, absorptance and transmittance depend on the type of radiation, the spectral composition, and the state of polarization of the incident radiation.

References

[1] BLEVIN, W. R., *Metrologia*, **8**, 146 (1972).
[2] Committee on Data for Science and Technology (CODATA) of the International Council of Scientific Unions (ICSU), *Recommended Consistent Values of the Fundamental Physical Constants, 1973*, CODATA Bulletin, No. 11 (December 1973).
[3] Commission Internationale de l'Eclairage (CIE) [International Commission on Illumination], Publication No. 15 (E-1.3.1), Bureau central de la CIE, Paris, 1971.
[4] Comité International des Poids et Mesures, *Procès-verbaux des séances*, **40**, 29, 145 (1972).
[5] QUINN and CHANDLER, in PLUMB, H. H. (Ed.), *Temperature: Its Measurement and Control in Science and Industry*, volume 4, part 1, Instrument Society of America, Pittsburgh, 1972, page 295.
[6] Commission Internationale de l'Eclairage (CIE) [International Commission on Illumination], *Internationales Wörterbuch der Lichttechnik*, 3rd ed., Publication No. 17 (E-1.1), Bureau central de la CIE, Paris, 1970; International Organization for Standardization (ISO), *Quantities and Units of Light and Related Electromagnetic Radiations*, International Standard ISO 31/VI, 1st ed., 1973.
[7] Comité International des Poids et Mesures, *Procès-verbaux des séances*, **20**, 119 (1946) and **21**, 67 (1948); Conférence Générale des Poids et Mesures, *Comptes rendus des séances de la 9ᵉ Conférence Générale des Poids et Mesures, Paris 1948*, Gauthier-Villars, Paris, 1949, page 54; Conférence Générale des Poids et Mesures, *Comptes rendus des séances de la 13ᵉ Conférence Générale des Poids et Mesures, Paris 1967–1968*, Bureau International des Poids et Mesures, Sèvres, 1969, pages 70 and 104.
[8] Conférence Générale des Poids et Mesures, *Comptes rendus des séances de la 16ᵉ Conférence Générale des Poids et Mesures, Paris 1979*, Bureau International des Poids et Mesures, Sèvres, 1979, page 100.

Acoustics

Quantity and definition[1]	SI unit	
	Name	Symbol
The **period** T is the time taken by a periodic phenomenon in an arbitrarily defined initial state to return to that state for the first time.	second	s
The **frequency** v or f of a periodic phenomenon is the reciprocal of the period: $f = 1/T$. The frequency of a sound determines the sensation of pitch.	hertz	Hz
Standard musical tuning pitch[2]: The A_4* of the musical scale has a frequency of 440 Hz.		
The **wavelength** λ of a sound wave is the distance between neighboring points in the same state of oscillation in the wave.	meter	m
The **velocity of sound** c is the velocity of propagation of a sound wave: $$c = \lambda f$$ The velocity of sound is a constant of the medium, and as such independent of the frequency and intensity of the sound wave. In air, it depends primarily on the temperature, and has the value $(331.4 + 0.607\,t)$ m s^{-1}, where t is the numerical value of the Celsius temperature in °C. *Note:* At very high intensities (sonic booms and explosions) the velocity of sound may have a higher value.	meter per second	m s^{-1}
The (instantaneous) **sound pressure** $p^\diamond$ is the instantaneous alternating pressure, produced by the sound process, superimposed on the static pressure p_s, i.e., on the pressure at the point concerned in the absence of sound waves; the sound pressure is thus the difference between the instantaneous total pressure and the static pressure.	pascal	Pa
The (instantaneous) **sound particle displacement** $\xi^\diamond$ is the instantaneous displacement of a particle[†] of the medium from the position it would have occupied in the absence of sound waves.	meter	m
The (instantaneous) **sound particle velocity** $u^\diamond$ or $v^\diamond$ is the momentary value of the alternating velocity of a particle of the medium set in motion by an acoustic phenomenon: $$u = \partial\xi/\partial t$$	meter per second	m s^{-1}

* In the original German text: a'.
$^\diamond$ Often also used for the effective (root mean square) values of these quantities, whereby the symbols for the instantaneous values are employed for the effective values without addition of any distinguishing mark such as the subscript 'eff'.

† The term 'particle' here means an element of the medium whose dimensions are small compared with the wavelength of the sound but large compared with the size of the molecules.

Quantity and definition[1]	SI unit	
	Name	Symbol
The (instantaneous) **sound particle acceleration** $a^\Diamond$ is the momentary value of the alternating acceleration of an oscillating particle: $$\mathrm{d}a = \partial u/\partial t$$	meter per second squared	m s^{-2}
The (instantaneous) **sound flux** or (instantaneous) **volume velocity** $q^\Diamond$ (or $U^\Diamond$) is the integral of the sound particle velocity over the flow cross section of the sound wave: $$q = \int u \, \mathrm{d}S$$	cubic meter per second	m^3 s^{-1}
The **sound energy** W is the mechanical energy radiated in the form of sound.	joule	J
The **sound energy density** w (or E) is the mean sound energy in a volume element $\mathrm{d}V$ divided by that volume element: $$w = \mathrm{d}W/\mathrm{d}V$$ If the energy density varies with time, the value to be taken is the mean value over a time interval during which the sound can be regarded as statistically stationary.	joule per cubic meter	J m^{-3}
The **sound power** or **sound energy flux** P or P_a is the sound energy transferred (emitted, transmitted, or received) through a cross section S during a given time interval $\mathrm{d}t$ divided by that time interval: $$P = \mathrm{d}W/\mathrm{d}t = \int p \, u \, \mathrm{d}S$$	watt	W
The **sound intensity** J for unidirectional sound energy flux is the sound power transferred through area S normal to the direction of propagation divided by that area: $$J = \mathrm{d}P/\mathrm{d}S = p \, u$$	watt per square meter	W m^{-2}
The **specific acoustic impedance** Z_s[§] is the complex representation of the sound pressure at a point in the sound wave divided by the complex representation of the particle velocity at that point: $$Z_s = p/u$$	pascal second per meter	Pa s m^{-1}
The **acoustic impedance** Z_a[§] is the complex representation of the mean sound pressure in an oscillating surface S divided by the complex representation of the sound flux through this surface: $$Z_a = p/q = Z_s/S$$	pascal second per cubic meter	Pa s m^{-3}
The **mechanical impedance** Z_m[§] is the complex representation of the force acting on a surface S (or at a point) of a mechanical system divided by the complex representation of the mean particle velocity at that surface (or at that point) in the direction of the force: $$Z_m = \int (p/u) \, \mathrm{d}S = Z_s \, S$$	pascal second meter	Pa s m
The **attenuation exponent** a in a plane wave is the natural logarithm of the ratio of the amplitudes of a field quantity (the sound pressure, for example) at two points at different distances from the source in the direction of propagation: $$a = \ln(p_1/p_2) = 20 \lg(p_1/p_2) \, \alpha$$ where $\alpha = (\ln 10)/20 \approx 0.115129$ The special name for the unit of attenuation exponent, not accepted by the committees of the Metric Convention, is the neper (Np), i.e., 1 Np can be equated with unity in numerical calculations: $$a = \ln(p_1/p_2) \, \mathrm{Np}$$ The unit decibel (dB), which is equal to α, is the attenuation exponent when $(p_1/p_2)^{20} = 10$, i.e., 1 dB can be given the value 0.115129 in numerical calculations: $$a = 20 \lg(p_1/p_2) \, \mathrm{dB}$$ In acoustics the attenuation exponent is almost always written in this form with logarithms to the base 10.	unity	1
The **phase exponent (or phase angle)** b in a plane wave is the difference between the phase angles of a field quantity (sound pressure, for example) at two points at different distances from the source in the direction of propagation: $$b = \varphi_1 - \varphi_2$$	radian	rad
The **propagation exponent** g is the complex sum of the attenuation exponent (real part) and the phase exponent (imaginary part) along the same path of propagation: $$g = a + \mathrm{j}b$$	unity	1

$\Diamond$ Often also used for the effective (root mean square) values of these quantities, whereby the symbols for the instantaneous values are employed for the effective values without addition of any distinguishing mark such as the subscript 'eff'.

§ The quantities in the numerators and denominators of these definitions are assumed to be sinusoidal.

Quantity and definition[1]	SI unit	
	Name	Symbol
The **attenuation coefficient** (or **attenuation constant**) α is the attenuation exponent divided by the distance x between the successive points in the direction of propagation: $\alpha = a/x$ Practical unit: Np/m.	reciprocal meter	m^{-1}
The **phase coefficient** (or **phase constant**) β is the phase exponent divided by the distance x between the successive points in the direction of propagation: $\beta = b/x$	radian per meter	$rad\ m^{-1}$
The **propagation coefficient** (or **propagation constant**) γ is the complex sum of the attenuation coefficient (real part) and the phase coefficient (imaginary part): $\gamma = \alpha + j\beta = g/x$	reciprocal meter	m^{-1}
The **damping coefficient** δ in a sound wave decaying exponentially with time is the natural logarithm of the ratio of the sound particle displacement ξ_0 to its e-th part ξ, divided by the time t in which ξ_0 decays to ξ: $\delta = \ln(\xi_0/\xi)/t$ Practical unit: Np/s.	reciprocal second	s^{-1}
The **time constant** or **relaxation time** τ in a sound wave decaying exponentially with time is the reciprocal of the damping coefficient: $\tau = 1/\delta$ Practical unit: s/Np.	second	s
The **logarithmic decrement** Λ of a sound wave of period T decaying exponentially with time is the natural logarithm of the ratio of two sound particle displacements one period apart: $\Lambda = \ln(\xi_n/\xi_{n+1}) = \delta T$ Practical unit: Np.	unity	1
The **sound pressure reflection coefficient** r is the complex ratio of the field quantity (sound pressure, for example) of a reflected plane wave to the same field quantity of the incident wave: $r = p_r/p_i$	unity	1
The **sound power reflection coefficient** ϱ is the ratio of the reflected sound power P_r to the incident sound power P_i: $\varrho = P_r/P_i$	unity	1
The **acoustic absorption coefficient** α is the ratio of the unreflected sound power P_α to the incident sound power P_i: $\alpha = P_\alpha/P_i = 1 - \varrho$	unity	1
The **acoustic dissipation coefficient** δ is the ratio of the sound power P_d dissipated by conversion into other energy (mostly heat) to the incident sound power P_i: $\delta = P_d/P_i$	unity	1
The **acoustic transmission coefficient** τ is the ratio of the sound power P_t transmitted to the incident sound power P_i: $\tau = P_t/P_i = 1 - (\varrho + \delta)$	unity	1
The **sound reduction index** or **transmission loss** R is the negative natural logarithm of the square root of the acoustic transmission coefficient: $R = \ln(1/\tau)^{1/2} = 0.5 \ln(1/\tau)\ \text{Np} = 10 \lg(1/\tau)\ \text{dB}$ (For the units Np and dB, see under the quantities 'attenuation exponent' above and 'sound pressure level' below.)	unity	1
The **reverberation time** T is the time during which the mean sound energy density w_1 in an enclosure drops to a millionth of its value: $w_2 = 10^{-6} w_1$. In practice the sound pressure level is measured rather than the sound energy, under the assumption that the sound energy density and the sound power are strictly proportional to the square of the sound pressure; the reverberation time is therefore the time during which, in accordance with the relation $w_1/w_2 = P_1/P_2 = (p_1/p_2)^2 = 10^6$, the sound power level (see below) decreases by $L_P = 10 \lg(P_1/P_2)\ \text{dB} = 60\ \text{dB}$ and the sound pressure level (see below) likewise by $L_p = 20 \lg(p_1/p_2)\ \text{dB} = 60\ \text{dB}$.	second	s

Quantity and definition[1]	SI unit		
	Name	Symbol	

Quantity and definition[1]	Name	Symbol
The **sound pressure level** L_p is defined as the natural logarithm of the pressure ratio p/p_0, where p is a given pressure and p_0 the reference pressure: $L_p = \ln(p/p_0) = 20 \lg(p/p_0)\alpha$ where $\alpha = (\ln 10)/20 \approx 0.115\,129$ The special name for the unit of sound pressure level, not accepted by the committees of the Metric Convention, is the neper (Np), i.e., 1 Np may be equated with unity in numerical calculations: $L_p = \ln(p/p_0)$ Np The unit decibel (dB), which is equal to α, is the sound pressure level when $(p/p_0)^{20} = 10$, i.e., 1 dB can be given the value $0.115\,129$ in numerical calculations: $L_p = 20 \lg(p/p_0)$ dB In acoustics the sound pressure level is almost always expressed in this form with logarithms to the base 10.	unity	1
The **sound power level** L_P is defined as ½ the natural logarithm of the ratio P/P_0, where P is a given sound power and P_0 the reference sound power: $L_P = 0.5 \ln(P/P_0) = 10 \lg(P/P_0)\,\alpha$ [where $\alpha = (\ln 10)/20 \approx 0.115\,129$] The special name for the unit of sound power level is the neper (Np), i.e., 1 Np may be equated with unity in numerical calculations: $L_P = 0.5 \ln(P/P_0)$ Np The unit decibel (dB), which is equal to α, is the sound power level when $(P/P_0)^{10} = 10$, i.e., 1 dB can be given the value $0.115\,129$ in numerical calculations: $L_P = 10 \lg(P/P_0)$ dB In acoustics the sound power level is almost always expressed in this form with logarithms to the base 10. As dimensionless units, neither the neper nor the decibel are, however, accepted by the International Organization for Standards. The sound power P is the area integral of the sound intensity J: $P = \int J \, dS$ The sound intensity is the product of the sound pressure p and the sound particle velocity u: $J = p \, u$ or, using the specific acoustic impedance Z_s: $J = Z_s u^2 = p^2/Z_s$ The sound power P and sound intensity J in an acoustic field are proportional to each other in space and time: $P_1/P_2 = J_1/J_2 = (p_1^2/p_2^2)(Z_{s2}/Z_{s1})$ For this reason the differences between the sound power levels L_P and the sound pressure levels L_p in an acoustic field at the same time t at two points X_1 and X_2, or at the same point X at two different times t_1 and t_2, are in general related by the equation: $L_P = 10 \lg(P_1/P_2)$ dB $\quad = 20 \lg(p_1/p_2)^2$ dB $+ 10 \lg(Z_{s2}/Z_{s1})$ $\quad = L_p + 10 \lg(Z_{s2}/Z_{s1})$ If Z_s is constant in space and in time in the acoustic field, i.e., $Z_{s2}/Z_{s1} = 1$, the sound power level L_P and the sound pressure level L_p will be the same, independent of the specific acoustic impedance Z_s, and the sound power ratio P_1/P_2 will be equal to the square of the sound pressure ratio p_1/p_2: $P_1/P_2 = (p_1/p_2)^2$	unity	1
The **loudness level** L_N is the natural logarithm of the pressure ratio $p_{eff}/p_{0,\,eff}$, where p_{eff} is the effective value of the sound pressure of a standard pure tone of 1 kHz judged by an observer with 'normal' hearing to be equally loud under standard listening conditions, and $p_{0,\,eff}$ is the effective value of the reference sound pressure 2×10^{-5} Pa: $L_N = \ln(p_{eff}/p_{0,\,eff})_{1\,kHz}$ The loudness level is in practice used only in the form $L_N = 20 \lg(p_{eff}/p_{0,\,eff})_{1\,kHz}\,\alpha,$ where $\alpha = (\ln 10)/20 \approx 0.115\,129$ The unit phon (phon), which is equal to α, is the loudness level when $(p_{eff}/p_{0,\,eff})^{20} = 10$, i.e., phon is a special name for the unit decibel in loudness level data, and 1 phon can be given the value $0.115\,129$ in numerical calculations: $L_N = 20 \lg(p_{eff}/p_{0,\,eff})_{1\,kHz}$ dB	unity	1

Quantity and definition[7]	SI unit	
	Name	Symbol
The **loudness** N is the normal observer's auditory estimate of the ratio between the loudness level L_N of a given sound and a reference sound with a loudness level $L_N = 40$ phon, and is a measure of the intensity of perception in that a doubling of the numerical value corresponds to a doubling of the perceptive intensity. The relation between the loudness of any sound and its loudness level is given by the formula	unity	1

$N = 2^{0.1\,[(L_N/\text{phon}) - 40]}$, or

$\lg N = 0.1\,[(L_N/\text{phon}) - 40] \times \lg 2$

$\quad \approx 0.03\,[20\,\lg(p_{\text{eff}}/p_{0,\,\text{eff}})_{1\,\text{kHz}} - 40]$

The special name for the unit of loudness, not accepted by the committees of the Metric Convention, is the sone (sone), i.e., 1 sone may be equated with unity in numerical calculations:

$N = 2^{0.1\,[(L_N/\text{phon}) - 40]}$ sone

The relation between loudness N and loudness level L_N results in values such as those given in the following table:

L_N	N	L_N	N	L_N	N
20 phon	0.25 sone	55 phon	2.83 sone	90 phon	32.0 sone
25 phon	0.35 sone	60 phon	4.00 sone	95 phon	45.3 sone
30 phon	0.50 sone	65 phon	5.66 sone	100 phon	64.0 sone
35 phon	0.70 sone	70 phon	8.00 sone	105 phon	90.5 sone
40 phon	1.00 sone	75 phon	11.3 sone	110 phon	128 sone
45 phon	1.41 sone	80 phon	16.0 sone	115 phon	181 sone
50 phon	2.00 sone	85 phon	22.6 sone	120 phon	256 sone

In this connection the following should be born in mind:
1. The loudness in sone is not directly measurable but can only be calculated from the loudness level in phon.
2. A loudness of 1 sone corresponds to a loudness level of 40 phon.
3. Doubling the loudness corresponds to a difference of 10 phon in the loudness level.
4. The relation is valid only between 20 and 120 phon; values outside these limits must be regarded as extrapolations.

The **(acoustic) interval** or **frequency interval** i is defined as the logarithm to the base 2 of the frequency ratio f/f_0:	octave	O

$i = \text{lb}(f/f_0) = \lg(f/f_0)/\lg 2 = \lg(f/f_0)/0.301030 \approx 3.32193\,\lg(f/f_0)$

The special name for the unit of the frequency interval, not accepted by the committees of the Metric Convention, is the octave (O); 1 O is the interval when the frequency ratio $f/f_0 = 2$, i.e., 1 O can be equated with unity in numerical calculations:

$i = \text{lb}(f/f_0)\,\text{O}$

Another interval unit is the cent (cent), equal to

$\dfrac{1}{1200}$ O; 100 cent $= \dfrac{1}{12}$ O is a semitone step.

Calculation of loudness levels

Loudness levels can also be calculated from noise analyses, the two best-known methods being those of STEVENS[3] and ZWICKER[4]. The precision of these methods, i.e., the agreement of their results with loudness levels measured subjectively in accordance with the ISO recommendations[1], is adequate for many purposes. Values calculated in this way, however, should not be given simply in 'phon' but should bear an indication that they have been arrived at using a particular method, for example 'phon by the method of ZWICKER'.

KRYTER and PEARSONS developed a particular procedure for the measurement of aircraft noise[5]. The values so obtained are known as 'perceived noise levels' L_{PN} (or PNL) and are expressed in dB, e.g., $L_{PN} = 70$ dB, or as the value '70 PNdB'. This is a standardized procedure for correlating objective measurements with subjective sensation. It was proposed to introduce a uniform procedure for measurement of a quantity as subjective as aircraft noise.

Sound level meters

In view of the difficult nature of the subjective hearing tests required for the measurement of loudness levels in phon, sound level meters have been standardized, their properties corresponding to some extent to those of the human ear[6]. For this purpose sound level meters contain three different frequency characteristics (A, B, C) which yield a 'weighted' sound pressure level. Each measurement must show the curve used, for example 'the sound pressure level L_{PN} (or simply the sound level L_A) measured with curve A is 45 dB'. Occasionally this is abbreviated to 'the sound level is 45 dB(A)'. Special requirements have been laid down for measurement of impulsive sounds and sounds of short duration[7].

Typical sound levels

The following examples from everyday life illustrate the range of the dB(A) sound level scale:

Source	Sound level L_A
Propeller aircraft at 5 m	130 dB
Pneumatic hammer at 1 m	120 dB
Brass foundry	110 dB
Automobile horn at 5 m....................	100 dB
Truck at 5 m	90 dB
Loud radio music	80 dB
Normal conversation at 1 m	70 dB
Automobile at 10 m	60 dB
Quiet stream or river.....................	50 dB
Residential district without traffic	40 dB
Quiet garden............................	30 dB
Ticking of a watch	20 dB
Limit of audible noise....................	10 dB
Absolute silence..........................	0 dB

References

[1] International Organization for Standardization (ISO), *Expression of the Physical and Subjective Magnitudes of Sound or Noise*, ISO Recommendation R 131, September 1959; *Quantities and Units of Acoustics*, Draft International Standard ISO/DIS 31/VII, 1975.

[2] International Organization for Standardization (ISO), *Standard Tuning Frequency*, ISO Recommendation R 16, November 1955.

[3] STEVENS, S. S., *J. acoust. Soc. Amer.*, **28**, 807 (1956).

[4] ZWICKER, E., *Acustica*, **10**, 304 (1960).

[5] KRYTER and PEARSONS, *J. acoust. Soc. Amer.*, **35**, 866 (1963).

[6] International Electrotechnical Commission (IEC), *Recommendations for Sound Level Meters*, IEC Publication 123 (1961), and *Precision Sound Level Meters*, IEC Publication 179 (1973), Geneva; Deutscher Normenausschuss, *Präzisionsschallpegelmesser, Allgemeine Anforderungen*, DIN 45633, part 1, Beuth, Berlin, 1970.

[7] International Electrotechnical Commission (IEC), *First Supplement to Publication 179 (1973), Precision Sound Level Meters, Additional Characteristics for Measurement of Impulsive Sounds*, Publication 179 A (1973), Geneva.

Amount of substance (n)

Dimension: N

Base SI unit: mole (mol)

Definition of amount of substance

Except in special cases, there is no practicable method of counting the numbers of particles involved in a chemical or physical process. For this reason the IUPAP[1] in 1957 introduced the basic quantity *amount of substance n* for use in chemical and molecular physics. The concept of amount of substance is founded on the 'countability' of identical entities (particles) in an atomic or other discontinuous system[2]. The value of n is proportional to the number of particles N, the proportionality factor being a fundamental constant, the Avogadro constant (see also page 47): $N_A = N/n$ (dimension: N^{-1}). The number of entities in a population having the amount of substance $n = 1$ mol is therefore $N = N_A \times 1$ mol; $N_A = 6.022045 \times 10^{23}$ mol^{-1} ($s = 31 \times 10^{17}$ mol^{-1}).

Base SI unit of amount of substance

The primary standard for the mole – as well as for the scale of relative atomic masses A_r and the (unified) atomic mass unit (u) – is the carbon nuclide ^{12}C on which the IUPAC and IUPAP agreed in 1960/61[3,4].

In accordance with the proposals of the IUPAP[5], the IUPAC[6] and the ISO[7], the Comité International des Poids et Mesures in 1967 and 1969[9] adopted a definition of the mole recommended by the Comité Consultatif des Unités[8]. This was finally accepted by the 14th General Conference on Weights and Measures (1971, Resolution 3)[7,10]:

'The mole is the amount of substance of a system which contains as many elementary entities as there are atoms in 0.012 kg of the nuclide ^{12}C; its unit symbol is the "mol".

The type of particle must be specified and may be an atom, a molecule, an ion, an electron, etc., or a group of such entities of precisely stated composition.'

Definition and unit of amount of equivalent

The concept of amount of substance may be extended to *Faraday's law of equivalence* and *chemical bonds*. Here use is made of the *amount of equivalent* $n_{eq} = z\,n$, where z is the charge number in the case of ions and the valency (single, double, etc.) in the case of bonds. The amount of equivalent n_{eq} is proportional to the electric charge $Q = N z e$ (e: elementary charge; see also page 48) of N ions of charge number z, the proportionality factor again being a fundamental constant, the Faraday constant (see also page 48) $F = Q/n_{eq} = e N/n = e N_A$ (dimension: T I N^{-1}). The *unit of amount of equivalent* is likewise the base unit mole[o]. The electric charge carried by the amount of equivalent $n_{eq} = z\,n = 1$ mol of a particular species of ion is therefore $Q = F n_{eq} = F \times 1$ mol; $F = 9.648456 \times 10^4$ C mol^{-1} ($s = 2.7 \times 10^{-1}$ C mol^{-1}).

When the concept of amount of substance is applied consistently, the term 'amount of equivalent' becomes superfluous and confusing. As recommended by the IUPAC[11], its use should therefore be avoided. Examples of amount of substance n are:

$n = 1$ mol HgCl has a mass of $m = 236.04$ g
$n = 1$ mol ½Ca^{2+} has a mass of $m = 20.04$ g and a charge $Q = F \times 1$ mol ÷ $F \approx 96485$ C mol^{-1}

1 mol ½H$_2$SO$_4$ contains the same amount of substance n(H) = 1 mol H as 1 mol HCl, 1 mol ⅓H$_3$PO$_4$ or 1 mol Na$_2$HPO$_4$

The quantity 'amount of equivalent' has been included in this chapter simply for information in view of its continued frequent use in chemistry.

Scale of relative atomic masses (A_r) and the (unified) atomic mass unit (u)

The unified scale of relative atomic masses A_r, with ^{12}C as reference nuclide or primary standard, is defined[3,4] by the assigned value

$$A_r(^{12}C) = 12$$

Using the mass $m(^{12}C)$ of an atom of the nuclide ^{12}C as primary standard, the (unified) atomic mass unit (u) is defined by the relation[3] (see page 14)

$$1\,u = m(^{12}C)/12$$

The atomic mass of any nuclide X can therefore be written as $m(X) = A_r(X)\,u$ with

$$1\,u = 10^{-3}\,(N_A\,\text{mol})^{-1}\,\text{kg}$$
$$= 1.6605655 \times 10^{-27}\,\text{kg}\ (s = 8.6 \times 10^{-33}\,\text{kg})$$

Tables of the relative atomic masses $m(X)$ of the nuclides have been published since 1960 at the instance of the Commission on Atomic Masses and Fundamental Constants of the IUPAP[13-15]. These data, together with the 'natural' or 'average' relative abundancies of the stable isotopes of the elements, have formed since 1961 the basis of the tables of relative atomic masses of the elements issued by the Commission on Atomic Weights of the IUPAC[16].

Quantities related to amount of substance

Apart from amount of substance n, a number of other quantities with amount of substance as reference quantity (whence, unfortunately, the designation 'molar') are widely used, especially in thermodynamics and statistics. Examples (dimensions in brackets) are molar volume $V_m = V/n$ (L^3 N^{-1}), molar mass $M = m/n$ (M N^{-1}), molar enthalpy $H_m = H/n$, molar internal energy $U_m = U/n$ (for H_m and U_m: L^2 M T^{-2} N^{-1}), molar entropy $S_m = S/n$, molar heat capacity $C_m = C/n$, and molar gas constant $R = R'/n$ (for S_m, C_m and R: L^2 M T^{-2} Θ^{-1} N^{-1}).

In analogy with the quantities related to amount of substance, the molar conductivity Λ (M^{-1} T^3 I^2 N^{-1}) has, for instance, been introduced as the conductivity κ of an electrolyte related to the molar (amount-of-substance) concentration $c = n/V$ (where V is the volume of the solution): $\Lambda = \kappa/c$.

On the basis of the 'amount of equivalent' concept, chemists still make use of the 'equivalent conductivity' Λ_{eq} (M^{-1} T^3 I^2 N^{-1}) as the conductivity κ related to the 'concentration of equivalent' $c_{eq} = n_{eq}/V$: $\Lambda_{eq} = \kappa/c_{eq}$.

Earlier 'physical' and 'chemical' scales of atomic masses

Before agreement was reached on the unified ^{12}C scale, different relative mass scales[2] were in use in physics and chemistry[2], namely the 'physical scale of atomic weights' based on the oxygen nuclide ^{16}O as primary standard and defined by $A_{ph}(^{16}O) = 16$, and the 'chemical scale of atomic weights' based on elementary oxygen, i.e., on the 'naturally' occurring mixture of the stable oxygen isotopes ^{16}O, ^{17}O and ^{18}O, the primary standard being a 'mean' oxygen atom $\bar{O}$ with the definition $A_{ch}(\bar{O}) = 16$.

---

[o] Previously the mole, as an 'individual (chemical) unit of mass', was defined by and employed[2] in equations of the type 1 mol = M_rg [M_r being the relative molecular mass (formerly 'molecular weight', 'molar weight') of the substance under consideration]. Besides the mole, this concept incorporated a further 'individual (electrochemical) unit of mass' for ions of a chemically homogeneous substance: the gram-equivalent or val, defined by equations of the type 1 val = (1/z) mol = (M_r/z) g (where M_r/z is the 'equivalent weight' of the appropriate ion). Instead of val, the symbol Eq (for gram-equivalent) was also recommended for the val[12]. On introduction of the base quantity amount of substance with the base unit mole one consciously abstained from giving an analogue definition for the val, the use of which is now obsolete. Instead, the additional quantity 'equivalent amount' $n_{eq} = z\,n$ was introduced, which has the same dimension as the amount of substance n. That is to say, the previously common statement of mass y val of ions of relative molecular mass M_r and valency z in this representation corresponds to the 'equivalent amount' $n_{eq} = y$ mol and the amount of substance $n = (y/z)$ mol of the same kind of ions.

Quantities of composition of mixed phases

Quantity	Symbol	Definition	SI unit*
Volume fraction of component i.................	φ_i	$\varphi_i = V_i / \sum\limits_{j=1}^{1} V_j$ (volume of component i in relation to the volume of all components l in a mixed phase)	[m^3 m^{-3}] or [L L^{-1}]
Mass fraction of component i....................	w_i	$w_i = m_i / \sum\limits_{j=1}^{1} m_j$ (mass of component i in relation to the mass of all components l in a mixed phase)	[kg kg^{-1}]
Substance fraction (mole fraction) of component i	x_i	$x_i = n_i / \sum\limits_{j=1}^{1} n_j$ (amount of substance of component i in relation to the amount of substance of all components l in a mixed phase)	[mol mol^{-1}]
Volume ratio of component i....................	ψ_{ik}	$\psi_{ik} = V_i / V_k$ (volume of component i in relation to the volume of a component k in a mixed phase)	[m^3 m^{-3}] or [L L^{-1}]
Mass ratio of component i	ξ_{ik}	$\xi_{ik} = m_i / m_k$ (mass of component i in relation to the mass of a component k in a mixed phase)	[kg kg^{-1}]
Substance (mole) ratio of component i	r_{ik}	$r_{ik} = n_i / n_k$ (amount of substance of component i in relation to that of a component k in a mixed phase)	[mol mol^{-1}]
Volume concentration of component i...........	σ_i	$\sigma_i = V_i / V$ (volume of component i in relation to the volume V of a mixed phase or solution)†	[m^3 m^{-3}] or [L L^{-1}]
Mass concentration of component i..............	ϱ_i	$\varrho_i = \bar{m}_i / V$ (mass of component i in relation to the volume V of a mixed phase or solution)	kg m^{-3} or kg L^{-1}
(Amount-of-)Substance concentration (molar concentration) of component i....................	c_i	$c_i = n_i / V$ (amount of substance of component i in relation to the volume V of a mixed phase or solution)§	mol m^{-3} or mol L^{-1}
Equivalent concentration of the ions i	$c_{eq,\,i}$	$c_{eq,\,i} = z_i\, c_i = z_i\, n_i / V$ $\quad\quad = n_{eq,\,i} / V$ (equivalents of the ions i in relation to the volume V of a mixed phase or solution)	mol m^{-3} or mol L^{-1}
Molality of the component i......................	m_i	$m_i = n_i / m_0$ (amount of substance of component i in relation to the mass m_0 of the solvent)	mol kg^{-1}
Ionic strength of a solution	I	$I = \dfrac{1}{2} \sum\limits_i z_i^2\, m_i = \dfrac{1}{2} \sum\limits_i z_i^2\, n_i / m_0$	mol kg^{-1}
Number concentration of component i	C_i	$C_i = N_i / V$ (number of stated particles of component i in relation to the volumen V of a mixed phase or solution)	m^{-3} or L^{-1}

* Units in brackets are not recommended since these quantities have the dimension 1.
† The volume concentration σ_i is equal to the volume fraction φ_i only when the mixing process entails no change in volume.

§ The following designations are also in use:
'y-molar' for a solution of substance concentration $c_i = y$ mol L^{-1} (with reference to the component i),
'y-molal' for a solution of molality $m_i = y$ mol kg^{-1} (with reference to the component i).

The abundance ratio of the three stable oxygen isotopes varies according to the source of the element, with the result that there was a scatter of at least 15 parts per million in experimental values of the conversion factor k_A (SMYTHE factor) between the two scales. This circumstance led the Commission on Atomic Weights of the IUPAC[17] to recommend a mean *conventional* value for k_A as follows: $k_A = A_{ph}/A_{ch} = mol_{ph}/mol_{ch} = 1.000275$.

The following relationships hold between the two earlier atomic weight scales $[A_{ph} = A_r(^{16}O = 16)$ and $A_{ch} = A_r(\bar{O} = 16)]$ and the newer unified scale of relative atomic masses $[A_r(^{12}C) = 12]$, and between the three corresponding units of amount of substance $mol(^{16}O = 16)$, $mol(\bar{O} = 16)$ and $mol(^{12}C = 12)$:

$$\frac{A_r(^{16}O = 16)}{A_r(^{12}C = 12)} = \frac{mol(^{16}O = 16)}{mol(^{12}C = 12)} = 1.00031791^{14}$$
$$(s = 1.5 \times 10^{-8})$$

$$\frac{A_r(\bar{O} = 16)}{A_r(^{12}C = 12)} = \frac{mol(\bar{O} = 16)}{mol(^{12}C = 12)} = \frac{1.000318}{k_A} = 1.000043$$
$$(s = 5 \times 10^{-6})$$

Quantities of flow (flux)

Quantity	Symbol	Definition	SI unit
Volume rate..................	$\dot{V}, q_v$	$\dot{V} = V/t$	$m^3 s^{-1}$ or $L s^{-1}$
Mass rate	$\dot{m}, q_m$	$\dot{m} = m/t$	$kg s^{-1}$
Substance rate	$\dot{n}, q_n$	$\dot{n} = n/t$	$mol s^{-1}$

References

[1] International Union of Pure and Applied Physics (IUPAP), *Report of the 9th General Assembly, Rome 1957*, page 7, also in *Ned. T. Natuurkde*, **23**, 327 (1957); and *Nuclear Phys.*, **7**, 299 (1958), *Phys. Bl.*, **14**, 259 (1958).
[2] For example, STILLE, U., *Rechnen und Messen in der Physik*, 2nd ed., Vieweg, Braunschweig, 1961.
[3] International Union of Pure and Applied Physics (IUPAP), *Report of the 10th General Assembly, Ottawa 1960*, page 24.

[4] International Union of Pure and Applied Chemistry (IUPAC): *Comptes rendus de la 20ᵉ conférence, Munich 1959*, Butterworth, London, page 202; *Information Bulletin*, No. 10, London, 1959, page 17; *Comptes rendus de la 21ᵉ conférence, Montreal 1961*, Butterworth, London, pages 221, 252, 281.
[5] International Union of Pure and Applied Physics (IUPAP), *Symbols, Units and Nomenclature in Physics*, Document U.I.P. 11 (S.U.N. 65-3), 1965, page 25.
[6] International Union of Pure and Applied Chemistry (IUPAC): *Comptes rendus de la 22ᵉ conférence, Londres 1963*, Butterworth, London, pages 156 and 178; *Comptes rendus de la 23ᵉ conférence, Paris 1965*, Butterworth, London, pages 131 and 149.
[7] International Organization for Standardization (ISO), *Quantities and Units of Physical Chemistry and Molecular Physics*, International Standard ISO, 31/VIII, 1st ed., 1973; Draft International Standard ISO/DIS 31/8, 1979.
[8] Comité International des Poids et Mesures, *Comité Consultatif des Unités, 1re session, Sèvres 1967*, Bureau International des Poids et Mesures, Sèvres, 1968, page U 17.
[9] Comité International des Poids et Mesures, *Comité Consultatif des Unités, 2e session, Sèvres 1969*, Bureau International des Poids et Mesures, Sèvres, 1970, page U 20.
[10] Conférence Generale des Poids et Mesures, *Comptes rendus des séances de la 14ᵉ Conférence Générale des Poids et Mesures, Paris 1971*, Bureau International des Poids et Mesures, Sèvres, 1972, pages 59 and 78; *Le Système International d'Unités (SI)*, Bureau International des Poids et Mesures, 3rd ed., Sèvres, 1977.
[11] International Union of Pure and Applied Chemistry, *Comptes rendus de la 27ᵉ conférence, Munich 1973*, Butterworth, London, pages 99 and 197.
[12] For example, World Health Organization, *Terminology Circular*, No. 4, 1st October 1964
[13] EVERLING et al., *Nuclear Phys.*, **18**, 529 (1960); KÖNIG et al., *Nuclear Phys.*, **31**, 18 (1962).
[14] MATTAUCH et al., *Nuclear Phys.*, **67**, 1 (1965).
[15] WAPSTRA and GOVE, in *Nucl. Data Tables*, **9**, 276 (1971).
[16] International Union of Pure and Applied Chemistry (IUPAC): *Comptes rendus de la 21ᵉ conférence, Montréal 1961*, Butterworth, London, pages 281 sq.; *Comptes rendus de la 22ᵉ conférence, Londres 1963*, Butterworth, London, page 196 sq.; *Comptes rendus de la 23ᵉ conférence, Paris 1965*, Butterworth, London, pages 169 and 173 sq.; *Comptes rendus de la 24ᵉ conférence, Prague 1967*, Butterworth, London, page 130; *Pure appl. Chem.*, **21**, 95 (1970); *Pure appl. Chem.*, **30**, 639 (1972); *Pure appl. Chem.*, **37**, 591 (1974); *Pure appl. Chem.*, **51**, 1 (1979).
[17] International Union of Pure and Applied Chemistry (IUPAC); *Comptes rendus de la 17ᵉ conférence, Stockholm 1953*, Société d'Edition d'Enseignement Supérieur, Paris, 1954, page 93; *Comptes rendus de la 18ᵉ conférence, Zurich 1955*, Société d'Edition d'Enseignement Supérieur, Paris, 1956, page 115.

Fundamental physical constants$^\diamond$ (for footnotes see page 49)

Name	Symbol and formula	Numerical values without powers of $10^\dagger$	Powers of $10^\dagger$ of SI unit	Powers of 10 of a different unit§	Relative standard deviation$^{\diamond\diamond}$ in 10^{-6}
1	2	3	4	5	6
Gravitational constant...........................	G	6.6720	10^{-11} N m² kg⁻²		615
Velocity of light in vacuum	c	2.99792458	10^8 m s⁻¹		0.004
	$1/c$	3.33564095	10^{-9} m⁻¹ s		0.004
	c^2	8.98755179	10^{16} m² s⁻²		0.006
	$1/c^2$	1.11265006	10^{-17} m⁻² s²		0.006
Magnetic field constant.....................	$\mu_0 = 1/\varepsilon_0 c^2$	1.25663706144	10^{-6} H m⁻¹		
Electric field constant	$\varepsilon_0 = 1/\mu_0 c^2$	8.85418782	10^{-12} F m⁻¹		0.008
Characteristic impedance of vacuum	$\Gamma_0 = \mu_0 c$	3.76730313	10^2 Ω		0.04
Universal (molar) gas constant††.................... ($p_0 = 101325$ Pa; $T_0 = 273.15$ K)	$R = p_0 V_0/T_0$	8.31441	J mol⁻¹ K⁻¹		31
Molar volume of an ideal gas at $T_0 = 273.15$ K and $p_0 = 101325$ Pa	$V_0 = R T_0/p_0$	2.241383	10^{-2} m³ mol⁻¹		31
Avogadro constant	N_A	6.022045	10^{23} mol⁻¹		5.1
Loschmidt constant	$n_0 = N_A/V_0$	2.68675	10^{25} m⁻³		32
Boltzmann entropy constant††	$k = R/N_A$	1.380662	10^{-23} J K⁻¹		32
Atomic mass constant	$m_u = m(^{12}C)/12$ $= (1/N_A)$ g mol⁻¹	1.6605655 1	10^{-27} kg	u	5.1 5.1
Rest mass of electron.....................	$m_e = 4\pi(e^*)^2 R_\infty/\alpha^3 c^2$	9.109534 5.4858026	10^{-31} kg	10^{-4} u	5.1 0.38
Rest mass of proton.....................	$m_p = A_{rp} m_u(^1H) - m_e$	1.6726485 1.007276470	10^{-27} kg	u	5.1 0.011
Rest mass of neutron	$m_n = A_{rn} m_u$	1.6749543 1.008665012	10^{-27} kg	u	5.1 0.037

Name	Symbol and formula	Numerical values without powers of $10^\dagger$	Powers of $10^\dagger$ of SI unit	Powers of 10 of a different unit§	Relative standard deviation◊◊ in 10^{-6}
1	2	3	4	5	6
Rest mass of muon	$m_\mu = A_r m_u$	1.883566 1.1342920	10^{-28} kg	10^{-1} u	5.6 2.3
Rest mass of ^{1}H atom	$m(^1\mathrm{H}) = A_r(^1\mathrm{H}) m_u$	1.673559 1.007825036	10^{-27} kg	u	5.1 0.011
Reduced mass of electron in ^{1}H atom	$\mu = m_e\, m_p/m(^1\mathrm{H})$	9.104576 5.4828166	10^{-31} kg	10^{-4} u	5.1 0.38
Ratio of rest masses of proton and electron	m_p/m_e	1.83615152	10^3		0.38
Ratio of rest masses of muon and electron	m_μ/m_e	2.0676865	10^2		2.3
Elementary charge	e e^* e^*/c	1.6021892 4.8032424 1.6021892	10^{-19} C	10^{-10} esu 10^{-20} emu	2.9 2.9 2.9
(Negative) specific charge of electron	e/m_e e^*/m_e $e^*/m_e\,c$	1.7588047 5.272764 1.7588047	10^{11} C kg^{-1}	10^{17} esu g^{-1} 10^7 emu g^{-1}	2.8 2.8 2.8
Specific charge of proton	e/m_p e^*/m_p $e^*/m_p\,c$	9.578756 2.871639 9.578756	10^7 C kg^{-1}	10^{14} esu g^{-1} 10^3 emu g^{-1}	2.8 2.8 2.8
Zeeman splitting constant	$e/4\pi m_e\,c$ $e^*/4\pi m_e\,c^2$	4.668604 4.668604	10 m^{-1} T^{-1}	10^{-5} cm^{-1} emu^{-1}	2.8 2.8
Faraday constant	$F = N_A\,e$ $F^* = N_A\,e^*$ $F^*/c = N_A\,e^*/c$	9.648456 2.892534 9.648456	10^4 C mol^{-1}	10^{14} esu mol^{-1} 10^3 emu mol^{-1}	2.8 2.8 2.8
Sommerfeld fine-structure constant	$\alpha = \mu_0\,c\,e^2/2h$ $1/\alpha$ α^2	7.2973506 1.3703604 5.325133	10^{-3} 10^2 10^{-5}		0.82 0.82 1.16
Planck constant	$h = 2\pi(e^*)^2/\alpha\,c$ $\hbar = h/2\pi$	6.626176 1.0545887	10^{-34} J s 10^{-34} J s		5.4 5.4
Fluxoid quantum§§	$\Phi_0 = h/2e$ h/e h/e^* $h\,c/e^*$	2.0678506 4.135701 1.379521 4.135701	10^{-15} Wb 10^{-15} J s C^{-1}	10^{-17} erg s esu^{-1} 10^{-7} erg s emu^{-1}	2.6 2.6 2.6 2.6
Josephson frequency-voltage ratio	$2e/h$	4.835939	10^{14} Hz V^{-1}		2.6
1st Planck radiation constant	$c_1 = 2\pi h\,c^2$ $c_1/2\pi = h\,c^2$	3.741832 5.955310	10^{-16} W m^2 10^{-17} W m^2		5.4 5.4
2nd Planck radiation constant	$c_2 = h\,c/k$ $c_2/c = h/k$	1.438786 4.799274	10^{-2} m K 10^{-11} s K		31 31
Wien shift law constant ($\varkappa = 4.96511423$)	$b = \lambda_{max}\,T = c_2/\varkappa$	2.897790	10^{-3} m K		31
Stefan-Boltzmann constant	$\sigma = (\pi^2/60)\,k^4/\hbar^3 c^2$	5.67032	10^{-8} W m^{-2} K^{-4}		125
Rydberg constant for an atom with a nucleus of infinite mass	R_∞	1.097373177	10^7 m^{-1}		0.075
Rydberg constant for ^{1}H atom	$R_H = R_\infty/(1 + m_e/m_p)$	1.096775854	10^7 m^{-1}		0.075
Rydberg frequency for an atom with a nucleus of infinite mass	$R'_\infty = R_\infty\,c$	3.28984202	10^{15} Hz		0.075
Rydberg frequency for ^{1}H atom	$R'_H = R_H\,c$	3.28805129	10^{15} Hz		0.075
Bohr radius (of single-quantum electron orbit of hydrogen atom)	$a_0 = \alpha/4\pi R_\infty$	5.2917706	10^{-11} m		0.82
(Classical) radius of electron	$r_e = \alpha^2\,a_0 = \alpha^3/4\pi R_\infty$	2.8179380	10^{-15} m		2.5
Compton wavelength of electron	$\lambda_{C,e} = h/m_e\,c = \alpha^2/2\,R_\infty$ $\lambdabar_{C,e} = \lambda_{C,e}/2\pi = \alpha\,a_0$	2.4263089 3.8615905	10^{-12} m 10^{-13} m		1.6 1.6
Compton wavelength of proton	$\lambda_{C,p} = h/m_p\,c$ $\lambdabar_{C,p} = \lambda_{C,p}/2\pi$	1.3214099 2.1030892	10^{-15} m 10^{-16} m		1.7 1.7
Compton wavelength of neutron	$\lambda_{C,n} = h/m_n\,c$ $\lambdabar_{C,n} = \lambda_{C,n}/2\pi$	1.3195909 2.1001941	10^{-15} m 10^{-16} m		1.7 1.7
Bohr magneton	$\mu_B = e\hbar/2m_e$ $\mu_B^* = e^*\hbar/2m_e\,c$	9.274078 9.274078	10^{-24} J T^{-1}	10^{-21} erg emu^{-1}	3.9 3.9
Nuclear magneton	$\mu_N = e\hbar/2m_p$ $\mu_N^* = e^*\hbar/2m_p\,c$	5.050824 5.050824	10^{-27} J T^{-1}	10^{-24} erg emu^{-1}	3.9 3.9
Magnetic moment of electron	$\mu_e = \mu_B\,(\mu_e/\mu_B)$ $\mu_e^* = \mu_B^*\,(\mu_e^*/\mu_B^*)$	9.284832 9.284832	10^{-24} J T^{-1}	10^{-21} erg emu^{-1}	3.9 3.9
Magnetic moment of proton	$\mu_p = \gamma_p\,\hbar/2$ $\mu_p^* = \gamma_p^*\,\hbar/2$	1.4106171 1.4106171	10^{-26} J T^{-1}	10^{-23} erg emu^{-1}	3.9 3.9
Magnetic moment of muon	μ_μ μ_μ^*	4.490474 4.490474	10^{-26} J T^{-1}	10^{-23} erg emu^{-1}	3.9 3.9

Name	Symbol and formula	Numerical values without powers of 10[†]	Powers of 10[†] of SI unit	Powers of 10 of a different unit[§]	Relative standard deviation[◊◊] in 10^{-6}
1	2	3	4	5	6
Ratio of magnetic moments of electron and proton	$\mu_e/\mu_p = \mu_e^*/\mu_p^*$	6.582106880	10^2		0.010
Ratio of magnetic moments of muon and proton	$\mu_\mu/\mu_p = \mu_\mu^*/\mu_p^*$	3.1833402			2.3
Magnetic moment of electron in Bohr magnetons	$\mu_e/\mu_B = \mu_e^*/\mu_B^*$ $= 1 + \alpha/2\pi - 0.328\,\alpha^2/\pi^2$	1.0011596567			0.0035
Magnetic moment of proton in Bohr magnetons........	$\mu_p/\mu_B = \mu_p^*/\mu_B^*$	1.521032209	10^{-3}		0.011
Magnetic moment of muon in Bohr magnetons	$\mu_\mu/\mu_B = \mu_\mu^*/\mu_B^*$	4.841963	10^{-3}		5.5
Magnetic moment of proton in nuclear magnetons	$\mu_p/\mu_N = \mu_p^*/\mu_N^*$	2.7928456			0.38
Magnetic moment of proton in nuclear magnetons in a spherical sample of distilled water	$\mu_p'/\mu_N = \mu_p^{*'}/\mu_N^*$	2.7927740			0.38
Gyromagnetic ratio of proton	γ_p	2.6751987	$10^8\ s^{-1}\ T^{-1}$		2.8
Gyromagnetic ratio of proton in a spherical sample of distilled water	γ_p' $\gamma_p'/2\pi$ γ_p'	2.6751301 4.257602 2.6751301	$10^8\ s^{-1}\ T^{-1}$ $10^7\ s^{-1}\ T^{-1}$	$10^4\ s^{-1}\ emu^{-1}$	2.8 2.8 2.8
Energy conversion factor[**] for electron volt...........	$eV = e \times (1\ V)$ J/eV	1.6021892 6.241460	10^{-19} J 10^{18}		2.9 2.9
Energy conversion factor[**] for rydberg	$Ry = h\,c\,R_\infty$ $h\,c\,R_H$	2.179907 1.3605804 2.178721 1.359840	10^{-18} J 10^{-18} J	10 eV 10 eV	5.4 2.6 5.4 2.6
Energy equivalent[**] of the second to the power minus one	$E(s^{-1}) = h \times (1\ s^{-1})$	6.626176 4.135701	10^{-34} J	10^{-15} eV	5.4 2.6
Energy equivalent[**] of the meter to the power minus one	$E(m^{-1}) = h\,c \times (1\ m^{-1})$	1.986478 1.239852	10^{-25} J	10^{-6} eV	5.4 2.6
Energy equivalent[**] of the kelvin	$E(K) = k \times (1\ K)$	1.380662 8.617347	10^{-23} J	10^{-5} eV	32 32
Energy equivalent[**] of the kilogram	$E(kg) = c^2 \times (1\ kg)$	8.987552 5.609545	10^{16} J	10^{35} eV	0.006 2.9
Energy equivalent[**] of the atomic mass unit...........	$E(u) = c^2 \times (1\ u)$	1.492442 9.315016	10^{-10} J	10^8 eV	5.1 2.8
Energy equivalent[**] of the mass of the electron	$E(m_e) = c^2\,m_e$	8.187241 5.110034	10^{-14} J	10^5 eV	5.1 2.8
Energy equivalent[**] of the mass of the proton	$E(m_p) = c^2\,m_p$	1.503302 9.382796	10^{-10} J	10^8 eV	5.1 2.8
Energy equivalent[**] of the mass of the neutron	$E(m_n) = c^2\,m_n$	1.505374 9.395731	10^{-10} J	10^8 eV	5.1 2.8
Energy equivalent[**] of the mass of the muon	$E(m_\mu) = c^2\,m_\mu$	1.692865 1.056595	10^{-11} J	10^8 eV	5.1 3.3

[◊] The values given are taken from a consistent set of values recommended by the General Convention of the Committee on Data for Science and Technology (CODATA) of the International Council of Scientific Unions (ICSU) in Stockholm (September 1973) for general use in science and technology[1]. This set of values is contained in recommendations of the international scientific unions comprising the ICSU and of various international technical organizations.

A detailed description of the experimental and mathematical considerations on which the consistent set is based as well as of the primary data so obtained for combinations of constants and their physical and mathematical evaluation, has been published by COHEN and TAYLOR[2].

The quantities elementary charge, Faraday constant, gyromagnetic ratio and magnetic moment not rationally defined in the three-dimensional symmetrical system of quantities are symbolized by e^*, F^*, γ^*, and μ^*, while the corresponding quantities rationally defined in the four-dimensional system of quantities are symbolized by e, F, γ, and μ: $e^*/e = F^*/F = (4\pi\,\varepsilon_0)^{-1/2}$; $\gamma^*/\gamma = \mu^*/\mu = (\mu_0/4\pi)^{1/2}$ (page 27).

[†] Column 3 gives the values of the constants in their SI units (column 4), column 5 the values in 'other units'; in each case the power of 10 of the unit is shown as factor preceeding the corresponding unit in column 4 and 5.

[§] Only the following units not coherent with the International System of Units (SI) appear in column 5: electron volt (eV) (see pages 24 and 25) and

atomic mass unit (u) (see page 14), as well as the Gaussian units, which are a combination of the 'electrostatic' and 'electromagnetic' CGS units (esu and emu, see page 27) and consistent with the three-dimensional, symmetrically defined quantities X^*.

[◊◊] Column 6 gives the relative standard deviation as degree of uncertainty.

[††] The values of the universal (molar) gas constant and the Boltzmann entropy constant, and the noncoherent energy units (see pages 24 and 25) still in use for them, are

$R = 8.20568 \times 10^{-2}$ L atm K^{-1} $mol^{-1} = 1.98719$ cal_{th} K^{-1} mol^{-1}
$= 1.98648$ cal_{15} K^{-1} $mol^{-1} = 1.98586$ cal_{IT} K^{-1} mol^{-1}
$k = 1.36261 \times 10^{-25}$ L atm $K^{-1} = 3.29986 \times 10^{-24}$ cal_{th} K^1
$= 3.29868 \times 10^{-24}$ cal_{15} $K^{-1} = 3.29765 \times 10^{-24}$ cal_{IT} K^{-1}

[§§] Also known as 'characteristic constant of macroscopic coherence in superconductors'.

[**] See under 'Units of energy and energy equivalents in atomic and nuclear physics', page 25.

References

[1] Committee on Data for Science and Technology (CODATA), *Recommended Consistent Values of the Fundamental Physical Constants, 1973*, CODATA Bulletin, No. 11 (December 1973).

[2] COHEN and TAYLOR, *J. phys. chem. Ref. Data*, **2**, 663 (1973).

Standard substances

Mercury

Density under standard conditions[1] (0 °C, 101325 Pa):
$$\varrho_n(Hg) = 13.59508 \text{ kg dm}^{-3}$$

The mean density of pure mercury at the temperature t_{68} (Celsius temperature) given in the International Practical Temperature Scale 1968 (see page 20) in a barometric column supported by the pressure p being measured is given with sufficient accuracy over the temperature range starting with 0 °C and for the pressures relevant to the IPTS-68, by the relation[2]:

$$\varrho\left(t_{68};\frac{p}{2}\right) = \frac{\varrho(20\,°C; p_0)}{\left[1 + A(t_{68}-20\,°C) + B(t_{68}-20\,°C)^2\right] \times \left[1 - \chi\left(\frac{p}{2}-p_0\right)\right]}$$

where
$A = 18115 \times 10^{-8} \text{ °C}^{-1}$
$B = 0.8 \times 10^{-8} \text{ °C}^{-2}$
$\chi = 4 \times 10^{-11} \text{ Pa}^{-1}$
$\varrho(20\,°C; p_0) = 13545.87 \text{ kg m}^{-3}$
$p_0 = 101325 \text{ Pa}$

Density relative to water:
$$d(Hg) = \varrho_n(Hg)/\varrho_{max}(H_2O) = 13.59546$$

Water (for the ice, triple and steam points see page 19)
Maximum density[3,4] (≈ 3.98 °C, 101325 Pa, air-free):
$$\varrho_{max}(H_2O) = (0.999972 \pm 0.000003) \text{ kg dm}^{-3}$$

Air

Standard density of dry air free of carbon dioxide[8] (0 °C, 101325 Pa):
$$\varrho_n(air) = 1.2928 \times 10^{-3} \text{ kg dm}^{-3}$$

Standard conditions for air in spectroscopy:
101325 Pa, 15 °C, dry, 0.03% CO_2

Density of heavy water (100% D_2O, 101325 Pa, air-free)[5]

Temperature	kg m^{-3}	Temperature	kg m^{-3}
3.813 °C	1105.46	20 °C	1105.34
5 °C	1105.62	25 °C	1104.45
10 °C	1105.99	30 °C	1103.23
11.185 °C	1106.00*	35 °C	1101.73
15 °C	1105.87	40 °C	1099.96

*Maximum density.

Density[4] of air-free water in kg m^{-3} as a function of Celsius temperature, given on the International Practical Temperature Scale 1968, between 0 °C and 40 °C and at 101325 Pa

t_{68} in °C	0.0	0.1	0.2	0.3	0.4	0.5	0.6	0.7	0.8	0.9	$\Delta\varrho/\Delta t$ in kg m^{-3} K^{-1}	$\Delta\varrho = \varrho_g - \varrho_f$* in kg m^{-3}
0	999.8396	999.8463	999.8528	999.8591	999.8653	999.8713	999.8771	999.8827	999.8882	999.8934	0.059	−0.0026
1	999.8985	999.9035	999.9082	999.9128	999.9172	999.9214	999.9254	999.9293	999.9330	999.9365	0.041	−0.0027
2	999.9399	999.9431	999.9461	999.9489	999.9516	999.9541	999.9565	999.9587	999.9607	999.9625	0.024	−0.0028
3	999.9642	999.9657	999.9670	999.9682	999.9692	999.9701	999.9708	999.9713	999.9717	999.9719	0.008	−0.0030
4	999.9720	999.9718	999.9716	999.9711	999.9705	999.9698	999.9689	999.9678	999.9666	999.9652	−0.008	−0.0031
5	999.9637	999.9620	999.9602	999.9582	999.9560	999.9537	999.9513	999.9487	999.9459	999.9430	−0.024	−0.0033
6	999.9399	999.9367	999.9334	999.9299	999.9262	999.9224	999.9184	999.9143	999.9101	999.9057	−0.039	−0.0034
7	999.9011	999.8964	999.8916	999.8866	999.8815	999.8762	999.8708	999.8652	999.8595	999.8537	−0.053	−0.0035
8	999.8477	999.8416	999.8353	999.8289	999.8223	999.8157	999.8088	999.8019	999.7947	999.7875	−0.068	−0.0035
9	999.7801	999.7726	999.7649	999.7571	999.7492	999.7411	999.7329	999.7246	999.7161	999.7075	−0.081	−0.0034
10	999.6987	999.6898	999.6808	999.6717	999.6624	999.6530	999.6434	999.6337	999.6239	999.6140	−0.095	−0.0033
11	999.6039	999.5937	999.5834	999.5729	999.5623	999.5516	999.5408	999.5298	999.5187	999.5074	−0.108	−0.0031
12	999.4961	999.4846	999.4730	999.4612	999.4494	999.4374	999.4253	999.4130	999.4007	999.3882	−0.121	−0.0029
13	999.3756	999.3628	999.3500	999.3370	999.3239	999.3106	999.2973	999.2838	999.2702	999.2565	−0.133	−0.0026
14	999.2427	999.2287	999.2146	999.2004	999.1861	999.1717	999.1571	999.1424	999.1276	999.1127	−0.145	−0.0023
15	999.0977	999.0826	999.0673	999.0519	999.0364	999.0208	999.0051	998.9892	998.9733	998.9572	−0.157	−0.0020
16	998.9410	998.9247	998.9083	998.8917	998.8751	998.8583	998.8414	998.8244	998.8073	998.7901	−0.168	−0.0017
17	998.7728	998.7553	998.7378	998.7201	998.7023	998.6845	998.6665	998.6483	998.6301	998.6118	−0.179	−0.0014
18	998.5934	998.5748	998.5562	998.5374	998.5185	998.4995	998.4804	998.4612	998.4419	998.4225	−0.190	−0.0011
19	998.4030	998.3833	998.3636	998.3438	998.3238	998.3037	998.2836	998.2633	998.2429	998.2224	−0.201	−0.0009
20	998.2019	998.1812	998.1604	998.1395	998.1185	998.0973	998.0761	998.0548	998.0334	998.0119	−0.212	−0.0006
21	997.9902	997.9685	997.9467	997.9247	997.9027	997.8805	997.8583	997.8360	997.8135	997.7910	−0.222	−0.0004
22	997.7683	997.7456	997.7227	997.6998	997.6767	997.6536	997.6303	997.6070	997.5835	997.5600	−0.232	−0.0002
23	997.5363	997.5126	997.4887	997.4648	997.4408	997.4166	997.3924	997.3680	997.3436	997.3191	−0.242	−0.0001
24	997.2944	997.2697	997.2449	997.2200	997.1950	997.1699	997.1446	997.1193	997.0939	997.0685	−0.252	0.0000
25	997.0429	997.0172	996.9914	996.9655	996.9396	996.9135	996.8873	996.8611	996.8347	996.8083	−0.261	0.0000
26	996.7818	996.7551	996.7284	996.7016	996.6747	996.6477	996.6206	996.5934	996.5661	996.5388	−0.270	0.0000
27	996.5113	996.4837	996.4561	996.4284	996.4005	996.3726	996.3446	996.3165	996.2883	996.2600	−0.280	0.0000
28	996.2316	996.2032	996.1746	996.1460	996.1172	996.0884	996.0595	996.0305	996.0014	995.9722	−0.289	0.0000
29	995.9430	995.9136	995.8842	995.8546	995.8250	995.7953	995.7655	995.7356	995.7056	995.6756	−0.298	0.0000
30	995.6454	995.6152	995.5848	995.5544	995.5239	995.4934	995.4627	995.4319	995.4011	995.3701	−0.306	0.0000
31	995.3391	995.3080	995.2768	995.2456	995.2142	995.1828	995.1512	995.1196	995.0879	995.0561	−0.315	0.0000
32	995.0243	994.9923	994.9603	994.9282	994.8960	994.8637	994.8313	994.7988	994.7663	994.7337	−0.323	0.0000
33	994.7010	994.6682	994.6353	994.6024	994.5693	994.5362	994.5030	994.4697	994.4364	994.4029	−0.332	0.0000
34	994.3694	994.3358	994.3021	994.2683	994.2345	994.2005	994.1665	994.1324	994.0982	994.0640	−0.340	0.0000
35	994.0296	993.9952	993.9607	993.9261	993.8915	993.8567	993.8219	993.7870	993.7521	993.7170	−0.348	0.0000
36	993.6819	993.6467	993.6114	993.5760	993.5406	993.5050	993.4694	993.4338	993.3980	993.3622	−0.356	0.0000
37	993.3263	993.2903	993.2542	993.2181	993.1818	993.1455	993.1092	993.0727	993.0362	992.9996	−0.363	0.0000
38	992.9629	992.9261	992.8893	992.8524	992.8154	992.7784	992.7412	992.7040	992.6668	992.6294	−0.371	0.0000
39	992.5920	992.5545	992.5169	992.4792	992.4415	992.4037	992.3658	992.3279	992.2899	992.2518	−0.378	0.0000
40	992.2136											

* ϱ_g saturated with air; ϱ_f air-free.

Specific heat capacity of air-free water[7] between 0 °C and 100 °C and at 101 325 Pa

°C	0	1	2	3	4	5	6	7	8	9
					$J\,g^{-1}\,K^{-1}$					
0	4.2174	4.2138	4.2104	4.2074	4.2045	4.2019	4.1996	4.1974	4.1954	4.1936
10	4.1919	4.1904	4.1890	4.1877	4.1866	4.1855	4.1846	4.1837	4.1829	4.1822
20	4.1816	4.1810	4.1805	4.1801	4.1797	4.1793	4.1790	4.1787	4.1785	4.1783
30	4.1782	4.1781	4.1780	4.1780	4.1779	4.1779	4.1780	4.1780	4.1781	4.1782
40	4.1783	4.1784	4.1786	4.1788	4.1789	4.1792	4.1794	4.1796	4.1799	4.1801
50	4.1804	4.1807	4.1811	4.1814	4.1817	4.1821	4.1825	4.1829	4.1833	4.1837
60	4.1841	4.1846	4.1850	4.1855	4.1860	4.1865	4.1871	4.1876	4.1882	4.1887
70	4.1893	4.1899	4.1905	4.1912	4.1918	4.1925	4.1932	4.1939	4.1946	4.1954
80	4.1961	4.1969	4.1977	4.1985	4.1994	4.2002	4.2011	4.2020	4.2029	4.2039
90	4.2048	4.2058	4.2068	4.2078	4.2089	4.2100	4.2111	4.2122	4.2133	4.2145
100	4.2156									

$cal_{15}\,g^{-1}\,K^{-1}$ (calculated by the editors from the CIPM values)[7]

°C	0	1	2	3	4	5	6	7	8	9
	1.0.	1.0.	1.0.	1.0.	1.0.	1.0.	1.0.	1.0.	1.0.	1.0.
0	00762	00676	00595	00523	00454	00392	00337	00284	00237	00194
10	00153	00117	00084	00053	00026	00000	99978	99957	99938	99921
20	99907	99892	99881	99871	99861	99852	99845	99838	99833	99828
30	99826	99823	99821	99821	99818	99818	99821	99821	99823	99826
40	99828	99830	99835	99840	99842	99849	99854	99859	99866	99871
50	99878	99885	99895	99902	99909	99919	99928	99938	99947	99957
60	99967	99978	99988	00000	00012	00024	00038	00050	00065	00076
70	00091	00105	00119	00136	00151	00167	00184	00201	00217	00237
80	00253	00272	00291	00311	00332	00351	00373	00394	00416	00440
90	00461	00485	00509	00533	00559	00585	00612	00638	00664	00693
100	00719									

Acceleration due to gravity

Standard acceleration due to gravity[9]:

$g_n = 980.665$ Gal (1 Gal $= 1\ cm\ s^{-2}$; see also page 22)

International gravity formula[10] (based on the international terrestrial ellipsoid):

$\gamma_0 = (980.632272 - 2.586145 \cos 2B + 0.002878 \cos 4B - 0.000004 \cos 6B)$ Gal

where γ_0 is the acceleration due to gravity at sea level, and B the latitude. This yields the following values for different degrees of latitude (calculated by the editors):

Latitude (degrees)	γ_0 in Gal	γ_0/g_n	g_n/γ_0	Latitude (degrees)	γ_0 in Gal	γ_0/g_n	g_n/γ_0
0	978.0490	0.997332	1.002675	46	980.7197	1.000056	0.999944
5	0881	372	635	47	8098	148	852
10	2043	491	516	48	8998	239	761
15	3940	684	321	49	9894	331	669
20	6517	947	057	50	981.0787	422	578
25	9694	0.998271	1.001732	51	1673	512	488
30	979.3378	647	355	52	2554	602	398
31	4165	727	275	53	3427	691	309
32	4968	809	193	54	4291	779	221
33	5785	892	109	55	5146	866	134
34	6614	977	025	56	5990	952	048
35	7456	0.999062	1.000938	57	6822	1.001037	0.998964
36	8308	149	851	58	7642	121	880
37	9170	237	763	59	8448	203	798
38	980.0041	326	674	60	9239	284	718
39	0920	416	585	65	982.2941	661	342
40	1805	506	494	70	6139	987	017
41	2696	597	403	75	8734	1.002252	0.997753
42	3591	688	312	80	983.0647	447	559
43	4490	780	220	85	1818	566	440
44	5391	872	128	90	2213	607	400
45	6294	964	036				

The true acceleration due to gravity is probably about 14 mGal less than the values calculated from the international gravity formula[11].

Viscosity of water between 0 °C and 40 °C[6]

Temperature	Viscosity ratio η_t/η_{20} °C	Dynamic viscosity η in dPa s	Kinematic viscosity v in $cm^2\,s^{-1}$
0 °C	1.7885	1.792	1.792
5 °C	1.5170	1.520	1.520
10 °C	1.3043	1.3069	1.3073
15 °C	1.1360	1.1383	1.1393
20 °C	1.0000	1.0020	1.0038
25 °C	0.8885	0.8903	0.8929
30 °C	0.7959	0.7975	0.8010
35 °C	0.7179	0.7193	0.7236
40 °C	0.6518	0.6531	0.6582

References

[1] Cook and Stone, *Phil. Trans. Roy. Soc.*, **250A**, 279 (1957); Cook, A. H., *Phil. Trans. Roy. Soc.*, **254A**, 125 (1961); Beattie et al., *Proc. Amer. Acad. Arts Sci.*, **74**, 371 (1941).

[2] Conférence Générale des Poids et Mesures, *Comptes rendus des séances de la 13ᵉ Conférence Générale des Poids et Mesures, Paris 1967/68*, Bureau International des Poids et Mesures, Sèvres, 1969, page A8.

[3] Guillaume et al., *Trav. Mém. Bureau Int. Poids Mes.*, **14**, 3–269 (1910); Weast, R. C. (Ed.), *CRC Handbook of Chemistry and Physics*, 58th ed., CRC Press, Cleveland, 1977, page F-11; Stille, U., *Messen und Rechnen in der Physik*, 2nd ed., Vieweg, Braunschweig, 1961, page 286.

[4] Wagenbreth and Blanke, *PTB-Mitteilungen*, **81**, 412 (1971).

[5] Kell, G. S., *J. chem. Engng Data*, **12**, 66 (1967); Kaye and Laby, *Tables of Physical and Chemical Constants and Some Mathematical Functions*, 14th ed., Longman, London, 1973, page 29.

[6] Weber, W., *Z. angew. Phys.*, **7**, 96 (1955).

[7] Comité International des Poids et Mesures, *Procès-verbaux des séances*, **22**, 79 and 92 (1950).

[8] Otto and Thomas, in Hausen, H. (Ed.), *Landolt-Börnstein, Physikalisch-chemische Tabellen*, 6th ed., volume IV, section 4, part a, Springer, Berlin, 1967, page 174.

[9] Conférence Générale des Poids et Mesures, *Comptes rendus des séances de la 3ᵉ Conférence Générale des Poids et Mesures, Paris 1901*, Gauthier-Villars, Paris, 1901, page 70.

[10] Heiskanen, W., *Gerlands Beitr. Geophys.*, **19**, 356 (1928); Union Géodésique et Géophysique Internationale, *Bull. géod. int.*, No. 27, 238 (1930); Cassinis, G., *Bull. géod. int.*, No. 26, 40 (1930); Cassinis, G., *Bull. géod. int.*, No. 32, 313 (1931); Cassinis et al., *R. Comm. géod. ital.* (NS), No. 13 (1937).

[11] Union Géodésique et Géophysique Internationale, *14ᵉ Assemblée générale, Zurich 1967*, Paris, 1968, page 146.

Element	Symbol	Atomic number	Relative atomic mass (1977)	Element	Symbol	Atomic number	Relative atomic mass (1977)
Actinium	Ac	89	227.0278	Molybdenum	Mo	42	95.94
Aluminum	Al	13	26.98154				
Americium	Am	95	(243)	Neodymium	Nd	60	144.24+
Antimony	Sb	51	121.75+	Neon	Ne	10	20.179+
Argon	Ar	18	39.948+	Neptunium	Np	93	[237.0482]
Arsenic	As	33	74.9216	Nickel	Ni	28	58.70
Astatine	At	85	(210)	Niobium	Nb	41	92.9064
				Niton	Nt	see Radon	
Barium	Ba	56	137.373	Nitrogen	N	7	14.0067
Berkelium	Bk	97	(247)	Nobelium	No	102	(259)
Beryllium	Be	4	9.01218				
Bismuth	Bi	83	208.9804	Osmium	Os	76	190.2
Boron	B	5	10.81	Oxygen	O	8	15.9994+
Bromine	Br	35	79.904				
				Palladium	Pd	46	106.4
Cadmium	Cd	48	112.41	Phosphorus	P	15	30.97376
Calcium	Ca	20	40.08	Platinum	Pt	78	195.09+
Californium	Cf	98	(251)	Plutonium	Pu	94	(244)
Carbon	C	6	12.011	Polonium	Po	84	(209)
Cassiopeium	Cp	see Lutetium		Potassium	K	19	39.0983+
Cerium	Ce	58	140.12	Praseodymium	Pr	59	140.9077
Cesium	Cs	55	132.9054	Promethium	Pm	61	(145)
Chlorine	Cl	17	35.453	Protactinium	Pa	91	[231.0359]
Chromium	Cr	24	51.996				
Cobalt	Co	27	58.9332	Radium	Ra	88	[226.0254]
Columbium	Cb	see Niobium		Radon	Rn	86	(222)
Copper	Cu	29	63.546+	Rhenium	Re	75	186.207
Curium	Cm	96	(247)	Rhodium	Rh	45	102.9055
				Rubidium	Rb	37	85.4678+
Dysprosium	Dy	66	162.50+	Ruthenium	Ru	44	101.07+
Einsteinium	Es	99	(252)	Samarium	Sm	62	150.4
Emanation	Em	see Radon		Scandium	Sc	21	44.9559
Erbium	Er	68	167.26+	Selenium	Se	34	78.96+
Europium	Eu	63	151.96	Silicon	Si	14	28.0855
				Silver	Ag	47	107.868
Fermium	Fm	100	(257)	Sodium	Na	11	22.98977
Fluorine	F	9	18.998403	Strontium	Sr	38	87.62
Francium	Fr	87	(223)	Sulfur	S	16	32.06
Gadolinium	Gd	64	157.25+	Tantalum	Ta	73	180.9479+
Gallium	Ga	31	69.72	Technetium	Tc	43	[98.9062]
Germanium	Ge	32	72.59+	Tellurium	Te	52	127.60+
Glucinium	Gl	see Beryllium		Terbium	Tb	65	158.9254
Gold	Au	79	196.9665	Thallium	Tl	81	204.37+
				Thorium	Th	90	[232.03811]
Hafnium	Hf	72	178.49+	Thulium	Tm	69	168.9342
Helium	He	2	4.00260	Tin	Sn	50	118.69+
Holmium	Ho	67	164.9304	Titanium	Ti	22	47.90+
Hydrogen	H	1	1.0079	Tungsten	W	74	183.85+
Indium	In	49	114.82	Unnilhexium◊	Unh	106	(263)
Iodine	I	53	126.9045	Unnilpentium◊	Unp	105	(262)
Iridium	Ir	77	192.22+	Unnilquadium◊	Unq	104	(261)
Iron	Fe	26	55.847+	Uranium	U	92	238.029
Krypton	Kr	36	83.80	Vanadium	V	23	50.9415+
Lanthanum	La	57	138.9055+	Wolfram	W	see Tungsten	
Lawrencium	Lr	103	(260)				
Lead	Pb	82	207.2	Xenon	Xe	54	131.30
Lithium	Li	3	6.941+				
Lutetium	Lu	71	174.967	Ytterbium	Yb	70	173.04+
				Yttrium	Yt	39	88.9059
Magnesium	Mg	12	24.305				
Manganese	Mn	25	54.9380	Zinc	Zn	30	65.38
Mendelevium	Md	101	(258)	Zirconium	Zr	40	91.22
Mercury	Hg	80	200.59+				

* Recommended values of the Commission on Atomic Weights of the International Union of Pure and Applied Chemistry (IUPAC) of 1977 (*Pure appl. Chem.*, **51**, 405 [1979]); they are based on the assigned value of **12** for the relative atomic mass of carbon ^{12}C (International Union of Pure and Applied Chemistry [IUPAC], *Comptes rendus de la 24ᵉ conférence, 1967*, Butterworth, London, 1968, page 130). The uncertainty is ± 1 in the last decimal place, except for the values marked +, for which it is ± 3. A value in round brackets is the nucleon number (mass number) of the most stable known isotope, a value in square brackets the relative atomic mass of the best-known isotope. See also page 45.

◊ These elements as well as their symbols are not yet internationally recognized.

Urine is voided even in utero (see section 'Amniotic Fluid', page 197). At birth, the bladder contains urine volumes ranging up to 44 mL (average 5.7 mL)[1]. The frequency of urination increases from 1–2 times a day in the first postnatal days to 6–8 times daily toward the end of the first week; in the further course of the first postnatal year the number of urinations averages 18–25 daily until involuntary voiding of urine is changed by education into voluntary micturition[2]. The bladder content is determined by bladder tone; in adults, it amounts to approximately 500 mL at a pressure of 3.4 kPa, which causes considerable urinary urgency[2].

The physical properties and the chemical composition of urine are highly variable and are determined in large measure by the quantity and the type of food consumed; moreover, the excretion of products of the endogenous metabolism is dependent on body mass. The composition of individual urine specimens is not entirely identical to that of the 24-hour urine; the excretion of many urine constituents is subject to a day/night rhythm[3–5]. Unless otherwise indicated, the values for adults given in the tables below refer to a mixed diet. The properties and composition of urine have been discussed in detail[6–9].

Appearance

At the moment of voiding the urine is clear and transparent; after a meal which turns the urine alkaline, however, it can sometimes be more or less turbid. If clear urine is allowed to stand for some time, flaky opacities (nubeculae) appear which are formed by mucin from the urinary passages and, in alkaline urine, by various crystals (alkaline earth phosphates). The urine may also be clouded by lipids.

Normally, the urine has a more or less deep-yellow color due to the presence of substances that have not been precisely identified (urochromes). The urochromes can be divided into a number of yellow, brown and red pigments, of which only porphyrins, bilirubin and urobilin have been reliably identified. Abnormal discoloration of the urine can be of endogenous or exogenous origin (see table on next page).

Odor

The faint, usually aromatic odor is due to unidentified substances. The odor changes completely after the ingestion of coffee, garlic or asparagus (S-methylthioester), for example. When acetone is present, the urine has a fruity odor; when there is decomposition, it smells of ammonia, putrefaction, or of hydrogen sulfide.

References

[1] ALEXANDER and NIXON, Brit. med. Bull., **17**, 112 (1961).
[2] HUNGERLAND, H., in BROCK, J. (Ed.), Biologische Daten für den Kinderarzt, 2nd ed., volume 2, Springer, Berlin, 1954, page 336.
[3] CONROY and MILLS, Human Circadian Rhythms, Churchill, London, 1970.
[4] DE VRIES et al., in STEWART and STRENGERS (Eds.), Symposium on Water and Electrolyte Metabolism, Elsevier, Amsterdam, 1961, page 77.
[5] MERTZ, D. P., Dtsch. med. Wschr., **89**, 2327 (1964).
[6] WERLE and SCHIEVELBEIN, in FLASCHENTRÄGER and LEHNARTZ (Eds.), Physiologische Chemie, volume II/2b, Springer, Berlin, 1957, page 1.
[7] COCKBURN, B. J., in LONG et al. (Eds.), Biochemists' Handbook, Spon, London, 1961, page 918; VAN PILSUM, J., in ALTMAN and DITTMER (Eds.), Biology Data Book, 2nd ed., volume 3, Federation of American Societies for Experimental Biology, Bethesda (Md.), 1974, page 1497.
[8] HINSBERG, K., in LANG et al. (Eds.), Hoppe-Seyler/Thierfelder Handbuch der physiologisch- und pathologisch-chemischen Analyse, 10th ed., volume 5, Springer, Berlin, 1953, page 181.
[9] COLOMBO and RICHTERICH, Die einfache Urinuntersuchung, Huber, Berne, 1977.

Volume rate and physicochemical data (references see page 57)

↓See text on page after next		SI unit	Mean	s	(Extreme range)	Other units	Mean	s	(Extreme range)	Reference
↓ **Volume rate**	....	...	...	...	...	...	...	...	...	...
↓ **Relative density**	Newborn (first few days)	...	1.012	–	–	...	...	...	...	15
	– After fluid intake	...	1.004	–	–	...	...	...	...	15
	Adults	...	1.015	–	(1.001–1.028)	...	...	...	...	8
↓ **Relative viscosity** ..	....	...	–	–	(1.0–1.14)	...	...	...	...	16
Surface tension	....	10^{-3} N m^{-1}	–	–	(64–69)	dyn cm^{-1}	–	–	(64–69)	17
↓ **Freezing-point depression**	.... (a)	K	–	–	(0.1–2.6)	°C	–	–	(0.1–2.6)	18
	(b)	K	–	–	(1.6–2.5)	°C	–	–	(1.6–2.5)	19
↓ **Osmolality**	.... (a)	mmol/kg	–	–	(50–1400)	mosm/kg	–	–	(50–1400)	18
	(b)	mmol/kg	–	–	(855–1335)	mosm/kg	–	–	(855–1335)	19
↓ **pH**	Newborn	...	...	...	...	...	6.2	–	(5.5–7.3)	21,22
	Children, adults.......	...	...	...	...	...	–	–	(4.5–8.2)	23

		Amount of substance				Mass				
		Unit	Mean	s	(Extreme range)	Unit	Mean	s	(Extreme range)	
↓ **Acidity**										
– titratable.........	Relative to body mass:									
	– 20 newborn	mmol d^{-1} kg^{-1}	0.30	–	–	...	...	...	...	21
	– 220 infants	mmol d^{-1} kg^{-1}	0.96	–	–	...	...	...	...	21
	– 11 young men	mmol d^{-1} kg^{-1}	0.64	0.125	–	...	...	...	...	6
↓ **CO$_2$ pressure**.......	....	...	...	...	...	...	...	...	...	
↓ **Dry mass**..........	....	...	...	...	...	g/d	–	–	(50–72)	32

Color changes of urine

(RICHTERICH, R.: Bulletin, Schweizerische Gesellschaft für klinische Chemie, 1973, page 7; COLOMBO and RICHTERICH, *Die einfache Urinuntersuchung,* Huber, Berne, 1977)

	Yellow to brown	Red to brown	Green*	Blue	Black
Physiological pigments in abnormal concentration	Bilirubin Erythrocytes Hemoglobin Myoglobin Porphobilin Porphyrins Urobilin	Bilirubin Erythrocytes Hemoglobin and derivatives Myoglobin Porphobilin Porphyrins Urobilin	Biliverdin Bile Indican (on standing) Verdoglobin		Blood (on standing) Homogentisic acid Indican (on standing) Melanogens Mesobilifuscin Porphobilin
Food derivatives and additives	Anthrone derivatives (e.g. rhubarb)◊ Betanidin (e.g. beets)◊ Carotenes (e.g. carrots) Flavins (e.g. riboflavin), yellow-green fluorescence	Anthrone derivatives◊ Betanidin◊ Food colors (e.g. rhodamine B, green fluorescence)	Indigo carmine	Indigo carmine	
Drugs (therapeutic and toxic)	Anisindione◊ Anthrone derivatives, aloin, aloe, cascara, emodin, senna)◊ Bromsulphalein◊ Quinine Chloroquine Fluorescein Congo red◊ Mepacrine Methocarbamol (on standing) Methyldopa (on standing) Nitrofurantoin Pamaquine Phenolphthalein◊ Phenolsulfon-phthalein◊ Primaquine Santonin◊	Aminophenazone Anisindione◊ Anthrone derivatives Bromsulphalein◊ Chlorzoxazone Chrysarobin◊ Cinchophen Clofazimine Deferoxamine Ethoxazene Furazolidone Furazolium Congo red◊ Levodopa (black on standing) Methocarbamol Methyldopa Metronidazole Niridazole Nitrofurantoin Phenacetin Phenazone◊ Phenazopyridine Phenindione◊ Phenolphthalein◊ Phenolsulfon-phthalein◊ Phensuximide Phenytoin Rifamycin Salazosulfapyridine Santonin◊ Sulfamethoxazole	Acriflavine (green fluorescence) Amitriptyline Azuresin (Diagnex Blue) Iodochlor-hydroxyquin Indigo carmine Copper Methylene blue Triam-terene (blue fluorescence)	Amitryp-tiline Evans Blue Azuresin (Diagnex Blue) Indigo carmine Copper salts Methylene blue Nitrofural	Cascara (on standing) Levodopa
Intoxications	Cresol Nitrobenzene	Cresol Nitrobenzene Pyrogallol	Creosote Phenyl-salicylate Resorcinol		Phenols Pyrogallol Resorcinol Thymol
Bacterial discoloration		Chromogenic bacteria (e.g. *Serratia marcescens*)	*Pseudomonas* pigments (fluorescein, pyocyanine)		

* Possibly blue pigments producing green color on mixing with yellow urine. ◊ Coloration dependent on pH.

Volume. Premature infants produce less urine than full-term infants of the same age[5]. See Table 2 for data on children and young males. Urinary volume rate is increased at high water and salt intakes and a protein-rich diet; it is decreased at low water intake, a diet rich in carbohydrates, and in case of profuse sweating. The volume rate is lower during the night than during the day (Fig.1)[9,10]; this rhythm is not observed in pregnant women[11]. See Table 3 for a definition of polyuria and anuria, and Tables 4 and 5 for pathological changes.

Relative density. Details on relative density may be found in the section 'Renal Function Values', page 103. Low values are seen in diabetes insipidus[12], and high values in diabetes mellitus, fever, and the nephrotic syndrome (proteinuria).

Relative viscosity. The relation between relative density and relative viscosity is indicated in Table 6. The viscosity is increased if the urine contains increased amounts of protein, blood or leukocytes.

Freezing-point depression and osmolality. (a) Limits of renal diluting and concentrating capacity; (b) after 14 hours fluid fasting. The values given do not apply to newborn infants. See Table 1 for additional values. See Figure 2 regarding the relation between the osmolality and the relative density of urine; the wide variance of the values is due to varying contributions of the solutes to the osmolality. Other details may be found in the section 'Renal Function Values', page 103. Under normal conditions, osmolality (virtually equivalent to osmolarity) is determined by diet and fluid intake and should reach 800–900 mmol/kg in the fasting morning urine (the urine osmolality/plasma osmolality ratio should amount to 3 or more)[20]. See Table 7 concerning the osmolality under abnormal hydration conditions.

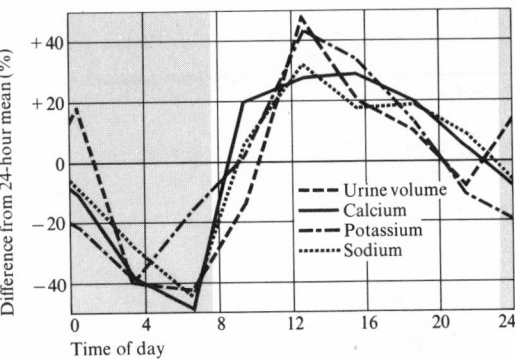

Fig. 1. Diurnal excretion of urine and electrolytes relative to mean value of 24-hour urine[9]. Shaded area: period of sleep.

pH (for additional values see Table 8). Normal urine generally reacts acid owing to the sulfuric and phosphoric acid derived from the degradation of proteins and phospholipids; on a vegetarian diet it can turn alkaline since organic acids of fruits and vegetables are broken down to bicarbonate. The urine pH (and titratable acidity) is subject to a day/night rhythm[26,27]: the urine is least acid (sometimes alkaline) after awakening, and most acid toward midnight. Under extreme conditions the urine can be acidified to a pH as low as 4.0[28]. Alkaline pH values can also be the result of bacterial decomposition of urea.

Acidity (see Table 8 for additional data; also the section 'Renal Function Values', page 104). *Total acidity* represents the sum of titratable acidity and ammonium concentration minus the bicarbonate concentration. Normally – except in the first postnatal year – about 60% of the hydrogen ions that are produced are excreted as NH_4^+, 40% as $H_2PO_4^-$, and small amounts of hydrogen ions are bound to urate and creatinine. At a pH below 6.0, the bicarbonate concentration may be neglected (page 58). The *titratable acidity* is determined by titration to pH 7.40. It consists predominantly of $H_2PO_4^-$. Because of a low rate of phosphate excretion there is little excretion of titratable acidity in the newborn infant[6,29]. The excretion of total acidity (net acid excretion) can reach 750 mmol/d in diabetic acidosis (titratable acidity 250 mmol/d), and in the terminal stage of nephritis it can drop to 2.5 mmol/d[30].

CO_2 pressure. The urinary CO_2 pressure in nearly all samples is higher than that in the plasma (Fig.3).

Dry mass. The concentration of solutes can be approximatively calculated from the relative density by multiplying the second and third digit after the decimal point by 2.6 (or by 1.6 in young children). Example: relative density 1.020; dry mass $\cong 20 \times 2.6 = 52$ g/L (adults)[33].

Table 1   *Urinary volume rate*

Age	Mean	s	(Extreme range)	Reference
	mL/d			
Newborn infants, 1st day	17	–	(0–68)	1
Newborn infants, 7th day	34	–	(0–84)	1
41 boys, 6–10 years	459	175	–	2
24 boys, 10–14 years	605	294	–	2
34 girls, 6–10 years	274	125	–	2
19 girls, 10–14 years	441	305	–	2
33 men	1360	443	(690–2690)	3
39 women (no ovulation inhibitors)	1130	423	(490–2260)	3
30 women (ovulation inhibitors)	980	449	(320–2290)	3
27 adults, >90 years	853	–	(275–2400)	4

Table 2   *Urinary volume rate and electrolyte excretion (relative to body mass) and osmolality in children and young males*

Age	Number	Urinary volume rate		Chloride		Sodium		Potassium		Osmolality		Reference
		Mean	s	Mean	s	Mean	s	Mean	s	Mean	s	
		mL d⁻¹ kg⁻¹		mmol d⁻¹ kg⁻¹						mmol/kg		
1st day	9	8.5	3.5	0.43	0.18	0.25	0.07	0.36	0.14	–	–	6
7th day (breast-fed)*	16	76	17	2.08	1.00	1.78	1.29	0.95	0.65	–	–	6
0–6 months	8	34	6	1.61	0.54	0.79	0.42	2.27	1.31	462	85	7
6 months to 1 year	19	29	12	3.19	0.99	2.52	1.14	3.55	0.81	880	283	7
1–2 years	14	25	7	3.49	0.95	3.36	0.98	4.06	0.56	1004	297	7
2–3 years	6	33	9	3.55	0.24	2.77	0.36	2.29	0.33	813	215	7
3–4 years	8	34	7	3.78	0.53	3.49	0.43	3.10	0.62	808	249	7
4–5 years	10	29	10	3.26	1.49	3.12	0.96	2.33	0.75	735	165	7
5–7 years	8	25	7	2.47	0.44	2.15	0.75	1.92	0.36	726	338	7
7–11 years	12	25	7	2.98	1.21	2.73	1.01	1.71	0.92	711	56	7
11–14 years	8	19	3	2.54	0.76	2.29	0.60	1.76	0.58	824	76	7
Young males	11◊	20	3.2	2.80	0.62	2.66	0.54	1.05	0.13	852	189	6

*Infants fed cow's milk: about 1½ times as much chloride and sodium; about twice as much potassium.   ◊Osmolality: values of 263 persons[8].

Table 3 *Evaluation of urinary volume rate[12,14]*

Severe polyuria	6000–15000 mL/d
Moderate polyuria	2000–6000 mL/d
Oliguria	$<$500 mL/d or $<$20 mL/h
Anuria	$<$100 mL/d
Total anuria	0 mL/d

Table 4 *Differentiation of pathological polyurias[12]*

Water	
Increased water intake	Psychogenic polydipsia Postencephalitic polydipsia
Inadequate reabsorption of filtered water	Central diabetes insipidus (lack of vasopressin secretion) *Congenital form* of nephrogenic diabetes insipidus (failure of response to vasopressin) *Acquired forms:* Chronic renal diseases Obstructive uropathy Multiple myeloma Amyloidosis Sjögren's syndrome Potassium deficiency Hyperaldosteronism Nephrocalcinosis, hypercalcemia Unilateral renal artery occlusion Postrenal transplantation Sickle-cell anemia
Solutes (osmotic diuresis)	
Inadequate reabsorption of glucose	Diabetes mellitus
Inadequate reabsorption of salts (mainly NaCl)	Chronic renal diseases (especially pyelonephritis)
	After diuretics, mannitol

Table 5 *Differentiation of oligurias and anurias[13]*

	Diagnostic criteria

Prerenal
Massive dehydration
Circulatory failure
  Blood loss
  Left ventricular failure
Terminal cirrhosis of the liver
	Urine sodium concentration $<$40 mmol/L
	
	$\dfrac{\text{Urine osmolality}}{\text{Plasma osmolality}} > 1.2$

Postrenal Ureterolith, papillary necrosis (single kidney) Uterine carcinoma Prostatic or bladder tumors Surgical ureteral ligature Retroperitoneal fibrosis	Urine sodium concentration $>$60 mmol/L
Acute renal Shock kidney Nephrotoxins Crush, hemolytic, 'heat' kidney Intravascular coagulation Acute glomerulonephritis Vasculitis Bilateral renal artery occlusion Bilateral renal vein thrombosis Hyperuratemia Hypercalcemia Myeloma	Urine sodium concentration $>$60 mmol/L $\dfrac{\text{Urine osmolality}}{\text{Plasma osmolality}} < 1.1$

Table 6 *Relation between relative density and relative viscosity[16]*

Relative density	Relative viscosity	
1.005	1.0	(Relative viscosity
1.016	1.02	of distilled
1.022	1.09	water = 1.00)
1.024	1.14	

Table 7 *Classification of abnormal states of hydration*

	Osmolality			Osmolality	
	Urine	Serum		Urine	Serum
Hypertonic dehydration Water loss $>$ NaCl loss Perspiration Diabetes insipidus	 ↑ ↓	 ↑ ↑	*Hypotonic dehydration* NaCl loss $>$ water loss Addison's disease	 ↑	 ↓
Hypertonic hydration NaCl uptake $>$ water uptake	↑	↑	*Hypotonic hydration* Water uptake $>$ NaCl uptake	↓	↓

Table 8 *Urinary pH and excretion of total acidity (A_{H^+}), titratable acidity (A_{TA}), and ammonium ions ($A_{NH_4^+}$)*

	pH		A_{H^+}		A_{TA}		$A_{NH_4^+}$		Reference
	Mean	(Extreme range)	Mean	(Extreme range)	Mean	(Extreme range)	Mean	(Extreme range)	
					mmol/d				
11 children, 2–11½ months*	5.9	(5.1–6.8)	64.4	(12.1–105)	36.7	(5.2–60.0)	29.4	(10.5–49.7)	24
6 children, 1–16 years*	6.2	(5.3–7.2)	42.0	(13.0–68.5)	17.1	(2.9–34.8)	30.1	(16.1–41.2)	24
11 adults	6.17	s 0.47	56.0	s 21.9	23.0	s 10.2	36.5	s 9.5	25

* For body surface of 1.73 m².

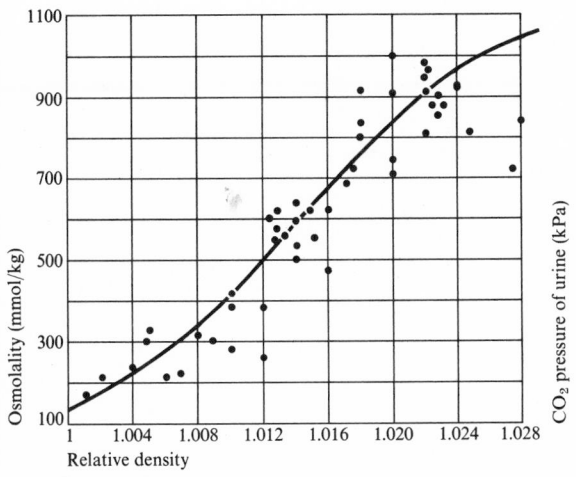

Fig. 2. Relation between osmolality and relative density of urine[8].

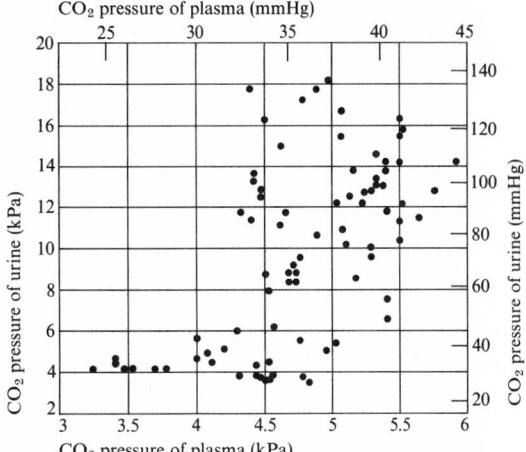

Fig. 3. Relation between CO_2 pressures of urine and plasma[31].

References

1 AAS, K., *Acta paediat. (Uppsala),* **50**, 361 (1961).
2 LIAPPIS and JÄKEL, *Mschr. Kinderheilk.,* **122**, 777 (1974).
3 LIAPPIS, N., *Z. klin. Chem.,* **11**, 279 (1973).
4 HOWELL, T. H., *J. Geront.,* **11**, 61 (1956).
5 CRANNY and CRANNY, *Amer. J. Dis. Child.,* **99**, 507 (1960).
6 McCANCE and WIDDOWSON, *Acta paediat. (Uppsala),* **49**, 409 (1960).
7 CHAPTAL et al., *Arch. franç. Pédiat.,* **20**, 905 (1963).
8 FORMAN and CHANGUS, *Clin. Chem.,* **14**, 38 (1968).
9 WISSER et al., *Klin. Wschr.,* **51**, 242 (1973).
10 ELITHORN et al., *Brit. med. J.,* **2**, 1620 (1966).
11 PARBOOSINGH and DOIG, *Amer. J. Obstet. Gynec.,* **116**, 609 (1973).
12 KLEEMAN, C. R., in MAXWELL and KLEEMAN (Eds.), *Clinical Disorders of Fluid and Electrolyte Metabolism,* 2nd ed., McGraw-Hill, New York, 1972, page 215.
13 THIEL, G., *Schweiz. med. Wschr.,* **102**, 917 (1972).
14 HARRINGTON and COHEN, *Arch. intern. Med.,* **131**, 810 (1973).
15 RUBIN, M. I., in NELSON, W. E. (Ed.), *Textbook of Pediatrics,* 8th ed., Saunders, Philadelphia, 1964, page 1092.
16 POSNER, C., *Berl. klin. Wschr.,* **52**, 1106 (1915).
17 WERLE and SCHIEVELBEIN, in FLASCHENTRÄGER and LEHNARTZ (Eds.), *Physiologische Chemie,* volume II/2b, Springer, Berlin, 1957, page 1.

18 CONSOLAZIO et al., *Physiological Measurements of Metabolic Functions in Man,* McGraw-Hill, New York, 1963, page 437.
19 JACOBSON et al., *Arch. intern. Med.,* **110**, 83 (1962).
20 FRICK, P. G., *Schweiz. med. Wschr.,* **98**, 1562 (1968).
21 WEBER, H., *Helv. paediat. Acta,* **15**, 186 (1960).
22 HUNGERLAND, H., in BROCK, J. (Ed.), *Biologische Daten für den Kinderarzt,* 2nd ed., volume 2, Springer, Berlin, 1954, page 543.
23 KILDEBERG, P., *Clinical Acid–Base Physiology,* Munksgaard, Copenhagen, 1968.
24 PEONIDES et al., *Arch. Dis. Childh.,* **40**, 33 (1965).
25 SIMPSON, D. P., *Medicine (Baltimore),* **50**, 503 (1971).
26 CONROY and MILLS, *Human Circadian Rhythms,* Churchill, London, 1970.
27 VIOLLE, P.-L., *Rev. Prat. (Paris),* **7**, 644 (1957).
28 RELMAN, A. S., *Advanc. intern. Med.,* **12**, 295 (1964).
29 McCANCE and HATEMI, *Lancet,* **1**, 293 (1961).
30 PITTS, R. F., *Physiology of the Kidney and Body Fluids,* 3rd ed., Year Book Medical Publishers, Chicago, 1974.
31 PITTS et al., *J. clin. Invest.,* **28**, 35 (1949).
32 DE VRIES et al., in STEWART and STRENGERS (Eds.), *Symposium on Water and Electrolyte Metabolism,* Elsevier, Amsterdam, 1961, page 77.
33 HINSBERG, K., in LANG et al. (Eds.), *Hoppe-Seyler/Thierfelder Handbuch der physiologisch- und pathologisch-chemischen Analyse,* 10th ed., volume 5, Springer, Berlin, 1953, page 181.

Inorganic substances in urine (for references see pages 61 and 62)

↓See text on next page			Amount of substance				Mass				Reference
			Unit	Mean	s	(Extreme range)	Unit	Mean	s	(Extreme range)	
↓ **Bicarbonate**	....		...	...	...	...	...	...	...	...	...
↓ **Chloride**	.....................(a)		mmol/d	135	–	(80–270)	g/d	4.8	–	(2.8–9.6)	–
↓ **Phosphorus**	Adults		mmol/d	–	–	(26–65)	g/d	–	–	(0.8–2.0)	4
Phosphate	33 children and young adults		mmol/d	20.0	9.0	–	...	...	...	...	11
↓ **Pyrophosphate**	33 children and young adults		µmol/d	38.9	18.6	–	...	...	...	...	11
↓ **Sulfur**											
Total S............	....		mmol/d	41.3	–	(39–47)	g/d	1.32	–	(1.24–1.49)	15
Inorganic sulfate S	....		mmol/d	36.6	–	(33–41)	g/d	1.17	–	(1.07–1.30)	15
Sulfuric acid ester S	....		mmol/d	2.8	–	(2.5–34.4)	g/d	0.09	–	(0.08–1.10)	15
Neutral S	....		mmol/d	2.2	–	(1.6–2.5)	g/d	0.07	–	(0.05–0.08)	15
SO_4^{2-}.................	....		mmol/d	–	–	(12–42)	...	...	...	...	90
$S_2O_3^{2-}$...............	31 adults...........		µmol/d	31.7	12.8	(12.4–67.5)	...	...	...	...	90
↓ **Thiocyanate**	Nonsmokers		mmol/L	0.07	–	(0–0.10)	mg/L	4	–	(0–6)	27
Cyanide............	....		µmol/d	–	–	(0.08–0.23)	µg/d	–	–	(2–6)	28

↓See text below and on next page		Amount of substance				Mass				Reference
		Unit	Mean	s	95% range (extreme range in brackets)	Unit	Mean	s	95% range (extreme range in brackets)	
↓**Fluoride**	Newborn	µmol/L	4.2	–	–	mg/L	0.08	–	–	20
	31 children 1–3 years ...... (a)	µmol/L	7.4	–	(2.6–16)	mg/L	0.14	–	(0.05–0.30)	21
	28 children 4–6 years ...... (a)	µmol/L	14.2	–	(2.6–37)	mg/L	0.27	–	(0.05–0.70)	21
	34 adults .... (a)	µmol/L	27.3	–	(16–45)	mg/L	0.52	–	(0.30–0.85)	21
	5 adults.................... (b)	µmol/d	–	–	(47–153)	mg/d	–	–	(0.9–2.9)	22
↓**Bromide**	15 adults......................	µmol/d	46	20	(20–84)	mg/d	3.7	1.6	(1.6–6.7)	76
	8 subjects	µmol/L	82.1	–	(37.2–107)	mg/L	6.56	–	(2.97–8.55)	18
↓**Iodide**		µmol/d	1.51	1.09	0.14–3.81	mg/d	0.191	0.138	(0.018–0.483)	25
	Relative to creatinine:									
	– 1224 children, 1–6 years.. (a)	mmol/mol	0.530	–	0.201–1.65	mg/g	0.600	–	0.225–1.85	26
	– 162 boys, 9–16 years	mmol/mol	0.426	0.189	–	mg/g	0.478	0.212	–	91
	– 215 girls, 9–16 years.........	mmol/mol	0.368	0.199	–	mg/g	0.413	0.223	–	91
↓**Boron**......		mmol/d	0.09	–	–	mg/d	1.0	–	–	19
↓**Potassium** ..	.... (a)	mmol/d	70	–	(40–100)	g/d	2.7	–	(1.6–3.9)	–
↓**Sodium**	.... (a)	mmol/d	150	–	(95–310)	g/d	3.5	–	(2.2–7.1)	–
	106 males......................	mmol/d	224	95	(80–560)	g/d	5.15	2.2	(1.8–12.9)	92

Bicarbonate. See Figure 1 for the relation between urinary pH and bicarbonate concentration. At a normal acid-base equilibrium, that is, up to an upper limit of the plasma bicarbonate level of 26–28 mmol/L, virtually all of the bicarbonate that has undergone glomerular filtration is reabsorbed so that the urine contains no bicarbonate[93]. If the plasma bicarbonate concentration exceeds this limit, bicarbonate appears in the urine in increasing amounts. Bicarbonate excretion is affected by the carbon dioxide tension of the arterial blood, the body's potassium stores, the plasma chloride level, and by corticosteroid secretion[93].

Chloride. (a) Calculated for an intake of 6–20 g/d of NaCl assuming that approximately 80% of the chloride ingested is excreted in the urine[1]. – The excretion rate is lower during the night than during the day[2,3]. See Table 2, page 55, regarding chloride excretion in children and young males. The excretion increases with increasing salt intake and is elevated under the action of diuretics, in salt-losing nephritis, potassium deficiency, and adrenocortical insufficiency. Chloride excretion is low in individuals on a low-sodium diet, in starvation, in cases of increased loss of chloride due to vomiting, sweating or diarrhea, in Cushing's syndrome and during corticosteroid therapy as well as in all forms of salt retention (e.g. edema).

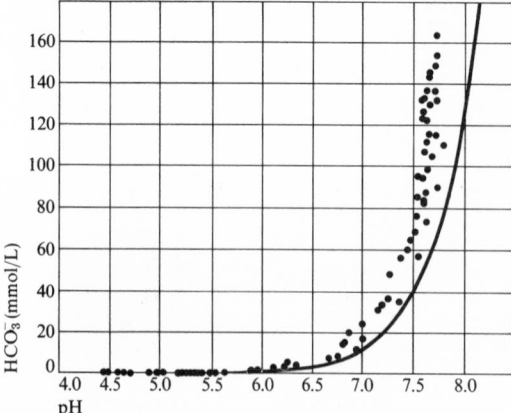

Fig. 1. Relation between urinary bicarbonate concentration and pH. The curve has been calculated by the Henderson-Hasselbalch equation on the assumption of a constant CO_2 pressure of 6.7 kPa (50 mmHg)[93].

Phosphorus. The phosphorus in urine is 95–100% inorganic, being present for the most part as primary phosphate (the proportion of secondary phosphate increasing with rising pH). Most of it comes from food; a smaller amount originates from the endogenous metabolism of organic phosphates. About 50–80% of alimentary phosphates appear in the urine[5]. The rate of excretion reaches a maximum during the night, and a minimum in the forenoon[2,6,7]. It is affected by parathyroid hormone and dependent on renal function. Urine formed in utero contains little phosphorus[8]. Values of phosphorus excretion in children and young men are given in Table 1. Values in relation to intake may be found in Table 2. Phosphate clearance, tubular phosphate reabsorption expressed as a percentage, the phosphate excretion index (PEI), and the index of phosphate excretion (IPE) are clinically evaluable parameters of phosphate excretion. FOURMAN and ROYER have cited normal values and pathologically induced changes therein[9].

Pyrophosphate excretion relative to body mass is greater in children than in adults[12]. It increases as phosphate intake increases[13,14].

Sulfur. The urinary sulfur consists mostly of free sulfate; small amounts of sulfate are in the form of organic esters (indoxylsulfonic acid)[15,16]. Neutral sulfur comprises thiocyanate, mercaptan, diethyl sulfide, and sulfur-containing amino acids[5]. Inorganic sulfate results from the metabolism of sulfur-containing amino acids; its excretion is therefore increased on a high-protein diet and is a measure of the quality of the dietary proteins[17]. Data on sulfate excretion in children and young men are given in Table 1.

Thiocyanate. Values higher in smokers.

Fluoride. (a) At a fluoride content of the drinking water of 26 to 32 µmol/L; (b) at an intake of 79–247 µmol/d. – Beginning with the 4th month of pregnancy, fluoride excretion decreases (down to 12 µmol/L in 8th month); within 16 weeks after the delivery it rises to the normal level again[23]. Data on fluoride excretion in relation to intake are given in Table 2. With a decline in renal function fluoride excretion diminishes[24].

Bromide. Approximately 90% of the bromine taken in is excreted in the urine[19].

Iodide. (a) Range: 10–90 centiles. – Data on iodide excretion in relation to intake are given in Table 2. The urinary iodide is composed of ingested iodide and iodide split off from thyroxine.

Boron. About 77% of the boron taken in is excreted in the urine[19].

Potassium. (a) Calculated for an intake of 45–110 mmol/d on the assumption that about 90% of the dietary potassium is excreted in the urine[29]. – In individuals with intact renal function, potassium excretion can increase to as much as 35–40 mmol/h[30]. With a potassium-free diet but adequate caloric intake, potassium excre-

Table 1 *Excretion of phosphate, sulfate, calcium and magnesium in relation to body mass in children and young males*

Age	Number	Phosphate (as P) Mean	s	Sulfate (as S) Mean	s	Calcium Mean	s	Magnesium Mean	s	Reference
		μmol d⁻¹ kg⁻¹								
1st day.................	9, 12	3.9	1.0	110	53	9.7	2.5	2.0	0.9	52, 53
7th day (breast-fed)*...	13, 16	10	6.1	190	66	110	60	25	17	52, 54
1 month to 12 years	38	–	–	–	–	90	60	115	45	55
1–15 years	52, 23	–	–	–	–	59	16	116	33	56
Young men	11	533	103	600	130	–	–	–	–	52

*When feeding cow's milk: P about 10 times, S about 3 times more; calcium and magnesium approximately one-half.

Table 2 *Excretion of fluoride, iodide, calcium and phosphate in relation to intake*

Fluoride[49] Intake	Urine Mean	Urine Range	Iodide[50] Intake	Urine Mean	Calcium[51] Intake	Urine Mean	Urine 95% range	Inorganic phosphate (as P)[14] Intake	Urine Mean	Urine (Extreme range)
μmol/d			μmol/d		mmol/d			mmol/d		
230	119	(79–163)	0.80	0.56	3.74	2.20	0.40–4.00	32.3	26.5	(17.1–35.5)
726	391	(316–488)	4.73	2.40	37.4	4.96	1.32–8.60	64.6	44.9	(32.3–58.1)
...	...	...	...	...	...	...	...	96.9	63.6	(44.6–96.9)

tion decreases to about 10 mmol/d within a few days[31,32]. Renal potassium loss is greater in individuals fasting completely[33]. The excretion rate is lower during the night than during the day[2,3,7,34] (Fig. 1, page 55). See Table 2 for potassium excretion in children and young men (page 55). Excretion is *elevated* under the action of diuretics (except potassium-retaining diuretics), in the polyuric phase of chronic kidney diseases and in the presence of tubular dysfunction (pyelonephritis, renal-tubular acidosis, Liddle's syndrome, medullary cystic kidney), under the action of corticosteroids (Cushing's syndrome, primary hyperaldosteronism, Bongiovanni's syndrome and Biglieri's syndrome, secondary hyperaldosteronism), in connection with an increased excretion of bicarbonate (alkalosis) and organic anions (metabolic acidoses). Potassium excretion is *depressed* under the action of potassium-retaining diuretics, in the anuric phase of renal failure, in acute tubular necrosis, adrenocortical insufficiency (Addison's disease), congenital adrenal hyperplasia and in connection with sodium deficiency. The determination of potassium excretion helps in the differential diagnosis of hypokalemia (Table 3).

Sodium. (a) Calculated for a NaCl intake of 6–20 g/d on the assumption that about 90–95% of the sodium ingested is excreted in the urine[35]. – Whereas the normal individual is capable of varying salt excretion (as NaCl) from virtually zero to values well in excess of 20 g/d, the range in the uremic patient is restricted[36]. Total fasting leads initially to increased natriuresis, which can be stopped by ingestion of carbohydrates. After a fast of about 20 days renal excretion of sodium ceases almost entirely[33,89] (Fig. 2). The excretion rate is lower during the night than during the day[2,3,7,34] (Fig. 1, page 55). Data on sodium excretion in children and young men are given in Table 2, page 55. Excretion increases with increasing salt intake and is *elevated* in adrenocortical insufficiency (Addison's disease, hypophyseal insufficiency), congenital adrenocortical

hyperplasia, certain forms of chronic renal failure (salt-losing kidney, pyelonephritis), under the action of certain diuretics (potassium-retaining diuretics), with increased excretion of bicarbonate (alkalosis) and glucose as well as in connection with water retention at continued sodium excretion (syndrome of inappropriate vasopressin secretion). Sodium excretion is *depressed* in cases of low salt intake, in cases of extrarenal sodium loss and simultaneous low sodium intake, under the action of corticosteroids (stress, Cushing's syndrome), and at reduced renal perfusion (functional renal failure).

Calcium. Calcium excretion is reduced in old age[39,40], increased after meals[41], and influenced by diet composition. It depends to a small extent only on calcium intake (Table 2) but increases with the supply of sodium[42], carbohydrates[43], and protein[44]. Continued calcium excretion during total fasting is probably related to the metabolic acidosis[33]. Diurnal variations[2,7,34] and reduced excretion during the night as compared with daytime values (Fig. 1, page 55) primarily reflect meals. See Table 1 for excretion in children and young men. Calcium excretion decreases in women using estrogen-containing ovulation-inhibitors[94]. The causes of pathological hypercalciuria are indicated in Table 4. They are either absolute or relative (in relation to the serum calcium level). Hypocalciuria is found mainly in cases of impaired calcium absorption

Table 3 *Interpretation of hypokaliuria[32]*

Initial procedure ...	Withdrawal of diuretics No potassium supplement Sodium intake > 100 mmol/d	
Potassium in urine	< 30 mmol/d	> 30 mmol/d
Diagnosis	Extrarenal potassium loss Diuretic-induced hypokalemia	Probable mineralocorticoid syndrome

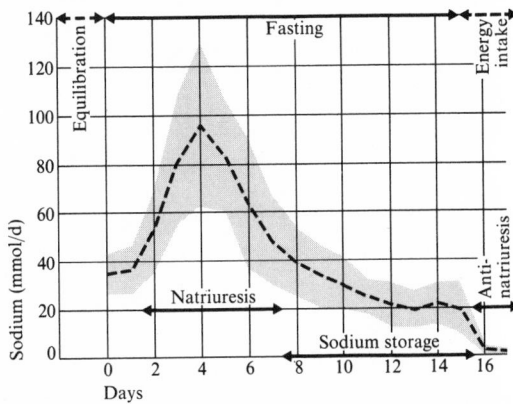

Fig. 2. Urinary excretion of sodium during 15-day fasting, following a period of equilibrium, at a constant sodium intake of 50 mmol/d (mean value and 95% range of 5 subjects)[89].

↑↓See text on page 59 and below		Amount of substance				Mass				Reference
		Unit	Mean	s	95% range (extreme range in brackets)	Unit	Mean	s	95% range (extreme range in brackets)	
↑ Calcium ...	75 men	mmol/d	5.94	1.9	<10	mg/d	238	75	<400	37
	98 women	mmol/d	4.54	1.5	<8.5	mg/d	182	62	<340	37
	13 adults	mmol/d	5.8	1.25	–	mg/d	232	50	–	38
↓ Magnesium	91 men	mmol/d	5.4	1.5	–	mg/d	131	36.5	–	46
	61 women	mmol/d	4.4	1.4	–	mg/d	107	34.0	–	46
	Adults.......................	mmol/d	–	–	(2.5–8.3)	mg/d	–	–	(60–200)	47
↓ Iron........	30 adults.............. (a)	µmol/d	1.6	–	0–2.2	µg/d	88	–	0–120	57
	10 subjects............. (b)	µmol/d	1.8	–	(0.7–2.7)	µg/d	100	–	(40–150)	58
	10 men .... (b)	µmol/d	0.45	–	(0.22–0.81)	µg/d	25	–	(12–45)	59
	13 adults.............. (c)	µmol/d	2.35	1.50	(0.91–6.30)	µg/d	131	84	(51–350)	76
	Relative to body mass:									
	– 38 children............ (a)	nmol d⁻¹ kg⁻¹	64.2	35.8	–	µg/d	3.6	2.0	–	97
↓ Copper.....	52 newborn.............. (a)	µmol/d	0.12	–	–	µg/d	7.9	–	–	62
	204 children, 2–6 years.... (a)	µmol/d	0.47	–	–	µg/d	30.1	–	–	62
	52 men .... (b)	µmol/d	0.38	–	0.20–0.68	µg/d	24.2	–	13–43	63
	46 women .... (b)	µmol/d	0.30	–	0.14–0.58	µg/d	19.2	–	9–37	63
	82 adults.............. (b)	µmol/d	0.57	–	(0.16–1.79)	µg/d	36	–	(10–114)	64
	16 adults.............. (c)	µmol/d	0.79	0.46	(0.06–1.81)	µg/d	50	29	(4–115)	76
↓ Zinc	Children, 7–9 years .... (b)	µmol/d	5.8	–	–	µg/d	380	–	–	71
	62 men .... (a)	µmol/d	8.03	3.88	(2.22–19.2)	µg/d	525	254	(145–1256)	70
	82 adults.............. (b)	µmol/d	5.40	3.18	(2.16–11.9)	µg/d	353	208	(141–779)	64
	16 adults.............. (c)	µmol/d	8.0	4.6	(2.1–18)	µg/d	520	300	(140–1200)	76

(malabsorption syndrome) and in chronic kidney diseases as well as in osteopetrosis[96]; see also review papers[9,10,45].

Magnesium. About one-third of dietary magnesium is usually excreted in the urine. After carbohydrate intake, magnesium excretion increases[43,48]. Continued excretion of magnesium during total fasting is probably related to the metabolic acidosis[33]. The slight diurnal variations[2,7] – excretion lower during the night than in the daytime – primarily reflect meals[41]. Data on magnesium excretion in children and young men are presented in Table 1. Magnesium excretion declines in women taking estrogen-containing ovulation inhibitors[94]. Magnesium excretion is pathologically *elevated* in hyperaldosteronism, renal-tubular acidosis, and under the action of kaliuretic diuretics; it is *depressed* in disorders of enteric absorption and renal failure[10].

Iron. Values cited determined (a) by means of atomic absorption, (b) colorimetrically, and (c) by neutron activation. Iron is present in higher concentrations than is indicated by the quantity of transferrin. The iron stems mostly from microhematuria and

Table 4   *Major causes of hypercalciuria[9,10]*

Increased enteric absorption of calcium	Excessive intake of vitamin D and calcium Sarcoidosis Milk-alkali syndrome Idiopathic forms
Increased bone resorption	Cushing's syndrome Immobilization Hyperthyroidism Hyperparathyroidism Paget's disease
Disturbance of renal reabsorption of calcium	Diuretics Salt-wasting kidney
Renal-tubular acidosis	Fanconi's syndrome Wilson's disease

from epithelial cells from the renal tubules and the bladder mucosa. Iron excretion is increased in diseases associated with intravascular hemolysis[60,61].

Copper. Determined (a) with the aid of dithiocarbamate, (b) by means of atomic absorption, and (c) by neutron activation. Approximately 3% of the dietary copper is excreted in the urine[19]. Copper excretion is lower during the night than during the day[65]. It is pathologically elevated in Wilson's disease (>1.6 µmol/d), in biliary cirrhosis as well as in proteinuria (e.g. in the nephrotic syndrome), 60–80% of the copper being in the form of ceruloplasmin[66,67].

Zinc. Determined (a) with dithizon, (b) by means of atomic absorption, and (c) by means of neutron activation. About 5% of the dietary zinc is excreted in the urine[19]. Zinc excretion is pathologically elevated in diabetes mellitus, cancer, alcohol-induced cirrhosis and in all forms of muscular catabolism and during total fasting[72,74].

Arsenic. About 20% of the arsenic supplied is excreted in the urine[19].

Chromium. Increased in insulin-dependent diabetics[80].

Lead. About 7% of the lead taken in is excreted in the urine[19]. An increase to more than 4.8 µmol/d after administration of 1.0 g Ca-EDTA – or of a dose commensurate to body mass in children – is suggestive of lead intoxication[84,85].

Lithium. About 40% of the dietary lithium is excreted in the urine[19].

Mercury. About 75% of the mercury administered is excreted in the urine[19].

Nickel. About 3% of the dietary nickel is excreted in the urine[19].

Strontium. About 10% of the dietary strontium is excreted in the urine[19].

Other elements. Elements that are contained in the diet in relatively large amounts, such as aluminum, tin, zirconium, strontium and vanadium, remain practically unabsorbed and more than 99% are excreted with the feces[19]. For quantitative data on urinary excretion of beryllium, barium, tellurium, titanium, niobium[19], bismuth[88] and of silicon[98] see the original publications[5]. Nitrite and nitrate are likewise found in the urine[5].

↑See text on page 60		Amount of substance				Mass				Reference
		Unit	Mean	s	(Extreme range)	Unit	Mean	s	(Extreme range)	
Trace metals of minor importance										
Antimony ...	16 adults	nmol/d	12	4.6	(0.43–21)	µg/d	1.5	0.57	(0.52–2.6)	76
↑Arsenic	16 adults........................	µmol/d	2.4	2.4	(0.41–8.1)	µg/d	180	180	(31–610)	76
	5 subjects	µmol/d	0.63	–	(0.05–2.68)	µg/d	47	–	(4–201)	82
Cadmium ..	16 adults........................	nmol/d	19	20	(2–75)	µg/d	2.1	2.3	(0.24–8.4)	76
	4 women at intake of 0.53–0.82 µmol/d	nmol/d	–	–	(124–480)	µg/d	–	–	(14–54)	77
	Relative to creatinine: – 169 adults	µmol/mol	1.26	1.03	–	µg/g	1.25	1.02	–	86
Cesium	13 adults........................	nmol/d	98	23	(61–140)	µg/d	13	3	(8.1–19)	76
↑Chromium .	18 children......................	µmol/d	0.11	0.06	–	µg/d	5.5	2.9	–	80
	20 adults........................	µmol/d	0.16	0.10	–	µg/d	8.4	5.2	–	80
	Relative to body mass: – 46 children	nmol d^{-1} kg^{-1}	11.8	5.5	–	µg d^{-1} kg^{-1}	0.61	0.29	–	97
Cobalt	Children at intake of 136–339 nmol/d	nmol/d	–	–	(5.1–32)	µg/d	–	–	(0.3-1.9)	75
	16 adults........................	nmol/d	12.4	8.1	(3.9–30)	µg/d	0.73	0.48	(0.23–1.8)	76
Gold.......	16 adults........................	pmol/d	56	127	(0.05–420)	ng/d	11	25	(0.01–83)	76
↑Lead......	....	µmol/L	0.17	–	<0.31	µg/L	35	–	<65	83
↑Lithium....	....	mmol/d	0.12	–	–	mg/d	0.8	–	–	19
Manganese	Children, at intake of 39–44 µmol/d...........	µmol/d	0.18–0.36	–	–	µg/d	10–20	–	–	68
	29 subjects, 14–61 years	µmol/d	0.30–0.44	–	–	µg/d	16.4–23.9	–	–	78
	230 males	µmol/L	–	–	<0.35	µg/L	–	–	<19	69
↑Mercury ...	16 adults........................	nmol/d	5.0	3.4	(0.8–12)	µg/d	1.0	0.69	(0.16–2.4)	76
	80 subjects	nmol/d	45	60	–	µg/d	9	12	–	95
	Relative to creatinine	µmol/mol	–	–	(0–6)	µg/g	–	–	(0–10)	87
Molybdenum	Children at intake of 0.45–0.84 µmol/d	µmol/d	–	–	(0.24–0.59)	µg/d	–	–	(23–57)	75
	4 women at intake of 0.48–1.00 µmol/d	µmol/d	–	–	(0.11–0.60)	µg/d	–	–	(11–58)	77
	16 adults........................	µmol/d	0.84	0.43	(0.24–1.9)	µg/d	81	41	(23–180)	76
↑Nickel	50 adults........................	nmol/d	44	24	(8.5–109)	µg/d	2.6	1.4	(0.5–6.4)	81
Rubidium ..	16 adults........................	µmol/d	28	7	(15–40)	mg/d	2.4	0.6	(1.3–3.4)	76
Scandium..	14 adults........................	nmol/d	1.6	2.2	(0.09–8.0)	ng/d	73	100	(3.9–360)	61
Selenium ..	Intake 0.76–1.90 µmol/d	µmol/d	–	–	(0.25–0.63)	µg/d	–	–	(20–50)	79
	4 women at intake of 0.23–0.33 µmol/d	µmol/d	–	–	(0.09–0.20)	µg/d	–	–	(7.5–16.1)	77
	16 adults........................	µmol/d	0.38	0.18	(0.04–0.66)	µg/d	30	14	(3–52)	76
Silver	14 adults........................	nmol/d	5.1	2.6	(1.7–10)	µg/d	0.55	0.28	(0.18–1.1)	76
↑Strontium..	....	µmol/d	2	–	–	mg/d	0.2	–	–	19
	Relative to body mass: – 12 newborn, 1st day	nmol d^{-1} kg^{-1}	20	13	–	µg d^{-1} kg^{-1}	1.74	1.15	–	53
Tungsten ..	16 adults........................	µmol/d	0.17	0.34	(0.01–1.5)	µg/d	32	63	(2.3–270)	76
↑Other elements ...	....	......	...	...	...	...	...	...	...	...

References

[1] COTLOVE and HOGBEN, in COMAR and BRONNER (Eds.), *Mineral Metabolism*, volume 2, part B, Academic Press, New York, 1962, page 109.
[2] WESSON, L. G., *Medicine (Baltimore)*, **43**, 547 (1964).
[3] ELITHORN et al., *Brit. med. J.*, **2**, 1620 (1966).
[4] CONSOLAZIO et al., *Physiological Measurements of Metabolic Functions in Man*, McGraw-Hill, New York, 1963, page 437.
[5] WERLE and SCHIEVELBEIN, in FLASCHENTRÄGER and LEHNARTZ (Eds.), *Physiologische Chemie*, volume II/2b, Springer, Berlin, 1957, page 1.
[6] SCHÄFER et al., *Z. klin. Med.*, **157**, 372 (1961/63).
[7] HEATON and HODGKINSON, *Clin. chim. Acta*, **8**, 246 (1963).
[8] MCCANCE and WIDDOWSON, *Acta paediat. (Uppsala)*, **49**, 409 (1960).
[9] FOURMAN and ROYER, *Calcium Metabolism and the Bone*, 2nd ed., Blackwell, Oxford, 1968.
[10] WALSER, M., in COMAR and BRONNER (Eds.), *Mineral Metabolism*, volume 3, Academic Press, New York, 1969, page 235.
[11] RUSSELL, R. G., *Lancet*, **2**, 461 (1965).
[12] FLEISCH and BISAZ, *Helv. physiol. pharmacol. Acta*, **21**, 88 (1963).
[13] FLEISCH et al., *Lancet*, **1**, 1065 (1964).
[14] O'BRIEN et al., *Canad. med. Ass. J.*, **96**, 100 (1967).
[15] FOLIN, O., *Amer. J. Physiol.*, **13**, 45 (1905).

[16] MÜTING et al., *Z. klin. Med.,* **157**, 391 (1961/63).
[17] SIMMONS, W. K., *Amer. J. clin. Nutr.,* **26**, 72 (1973).
[18] CONWAY and FLOOD, *Biochem. J.,* **30**, 716 (1936).
[19] SCHROEDER and NASON, *Clin. Chem.,* **17**, 461 (1971).
[20] WESPI and BÜRGI, *Caries Res.,* **5**, 89 (1971).
[21] GEDALIA, J., *J. dent. Res.,* **37**, 601 (1958).
[22] MCCLURE et al., *J. industr. Hyg.,* **27**, 159 (1945).
[23] GEDALIA et al., *J. dent. Res.,* **38**, 548 (1959).
[24] PARSONS et al., *Brit. med. J.,* **1**, 128 (1975).
[25] BRUGER et al., *J. Lab. clin. Med.,* **26**, 1942 (1941).
[26] GARRY et al., *Clin. Chem.,* **19**, 950 (1973).
[27] RHEINWALD, U., *Dtsch. zahnärztl. Z.,* **10**, 477 (1955).
[28] BOXER and RICKARDS, *Arch. Biochem.,* **30**, 392 (1951).
[29] BLACK, D. A., in MAXWELL and KLEEMAN (Eds.), *Clinical Disorders of Fluid and Electrolyte Metabolism,* 2nd ed., McGraw-Hill, New York, 1972, page 121.
[30] KAPLAN, N. M., *Ann. intern. Med.,* **71**, 363 (1969).
[31] SQUIRES and HUTH, *J. clin. Invest.,* **38**, 1134 (1959).
[32] KAPLAN, N. M., *Ann. intern. Med.,* **66**, 1079 (1967).
[33] DRENICK, E. J., in MAXWELL and KLEEMAN (Eds.), *Clinical Disorders of Fluid and Electrolyte Metabolism,* McGraw-Hill, New York, 2nd ed., 1972, page 1117.
[34] WISSER et al., *Klin. Wschr.,* **51**, 242 (1973).
[35] FORBES, G. B., in COMAR and BRONNER (Eds.), *Mineral Metabolism,* volume 2, part B, Academic Press, New York, 1962, page 1.
[36] BRICKER et al., in MAXWELL and KLEEMAN (Eds.), *Clinical Disorders of Fluid and Electrolyte Metabolism,* 2nd ed., McGraw-Hill, New York, 1972, page 697.
[37] DAVIS et al., *Clin. Sci.,* **39**, 1 (1970).
[38] BHANDARKAR and NORDIN, *Brit. med. J.,* **1**, 145 (1962).
[39] PANSU et al., in HIOCO, D. J. (Eds.), *L'ostéoporose,* Masson, Paris, 1964, page 176.
[40] SALEH and COENEGRACHT, *Clin. chim. Acta,* **21**, 445 (1968).
[41] HODGKINSON and HEATON, *Clin. chim. Acta,* **11**, 354 (1965).
[42] EPSTEIN, F. H., *Amer. J. Med.,* **45**, 700 (1968).
[43] LINDEMAN et al., *J. Lab. clin. Med.,* **70**, 236 (1967).
[44] WALKER and LINKSWILER, *J. Nutr.,* **102**, 1297 (1972).
[45] NORDIN and HODGKINSON, *Advanc. intern. Med.,* **13**, 155 (1967); NORDIN et al., *Clin. Endocr. Metab. (Lond.),* **1**, 169 (1972).
[46] EVANS and WATSON, *Lancet,* **1**, 522 (1966).
[47] WACKER and VALLEE, *Med. Clin. N. Amer.,* **44**, 1357 (1960).
[48] MEYER et al., *Amer. J. Nutr.,* **25**, 677 (1972).
[49] SPENCER et al., *Amer. J. Med.,* **49**, 807 (1970).
[50] HARRISON, M. T., *Postgrad. med. J.,* **44**, 69 (1968).
[51] MCINTOSH and SERAGLIA, *Canad. med. Ass. J.,* **89**, 1242 (1963).
[52] MCCANCE and WIDDOWSON, *Acta paediat. (Uppsala),* **49**, 409 (1960).
[53] WIDDOWSON et al., *Lancet,* **2**, 373 (1962).
[54] SLATER, J. E., *Brit. J. Nutr.,* **15**, 83 (1961).

[55] PAUNIER et al., *Helv. paediat. Acta,* **25**, 577 (1970).
[56] GHAZALI and BARRATT, *Arch. Dis. Childh.,* **49**, 97 (1974).
[57] WASHINGTON and BOGGS, *J. Lab. clin. Med.,* **86**, 17 (1975).
[58] HWANG and BROWN, *Arch. intern. Med.,* **114**, 741 (1964).
[59] TAVENIER et al., *Clin. chim. Acta,* **32**, 63 (1971).
[60] MOORE and BROWN, *Der Eisenstoffwechsel,* Documenta Geigy, Acta clinica, No. 7, Basle, 1967.
[61] SLATER and FELL, *Clin. Sci.,* **42**, 545 (1972).
[62] KLEINBAUM, H., *Z. Kinderheilk.,* **90**, 184 (1964).
[63] PIRKE and STAMM, *Z. klin. Chem.,* **8**, 449 (1970).
[64] MERET and HENKIN, *Clin. Chem.,* **17**, 369 (1971).
[65] LIFSCHITZ and HENKIN, *J. appl. Physiol.,* **31**, 88 (1971).
[66] SCHEINBERG and STERNLIEB, *Ann. Rev. Med.,* **16**, 119 (1965).
[67] CARTWRIGHT and WINTROBE, *Amer. J. clin. Nutr.,* **15**, 94 (1964).
[68] PRICE et al., *Amer. J. clin. Nutr.,* **23**, 258 (1970).
[69] HORIUCHI et al., *Osaka Cy med. J.,* **13**, 151 (1967).
[70] HELWIG et al., *Amer. J. clin. Path.,* **45**, 160 (1966).
[71] RITCHEY et al., *Amer. J. clin. Nutr.,* **32**, 799 (1979).
[72] MIKAC-DEVIĆ, D., *Advanc. clin. Chem.,* **13**, 271 (1970).
[73] PRASAD et al., *Amer. J. clin. Nutr.,* **23**, 581 (1970).
[74] Editorial, *Lancet,* **1**, 299 (1973); DAVIES and FELL, *Clin. chim. Acta,* **51**, 83 (1974).
[75] ENGEL et al., *J. Nutr.,* **92**, 197 (1967).
[76] WESTER, O. P., *Acta med. scand.,* **194**, 505 (1973).
[77] ROBINSON et al., *Brit. J. Nutr.,* **30**, 195 (1973).
[78] MERTZ et al., *Res. exp. Med.,* **169**, 21 (1976).
[79] SCHROEDER et al., *J. chron. Dis.,* **23**, 227 (1970).
[80] HAMBIDGE, K. M., *Amer. J. clin. Nutr.,* **27**, 505 (1974).
[81] HORAK and SUNDERMAN, *Clin. Chem.,* **19**, 429 (1973).
[82] WAGNER and WESWIG, *Arch. environm. Hlth,* **28**, 77 (1974).
[83] GOLDWATER and HOOVER, *Arch. environm. Hlth,* **15**, 60 (1967).
[84] MORGAN and BURCH, *Amer. J. intern. Med.,* **130**, 335 (1972).
[85] US Public Health Service, Bureau of Community Environmental Management, *Pediatrics,* **48**, 464 (1971).
[86] SZADKOWSKI et al., *Z. klin. Chem.,* **7**, 551 (1969).
[87] TAYLOR and MARKS, *Brit. J. industr. Med.,* **30**, 293 (1973).
[88] MELTZER et al., *Amer. J. med. Sci.,* **244**, 282 (1962).
[89] BOULTER et al., *J. clin. Endocr.,* **38**, 248 (1974).
[90] SÖRBO and ÖHMAN, *Scand. J. clin. Lab. Invest.,* **38**, 521 (1978).
[91] TROWBRIDGE et al., *Pediatrics,* **56**, 82 (1975).
[92] LOEW and MENG, *Klin. Wschr.,* **53**, 1131 (1975).
[93] PITTS et al., *J. clin. Invest.,* **28**, 35 (1949); PITTS, R. F., *Physiology of the Kidney and Body Fluids,* 3rd ed., Year Book Medical Publishers, Chicago, 1974.
[94] GOLDSMITH and JOHNSTON, *J. Bone Jt Surg.,* **57-A**, 657 (1975).
[95] PETERS-HAEFELI et al., *Schweiz. med. Wschr.,* **106**, 171 (1976).
[96] BOUILLIÉ et al., *Ann. Pédiat.,* **23**, 17 (1976).
[97] CARR and WILKINSON, *Clin. chim. Acta,* **96**, 73 (1979).
[98] KELSAY et al., *Amer. J. clin. Nutr.,* **32**, 1876 (1979).

Nitrogenous substances (for references see page 77)

↓See text on next page		Amount of substance				Mass				Reference
		Unit	Mean	s	(Extreme range)	Unit	Mean	s	(Extreme range)	
↓ **Total nitrogen** ...	7 newborn, birth	mmol/L	53	26	–	g/L	0.74	0.36	–	[1]
	9 newborn, 2nd day ...	mmol/L	457	106	–	g/L	6.40	1.48	–	[1]
	12 adults	mmol/L	656	–	–	g/L	9.19	–	–	[2]
	12 children, 3–11 years	mmol/d	–	–	(380–1490)	g/d	–	–	(5.3–20.9)	[3]
	54 adults	mmol/d	820	160	–	g/d	11.5	2.3	–	[4]
	Relative to body mass:									
	– 9 newborn, 1st day ..	mmol d⁻¹ kg⁻¹	2.78	1.31	–	mg d⁻¹ kg⁻¹	38.9	18.4	–	[1]
	– 9 newborn, 2nd day .	mmol d⁻¹ kg⁻¹	5.39	1.85	–	mg d⁻¹ kg⁻¹	75.4	25.9	–	[1]
	– 16 newborn, 7th day, breast-fed	mmol d⁻¹ kg⁻¹	7.71	1.51	–	mg d⁻¹ kg⁻¹	108	21.1	–	[1]
	– 11 young men	mmol d⁻¹ kg⁻¹	14.8	1.73	–	mg d⁻¹ kg⁻¹	207	24.2	–	[1]
↓ **Urea**	53 subjects ....(a)	mmol/d	343	67	–	g/d	20.6	4.0	–	[4]
↓ **Creatine**	14 subjects ....(a)	mmol/d	0.65	0.08	–	mg/d	85	11	–	[8]
	Men ....(b)	mmol/d	0.397	–	(0.08–1.44)	mg/d	52.1	–	(11–189)	[9]
	Women ....(b)	mmol/d	0.702	–	(0.14–2.06)	mg/d	92.1	–	(19–270)	[9]
	27 adults, >90 years ..	mmol/d	0.69	–	(0.19–1.75)	mg/d	90	–	(25–230)	[10]
	Relative to body mass:									
	– 10 premature infants, 2–12 weeks	µmol d⁻¹ kg⁻¹	18	–	(2.3–33)	mg d⁻¹ kg⁻¹	2.3	–	(0.3–4.3)	[11]
	– 6 full-term infants, 2–12 weeks	µmol d⁻¹ kg⁻¹	214	–	(116–273)	mg d⁻¹ kg⁻¹	28.0	–	(15.2–35.8)	[12]
	– 5 children, 6–12 months	µmol d⁻¹ kg⁻¹	81	–	(27–117)	mg d⁻¹ kg⁻¹	10.6	–	(3.6–15.3)	[12]
	– 10 adults ....(b)	µmol d⁻¹ kg⁻¹	3.2	4.1	–	mg d⁻¹ kg⁻¹	0.42	0.54	–	[13]

Table 1 *Nitrogen fractions in urine*

Subjects	Diet	N intake	Urinary excretion of nitrogen										Reference
			Total N	Urea N		Creatinine N		NH₃-N		Uric acid N			
		g/d	g/d	g/d	% *	g/d	% *	g/d	% *	g/d	% *		
2 adults (obese)	Adequate energy, 80 g protein/d	12.6	11.1	8.9	80	0.71	6.4	0.82	7.4	–	–		34
3 adults (obese)	Adequate energy, 120 g protein/d	18.9	16.1	12.2	76	0.59	3.7	1.15	7.1	–	–		34
6 women (obese)	Adequate energy, adequate protein	12.3	10.2	8.9	88	0.52	5.1	–	–	0.18	1.8		35
	Adequate energy, no protein	0.31	2.36	1.2	51	0.50	21	–	–	0.16	6.8		35
83 young men	Adequate energy, protein minimal	<1	2.69 (s0.45)	–	–	0.64	24	–	–	–	–		36
		Urinary excretion of nitrogen relative to body mass											
		mg d⁻¹ kg⁻¹	mg d⁻¹ kg⁻¹	mg d⁻¹ kg⁻¹	% *	mg d⁻¹ kg⁻¹	% *	mg d⁻¹ kg⁻¹	% *	mg d⁻¹ kg⁻¹	% *		
13 newborn, 7th day	Breast-fed	400	117	77	64	1.7	1.4	–	–	3.9	3.2		37
9 newborn, 7th day	Cow's milk	600	221	181	79	1.7	0.7	–	–	3.6	1.5		37

* Percent of total nitrogen in urine.

Total nitrogen. Total nitrogen excretion is a measure of protein intake[5, 6]. At a nitrogen-free but energetically adequate diet the amount excreted is 2–3 g/d. During a total fast the urinary loss of nitrogen due to increased degradation of endogenous protein is 2–6 g/d[7]. With a high-protein diet, up to 90% and with a protein-free diet 50–60% of the urinary nitrogen consists of urea. Data on excretion of the most important nitrogenous substances in relation to diet are given in Table 1. Newborn infants excrete little nitrogen, hence urea, owing to their anabolic status (Table 1); in these cases, amino-acid nitrogen accounts for a significant proportion of the urinary nitrogen (see Table 2).

Urea. (a) Diet of adequate protein content. – For other data see Table 1. Urea excretion is proportionate to protein intake and dependent on the protein metabolism: it is increased on a high-protein diet and a negative nitrogen balance (postoperatively; under the action of thyroid hormone); it is decreased at a positive nitrogen balance (during growth; pregnancy; under the action of insulin, growth hormone, testosterone), in cases of reduced urea formation (liver diseases), and in nephropathies.

Creatine. (a) Fluorimetrically; (b) enzymatically determined; for all other values: Jaffé reaction[14]. – Creatine excretion is greater in children than in adults, and greater in boys than in girls. In women, it fluctuates with the cycle and is increased during pregnancy and at the beginning of the puerperium. It increases at a high creatine intake (raw meat) and in muscular catabolism: values up to 6 mmol/d were found after 11–17 days of immobilization (bed rest)[15]. Creatine excretion is pathologically elevated in muscle diseases, under the action of ACTH, corticosteroids and thyroxine (hyperthyroidism), and when renal reabsorption is impaired; it is depressed in hypothyroidism and under the action of testosterone.

Creatinine. The values were determined by the Jaffé reaction[14]. See Figure 1 on creatinine excretion in the young. It is dependent primarily on muscle mass and is closely correlated with total body potassium[38]. In children, it increases with age[19, 20], and it is lower in girls and women than in boys and men and decreases in old age[10, 21]. Creatinine excretion in relation to body length has been used to evaluate the state of nutrition[22, 23]. Creatinine excretion is greater on a diet of high meat content (high in creatine) than on a meatless diet[24]; however, intraindividual variations from day to day cannot be explained by differences in diet alone[24, 25]. After a 24-hour fast, creatinine excretion is increased[26] but it decreases after prolonged fasting[27]. Diurnal fluctuations in creatinine excretion are small (values tend to be higher in the afternoon than during the night)[28]. Creatinine excretion is *pathologically* increased in hypothyroidism, acromegaly and diabetes mellitus; it is depressed in muscle diseases, hyperthyroidism, and advanced renal damage.

Guanidine and its derivatives. The excretion of these compounds is increased in uremia.

Ammonia. At a pH of 7.3 and below, nearly all the NH₃ is present as NH₄⁺. Under normal conditions about 60% of the hydrogen ions produced in the body are excreted in the form of NH₄⁺ (page 55). Ammonium excretion decreases as the urine pH rises (Fig.2). It is high when hydrogen ion production is increased, e.g. on a diet of high meat content or in metabolic acidosis (up to 500 mmol/d in diabetic acidosis); it is reduced when hydrogen ion production is decreased – e.g. in metabolic alkalosis – as well as in the presence of damage to the distal renal tubules (down to 0.5 mmol/d)[245].

α-Amino nitrogen. (a, b) Determined colorimetrically with ninhydrin; (a) values of total α-amino nitrogen determined after hy-

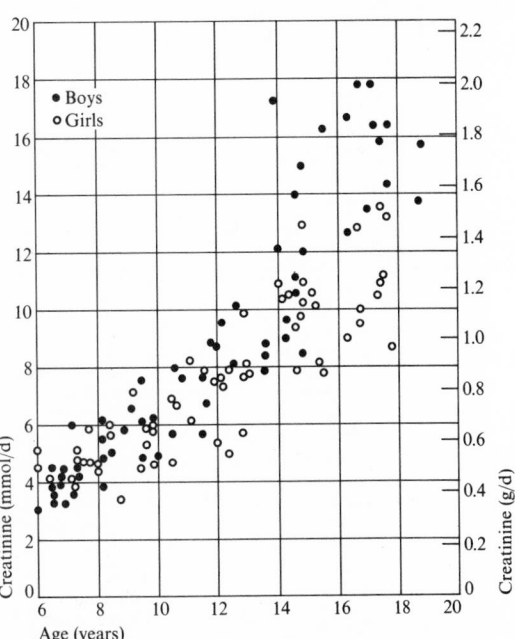

Fig. 1. Urinary excretion of creatinine in children[19].

↑See text on page 63		Amount of substance				Mass				Reference
		Unit	Mean	s	(Extreme range)	Unit	Mean	s	(Extreme range)	
↑ **Creatinine**	10 newborn, 1st day ...	mmol/L	3.5	–	(1.5–16)	g/L	0.40	–	(0.17–1.80)	[16]
	138 adults............	mmol/L	13.2	4.1	–	g/L	1.49	0.46	–	[17]
	138 adults............	mmol/d	12.9	3.4	–	g/d	1.46	0.39	–	[17]
	8 men, 20–45 years....	mmol/d	15.9	3.1	–	g/d	1.80	0.35	–	[18]
	10 women, 20–45 years	mmol/d	10.3	0.7	–	g/d	1.17	0.08	–	[18]
	27 adults, >90 years ..	mmol/d	4.2	–	(0.35–8.8)	g/d	0.47	–	(0.04–1.0)	[12]
	Relative to body mass:									
	– 10 premature infants, 2–12 weeks.........	μmol d^{-1} kg^{-1}	126	–	(73.4–176)	mg d^{-1} kg^{-1}	14.3	–	(8.3–19.9)	[11]
	– 6 full-term infants, 2–12 weeks.........	μmol d^{-1} kg^{-1}	105	–	(97.2–129)	mg d^{-1} kg^{-1}	11.9	–	(11.0–14.6)	[12]
	– 5 children, 6–12 months	μmol d^{-1} kg^{-1}	86.6	–	(46.0–180)	mg d^{-1} kg^{-1}	9.8	–	(5.2–20.4)	[12]
	– 10 adults	μmol d^{-1} kg^{-1}	165	42	–	mg d^{-1} kg^{-1}	18.7	4.7	–	[13]
↑ **Guanidine**	8 subjects	μmol/d	6.4	3.7	–	mg/d	0.38	0.22	–	[29]
↑ **Methylguanidine** .	6 subjects	μmol/d	19	11	(8–40)	mg/d	1.4	0.8	(0.6–2.9)	[30]
↑ **Guanidinoacetic acid**	15 subjects	μmol/d	235	147	–	mg/d	27.5	17.2	–	[31]
↑ **Guanidinosuccinic acid**	21 subjects	μmol/d	58.8	29.1	–	mg/d	10.3	5.1	–	[31]
	15 subjects	μmol/L	97.6	91.4	(21–390)	mg/L	17.1	16.0	(3.6–68)	[32]
↑ **Ammonia** .... (ammonium)	20 men	mmol/d	42.7	14.4	–	mg d	770	260	–	[39]
	Relative to body mass:									
	– 9 newborn, 1st day ..	mmol d^{-1} kg^{-1}	0.26	0.12	–	mg d^{-1} kg^{-1}	4.7	2.2	–	[1]
	– 16 newborn, 7th day .	mmol d^{-1} kg^{-1}	0.56	0.15	–	mg d^{-1} kg^{-1}	10.1	2.7	–	[1]
	– 11 young men	mmol d^{-1} kg^{-1}	0.80	0.14	–	mg d^{-1} kg^{-1}	14.4	2.5	–	[1]
↑ α-**Amino nitrogen**										
– total...........	20 men ....(a)	mmol/d	29.6	10.9	–	mg/d	414	152	–	[39]
– free	20 men ....(b)	mmol/d	11.4	2.5	–	mg/d	160	35	–	[39]

drolysis. – The α-amino nitrogen primarily comprises the free amino groups of the amino acids, in addition to free amino groups of peptides and other substances. Values obtained by different methods show agreement to a limited extent (Table 2)[44–46]; the gasometric ninhydrin technique is used as the reference method. α-Amino nitrogen in non-hydrolyzed urine (free amino acids) represents 1–2% of the total urinary nitrogen in older children and adults[44]; in newborn infants it amounts to 5–10%[47]. The proportion of α-amino nitrogen to total nitrogen is increased in aminoacidurias; in a case of pyroglutamic aciduria, for example, it amounted to 30–50%[48].

Amino acids

Approximately 40% of the amino acids in the urine are present in free form (see Table 3); the remainder is present in peptide-type linkages (peptides, proteins) or in nonpeptide-type linkages (hippuric acid, phenylacetylglutamine, etc.). *Separation* of amino acids can be accomplished by high-voltage electrophoresis[51], paper chromatography[51–53], thin-layer chromatography[51,54], column chromatography (ion exchanger)[51,55], or by gas chromatography[56]. The individual amino acids can also be determined microbiologically, and a few by specific chemical methods. Separation by column chromatography uncovered as many as 175 substances reacting with ninhydrin but only some of them were identified as amino acids[57].

Free amino acids. Normal values of excretion of the individual free amino acids are given in Tables 4–6. Normal values relative to creatinine excretion have been cited by PRZYREMBEL et al.[58] (premature infants), ARMSTRONG et al.[16] (full-term infants), LIAPPIS and JÄKEL[65] (children), EMERY and BURT[59] and by PETERS et al.[60] (adults), and in relation to α-amino nitrogen by GEER et al.[61] (children). In evaluating amino acid excretion, use should be made of age and sex-specific reference values; in women, the use of oral contraceptives also needs to be taken into consideration[240]. In adults, sex-related differences are cancelled out in large part if the

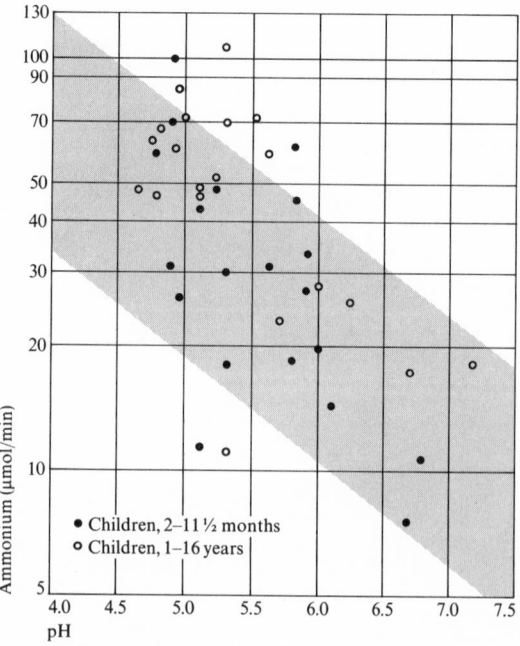

Fig. 2. Relation between ammonium excretion at a body surface of 1.73 m² and urinary pH in adults (shaded area, 95% confidence limits[243]) and children[244].

(y-axis: Ammonium (μmol/min); x-axis: pH)

● Children, 2–11 ½ months
○ Children, 1–16 years

Table 2 *Free α-amino nitrogen in urine*

Method	Number		α-Amino N		α-Amino N relative to body mass	$\dfrac{\text{α-Amino N}}{\text{Creatinine}}$	Reference
			Mean (in brackets: *s* or extreme range)				
			mmol/d	mg/d	mg d⁻¹ kg⁻¹	g/g	
Spectrophotometrically with dinitrofluorobenzene	20	Children, 5–7 months .	...	...	4.67(3.80–6.50)	...	40
	28	Children, 3–12 years ..	...	...	3.22(s 1.09)	...	40
Colorimetrically as copper complex	10	Premature infants, 2–12 weeks............	...	...	20.7(10.0–26.8)	...	11
	6	Full-term infants, 2–12 weeks............	...	...	12.9(6.8–20.7)	...	12
	5	Children, 6–12 months	...	...	6.3(3.4–8.5)	...	12
	14	Children, 0–2 years....	1.70(s 0.86)	23.8(s 12.1)	2.40(s 0.83)	0.58(s 0.58)	41
	14	Children, 2–3 years....	5.83(s 1.68)	81.7(s 23.5)	6.31(s 2.24)	0.36(s 0.07)	41
	13	Children, 3–5 years....	7.03(s 2.48)	98.5(s 34.8)	5.97(s 1.94)	0.33(s 0.08)	41
	14	Children, 5–6 years....	8.13(s 1.61)	113.9(s 22.6)	5.97(s 1.24)	0.30(s 0.09)	41
	16	Children, 6–8 years....	8.87(s 2.07)	124.3(s 29.0)	5.64(s 1.60)	0.28(s 0.08)	41
	12	Children, 8–10 years...	10.83(s 3.12)	151.7(s 43.7)	5.86(s 2.06)	0.28(s 0.09)	41
	15	Children, 10–12 years .	10.12(s 4.07)	141.8(s 57.0)	4.66(s 1.91)	0.26(s 0.07)	41
	29	Men..................	15.99(s 4.29)	244.0(s 60.1)	3.15(s 0.92)	0.15(s 0.04)	41
	16	Women	12.98(s 4.92)	181.8(s 68.9)	3.14(s 1.09)	0.20(s 0.06)	41
Colorimetrically with ninhydrin	50	Children, 0–1 year.....	3.00(s 1.40)	42(s 19.6)	...	0.47(s 0.21)	42
	42	Children	...	...	...	0.35(s 0.16)	42
	34	Children	...	...	...	0.24(s 0.10)	42
	20	Men..................	11.4(s 2.5)	160(s 35)	2.19(s 0.40)	0.08(s 0.02)	39
Gasometrically with ninhydrin	13	Men..................	7.21(s 2.8)	101(s 39)	...	...	43
	11	Women	9.00(s 4.8)	126(s 67)	...	...	43
Ion exchanger, copper complex	12	Children, 6 months to 13 years	...	...	3.1(1.5–4.0)	...	44
	17	Adults................	7.50(s 2.6)	105(s 37)	...	...	44

amino acid excretion is related to body mass[49]. In addition to inter-individual *variations,* there are considerable intraindividual variations[241]. The values are influenced to some extent by diet. The excretion of Nᵀ-methylhistidine, for example, increases on a diet of high meat content; excretion of β-aminoisobutyric acid increases in starvation and malnutrition. In relation to nitrogen excretion, amino acid excretion is greater in *newborns* and *breast-fed infants* (particularly premature infants) than in adults. In the newborn, taurine excretion before the first intake of food is greater than excretion of all the other amino acids combined[16]. In the first two weeks of life the excretion of proline shows a massive temporary increase[62]. In premature infants, increase of protein intake is associated not only with increases in the plasma levels of amino acids but also with increases in amino acid excretion and notably increased excretion of citrulline, homocitrulline and cystathionine[58]. Amino acid excretion is increased during *pregnancy.* Some amino acids (histidine, threonine, serine) are then excreted in 4–5 times larger quantities[50]. Taurine excretion declines markedly in the first week post partum[63].

Amino acid excretion is pathologically elevated at increased plasma levels of amino acids provided the renal function is normal, at an increased protein catabolism, and in various renal tubular disorders (Table 10). Hereditary aminoacidurias are presented in Table 9. Normal and pathological amino acid excretion has been discussed in the literature[64].

Table 3 *Total free amino acids in urine*

	Mean	s	Reference
	mmol/d		
41 boys, 6–10 years.....................	2.18	0.89	65
24 boys, 10–14 years....................	3.44	2.42	65
34 girls, 6–10 years	1.49	0.70	65
19 girls, 10–14 years	2.22	1.36	65
33 men................................	5.86	2.22	49
39 women..............................	5.68	2.23	49
10 women up to 20 weeks pregnant......	11.6	–	50
10 women, 20–29 weeks pregnant.......	15.9	–	50
10 women more than 30 weeks pregnant	15.5	–	50
10 women, 8 weeks post partum	4.05	–	50

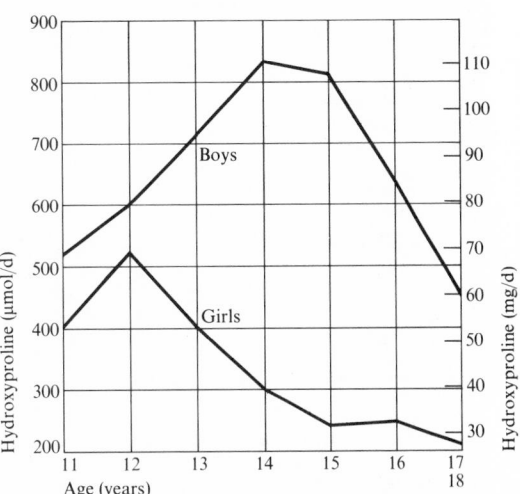

Fig. 3. Mean values of hydroxyproline excretion in boys and girls[20].

Table 4   *Free amino acids in urine (µmol/d)*

	5 newborn, 5 days[47]	Children, 6–10 years[65]				Children, 10–14 years[65]				Adults			
		41 boys		34 girls		24 boys		19 girls		33 men		39 women	
	(Extreme range)	Mean	s	Mean	s	Mean	s	Mean	s	Mean	s	Mean	s
Alanine	(15.7–53.9)	187	86.4	126	69.2	270	154	212	187	340	167	335	161
α-Aminobutyric acid	(0–1.0)	–	–	–	–	–	–	–	–	–	–	–	–
β-Aminobutyric acid	(2.9–14.5)	–	–	–	–	–	–	–	–	–	–	–	–
γ-Aminobutyric acid	(0–42.7)	–	–	–	–	–	–	–	–	–	–	–	–
β-Aminoisobutyric acid	–	65.3	43.6	58.5	65.7	67.4	71.3	53.1	47.7	146	138	108	101
Arginine	(0–trace)	12.6	6.6	6.6	4.4	16.3	10.6	9.4	6.8	30.2	17.5	20.5	13.6
Aspartic acid	(4.5–6.8)	–	–	–	–	–	–	–	–	–	–	–	–
Carnosine	–	68.7	58.0	48.6	66.2	62.9	48.5	35.7	31.7	53.2	41.4	60.2	39.1
Citrulline	(0–trace)	7.7	8.3	7.2	8.4	20.6	13.0	14.8	18.1	16.8	12.8	15.1	10.5
½ Cystine	(1.7–3.3)	55.0	33.4	39.5	24.9	62.0	49.6	52.6	36.8	136	46.7	111	41.7
Glutamine + asparagine	(0–41)	–	–	–	–	–	–	–	–	–	–	–	–
Glutamic acid	(2.0–15.0)	–	–	–	–	–	–	–	–	–	–	–	–
Glycine	(149–353)	650	356	451	285	1090	1008	760	526	1400	599	2120	1310
Histidine	(18.0–51.6)	468	227	271	137	704	450	475	342	1290	505	947	432
Hydroxyproline	(32.8–51.1)	–	–	–	–	–	–	–	–	–	–	–	–
Isoleucine	(0–trace)	14.4	10.2	9.9	6.7	25.0	16.9	12.5	7.9	27.6	15.2	47.8	21.7
Leucine	(0–3.0)	38.3	17.8	24.7	18.3	48.9	35.6	31.7	24.1	47.8	21.7	38.2	19.5
Lysine* (see footnote Table 5)	(2.7–28.0)	136	85.6	112	95.4	347	396	118	70.8	492	415	448	331
Methionine	(0–2.0)	9.3	6.9	5.7	5.7	10.8	12.6	10.6	8.6	19.9	14.8	17.1	13.7
Ornithine	(0–1.5)	11.8	5.6	8.9	5.1	22.7	16.6	19.1	18.0	47.2	22.3	41.0	19.7
Phenylalanine	(1.2–5.4)	38.9	19.2	24.6	15.4	53.6	40.6	38.6	27.0	68.3	28.5	62.6	26.8
Proline	(7.8–30.4)	–	–	–	–	–	–	–	–	–	–	–	–
Serine	(5.7–75.2)	217	90.0	135	70.8	311	209	175	110	459	208	400	153
Taurine	(4.0–23.2)	–	–	–	–	–	–	–	–	–	–	–	–
Threonine	(2.5–36.9)	116	59.4	74.3	37.2	195	148	128	71.9	274	147	243	139
Tyrosine	(2.8–21.0)	64.0	28.2	41.0	24.3	96.3	64.9	60.1	43.0	134	69.7	106	45.5
Valine	(4.3–20.4)	25.5	12.2	20.6	24.3	33.6	26.9	16.5	13.3	46.7	15.6	34.9	18.3

Table 5   *Free amino acids in urine (µmol/min for 1.73 m² body surface)[66]*

	Premature infants, 6th week	Full-term infants, 6th week	Children, 2–12 years	Adults
Alanine	0.5–0.7	1.2–2.1	0.04–0.35	0.09–0.27
α-Aminoadipic acid	0.1–0.23	0.17–0.23	–	0–0.02
α-Aminobutyric acid	trace	0	trace–0.06	0.01–0.04
γ-Aminobutyric acid	0–trace	0–trace	–	trace
β-Aminoisobutyric acid	0.09–0.16	0.17–0.42	0–0.19	0.01–0.09
Arginine	0	trace–0.1	0.01–0.04	0.02–0.20
Aspartic acid	trace–0.04	trace–0.32	trace–0.07	0.03–0.09
Asparagine + glutamine	0.5	1.1–2.0	0.04–0.75	0.17–0.48
Citrulline	0.02–0.17	trace–0.04	trace–0.03	0–trace
Cystathionine	–	–	0–0.019[†]	0–0.021
½ Cystine	0.04–0.25	0.14–0.34	–	0.02–0.08
Glutamic acid	0.02–0.13	0.04–0.62	0.01–0.13	0.008–0.16
Glycine	2.5–4.2	3.7–8.4	0.33–1.5	0.40–0.9
Histidine	0.34–0.83	0.8–1.8	0.11–1.0	0.15–0.53
Homocitrulline	0.13–0.37	0.12–0.24	–	0.02–0.04
Hydroxylysine	0.13–0.27	0.05–0.11	–	0–0.02
Hydroxyproline	1.1–2.1	0.7–2.6	0	0
Isoleucine	0.03–0.07	0.10–0.16	0.01–0.07	0.01–0.04
Leucine	0.04–0.08	0.15–0.18	0.02–0.11	0.02–0.5
Lysine*	0.2–0.6	0.7–1.4	0.04–0.21	0.02–0.20
Methionine	0.08–0.14	0.12–0.14	0.01–0.04	0.02–0.04
Nπ-Methylhistidine (1-methylhistidine)	0	0–0.03	0.12◊	0.58–0.9
Nτ-Methylhistidine (3-methylhistidine)	0	0–0.07	0.20◊	0.08–0.28
Ornithine	0–0.08	0.05–0.08	0.01–0.03	trace
Phenylalanine	0.08–0.13	0.11–0.14	0.01–0.11	0.04–0.07
Proline	0.6–1.7	0.7–5.4	trace–0.04	0
Serine	0.8–1.3	1.1–2.3	0.09–0.34	0.09–0.31
Taurine	0.03–0.08	0.01–0.18	0.76–1.9	0.4–1.3
Threonine	0.9–1.9	0.67–1.4	0.04–0.17	0.09–0.14
Tyrosine	0.17–0.60	0.22–0.38	0.03–0.12	0.06–0.10
Valine	trace–0.2	0.1–0.16	trace–0.08	trace–0.05

* About 30% of the total lysine is in the form of methyllysines[67] (see also Table 6).   ◊ Children, 7–13 years[99].   † Children, 3 days to 14 years[253].

Table 6 *Other amino acids and related compounds in urine*

		Unit	Mean	s	(Extreme range)	Reference
N-Acetylcysteine............	11 men..............	µmol/d	37.1	14.6	–	[96]
	11 women............	µmol/d	24.1	11.1	–	[96]
N-Acetylhistidine............	5 children..........	µmol/d	9.1	–	(4.1–11.7)	[158]
	9 adults............	µmol/d	29	–	(6.6–54)	[158]
N^α-Acetyllysine............	Relative to creatinine, 6 women	mmol/mol	2.0	0.8	–	[67]
N^ϵ-Acetyllysine............	Relative to creatinine............	mmol/mol	2.8	–	–	[67]
N-Acetyltryptophan	....	–	trace	–	–	[155]
β-Alanine................	Relative to creatinine, 125 men	µmol/mol	0.68	0.49	–	[254]
	Relative to creatinine, 121 women ..	µmol/mol	0.70	0.75	–	[254]
Anserine................	....	µmol/d	–	–	(20–30)	[72]
Argininosuccinic acid	....	µmol/d	–	–	(<6.5)	[91]
γ-Carboxyglutamic acid..........	3 men..............	µmol/d	–	–	(27–42)	[248]
	6 women............	µmol/d	–	–	(19–32)	[248]
Cysteic acid................	Relative to creatinine, newborn.....	mmol/mol	~1.1	–	–	[16]
sym-Dimethylarginine	32 adults	µmol/d	41.7	10.9	(25.5–62.5)	[255]
unsym-Dimethylarginine	32 adults	µmol/d	42.7	13.1	(21.7–74.3)	[255]
Homoarginine	Relative to creatinine............	mmol/mol	~0.28	–	–	[67]
Homocarnosine	....	µmol/d	4.6	–	(2–10)	[73]
Homocitrulline	Relative to creatinine, newborn.....	mmol/mol	–	–	(2.3–36)	[16]
Isovalerylglycine.............	7 children, 3–5¼ years	µmol/d	–	–	(<15)	[95]
Mercaptoacetate-cysteine disulfide .	11 men..............	µmol/d	10.8	1.7	–	[96]
	11 women............	µmol/d	7.8	1.7	–	[96]
β-Mercaptolactate-cysteine disulfide	11 men..............	µmol/d	48.2	13.7	–	[96]
	11 women............	µmol/d	26.7	7.6	–	[96]
N^ϵ-Methyllysines:						
Methyllysine	Relative to body mass, 6 adults	$\mu mol\ d^{-1}\ kg^{-1}$	0.37	0.29	(0.16–0.87)	[69]
Dimethyllysine............	Relative to body mass, 6 adults	$\mu mol\ d^{-1}\ kg^{-1}$	0.88	0.44	(0.42–1.54)	[69]
Trimethyllysine.............	Relative to body mass, 6 adults	$\mu mol\ d^{-1}\ kg^{-1}$	0.92	0.27	(0.55–1.25)	[69]
Putreanine..............	....	µmol/d	~2	–	–	[74]
2-Pyrrolecarboxylic acid .... (2-carboxypyrrole)	16 adults	µmol/d	0.51	0.31	(0.20–1.3)	[70]
Sarcosine (methylglycine).........	Children and adults	µmol/d	–	–	(<22)	[71]
Amino acids bound to carbohydrates						
Galactosylhydroxylysine..........	....	µmol/d	17.7	–	(12.4–23.0)	[100]
Glucosylgalactosylhydroxylysine...	....	µmol/d	26.3	–	(21.8–30.4)	[100]
Xylosylserine	Relative to body surface, 33 subjects	$\mu mol\ d^{-1}\ m^{-2}$	23	6.7	–	[101]
Glucosylfucosylthreonine	....	mmol/L	–	–	(0.4–0.6)	[249]
Amino acids bound to aromatic acids						
o-Aminohippuric acid.............	20 subjects	µmol/d	5.87	–	(2.3–8.8)	[90]
Hippuric acid (benzoylglycine).....	....	mmol/d	–	–	(5.6–14)	[92]
	12 subjects	mmol/d	2.19	–	(0.69–4.12)	[93]
	Relative to creatinine, 15 newborn..	mmol/mol	11	–	(3–30)	[250]
	Relative to creatinine, 10 adults	mmol/mol	251	–	(132–395)	[250]
m-Hydroxyhippuric acid	....	µmol/d	31	–	(10–770)	[94]
o-Hydroxyhippuric acid*..........	....	...	...	...	...	...
Phenylacetylglutamine............	....	mmol/d	–	–	(0.95–1.9)	[92]

* Normal urinary constituent; also metabolite of salicylates[97,98].

Table 7 *Total hydroxyproline excretion in urine*

Age	Number	Hydroxyproline		Reference
		µmol/d	mg/d	
0–1 year ...	7	249 (134–328)	32.7 (17.6–43.0)	[82]
1–10 years .	21	374 (114–1140)	49.0 (14.9–150)	[82]
22–44 years	20	210 (142–275)	27.6 (18.6–36.1)	[83]
21–63 years	20	178 (s 61)	23.3 (s 8.0)	[84]
Adults	35	40–200	5.2–26.2	[85]

Table 8 *Urinary excretion of proline and hydroxyproline in children, relative to creatinine*[62]

Age	Total proline	Peptide-bound proline	Total hydroxyproline	Peptide-bound hydroxyproline
	mg/g	%	mg/g	%
1st day	310	71	380	72
15th day	1100	60	660	50
7–14 years	96	89	110	–

Amino acids bound to carbohydrates (Table 6). Amino acids bound to carbohydrates are contained in mucopolysaccharides, glycoproteins and collagen. Hydroxylysine in the urine is 80% glycoside (8% free, 11% as peptide)[100]. The excretion of hydroxylysine[102] and xylosylserine[101] is increased in metabolic diseases of bone and collagen.

Amino acids bound to aromatic acids (Table 6). More than 50% of the glycine in the urine is bound to benzoic acid (hippuric acid).

Table 9 *Hereditary aminoacidurias*[51]

Disease	Amino acids with elevated excretion levels
Phenylketonuria	Phenylalanine
Hypertyrosinemia.........	Tyrosine, methionine
Hyperhistidinemia	Histidine
Hypervalinemia...........	Valine
Homocystinuria...........	Homocystine (0.1–1.0 mmol/d), methionine
Hypermethioninemia	Methionine
Ketotic hyperglycinemia .. (propionic acidemia)	Glycine
Nonketotic hyperglyci- nemia....................	Glycine (up to 40 mmol/d)
Hypersarcosinemia	Sarcosine
Hyperprolinemia type I ...	Proline, hydroxyproline, glycine
Hyperprolinemia type II ..	Proline, hydroxyproline, glycine, Δ^1-pyrroline-5-carboxylic acid
Hydroxyprolinemia	Hydroxyproline
Hyperpipecolatemia	Pipecolic acid, generalized aminoaciduria
Hyperammonemia type I	Glutamine, glycine, possibly homocitrulline
Hyperammonemia type II	Glutamine
Hyperornithinemia	Possibly ornithine
Citrullinemia.............	Citrulline
Argininosuccinic-aciduria .	Argininosuccinic acid (>8 mmol/d)
Persistent hyperlysinemia .	Lysine, homocitrulline, homo-arginine
Cystathioninuria..........	Cystathionine (>4.5 mmol/d)
Hypophosphatasia	Phosphoethanolamine (>1 mmol/d)
β-Aminoisobutyric-aciduria...................	β-Aminoisobutyric acid
Hyper-β-alaninemia	β-Aminoisobutyric acid, γ-aminobutyric acid, taurine
Carnosinemia.............	Carnosine (0.1–0.5 mmol/d)
Hypertryptophanemia	Tryptophan
Aspartylglycosylaminuria .	Aspartylglycosylamine
Pyroglutamic-aciduria	5-Oxoproline (up to 150 mmol/d)
Cystinuria	Cystine, lysine, arginine, ornithine
Isolated hypercystinuria...	Cystine
Protein intolerance with lysinuria	Lysine, arginine, ornithine
Iminoglycinuria..........	Proline (5 mmol/d), hydroxy-proline, glycine
Hartnup disease..........	Neutral monoaminomonocarboxylic acids
Methionine malabsorption	Methionine (after high methionine intake)
Hyperglycinuria	Glycine
Dicarboxylamino-aciduria .	Glutamic acid, aspartic acid
Fanconi's syndrome.......	Generalized aminoaciduria
Oculocerebrorenal syndrome (Lowe syndrome)..	Generalized aminoaciduria
Busby's syndrome.........	Generalized aminoaciduria
Wilson's disease..........	Glycine, serine, cystine
Galactosemia.............	Generalized aminoaciduria

Table 10 *Acquired alterations of amino-acid excretion*[51]

Malnutrition.............	Decreased hydroxyproline excretion
Vitamin D deficiency.....	Generalized aminoaciduria
Ascorbic acid deficiency..	Generalized aminoaciduria
Vitamin B_6 deficiency	Xanthurenic aciduria
Neuroblastoma, ganglio-neuroma, ganglioneuroblastoma, carcinoid with liver metastases	Cystathioninuria
Malignant melanoma	Increased phosphoserine excretion; reduced 1-methylhistidine excretion and 3-methylhistidine
Hyperthyroidism.........	Increased hydroxyproline excretion
Hypothyroidism	Decreased hydroxyproline excretion
Pituitary hypofunction in children	Decreased hydroxyproline excretion
Acromegaly..............	Increased hydroxyproline excretion
Hyperparathyroidism	Increased hydroxyproline excretion
Paget's disease	Increased hydroxyproline excretion
Fibrous dysplasia	Increased hydroxyproline excretion
Marfan's syndrome	Increased hydroxyproline excretion
Malabsorption	Increased hippuric-acid excretion
Muscular dystrophy......	Generalized aminoaciduria; decreased hydroxyproline excretion
Liver necrosis............	Aminoaciduria with increased excretion of tyrosine, leucine and proline
Nephrotic syndrome	Generalized aminoaciduria
Following renal transplantation	Generalized aminoaciduria or increased cystine and lysine excretion
Burns	Increased hydroxyproline excretion
Xeroderma pigmentosum	Increased excretion of cystine, cysteine, histidine, lysine, arginine, aspartic acid, glutamine, serine and alanine
Heavy-metal poisoning .. (lead, mercury, cadmium, uranium, thallium)	Generalized aminoaciduria
Salicylate intoxication....	Generalized aminoaciduria
Nitrobenzene intoxication	Generalized aminoaciduria

The urinary glutamic acid is mostly in the form of phenylacetyl-glutamine. Hippuric acid excretion is increased after ingestion of large quantities of fruits and vegetables; it is lowered in renal failure. The determination of hippuric acid excretion after a sodium benzoate challenge serves as a liver function test[93].

Peptides (carnosine Table 4; anserine and homocarnosine Table 6). The urine contains a number of poorly defined peptides that vary in relative molecular mass; some originate from body proteins (notably collagen) and others from dietary proteins[76-79]. The excretion of a fraction of hydroxyproline-free peptides (relative molecular mass 5000–8000) amounts to 30–120 mg/d[75]. Pathological peptiduria is seen in burns, active bone diseases (Tables 9 and 10), in Wilson's disease and in other hereditary aminoacidurias[76,81]. – *Proline* and *hydroxyproline* are found in adult urine almost entirely in the form of peptides[80]: thus, 96–97% of hydroxyproline is bound to peptides and only 3–4% is free. 60% of hydroxyproline is in the form of prolylhydroxyproline, 15% as glycylhydroxyproline, and 25% of the peptides have longer chains with a relative molecular mass of more than 1000[78,80,86]. In the body, hydroxyproline is principally bound in collagen (13% of total collagen amino acids) which, as a constituent of the bony matrix, is subject to continuous anabolism and catabolism. A small portion of the urinary hydroxyproline comes from the diet, and for evaluation a strictly gelatin-free diet needs to be maintained. The values have to be evaluated in relation to age and also, in older children, in relation to sex (Tables 7 and 8 and Fig.3)[20,80,82,87,88]. In growth phases there is increased synthesis of collagen precursors, which also appear in the urine. Beginning with the third decade, hydroxyproline excretion declines[89]. The determination of hydroxyproline excretion is mainly suitable for following up the

↓See text below		Amount of substance				Mass				Reference
		Unit	Mean	s	(Extreme range)	Unit	Mean	s	(Extreme range)	
Betaines, nitriles										
Choline	....	µmol/d	–	–	(46–74)	mg/d	–	–	(5.6–9.0)	103
	21 boys, 4–12 years....	µmol/d	97	95	(11–433)	mg/d	11.8	11.5	(1.3–52.5)	251
Carnitine	121 men	µmol/d	358	60	–	mg/d	57.7	9.6	–	104
	101 women	µmol/d	274	18	–	mg/d	44.1	2.9	–	104
	28 men	µmol/d	175	81	–	mg/d	28.2	13.1	–	238
	42 women	µmol/d	86	73	–	mg/d	13.9	11.8	–	238
Acetonitrile......	Nonsmokers	µmol/L ·	0.07	–	–	µg/L	2.9	–	–	105
	Smokers	µmol/L	2.87	–	–	µg/L	118	–	–	105
Aliphatic and aromatic amines										
Ethanolamine....	15 subjects	µmol/d	449	118	–	mg/d	27.4	7.2	–	65
	Relative to body mass:									
	– 33 men.............	µmol d^{-1} kg^{-1}	5.99	1.78	(2.28–10.4)	µg d^{-1} kg^{-1}	366	109	(139–635)	49
	– 39 women	µmol d^{-1} kg^{-1}	6.63	1.48	(4.14–9.99)	µg d^{-1} kg^{-1}	405	90	(253–610)	49
	Relative to creatinine:									
	– newborn	mmol/mol	205	–	(trace–457)	mg/g	111	–	(trace–247)	16
↓o-Phospho-ethanolamine	15 subjects	µmol/d	125	31	–	mg/d	17.7	4.4	–	65
	Relative to body mass:									
	– 33 men.............	µmol d^{-1} kg^{-1}	1.41	0.70	(0.45–2.96)	µg d^{-1} kg^{-1}	199	99	(63–418)	49
	– 39 women..........	µmol d^{-1} kg^{-1}	1.09	0.59	(0.34–3.13)	µg d^{-1} kg^{-1}	154	83	(48–442)	49
	Relative to creatinine:									
	– newborn	mmol/mol	35	–	(trace–82)	mg/g	44	–	(trace–102)	16
Methylamine	....	mmol/d	0.16	–	(0.15–0.19)	mg/d	5.0	–	(4.6–6.0)	106
Dimethylamine ..	....	mmol/d	0.38	–	(0.34–0.43)	mg/d	17.0	–	(15.2–19.3)	106
Cystamine	....	µmol/d	9.2	–	–	mg/d	1.4	–	–	107
↓Piperidine	....	µmol/d	67	–	(55–83)	mg/d	5.7	–	(4.7–7.1)	106
↓Polyamines										
Spermidine	10 subjects	µmol/d	17	3	–	mg/d	2.4	0.4	–	109
		µmol/d	~7	–	(<14)	mg/d	~1	–	(<2)	110
Spermine	10 subjects	µmol/d	2	1	–	mg/d	0.4	0.2	–	109
		µmol/d	–	–	(<2.5)	mg/d	–	–	(<0.5)	110
Putrescine	10 subjects	µmol/d	28	7	–	mg/d	2.5	0.6	–	109
		µmol/d	~57	–	–	mg/d	~5	–	–	110
Cadaverine	....	µmol/d	~20	–	–	mg/d	~2	–	–	110
p-Aminobenzoic acid..............	....	µmol/d	5.5	–	(2.3–9.6)	mg/d	0.76	–	(0.31–1.32)	111
↓o-Aminobenzoic acid..............	....	µmol/d	6.5	–	(2.3–16.3)	mg/d	0.89	–	(0.32–2.24)	111
m-Tyramine......	....	µmol/d	~0.15	–	–	µg/d	~20	–	–	112

development of bone diseases: increased excretion reflects increased activity of the skeletal metabolism (in Paget's disease the rate of excretion may increase to 25 times the normal value[80]).

o-Phosphoethanolamine. Excretion is increased at a high protein intake, in acromegaly and hypophosphatasia[256].

Piperidine. Probably mostly of bacterial origin (colon)[108].

Polyamines. Present mostly as acetylated compounds. The formation of spermidine, spermine and putrescine is linked to tissue growth and the excretion of these polyamines is therefore frequently increased in cancer patients; cadaverine is probably a product of bacterial metabolism[246]. In pregnancy, the excretion of putrescine and particularly that of spermine is increased[257].

o-Aminobenzoic acid (anthranilic acid). This is excreted predominantly in the form of *o*-aminohippuric acid (Table 6).

p-Tyramine. Excretion is increased in Parkinson's disease[114].

Dopa. Values determined fluorimetrically. – Excretion increased in neuroblastoma[124, 126] and myocardial infarction[243].

Dopamine, epinephrine, norepinephrine. Determination (a) by gas chromatography, (b) fluorimetrically. – Excretion of these catecholamines is lower in women than in men; in children (relative to body surface) it is approximately equal to that in adults[120]. Dopamine excretion is influenced by diet composition[122]; it is increased in neuroblastoma[124]. During sleep, less epinephrine and norepinephrine is excreted than during the day[121]. The excretion of epinephrine and norepinephrine combined is normally below 600 nmol/d; values between 600 nmol/d and 1200 nmol/d are suggestive of hypertension, and higher values – up to 60 µmol/d and more – are found in pheochromocytoma[123–125].

↑↓See text on page 69 and on next page		Amount of substance				Mass				Reference
		Unit	Mean	s	95% range (extreme range in brackets)	Unit	Mean	s	95% range (extreme range in brackets)	
↑ p-Tyramine										
– free	8 subjects	µmol/d	5.8	–	(3.6–12)	mg/d	0.8	–	(0.5–1.7)	113
– conjugated	8 subjects	µmol/d	10	–	(5–46)	mg/d	1.4	–	(0.7–6.3)	113
2-Phenylethyl-amine										
– free	Relative to creatinine: – 12 subjects	µmol/mol	6.9	1.9	–	µg/g	7.4	2.0	–	115
– conjugated	Relative to creatinine: – 12 subjects	µmol/mol	19.7	20.8	–	µg/g	21.1	22.3	–	115
p-Hydroxyphenyl-ethanolamine (octopamine)	17 subjects	nmol/d	368	46	–	µg/d	56.4	7.0	–	116
↑ Dopa, free (dihydroxy-phenylalanine)	29 children	nmol/d	120	–	(55–210)	µg/d	24	–	(11–42)	126
	8 adults	nmol/d	110	–	(81–170)	µg/d	22	–	(16–33)	126
	20 adults	nmol/d	208	51	–	µg/d	41.1	10.1	–	242
↑ Dopamine										
– free	8 subjects (a)	µmol/d	2.62	0.56	(1.88–3.49)	µg/d	402	86	(288–535)	117
	98 subjects (b)	µmol/d	1.53	–	1.01–2.44	µg/d	234	–	155–374	118
	(b)	µmol/d	1.49	–	–	µg/d	229	–	–	119
– conjugated	(b)	µmol/d	2.72			µg/d	416			119
↑ Epinephrine										
– free	8 subjects (a)	nmol/d	132	22	(84–155)	µg/d	24.2	4.0	(15.3–28.4)	117
	98 subjects (b)	nmol/d	32	–	15–80	µg/d	5.8	–	2.7–14.6	118
	(b)	nmol/d	26	–	–	µg/d	4.7	–	–	119
– conjugated	(b)	nmol/d	33	–	–	µg/d	6.1	–	–	119
↑ Norepinephrine										
– free	8 subjects (a)	nmol/d	308	89	(174–394)	µg/d	52.1	15.0	(29.4–66.6)	117
	98 subjects (b)	nmol/d	210	–	95–490	µg/d	36	–	16–83	118
	(b)	nmol/d	170	–	–	µg/d	29	–	–	119
– conjugated	(b)	nmol/d	350	–	–	µg/d	59	–	–	119
↓ Metanephrine										
– total	23 subjects (a)	nmol/d	674	380	(180–1540)	µg/d	133	75	(36–303)	127
	15 subjects (b)	nmol/d	85.7	57.8	(17–213)	µg/d	16.9	11.4	(3.3–42)	258
– free	15 subjects (b)	nmol/d	17.7	5.3	(8.6–30)	µg/d	3.49	1.04	(1.7–5.9)	258
↓ Normetanephrine										
– total	23 subjects	nmol/d	955	573	(380–2280)	µg/d	175	105	(70–417)	127
↓ 3-Methoxytyra-mine										
– total	23 subjects	µmol/d	1.96	1.00	(0.96–5.10)	µg/d	327	168	(160–852)	127
– free	14 children	µmol/d	0.22	–	(0.08–0.43)	µg/d	37	–	(13–72)	128
	14 adults	µmol/d	0.53	–	(0.18–1.05)	µg/d	88	–	(30–175)	128
3,4-Dimethoxy-phenylethylamine	80 adults	nmol/d	0.42	–	<1.24	ng/d	77	–	<225	247
↓ Metabolites of tryptophan										
↓ 5-Hydroxytrypto-phan		…	…	…	…	…	…	…	…	…
↓ Serotonin (5-hydroxytryptamine)										
– free	6 children	µmol/d	0.47	–	(0.24–0.70)	µg/d	83	–	(43–123)	141
	20 men	µmol/d	0.41	–	(0.26–0.62)	µg/d	72	–	(45–110)	138
	6 women	µmol/d	0.31	–	(0.06–0.48)	µg/d	55	–	(10–85)	138
	21 subjects	µmol/d	0.74	–	(0.18–1.68)	µg/d	131	–	(31–296)	142
– as glucuronide		µmol/d	0.53	–	(0.12–2.01)	µg/d	93	–	(21–355)	142
– as sulfate		µmol/d	0.33	–	(0–0.72)	µg/d	59	–	(0–127)	142

See text below		Amount of substance				Mass				Reference
		Unit	Mean	s	(Extreme range)	Unit	Mean	s	(Extreme range)	
Bufotenine.......	50 subjects	μmol/d	0.31	0.03	–	μg/d	63	7	–	[150]
↓**5-Hydroxyindole-acetic acid**	19 children............	μmol/d	45	–	(7.3–69)	mg/d	8.6	–	(1.4–13.2)	[141]
	30 adults...............	μmol/d	–	–	(5.2–77)	mg/d	–	–	(1.0–14.7)	[143]
	15 adults.............	μmol/d	24	5.8	–	mg/d	4.5	1.1	–	[144]
	13 adults.............	μmol/d	15	7.1	–	mg/d	2.9	1.4	–	[145]
↓**5-Methoxytrypt-amine**..........	....	nmol/d	–	–	(<50)	μg/d	–	–	(<10)	[168]

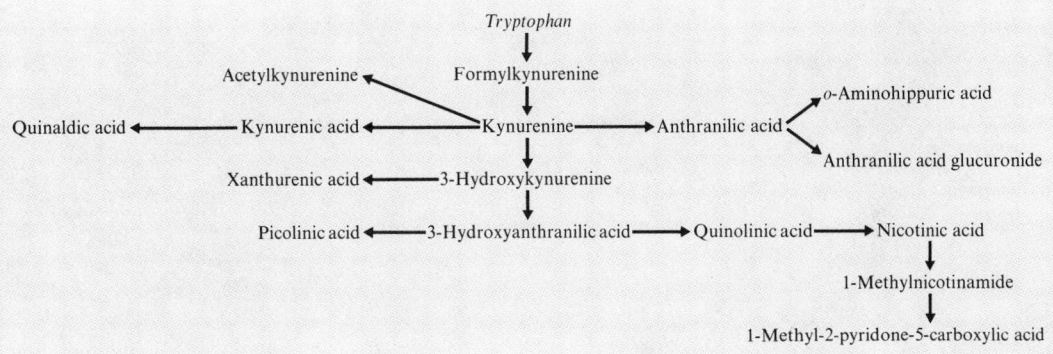

Fig. 4. Schematic representation of tryptophan-nicotinic acid metabolism[145].

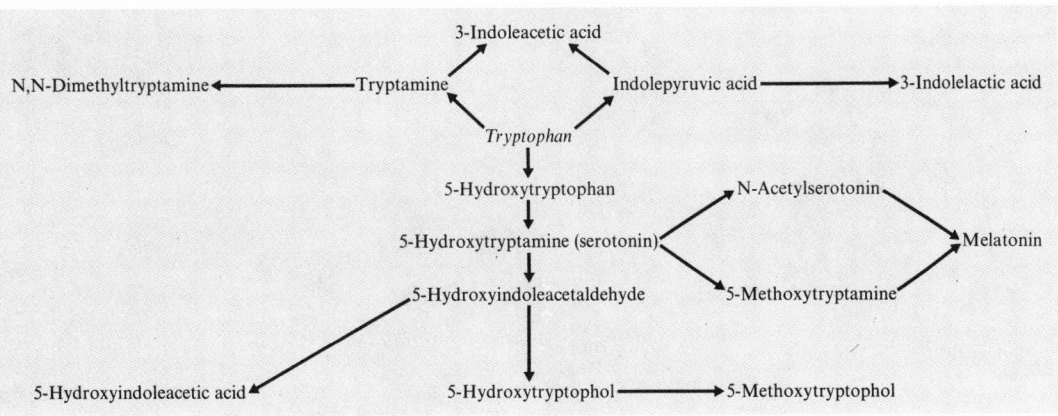

Fig. 5. Metabolic interrelations of indole compounds[145].

Metanephrine, normetanephrine. Values determined (a) fluorimetrically, (b) radioimmunologically. – For excretion in children, see also WINKEL and SLOB[129]. 80–90% of the methylated catecholamines are conjugated[123]. The excretion of metanephrine and normetanephrine is considerably increased in pheochromocytoma (up to about 530 μmol/d)[123, 124].

3-Methoxytyramine. Values determined fluorimetrically. – Excretion is increased in neuroblastoma[124].

Metabolites of tryptophan. The excretion rates of tryptophan-nicotinic acid metabolites (Fig.4) are presented in Table 11. In women, the excretion of 3-hydroxykynurenine varies with the cycle[131]. The excretion of xanthenuric acid, kynurenine and 3-hydroxykynurenine is increased in pregnancy, in women taking estrogen-containing contraceptives and in vitamin B_6 deficiency; these changes become most clearly apparent after oral administration of tryptophan (tryptophan loading test; see Table 12 for normal values)[132–135]. The increased excretion of kynurenine and

3-hydroxyanthranilic acid in rheumatoid arthritis is probably related to altered renal function[136].

5-Hydroxytryptophan. Demonstrable in urine of patients with carcinoid tumors[252].

Serotonin. The excretion of conjugated serotonin in particular is increased in the presence of carcinoids.

5-Hydroxyindoleacetic acid. Usual normal range according to the literature: 10–50 μmol/d[146]. However, allowing for losses during workup of the urine, up to 130 μmol/d is excreted[147]. Excretion of this serotonin metabolite (Fig.5) is increased after consumption of serotonin-containing foods (bananas, tomatoes, plums, walnuts) and after intake of various drugs (e.g. caffeine, nicotine)[143,148]; it is *pathologically elevated* in the presence of carcinoids (0.15–8 mmol/d)[149].

5-Methoxytryptamine. 0.2–1.1 μmol/d was found in the urine in patients with rheumatic fever and scarlet fever[141, 168].

Table 11   *Tryptophan metabolites in urine (basal values)*

	Children[235]*		Adults[236]◊		Adults[145]†	
	Mean	95% range	Mean	(Extreme range)	Mean	s
	µmol d^{-1} kg^{-1}		µmol/d			
Kynurenic acid...	0.32	0.01–1.40	23	(10–62)	20.4	4.6
Xanthurenic acid...	0.55	0.04–1.0	15	(9–36)	19.6	6.8
o-Aminohippuric acid (o-aminobenzoylglycine)	0.41	0.02–0.73	22	(7–45)	76	59
Anthranilic acid glucuronide	0.16	0.05–0.66	6	(3–14)	–	–
Anthranilic acid (o-aminobenzoic acid).............................	–	0–0.13	–	–	11.7	9.6
Acetylkynurenine	0.47	0.04–1.05	12	(8–16)	26.9	19.6
Kynurenine	0.78	0.18–6.0	14	(4–28)	43.4	29.6
3-Hydroxykynurenine...	4.30	0.15–13.2	27	(7–78)	–	–
3-Hydroxyanthranilic acid	–	–	50	(7–79)	–	–
1-Methyl-2-pyridone-5-carboxamide	3.10	0.10–10.8	96	(87–156)	–	–

* Relative to body mass.   ◊ Literature review.   † Tryptophan intake 1.1 g/d (s 0.315 g/d).

Table 12   *Tryptophan metabolites in urine after oral loading with 2 g (∼ 10 mmol) of tryptophan*

	Adults[236]*		Women[135]			
			No oral contraceptives		Oral contraceptives	
	Mean	(Extreme range)	Mean	s	Mean	s
	µmol/d					
Kynurenic acid...	56	(40–67)	–	–	–	–
Xanthurenic acid...	34	(28–41)	50	19	371	205
o-Aminohippuric acid (o-aminobenzoylglycine)	43	(15–57)	–	–	–	–
Anthranilic acid glucuronide	8	(6–12)	–	–	–	–
Acetylkynurenine	16	(9–19)	–	–	–	–
Kynurenine	36	(22–67)	–	–	–	–
3-Hydroxykynurenine...	34	(16–52)	38	18	131	129
3-Hydroxyanthranilic acid	–	–	28	14	59	32
1-Methyl-2-pyridone-5-carboxamide................................	136	(120–158)	–	–	–	–
Quinolinic acid	–	–	38	17	88	67

* Literature review.

↓See text on next page		Amount of substance				Mass				Refer-ence
		Unit	Mean	s	(Extreme range)	Unit	Mean	s	(Extreme range)	
Melatonin .... (N-acetyl-5-methoxytrypt-amine)	6 adults	pmol/d	–	–	(9–90)	ng/d	–	–	(2–21)	[139]
↓ **Tryptamine**	20 children............	µmol/d	–	–	(0.41–2.31)	µg/d	–	–	(66–370)	[137]
	13 men	µmol/d	0.40	–	(0.12–0.75)	µg/d	64	–	(20–120)	[138]
	6 women.............	µmol/d	0.35	–	(0.25–0.45)	µg/d	56	–	(40–72)	[138]
N,N-Dimethyl-tryptamine	....	µmol/d	0.23	0.046	–	µg/d	43.0	8.6	–	[140]
3-Indolelactic acid.............	....	µmol/d	–	–	(1.5–15)	mg/d	–	–	(0.3–3)	[155]
3-Indoleacetic acid										
– total	11 subjects	µmol/d	–	–	(30–79)	mg/d	–	–	(5.2–13.8)	[154]
– free	11 subjects	µmol/d	–	–	(18–46)	mg/d	–	–	(3.1–8.1)	[154]
	7 adults	µmol/d	32.3	15.8	–	mg/d	5.65	2.77	–	[145]
Indoleacetyl-glutamine........	....	µmol/d	–	–	(3–26)	mg/d	–	–	(1–8)	[155]

↓See text below		Amount of substance				Mass				Refer-ence
		Unit	Mean	s	(Extreme range)	Unit	Mean	s	(Extreme range)	
3-Indolecarbox-ylic acid glu-curonide	....	μmol/d	–	–	(0–178)	mg/d	–	–	(0–60)	156
Indoleacryloyl-glycine.........	Relative to creatinine: – 19 subjects	mmol/mol	–	–	(0.05–3.7)	mg/g	–	–	(0.1–8)	157
↓ Indoxylsulfuric acid	19 children..........	mmol/d	1.97	–	(0.69–2.91)	mg/d	420	–	(148–620)	141
	8 adults	mmol/d	0.94	–	(0.66–1.17)	mg/d	200	–	(140–250)	141
	56 men	mmol/d	0.30	0.08	–	mg/d	64	18	–	151
	44 women	mmol/d	0.27	0.10	–	mg/d	57	22	–	151
	7 adults	mmol/d	0.42	0.21	–	mg/d	90	45	–	145
6-Sulfatoxy-skatole.........	10 subjects	μmol/d	–	–	(0.22–21)	mg/d	–	–	(0.05–4.7)	169
5-Sulfatoxy-skatole.........	10 subjects	μmol/d	–	–	(0–11)	mg/d	–	–	(0–2.4)	169
Imidazoles, metabolites of histidine										
↓ Histamine	17 adults.............	nmol/d	107	–	(55–170)	μg/d	11.9	–	(6.1–19)	159
↓ N-Acetylhista-mine	20 children..........	μmol/d	–	–	(0.11–12.0)	μg/d	–	–	(17–1840)	137
	17 adults.............	μmol/d	0.14	–	(0.02–0.37)	μg/d	22.0	–	(2.3–56)	159
↓ Methylhistamine	20 subjects	μmol/d	1.5	–	(0.5–2.8)	μg/d	190	–	(60–350)	160
Imidazolelactic acid............	5 children, 1–2 years	μmol/d	7.7	–	(2.6–16.6)	mg/d	1.20	–	(0.40–2.59)	158
	9 adults	μmol/d	85.8	–	(53.1–109)	mg/d	13.4	–	(8.29–17.0)	158
Imidazoleacetic acid............	5 children..........	μmol/d	3.2	–	(1.6–4.8)	mg/d	0.40	–	(0.20–0.61)	158
	9 adults	μmol/d	23.4	–	(6.3–53.1)	mg/d	2.95	–	(0.79–6.70)	158
↓ 1,4-Methylimid-azoleacetic acid............	20 subjects	μmol/d	19	–	(12–54)	mg/d	2.7	–	(1.7–7.5)	160
↓ 1,5-Methylimid-azoleacetic acid............	20 subjects	μmol/d	–	–	(<4–51)	mg/d	–	–	(<0.5–7.2)	160
↓ Urocanic acid...	6 subjects	μmol/d	4.5	–	(0–12)	mg/d	0.62	–	(0–1.7)	164
↓ Formimino-glutamic acid ... (formamidino-glutaric acid)	6 subjects	μmol/d	7.2	–	(0–12)	mg/d	1.3	–	(0–2.1)	164

Tryptamine. Excretion is increased in Parkinson's disease[114].

Indoxylsulfuric acid. The excretion of indoxylsulfuric acid is increased in the presence of intensified bacterial decomposition of the intestinal contents (e.g. in intestinal obstruction)[152] and in the nephrotic syndrome[153]; it is reduced in rheumatic fever[141].

Histamine. The excretion is dependent on the protein intake; it is increased in mastocytosis[161, 162].

N-Acetylhistamine. Likely to be of predominantly bacterial origin (colon)[108, 163].

Methylhistamine. Values on low-histamine diet.

1,4-Methylimidazoleacetic acid, 1,5-methylimidazoleacetic acid. Values on low-histamine diet. The excretion of 1,4-methyl-imidazoleacetic acid may increase to more than 70 μmol/d on a high-protein diet[160], and it is elevated in mastocytosis[161].

Urocanic acid, formiminoglutamic acid. Excretion of these histamine metabolites is reduced in pregnant women[165]; it is increased after oral administration of histidine (Table 13), in folic acid and

Table 13 *Histidine loading test*

Oral histidine loading	Urocanic acid excretion	Formimino-glutamic acid excretion
19 mmol/d (3 g/d)[164]	20 μmol/d (2.8 mg/d)	35 μmol/d (6 mg/d)
97 mmol/d (15 g/d)[166]	100 μmol/d (17 mg/d)	

vitamin B_{12} deficiency, and occasionally also in liver diseases and sarcoidosis[164, 166, 167].

γ,δ-Dioxovaleric acid. Excretion of this metabolite of δ-amino-levulinic acid is increased in porphyria cutanea tarda.

δ-Aminolevulinic acid. Greatly increased excretion in porphyria acuta intermittens[171, 176–178] as well as in lead poisoning[171, 179, 180] (up to 1140 μmol/d[180]). For assessment of the values, see Table 14. For excretion in children of various ages, see KÄSER et al.[181].

↑↓See text on page 73 and below		Amount of substance				Mass				Reference
		Unit	Mean	s	95% range (extreme range in brackets)	Unit	Mean	s	95% range (extreme range in brackets)	
Porphyrins and related compounds										
Aminoacetone	....	μmol/L	30	–	(21–42)	mg/L	2.2	–	(1.5–3.1)	[170]
↑ **γ,δ-Dioxovaleric acid**	25 subjects	nmol/d	34	23	–	μg/d	4.4	3.0	–	[171]
↑ **δ-Aminolevulinic acid**	50 children, <15 years	μmol/L	19.6	8.77	–	mg/L	2.57	1.15	–	[172]
	100 adults............	μmol/L	22	11	–	mg/L	2.9	1.4	–	[173]
	13 subjects	μmol/d	20.1	10.3	–	mg/d	2.63	1.35	–	[174]
	25 subjects	μmol/d	19.2	1.6	–	mg/d	2.52	0.21	–	[171]
	22 subjects	μmol/d	27.4	7.1	–	mg/d	3.59	0.93	–	[175]
↓ **Porphobilinogen** ..	50 children, <15 years	μmol/L	4.64	2.0	–	mg/L	1.05	0.46	–	[172]
	100 adults............	μmol/L	4.4	2.2	–	mg/L	1.0	0.5	–	[173]
	13 subjects	μmol/d	6.2	2.3	–	mg/d	1.40	0.51	–	[174]
↓ **Porphyrins**										
Coproporphyrin ..	9 subjects .... (a)	nmol/d	200	–	(120–340)	μg/d	130	–	(80–220)	[183]
	72 subjects .... (b)	nmol/d	55	23	–	μg/d	36	15	–	[184]
	34 subjects .... (b)	nmol/d	–	–	0–246	μg/d	–	–	0–161	[185]
Uroporphyrin.....	9 subjects .... (a)	nmol/d	47	–	(34–76)	μg/d	39	–	(28–63)	[183]
	72 subjects .... (b)	nmol/d	14	5	–	μg/d	12	4	–	[184]
	34 subjects .... (b)	nmol/d	–	–	0–31	μg/d	–	–	0–26	[185]
↓ **Bilirubin**	....	μmol/L	∼0.5	–	(0.03–3.2)	mg/L	∼0.3	–	(0.02–1.9)	[189, 190]
↓ **Urobilinoids** ...... (urobilinogen)	46 subjects	...	...	...	...	mg/d	0.36	–	(0.05–2.5)	[192]
↓ **Fuscins**	....	...	...	...	...	...	...	...	...	...
↓ **Hemoproteins**.....	....	...	...	...	...	...	...	...	...	...
Myoglobin	24 adults.............	...	...	...	...	μg/d	1.2	–	(0.1–4)	[259]

Table 14 *Evaluation of urine concentration of δ-aminolevulinic acid in persons with lead intoxication[182]*

	μmol/L	mg/L
Normal.....................................	<45	<6
Still tolerable	45–90	6–12
No longer tolerable	150–300	20–40
Dangerous................................	>300	>40

Porphobilinogen. Excretion greatly increased in acute intermittent porphyria[171, 176–178] (Table 16).

Porphyrins. Values determined (a) fluorimetrically, (b) spectrophotometrically. – Relative to body mass, excretion in children is about the same as in adults[183]. Besides coproporphyrin (4 carboxyl groups) and uroporphyrin (8 carboxyl groups), the urine contains small quantities of porphyrins with 3, 5, 6 and 7 carboxyl groups (Table 15). The I-isomer predominates in both coproporphyrin

and uroporphyrin[176]. For differentiation of porphyrinurias, see Table 16 and other pertinent literature[176–180, 187].

Bilirubin. The values are applicable to children and adults[190, 191]. The urine normally contains only unconjugated bilirubin. Excretion is increased in hepatic and obstructive jaundice, in the Dubin-Johnson syndrome, and in an idiopathic form of bilirubinuria[190].

Urobilinoids. The values show a log-normal distribution. Excretion increases with rising urinary pH[193]; it is rather lower in children and increased during pregnancy[190]. It is pathologically reduced in complete occlusion of the bile ducts; it is pathologically increased in cases of damage to the liver parenchyma and intravascular hemolysis[190, 192, 194].

Fuscins. The normal urinary pigment urochrome B is probably a fuscin[190]. The excretion of fuscins may be increased in certain hemoglobinopathies[190, 195].

Hemoproteins. Hemoglobin that is not contained in the red blood cells, as well as myoglobin, is not normally found in the urine.

Table 15 *Excretion of individual porphyrins (TLC separation)*

	Number	Total porphyrin			Individual porphyrins						Reference
		Mean	s	(Extreme range)	Carboxyl groups						
					3	4	5	6	7	8	
		μg/d			Relative to total porphyrins (%)						
Normal subjects....................	25	85.4	34.4	–	0.3	69.9	1.7	0.9	5.7	21.1	[180]
Lead poisoning	7	1290	–	(338–2550)	0.3	90.5	4.9	0.4	0.9	3.0	[180]
Porphyria cutanea tarda................	1	6500	–	–	–	8.4	6.4	6.0	25.5	53.6	[186]

Table 16 *Results of qualitative tests for differentiation of porphobilinogenuria and porphyrinuria*[188]

Porpho-bilinogen	Porphyrins	Probable diagnosis
Positive	Negative	Acute intermittent porphyria
Positive	Positive	Acute intermittent porphyria* Hereditary coproporphyria Porphyria variegata (Severe lead intoxication)
Negative	Positive	Chronic hepatic porphyria Porphyria cutanea tarda Lead intoxication Alcohol abuse Chronic liver and blood diseases Congenital erythropoietic porphyria
Negative	Negative	Erythropoietic protoporphyria

*Porphyrins positive owing to formation of porphobilinogen in acidic medium.

Table 17 *Differentiation of pigmenturias by chemical and clinical criteria*[202]

	Hemo-globinuria	Myoglobin-uria*	Porphyria
Color of urine............	Red-brown	Brown	Red-brown
Benzidine test.............	+	+	–
Porphobilinogen in urine..	Normal	Normal	Elevated
Color of serum...........	Rose	Normal	Normal
Serum enzymes◊.........	Normal to elevated	Elevated	Normal
Muscular pains...........	None	Yes	None
Peripheral neuropathy	None	None	Yes

*Excretion is increased up to 410 mg/L in some patients after physical exertion[205].
◊Lactate dehydrogenase, glucosephosphate isomerase, aspartate aminotransferase.

↓See text below		Amount of substance				Mass				Reference
		Unit	Mean	s	(Extreme range)	Unit	Mean	s	(Extreme range)	
Purines and related compounds										
↓**Aminoimidazole-carboxamide**.....	15 subjects	μmol/d	3.2	–	(0.8–8.0)	mg/d	0.4	–	(0.1–1.0)	206
	15 men	μmol/d	7.1	–	(2.9–12.6)	mg/d	0.90	–	(0.36–1.58)	207
↓**Purine bases**										
Hypoxanthine ...	....	μmol/d	71	–	(43–97)	mg/d	9.7	–	(5.9–13.2)	208
Xanthine	....	μmol/d	40	–	(34–57)	mg/d	6.1	–	(5.1–8.6)	208
Adenine	....	μmol/d	10	–	(8–13)	mg/d	1.4	–	(1.1–1.7)	208
Guanine.........	....	μmol/d	3	–	(1.3–4.0)	mg/d	0.4	–	(0.2–0.6)	208
1-Methylhypo-xanthine	....	μmol/d	3	–	(1.3–4.7)	mg/d	0.4	–	(0.2–0.7)	208
6-Succinoamino-purine	....	μmol/d	4.8	–	(3.2–6.0)	mg/d	1.2	–	(0.8–1.5)	208
1-Methylguanine + 7-methylgua-nine	....	μmol/d	39	–	(33–47)	mg/d	6.5	–	(5.5–7.8)	208
N^2-Methylguanine	....	μmol/d	3	–	(2.4–3.6)	mg/d	0.5	–	(0.4–0.6)	208
7-Methyl-8-hy-droxyguanine	....	μmol/d	9	–	(6–11)	mg/d	1.6	–	(1.1–2.0)	208
Nucleosides										
N^2,N^2-Dimethyl-guanosine........	Relative to body mass: – 17 adults	μmol d^{-1} kg^{-1}	0.2	0.06	(0.1–0.3)	mg d^{-1} kg^{-1}	0.06	0.017	(0.03–0.09)	212
1-Methylinosine .	– 17 adults	μmol d^{-1} kg^{-1}	0.1	0.05	(trace–0.2)	mg d^{-1} kg^{-1}	0.03	0.014	(trace–0.06)	212

Hemoglobin enters the glomerular filtrate only if the binding capacity of haptoglobin for hemoglobin is exceeded. It undergoes tubular reabsorption and appears in the urine only after a certain threshold value has been passed[196]: a hemoglobinuria may be expected beginning at plasma levels of 0.5–1.4 g/L[197, 198]. Myoglobin released from the tissues is not bound to specific proteins in the plasma and can easily be filtered by the glomeruli owing to its small relative molecular mass: myoglobin is also detectable in the urine of normal subjects by radioimmunoassay[259]. Hemoproteins are most readily identified by immunoelectrophoresis[198]. See Table 17 for simple differentiation. – *Hemoglobinuria:* in black-water fever; after transfusion of inappropriate blood; paroxysmally (paroxysmal nocturnal hemoglobinuria, paroxysmal cold hemoglobinuria); after intensive track training (march hemoglobinuria)[199, 200]. In blackwater fever, a reddish-brown pigment showing no peroxidase activity may also be excreted[201]. – *Myoglo-*

binuria: Myoglobin in the urine, detected by routine methods, is indicative of extensive muscular injury. Myoglobinuria can be of hereditary origin (as in phosphorylase or phosphofructokinase deficiency) or occur sporadically (as after severe physical exertion, after muscular injury, after myocardial infarction, after infections, in hypokalemia; in intoxications, e.g. with alcohol, heroin)[198, 202–204].

Aminoimidazolecarboxamide is an intermediate product of purine synthesis; its excretion is increased in cases of vitamin B$_{12}$ deficiency.

Purine bases. Methylated xanthines in the urine are metabolites of dietary purines (from coffee, tea, cocoa)[209, 210]. The excretion of hypoxanthine and uric acid is greatly increased in cases of deficiency of hypoxanthine/guanine-phosphoribosyltransferase[211].

↓See text below and on next page		Amount of substance				Mass				Reference
		Unit	Mean	s	(Extreme range)	Unit	Mean	s	(Extreme range)	
↓ Cyclic nucleotides										
Adenosine 3',5'-phosphate	25 men	µmol/d	5.82	1.2	–	mg/d	1.74	0.40	–	213
	32 women	µmol/d	5.10	1.3	–	mg/d	1.68	0.43	–	213
	Relative to body surface:									
	– 41 children, 3 months to 9½ years	µmol d⁻¹ m⁻²	4.45	1.71	–	mg d⁻¹ m⁻²	1.46	0.56	–	216
	– 30 children, 9½–16 years	µmol d⁻¹ m⁻²	2.22	0.66	–	mg d⁻¹ m⁻²	0.73	0.22	–	216
	Relative to creatinine:									
	– children, 3 months to 4 years	mmol/mol	1.05	0.17	–	µmol/g	9.26	1.49	–	216
	– children, 12–16 years	mmol/mol	0.53	0.12	–	µmol/g	4.67	1.05	–	216
	– adults	mmol/mol	0.49	0.14	–	µmol/g	4.34	1.25	–	216
	– 12 adults	mmol/mol	0.28	0.05	–	µmol/g	2.5	0.45	–	214
Guanosine 3',5'-phosphate	25 men..............	µmol/d	0.56	0.15	–	mg/d	0.19	0.052	–	213
	32 women............	µmol/d	0.38	0.11	–	mg/d	0.13	0.038	–	213
	Relative to body surface:									
	– children, <4 years ..	µmol d⁻¹ m⁻²	0.72	0.13	–	mg d⁻¹ m⁻²	0.25	0.045	–	237
	– children, 10–12 years	µmol d⁻¹ m⁻²	0.22	0.02	–	mg d⁻¹ m⁻²	0.08	0.008	–	237
	– youths, 16–18 years..	µmol d⁻¹ m⁻²	0.46	0.08	–	mg d⁻¹ m⁻²	0.16	0.027	–	237
	Relative to creatinine:									
	– 12 adults	µmol/mol	62	31	–	µmol/g	0.55	0.27	–	214
↓ Uric acid	20 subjects .... (a)	mmol/d	3.14	1.33	–	mg/d	528	224	–	220
	22 men............ (b)	mmol/d	2.53	0.48	–	mg/d	426	81	–	221
	Relative to body mass:									
	– 8 newborn, 0–2 days	µmol d⁻¹ kg⁻¹	29	–	–	mg d⁻¹ kg⁻¹	4.8	–	–	2
	– 4 adults	µmol d⁻¹ kg⁻¹	52	–	–	mg d⁻¹ kg⁻¹	8.7	–	–	2
Allantoin	5 adults	mmol/d	0.30	0.16	(0.15–0.58)	mg/d	47	26	(24–91)	226
Pyrimidines and related compounds										
↓ 5-Ribosyluracil (pseudouridine)	26 subjects .... (a)	µmol/d	190	–	(98–310)	mg/d	46	–	(24–75)	227
	Relative to body mass:									
	– 17 adults	µmol d⁻¹ kg⁻¹	3.5	0.98	(1.5–4.34)	mg d⁻¹ kg⁻¹	0.86	0.24	(0.37–1.06)	212
	– 49 children, 2–10 years..........	µmol d⁻¹ kg⁻¹	–	–	(6.31–18.4)	mg d⁻¹ kg⁻¹	–	–	(1.54–4.49)	228
↓ Uracil............	2 subjects .... (a)	µmol/d	–	–	(36–54)	mg/d	–	–	(4–6)	231
Carbamoylaspartic acid..........	For body surface of 1.73 m²:									
	– 7 children	µmol/d	15.7	5.7	–	mg/d	2.77	1.0	–	239
	– 10 adults	µmol/d	10.7	3.6	–	mg/d	1.88	0.63	–	239
↓ Orotic acid	6 adults	µmol/d	9.6	3.2	–	mg/d	1.5	0.5	–	232
Orotidine........	6 adults	µmol/d	17	3	–	mg/d	5.0	0.9	–	232
↓ β-Aminoisobutyric acid	Relative to creatinine:									
	– 125 men	µmol/mol	4.27	1.93	–	nmol/g	38	17	–	254
	– 120 women..........	µmol/mol	5.81	4.11	–	nmol/g	51	36	–	254

Cyclic nucleotides. Excretion of cyclic adenosine monophosphate is low on the first day of life[215] and it increases with increasing age[216]; it varies in the course of the day (highest values toward noon)[217]. Excretion of cyclic nucleotides is promoted by parathyroid hormone, and hyperparathyroidism can be associated with increased excretion rates[214,218,219].

Uric acid. (a) On normal diet; (b) on low-purine diet. – Data in relation to age are given in Figure 6. Uric acid excretion is dependent on the purine content of the diet; on a high-purine diet, 12 mmol of uric acid or more may be excreted daily[222]. Uric acid excretion is pathologically elevated in the Lesch-Nyhan syndrome, in chronic granulocytic leukemia and various acute leukemias (but not in chronic lymphocytic leukemia), in polycythemia vera, in Wilson's disease, and occasionally in psoriasis[223,224]. Uric acid excretion is increased in some forms of gout and reduced in others (renal insufficiency)[221].

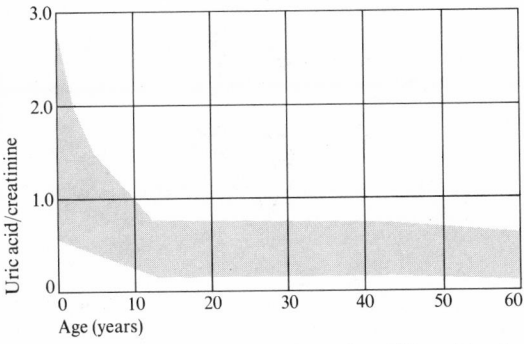

Fig. 6. Normal range of mass fraction uric acid/creatinine in urine[225].

5-Ribosyluracil. On purine-free diet. In 1 subject on purine-free diet, excretion ranged up to 560 µmol/d[229]. Excretion is increased in some cases of leukemia and macroglobulinemia[227, 230].

Uracil. On purine-free diet.

Orotic acid. Excretion is slightly increased in pregnant women[233]. Values exceed 12 mmol/d in hereditary orotic-aciduria; after azauridine therapy they reach 64–77 mmol/d[234].

β-Aminoisobutyric acid. See page 66 for normal values. For genetic reasons, excretion is increased in 5–10% of the white population and in a higher percentage of Asiatics[234].

References

[1] McCance and Widdowson, *Acta paediat. (Uppsala),* **49**, 409 (1960).
[2] Barlow and McCance, *Arch. Dis. Childh.,* **23**, 225 (1948).
[3] Carver and Paska, *Clin. chim. Acta,* **6**, 721 (1961).
[4] Jellinek and Looney, *J. biol. Chem.,* **128**, 621 (1939).
[5] Dugdale and Edkins, *Lancet,* **1**, 1062 (1964).
[6] Simmons, W. K., *Amer. J. clin. Nutr.,* **25**, 539 (1972).
[7] Owen et al., *Clin. Res.,* **16**, 348 (1968); Runcie and Hilditch, *Brit. med. J.,* **2**, 352 (1974).
[8] Cuthbertson et al., *Brit. J. Surg.,* **59**, 925 (1972).
[9] Kibrick, A. C., *Clin. chim. Acta,* **11**, 408 (1965).
[10] Howell, T. H., *J. Geront.,* **11**, 61 (1956).
[11] Bergstedt et al., *J. Pediat.,* **56**, 635 (1960).
[12] de Leo and di Francesco, *Pediatria (Napoli),* **67**, 239 (1959).
[13] Emery and Burt, *Clin. chim. Acta,* **39**, 361 (1972).
[14] Taussky, H. H., *Clin. chim. Acta,* **1**, 210 (1956); Taussky, H. H., *Stand. Meth. clin. Chem.,* **3**, 99 (1961).
[15] Heilskov and Schønheyder, *Acta med. scand.,* **151**, 51 (1955).
[16] Armstrong et al., *Pediatrics,* **33**, 975 (1964).
[17] Szadkowski et al., *Z. klin. Chem.,* **8**, 529 (1970).
[18] Vestergaard and Leverett, *J. Lab. clin. Med.,* **51**, 211 (1958).
[19] Clark et al., *Amer. J. Dis. Child.,* **81**, 774 (1951).
[20] Zorab, P. A., *Lancet,* **2**, 1164 (1969).
[21] Friedman et al., *Ann. intern. Med.,* **76**, 41 (1972).
[22] Arroyave and Wilson, *Amer. J. clin. Nutr.,* **9**, 170 (1961).
[23] Viteri and Alvarado, *Pediatrics,* **46**, 696 (1970).
[24] Chattaway et al., *Clin. chim. Acta,* **26**, 567 (1969).
[25] Edwards et al., *Lancet,* **2**, 1165 (1969).
[26] Tocci et al., *Clin. chim. Acta,* **40**, 449 (1972).
[27] Peters et al., *Clin. chim. Acta,* **39**, 273 (1972).
[28] Mautalen, C. A., *J. Lab. clin. Med.,* **75**, 11 (1970).
[29] Menichini and Giovannetti, *Experientia (Basel),* **29**, 506 (1973).
[30] Stein et al., *J. Lab. clin. Med.,* **77**, 1020 (1971).
[31] Cohen, B. D., *Arch. intern. Med.,* **126**, 846 (1970).
[32] Stein et al., *New Engl. J. Med.,* **280**, 926 (1969).
[33] Simpson, D. P., *Medicine (Baltimore),* **50**, 503 (1971).
[34] Bortz et al., *Amer. J. clin. Nutr.,* **21**, 1291 (1968).
[35] Jourdan et al., *Amer. J. clin. Nutr.,* **27**, 3 (1974).
[36] Scrimshaw et al., *J. Nutr.,* **102**, 1595 (1972).
[37] Slater, J. E., *Brit. J. Nutr.,* **15**, 83 (1961).
[38] Turner and Cohn, *Clin. Pharmacol. Ther.,* **18**, 405 (1975).
[39] Clarkson and Ferraio, *Clin. Sci.,* **15**, 433 (1969).
[40] Goodwin, J. F., *Clin. chim. Acta,* **21**, 231 (1968); Goodwin, J. F., *Stand. Meth. clin. Chem.,* **6**, 89 (1970).
[41] Peters, W. H., *Clin. chim. Acta,* **45**, 387 (1973).
[42] Applegarth et al., *Clin. chim. Acta,* **22**, 131 (1968).
[43] Thompson and Abdulnabi, *J. biol. Chem.,* **185**, 625 (1950).
[44] Ruskin and Sunderman, in Sunderman and Sunderman (Eds.), *The Clinical Pathology of Infancy,* Thomas, Springfield, 1967, page 132.
[45] Bigwood et al., *Advanc. clin. Chem.,* **2**, 201 (1959).
[46] Khachadurian et al., *J. Lab. clin. Med.,* **56**, 321 (1960).
[47] Baumgartner et al., *Helv. paediat. Acta,* **23**, 77 (1968).
[48] Eldjarn et al., *Clin. chim. Acta,* **40**, 461 (1972).
[49] Liappis, N., *Z. klin. Chem.,* **11**, 279 (1973).

[50] Hytten and Lind, *Diagnostic Indices in Pregnancy,* CIBA-GEIGY LTD, Basle, 1973.
[51] Saifer, A., *Advanc. clin. Chem.,* **14**, 145 (1971).
[52] O'Brien et al., *Laboratory Manual of Pediatric Microbiochemical Techniques,* 4th ed., Harper, New York, 1968; O'Brien et al., *Progr. clin. Path.,* **1**, 512 (1966).
[53] Leonard, C. A., *Stand. Meth. clin. Chem.,* **7**, 267 (1972).
[54] Sunderman, F. W., in Sunderman and Sunderman (Eds.), *The Clinical Pathology of Infancy,* Thomas, Springfield, 1967, page 145.
[55] King, J. S., *Clin. chim. Acta,* **9**, 441 (1964).
[56] McGregor et al., *Clin. chim. Acta,* **48**, 65 (1973).
[57] Hamilton, P. B., in Sober, H. A. (Eds.), *Handbook of Biochemistry,* The Chemical Rubber Co., Cleveland, 1968, page B-43.
[58] Przyrembel et al., *Clin. chim. Acta,* **49**, 27 (1973).
[59] Emery and Burt, *Clin. chim. Acta,* **39**, 361 (1972).
[60] Peters et al., *Proc. Soc. exp. Biol. (N.Y.),* **131**, 281 (1969).
[61] Geer et al., *Clin. Chem.,* **14**, 12 (1968).
[62] Danelatos-Athanassiadis et al., *Clin. chim. Acta,* **23**, 153 (1969).
[63] Armstrong, M. D., *Clin. chim. Acta,* **46**, 253 (1973).
[64] Soupart, P., in Holden, J. T. (Ed.), *Amino Acid Pools,* Elsevier, Amsterdam, 1962, page 220; Scriver and Rosenberg, *Amino Acid Metabolism and Its Disorders,* Saunders, Philadelphia, 1973.
[65] Liappis and Jäkel, *Mschr. Kinderheilk,* **122**, 777 (1974).
[66] O'Brien et al., *Laboratory Manual of Pediatric Microbiochemical Techniques,* 4th ed., Harper, New York, 1968, page 35.
[67] Armstrong and Robinow, *Pediatrics,* **39**, 546 (1967).
[68] Soupart. P., *Clin. chim. Acta,* **4**, 265 (1959).
[69] Löwer et al., *Clin. chim. Acta,* **58**, 155 (1975).
[70] Heacock and Mahler, *Clin. chim. Acta,* **54**, 810 (1974).
[71] Gerritsen and Waisman, in Stanbury et al. (Eds.), *The Metabolic Basis of Inherited Disease,* 3rd ed., McGraw-Hill, New York, 1972, page 459.
[72] Westall, R. G., *Biochem. J.,* **60**, 247 (1955).
[73] Abraham et al., *Arch. Biochem.,* **99**, 210 (1962).
[74] Nakajima et al., *Biochim. biophys. Acta (Amst.),* **222**, 405 (1970).
[75] Rudman et al., *Amer. J. Med.,* **46**, 174 (1969).
[76] Skarżyński and Sarnecka-Keller, *Advanc. clin. Chem.,* **5**, 107 (1962).
[77] Klosse et al., *Clin. chim. Acta,* **42**, 409 (1972).
[78] Smiley and Ziff, *Physiol. Rev.,* **44**, 30 (1964).
[79] Lutz et al., *Clin. chim. Acta,* **39**, 425 (1972).
[80] Nusgens and Lapiere, *Clin. chim. Acta,* **48**, 203 (1973).
[81] Ben-Ami et al., *Clin. chim. Acta,* **45**, 335 (1973).
[82] Jasin et al., *J. clin. Invest.,* **41**, 1928 (1962).
[83] Klein, L., *Stand. Meth. clin. Chem.,* **6**, 41 (1970).
[84] Mautalen, C. A., *J. Lab. clin. Med.,* **75**, 11 (1970).
[85] Zender, R., *Clin. chim. Acta,* **37**, 263 (1972).
[86] Raab, W., *Z. klin. Chem.,* **10**, 195 (1972).
[87] Yamamoto et al., *Clin. chim. Acta,* **37**, 165 (1972).
[88] Leroy, E. C., *Advanc. clin. Chem.,* **10**, 213 (1967).
[89] Saleh and Coenegracht, *Clin. chim. Acta,* **21**, 445 (1968); Burkhardt et al., *Z. klin. Chem.,* **12**, 108 (1974).
[90] Musajo and Benassi, *Advanc. clin. Chem.,* **7**, 63 (1964).
[91] Palmer et al., *Clin. chim. Acta,* **47**, 443 (1973).
[92] Stein et al., *J. Amer. chem. Soc.,* **76**, 2848 (1954).
[93] van Sumere et al., *Clin. chim. Acta,* **26**, 85 (1969).
[94] Armstrong et al., *J. biol. Chem.,* **218**, 921 (1956).
[95] Tanaka, K., in Hommes and van den Berg (Eds.), *Inborn Errors of Metabolism,* Academic Press, London, 1973, page 269.
[96] Hannestad and Sörbo, *Clin. chim. Acta,* **95**, 189 (1979).
[97] Coward and Smith, *J. Chromatogr.,* **45**, 230 (1969).
[98] Altschule and Hegedus, *Clin. Pharmacol. Ther.,* **15**, 111 (1974).
[99] Holmgren, G., *Nutr. Metab.,* **16**, 223 (1974).
[100] Askenasi, R., *Biochim. biophys. Acta (Amst.),* **304**, 375 (1973).
[101] Kay et al., *Arthr. and Rheum.,* **14**, 393 (1971).
[102] Askenasi, R., *J. Lab. clin. Med.,* **83**, 673 (1974).
[103] Luecke and Pearson, *J. biol. Chem.,* **153**, 259 (1944).
[104] Maebashi et al., *Nature,* **249**, 173 (1974).
[105] Medical News, *J. Amer. med. Ass.,* **181**, No. 5, 26 (1962).
[106] Blau, K., *Biochem. J.,* **80**, 193 (1961).
[107] Mondovì et al., *Ital. J. Biochem.,* **10**, 42 (1961).
[108] Perry et al., *Clin. chim. Acta,* **14**, 116 (1966).
[109] Marton et al., *Clin. Chem.,* **19**, 923 (1973).
[110] Dreyfuss et al., *Clin. chim. Acta,* **49**, 65 (1973).
[111] Tompsett, S. L., *Clin. chim. Acta,* **5**, 415 (1960).
[112] King, *Clin. chim. Acta,* **51**, 105 (1974).
[113] Smith and Kellow, *Clin. chim. Acta,* **40**, 353 (1972).
[114] Smith and Kellow, *Nature,* **181**, 1261 (1969).
[115] Reynolds et al., *Clin. chim. Acta,* **83**, 33 (1978).
[116] Manghani et al., *Lancet,* **2**, 943 (1975).
[117] Ping Sung et al., *Clin. chim. Acta,* **47**, 215 (1973).
[118] Wisser, H., *Z. klin. Chem.,* **8**, 637 (1970).
[119] Hoeldtke and Sloan, *J. Lab. clin. Med.,* **75**, 159 (1970).
[120] Voorhess, M. L., *Pediatrics,* **39**, 252 (1967).
[121] Townshend and Smith, *Clin. Sci.,* **44**, 253 (1973).
[122] Weil-Malherbe and van Buren, *J. Lab. clin. Med.,* **74**, 305 (1969).
[123] Sandhu and Freed, *Stand. Meth. clin. Chem.,* **7**, 231 (1972).
[124] Käser, H., *Helv. paediat. Acta,* suppl. 29, 7 (1972).
[125] Louis et al., *Brit. med. J.,* **4**, 325 (1972).
[126] Türler and Käser, *Clin. chim. Acta,* **32**, 41 (1971).
[127] Geissbuhler, F., *Clin. chim. Acta,* **30**, 543 (1972).
[128] Käser and Thomke, *Clin. chim. Acta,* **27**, 203 (1970).
[129] Winkel and Slob, *Clin. chim. Acta,* **45**, 113 (1973).
[130] Käser et al., *Schweiz. med. Wschr.,* **104**, 642 (1974).
[131] Brown et al., *J. clin. Invest.,* **40**, 617 (1961).

[132] PRICE et al., *Advanc. metab. Disord.*, **2**, 159 (1965).
[133] MUSAJO and BENASSI, *Advanc. clin. Chem.*, **7**, 63 (1964).
[134] PRICE et al., *Amer. J. clin. Nutr.*, **25**, 494 (1972); ROSE et al., *Clin. Sci.*, **42**, 465 (1972); ROSE, D. P., *J. clin. Path.*, **25**, 17 (1972).
[135] ROSE and TOSELAND, *Metabolism*, **22**, 165 (1973).
[136] SPIERA, H., *Arth. and Rheum.*, **9**, 318 (1966); SPIERA and VALLARINO, *J. clin. Invest.*, **48**, 856 (1969).
[137] PERRY et al., *Pediatrics*, **30**, 576 (1962).
[138] RODNIGHT, R., *Int. Rev. Neurobiol.*, **3**, 251 (1961).
[139] LYNCH et al., *Science*, **187**, 169 (1975).
[140] GROSS and FRANZEN, *Z. klin. Chem.*, **3**, 99 (1965).
[141] HADDOX and SASLAW, *J. clin. Invest.*, **42**, 435 (1963).
[142] DAVIS et al., *J. Lab. clin. Med.*, **66**, 390 (1965).
[143] STURM, A., *Clin. chim. Acta*, **7**, 714 (1962).
[144] MUSTALA et al., *Scand. J. clin. Lab. Invest.*, **16**, 655 (1964).
[145] PAYNE et al., *Amer. J. clin. Nutr.*, **27**, 565 and 572 (1974).
[146] FELDMAN et al., *Clin. chim. Acta*, **51**, 75 (1974).
[147] GARTZKE and MAJEWSKI, *Z. klin. Chem.*, **10**, 108 (1972).
[148] SCHIEVELBEIN et al., *Klin. Wschr.*, **40**, 52 (1962).
[149] DALGLIESH, C. E., *Advanc. clin. Chem.*, **1**, 193 (1958); RESNICK and GRAY, *Med. Clin. N. Amer.*, **44**, 1323 (1960); WEISSBACH, H., *Stand. Meth. clin. Chem.*, **4**, 121 (1963).
[150] GROSS and FRANZEN, *Biochem. Z.*, **340**, 403 (1964).
[151] MÜTING et al., *Z. klin. Med.*, **157**, 538 (1964).
[152] CURZON and WALSH, *Clin. chim. Acta*, **7**, 657 (1962).
[153] MÜTING et al., *Z. klin. Med.*, **157**, 544 (1963).
[154] WEISSBACH et al., *J. biol. Chem.*, **234**, 81 (1959).
[155] ARMSTRONG et al., *J. biol. Chem.*, **232**, 17 (1958).
[156] BALAKRISHNAN and RODNIGHT, *Biochem. J.*, **76**, 61P (1960).
[157] MARKLOVÁ and HAIS, *Clin. chim. Acta*, **40**, 455 (1972).
[158] WADMAN et al., *Clin. chim. Acta*, **31**, 215 (1971).
[159] DUNER and PERNOW, *Scand. J. clin. Lab. Invest.*, **8**, 296 (1956).
[160] GRANERUS, G., *Scand. J. clin. Lab. Invest.*, **22**, suppl. 104, 49 and 59 (1968).
[161] DEMIS, D. J., in *XXII. International Congress of Physiological Sciences, Leiden 1962*, volume 2, Excerpta Medica Foundation, Amsterdam, 1962, abstract No. 695; DEMIS and ZIMMER, *Arch. intern. Med.*, **111**, 309 (1963).
[162] BEAVEN et al., *Clin. chim. Acta*, **37**, 91 (1972).
[163] VAN DER HEIDEN et al., *Clin. chim. Acta*, **39**, 201 (1972).
[164] MERRITT et al., *J. clin. Invest.*, **41**, 1472 (1962).
[165] BERRY et al., *Brit. med. J.*, **2**, 1103 (1963).
[166] BENNETT and CHANARIN, *Nature*, **196**, 271 (1962); CHANARIN, I., *Proc. roy. Soc. Med.*, **57**, 384 (1964).
[167] LUHBY and COOPERMAN, *Advanc. metab. Disord.*, **1**, 263 (1964); WILMANNS, W., *Wiss. Veröff. dtsch. Ges. Ernähr.*, **19**, 30 (1971).
[168] DREUX, *Clin. chim. Acta*, **30**, 519 (1970).
[169] MAHON and MATTOK, *Canad. J. Biochem.*, **45**, 1317 (1967).
[170] WALDRON, H. A., *J. clin. Path.*, **18**, 230 (1965).
[171] KISSEL et al., *Germ. med. Mth.*, **14**, 405 (1969).
[172] HAEGER, B., *Lancet*, **2**, 606 (1958).
[173] HAEGER-ARONSEN, B., *Scand. J. clin. Lab. Invest.*, **12**, suppl. 47, 1 (1960).
[174] MALOOLY and HIGHTOWER, *J. Lab. clin. Med.*, **59**, 568 (1962).
[175] RIJKS, L. G., *Clin. chim. Acta*, **53**, 23 (1974).
[176] LEVERE and KAPPAS, *Advanc. clin. Chem.*, **11**, 133 (1968).
[177] MIYAGI et al., *J. Lab. clin. Med.*, **78**, 683 (1971).
[178] MEYER et al., *New Engl. J. Med.*, **286**, 1277 (1972).
[179] MORGAN and BURCH, *Arch. intern. Med.*, **130**, 335 (1972).
[180] SCHMIDT and STICH, *Dtsch. med. Wschr.*, **97**, 1176 (1972).
[181] KÄSER et al., *Schweiz. med. Wschr.*, **93**, 1052 (1963).
[182] HOEFLMAYR et al., *Dtsch. med. Wschr.*, **100**, 187 (1975).
[183] TALMAN, E. L., *Stand. Meth. clin. Chem.*, **2**, 137 (1958).
[184] REINKINGH and VAN KAMPEN, *Clin. chim. Acta*, **9**, 592 (1964).
[185] FERNANDEZ et al., *Clin. Chem.*, **12**, 463 (1966); FERNANDEZ and JACOBS, *Stand. Meth. clin. Chem.*, **6**, 57 (1970).
[186] PINELLI and GASPARI, *Clin. chim. Acta*, **39**, 135 (1972).
[187] WALDENSTRÖM and HAEGER-ARONSEN, *Münch. med. Wschr.*, **106**, 1333 (1964).
[188] DOSS, M., *Diagnostik*, **7**, 489 (1974).
[189] GUNDERMANN and KÜBLER, *Dtsch. med. Wschr.*, **87**, 306 (1962).
[190] WITH, T. K., *Bile Pigments*, Academic Press, New York, 1968.
[191] MICHAÉLSSON, M., *Scand. J. clin. Lab. Invest.*, **13**, suppl. 56, 1 (1961).
[192] BALIKOV, B., *Stand. Meth. clin. Chem.*, **2**, 192 (1958).

[193] BOURKE et al., *Brit. med. J.*, **2**, 1510 (1965).
[194] ROOT, W. S., *Meth. med. Res.*, **8**, 122 (1960).
[195] KREIMER-BIRNBAUM et al., *Brit. med. J.*, **2**, 396 (1966).
[196] BUNN and JANDL, *J. exp. Med.*, **129**, 925 (1969).
[197] LAURELL and NYMAN, *Blood*, **12**, 493 (1957).
[198] ROWLAND and PENN, *Med. Clin. N. Amer.*, **56**, 1233 (1972).
[199] DACIE, J. V., *Proc. roy. Soc. Med.*, **56**, 587 (1963).
[200] SCHLATTER and FORSTER, *Schweiz. med. Wschr.*, **95**, 979 (1965); PAYNE, R. B., *J. clin. Path.*, **19**, 170 (1966); SPICER, A. J., *Brit. med. J.*, **1**, 155 (1970).
[201] RICK, W., personal communication.
[202] ROWLAND et al., *Arch. Neurol. (Chic.)*, **10**, 537 (1964).
[203] BERLIN et al., *J. Amer. med. Ass.*, **227**, 1414 (1974).
[204] SARANCHAK and BERNSTEIN, *J. Amer. med. Ass.*, **228**, 1251 (1974).
[205] SMITH, R. F., *Arch. intern. Med.*, **121**, 313 (1968).
[206] LUHBY and COOPERMAN, *Lancet*, **2**, 1381 (1962).
[207] CONWARD and SMITH, *Clin. chim. Acta*, **12**, 206 (1965).
[208] WYNGAARDEN and KELLEY, in STANBURY et al. (Eds.), *The Metabolic Basis of Inherited Disease*, 3rd ed., McGraw-Hill, New York, 1972, page 889.
[209] VAN GENNIP et al., *Clin. chim. Acta*, **45**, 119 (1973).
[210] SIMMONDS, H. A., *Clin. chim. Acta*, **23**, 353 (1969).
[211] DANCIS et al., *J. clin. Invest.*, **52**, 2068 (1973).
[212] CHANG et al., *J. Lab. clin. Med.*, **83**, 816 (1974).
[213] TUCCI and KOPP, *J. clin. Endocr.*, **43**, 1323 (1976).
[214] MURAD and PAK, *New Engl. J. Med.*, **286**, 1382 (1972).
[215] LINARELLI, L. G., *Pediatrics*, **50**, 14 (1972); McCRORY, W. W., *Pediatrics*, **50**, 3 (1972).
[216] VITEK and LANG, *J. clin. Endocr.*, **42**, 781 (1976).
[217] SAGEL et al., *J. clin. Endocr.*, **37**, 570 (1973).
[218] GERBITZ and WIELAND, *Z. klin. Chem.*, **11**, 224 (1973).
[219] NEELON et al., *Lancet*, **1**, 631 (1973).
[220] KUHL et al., *Metabolism*, **4**, 143 (1955).
[221] SEEGMILLER et al., *New Engl. J. Med.*, **268**, 712 (1963).
[222] NATELSON, S., *Stand. Meth. clin. Chem.*, **1**, 123 (1953).
[223] EISEN and SEEGMILLER, *J. clin. Invest.*, **40**, 1486 (1961).
[224] BALIS, M. E., *Advanc. clin. Chem.*, **10**, 157 (1967).
[225] KAUFMAN et al., *J. Pediat.*, **73**, 583 (1968).
[226] JANZEN et al., *Klin. Wschr.*, **55**, 1071 (1977).
[227] WEISSMAN et al., *J. Lab. clin. Med.*, **59**, 852 (1962).
[228] LIS et al., *Clin. Chem.*, **16**, 714 (1970).
[229] BYRNE and CHAPMAN, *Clin. chim. Acta*, **48**, 341 (1973).
[230] WEISSMAN, S. M., *J. Amer. med. Ass.*, **195**, 27 (1966).
[231] EISEN et al., *J. Lab. clin. Med.*, **59**, 620 (1962).
[232] TAX et al., *Clin. chim. Acta*, **90**, 217 (1978).
[233] WOOD and O'SULLIVAN, *Amer. J. Obstet. Gynec.*, **116**, 57 (1973).
[234] SMITH, L. H., *New Engl. J. Med.*, **288**, 764 (1973).
[235] VASSELLA et al., *Helv. paediat. Acta*, **23**, 22 (1968).
[236] LEKLEM, J. E., *Amer. J. clin. Nutr.*, **24**, 659 (1971).
[237] MURAD et al., *J. clin. Endocr.*, **40**, 552 (1975).
[238] CEDERBLAD and LINDSTEDT, *Clin. chim. Acta*, **33**, 117 (1971).
[239] SMITH and GILMOUR, *J. Lab. clin. Med.*, **86**, 1047 (1975).
[240] DIRREN et al., *Clin. Chem.*, **21**, 1970 (1975).
[241] LIAPPIS, N., *Münch. med. Wschr.*, **117**, 1839 (1975).
[242] WOCIAL et al., *Clin. chim. Acta*, **66**, 273 (1976).
[243] WRONG and DAVIES, *Quart. J. Med.*, **28**, 259 (1959).
[244] PEONIDES et al., *Arch. Dis. Childh.*, **40**, 33 (1965).
[245] PITTS, R. F., *Physiology of the Kidney and Body Fluids*, 3rd ed., Year Book Medical Publishers, Chicago, 1974.
[246] DREYFUSS et al., *Israel J. med. Sci.*, **11**, 785 (1975).
[247] KNOLL and WISSER, *Clin. chim. Acta*, **68**, 327 (1976).
[248] FERNLUND, P., *Clin. chim. Acta*, **72**, 147 (1976).
[249] HALLGREN et al., *J. biol. Chem.*, **250**, 5312 (1975).
[250] BJÖRKMAN et al., *Clin. Chem.*, **22**, 49 (1976).
[251] DiMAURO and ROWLAND, *Arch. Neurol.*, **33**, 204 (1976).
[252] ARTERBERRY and CONLEY, *Clin. chim. Acta*, **17**, 431 (1967).
[253] ENDRES and SEIBOLD, *Clin. chim. Acta*, **87**, 425 (1978).
[254] KUO et al., *Clin. Chem.*, **24**, 1373 (1978).
[255] CARNEGIE et al., *Metabolism*, **26**, 531 (1977).
[256] LICATA et al., *Amer. J. Med.*, **64**, 133 (1978).
[257] RUSSELL et al., *Amer. J. Obstet. Gynec.*, **132**, 649 (1978).
[258] LAM et al., *Clin. Chem.*, **23**, 1264 (1977).
[259] ROXIN et al., *Scand. J. clin. Lab. Invest.*, **39**, 37 (1979).

Non-dialyzable material and protein

(for references see pages 80 and 81)

Table 1 *Constituents of non-dialyzable material in urine*[4]

	%
N-Acetylneuraminic acid	10.2
Fucose	2.5
Hexoses (orcin reaction)	15.7
Hexosamine	11.6
Hexuronic acid (carbazole reaction)	3.0
Protein	39(35–44)
Inorganic substances	9.6

The varying data reported on the excretion of high-molecular substances (between 30 mg/d and 750 mg/d[7]) are attributable in some measure to the difficulty of concentrating urine. The non-dialyzable material consists of about 40% carbohydrates and about 40% protein (Table 1)[4, 8]. It is a complex mixture of plasma proteins and other proteins (Tables 3 and 4), glycosaminoglycans (see below) and glycopeptides[7, 14]. Approximately 30 different plasma proteins have been identified in the urine[15]; other proteins, such as the Tamm-Horsfall glycoprotein, originate from the kidneys[12, 16].

When glomerular permeability is impaired, high-molecular proteins in particular appear in the urine (albumin and larger molecules); when tubular function is impaired, the normally filtered low-molecular proteins are not adequately reabsorbed and appear in the urine in increased quantities (albumin and smaller molecules)[15, 17–19] (Table 5). Upon severe physical exertion protein

Table 2 *Non-dialyzable material and protein (mean and s or extreme range or 95% range)*

Method	Number	Non-dialyzable material	Protein	Reference
		mg/d		
Dialysis, fractionation with Millipore® filter	7 newborn	87.9(s26.8)	10.5(s0.84)	1
	3 infants	125	13.0	1
	11 adults...............	474(s27)	61.6(s7.3)	1
Ultrafiltration, dialysis, protein after KJELDAHL ...	14 premature infants....	–	6.56(s4.55)	2
	14 full-term infants	–	15.4(s6.17)	2
	14 infants..............	–	12.2(s8.89)	2
	12 children, 1–4 years ...	–	8.76(s6.68)	2
	13 children, 5–6 years ...	–	6.6(s6.11)	2
	12 children, 7–12 years..	–	5.62(s4.25)	2
	11 children, 13–16 years.	–	21.5(s23.1)	2
Dialysis, protein after LOWRY	49 subjects, 4–66 years ..	–	216(95% range: 38–394)	3
Dialysis, protein after KJELDAHL	49 subjects, 4–66 years ..	–	96(95% range: 2–190)	3
Ultrafiltration, dialysis, protein after KJELDAHL ...	15 adults...............	170(95% range: 150–310)	66(95% range: 59–121)	4
Ultrafiltration, precipitation with phosphotungstic acid, biuret reaction	48 adults...............	–	50.9(8–133)	5
Immunoassay of proteins	Adults	–	103(50–187)	6

Table 3 *Urinary excretion of various proteins at different ages[9]*

	All age groups (239 subjects)		<10 years (18 subjects)	10–69 years (209 subjects)	>70 years (12 subjects)
	Median	95% range	Median	Median	Median
	mg/d				
Albumin........	6.10	1.64–34.2	3.8	6.2	5.5
Haptoglobin	0.09	0.00–0.95	0.04	0.10	0.18
Transferrin	0.69	0.00–3.50	0.33	0.68	0.88
β_2-Microglobulin	0.04	0.00–0.14	0.014	0.033	0.049
IgG	1.98	0.20–6.50	2.11	1.93	1.87
IgA	0.54	0.00–2.25	0.13	0.58	0.82
IgM............	0.30	0.00–1.34	0.04	0.34	0.36
λ-Chains........	1.30	0.00–7.60	0.45	1.40	1.35
ϰ-Chains........	2.20	0.00–9.00	0.45	2.30	2.70
Lysozyme.......	0.15	0.02–0.45	0.07	0.16	0.12

Table 4
Urinary excretion of some proteins and mucopolysaccharides

	Number	Unit	Mean	95% range (extreme range)	Reference
Albumin (relative to creatinine)	8 newborn	mg/g	78	15–390	10
	16 adults	mg/g	19	7–49	10
β-Trace protein	15 adults	mg/d	18	(3.6–54)	11
Fc fragment	....	mg/d	0.2	(0.1–0.4)	6
Tamm-Horsfall glyco-protein	35 adults	mg/d	38.9	s16.5	16
Glycosaminoglycans – as chondroitin sulfate	....	mg/d	–	~5–15	42
– as uronic acid	9 adults	mg/d	2.4	(0.9–3.0)	43

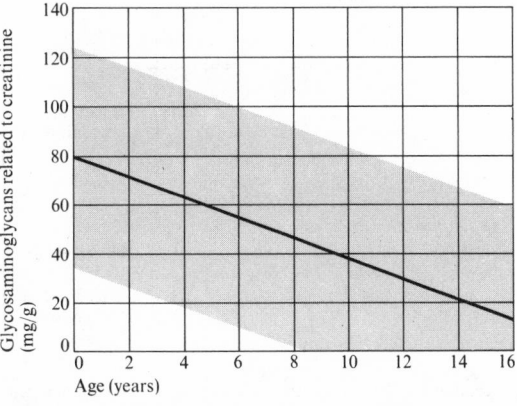

Fig. 1. Excretion of glycosaminoglycans in children (calculated from uronic acid excretion)[37].

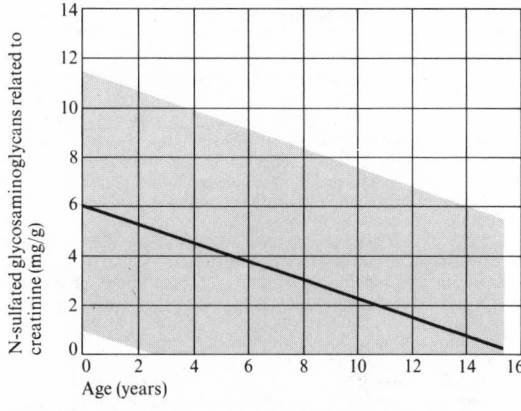

Fig. 2. Excretion of N-sulfated glycosaminoglycans (heparan sulfate) in children (calculated from N-sulfate hexosamine excretion)[37].

Table 5   *Causes of, and diagnostic criteria for, proteinurias*

Glomerular proteinurias[17]	Tubular proteinurias[17]	Prerenal proteinurias[19]	Postrenal proteinurias[19]
Immune complexes (nephritis in lupus erythematosus) Antibodies against antiglomerular basement membrane (e.g. Goodpasture's syndrome) Deposition of abnormal material (amyloidosis, diabetes mellitus) Pyelonephritis Vascular diseases (e.g. hypertension, congestive heart failure) Congenital renal diseases (e.g. Alport's syndrome) Lipoid nephrosis Physiologic: exercise, orthostatic reaction, fever	Fanconi's syndrome Cystinosis Wilson's disease Oculocerebrorenal syndrome Sarcoidosis Renal tubular acidosis Cadmium intoxication Balkan nephropathy Medullary cystic disease Renal transplantation Physiologic: food deprivation (potassium deficiency?)[20]	Increase of blood concentrations of low-molecular proteins: Hemoglobinuria Myoglobinuria Bence-Jones proteinuria Paraproteinurias	Inflammatory exudate from mucosa of urinary tract: Infections Tumors
Protein excretion (15 cases)[15]	Protein excretion (15 cases)[15]	Protein excretion	
Total protein: 0.31–54.1 g/d $\dfrac{\text{Albumin}}{\beta_2\text{-Microglobulin}}$: 1 100–14200	Total protein: 0.13–1.57 g/d $\dfrac{\text{Albumin}}{\beta_2\text{-Microglobulin}}$: 1.0–13.3	Specifically proteins in urine	

Table 6   *Individual mucopolysaccharides in urine[28] (relative to total mucopolysaccharides)*

	%	Carbohydrate components
Chondroitin 4-sulfate (chondroitin sulfate A)	34	Galactosamine, glucuronic acid
Chondroitin 6-sulfate (chondroitin sulfate C)	31	Galactosamine, glucuronic acid
Dermatan sulfate (chondroitin sulfate B)	1	Galactosamine, iduronic acid
Nonsulfated chondroitin	25	Galactosamine, glucuronic acid
Heparan sulfate (heparitin sulfate)*.	8	Glucosamine, glucuronic acid
Keratan sulfate (keratosulfate)	1	Glucosamine, galactose
Hyaluronic acid.....................	1	Glucosamine, glucuronic acid

* Heparin is not found in the urine[29, 30].

Table 7   *Mucopolysaccharide-bound uronic acid in urine*

Method	Number	Mean	(Extreme range)	Reference
		mg/d		
Precipitation with cetyltrimethylammonium bromide	1 infant .. 4 girls* ... 25 boys◊ . 6 men .... 9 women .	2.6 5.80 7.45 6.00 3.77	– (4.80–8.10) (4.10–14.7) (4.40–7.28) (2.73–5.40)	32 33 33 33 33
Precipitation with cetylpyridinium chloride	16 men... 15 women	5.3 3.7	s1.1 s0.9	34 34
Separation with epichlorohydrin triethanolamine cellulose column	16 men... 15 women	5.7 4.1	s1.2 s1.1	34 34
Separation with cetylpyridinium chloride cellulose column	42 men... 14 women	2.51 2.19	s2.38 s1.85	35 35

* 7–8 years.   ◊ 7–16 years.

excretion may temporarily increase to 50–100 times the normal level[21, 22].

IgM components. In multiple myeloma and in macroglobulinemia, a number of IgM-related proteins are excreted with the urine, among them Bence-Jones globulins[6]. The Bence-Jones globulins (relative molecular mass between 24000 and 90000) are demonstrable by precipitation with sulfosalicylic acid and dissolution of the precipitate at 90–100 °C[23].

Fibrinogen and fibrin degradation products stem either from the blood or from fibrin deposits in the kidney[24, 25]. At most, only traces of these compounds are found in normal urine[26]. They are excreted in large amounts in some cases of glomerulonephritis (up to 0.1 g/L[27]), preeclampsia, malignant tumors and after renal transplantation (up to 0.4 g/L or more after rejection[24, 26]).

Glycosaminoglycans (mucopolysaccharides). This fraction accounts for approximately 10% of the non-dialyzable material in the urine[4] and consists predominantly of chondroitin sulfates (Table 6). The acid mucopolysaccharides are easily determinable by assay of the uronic acid component although the individual techniques yield varying results (Table 7)[31]. The amount of kera-

tan sulfate can be inferred from the proportion of galactose[36], and the amount of heparan sulfate from the proportion of N-sulfate hexosamine[37]. Mucopolysaccharide excretion shows a relative increase in the growing child (Figs. 1 and 2)[37–39]. The excretion of acid mucopolysaccharides is increased in active, rheumatoid arthritis[40] and can increase to 40 times the normal value in hereditary mucopolysaccharidoses[13, 37, 41].

References

[1] KEUTEL and KING, *Clin. chim. Acta*, **11**, 341 (1965).
[2] DA FONSECA-WOLLHEIM and ROHWEDDER, *Arch. Kinderheilk.*, **183**, 122 (1971).
[3] HEMMINGSEN and SKOV, *Clin. chim. Acta*, **19**, 81 (1968).
[4] GRÄSSLIN et al., *Z. klin. Chem.*, **8**, 288 (1970).
[5] ANH CAO et al., *Schweiz. med. Wschr.*, **105**, 421 (1975).
[6] PRUZANSKI and OGRYZLO, *Advanc. clin. Chem.*, **13**, 335 (1970).
[7] MAXFIELD, M., *Ann. Rev. Med.*, **14**, 99 (1963).
[8] BOURRILLON and KAPLAN, *Clin. chim. Acta*, **5**, 732 (1960).
[9] HEMMINGSEN and SKAARUP, *Scand. J. clin. Lab. Invest.*, **35**, 347 (1975).
[10] BARRATT et al., *Arch. Dis. Childh.*, **45**, 496 (1970).
[11] WHITSED and PENNY, *Clin. chim. Acta*, **50**, 111 (1974).

[12] GRANT et al., *Clin. Sci.*, **44**, 377 (1973).

[13] KAPLAN, D., *Amer. J. Med.*, **47**, 721 (1969); BERMAN et al., *Clin. Chem.*, **17**, 886 (1971).

[14] HITZIG, W. H., *Die Plasmaproteine in der klinischen Medizin*, Springer, Berlin, 1963, page 209; KING and BOYCE, *High Molecular Weight Substances in Human Urine*, Thomas, Springfield, 1963.

[15] PETERSON et al., *J. clin. Invest.*, **48**, 1189 (1969).

[16] SAMUELL, C. T., *Clin. chim. Acta*, **85**, 285 (1978).

[17] HEINEMANN et al., *Amer. J. Med.*, **56**, 71 (1974).

[18] HALL and HARDWICKE, *Ann. Rev. Med.*, **30**, 199 (1979).

[19] BOESKEN et al., *Nieren- u. Hochdruck-Kr.*, **2**, 183 (1973); BOESKEN, W. H., *Klin. Wschr.*, **53**, 473 (1975).

[20] KJELLBERG et al., *Acta med. scand.*, **190**, 519 (1971).

[21] BICHLER et al., *Dtsch. med. Wschr.*, **97**, 1229 (1972).

[22] POORTMANS and JEANLOZ, *J. clin. Invest.*, **47**, 386 (1968).

[23] SNAPPER and ORES, *J. Amer. med. Ass.*, **173**, 1137 (1960); NAUMANN, H. N., *Amer. J. clin. Path.*, **44**, 413 (1965).

[24] THÖNI and GROB, *Schweiz. med. Wschr.*, **103**, 965 (1973).

[25] CLARKSON et al., *Brit. med. J.*, **3**, 447 (1971); CORTES et al., *J. Lab. clin. Med.*, **82**, 377 (1973); NAISH et al., *Brit. med. J.*, **1**, 544 (1974).

[26] BENDEL et al., *Schweiz. med. Wschr.*, **105**, 1040 (1975).

[27] REICHEL et al., *Nieren- u. Hochdruck-Kr.*, **2**, 209 (1973).

[28] VARADI et al., *Biochim. biophys. Acta (Amst.)*, **141**, 103 (1967).

[29] TANIGUCHI, N., *Clin. chim. Acta*, **37**, 225 (1972).

[30] MCKUSICK, V. A., *Amer. J. Med.*, **47**, 730 (1969).

[31] DORFMAN and MATALON, in STANBURY et al. (Eds.), *The Metabolic Basis of Inherited Disease*, 3rd ed., McGraw-Hill, New York, 1972, page 1218.

[32] RICH et al., *J. Lab. clin. Med.*, **50**, 686 (1957).

[33] DI FERRANTE and RICH, *J. Lab. clin. Med.*, **48**, 491 (1956).

[34] DI FERRANTE, N. M., *Analyt. Biochem.*, **21**, 98 (1967).

[35] DELBRÜCK et al., *Z. klin. Chem.*, **5**, 10 (1967).

[36] HUMBEL, R., *Clin. chim. Acta*, **52**, 173 (1974).

[37] LAGUNOFF et al., *Proc. Soc. exp. Biol. (N. Y.)*, **126**, 34 (1967).

[38] TELLER et al., *J. Lab. clin. Med.*, **59**, 95 (1962).

[39] GOLDBERG and COTLIER, *Clin. chim. Acta*, **41**, 19 (1972).

[40] DELBRÜCK et al., *Z. klin. Chem.*, **5**, 16 (1967).

[41] MUIR, H., *Amer. J. Med.*, **47**, 673 (1969).

[42] RITCHIE et al., *Amer. J. clin. Path.*, **67**, 585 (1977).

[43] MURATA and TAKEDA, *Clin. chim. Acta*, **108**, 49 (1980).

Enzymes[1,3] (for references see next page)

The most important of the 30 or so enzymes identified in the urine are listed in the adjoining table. They originate from the serum (glomerular filtration of low-molecular enzymes), erythrocytes and leukocytes, renal and urinary passages, genital secretions (prostatic secretion), or from bacteria[38].

The excretion of certain enzymes, notably of arylsulfatase and β-galactosidase, is subject to diurnal fluctuations (highest values between 6 a.m. and noon, followed by a rapid decline toward evening)[43].

In evaluating enzyme activity in the urine, account has to be taken of urine volume and the state of urine flow; thus, the demonstrable activity of certain enzymes in terms of unit volume proved to be higher in antidiuresis than in diuresis[4,11,12]. Enzyme inhibitors occurring in the urine and variation of pH in the bladder can lead to decreases in activity[2,3].

Urinary enzyme determinations are of little diagnostic value[44]. High activities of high-molecular enzymes in the urine, which are found mainly in the renal parenchyma (β-glucuronidase, γ-glutamyl transferase), are suggestive of acute processes in the renal tubules[12,39]. The hereditary deficiency of some lysosomal enzymes (for example, α-galactosidase in Fabry's disease) is detectable by an almost complete absence of activity of the enzyme in the urine[33,34].

EC number	Name of enzyme	Reference
1.1.1.27	Lactate dehydrogenase	4–10
2.3.2.2	γ-Glutamyltransferase	11–14
2.6.1.1	Aspartate aminotransferase	6,7,15
2.7.4.3	Adenylate kinase	16
3.1.3.1	Alkaline phosphatase	4,8,10,17,18
3.1.3.2	Acid phosphatase	10,17
3.1.6.1	Arylsulfatase	10,21,22
3.1.27.5	Ribonuclease (pancreatic)	19,20
3.2.1.1	α-Amylase	23–27
3.2.1.17	Lysozyme	28–31
3.2.1.21	β-D-Glucosidase	32
3.2.1.22	α-D-Galactosidase	33,34
3.2.1.23	β-D-Galactosidase	34–36,47
3.2.1.24	α-D-Mannosidase	32
3.2.1.30	β-N-Acetyl-D-glucosaminidase	32,33,35–37,47
3.2.1.31	β-D-Glucuronidase	10,32,36,38,39
3.4.11.1	Aminopeptidase (leucine aminopeptidase)	4,10,40,41
3.4.22.1	Cathepsin B	42

↓See text below	SI unit	Mean	s	95% range (extreme range in brackets)	Other units*	Mean	s	95% range (extreme range in brackets)	Reference
↓ **Lactate dehydrogenase**...... Substrate pyruvate, 25 °C:									
– 25 subjects	nmol s⁻¹/d	–	–	(<223)	U/d	–	–	(<13.4)	7,44
γ-Glutamyl transferase..... Substrate γ-glutamyl-p-nitro-anilide, 25 °C:									
– night urine, 23 men	nmol s⁻¹/8 h	182	–	65–298	U/8 h	10.9	–	3.9–17.9	11
– night urine, 21 women	nmol s⁻¹/8 h	125	–	35–213	U/8 h	7.5	–	2.1–12.8	11
↓ **α-Amylase** ...... After SMITH and ROE, 37 °C:									
– 292 subjects.....................	µmol s⁻¹/h	–	–	(0.5–7.5)	U/h	–	–	(30–450)	26
After STREET and CLOSE, 37 °C:									
– 146 subjects.....................	µmol s⁻¹/L	–	–	1.67–26.7	U/L	–	–	100–1600	24
↓ **Lysozyme**	....	...	...	...	...	...	...	...	...

* U ≡ µmol min⁻¹.

Lactate dehydrogenase. Among the 5 isoenzymes, LDH-1 and LDH-2 predominate. LDH-4 and LDH-5 are not always detectable under normal conditions[9]. The enzyme activity is increased in many diseases of the genitourinary tract.

α-Amylase. Age, sex and state of diuresis have no effect on the rate of excretion[26]. The isoenzyme from the pancreas predomi-

nates in the urine[27,46]. The excretion rate is increased in acute pancreatitis, and reduced in pancreatic insufficiency.

Lysozyme. See Table 3 for normal excretion values (page 79). The enzyme is found mostly in the monocytes, and its excretion is increased in leukemia (particularly monocytic and myelomonocytic), with values ranging up to 1000 times the normal le-

↓See text below		SI unit	Mean	s	95% range (extreme range in brackets)	Other units*	Mean	s	95% range (extreme range in brackets)	Reference
β-Galactosidase	Substrate 4-nitrophenyl-β-D-galactopyranoside, 37°C:	nmol s⁻¹/L	83	–	(1.7–280)	U/L	5.0	–	(0.1–16.8)	47
↓ β-N-Acetylglu-cosaminidase ..	Substrate 4-nitrophenyl-N-acetyl-β-D-glucosaminide, 37°C:	nmol s⁻¹/L	135	–	(2.5–497)	U/L	8.1	–	(1.5–29.8)	47
	Substrate 4-methylumbelliferyl-2-acetamido-2-deoxy-β-D-gluco-pyranosid, 37 °C:									
	– 9 men....................	nmol s⁻¹/L	12	7.1	–	U/L	0.70	0.43	–	37
	– 8 women...................	nmol s⁻¹/L	16	7.5	–	U/L	0.98	0.45	–	37
↓ Uropepsinogen.	Substrate hemoglobin, 37°C:									
	– 21 men.................	μmol s⁻¹/d	0.67	0.31	–	U/d	40	19	–	45
	– 18 women.................	μmol s⁻¹/d	0.38	0.23	–	U/d	23	14	–	45

*U ≡ μmol min⁻¹.

vels[28, 30, 31]; it may therefore account for as much as 97% of total urinary protein[28].

β-N-Acetylglucosaminidase. Excretion – especially of isoenzyme B – is increased in kidney diseases[37]. An increased activity of the enzyme in the urine may be the first sign of the rejection of a kidney transplant[37].

Uropepsinogen. A small portion of the pepsinogen secreted by the gastric mucosa enters the blood and is excreted via the kidneys; however, uropepsinogen excretion is poorly correlated with pepsinogen secretion in the gastric juice. The absence of uropepsinogen in the urine is indicative of atrophy of the gastric mucosa.

References

[1] DUBACH, U. C. (Ed.), *Current Problems in Clinical Biochemistry*, volume 2, Huber, Berne, 1968.
[2] MATTENHEIMER, H., *Med. Clin. N. Amer.*, **55**, 1493 (1971).
[3] MATTENHEIMER, H., in BERGMEYER, H. U. (Ed.), *Methoden der enzymatischen Analyse*, 3rd ed., volume 1, Verlag Chemie, Weinheim/Bergstrasse, 1974, page 64.
[4] JÖSCH and DUBACH, *Clin. chim. Acta*, **15**, 325 (1967).
[5] WACKER and DORFMAN, *J. Amer. med. Ass.*, **181**, 972 (1962).
[6] BRENNER and GILBERT, *Amer. J. med. Sci.*, **245**, 31 (1963).
[7] ROSALKI and WILKINSON, *Lancet*, **2**, 327 (1959).
[8] AMADOR et al., *Ann. intern. Med.*, **62**, 30 (1965).
[9] HEMMINGSEN and SKOV, *Clin. chim. Acta*, **19**, 81 (1968).
[10] WERNER et al., *Clin. chim. Acta*, **29**, 437 (1970).
[11] SZASZ, G., *Z. klin. Chim.*, **8**, 1 (1970).
[12] LÉVY and DUBACH, *Klin. Wschr.*, **50**, 438 (1972).
[13] THIELE, K. G., *Klin. Wschr.*, **51**, 339 (1973).
[14] BAHRE et al., *Dtsch. med. Wschr.*, **99**, 2214 (1974); ROSALKI, S. B., *Advanc. clin. Chem.*, **17**, 53 (1975).
[15] SEPAHA et al., *Indian J. med. Res.*, **49**, 68 (1961).
[16] SACHSENHEIMER et al., *Klin. Wschr.*, **53**, 617 (1975).
[17] BURGEN, A. S., *Lancet*, **1**, 329 (1947).

[18] AMADOR et al., *J. Amer. med. Ass.*, **185**, 769 (1963); BUTTERWORTH et al., *Clin. chim. Acta*, **11**, 212 (1965); DIETZ and HODGES, *Clin. chim. Acta*, **15**, 393 (1967).
[19] LEVY and ROTTINO, *Clin. Chem.*, **6**, 43 (1960).
[20] SIGULEM et al., *Amer. J. clin. Nutr.*, **26**, 793 (1973).
[21] BAUM et al., *Clin. chim. Acta*, **4**, 453 (1969); DZIAŁOSZYŃSKI and GNIOT-SZULŻYCKA, *Clin. chim. Acta*, **15**, 381 (1967).
[22] CLAUSEN and ASBOE-HANSEN, *Clin. chim. Acta*, **16**, 131 (1967).
[23] TIERNEY et al., *Ann. intern. Med.*, **58**, 229 (1963).
[24] VAN RIET and HOEKE, *Clin. chim. Acta*, **19**, 459 (1968).
[25] CESKA et al., *Clin. chim. Acta*, **26**, 445 (1969).
[26] EBERHAGEN et al., *Z. klin. Chem.*, **8**, 284 (1970).
[27] ADLERCREUTZ et al., *Clin. chim. Acta*, **43**, 187 (1973).
[28] PRUZANSKI and OGRYZLO, *Advanc. clin. Chem.*, **13**, 335 (1970).
[29] BARTHELEMY et al., *Clin. chim. Acta*, **50**, 257 (1974).
[30] BRIERE et al., *Clin. chim. Acta*, **50**, 265 (1974).
[31] ZUCKER and WEBB, *Stand. Meth. clin. Chem.*, **7**, 9 (1972).
[32] HULTBERG et al., *Clin. chim. Acta*, **52**, 239 (1974).
[33] RIETRA et al., *Clin. chim. Acta*, **40**, 229 (1972).
[34] DESNICK et al., *J. Lab. clin. Med.*, **81**, 157 (1973).
[35] DANCE et al., *Clin. chim. Acta*, **27**, 87 (1970).
[36] SANDMAN et al., *Clin. chim. Acta*, **45**, 349 (1973).
[37] TUCKER et al., *Clin. chim. Acta*, **62**, 333 (1975); WELLWOOD et al., *Brit. med. J.*, **3**, 408 (1975); ELLIS et al., *Clin. chim. Acta*, **64**, 195 (1975).
[38] RICHTERICH and DAUWALDER, *Z. klin. Chem.*, **4**, 105 (1966).
[39] GONICK et al., *Arch. intern. Med.*, **132**, 63 (1973).
[40] ROTH, M., *Clin. chim. Acta*, **9**, 448 (1964); BERGMANN and SCHELER, *Klin. Wschr.*, **42**, 275 (1964).
[41] LUCKMANN and KÖRNER, *Klin. Wschr.*, **50**, 1003 (1972).
[42] PETERS et al., *Clin. chim. Acta*, **36**, 289 (1972).
[43] MARUHN et al., *Z. klin. Chem.*, **12**, 270 (1974); MARUHN et al., *Clin. chim. Acta*, **75**, 427 (1977).
[44] WILKINSON, J. H., in DUBACH, U. C. (Ed.), *Current Problems in Clinical Biochemistry*, volume 2, Huber, Berne, 1968, page 207.
[45] VAN GOIDSENHOVEN et al., *Gastroenterology*, **34**, 421 (1958).
[46] FRIDHANDLER et al., *Clin. Chem.*, **18**, 1493 (1972).
[47] MARUHN, D., *Clin. chim. Acta*, **73**, 453 (1976).

Carbohydrates (for references see page 85)

The carbohydrates in the urine are present partly in free form and partly in the form of glycoproteins, mucopolysaccharides and glycopeptides, or in the form of glucuronic acid bound to phenols and acids. Unless otherwise indicated, reference is made below to the excretion of free carbohydrates. These are partly derived from foods and partly formed endogenously[7–9].

The classic methods of determining 'urinary sugar' are based on the reducing power of certain carbohydrates. They are not specific for glucose (see adjoining table) but give positive results also with other urine constituents, such as uric acid, creatinine, glucuronic acid, homogentisic acid, ascorbic acid, fructose, lactose, and pentoses. Further, they can be positive in patients who have been treated with certain antibiotics[3] (penicillin, streptomycin, tetracyclines). Measurement by polarization is even more susceptible to interference since a majority of endogenous substances as well as many drugs (e.g. penicillin, tetracyclines) are optically active[4]. The o-toluidine method and that using hexokinase/glucose-6-phosphate dehydrogenase are best suited for glucose assays[5, 6].

Excretion of reducing substances ('urinary sugar') in urine

Method	Number	Mean	(Extreme range)	Reference
		mg/d		
Ferricyanide (automated)	–	1620	(520–3680)	1
Folin-Wu	–	1140	(300–2500)	1
Somogyi-Nelson	–	490	(70–1090)	1
Dinitrosalicylic acid......	–	190	(50–450)	1
o-Toluidine	–	180	(30–390)	1
Fermentation with yeast .	–	50	(0–100)	1
		mg/L		
Somogyi-Nelson	30	515	(242–845)	2
Glucose oxidase	30	72	(16–132)	2

↓See text below		Amount of substance				Mass				Reference
		Unit	Mean	s	(Extreme range)	Unit	Mean	s	(Extreme range)	
↓ Aldopentoses										
Arabinose	11 adults .... (a)	μmol/d	133	–	(93–180)	mg/d	20	–	(14–27)	10
	Relative to body mass: – 8 men .... (b)	μmol d⁻¹ kg⁻¹	4.29	1.93	–	mg d⁻¹ kg⁻¹	0.644	0.290	–	11
Xylose	11 adults .... (a)	μmol/d	80	–	(60–107)	mg/d	12	–	(9–16)	10
	Relative to body mass: – 8 men .... (b)	μmol d⁻¹ kg⁻¹	2.56	1.46	–	mg d⁻¹ kg⁻¹	0.385	0.219	–	11
Ribose	11 adults .... (a)	μmol/d	47	–	(40–67)	mg/d	7	–	(6–10)	10
	Relative to body mass: – 8 men .... (b)	μmol d⁻¹ kg⁻¹	0.366	0.679	–	mg d⁻¹ kg⁻¹	0.055	0.102	–	11
Fucose	11 adults .... (a)	μmol/d	146	–	(97–244)	mg/d	24	–	(16–40)	10
Rhamnose	Relative to body mass: – 8 men .... (b)	μmol d⁻¹ kg⁻¹	0.231	0.457	–	mg d⁻¹ kg⁻¹	0.038	0.075	–	11
↓ Ketopentoses	15 men	μmol/d	29	13	–	mg/d	4.3	1.9	–	14
↓ Glucose	18 children, 1 week to 4 months .... (a)	μmol/d	–	–	(0–233)	mg/d	–	–	(0–42)	16
	25 adults .... (b)	μmol/d	393	210	(0–1070)	mg/d	71	38	(0–193)	17
	Relative to creatinine: – newborn .... (c)	mmol/mol	15	–	(<50)	mg/g	24	–	(<80)	18
	– adolescents .... (c)	mmol/mol	–	–	(<19)	mg/g	–	–	(<30)	18
	– adults .... (c)	mmol/mol	5	–	(<38)	mg/g	8	–	(<61)	18
	Relative to body mass: – 8 men .... (d)	μmol d⁻¹ kg⁻¹	3.67	0.66	–	mg d⁻¹ kg⁻¹	0.662	0.119	–	11
↓ Galactose	18 children, 1 week to 4 months .... (a)	μmol/d	–	–	(0–500)	mg/d	–	–	(0–90)	16
	Relative to creatinine: – newborn .... (b)	mmol/mol	5.0	–	(<19)	mg/g	8	–	(<30)	18
	– adolescents .... (b)	mmol/mol	3.8	–	(<11)	mg/g	6	–	(<17)	18
	– adults .... (b)	mmol/mol	4.4	–	(<31)	mg/g	7	–	(<50)	18
	Relative to body mass: – 8 men .... (c)	mmol d⁻¹ kg⁻¹	3.03	1.09	–	mg d⁻¹ kg⁻¹	0.545	0.196	–	11
↓ Mannose	Relative to creatinine: – newborn	mmol/mol	2.5	–	(<12.6)	mg/g	4	–	(<20)	18
	– adolescents	mmol/mol	–	–	(<2.5)	mg/g	–	–	(<4)	18
	– adults	mmol/mol	–	–	(<2.5)	mg/g	–	–	(<4)	18

Aldopentoses. Values determined (a) by thin-layer chromatography; (b) by high-pressure liquid chromatography. – The excretion of arabinose and xylose is increased after ingestion of fruits and vegetables[10, 12]. After oral administration of 25 g of D-xylose, 25% of the dose appears in the urine within 5 hours if intestinal absorption and kidney function are normal (xylose loading test for detection of malabsorption)[13].

Ketopentoses. Mostly L-xylulose as well as traces of ribulose and sedoheptulose. In essential pentosuria, 1–5 g of L-xylulose is excreted daily regardless of diet[15].

Glucose. Values determined (a) by means of glucose oxidase; (b) by means of hexokinase/glucose-6-phosphate dehydrogenase; (c) by gas chromatography; and (d) by high-pressure liquid chromatography. (See also table on 'Reducing substances', page 82.) – Glucose excretion is irregularly and at times markedly increased during pregnancy[6]. It increases with increasing glucose intake (Fig. 1) and is pathologically elevated in certain types of renal damage, in various endocrine diseases (diabetes mellitus, Cushing's syndrome, adrenocortical hyperplasia), and in cases of head injuries and intracranial tumors.

Galactose. Determination (a) enzymatically; (b) by gas chromatography; (c) by high-pressure liquid chromatography. – Excretion increases after copious intake of lactose[20]. Infants put on a high-milk diet can excrete in the urine up to 2 mmol/L, and infants with galactosemia up to 55 mmol/L[21].

Mannose. Determined by high-pressure liquid chromatography.

Fructose. Determined by high-pressure liquid chromatography. – The excretion of fructose is increased after copious ingestion of fructose including sucrose intake[20] and in essential fructosuria.

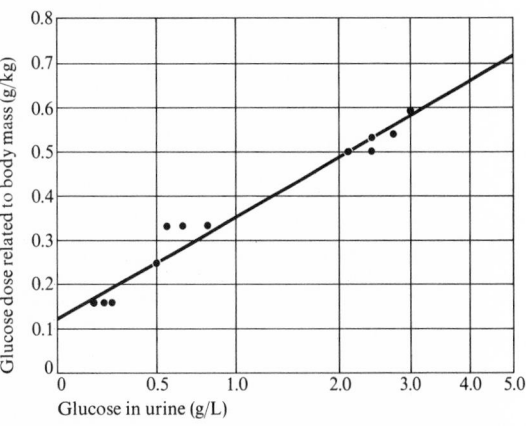

Fig. 1. Glucose excreted in urine related to glucose given intravenously[19].

↑↓See text on page 83 and on next page		Amount of substance				Mass				Reference
		Unit	Mean	s	(Extreme range)	Unit	Mean	s	(Extreme range)	
↑ **Fructose**	Relative to body mass: – 8 men	µmol d⁻¹ kg⁻¹	1.44	0.79	–	mg d⁻¹ kg⁻¹	0.260	0.143	–	11
Mannoheptulose	Relative to body mass: – 8 men	µmol d⁻¹ kg⁻¹	0.285	0.119	–	mg d⁻¹ kg⁻¹	0.060	0.025	–	11
↓ **Lactose**	18 children, 1 week to 4 months .... (a)	µmol/d	–	–	(204–727)	mg/d	–	–	(70–249)	16
	15 adults .... (a)	µmol/d	22	–	(9.6–52.3)	mg/d	7.6	–	(3.3–17.9)	22
	Relative to body mass: – 8 men .... (b)	µmol d⁻¹ kg⁻¹	3.77	1.84	–	mg d⁻¹ kg⁻¹	1.29	0.63	–	11
↓ **Sucrose**	Relative to body mass: – 8 men	µmol d⁻¹ kg⁻¹	0.853	0.368	–	mg d⁻¹ kg⁻¹	0.292	0.126	–	11
Fucosylglucose..	....	–	–	–	traces	–	–	–	traces	24
Xylosylglucose..	....	–	–	–	traces	–	–	–	traces	24
↓ **Raffinose**	Relative to body mass: – 8 men	µmol d⁻¹ kg⁻¹	0.11	0.048	–	mg d⁻¹ kg⁻¹	0.056	0.024	–	11
↓ **Tetrasaccharide** (consisting of glucose).........	2 boys	µmol/d	∼1.5	–	–	mg/d	∼1	–	–	25
↓ **Polyols**										
D-Threitol	Relative to creatinine: – adults	mmol/mol	10	–	(5.6–15)	mg/g	11	–	(6–16)	18
Erythritol.......	7 subjects..............	µmol/d	912	355	–	mg/d	111	43	–	26
Ribitol..........	7 subjects..............	µmol/d	53	34	–	mg/d	8	5	–	26
Arabitol	7 subjects..............	µmol/d	293	96	–	mg/d	45	14	–	26
Xylitol..........	7 subjects..............	µmol/d	53	36	–	mg/d	8	5	–	26
Mannitol	7 subjects..............	µmol/d	156	139	–	mg/d	28	25	–	26
	Relative to creatinine: – 20 children	mmol/mol	–	–	(0–245)	mg/g	–	–	(0–395)	41
Sorbitol.........	7 subjects..............	µmol/d	53	34	–	mg/d	10	6	–	26
Myoinositol.....	7 subjects..............	µmol/d	804	725	–	mg/d	146	132	–	26
Galactitol.......	Relative to creatinine: – 20 children	–	–	–	0	–	–	–	0	41
	– adults	mmol/mol	3.7	–	(<12)	mg/g	6	–	(<19)	18
↓ **Galactonic acid** .	....	...	...	...	...	...	...	...	...	...
↓ **D-Glucaric acid** . (as glucaro-1,4-lactone)	26 men	µmol/d	39.0	17.9	–	mg/d	7.5	3.4	–	30
	13 women	µmol/d	18.1	9.7	–	mg/d	3.5	1.9	–	30
	Relative to creatinine: – 16 newborn..........	mmol/mol	1.56	–	(0.27–4.00)	µmol/g	13.8	–	(2.4–35.2)	40
	– 45 children	mmol/mol	1.49	0.66	–	µmol/g	13.2	5.8	–	40
↓ **Glucuronic acid**										
– total	56 men	mmol/d	2.22	0.41	–	mg/d	431	80	–	32
	44 women	mmol/d	1.91	0.46	–	mg/d	371	89	–	32
	Relative to body mass: – 14 newborn, 0–2 weeks	µmol d⁻¹ kg⁻¹	84.5	10.9	–	mg d⁻¹ kg⁻¹	16.4	2.12	–	33
	– 10 children, 2–7 weeks	µmol d⁻¹ kg⁻¹	43.8	7.6	–	mg d⁻¹ kg⁻¹	8.5	1.48	–	33
↓ **Carbohydrates, non-dialyzable**										
Hexoses	4 adults	µmol/d	403	106	–	mg/d	72.6	19.1	–	38
Hexosamines ...	4 adults	µmol/d	148	34	–	mg/d	26.5	6.1	–	38
Sialic acid	4 adults	µmol/d	132	24	–	mg/d	40.7	7.5	–	38
	Relative to creatinine: – 6 subjects.............	mmol/mol	7.28	2.74	–	mg/g	19.9	7.5	–	43
Glucuronic acid.	children	µmol/d	–	–	(21–76)	mg/d	–	–	(4.1–14.7)	39
	adults	µmol/d	–	–	(14–38)	mg/d	–	–	(2.7–7.3)	39

Lactose. Determination (a) enzymatically; (b) by high-pressure liquid chromatography. – Excretion is increased after copious intake of lactose[20] and in pregnant and lactating women as a result of endogenous lactose formation[6]; with a lactose-free diet, no lactose is excreted in the urine.

Sucrose. Determined by high-pressure liquid chromatography. – Excretion increased after copious sucrose intake[20,23].

Raffinose. Determined by high-pressure liquid chromatography.

Tetrasaccharide consisting of glucose. Excretion increased in glycogen storage disease type II (Pompe's disease)[25].

Polyols. Determined by gas chromatography. – See PFAFFENBERGER et al.[18] regarding age-related differences in the excretion of polyhydric alcohols. The excretion of myoinositol is increased in diabetes mellitus and chronic renal failure[26,27]. The excretion of galactitol is increased after oral galactose loading[28] and in galactosemia[28,29].

Galactonic acid. Demonstrable in the urine after oral galactose loading, particularly in galactosemia[28].

D-*Glucaric acid.* The excretion in newborn infants provides information on the effectiveness of the glucuronic acid-producing system[42].

Glucuronic acid. Glucuronic acid is bound for the most part to phenols (also to steroidal hormones) and acids. The liver is able to supply large quantities of glucuronic acid for the detoxification and excretion of such substances. In women, excretion varies with the cycle[34]. The glucuronic acid excretion is *increased* in severe burns and in malignant neoplastic diseases[35]; it is *decreased* in rheumatoid diseases[34], liver diseases[36], and in the nephrotic syndrome[37].

Carbohydrates, non-dialyzable. These carbohydrates are present in the form of glycoproteins, mucopolysaccharides and glycopeptides (see also page 78). The following hexoses have been identified: galactose, mannose, glucose and fucose; hexosamines: glucosamine and galactosamine. Glucuronic acid excretion serves as a measure of the excretion of mucopolysaccharides (see also page 80).

References
[1] CARAWAY, W. T., *Clin. Chem.*, **17**, 63 (1971).
[2] FROESCH and RENOLD, *Diabetes*, **5**, 1 (1956).
[3] FISHER et al., *Ann. paediat. (Basel)*, **185**, 254 (1955).
[4] SCHMIDT, F. H., *Dtsch. med. Wschr.*, **92**, 2025 (1967).
[5] FÖRSTER and HASLBECK, *Diagnostik*, **5**, 311 (1972).
[6] HYTTEN and LIND, *Diagnostic Indices in Pregnancy*, CIBA-GEIGY LTD., Basle, 1974.
[7] SIDBURY, J. B., *Advanc. clin. Chem.*, **4**, 29 (1961).
[8] YOUNG, D. S., *Amer. J. clin. Path.*, **53**, 803 (1970).
[9] BUTTS and JOLLEY, *Clin. Chem.*, **16**, 722 (1970).
[10] BELL and TALUKDER, *Clin. chim. Acta*, **40**, 13 (1972).
[11] JOLLEY et al., *Amer. J. clin. Path.*, **53**, 793 (1970).
[12] BICKEL, H., *Mod. Probl. Pädiat.*, **4**, 136 (1959).
[13] *Nutr. Rev.*, **30**, 84 (1972).
[14] BAKER et al., *Metabolism*, **9**, 478 (1960).
[15] Annotation, *Brit. med. J.*, **1**, 1628 (1963).
[16] TENGSTRÖM and WRANNE, *Scand. J. clin. Lab. Invest.*, **22**, 137 (1968).
[17] RENSCHLER et al., *Dtsch. med. Wschr.*, **90**, 2349 (1965).
[18] PFAFFENBERGER et al., *Analyt. Biochem.*, **63**, 501 (1975).
[19] KRUSE-JARRES et al., *Dtsch. med. Wschr.*, **96**, 1424 (1971).
[20] NAKAMURA and TAMURA, *Clin. chim. Acta*, **39**, 367 (1972).
[21] WOOLF, L. I., *Advanc. clin. Chem.*, **5**, 1 (1962).
[22] VITEK et al., *Clin. chim. Acta*, **58**, 109 (1975).
[23] HAWORTH, J. C., *Lancet*, **2**, 725 (1962).
[24] NORDÉN et al., *Clin. chim. Acta*, **44**, 95 (1973).
[25] HALLGREN et al., *Europ. J. clin. Invest.*, **4**, 429 (1974).
[26] PITKÄNEN, E., *Clin. chim. Acta*, **38**, 221 (1972).
[27] ALOIA, J. F., *J. Lab. clin. Med.*, **82**, 809 (1973).
[28] BERGREN et al., *Science*, **176**, 683 (1972).
[29] BLAU, K., *Clin. chim. Acta*, **38**, 441 (1972).
[30] SIMMONS et al., *Clin. chim. Acta*, **51**, 47 (1974).
[31] CASSIMOS et al., *J. Pediat.*, **84**, 871 (1974).
[32] MÜTING et al., *Z. klin. Med.*, **157**, 538 (1963).
[33] PULKKINEN et al., *Ann. paediat. Fenn.*, **8**, 50 (1962).
[34] HOLOPAINEN, T., *Ann. Med. exp. Fenn.*, **36**, suppl. 8 (1958).
[35] CORNILLOT, P., *Clin. chim. Acta*, **7**, 42 (1962).
[36] MÜTING, D., *Dtsch. med. Wschr.*, **88**, 130 (1963).
[37] MÜTING et al., *Z. klin. Med.*, **157**, 544 (1963).
[38] KING et al., *J. clin. Invest.*, **37**, 315 (1958).
[39] DI FERRANTE and RICH, *J. Lab. clin. Med.*, **48**, 491 (1956).
[40] MALAKA-ZAFIRIU et al., *Helv. paediat. Acta*, **30**, 201 (1975).
[41] NG et al., *Clin. chim. Acta*, **64**, 39 (1975).
[42] TALAFANT et al., *Pediat. Res.*, **9**, 480 (1975).
[43] OKADA et al., *Clin. chim. Acta*, **86**, 159 (1978).

Nitrogen-free substances (for references see pages 92 and 93)

↓See text on page after next		Amount of substance				Mass				Reference
		Unit	Mean	s	(Extreme range)	Unit	Mean	s	(Extreme range)	
↓ Organic acids	Men	mmol/d	55	–	–	...	...	...	...	1
	Women	mmol/d	64	–	–	...	...	...	...	1
Aliphatic acids and related compounds										
Formic acid	20 adults	mmol/d	0.31	0.18	(0.04–0.73)	mg/d	14.1	8.2	(1.8–33.4)	4
Acetic acid.......	19 subjects	mmol/d	0.68	0.80	(0.11–3.7)	mg/d	41	48	(6.6–220)	5
	Relative to creatinine: – 16 subjects	mmol/mol	200	164	(36–716)	mg/g	106	87	(19–380)	6
Propionic acid ...	19 subjects	µmol/d	45	42	(0–189)	mg/d	3.3	3.1	(0–14)	5
	Relative to creatinine: – 5 children, < 1 year ...	mmol/mol	–	–	(11.4–18.3)	µmol/g	–	–	(101–162)	63
Isobutyric acid ...	Relative to creatinine: – 5 children, < 1 year ...	mmol/mol	–	–	(12–27)	µmol/g	–	–	(110–240)	63
	– 5 subjects	mmol/mol	39	–	(9–122)	mg/g	30	–	(7–95)	6
Butyric acid	Relative to creatinine: – 5 children, < 1 year ...	mmol/mol	–	–	(0–6.4)	µmol/g	–	–	(0–57)	63
	– 3 subjects	mmol/mol	42	–	(21–81)	mg/g	33	–	(16–63)	6
Isovaleric acid ...	7 children, 3–5 years	µmol/d	–	–	(<2)	mg/d	–	–	(<0.2)	73
	Relative to creatinine: – 5 children, < 1 year ...	mmol/mol	–	–	(1.1–6.7)	µmol/g	–	–	(10–59)	63
	– 10 subjects	mmol/mol	41	25	(16–75)	mg/g	37	23	(14–68)	6
Caproic acid	Relative to creatinine: – 5 children, < 1 year ...	mmol/mol	–	–	(0–1.0)	µmol/g	–	–	(0–9)	63

↓See text on next page		Amount of substance				Mass				Reference
		Unit	Mean	s	(Extreme range)	Unit	Mean	s	(Extreme range)	
↓ Long-chain fatty acids										
Non-esterified (free), total.......	25 adults...............	µmol/L	10.8	2.7	–	mg/L	3.05	0.76	–	7
Lauric acid.......	25 adults...............	µmol/L	0.4	0.3	–	mg/L	0.08	0.06	–	7
Myristic acid.....	25 adults...............	µmol/L	0.9	0.4	–	mg/L	0.21	0.09	–	7
Palmitic acid.....	25 adults...............	µmol/L	4.5	1.3	–	mg/L	1.15	0.33	–	7
Palmitoleic acid..	25 adults...............	µmol/L	0.4	0.3	–	mg/L	0.10	0.08	–	7
Stearic acid	25 adults...............	µmol/L	1.5	0.4	–	mg/L	0.43	0.11	–	7
Oleic acid........	25 adults...............	µmol/L	2.4	1.2	–	mg/L	0.68	0.34	–	7
Linoleic acid.....	25 adults...............	µmol/L	0.7	0.7	–	mg/L	0.20	0.20	–	7
↓ Glycolic acid.....	19 adults	µmol/d	462	–	(240–800)	mg/d	35.1	–	(18–61)	8
	For body surface of 1.73 m²:									
	– 15 children	µmol/d	550	–	(200–790)	mg/d	42	–	(15–60)	8
↓ Glyoxylic acid ...	12 adults	µmol/d	50	–	(30–81)	mg/d	3.7	–	(2.2–6.0)	8
	For body surface of 1.73 m²:									
	– 15 children...........	µmol/d	22	–	(7–59)	mg/d	1.6	–	(0.5–4.4)	8
↓ Oxalic acid	150 adults .... (a)	µmol/d	280	100	80–500	mg/d	25.2	9.0	7.2–45	80
	22 adults .... (b)	µmol/d	301	79	(90–420)	mg/d	27.1	7.1	(8–38)	11
	27 adults .... (c)	µmol/d	327	–	(200–520)	mg/d	29.4	–	(18–47)	8
	For body surface of 1.73 m²:									
	– 15 children .... (c)	µmol/d	365	–	(110–620)	mg/d	32.9	–	(10–56)	8
Succinic acid	12 subjects	µmol/d	59	–	(19–102)	mg/d	7.0	–	(2.3–12)	14
	Relative to body mass:									
	– 13 children, 0–29 days.	µmol d⁻¹ kg⁻¹	3.1	3.2	–	mg d⁻¹ kg⁻¹	0.37	0.38	–	27
	– 8 children, 1–23 months	µmol d⁻¹ kg⁻¹	2.8	2.7	–	mg d⁻¹ kg⁻¹	0.33	0.32	–	27
	– 6 children, 2–14 years .	µmol d⁻¹ kg⁻¹	1.6	0.8	–	mg d⁻¹ kg⁻¹	0.19	0.1	–	27
Glutaric acid	....	µmol/d	–	–	(<19)	mg/d	–	–	(<2.5)	15
	4 newborn	µmol/L	10	–	–	mg/L	1.3	–	–	18
	Relative to creatinine:									
	– 5 children, <1 year ...	mmol/mol	–	–	(<11)	µmol/g	–	–	(<100)	63
↓ Adipic acid	....	µmol/d	–	–	(9–17)	mg/d	–	–	(1.3–2.5)	16
	Relative to body mass:									
	– 21 adults..............	µmol d⁻¹ kg⁻¹	0.42	0.23	–	µg d⁻¹ kg⁻¹	62	33	–	17
	Relative to creatinine:									
	– 5 children, <1 year ...	mmol/mol	6	–	(2–11)	mg/g	8	–	(3–14)	78
↓ Suberic acid	4 newborn	µmol/L	30	–	–	mg/L	5.2	s	–	18
	Relative to creatinine:									
	– 5 children, <1 year ...	mmol/mol	9	–	(4–20)	mg/g	12	–	(5–26)	78
Sebacic acid	4 newborn	µmol/L	20	–	–	mg/L	4	–	–	18
↓ Methylmalonic acid	10 subjects.......... (a)	µmol/d	24	–	(0–50)	mg/d	2.8	–	(0–6)	64
	Relative to creatinine:									
	– 6 newborn ....(b)	mmol/mol	2.0	0.7	–	mg/g	2.1	0.7	–	20
	– 5 children, 2–12 years (b)	mmol/mol	4.0	0.9	–	mg/g	4.2	0.9	–	20
	– 8 adults.............(b)	mmol/mol	1.7	0.9	–	mg/g	1.8	0.9	–	20
Ethylmalonic acid	Adults.................	µmol/d	–	–	(8–60)	mg/d	–	–	(1–8)	29
	Relative to creatinine:									
	– 5 children, <1 year ...	mmol/mol	–	–	(<40)	µmol/g	–	–	(<350)	63

↓See text below		Amount of substance				Mass				Reference
		Unit	Mean	s	(Extreme range)	Unit	Mean	s	(Extreme range)	
3-Methylsuccinic acid	4 adults..............	µmol/d	–	–	(10–20)	mg/d	–	–	(1.3–2.6)	21
	Relative to creatinine:									
	– 6 newborn	mmol/mol	1.2	0.8		mg/g	1.4	0.9	–	20
	– 5 children, 2–12 years .	mmol/mol	1.9	0.7	–	mg/g	2.2	0.8	–	20
	– 8 adults	mmol/mol	0.9	0.8		mg/g	1.1	0.9	–	20
3-Methylglutaric acid	4 adults..............	µmol/d	–	–	(20–30)	mg/d	–	–	(2.9–4.4)	21
3-Methyladipic acid	4 adults..............	µmol/d	–	–	(100–190)	mg/d	–	–	(16–30)	21
	Relative to body mass:									
	– 21 adults	µmol d⁻¹ kg⁻¹	0.87	0.54	–	µg d⁻¹ kg⁻¹	139	86	–	17
3,4-Methylene-adipic acid	....	µmol/d	~100	–	–	mg/d	~16	–	–	22
3-Methylpimelic acid	4 adults..............	µmol/d	–	–	(<10–30)	mg/d	–	–	(<1.7–5)	21
3-Methylsuberic acid	4 adults..............	µmol/d	–	–	(<10)	mg/d	–	–	(<1.8)	21
Fumaric acid.....	Relative to body mass:									
	– 13 children, 0–29 days	µmol d⁻¹ kg⁻¹	0.7	0.09	–	mg d⁻¹ kg⁻¹	0.08	0.01	–	27
	– 8 children, 1–23 months	µmol d⁻¹ kg⁻¹	0.7	0.7	–	mg d⁻¹ kg⁻¹	0.08	0.08	–	27
	– 6 children, 2–14 years .	µmol d⁻¹ kg⁻¹	0.3	0.2	–	mg d⁻¹ kg⁻¹	0.03	0.02	–	27
↓Lactic acid	30 men	µmol/d	508	293	(178–1700)	mg/d	45.8	26.4	(16–153)	23
	17 women	µmol/d	513	188	(244–1070)	mg/d	46.2	16.9	(22–96)	23
	Relative to body mass:									
	– 13 children, 0–29 days	µmol d⁻¹ kg⁻¹	9.7	5.0	–	mg d⁻¹ kg⁻¹	0.87	0.45	–	27
	– 8 children, 1–23 months	µmol d⁻¹ kg⁻¹	8.8	7.4	–	mg d⁻¹ kg⁻¹	0.79	0.67	–	27
	– 6 children, 2–14 years .	µmol d⁻¹ kg⁻¹	9.7	4.9	–	mg d⁻¹ kg⁻¹	0.87	0.44	–	27
	Relative to creatinine:									
	– 18 newborn	mmol/mol	65.6	30.5	–	mg/g	52.2	24.3	–	24
	– 71 children	mmol/mol	17.0	10.2	–	mg/g	13.5	8.1	–	24
↓Pyruvic acid	21 children	µmol/d	64	20.8	–	mg/d	5.6	1.83	–	25
	3 men	µmol/d	109	–	–	mg/d	9.6	–	–	26
	3 women	µmol/d	129	–	–	mg/d	11.4	–	–	26
	Relative to body mass:									
	– 13 children, 0–29 days	µmol d⁻¹ kg⁻¹	8.9	6.1	–	mg d⁻¹ kg⁻¹	0.78	0.54	–	27
	– 8 children, 1–23 months	µmol d⁻¹ kg⁻¹	6.9	3.3	–	mg d⁻¹ kg⁻¹	0.61	0.29	–	27
	– 6 children, 2–14 years .	µmol d⁻¹ kg⁻¹	6.8	4.7	–	mg d⁻¹ kg⁻¹	0.60	0.41	–	27

Organic acids. Aliphatic acids dominate in infant urine, and after ingestion of fruits and vegetables aromatic acids dominate in adult urine, but they are for the most part bound to amino acids (page 67). See also NORDMANN and NORDMANN[2] as well as WERLE and SCHIEVELBEIN[3]. Very large quantities of organic acids are excreted in certain hereditary disorders of amino-acid metabolism – thus, about 2 mol of propionic acid to 1 mol of creatinine are excreted in propionic-aciduria and methylmalonic-aciduria[6].

Long-chain fatty acids. Values of individuals with normal renal function, determined by gas chromatography. (a) Mean relative molecular mass: 282.

Glycolic acid. In most cases of primary hyperoxaluria excretion amounts to more than 1.3 mmol/d[8].

Glyoxylic acid. Values in children relative to age have been cited by RAMPINI et al.[9]. Increased in certain cases of primary hyperoxaluria[8].

Oxalic acid. Values determined (a) by gas chromatography, (b) enzymatically, (c) by isotope dilution. – The uncorrected daily excretion is lower in children; it reaches adult values at about age 14[12]. Oxalic acid excretion increases with the urinary volume rate and is greater on a high-oxalate than on a low-oxalate diet[10]. Presumably, 35–50% of the oxalic acid in the urine is formed from ascorbic acid[13]. Some patients with renal calculi excrete increased quantities of oxalate (up to 1 mmol/d)[10]; in primary hyperoxaluria excretion exceeds 1 mmol/d[8,10].

Adipic acid, suberic acid. These acids are excreted in increased amounts in ketosis (particularly diabetes mellitus)[19].

Methylmalonic acid. Values determined (a) by thin-layer chromatography, (b) by gas chromatography. – Excretion is increased in vitamin B_{12} deficiency[5,64].

Lactic acid. Excretion is increased after vigorous muscular work; high values are found in congenital lactacidosis[18]. The lactic acid concentration in urine is increased in pyelonephritis and urethral obstruction, but not in lower urinary tract infection[82].

Pyruvic acid. Excretion is increased in uncompensated diabetes mellitus.

		Amount of substance				Mass				Reference
		Unit	Mean	s	(Extreme range)	Unit	Mean	s	(Extreme range)	
2(α)-Hydroxy-butyric acid	5 children, <1 year	µmol/L	–	–	(<10)	mg/L	–	–	(<1.0)	63
	Relative to body mass: – 21 adults	µmol d^{-1} kg^{-1}	–	–	(<1)	mg d^{-1} kg^{-1}	–	–	(<0.1)	17
3(β)-Hydroxy-butyric acid	Relative to body mass: – 21 adults	µmol d^{-1} kg^{-1}	5.96	3.84	–	mg d^{-1} kg^{-1}	0.62	0.40	–	17
	Relative to creatinine: – 10 children, 3 months to 5 years	mmol/mol	–	–	(1–27)	mg/g	–	–	(1–25)	66
3(β)-Hydroxy-isobutyric acid	Relative to creatinine: – 10 children, 3 months to 5 years	mmol/mol	–	–	(2–24)	mg/g	–	–	(2–22)	66
erythro-**2,3-Dihydroxybuty-ric acid** (4-deoxyery-thronic acid)	Relative to creatinine: – 8 newborn – 8 adults	mmol/mol mmol/mol	trace 5	– 3	(0–trace) (3–8)	mg/g mg/g	trace 5	– 3	(0–trace) (3–8)	67 67
threo-**2,3-Dihydroxybutyric acid** (4-deoxythreonic acid)	Relative to creatinine: – 8 newborn – 8 adults	mmol/mol mmol/mol	14 25	7 10	(5–27) (14–43)	mg/g mg/g	15 27	7 11	(5–29) (15–46)	67 67
2,3-Dihydroxyisobutyric acid (2-methylgly-ceric acid)	Relative to creatinine: – 8 newborn – 8 adults	– mmol/mol	– 1	– –	0 (0–2)	– mg/g	– 1	– –	0 (0–2)	67 67
3,4-Dihydroxyisobutyric acid (2-deoxytetronic acid)	Relative to creatinine: – 8 newborn – 8 adults	mmol/mol mmol/mol	73 8	24 3	(37–105) (6–13)	mg/g mg/g	78 9	25 3	(39–111) (6–14)	67 67
2,4-Dihydroxybutyric acid (3-deoxytetronic acid)	Relative to creatinine: – 8 newborn – 8 adults	mmol/mol mmol/mol	trace 2	– 2	(0–trace) (0–6)	mg/g mg/g	trace 2	– 2	(0–trace) (0–6)	67 67
erythro-**2,3,4-Trihydroxybutyric acid** (erythronic acid)	Relative to creatinine: – 8 newborn – 8 adults	mmol/mol mmol/mol	109 20	19 8	(76–133) (15–37)	mg/g mg/g	131 24	23 10	(91–160) (18–44)	67 67
threo-**2,3,4-Trihydroxybutyric acid** (threonic acid)	Relative to creatinine: – 8 newborn – 8 adults	mmol/mol mmol/mol	63 10	21 7	(39–101) (4–22)	mg/g mg/g	76 12	25 8	(47–122) (5–27)	67 67
2-Methyl-3-hydroxybutyric acid	Relative to creatinine: – 10 children, 3 months to 5 years	mmol/mol	–	–	(1–9)	mg/g	–	–	(1–9)	66

β-Hydroxyisovaleric acid. Up to 30 times higher in ketoacidosis[30].

α-Oxoglutaric acid. Excretion is reduced in chronic renal failure[31].

Citric acid. Values determined (a) enzymatically, (b) colorimetrically, (c) by column chromatography. – Excretion higher on high-carbohydrate diet than on high-protein diet; *elevated* with administration of estrogens (hence cycle-dependent in women) and of vitamin D; *reduced* with vigorous muscular activity, in acidosis, diabetes mellitus, hypoparathyroidism, and in chronic renal failure[31].

Ketone bodies. (a) As acetone, (b) as acetoacetic acid + 3-hydroxybutyric acid. – The ketone bodies consist of acetoacetic acid, 3-hydroxybutyric acid (see above) and acetone; with increasing excretion of ketone bodies the proportion of 3-hydroxybutyric acid increases[34]. The excretion of ketone bodies is increased during fasting, particularly when this is accompanied by muscular work, and at low environmental temperatures; it is reduced in states of dehydration. It is *pathologically* elevated in diabetes (>100 mmol/L in poorly controlled diabetes), in thyrotoxicosis and in fever. Children show a greater tendency to hyperketonuria than adults.

↑See text on page 88		Amount of substance				Mass				Refer-ence
		Unit	Mean	s	(Extreme range)	Unit	Mean	s	(Extreme range)	
2-Ethylhydra-crylic acid	Relative to creatinine ...	mmol/mol	~3	–	–	mg/g	~3	–	–	28
2(α)-Hydroxy-isovaleric acid....	Relative to creatinine: – 5 children, <1 year ...	mmol/mol	–	–	(<4.5)	μmol/g	–	–	(<40)	63
3(β)-Hydroxy-isovaleric acid ...	7 children, 3–5 years	μmol/d	–	–	(<60)	mg/d	–	–	(<7)	73
	Relative to body mass: – 21 adults	μmol d⁻¹ kg⁻¹	1.9	1.5	–	mg d⁻¹ kg⁻¹	0.22	0.18	–	17
	Relative to creatinine: – 10 children, 3 months to 5 years	mmol/mol	–	–	(5–26)	mg/g	–	–	(5–27)	66
Malic acid	12 subjects.............	μmol/d	40	–	–	mg/d	5.4	–	–	31
	Relative to body mass: – 13 children, 0–29 days	μmol d⁻¹ kg⁻¹	6.2	3.9	–	mg d⁻¹ kg⁻¹	0.83	0.52	–	27
	– 8 children, 1–23 months	μmol d⁻¹ kg⁻¹	6.0	4.9	–	mg d⁻¹ kg⁻¹	0.81	0.66	–	27
	– 6 children, 2–14 years .	μmol d⁻¹ kg⁻¹	2.7	1.4	–	mg d⁻¹ kg⁻¹	0.36	0.19	–	27
Tartaric acid.....	Relative to body mass: – 21 adults	μmol d⁻¹ kg⁻¹	0.87	0.33	–	mg d⁻¹ kg⁻¹	0.13	0.05	–	17
↑ α-Oxoglutaric acid.............	21 children, 5–10 years..	μmol/d	64	30	–	mg/d	9.3	4.4	–	25
	3 men..................	μmol/d	82	–	–	mg/d	12.0	–	–	26
	3 women...............	μmol/d	128	–	–	mg/d	18.7	–	–	26
	Relative to body mass: – 13 children, 0–29 days	μmol d⁻¹ kg⁻¹	13.8	7.0	–	mg d⁻¹ kg⁻¹	2.01	1.02	–	27
	– 8 children, 1–23 months	μmol d⁻¹ kg⁻¹	4.4	2.0	–	mg d⁻¹ kg⁻¹	0.64	0.29	–	27
	– 6 children, 2–14 years .	μmol d⁻¹ kg⁻¹	4.0	2.7	–	mg d⁻¹ kg⁻¹	0.59	0.40	–	27
3-Hydroxy-3-methylglutaric acid.............	Relative to creatinine: – 15 newborn	mmol/mol	27	–	(6–73)	mg/g	38	–	(9–105)	65
	– 10 adults.............	mmol/mol	1.4	–	(0.7–3)	mg/g	2	–	(1–4)	65
↑ Citric acid	35 subjects...........(a)	mmol/d	1.5	–	(0.4–3.4)	mg/d	290	–	(80–650)	32
	30 men ....(b)	mmol/d	2.75	1.47	(0.21–6.35)	mg/d	528	283	(40–1220)	23
	17 women ....(b)	mmol/d	3.68	1.97	(1.04–8.80)	mg/d	707	378	(199–1690)	23
	Relative to body mass: – 13 children, 0–29 days ....(c)	μmol d⁻¹ kg⁻¹	19.9	8.7	–	mg d⁻¹ kg⁻¹	3.83	1.67	–	27
	– 8 children, 1–23 months ....(c)	μmol d⁻¹ kg⁻¹	16.4	10.3	–	mg d⁻¹ kg⁻¹	3.15	1.98	–	27
	– 6 children, 2–14 years ....(c)	μmol d⁻¹ kg⁻¹	15.4	7.5	–	mg d⁻¹ kg⁻¹	2.95	1.44	–	27
Isocitric acid.....	Relative to creatinine: – 15 newborn	mmol/mol	19	–	(5–34)	mg/g	32	–	(9–58)	65
	– 10 adults.............	mmol/mol	7.7	–	(5–12)	mg/g	13	–	(8–20)	65
cis-Aconitic acid.............	Relative to body mass: – 13 children, 0–29 days.	μmol d⁻¹ kg⁻¹	2.0	1.8	–	mg d⁻¹ kg⁻¹	0.35	0.31	–	27
	– 8 children, 1–23 months	μmol d⁻¹ kg⁻¹	0.80	0.80	–	mg d⁻¹ kg⁻¹	0.14	0.14	–	27
	– 6 children, 2–14 years .	μmol d⁻¹ kg⁻¹	0.63	0.46	–	mg d⁻¹ kg⁻¹	0.11	0.08	–	27
↑ Ketone bodies	Adults...............(a)	mmol/d	–	–	(0.17–1.7)	mg/d	–	–	(10–100)	33
	10 adults ....(b)	μmol/d	98	56	–	...	...	...	...	68
	Relative to creatinine: – 12 adults........... (a)	mmol/mol	99	64	(21–125)	mg g	51	33	(11–64)	6
Acetaldehyde	16 infants..............	μmol/L	360	–	(1–660)	mg/L	16	–	(0.04–29)	69
Acetone.........	22 infants..............	μmol/L	64	–	(15–233)	mg/L	3.7	–	(0.87–13.5)	69
	10 subjects.............	μmol/L	14	–	(3–43)	mg/L	0.8	–	(0.2–2.5)	35

↓See text on next page and on page after next		Amount of substance				Mass				Reference
		Unit	Mean	s	(Extreme range)	Unit	Mean	s	(Extreme range)	
Butanone	16 infants..............	μmol/L	1	–	(0–4.0)	μg/L	70	–	(0–290)	69
	Relative to creatinine:									
	– 2 adults..............	mmol/mol	–	–	(trace–11)	mg/g	–	–	(trace–7)	6
Dimethylsulfone .	11 subjects..............	μmol/d	–	–	(39–114)	mg/d	–	–	(3.7–10.7)	62
α-Oxo-γ-methyl-thiobutyric acid ..	children	μmol/d	0.33	–	–	μg/d	49	–	–	79
Heterocyclic compounds										
Furan-2,5-dicar-boxylic acid......	Relative to body mass:									
	– 21 adults..............	μmol d^{-1} kg^{-1}	0.70	0.77	–	mg d^{-1} kg^{-1}	0.11	0.12	–	17
	Relative to creatinine:									
	– 20 adults..............	mmol/mol	–	–	(0.36–5.9)	mg/g	–	–	(0.5–8.2)	36
5-Hydroxymethyl-furan-2-carbox-ylic acid	Relative to body mass:									
	– 21 adults..............	μmol d^{-1} kg^{-1}	1.5	1.9	–	mg d^{-1} kg^{-1}	0.22	0.27	–	17
Phenols, aromatic acids										
↓ **Phenol**..........	....	μmol/d	106	–	(85–140)	mg/d	10	–	(8–13)	37
↓ **p-Cresol**		mmol/d	0.80	–	(0.59–1.08)	mg/d	87	–	(64–117)	37
Pyrocatechol		μmol/d	52	–	–	mg/d	5.7	–	–	39
↓ **Benzoic acid**	Relative to creatinine:									
	– 27 subjects.............	mmol/mol	106	41	–	mg/g	115	44	–	40
↓ **Phenylacetic acid**	4 children, >1 year.....	mmol/d	0.16	–	(0.04–0.46)	mg/d	21.7	–	(5.3–62)	41
	17 children, 1–8 years...	mmol/d	0.31	0.16	(0.10–0.57)	mg/d	42.0	21.9	(13–77)	41
	8 adults................	mmol/d	1.17	0.70	(0.46–2.7)	mg/d	159	95	(62–370)	41
	Relative to creatinine:									
	– 27 subjects.............	mmol/mol	96	50	–	mg/g	116	60	–	40
↓ **Phenylpropionic acid**										
– total...........	10 adults	μmol/d	–	–	(0.33–4.20)	μg/d	–	–	(50–630)	43
– free	10 adults	μmol/d	–	–	(0.07–1.40)	μg/d	–	–	(10–210)	43
↓ **p-Hydroxybenzoic acid**..............	Relative to creatinine:									
	– 7 subjects	mmol/mol	10.8	11.5	–	mg/g	13.2	14.1	–	71
	– 27 subjects	mmol/mol	16	9	–	mg/g	19	11	–	40
↓ **p-Hydroxyphenyl-acetic acid**	Relative to creatinine:									
	– 19 subjects............	mmol/mol	8.0	2.2	–	mg/g	10.7	2.9	–	71
	– 27 subjects............	mmol/mol	27	17	–	mg/g	36	23	–	40
m-Hydroxyphenyl-acetic acid	Relative to creatinine:									
	– 19 subjects............	mmol/mol	6.1	4.1	–	mg/g	8.2	5.5	–	71
p-Hydroxyphenyl-lactic acid	Relative to creatinine:									
	– 20 men	mmol/mol	1.05	0.43	(0.3–2.2)	mg/g	1.69	0.70	(0.5–3.5)	44
4-Hydroxy-3-methoxybenzoic acid.............. (vanillic acid)	....	μmol/d	–	–	(<30)	mg/d	–	–	(<5)	45
↓ **4-Hydroxy-3-methoxy-phenylethanol**	9 men	μmol/d	1.42	0.27	(0.49–2.77)	μg/d	239	46	(82–465)	46
3,4-Dihydroxy-phenylglycol	8 men	μmol/d	3.8	–	–	mg/d	0.64	–	–	74

↓See text on next page		Amount of substance				Mass				Refer-ence
		Unit	Mean	s	95% range (extreme range in brackets)	Unit	Mean	s	95% range (extreme range in brackets)	
4-Hydroxy-3-methoxy-phenylglycol	18 subjects.............	µmol/d	16	4	(7.6–25)	mg/d	3.0	0.8	(1.4–4.6)	47
	20 adults	µmol/d	13	4	–	mg/d	2.4	0.8	–	48
	9 men	µmol/d	10.1	0.60	(6.13–12.1)	mg/d	1.86	0.11	(1.13–2.22)	46
3,4-Dihydroxy-phenylacetic acid.............	5 children .... (a)	µmol/d	0.71	–	(0.30–1.78)	mg/d	0.12	–	(0.05–0.30)	49
	10 adults .... (a)	µmol/d	4.1	–	(2.4–8.9)	mg/d	0.69	–	(0.41–1.5)	49
	12 men .... (b)	µmol/d	17.7	7.6	(5.9–26.1)	mg/d	2.98	1.28	(1.0–4.4)	50
↓ **4-Hydroxy-3-meth-oxyphenylacetic acid**............. (homovanillic acid)	15 subjects......... (a)	µmol/d	29.4	6.0	–	mg/d	5.35	1.1	–	53
	12 men .... (a)	µmol/d	51.7	13.6	(23.6–70.3)	mg/d	9.41	2.47	(4.3–12.8)	50
	80 men .... (b)	µmol/d	26.8	7.1	(13–48)	mg/d	4.89	1.30	(2.4–8.8)	51
	43 women .... (b)	µmol/d	27.1	7.3	(14–47)	mg/d	4.93	1.33	(2.6–8.6)	51
	20 adults .... (c)	µmol/d	23	8.2	–	mg/d	4.2	1.5	–	48
	Relative to creatinine: – 20 subjects........ (c)	mmol/mol	2.31	–	(1.06–3.89)	mg/g	3.72	–	(1.70–6.26)	54
↓ **3-Hydroxy-4-meth-oxyphenylacetic acid**.............. (*iso*-homovanil-lic acid)	Relative to creatinine: – 20 subjects.............	mmol/mol	0.17	–	(0.012–0.60)	mg/g	0.28	–	(0.02–0.97)	54
↓ **3,4-Dihydroxyman-delic acid**	8 men .... (a)	µmol/d	0.49	0.26	(0.20–0.97)	µg/d	91	48	(36–178)	58
	12 men .... (b)	µmol/d	1.86	0.73	(0.67–2.59)	µg/d	343	134	(124–477)	50
↓ **4-Hydroxy-3-meth-oxymandelic acid** (vanillylman-delic acid)	20 adults .... (a)	µmol/d	29	6.6	–	mg/d	5.7	1.3	–	48
	12 men .... (b)	µmol/d	18.1	6.1	(8.6–32)	mg/d	3.58	1.20	(1.7–6.3)	50
	51 men .... (c)	µmol/d	23	–	17–32	mg/d	4.6	–	3.4–6.3	56
	47 women .... (c)	µmol/d	22	–	16–31	mg/d	4.4	–	3.1–6.2	56
	80 men .... (d)	µmol/d	16.7	4.8	(8.1–38)	mg/d	3.30	0.95	(1.6–7.5)	51
	43 women .... (d)	µmol/d	16.3	4.7	(12–32)	mg/d	3.24	0.93	(2.3–6.4)	51
↓ **2,5-Dihydroxyphe-nylacetic acid**	....	...	...	...	...	...	...	...	...	...
↓ **3,4-Dihydroxyphe-nylpropionic acid**	Relative to body mass: – 21 adults..............	µmol d⁻¹ kg⁻¹	13	40	–	mg d⁻¹ kg⁻¹	2.3	7.3	–	17

Phenol and *p-cresol* are bound for the most part to sulfuric and glucuronic acid; the volatile urinary phenols are presumably formed by bacterial action on tyrosine in the intestine[38].

Benzoic acid. Values determined by gas chromatography. – The acid in the urine is bound to glycine (see hippuric acid, page 67). It is a metabolite of phenylalanine and forms in the intestine as a result of bacterial action.

Phenylacetic acid. Values determined by gas chromatography. The acid in the urine is bound to glutamic acid by more than 99% (see phenylacetylglutamine, page 67)[70]. It is a metabolite of phenylalanine and is formed in the urine by bacterial action. Excretion is increased in cystic fibrosis, in celiac disease, and in ascorbic acid deficiency[41,42].

Phenylpropionic acid. Formed from phenylalanine by bacterial action in the intestine.

p-Hydroxybenzoic acid, p-hydroxyphenylacetic acid. Values determined by gas chromatography. – Both acids are metabolites of tyrosine, which are formed through bacterial action in the intestine.

Table 1 *Excretion of vanillylmandelic acid and homovanillic acid in children*[55]

Age	Num-ber	Vanillylman-delic acid		Homovanillic acid	
		Mean	Upper limit of normal	Mean	Upper limit of normal
		µmol/d			
<2 weeks..............	15	1.26	4.29	3.1	8.2
2–8 weeks..............	27	2.07	6.56	5.5	11.0
2–6 months	30	3.13	7.57	7.1	15.9
7–12 months	50	3.63	8.58	8.8	18.7
1–5 years	60	5.70	11.1	12.1	26.3
6–10 years	50	10.1	18.2	21.4	37.9
11–15 years	50	13.6	24.2	28.0	48.3
16–20 years	50	16.1	28.3	30.2	54.9

↓See text below		Amount of substance				Mass				Refer ence
		Unit	Mean	s	95% (extreme range in brackets)	Unit	Mean	s	95% (extreme range in brackets)	
Lipids										
↓ **Total lipids**.......	....	...	...	...	...	mg/d	15.6	8.1	–	59
↓ **Bile acids**	5 adults................	µmol/d	–	–	(6.4–11)	...	...	...	...	81
↓ **Prostaglandins**										
PGE$_2$	Women, 40–60 years	nmol/d	0.52	0.23	0.22–0.80	ng/d	185	81	76–281	75
	19 women	nmol/d	0.88	0.31	–	ng/d	311	108	–	76
	6 men	nmol/d	1.89	0.39	–	ng/d	668	139	–	76
PGF$_{2\alpha}$	Women, 40–60 years	nmol/d	1.58	0.40	1.19–2.46	ng/d	560	141	422–871	75
	19 women	nmol/d	3.32	0.81	–	ng/d	1172	285	–	76
	6 men	nmol/d	4.81	1.89	–	ng/d	1702	669	–	76
Prostaglandin metabolite	18 men	nmol/d	84	50	(40–252)	µg/d	22.2	13.2	(10.6–66.9)	77
	17 women	nmol/d	44	14	(25–71)	µg/d	11.6	3.7	(6.5–18.8)	77
	Women, 40–60 years	nmol/d	28	12	12–54	µg/d	7.3	3.2	3.2–14.2	75

4-Hydroxy-3-methoxyphenylethanol. Values determined by gas chromatography. – Present almost entirely as sulfate[46].

4-Hydroxy-3-methoxyphenylglycol. Values determined (a) by column chromatography, (b) by gas chromatography. – Present by 95% in conjugated form (as glucuronate or sulfate)[46]. The compound is a metabolite of epinephrine and norepinephrine. The excretion is increased in neuroblastoma (as much as 1000 times) and in pheochromocytoma[57].

3,4-Dihydroxyphenylacetic acid. Values determined (a) enzymatically with labelled substrate, and (b) by column chromatography. – The substance is a metabolite of dopamine; about one-half is present in conjugated form[52]. Excretion is increased in cases of neuroblastoma and after administration of dihydroxyphenylalanine.

4-Hydroxy-3-methoxyphenylacetic acid. Values determined (a) by column chromatography, (b) by paper chromatography, and (c) by gas chromatography. – The compound is a metabolite of dopamine. See Table 1 for excretion in children as related to age. The excretion is increased in neuroblastoma[55].

3-Hydroxy-4-methoxyphenylacetic acid. Values determined by gas chromatography.

3,4-Dihydroxymandelic acid. Values determined (a) enzymatically with labelled substrate; (b) by column chromatography.

4-Hydroxy-3-methoxymandelic acid. Values determined (a) by gas chromatography; (b) by periodate oxidation following separation by column chromatography; (c) by periodate oxidation following separation with ethyl acetate; and (d) by paper chromatography. – The compound is a metabolite of norepinephrine and epinephrine. Excretion is higher during the day than during the night[72]. See Table 1 regarding excretion in children in relation to age. Excretion is increased in pheochromocytoma and neuroblastoma[55].

2,5-Dihydroxyphenylacetic acid (homogentisic acid). Excreted in the urine in measurable amounts only in alkaptonuria (18–30 mmol/d)[57].

3,4-Dihydroxyphenylpropionic acid. Values determined by gas chromatography.

Lipids. See page 86 for excretion of individual fatty acids. Lipid excretion is increased in kidney diseases, particularly in the nephrotic syndrome (Table 2).

Bile acids. About 30 different bile acids are excreted in urine. Cholic acid, chenodeoxycholic acid, deoxycholic acid and lithocholic acid constitute 40–80% of total bile acids; the major part of these acids is sulfated. Greatly increased bile acid excretion is frequently noted in hepatobiliary diseases[61].

Prostaglandins. In children the excretion is lower than in adults. It is increased in children with Bartter's syndrome.

Table 2   *Lipids in the urine of healthy individuals and patients with renal disease[60]*

	Triglycerides				Cholesterol				Phospholipids				Free fatty acids			
	Mean	s	Mean	s	Mean	s	Mean	s	Mean	s	Mean	s	Mean	s	Mean	s
	µmol/d		mg/d		µmol/d		mg/d		µmol/d		mg/d		µmol/d		mg/d	
Normal kidneys...........	1.8	0.8	1.6	0.7	2.6	1.3	1	0.5	5.8	2.2	4.5	1.7	14.9	8.2	4.2	2.3
Nephrotic syndrome	2.54	2.1	2.25	1.9	10.6	7.2	4.1	2.8	16.9	10.2	13.1	7.9	40.8	24.1	11.5	6.8
Uremia	2.3	0.9	2	0.8	3.93	3.28	1.52	1.27	11.7	6.1	9.05	4.7	26.3	11.7	7.42	3.3

References

[1] SCHWAB and KÜHNS, *Die Störungen des Wasser- und Elektrolytstoffwechsels*, Springer, Berlin, 1959, page 171.
[2] NORDMANN and NORDMANN, *Advanc. clin. Chem.*, **4**, 53 (1961).
[3] WERLE and SCHIEVELBEIN, in FLASCHENTRÄGER and LEHNARTZ (Eds.), *Physiologische Chemie*, volume II/2b, Springer, Berlin, 1957, page 1.
[4] TRIEBIG and SCHALLER, *Clin. chim. Acta*, **108**, 355 (1980).
[5] WILLIAMS and SPRAY, *Brit. J. Haemat.*, **26**, 185 (1974).
[6] CHALMERS et al., *Clin. chim. Acta*, **52**, 31 (1974).
[7] HAGENFELDT, L., *Clin. chim. Acta*, **32**, 471 (1971).
[8] HOCKADAY et al., *J. Lab. clin. Med.*, **65**, 677 (1965).
[9] RAMPINI et al., *Helv. paediat. Acta*, **22**, 135 (1967).
[10] ZAREMBSKI and HODGKINSON, *Clin. chim. Acta*, **25**, 1 (1969).
[11] HALLSON and ROSE, *Clin. chim. Acta*, **55**, 29 (1974).
[12] GIBBS and WATTS, *J. Lab. clin. Med.*, **73**, 901 (1969).
[13] HAGLER and HERMAN, *Amer. J. clin. Nutr.*, **26**, 758 (1973).
[14] WEITZEL, G., *Hoppe-Seylers Z. physiol. Chem.*, **282**, 174 (1947).
[15] THOMAS and STALDER, *Hoppe-Seylers Z. physiol. Chem.*, **317**, 269 (1959).
[16] THOMAS et al., *Hoppe-Seylers Z. physiol. Chem.*, **317**, 276 (1959).
[17] WITTEN et al., *Clin. Chem.*, **19**, 586 (1973).
[18] BORG et al., *Clin. chim. Acta*, **41**, 363 (1972).
[19] PETTERSEN et al., *Clin. chim. Acta*, **38**, 17 (1972); PETTERSEN, J. E., *Diabetes*, **23**, 16 (1974).
[20] NAKAMURA et al., *Clin. chim. Acta*, **68**, 127 (1976).
[21] PETTERSEN and STOKKE, *Biochim. biophys. Acta (Amst.)*, **304**, 316 (1973).
[22] LINDSTEDT et al., *Clin. chim. Acta*, **53**, 143 (1974).
[23] ELLIOT and RIBEIRO, *Invest. Urol.*, **10**, 102 (1972).
[24] DAALMANS-DE LANGE and HOMMES, *Helv. paediat. Acta*, **29**, 599 (1974).

5 ZELNIČEK, E., *Clin. chim. Acta,* 7, 592 (1962).
16 ZELNIČEK, E., *Nature,* 185, 928 (1960).
27 AKSU et al., *Clin. Chem.,* 20, 603 (1974).
28 MAMER and TJOA, *Clin. chim. Acta,* 55, 199 (1974).
29 GIORGIO, A. J., quoted by MAMER and TJOA[28].
30 LANDAAS, S., *Clin. chim. Acta,* 54, 39 (1974).
31 NORDMANN et al., *Clin. chim. Acta,* 12, 304 (1965).
32 WELSHMAN and MCCAMBRIDGE, *Clin. chim. Acta,* 46, 243 (1973).
33 CONSOLAZIO et al., *Physiological Measurements of Metabolic Functions in Man,* McGraw-Hill, New York, 1963, page 437.
34 PASSMORE, R., *Lancet,* 1, 839 (1961).
35 LEVEY et al., *J. Lab. clin. Med.,* 63, 574 (1964).
36 PETTERSEN and JELLUM, *Clin. chim. Acta,* 41, 199 (1972).
37 SCHMIDT, E. G., *J. biol. Chem.,* 179, 211 (1949).
38 DURAN et al., *Clin. chim. Acta,* 45, 341 (1973); BONE et al., *Amer. J. clin. Nutr.,* 29, 1448 (1976).
39 SMITH, A. A., *Nature,* 190, 167 (1961).
40 VAN DER HEIDEN et al., *Clin. chim. Acta,* 34, 289 (1971).
41 SEAKINS, J. W., *Clin. chim. Acta,* 35, 121 (1971).
42 TOCCI et al., *Clin. chim. Acta,* 40, 449 (1972).
43 POLLITT, R. J., *Clin. chim. Acta,* 55, 317 (1974).
44 COWARD and SMITH, *J. Chromatogr.,* 41, 262 (1969).
45 STURM, A., *Dtsch. med. Wschr.,* 88, 1000 (1963).
46 KAROUM et al., *Clin. chim. Acta,* 43, 127 (1973).
47 RUTHVEN and SANDLER, *Clin. chim. Acta,* 12, 318 (1965).
48 KAROUM et al., *Clin. chim. Acta,* 24, 341 (1969).
49 COMOY and BOHUON, *Clin. chim. Acta,* 36, 207 (1972).
50 MESSIHA et al., *Clin. chim. Acta,* 45, 159 (1973).
51 STOTT et al., *Clin. chim. Acta,* 63, 7 (1975).
52 WEG et al., *Clin. chim. Acta,* 59, 249 (1975).
53 RUTHVEN and SANDLER, *Clin. chim. Acta,* 14, 511 (1966).
54 DZIEDZIC et al., *J. Lab. clin. Med.,* 82, 829 (1973).

55 KÄSER, H., *Helv. paediat. Acta,* 27, suppl. 29 (1972).
56 WISSER and STAMM, *Z. klin. Chem.,* 8, 21 (1970).
57 WILK et al., *Clin. chim. Acta,* 16, 403 (1967).
58 SATO and DEQUATTRO, *J. Lab. clin. Med.,* 74, 672 (1969).
59 KING et al., *J. clin. Invest.,* 37, 315 (1958).
60 KLEINKNECHT et al., in FELBER and SCHEIDEGGER (Eds.), *Hormones, Lipids and Miscellaneous,* volume 3, 7th International Congress of Clinical Chemistry, Geneva 1969, Karger, Basle, 1970, page 279.
61 MAKINO et al., *Gastroenterology,* 68, 545 (1975).
62 WILLIAMS et al., *Arch. Biochem.,* 113, 251 (1966).
63 PRZYREMBEL et al., *Clin. chim. Acta,* 66, 227 (1976).
64 DAS et al., *Clin. chim. Acta,* 66, 263 (1976).
65 BJÖRKMAN et al., *Clin. Chem.,* 22, 49 (1976).
66 LANDAAS, S., *Clin. chim. Acta,* 64, 143 (1975).
67 THOMPSON et al., *Clin. Chem.,* 21, 1892 (1975).
68 WILDENHOFF, K. E., *Acta med. scand.,* 198, 127 (1975).
69 BACHMANN et al., *Clin. chim. Acta,* 66, 287 (1976).
70 GOODWIN et al., *Clin. chim. Acta,* 62, 439 (1975).
71 RUGE, W., *Med. Welt (Stuttg.),* 23, 149 (1972).
72 DECK et al., *Klin. Wschr.,* 54, 131 (1976).
73 TANAKA, K., in HOMMES and VAN DEN BERG (Eds.), *Inborn Errors of Metabolism,* Academic Press, London, 1973, page 269.
74 KAHANE et al., *Clin. chim. Acta,* 73, 203 (1976).
75 GILL et al., *Amer. J. Med.,* 61, 43 (1976).
76 BENZONI et al., *Clin. chim. Acta,* 111, 9 (1981).
77 BRASH et al., *Biochem. Med.,* 16, 77 (1976).
78 TRUSCOTT et al., *Clin. chim. Acta,* 94, 31 (1979).
79 FAVIER and CAILLAT, *Clin. chim. Acta,* 79, 419 (1977).
80 FARRINGTON and CHALMERS, *Clin. Chem.,* 25, 1993 (1979).
81 ALMÉ et al., *J. Lipid Res.,* 18, 339 (1977).
82 BROOK et al., *Amer. J. clin. Path.,* 75, 110 (1981).

Vitamins (for references see page 95)

↓See text below		Amount of substance				Mass				Reference
		Unit	Mean	s	(Extreme range)	Unit	Mean	s	(Extreme range)	
Coenzyme Q$_{10}$		...	...	...	...	µg/d	15.4	–	(0–58)	1
↓ **Thiamine**	31 subjects (a)	µmol/L	3.4	–	(3.0–9.0)	µg/L	900	–	(800–2400)	2
	27 subjects (b)	µmol/L	–	–	(0.41–1.4)	µg/L	–	–	(110–370)	3
	24 newborn, 1st to 3rd day (c)	µmol/L	0.36	0.083	–	µg/L	96	22	–	4
	20 children, 3½–5½ years (d)	µmol/d	1.88	1.39	–	µg/d	498	368	–	14
↓ **Riboflavin**	24 newborn, 1st to 3rd day (a)	µmol/L	0.582	0.082	–	µg/L	219	31	–	4
	20 children, 3½–5½ years (b)	µmol/d	3.69	3.61	–	mg/d	1.39	1.36	–	14
	85 subjects (c)	µmol/d	2.7	1.3	(0.8–6.6)	mg/d	1.0	0.5	(0.3–2.5)	10
	41 adults (d)	µmol/d	2.71	1.20	–	mg/d	1.02	0.45	–	7

Thiamine. Values determined (a) with *Ochromonas danica,* (b) with *Ochromonas malhamensis,* (c) with *Lactobacillus fermentum,* and (d) chemically. – With ingestion of 0.5–0.6 mg/d and more, excretion increases linearly with ingestion and on a good diet amounts to 0.4 µmol/d (100 µg/d); in addition, degradation products such as pyrimidines and thiazoles are found in the urine[32]. In cases of thiamine deficiency, excretion of the vitamin decreases rapidly (see Table 1 for interpretation of the data). In beriberi, thiamine excretion amounts to 0–0.05 µmol/d[5]. The excretion is in-creased in individuals receiving mercurial diuretics but not with thiazide administration[6].

Riboflavin. Values determined (a) with *Lactobacillus casei,* (b) fluorimetrically, (c) with *Tetrahymena pyriformis,* (d) by competitive protein binding. – At a riboflavin intake of less than 1 mg/d, approximately 10% of the amount ingested is excreted; at higher intakes, 30% or more is excreted[32]. Excretion is reduced in riboflavin deficiency (see Table 1 for interpretation of the data).

Table 1   *Interpretation of excretion of thiamine, riboflavin and vitamin B$_6$ relative to creatinine excretion*

Age	Thiamine[12]			Riboflavin[12]			Vitamin B$_6$[13]*	
	Deficient	Low	Adequate	Deficient	Low	Adequate	Too low	Adequate
	µg/g							
1–3 years	<120	120–175	≥176	<150	150–499	≥500	<90	≥90
4–6 years	<85	85–120	≥121	<100	100–299	≥300	<80	≥80
7–9 years	<70	70–180	≥181	<85	85–269	≥270	<60	≥60
10–12 years	<60	60–180	≥181	} <70	70–199	≥200 {	<40	≥40
13–15 years	<50	50–150	≥151				<30	≥30
Adults◊	<27	27–65	≥66	<27	27–79	≥80	<20	≥20

* Determined in non-hydrolyzed urine by means of *Saccharomyces carlsbergensis.*   ◊ Pregnant and nursing women excepted.

↓See text below and on next page		Amount of substance				Mass				Reference
		Unit	Mean	s	(Extreme range)	Unit	Mean	s	(Extreme range)	
↓ **Vitamin B₆**...	36 samples	...	...	...	...	µg/d	40	18	(20–120)	8
↓ **4-Pyridoxic acid**	Women	µmol/d	3.9	1.4	–	mg/d	0.71	0.26	–	11
	Men	µmol/d	4.10	0.55	–	mg/d	0.75	0.10	–	11
↓ **Nicotinic acid**	Adults .... (a)	µmol/L	–	–	(9.42–12.5)	mg/L	–	–	(1.16–1.54)	3
	20 children, 3½–5½ years....... (b)	µmol/d	2.0	0.6	–	mg/d	0.25	0.07	–	14
↓ **1-Methylnicotinamide**	14 newborn, 4–50 days ...	µmol/d	12.5	–	(4.0–35.5)	mg/d	1.71	–	(0.55–4.87)	15
	29 children, 6–11 years ...	µmol/d	19.7	–	(5.6–39.7)	mg/d	2.70	–	(0.77–5.45)	16
	25 men, <35 years.......	µmol/d	53.8	–	(20.8–89.7)	mg/d	7.38	–	(2.85–12.3)	17
	25 women, <35 years....	µmol/d	44.1	–	(17.1–92.6)	mg/d	6.05	–	(2.34–12.7)	17
	25 men, >50 years.......	µmol/d	26.2	–	(12.8–76.6)	mg/d	3.60	–	(1.76–10.5)	17
	25 women, >50 years....	µmol/d	25.2	–	(10.9–67.1)	mg/d	3.45	–	(1.50–9.20)	17
	Relative to body mass: – 15 children	µmol d⁻¹ kg⁻¹	16	9.2	–	mg d⁻¹ kg⁻¹	2.2	1.3	–	36
↓ **1-Methyl-2-pyridone-5-carboxamide** .	14 newborn, 4–50 days ...	µmol/d	10.8	–	(2.0–43.8)	mg/d	1.64	–	(0.30–6.67)	15
	29 children, 6–11 years ...	µmol/d	29.3	–	(10.2–77.6)	mg/d	4.47	–	(1.55–11.8)	16
	25 men, <35 years.......	µmol/d	87.4	–	(29.2–192)	mg/d	13.3	–	(4.44–29.2)	17
	25 women, <35 years....	µmol/d	73.0	–	(28.3–212)	mg/d	11.1	–	(4.30–32.2)	17
	25 men, >50 years.......	µmol/d	40.7	–	(5.3–139)	mg/d	6.20	–	(0.80–21.1)	17
	25 women, >50 years....	µmol/d	80.8	–	(11.5–194)	mg/d	12.3	–	(1.75–29.5)	17
	Relative to body mass: – 15 children	µmol d⁻¹ kg⁻¹	1.9	1.2	–	mg d⁻¹ kg⁻¹	0.29	0.18	–	36
↓ **Vitamin B₁₂**..	16 non-smokers	pmol/d	44.5	23.3	–	ng/d	60.3	31.6	–	22
↓ **Folic acid**	15 adults	nmol/d	21.5	–	(0.2–41)	µg/d	9.5	–	(0.1–18.0)	30
	68 women...............	nmol/d	10	–	(1.4–21)	µg/d	4.5	–	(0.6–9.4)	23
↓ **Pteridines**....	60 adults	µmol/L	8.9	6.3	–	mg/L	2.1	1.5	–	31
		µmol/d	8.9	1.3	(6.3–10.1)	mg/d	2.1	0.3	(1.5–2.4)	29
Biopterin	Relative to creatinine: – 12 adults	mmol/mol	0.71	0.16	(0.46–0.99)	mg/g	1.49	0.34	(0.97–2.08)	37
	– 6 children	mmol/mol	1.13	0.54	(0.45–1.88)	mg/g	2.36	1.12	(0.94–3.93)	37
	– 12 men................	mmol/mol	0.24	0.07	–	mg/g	0.51	0.15	–	38
	– 11 women	mmol/mol	0.32	0.13	–	mg/g	0.68	0.27	–	38
	– 7 children	mmol/mol	0.48	0.17	–	mg/g	1.01	0.35	–	38
Neopterin ...	Relative to creatinine: – 12 adults	mmol/mol	0.28	0.05	(0.23–0.38)	mg/g	0.63	0.11	(0.52–0.87)	37
	– 6 children	mmol/mol	0.67	0.32	(0.24–1.13)	mg/g	1.50	0.71	(0.55–2.52)	37
	– 12 men................	mmol/mol	0.21	0.08	–	mg/g	0.47	0.18	–	38
	– 11 women	mmol/mol	0.23	0.08	–	mg/g	0.52	0.18	–	38
	– 7 children	mmol/mol	0.36	0.07	–	mg/g	0.80	0.17	–	38
Xanthopterin	Relative to creatinine: – 12 adults	mmol/mol	0.23	0.07	(0.11–0.34)	mg/g	0.36	0.12	(0.18–0.55)	37
	– 6 children	mmol/mol	0.37	0.12	(0.20–0.53)	mg/g	0.58	0.19	(0.31–0.83)	37

Vitamin B₆. Total activity, determined with *Tetrahymena pyriformis*. See Table 2 for excretion of the individual components of the vitamin. The phosphates of this vitamin apparently do not occur in the urine[9]. In vitamin B₆ deficiency, excretion declines (see Table 1 for interpretation of the data).

4-Pyridoxic acid. 40–50% of the vitamin B₆ ingested is excreted in the urine as pyridoxic acid.

Nicotinic acid. Total activity, determined (a) with *Tetrahymena pyriformis,* (b) with *Lactobacillus arabinosus.*

1-Methylnicotinamide. Excretion of this nicotinic acid metabolite is reduced in pellagra.

Table 2   *Vitamin B₆ components in the urine[9]*

	Pyridoxal		Pyridoxin		Pyridoxamine		4-Pyridoxic acid	
	Mean	s	Mean	s	Mean	s	Mean	s
	µmol/d							
Men	0.27	0.067	0.46	0.19	1.24	0.39	7.23	4.26
Women	0.15	0.074	0.56	0.21	0.72	0.29	6.62	4.63
Pregnant women	0.19	0.052	0.42	0.12	0.78	0.11	7.93	2.59

↓See text below		Amount of substance				Mass				Refer-ence
		Unit	Mean	s	(Extreme range)	Unit	Mean	s	(Extreme range)	
↓**Biotin**.......	....	nmol/L	–	–	(25.6–134)	µg/L	–	–	(6.26–32.7)	3
	Relative to creatinine: – 12 children, 4 years.....	µmol/mol	14.0	–	(2.0–44.0)	µg/g	30.2	–	(4.3–95.0)	39
↓**Pantothenic acid**.........	.... (a)	µmol/L	13.2	–	(3.5–19)	mg/L	2.90	–	(0.76–4.1)	3
	20 children, 3½–5½ years...... (b)	µmol/d	15.3	9.62	–	mg/d	3.36	2.11	–	14
	12 subjects .... (c)	µmol/d	17.4	5.0	–	mg/d	3.83	1.1	–	24
	Relative to creatinine: – 8 young men .... (d)	mmol/mol	2.7	0.9	(1.4–3.7)	mg/g	5.3	1.7	(2.7–7.2)	25
	– 5 young women .... (e)	mmol/mol	1.2	0.4	(0.8–1.7)	mg/g	2.3	0.7	(1.6–3.3)	25
↓**Ascorbic acid**	24 newborn, 1st to 3rd day	µmol/L	258	39	–	mg/L	45.4	6.8	–	4
	9 women: – normal diet	µmol/L	162	85	–	mg/L	28.6	15.0	–	26
	– high-ascorbic acid diet .	µmol/L	290	16	–	mg/L	51.0	2.8	–	26
	– low-ascorbic acid diet ..	µmol/L	49	16	–	mg/L	8.7	2.9	–	26

1-Methyl-2-pyridone-5-carboxamide. Besides 1-methyl-2-pyridone-5-carboxamide, the urine contains 1-methyl-4-pyridone-5-carboxamide[18]. Excretion is increased during pregnancy[19] and is dependent on the cycle in women[19, 20]. It is reduced in pellagra and diabetes mellitus[21].

Vitamin B_{12}. Values determined by the radioisotope method. – Excretion increases as the concentration in the serum increases[33].

Folic acid. Values determined with *Lactobacillus casei*. – Excretion increases as the serum level of folic acid increases[23]. It is increased during pregnancy[23] and in cirrhosis[30].

Biopterin. Total activity, determined with *Crithidia fasciculata*. – Excretion is increased particularly in patients with uremia[29, 31].

Pteridines. Determined with *Ochromonas danica*. – It is present in the urine in free form.

Pantothenic acid. Total activity, determined (a), (c), (d), (e) with *Lactobacillus plantarum*, (b) with *Lactobacillus casei*. Values (a) on normal diet, (b) at pantothenic acid intake of 4 mg/d, (d) at pantothenic acid intake of 12 mg/d.

Ascorbic acid. Excretion is dependent on the serum concentration, and this in turn depends on intake and the degree of tissue saturation. At a serum level of ascorbic acid of 80 µmol/L (14 mg/L), the renal threshold value is reached and ascorbic acid excretion is determined by the renal clearance of 1–3 mL/min[34]. When large quantities of ascorbic acid are administered, 60–80% appear in the urine, and the tissue deficit may be inferred from the amount retained[27]. In women, excretion changes in the course of the cycle[35]. It is reduced during use of ovulation inhibitors[28].

References

[1] NAPIER et al., *Nature,* **202**, 806 (1964).
[2] BAKER et al., *Amer. J. clin. Nutr.,* **14**, 197 (1964).
[3] BAKER and SOBOTKA, *Advanc. clin. Chem.,* **5**, 173 (1962).
[4] DAHL et al., *Acta paediat.* (*Uppsala),* **50**, 127 (1961).
[5] GOLDSMITH, G. A., in BEATON and McHENRY (Eds.), *Nutrition,* volume 2, Academic Press, New York, 1964, page 109.
[6] DUBEL and SOLOFF, *Amer. J. med. Sci.,* **245**, 58 (1963).
[7] FAZEKAS et al., *J. clin. Invest.,* **52**, 27a (1973).
[8] BAKER et al., *Amer. J. clin. Nutr.,* **18**, 123 (1966).
[9] CONTRACTOR and SHANE, *Amer. J. Obstet. Gynec.,* **107**, 635 (1970).
[10] BAKER et al., *Amer. J. clin. Nutr.,* **19**, 17 (1966).
[11] PRICE et al., *Advanc. metab. Disord.,* **2**, 159 (1965).
[12] SANDSTEAD and PEARSON, in GOODHART and SHILS (Eds.), *Modern Nutrition in Health and Disease,* 5th ed., Lea & Febiger, Philadelphia, 1973, page 572.
[13] SAUBERLICH et al., *Amer. J. clin. Nutr.,* **25**, 629 (1972).
[14] KERREY et al., *Amer. J. clin. Nutr.,* **21**, 1274 (1968).
[15] APOLLONIO et al., *Acta vitamin.* (*Milano),* **17**, 65 (1963).
[16] MAINARDI et al., *Acta vitamin.* (*Milano),* **17**, 153 (1963).
[17] MAINARDI et al., *Acta vitamin.* (*Milano),* **16**, 255 (1962).
[18] CHANG and JOHNSON, *J. biol. Chem.,* **236**, 2096 (1961).
[19] BROWN et al., *J. clin. Invest.,* **40**, 617 (1961).
[20] MAINARDI et al., *Acta vitamin.* (*Milano),* **19**, 15 (1965).
[21] PASQUARIELLO, G., *Acta vitamin.* (*Milano),* **18**, 225 (1964).
[22] LINNELL et al., *Brit. med. J.,* **2**, 215 (1968).
[23] SHOJANIA, A. M., *J. Lab. clin. Med.,* **85**, 185 (1975).
[24] HATANO et al., *Amer. J. clin. Nutr.,* **20**, 960 (1967).
[25] COHENOUR and CALLOWAY, *Amer. J. clin. Nutr.,* **25**, 512 (1972).
[26] HARRIS and AJOSE, *Lancet,* **1**, 671 (1973).
[27] CHATTERJEE, G. C., in SEBRELL and HARRIS (Eds.), *The Vitamins,* 2nd ed., volume 1, Academic Press, New York, 1967, page 399.
[28] HARRIS et al., *Lancet,* **2**, 201 (1973).
[29] BAKER et al., *Amer. J. clin. Nutr.,* **27**, 1247 (1974).
[30] RETIEF and HUSKISSON, *Brit. med. J.,* **2**, 150 (1969).
[31] LEEMING et al., *J. clin. Path.,* **29**, 444 (1976).
[32] PEARSON, W. N., *Amer. J. clin. Nutr.,* **20**, 514 (1967).
[33] ADAMS, J. F., *Brit. med. J.,* **1**, 138 (1970).
[34] KNOX and GOSWAMI, *Advanc. clin. Chem.,* **4**, 121 (1961).
[35] LOH and WILSON, *Lancet,* **1**, 110 (1971).
[36] BARLOW et al., *Clin. chim. Acta,* **75**, 337 (1977).
[37] DHONDT et al., *Clin. chim. Acta,* **110**, 205 (1981).
[38] ROKOS et al., *Clin. chim. Acta,* **105**, 275 (1980).
[39] MOCK et al., *New Engl. J. Med.,* **304**, 820 (1981).

Sediment (for references see page 97)

Cells and casts

Normal cell count values are presented in Tables 1 and 2. In view of the considerable differences between results of individual studies, the value of cell counting has been in dispute, however. The leukocytes in the urine are almost exclusively neutrophil granulocytes[1]. The size and shape of the erythrocytes depend on the osmolality or relative density as well as on the urinary pH; the size of the leukocytes, too, is affected by the relative density of the urine (Table 3).

Upon centrifugation, some erythrocytes and leukocytes are lost so that the cell count in the urinary sediment is lower than it is in fresh urine[11]. Counts in uncentrifuged urine, however, result in large errors[3].

Casts – i.e. exclusively hyaline ones – are found in normal individuals only in a certain percentage of urine specimens[4, 8, 10]. Table 4 shows the significance of the detection of casts in the urine.

Bacteria

Urine collected by bladder puncture is normally sterile. In judging what number of bacteria in midstream specimens is diagnostically significant, the method of collection and the composition of the microflora have to be taken into account[12, 13]. First of all, the urethra is colonized by microorganisms in men as well as in women; second, when collection is not done carefully in women, a considerable number of bacteria – particularly from the intestinal flora – can pass into the urine (Fig. 1).

Table 1　*Erythrocytes, leukocytes and renal tubular cells in urine[3]*

	Erythrocytes				Leukocytes				Renal tubular cells			
	Mean	s	(Extreme range)	Upper limit of normal	Mean	s	(Extreme range)	Upper limit of normal	Mean	s	(Extreme range)	Upper limit of normal
	$10^3\ h^{-1}$											
42 men												
Overnight urine...	32.0	11.7	(0–217)		31.4	14.9	(0–956)		74.4	14.3	(12–239)	
Morning urine	43.8	14.9	(5–380)	} 105	27.8	15.6	(0–307)	} 95	86.3	16.8	(17–222)	} 140
Afternoon urine...	46.1	15.6	(4–915)		24.0	13.6	(0–215)		78.3	16.2	(14–262)	
40 women												
Overnight urine...	23.3	8.2	(0–473)		107.1	82.2	(0–5042)		57.4	12.6	(5–234)	
Morning urine	32.9	12.6	(0–396)	} 80	111.5	89.2	(0–2774)	} 470	81.7	17.1	(22–243)	} 140
Afternoon urine...	35.6	15.2	(0–442)		105.4	80.3	(0–1195)		75.3	15.8	(13–199)	

Table 2　*Cellular elements in urine at different ages*

	Erythrocytes			Leukocytes and renal tubular cells				
	Mean	s	(Extreme range)	Mean	s	(Extreme range)	Upper limit of normal	Reference
	$10^3\ h^{-1}$							
45 adults............................	12.2	–	(0–128)	45	–	(2–283)	–	4
75 men	34.3	66.0	(0.6–475)	58.9	56.0	(4–267)	–	5
17 men	–	–	–	46	–	(0–220)	–	6
50 women	–	–	–	74	–	(0–574)	–	6
119 newborn.........................	7.5	–	(0–53)	155	–	(4–1125)	–	7
74 children, 4–12 years	1.3	1.5	(0–11)	26.8	27.0	(1–235)	–	8
Children, body surface up to 0.55 m² ...	–	–	–	–	–	–	50	9
Children, body surface 0.6–0.8 m²	–	–	–	–	–	–	100	9
Children, body surface 0.8–1.0 m²	–	–	–	–	–	–	200	9

Table 3　*Mean diameter of erythrocytes and leukocytes in urine[2]*

Relative density of urine	Mean	s
	μm	
Erythrocytes		
1.0075	8.31	0.67
1.0125	8.07	0.72
1.0180	7.12	0.57
1.0240	6.21	0.43
1.0300	5.85	0.26
Leukocytes		
1.0068	12.9	1.14
1.0123	11.3	1.03
1.0177	9.94	0.95
1.0232	9.24	0.48
1.0286	8.75	0.58

Urinary calculi

Urinary calculi can occur in all segments of the urinary tract. Renal and ureteral calculi predominate in the United States and in Europe; bladder stones frequently occur in certain regions of the Near and Far East[14]. Crystals composed of a single chemical substance are rare (Table 5)[14–16]. Some crystals are recognizable in pure form at the surface of the stones in some circumstances (Fig.2). Sulfonamides, 6-mercaptopurine and ampicillin may appear in the urine as crystals.

Urinary calculi consist of a mucoprotein matrix around which the crystals are deposited. In terms of dry mass, calcium and uric acid-bearing calculi contain approximately 2.5% of mucoprotein, while cystine stones have a matrix content of about 10%; the rare 'matrix calculi' contain about 60% of organic substance[17].

Whether or not a urine is saturated with crystal components can be determined from the nomograms shown (pages 99–100).

The saturation values are presented in two ways. Firstly they are expressed in absolute values as −$\log_{10}$ (activity products) and

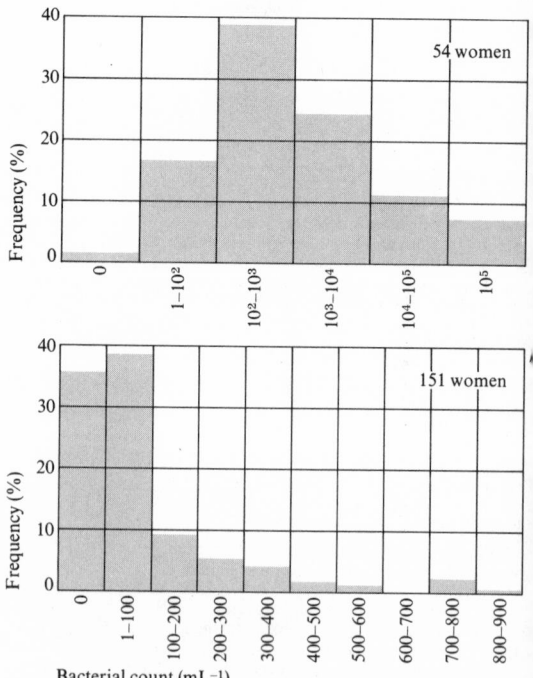

Fig. 1. Frequency distribution of bacterial counts in women with sterile bladder urine, the midstream urine having been collected under conventional conditions (*a*) and under special precautions on the cytoscopy table (*b*)[12].

Table 4   *Properties and significance of urinary casts*[1,18]

Type of cast	Definition	Clinical significance
Hyaline casts	Unstructured casts from distal tubules, consisting solely of Tamm-Horsfall mucoprotein	Excretion after physical exertion, fever, diuretics
Granular casts	Hyaline matrix with embedded droplets of plasma proteins	Formed at elevated protein concentration in tubular lumen. Generally associated with proteinuria
Waxy casts	Composed entirely or predominantly of plasma proteins. More refractive than hyaline casts	Formed at high protein level and low pH in tubular lumen. Associated with severe proteinuria. Indicative of nephropathy
Hemoprotein casts	Homogeneous casts of hemoglobin or myoglobin, with characteristic brown color	Formed in hemoglobinuria or myoglobinuria
Erythrocyte casts	Casts consisting of mucoprotein matrix with embedded, generally densely packed erythrocytes	Formed on passage of erythrocytes into glomerular filtrate. Associated with glomerulonephritis, acute renal allograft rejection and acute tubular necrosis
Leukocyte casts	Casts consisting of mucoprotein matrix with embedded leukocytes	Formed on passage of leukocytes from peritubular space into tubular lumen. Pointing to bacterial infections
Epithelial casts	Double rows of renal epithelial cells, or casts consisting of mucoprotein matrix with embedded epithelial cells	Indicative of tubular nephropathy or necrosis. Commonly observed during acute renal allograft rejection
Lipid casts	Casts consisting of mucoprotein matrix with embedded drop- or needle-shaped or intracellular lipids. Usually birefringent	Indicative of nephrotic syndrome

compared with the known thermodynamic solubility and formation products of the various stone constituents. Secondly they are defined on $\log_{10}$ (relative supersaturation) scale i.e.

$$\log_{10} \frac{\text{activity product}}{K_{sp}} \text{ divided by } \log_{10}\left(\frac{K_t}{K_{sp}}\right)$$

where K_t and K_{sp} are the thermodynamic formation and solubility products of the salt.

On this scale a urine at the solubility product has a $\log_{10}$ (relative supersaturation) value of 0, and a urine at the formation product has a value of 1. Thus a negative value indicates that the urine is undersaturated with the constituent concerned and should redissolve any preexisting crystals of that material. A value between 0 and 1 indicates that the urine lies in the metastable region of supersaturation and therefore may support the growth, and possibly aggregation, of preexisting crystals but will not allow the spontaneous formation of new crystals in the absence of some nucleating agent. Finally, a value greater than 1 indicates that spontaneous precipitation of the material is likely to occur.

References

[1] COLOMBO and RICHTERICH, *Die einfache Urinuntersuchung,* Huber, Berne, 1977.
[2] GADEHOLT, H., *Erythrocytes and Leucocytes in Urine,* Norwegian Universities Press, Bergen, 1968.
[3] PRESCOTT, L. F., *Clin. Sci.,* **31**, 425 (1966).
[4] GOLDRING, W., *J. clin. Invest.,* **10**, 355 (1931).
[5] GADEHOLT, H., *Acta med. scand.,* **183**, 369 (1968).
[6] LITTLE, P. J., *Lancet,* **1**, 1149 (1962).
[7] AAS, K., *Acta paediat. (Uppsala),* **50**, 361 (1961).
[8] LYTTLE, J. D., *J. clin. Invest.,* **12**, 87 (1933).
[9] HOUSTON, I. B., *Arch. Dis. Childh.,* **40**, 313 (1965).
[10] LIPPMAN, R. W., *Urine and the Urinary Sediment,* 2nd ed., Thomas, Springfield, 1957.
[11] GADEHOLT, H., *Brit. med. J.,* **1**, 1547 (1964).
[12] STAMEY et al., *Medicine (Baltimore),* **44**, 1 (1965).
[13] FUCHS, T., *Nieren- u. Hochdruck-Kr.,* **2**, 188 (1973); FREEDMAN, L. R., in STRAUSS and WELT (Eds.), *Diseases of the Kidney,* 2nd ed., Little, Brown, Boston, 1971, page 667.
[14] LONSDALE, K., *Science,* **159**, 1199 (1968).
[15] PRIEN and PRIEN, *Amer. J. Med.,* **45**, 654 (1968).
[16] LA GANGA, T. S., in HENRY et al. (Eds.), *Clinical Chemistry,* 2nd ed., Harper & Row, Hagerstown (Md.), 1974, page 1570.
[17] BOYCE, W. H., *Amer. J. Med.,* **45**, 673 (1968).
[18] SCHUMANN et al., *Amer. J. clin. Path.,* **69**, 18 (1978).

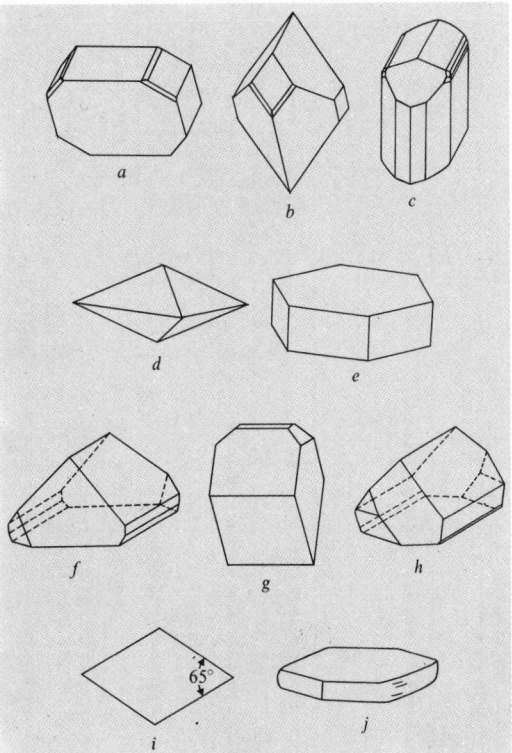

Fig. 2. Crystal forms observed at surface of urinary calculi[15]: *a–c* calcium oxalate monohydrate, rare (size 0.03–0.1 mm). *d* Calcium oxalate dihydrate, common (size up to 2.0 mm). *e* Cystine, common (size 0.1–0.2 mm). *f–h* Magnesium ammonium phosphate, common (size 0.5–1.0 mm). *i, j* Uric acid, rare (size 0.2 mm).

Table 5 *Endogenous urinary calculi*[15,16]

Name	Occurrence	Incidence*	Description
Calcium oxalate monohydrate: whewellite, $CaC_2O_4 \cdot H_2O$	Generally in acid urine	13.7%	Very hard, porous, smooth, lustrous surface; light honey-brown, red-brown, or black-brown. Three types: (a) small, smooth, ovoid 'hemp seed', usually multiple with concentric laminations; (b) 'mulberry', variable size and shape with irregular rounded mammillary processes; (c) 'jack stone', dense central mass with radiating spicules
Calcium oxalate dihydrate: weddelite, $CaC_2O_4 \cdot 2H_2O$	Generally in acid urine	0.4%	Pale yellow-white to honey-brown, octahedral crystals, loose or compactly interlocking aggregates
Calcium oxalate monohydrate and calcium oxalate dihydrate	Generally in acid urine	18.6%	Similar to calcium oxalate monohydrate
Calcium oxalate monohydrate with apatite	Generally in acid urine	7.2%	Porous, granular. Apatite exists in interstices or cavities
Calcium oxalate dihydrate with apatite	Generally in acid urine	4.7%	
Calcium oxalate monohydrate and calcium oxalate dihydrate with apatite	Generally in acid urine	22.4%	
Apatite: carbonate apatite, $Ca_{10}(PO_4,CO_3,OH)_6(OH)_2$ hydroxyl apatite, $Ca_{10}(PO_4)_6(OH)_2$	Alkaline or acid urine	3.4%	Fine grained, soft, and compact, usually laminated; chalk white, cream white, yellow-brown
Magnesium ammonium phosphate hexahydrate (struvite) $MgNH_4PO_4 \cdot 6H_2O$	Usually in alkaline, infected urine	0.3%	Densely granular, creamy white, resembling lump sugar
Magnesium ammonium phosphate hexahydrate with apatite	Generally in alkaline, infected urine	15.5%	Dirty to cream white, resembling cancellous bone in structure. Forms the 'staghorn' calculi
Magnesium ammonium phosphate hexahydrate with apatite and calcium oxalates	Generally in alkaline, infected urine	3.2%	Similar to magnesium ammonium phosphate hexahydrate with apatite
Calcium hydrogen phosphate dihydrate: brushite, $CaHPO_4 \cdot 2H_2O$	In acid urine	0.2%	Cream white or light brown, moderately soft, fracture surfaces pearly or silky luster, radially fibrous or bladed structure
Calcium hydrogen phosphate dihydrate with apatite or calcium oxalate monohydrate	In acid urine	1.7%	
Uric acid	In acid urine	4.7%	Dense, fine grain, typical oblate or flattened pebblelike with smooth but not polished surface (somewhat warty); usually laminated brown, relatively soft, and easily crushed
Uric acid with calcium oxalate monohydrate	—	1.1%	
Cystine	In acid urine	2.2%	Porous aggregates of relatively well formed short hexagonal prisms or tablets, sometimes compact granular center. Honey-yellow to yellow-white. Waxy luster, very soft unless densely granular
Cystine with apatite	In acid urine	0.7%	
Urostealith (fatty stone)	In acid urine	0.1%	Brown elastic stones having the consistency of beeswax. Free fatty acid content of about 50%
Cholesterol	In acid urine	Rare	Small pale-yellow stones with consistency of beeswax. Cholesterol content up to 95%
Xanthine		Very rare	Yellowish-brown to dark-brown, smooth, oval, not very hard stones. Xanthine content 5–100%.

* Incidence in a series of 1000 calculi examined in USA.   ° Partly as monoammonium urate and monosodium urate.

Nomograms for determination of saturation of urine with calcium oxalate, calcium hydrogen phosphate, octacalcium phosphate and magnesium ammonium phosphate (Marshall and Robertson, *Clin. chim. Acta,* **72**, 253 [1976])

RS: relative supersaturation; AP: activity product

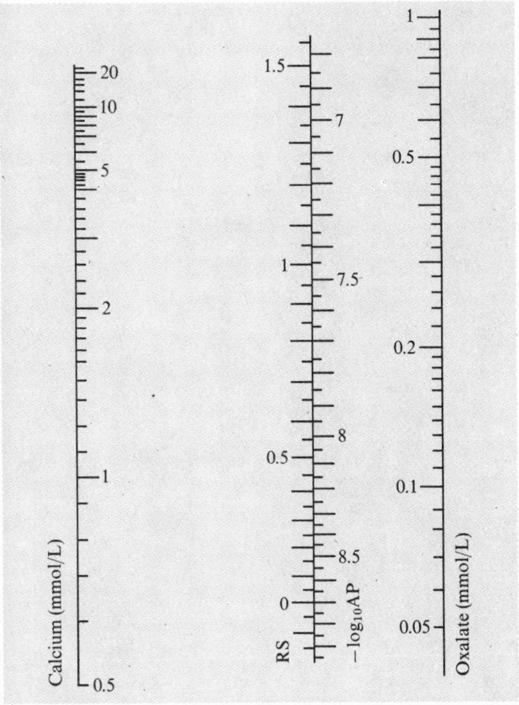

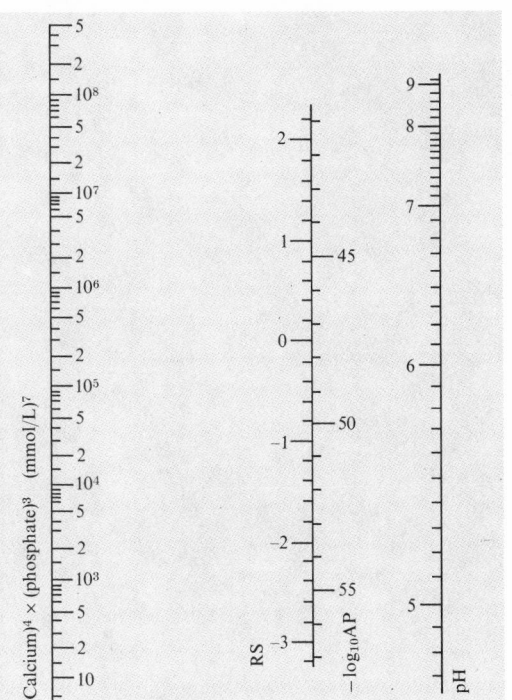

Fig. 3. Calcium oxalate: $\{Ca^{2+}\}\{oxalate^{2-}\}$.

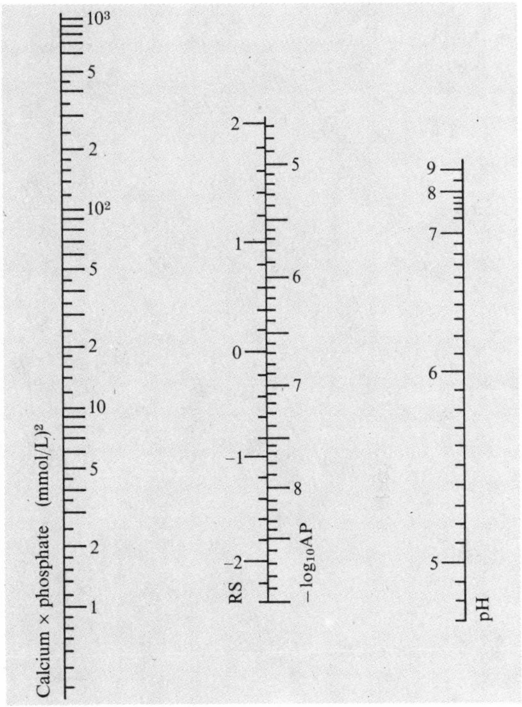

Fig. 5. Octacalcium phosphate: $\{Ca^{2+}\}^4\{H^+\}\{PO_4^{3-}\}^3$.

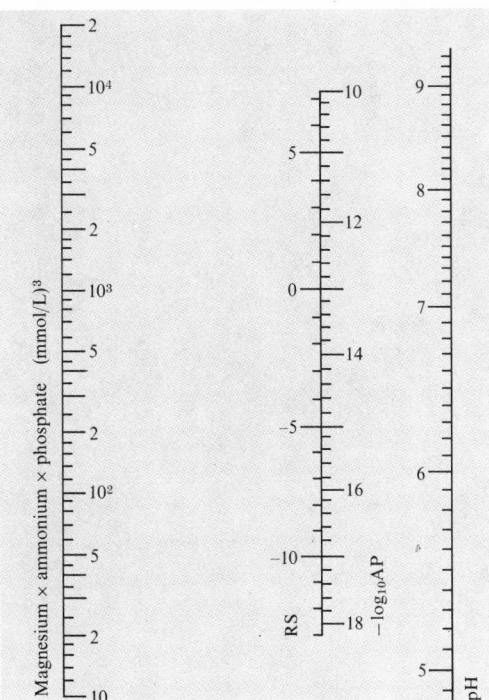

Fig. 4. Calcium hydrogen phosphate: $\{Ca^{2+}\}\{HPO_4^{2-}\}$.

Fig. 6. Magnesium ammonium phosphate: $\{Mg^{2+}\}\{NH_4^+\}\{PO_4^{3-}\}$.

Nomograms for determination of saturation of urine with uric acid, monosodium urate, monoammonium urate, and cystine (MARSHALL and ROBERTSON, *Clin. chim. Acta,* **72**, 253 [1976])

RS: relative supersaturation; AP: activity product

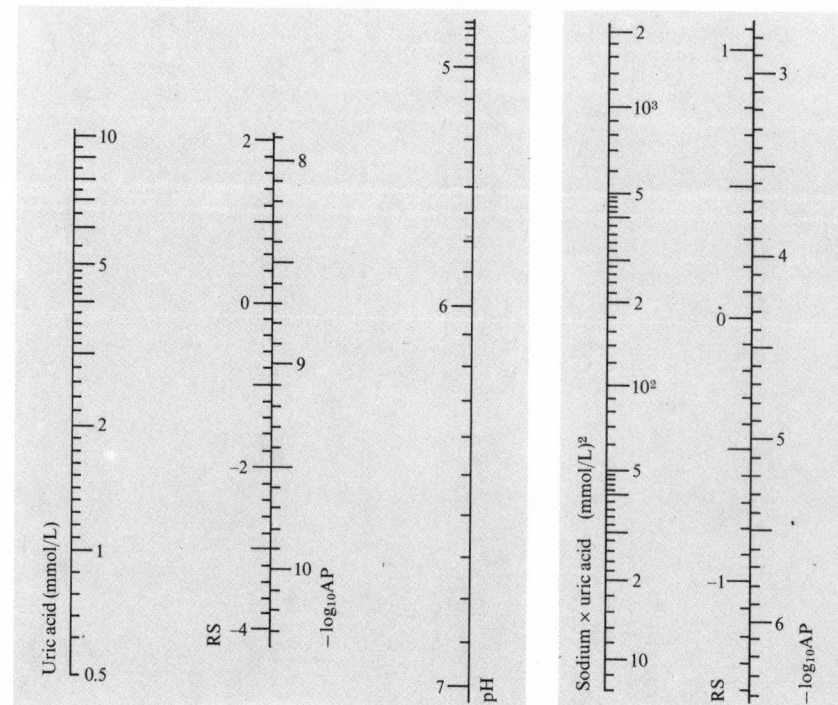

Fig. 7. Uric acid: {H+} {urate−}.

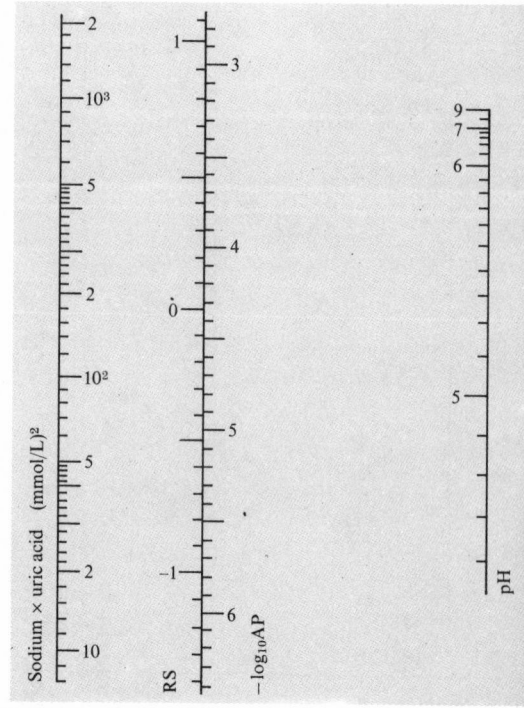

Fig. 8. Monosodium urate: {Na+} {urate−}.

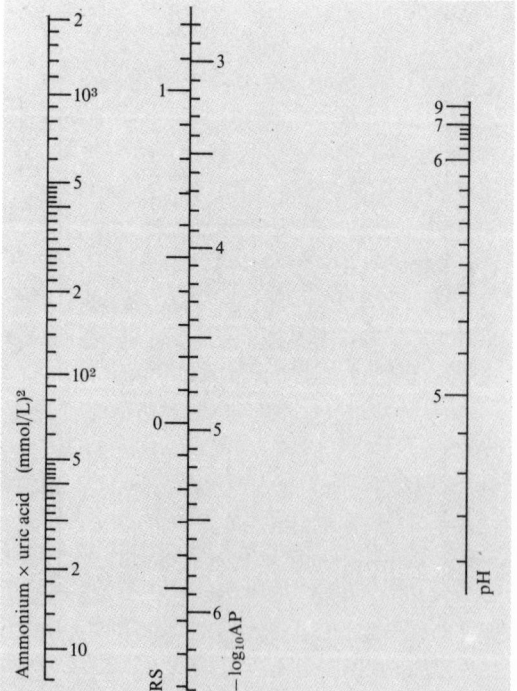

Fig. 9. Monoammonium urate: {NH4+} {urate−}.

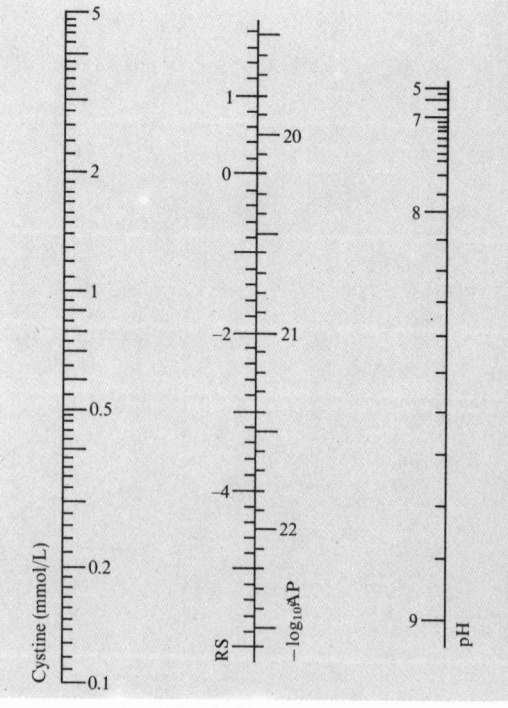

Fig. 10. Cystine: {H+}² {cystine²−}.

The individual functions of the kidneys can be assessed by means of quantitative as well as so-called semiquantitative tests. The quantitative tests are mostly based on the clearance principle and their use is not in all cases practicable or necessary; some are very time-consuming and may involve referring the patient to a specialized clinic. The semiquantitative tests include determinations of nonprotein nitrogen (NPN), or urea, and 'true' endogenous creatinine in the plasma, the phenolsulfonphthalein (PSP) test, and the fluid deprivation test for determining the ability of the kidneys to concentrate urine. The sensitivity of semiquantitative tests can be established by comparing their results with those of precise quantitative methods of determining the renal functions concerned.

Renal hemodynamics

Quantitative methods

In these tests the plasma clearance (C)[1,2] of certain substances is calculated by means of the formula:

$$C = \frac{U \times \dot{V}}{P}$$

where U and P are the concentrations of the clearance substance in the urine and plasma respectively in mg/L and $\dot{V}$ is the rate of urinary secretion in mL/min. A venous plasma concentration value is valid in the usual clearance formula only if measured under conditions of constancy of the concentrations of the clearance substance in the plasma and other body fluids. The standard plasma clearance of a substance is related to the 'normal' body surface (1.73 m²)[3,4].

Provided that a clearance substance is neither synthesized nor destroyed in the body and is physiologically inert, its plasma clearance is a measure of the *glomerular filtration rate*. The most suitable substance in this respect so far found is *inulin*[5,6], though it has recently been shown[7] that a poly(fructose)saccharide resembling inulin gives equally good results. (The urea clearance is of no use in determining renal hemodynamic values since in addition to being filtered by the glomeruli, urea also undergoes tubular reabsorption to an extent depending on the urinary flow[8].)

On account of its physicochemical and physiological properties, *p-aminohippuric acid* (PAH) is superior to all other substances for the determination of the *effective renal plasma flow* (C_{PAH})[2,9]:

$$C_{PAH} = \frac{U_{PAH} \times \dot{V}}{P_{PAH}}$$

The *total renal plasma flow*[2] is

$$RPF = \frac{C_{PAH}}{E_{PAH}}$$

E_{PAH} is the renal extraction:

$$E_{PAH} = \frac{P_{a_{PAH}} - P_{rv_{PAH}}}{P_{a_{PAH}}}$$

where $P_{a_{PAH}}$ is the concentration of PAH in the arterial plasma, $P_{rv_{PAH}}$ that in the renal venous blood.

For plasma PAH concentrations up to 30 mg/L the normal value of E_{PAH} is 0.925 (range 0.875–1.000)[10].

The *effective renal blood flow*[2] $= \dfrac{C_{PAH}}{1 - Hct}$

(Hct = peripheral hematocrit value)

The *total renal blood flow*[2] is

$$RBF = \frac{C_{PAH}}{E_{PAH}(1 - Hct)}$$

The 'normal' values of the renal inulin and PAH clearances (Table 1) are dependent on the water and salt balance[11,13] as well as on protein intake[14]. In the steady state, severe restriction of sodium intake causes C_{In} to fall markedly but has no effect on C_{PAH}. The diagnostically important filtration fraction (FF) is thus reduced:

$$FF = \frac{C_{In}}{C_{PAH}}$$

The clearances are increased on a protein-rich diet[14], as they are – without any characteristic change in the filtration fraction – when the daily urinary volume is high (hydration)[11,13]. Apart from

Table 1 *Normal values in renal hemodynamics (for body surface of 1.73 m²)*

Normal conditions (mixed diet, urinary volume rate 1–3 mL/min)		
Women[2]	C_{In}	108.8 ± 13.5 mL/min
	C_{PAH}	592 ± 153 mL/min
	FF	0.194 ± 0.039
	RBF[1]	982 ± 184 mL/min
Men[2]	C_{In}	124.1 ± 25.8 mL/min
	C_{PAH}	654 ± 163 mL/min
	FF	0.192 ± 0.035
	RBF[1]	1209 ± 256 mL/min
Men and women[11]	C_{In}	124.5 ± 9.7 mL/min
	C_{PAH}	638.6 ± 84.5 mL/min
	FF	0.197 ± 0.018
	RBF[12]	1165 mL/min
Hydration (urinary volume rate 6–12 mL/min)		
Men and women[11]	C_{In}	152.6 ± 14.7 mL/min
	C_{PAH}	711.7 ± 136.5 mL/min
	FF	0.220 ± 0.037
'Steady state' in dietetic restriction of sodium to 30 mmol/d; protein intake 0.5–1.0 g d⁻¹ kg⁻¹; urinary volume rate 1–3 mL/min		
Men and women[11]	C_{In}	107.6 ± 11.4 mL/min
	C_{PAH}	631.2 ± 87.8 mL/min
	FF	0.172 ± 0.018

this, the standard clearance values are dependent on age[15]. Between the 20th and 90th years of life C_{In} and C_{PAH} diminish roughly in proportion, so that the filtration fraction remains practically unchanged. The standard values at any age are given by the following equations:

C_{In} = 157.0 − (1.16 × age in years)
C_{PAH} = 820.2 − (6.75 × age in years)

The renal fraction of the minute output of the heart amounts normally to about 20%[2].

Semiquantitative methods

There exists no simple linear relationship between the glomerular filtration rate and the plasma creatinine or nonprotein nitrogen (NPN) levels[5,16–20] (Figs. 1 and 2), so that these determinations could fail to give an indication of even a considerable reduction in the glomerular function. A better indicator in this respect is the plasma concentration of 'true' endogenous creatinine (P_{Cr}), which is largely independent of the nitrogen metabolism.

In general, P_{Cr} is sensitive to a reduction of two-thirds or more in the normal glomerular filtration rate[5,18,20] (Fig. 1). The plasma NPN on the other hand is dependent on both the nitrogen turnover and urinary output; it may even be increased in persons with healthy kidneys[6] and may fail to react to a reduction in the glomerular filtration rate until this has fallen to a quarter of the normal value[19] (Fig. 2). In individual cases even a minor disturbance of renal function may result in an increased plasma creatinine level[18,20], while in persons with healthy kidneys the value may vary according to the method of measurement.

The different values for the two sexes given by most authorities are due to differences in the muscle mass of the body, since it is in this tissue that most of the creatinine is formed[22]. In determining plasma creatinine care should always be taken that the reaction mixture is freed of noncreatinine chromogens (including acetone, acetoacetic acid, bromsulfophthalein, glucose, barbiturates, pyruvic acid), which are treated differently by the kidney. When the plasma creatinine level is normal these chromogens, the proportion of which in the plasma creatinine shows marked individual variations but is of the order of 15%[17,23], are a disturbing factor in the test, whereas in renal insufficiency their importance becomes less in inverse proportion to the true plasma creatinine level.

The upper limit of the normal range of *plasma NPN concentration* is considered to be 400 mg/L[24]. Increases in this level are known to be dependent on an increase in the *urea fraction*. The proportion of the NPN due to the urea fraction can be calculated

*This chapter on 'Renal Function Values' (pages 101–107) has been compiled in collaboration with D.P.MERTZ, Kurklinik am Park, Horn-Bad Meinberg (FRG).

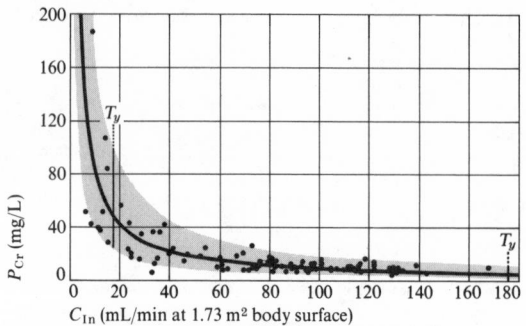

Fig. 1. Nonlinear relationship between the concentration of 'true' endogenous creatinine in plasma (P_{Cr}, as measured by the method of LØKEN[21]) and the renal inulin clearance (C_{In}). Ty: 95% tolerance range for $Y|x$[18].

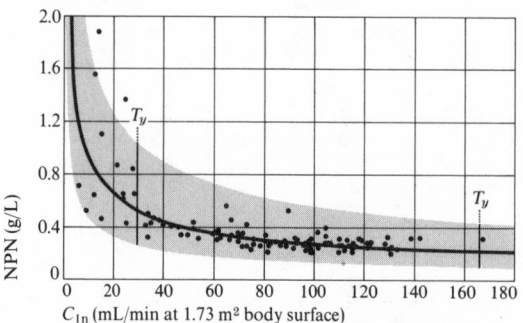

Fig. 2. Nonlinear relationship between the concentration of nonprotein nitrogen (NPN) in plasma and the renal inulin clearance (C_{In}). Ty: 95% tolerance range for $X|y$[19].

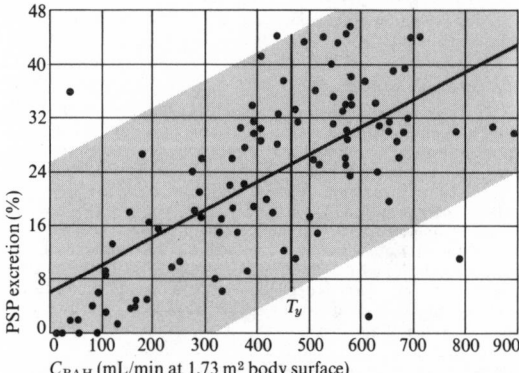

Fig. 3. Linear relationship between the percentage excretion of phenolsulfonphthalein (PSP: 15-minute value after a single intravenous injection of 6 mg) and the renal PAH clearance (C_{PAH}). Ty: 95% tolerance range for $Y|x$[26].

roughly from the urea nitrogen by means of the formula of PETERS and VAN SLYKE[25] (urea N and NPN in mg/L):

$$\text{Urea N} = \frac{\text{NPN} - 100}{1.07}$$

Here it should be borne in mind that in chronic renal insufficiency the rise in the NPN is not due to urea nitrogen to the extent indicated by the above formula. Whereas in acute renal failure up to 90% of the NPN is represented by urea, in chronic renal insufficiency there is a relatively larger increase in other NPN components.

The 15-minute *phenolsulfonphthalein test* (after a single intravenous injection of 6 mg of the dye) is not sufficiently sensitive to

reveal small changes in the excretory function of the renal tubules[26]. The marked variance of the sample values around the regression line (Fig. 3) is due in the main to the combination of PSP with plasma proteins (dependent on various factors), the absence of a flow equilibrium of PSP in the body fluid compartments after a single injection, failure to take account of body mass in evaluating the results, and the use of spontaneous urine samples[26].

Dilution and concentration of urine

Tests of the diluting capacity of the kidneys are usually now dispensed with. If the organ can concentrate urine it must also be able to dilute it, and in any case concentration tests are less dependent on extrarenal factors and therefore more sensitive. Moreover, a dilution test could have a disturbing effect on a subsequent concentration test[20, 24, 27].

Quantitative methods

When ADH (antidiuretic hormone) activity is at a maximum, the urinary concentrating capacity is limited by two factors[28]: (a) during hydropenia and oliguria by the maximum value of the ratio between the osmotic concentrations of the urine and plasma (U_{osm}/P_{osm}), i.e., by the maximum osmotic concentration effect; (b) during osmotic diuresis, which does not normally occur under physiological conditions, by the maximum reabsorption of osmotically free water ($Tm^c_{H_2O}$) into the hypertonic interstices of the renal medulla. A number of conditions are known in which the latter is the more sensitive factor, and it may have a pathological value even when the concentration test (determination of maximum urinary osmolality) is still completely normal.

Normal values	
Maximum urinary osmolality ..	1027 $\pm$ 110 mmol/kg[29]
	1067 (918–1230) mmol/kg[32]
(Deamino-arginine vasopressin test)	1042 $\pm$ 108 mmol/kg[31]
Maximum value of U_{osm}/P_{osm}	2.77 $\pm$ 0.36[33]
	3.63–4.65[34]
$Tm^c_{H_2O}$ (with intravenous infusion of hypertonic mannitol solution).....................	5.7 $\pm$ 2.0 mL/min[35]
$Tm^c_{H_2O} \times 100/C_{In}$ (with intravenous infusion of hypertonic mannitol solution)..........	5.1 $\pm$ 1.5[36]

Calculation according to WESSON and ANSLOW[42]:

$$T^c_{H_2O} = C_{osm} - \dot{V}$$

$$C_{osm} = \frac{U_{osm} \times \dot{V}}{P_{osm}}$$

$$U_{osm}/P_{osm} = 1 + \frac{T^c_{H_2O}}{\dot{V}} \quad \text{(see Fig. 4)}^{[36]}$$

With increasing osmolar clearance (C_{osm}) from 1 mL/min to 15 mL/min (for a body surface of 1.73 m²), $T^c_{H_2O}$ increases steadily up to its maximum value $Tm^c_{H_2O}$. When C_{osm} exceeds about 25 mL/min the latter tends to diminish slightly[37]. It has been shown that with increasing osmotic saline diuresis the value of $T^c_{H_2O}$ rises continuously and not to the expected individual maximum. This applies not only to normotensive subjects with healthy kidneys[38, 39] but also to patients with essential hypertension[39] provided their renal function is not noticeably impaired. This progressive increase in $T^c_{H_2O}$ also occurs in the diuretic range where its value for mannitol diuresis already shows a tendency to decrease (Fig. 5). In contrast to the views of some authorities it therefore seems that in man the behavior of $T^c_{H_2O}$ is not constant during osmotic diuresis with different substances such as sodium chloride, mannitol, urea or glucose under conditions of comparable total excretion of osmotically active material. The upper limit for the net withdrawal of osmotically free water during osmotic diuresis with mannitol, urea or glucose is a 'pseudomaximum'. Sodium transport in the interstitium of the renal medulla is no more subject to a maximum value in man than it is in the experimental animal. In the view of the present author[39], the ratio U_{osm}/P_{osm} during hydropenia and oliguria affords the best measure of the concentrating capacity of the kidney. In many cases, determination of '$Tm^c_{H_2O}$' during hypertonic mannitol diuresis offers at best certain advantages over the usual methods in respect of localization of the site of disturbances in the urinary concentration mechanism.

At maximum diuresis the excess of osmotically free water compared to a hypothetical isosmotic urinary portion can be determined as the maximum free-water clearance ($Tm^d_{H_2O}$).

$Tm^d_{H_2O}$ (maximal C_{H_2O})

Young men .... 6.9–16.9 mL/min[40]
Diabetes insipidus .... up to 23 mL/min[41]

Calculation according to WESSON and ANSLOW[42]:

$$T^d_{H_2O} = C_{H_2O} = \dot{V} - C_{osm}$$

There are considerable discrepancies in the 'normal' values given in the literature for some of the parameters of renal concentrating capacity, a result of differences in the experimental methods. The concentrating capacity of the kidneys can be increased by means of a protein-rich diet[44]; it is decreased under conditions of inadequate dehydration[45] and in man (fluid deprivation test) is independent of the sodium chloride intake[46].

For persons between the ages of 24 and 72 years with healthy kidneys the age dependence of maximum urinary osmolality as found by a 24-hour fluid deprivation test is given by the formula[47]:

$$U_{osm} = 1134 - (4.1 \times \text{age in years})$$

Semiquantitative methods

While the underlying physiological process in the concentration of urine consists of the removal of osmotically free water, the various electrolytes and nonelectrolytes present contribute in different degrees to the relative density ϱ_U and osmotic pressure. The determination of the *maximum relative density of urine* in the fluid deprivation test[48] must therefore be regarded as a semiquantitative test of renal function.

Glucose, phosphate and sulfate cause a high relative density of urine at fairly low osmotic concentrations[49], whereas chloride and urea exert a relatively high osmotic pressure for a given urinary relative density (Fig. 6). In persons with healthy kidneys the maximum urinary osmolarity reached in the fluid deprivation test is only loosely related to the maximum relative density[29]. The variance in the relationship between these two parameters increases in renal disease (Fig. 7)[30].

ϱ_U (24-hour test; 15 °C | 4 °C)

Normal value .... 1.035 ± 0.004[27]
Lower limit of normal (healthy kidney) ..... 1.026[24,27,30]

The maximum urinary relative density falls from an average of 1.032 at 20 years to an average of 1.024 between 80 and 90 years[50].

Dependence of the 24-hour urinary volume on the amounts of solutes removed in the urine and the concentrating capacity of the kidneys

The amounts of solutes removed in the urine depend both on the dietary intake, particularly of proteins and salts, and on the energy turnover of the body[51]. A mixed diet yields about 1200 mmol of urinary solutes per day[52], an amount reduced by fasting to about 800 mmol. In fasting subjects given 100 g glucose per day the urinary solutes fall to 400 mmol/d, while a diet low in protein and salt but rich in carbohydrates (with maintenance of the basal metabolic rate) results in a further reduction to 200 mmol/d. On the basis of a maximum urinary osmolality of 1400 mmol/kg the amounts of water required for the excretion of these amounts are 857, 571, 286 and 143 mL respectively. In isosthenuria (urinary osmolality of 300 mmol/kg) the renal elimination of 1200, 800, 400 and 200 mmol of urinary solutes requires respectively 4000, 2667, 1333 and 667 mL of water. The relationship between the renal water requirement and the urinary osmolality for different daily amounts of solutes removed in the urine is shown in Figure 8.

Tubular transport functions

Clearance techniques enable an assessment to be made of the state of functioning of the active local transport mechanisms in the

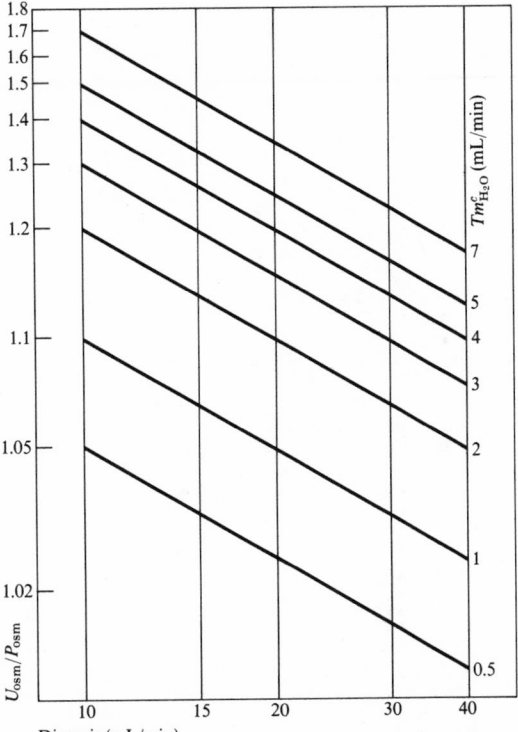

Fig. 4. Diagram for reading off values of $Tm^c_{H_2O}$ from those of U_{osm}/P_{osm} and the simultaneous urinary minute volume in osmotic diuresis[43].

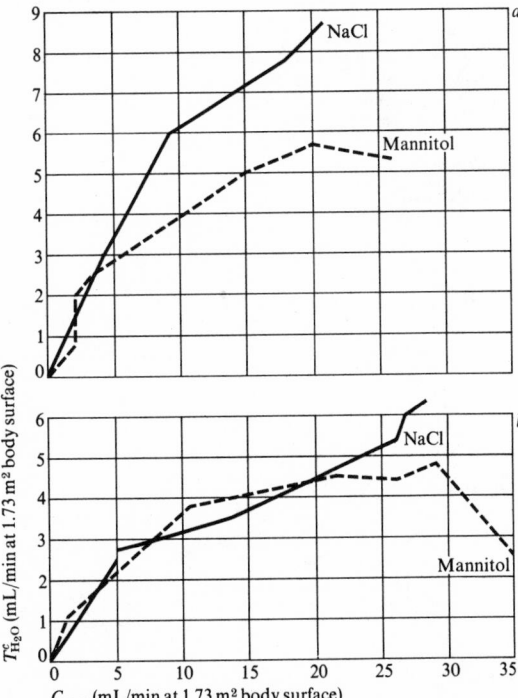

Fig. 5. Plots of $T^c_{H_2O}$ during saline diuresis and mannitol diuresis in (a) a healthy man and (b) a man with essential hypertension[39].

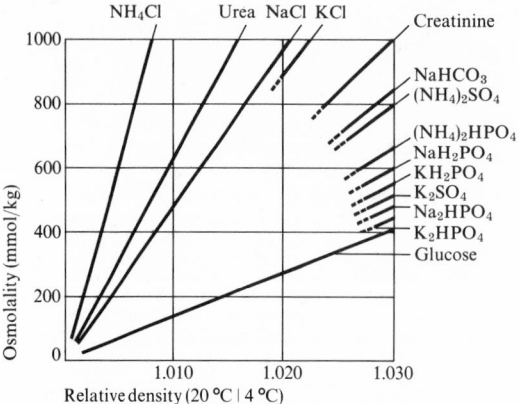

Fig. 6. Contributions of various urinary components to the relative density and osmolality of the urine[49].

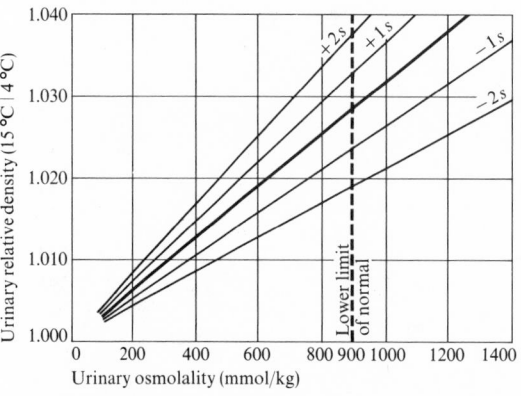

Fig. 7. Relationship between the maximum urinary relative density achieved in the 18-hour fluid deprivation test and the corresponding osmolality (U_{osm}) of the urine in 112 persons with healthy and diseased kidneys: $1000 \times (\varrho_U - 1)/U_{osm} = 0.0318 \pm 0.0053$[30].

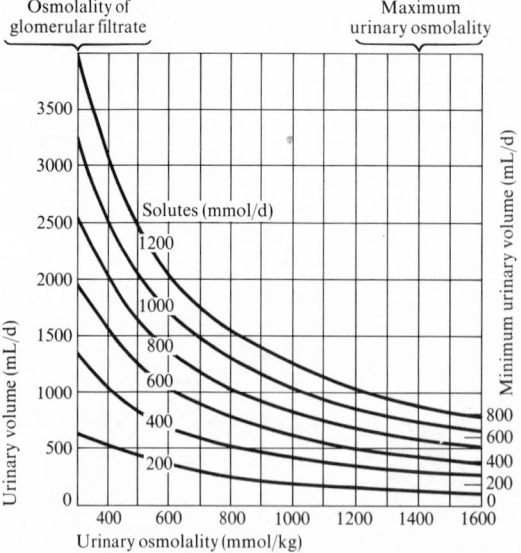

Fig. 8. Relationship between urinary volume and osmolality at various solute concentrations[51,52].

proximal tubular convolution. Both the tubular secretion of p-aminohippuric acid (PAH) and the reabsorption of glucose (G) from the tubular urine are limited by transport maxima (Tm)[1].

$$Tm_{PAH} = (U_{PAH} \times \dot{V}) - (P_{PAH} \times C_{In} \times k)^9$$

where U_{PAH} and P_{PAH} are the concentrations of PAH in urine and plasma respectively and k is a correction factor for the plasma PAH fraction that is protein-bound and not filtrable by the glomeruli. The normal value of k is 0.83.

$$Tm_G = (P_G \times C_{In}) - (U_G \times \dot{V})$$

Normal values (for 1.73 m² body surface)

Tm_{PAH}	Men	79.8 ± 16.7 mg/min²
	Women	77.2 ± 10.8 mg/min²
Tm_G	Men	375 ± 79.7 mg/min[1,2]
	Women	303 ± 55.3 mg/min[1,2]

These renal functions can be differentiated more precisely by relating Tm_{PAH} (as a measure of the functioning secretory renal tissue) and Tm_G (as a measure of the reabsorptive renal tissue) to C_{In} and C_{PAH} respectively. The ratios C_{In}/Tm_{PAH}, C_{PAH}/Tm_{PAH} and Tm_G/C_{In} are measures of glomerular activity, i.e., of the effective renal plasma flow per unit of the secretory or reabsorptive tissue.

Normal values

C_{In}/Tm_{PAH}	1.54 ± 0.4 mL/mg²
C_{PAH}/Tm_{PAH}	8.28 ± 2.2 mL/mg²
Tm_G/C_{In}	2.41 ± 0.35 mg/mL[1]

All these functions show age regression between the 20th and 90th years of life:

$$Tm_{PAH} = 120.6 - (0.865 \times \text{age in years})^{15}$$
$$Tm_G = 432.8 - (2.604 \times \text{age in years})^{50}$$
$$C_{In}/Tm_{PAH} = 1.382 - (0.00158 \times \text{age in years})^{50}$$
$$C_{PAH}/Tm_{PAH} = 7.710 - (0.0278 \times \text{age in years})^{50}$$

Excretion of acids and electrolytes

The *total acid excretion* (A_{H^+}) is made up of potentially ionizable hydrogen ions (titratable acidity, TA) and bound (nonionizable) hydrogen ions in the form of ammonium ions (NH_4^+):

$$A_{H^+} = A_{TA} + A_{NH_4^+}$$
$$(A_{H^+} : U_{H^+} \times \dot{V}; A_{TA} : U_{TA} \times \dot{V}; A_{NH_4^+} : U_{NH_4^+} \times \dot{V})$$

Normal values (on a mixed diet)

Total acid excretion (A_{H^+})	30–80 mmol/d[53]
Titratable acidity (A_{TA})	10–30 mmol/d[53]
NH_4^+ excretion ($A_{NH_4^+}$)	20–50 mmol/d[53]
$A_{NH_4^+}/A_{TA}$	1.0–2.5[53]
	1.28 ± 0.14[54]

The difference between the sum of the TA and NH_4^+ excretions and the bicarbonate excretion (HCO_3^-) is known as the *effective acid excretion* ($A_{H_{eff}^+}$).

$$A_{H_{eff}^+} = A_{H^+} - A_{HCO_3^-} = A_{TA} + A_{NH_4^+} - A_{HCO_3^-}$$

In alkaline urine the effective acid excretion has a negative value since mainly bicarbonate ions are excreted.

The pH value of urine may vary between 4.5 and 8.2[2,55].

Since the hydrogen ion clearance is not determinable, the serum bicarbonate level has been used to obtain a *hydrogen ion clearance index* as a measure of the hydrogen ion retention[56,57]. This index is used for the detection of renal tubular acidosis ($S_{HCO_3^-}$: serum bicarbonate in mmol/L):

$$I_{C_{H^+}} = \frac{U_{H^+} \times \dot{V}}{1/S_{HCO_3^-}}$$

$$I_{C_{TA}} = \frac{U_{TA} \times \dot{V}}{1/S_{HCO_3^-}}$$

$$I_{C_{NH_4^+}} = \frac{U_{NH_4^+} \times \dot{V}}{1/S_{HCO_3^-}}$$

To be informative, this index must be determined on the third day after the start of daily loading with 0.1 g ammonium chloride per 1 kg body mass.

Normal values for body surface of 1.73 m²[56,57]	Mean	Maximum	Minimum
I_{CH^+}	2.07	3.4	1.4
I_{CTA}	0.75	1.0	0.6
$I_{C_{NH4}^+}$	1.32	2.4	0.8

An accurate assessment of the tubular treatment of an *electrolyte* from the excreted proportion of the amount filtered by the glomeruli is possible only when the substance concerned is freely filtrable and is exclusively reabsorbed in the tubules and not secreted. The only important electrolytes at present considered to fulfil this condition in man are sodium, chloride and bicarbonate.

Table 2 gives the mean values for the glomerular filtration and total excretion of some electrolytes in the 24-hour urine[24].

The *glomerular filtration* of a completely filtrable electrolyte (E) is calculated as follows (GF_E in μmol/min):

$$GF_E = k \times P_E \times C_{In}$$

where P_E is the plasma concentration of the electrolyte (in μmol/mL) and k a correction factor for the small differences between the concentrations in plasma and glomerular filtrate resulting from the Gibbs-Donnan equilibrium and the lowering of the water content of the plasma by the proteins.

The value of k is normally 1.02 for Cl^- and HCO_3^-[58], 0.96[59] for Na^+ and 0.92[59] for K^+. For calculation of the amounts of partly plasma-protein-bound electrolytes filtered by the glomeruli it is important to know the filtrable part. This is dependent on the concentration and composition of the plasma proteins and on the pH value and other physicochemical conditions. 54% of the plasma calcium and 68% of the plasma magnesium are normally ultrafiltrable[60]. For phosphate, the ratio of the concentrations in the glomerular filtrate and plasma has been found to be 0.93 in rats[61].

The glomerular filtration of proteins depends on the size and on the steric and electrical properties of the molecules[62]. The albumin concentration in the glomerular filtrate is less than 1% of that in the plasma. On account of the high albumin content of the plasma, however, approximately 32 g/d passes into the glomerular filtrate, though only 50 mg/d of this appears in the urine.

So-called 'normal values' for the clearance of electrolytes have little significance since they are very largely dependent on exogenous factors. Clearance values for amino acids are shown in Table 3.

Partial functions of tubular excretion of sodium[63]

(a) Estimation of the proportion of sodium chloride to the total solutes excreted by calculation of the contribution of sodium chloride to urinary osmolality:

$$\frac{U_{Na} + U_{Cl}}{U_{osm}}$$

(U_{Na} and U_{Cl}: urinary Na or Cl concentration in mmol/L; U_{osm}: urinary osmolality in mmol/kg)

(b) Calculation of the quantity of sodium supplied to the distal tubular segment as the sum of the sodium that has to be reabsorbed in the production of osmotically free water during water excretion and the sodium simultaneously appearing in the urine:

$$U_{Na} \times \dot{V} + P_{Na} \times C_{H_2O}$$

This represents the minimum amount of sodium reaching the distal segment of the tubule via the proximal segment. In the proximal tubule, iso-osmotic reabsorption of sodium takes place, while in the distal segment osmotically free water is formed by selective reabsorption of sodium (in water excretion).

(c) Estimation of that part of the sodium fraction not proximally reabsorbed by calculating the ratio of the amount of sodium supplied to the distal tubule – see (b) above – to the amount undergoing glomerular filtration:

$$\frac{U_{Na} \times \dot{V} + P_{Na} \times C_{H_2O}}{C_{In} \times P_{Na}}$$

(d) Estimation of the percentage fractional reabsorption of sodium in the distal 'diluting' segment of the nephron as the ratio of the amount of sodium appearing in the urine to the amount supplied to the distal tubule:

$$\frac{U_{Na} \times \dot{V}}{U_{Na} \times \dot{V} + P_{Na} \times C_{H_2O}}$$

(e) Calculation of volume of water undergoing glomerular filtration (GF_{H_2O} in mL/min):

$$GF_{H_2O} = (1 - P_{Pr}) \times C_{In}$$

(P_{Pr}: plasma concentration of protein in g/mL)

Clearance studies in advanced kidney disease[64]

Under physiological conditions, there is satisfactory agreement between the clearance values of endogenous creatinine and inulin in man. However, in patients whose glomerular filtration rate has fallen to 40 mL/min or less, the C_{Cr}/C_{In} ratio may rise to a value above 2. As far as informative value is concerned, the creatinine clearance – in the absence of renal insufficiency – is superior to the plasma creatinine level for the early detection of disturbances of renal function or for serial observations of renal function. In patients with kidney disease, the creatinine clearance is generally between 30% and >50% higher than the inulin clearance. Wide

Table 2 *Amounts of various electrolytes filtered and excreted daily at a glomerular filtration rate of 120 mL/min*

	Filtered	Excreted in urine
	mmol	mmol
Bicarbonate	4400	1–2
Chloride	18300	80–270
Phosphate	160	5–40
Potassium	650	40–100
Sodium	23200	95–310
Calcium	230	1.5–8
Magnesium	95	2.5–8
Water	$10^3 \times 9000$	$10^3 \times 40$–100

Table 3 *Endogenous renal clearance of amino acids*

	12 children[90]				4 adults[91]
	16 days to 4 months		2–13 years		
	Mean	s	Mean	s	(Extreme range)
	mL/min for body surface of 1.73 m²				
Alanine	1.65	0.75	0.82	0.38	(0.3–0.9)
Arginine	0.36	0.08	0.28	0.10	(0.2–0.8)
Asparagine + glutamine	–	–	–	–	(0.7–1.8)
Asparagine + threonine	2.00	1.39	1.01	0.24	–
Aspartic acid	–	–	3.61	0.88	(0–2.4)
Cystine	1.07	0.27	0.79	0.20	(0.7–2.9)
Glutamic acid	–	–	–	–	(0.3–0.7)
Glycine	7.39	3.24	4.24	1.41	(2.7–5.8)
Histidine	8.52	4.46	9.51	2.63	(4.7–9.1)
Hydroxyproline	–	–	–	–	–
Isoleucine	0.30	0.16	0.32	0.09	(0.2–1.0)
Leucine	0.79	0.53	0.49	0.15	(0.2–0.9)
Lysine	1.29	0.37	1.16	0.38	(0.2–1.9)
Methionine	0.79	0.56	0.81	0.27	1.1
Ornithine	0.39	0.14	0.38	0.12	trace
Phenylalanine	1.74	0.91	1.50	0.29	(0.7–1.4)
Proline	1.01	0.66	0.35	0.21	0
Serine	4.06	1.94	2.43	0.51	(1.9–3.0)
Taurine	–	–	–	–	(1.7–14)
Threonine	–	–	–	–	(0.8–1.5)
Tyrosine	1.79	0.41	2.04	0.80	(1.0–1.7)
Valine	0.29	0.12	0.23	0.11	(0.1–0.3)

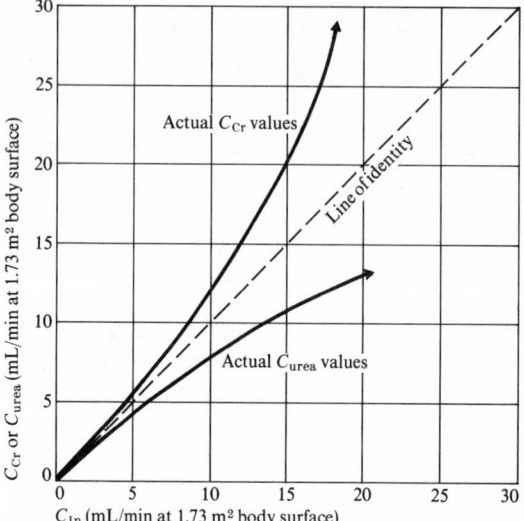

Fig. 9. Comparison of clearance values of endogenous creatinine and urea with the simultaneously measured inulin clearance values[64].

individual variations in the endogenous creatinine clearance, with C_{Cr}/C_{In} ratios between 0.8 and >4.0, have repeatedly been observed. This instability must be regarded as due to day-to-day variations in the tubular secretion of creatinine and to possible tubular rediffusion. The binding of creatinine to protein in the glomerular filtrate is another possible source of error. Assuming that the secretion of creatinine has an upper limit[2], the ratio of the amount secreted to total excretion should decrease as the plasma level rises. The creatinine clearance then approaches the inulin clearance as the plasma creatinine level continues to increase, that is, as the glomerular filtration rate decreases (Fig. 9). This theoretical condition, however, is not met in all cases of renal insufficiency. For this reason the clearance of endogenous creatinine cannot be regarded as a measure of the glomerular filtration rate in chronic renal insufficiency.

Theoretical considerations suggest that in severe renal insufficiency urea clearance should approach the glomerular filtration rate, namely when the fractional reabsorption of salt and water decreases to the same extent as the number of functioning nephrons. The lower the ratio between the urinary and plasma inulin levels, the smaller the proportion of reabsorbed water. Theoretically, therefore, urea clearance should be the same as inulin clearance when the concentration of inulin in the urine is no higher than that in the plasma, i.e., when the ratio of urinary inulin to plasma inulin is 1.0. The excretion of filtered water then amounts to 100%. Experimental findings support this assumption (Fig. 9).

Clearance studies are superfluous in patients with advanced chronic kidney disease. In such cases the plasma creatinine level also reflects the extent of the damage. In the early stage of renal insufficiency it is quite possible for this parameter to be normal in some individuals despite a considerable loss of function. When conventional semiquantitative tests are no longer sufficiently sensitive for evaluation after improvement of renal function, the standard clearance values should certainly be measured.

Renal function in the fetus and in infants and children

Renal function in the newborn can be compared with that in adults only to a limited extent since the physiological functions have to meet different requirements[65]. Thus, the kidney of the newborn infant functions entirely satisfactorily – unless subjected to nonphysiological stress – even though it is immature by adult standards.

The fetal glomeruli are not completely developed until the 35th week of pregnancy; however, in premature infants maturation takes place immediately after delivery[66]. Once the fetal mass has reached 2100–2500 g, the formation of new glomeruli usually ceases. For the number of glomeruli present at birth, the glomerular filtration rate is initially inhibited, a result of the persistence of fetal cuboid epithelium. During the first two years of life, this epi-

thelium is slowly replaced by the final, thin epithelial layer from the juxtamedullary to the cortical region[67]. At term, the proximal tubules of the fetus are still primitive but in tissue cultures they are already capable of secreting phenolsulfonphthalein in the 2nd to 3rd months of pregnancy[68]. As far as their function as countercurrent multiplier is concerned, the length of the loops of Henle is important for the production of a concentrated urine. At birth the loops are short[69], and with age they increase in length[70].

> *Normal hemodynamic kidney values in newborn infants 29 to 72 hours old (for body surface of 1 m²)[71]*
>
> C_{In} .... 9.3 (6.0–14.8) mL/min
> C_{PAH} .... 23.2 (15.0–27.7) mL/min
> FF 0.406 (0.23–0.58)

During the first two weeks of life the clearance values of inulin and PAH are doubled[72], as a result of which the serum creatinine level, which is elevated at birth, decreases sharply[73]. Since the renal extraction of PAH is low in the newborn[74], the PAH clearance significantly underestimates true renal plasma flow. On the whole, however, glomerular function develops more rapidly than tubular function. By the 5th or 6th postnatal month the glomerular filtration rate in relation to body surface area reaches adult values. Glomerular filtration rate and kidney mass increase uniformly[75]. After the first 6 months of life the other renal functions mature more slowly. PAH clearance reaches adult values by the 7th month at the earliest. With normal development, however, children do not reach full maturity of all tubular functions until they are 2 years old[75,76], although Tm_{PAH} may on occasion be fully developed at a much earlier age. While the filtration fraction, which is considerably elevated in the first weeks of life, decreases concurrently with maturation of the PAH transport mechanism, it remains moderately elevated in the second and third years.

The fetal kidney, which is not subject to the influence of antidiuretic hormone, is able to produce only a hypotonic urine. After birth, the ability of the kidney to produce a concentrated urine rapidly grows, and at the age of 1–2 months some children are already able to produce urine with an osmolality of 1000 mmol/kg or more[77,78]. However, copious excretion of urea (high protein intake) appears to be a prerequisite[79].

> *Normal values of renal concentrating capacity in the fetus and newborn*
>
> U_{osm}:
> Urine before birth .... 137 (97–232) mmol/kg[80]
> First urine after birth .... 317 (151–480) mmol/kg[80]
> First 48 hours after birth .... 420 (288–536) mmol/kg[81]
>
> U_{osm}/P_{osm}:
> First 3 hours after birth .... 0.98 (0.49–1.49)[82]
>
> Maximum urinary osmolality (deamino-arginine vasopressin test)[83]:
>
> 1–3 weeks .... 385 (350–430) mmol/kg
> 4–6 weeks .... 565 (480–630) mmol/kg

In view of the large individual variations in the concentrating capacity of the infantile kidney it is advisable to restrict the osmolar load by reducing the energy ion content of the diet to not more than 100 kcal/100 mL (420 kJ/100 mL) and to withhold NaCl-rich foods[84]. For children at risk (small-for-dates premature infants, congenital heart defects) the diet should be such that urinary osmolality does not exceed 400 mmol/kg[85].

Unlike the renal concentrating mechanism, the diluting mechanism is fully functional even in underweight premature infants: urinary dilution down to 40–50 mmol/kg is possible[86,87].

The ability of the newborn to excrete hydrogen ions differs from that of older children and adults insofar as the urine as yet contains little phosphate and thereby titratable acid, while ammonium formation in the kidney is not yet fully developed[55,65]. If therefore the dietary intake of phosphate is low, ammonium formation may easily prove inadequate to control an acidosis. The low bicarbonate concentration in the neonatal serum appears to be due to the lower renal bicarbonate threshold: in the newborn, bicarbonate appears in the urine even at a serum bicarbonate level of 22 mmol/L, whereas this happens in the adult only at 24–26 mmol/L[88]. In premature infants the capacity for hydrogen ion excretion is reduced by comparison with infants born at term; this difference diminishes, however, and disappears within 4–6 weeks of birth[89].

Determination of the endogenous clearance of amino acids has assumed some importance for the classification of aminoacidurias (page 68). The lag in the maturation of tubular as compared with glomerular function is reflected in clearance values that are higher in infants than in children and adults (Table 3).

References

[1] SMITH, H.W., *Lectures on the Kidney,* University of Kansas, Lawrence, 1943.
[2] SMITH, H.W., *The Kidney: Structure and Function in Health and Disease,* Oxford University Press, New York, 1951.
[3] MCINTOSH et al., *J. clin. Invest.,* **6**, 467 (1928).
[4] MÖLLER et al., *J. clin. Invest.,* **6**, 427 (1928).
[5] REUBI, F., *Schweiz. med. Wschr.,* **88**, 1084 (1958).
[6] SARRE and SCHADKHU, *Klin. Wschr.,* **40**, 179 (1962).
[7] HARTH, O., *Klin. Wschr.,* **41**, 769 (1963); MERTZ and SARRE, *Klin. Wschr.,* **41**, 868 (1963).
[8] AUSTIN et al., *J. biol. Chem.,* **46**, 91 (1921).
[9] SMITH et al., *J. clin. Invest.,* **24**, 388 (1945).
[10] BRADLEY et al., *Fed. Proc.,* **6**, 79 (1947).
[11] MERTZ, D.P., *Z. klin. Med.,* **157**, 1 (1961).
[12] AAS and BLEGEN, *Scand. J. clin. Lab. Invest.,* **1**, 22 (1949).
[13] MERTZ, D.P., *Die extracelluläre Flüssigkeit,* Thieme, Stuttgart, 1962.
[14] PULLMAN et al., *J. Lab. clin. Med.,* **44**, 320 (1954).
[15] WATKIN and SHOCK, *J. clin. Invest.,* **34**, 969 (1955).
[16] STEINITZ and TÜRKAND, *J. clin. Invest.,* **19**, 285 (1940); SARRE et al., *Dtsch. med. Wschr.,* **82**, 1093 (1957); EFFERSØE, P., *Acta med. scand.,* **156**, 429 (1957); EDWARDS and WHYTE, *Aust. Ann. Med.,* **8**, 218 (1959).
[17] DOOLAN et al., *Amer. J. Med.,* **32**, 65 (1962).
[18] MERTZ et al., *Klin. Wschr.,* **40**, 687 (1962).
[19] MERTZ et al., *Klin. Wschr.,* **40**, 889 (1962).
[20] REUBI, F., *Nierenkrankheiten,* 2nd ed., Huber, Berne, 1970.
[21] LØKEN, F., *Scand. J. clin. Lab. Invest.,* **6**, 325 (1954).
[22] BORSOOK and DUBNOFF, *J. biol. Chem.,* **168**, 493 (1947).
[23] LENTNER and EGGSTEIN, *Leading Symptoms: Laboratory Values,* CIBA-GEIGY Ltd., Basle, 1976.
[24] SARRE, H., *Nierenkrankheiten,* 4th ed., Thieme, Stuttgart, 1976.
[25] PETERS and VAN SLYKE, *Quantitative Clinical Chemistry,* 2nd ed., volume 1, Williams & Wilkins, Baltimore, 1946.
[26] MERTZ and SARRE, *Klin. Wschr.,* **40**, 692 (1962).
[27] BOCK and KRECKE, *Dtsch. Arch. klin. Med.,* **204**, 499 (1957).
[28] SMITH, H.W., *Principles of Renal Physiology,* Oxford University Press, New York, 1956.
[29] ISAACSON, L.C., *Lancet,* **1**, 467 (1960).
[30] MERTZ, D.P., *Z. klin. Med.,* **157**, 517 and 529 (1963).
[31] CURTIS and DONOVAN, *Brit. med. J.,* **1**, 304 (1979).
[32] HULET and SMITH, *Amer. J. Med.,* **30**, 8 (1961).
[33] BOYARSKY and SMITH, *J. Urol. (Baltimore),* **78**, 511 (1957).
[34] RAISZ and SCHEER, *J. clin. Invest.,* **38**, 1 (1959).
[35] ZAK et al., *J. clin. Invest.,* **33**, 1064 (1954).
[36] BALDWIN et al., *J. clin. Invest.,* **34**, 800 (1955).
[37] RAISZ et al., *J. clin. Invest.,* **38**, 1725 (1959); EISNER et al., *J. Mt Sinai Hosp.,* **29**, 38 (1962).
[38] GOLDBERG et al., *J. clin. Invest.,* **44**, 182 (1965).
[39] MERTZ, D.P., *Pflügers Arch. ges. Physiol.,* **290**. 1 (1966).
[40] KLEEMAN et al., *J. clin. Invest.,* **35**, 749 (1956); BUCHBORN et al., *Klin. Wschr.,* **37**, 347 (1959).
[41] KLEEMAN et al., *J. clin. Invest.,* **39**, 1472 (1960).
[42] WESSON and ANSLOW, *Amer. J. Physiol.,* **170**, 255 (1952).

[43] BUCHBORN and ANASTASAKIS, *Internist (Berl.),* **2**, 611 (1961).
[44] EPSTEIN et al., *J. clin. Invest.,* **36**, 635 (1957).
[45] KLEEMAN and MAXWELL, *Clin. Res. Proc.,* **5**, 43 (1957); EPSTEIN et al., *J. clin. Invest.,* **36**, 629 (1957).
[46] LEVITT et al., *J. clin. Invest.,* **38**, 463 (1959).
[47] LINDEMAN et al., *New Engl. J. Med.,* **262**, 1306 (1960).
[48] VOLHARD, F., *Verh. dtsch. Ges. inn. Med.,* **27**, 735 (1910).
[49] ISAACSON, L.C., *Lancet,* **1**, 72 (1959).
[50] SHOCK, N.W., in WOLSTENHOLME and O'CONNOR (Eds.), *Ciba Foundation Colloquia on Ageing,* volume 4, Churchill, London, 1958, page 229.
[51] GAMBLE, J.L., *Chemical Anatomy, Physiology and Pathology of Extracellular Fluid,* 6th ed., Harvard University Press, Cambridge, 1954.
[52] GAMBLE and BUTLER, *Trans. Ass. Amer. Phycns,* **58**, 157 (1944).
[53] KRÜCK, F., *Klin. Wschr.,* **36**, 946 (1958).
[54] SCHWAB, M., *Verh. dtsch. Ges. inn. Med.,* **67**, 595 (1961).
[55] KILDEBERG, P., *Clinical Acid–Base Physiology,* Munksgaard, Copenhagen, 1968.
[56] ELKINTON et al., *Amer. J. Med.,* **29**, 554 (1960).
[57] ELKINTON, J.R., *Med. Clin. N. Amer.,* **47**, 935 (1963).
[58] HASTINGS et al., *J. gen. Physiol.,* **8**, 701 (1927).
[59] FOLK et al., *Amer. J. Physiol.,* **153**, 381 (1948).
[60] WALSER, M., *J. clin. Invest.,* **40**, 723 (1961); WALSER, M., in COMAR and BRONNER (Eds.), *Mineral Metabolism,* volume 3, Academic Press, New York, 1969, page 235.
[61] HARRIS et al., *Amer. J. Physiol.,* **227**, 972 (1974).
[62] PITTS, R.F., *Physiology of the Kidney and Body Fluids,* 3rd ed., Year Book Medical Publishers, Chicago, 1974.
[63] MERTZ, D.P., *Elektrolytstoffwechsel und arterielle Hypertension,* Schattauer, Stuttgart, 1971.
[64] MERTZ, D.P., in KLUTHE et al. (Eds.), *Uremia,* Thieme, Stuttgart, 1972, page 108.
[65] NASH and EDELMANN, *Nephron,* **11**, 71 (1973).
[66] MÜHLMANN, M., *Ergebn. anat. Entwickl.-Gesch.,* **27**, 1 (1927).
[67] CLARA, M., *Z. mikr.-anat. Forsch.,* **40**, 147 (1936).
[68] CAMERON and CHAMBERS, *Amer. J. Physiol.,* **123**, 482 (1938).
[69] VESTERDAL, J., in WOLSTENHOLME and O'CONNOR (Eds.), *Somatic Stability in the Newly Born,* Ciba Foundation Symposium, Churchill, London, 1961, page 16.
[70] PETERS, K. (Ed.), *Untersuchungen über Bau und Entwicklung der Niere,* Fischer, Jena, 1909.
[71] GUIGNARD et al., *J. Pediat.,* **88**, 845 (1976).
[72] GUIGNARD et al., *J. Pediat.,* **87**, 268 (1975).
[73] SERTEL and SCOPES, *Arch. Dis. Childh.,* **48**, 717 (1973).
[74] CALCAGNO and RUBIN, *J. clin. Invest.,* **42**, 1632 (1963).
[75] RUBIN et al., *J. clin. Invest.,* **28**, 1144 (1949).
[76] WEST et al., *J. Pediat.,* **32**, 10 (1948).
[77] PRATT et al., *Pediatrics,* **1**, 181 (1948).
[78] POLÁČEK et al., *Arch. Dis. Childh.,* **40**, 291 (1965).
[79] EDELMANN et al., *J. clin. Invest.,* **39**, 1062 (1960).
[80] MCCANCE and WIDDOWSON, *Proc. roy. Soc. B,* **141**, 488 (1953), and *Cold Spr. Harb. Symp. quant. Biol.,* **19**, 155 (1954).
[81] MCCANCE and WIDDOWSON, *Arch. Dis. Childh.,* **29**, 495 (1954).
[82] STRAUSS et al., *Amer. J. Obstet. Gynec.,* **91**, 286 (1965).
[83] SVENNINGSEN and ARONSON, *Biol. Neonat. (Basel),* **25**, 230 (1974).
[84] ZIEGLER and FOMON, *J. Pediat.,* **78**, 561 (1971).
[85] BERGMANN et al., in FOMON, S.J., *Infant Nutrition,* 2nd ed., Saunders, Philadelphia, 1974, page 245.
[86] BARNETT et al., *J. clin. Invest.,* **31**, 1069 (1952).
[87] CALCAGNO et al., *J. clin. Invest.,* **33**, 91 (1954).
[88] EDELMANN, C.M., *Pediatrics,* **51**, 854 (1973).
[89] SVENNINGSEN, N.W., *Pediat. Res.,* **8**, 659 (1974).
[90] BRODEHL and GELLISSEN, *Pediatrics,* **42**, 395 (1968).
[91] CUSWORTH and DENT, *Biochem. J.,* **74**, 550 (1960).

Insensible perspiration

Early measurements of the total insensible perspiration were made by recording the loss of an individual's body mass. There are several components of water elimination macroscopally not visible[1,2]:

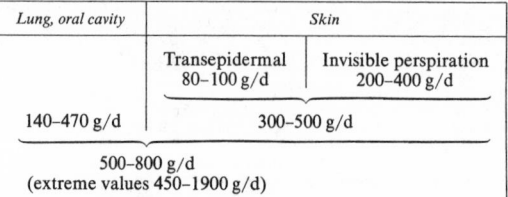

Lung, oral cavity	Skin	
	Transepidermal 80–100 g/d	Invisible perspiration 200–400 g/d
140–470 g/d	300–500 g/d	
500–800 g/d (extreme values 450–1900 g/d)		

Number of sweat glands[3]

Total	2 million
Flexure of elbow	751/cm²
Palm	373/cm²
Chest	155–250/cm²
Buttocks	57/cm²

Glandular sweating

The sweat is secreted by two types of sweat glands, the small, eccrine (minores) and the larger, apocrine (majores) ones. The eccrine sweat glands are far greater in number and are found mostly in hairless skin areas, while the apocrine ones are found more in hairy regions (particularly in the axillae). Unless otherwise indicated, the values apply to eccrine sweat.

Eccrine sweat. The composition – reviewed in several papers[1,4–10] – varies with the nature of the stimulus, the rate of sweating, and the site of collection[11]. Formation may be stimulated thermally (heat sweat), by physical activity (work sweat), or pharmacologically. Stimulation by introduction of pilocarpine into the skin with the aid of iontophoresis (pilocarpine sweat) has been found especially effective[12].

The primary eccrine sweat elaborated by the secretory coil of the glands is presumably isotonic with the plasma; however, since sodium and chloride along the excretory ducts are reabsorbed in excess to water, the resulting sweat is hypotonic relative to the plasma[13–16]. This mechanism is disturbed in cystic fibrosis[17,18].

Except for heat regulation, sweating seems not to be important for the body's homeostasis[10].

Apocrine sweat. Little is known about the composition. The secretion can be collected by expression and has a milk-like appearance[19,20].

Appearance

Eccrine sweat: clear, watery, odorless.

Apocrine sweat: cloudy, viscous, often slightly yellow and fluorescent, at times bluish to nearly black (chromhidrosis: excessive coloration); sterile apocrine sweat is odorless but quickly takes on a characteristic odor under the action of bacteria (bromhidrosis: excessive odor development).

Rate of eccrine sweating

Rates of sweating for various age groups and ethnic groups are summarized in the table below. In measurements on single glands, higher rates are obtained after pilocarpine stimulation than after thermal stimulation[28]. In the newborn, the flow for the individual gland amounts to only about one-half of that of older children and adults[23].

Daily sweat production for a man of 65 kg body mass doing light work at an ambient temperature of 29 °C measures 2–3 L[1]. A maximum of 2–4 L/h may be produced for a short time; as the duration of the perspiration increases, the rate of production decreases, reaching a value of about 0.5 L/h in a 24-hour period[1,8,24]. Adaptation to heat leads to increased sweat production[25,26]. This increases with increasing water intake[24].

Mass rate for pilocarpine sweat relative to body surface

	Number	Mean	s	(Extreme range)	Reference
		g min⁻¹ m⁻²			
Americans					
1–12 months:					
Boys	22	7.8	4.5	(1.7–19.7)	21
Girls	8	6.1	2.0	(3.2–9.1)	21
1–5 years:					
Boys	25	6.1	3.0	(2.5–14.1)	21
Girls	17	5.6	2.8	(2.1–12.4)	21
6–10 years:					
Boys	15	3.7	1.6	(2.1–7.7)	21
Girls	13	3.9	2.1	(1.2–9.0)	21
11–19 years:					
Boys	20	5.7	3.3	(0.9–15.9)	21
Girls	18	4.3	3.4	(0.9–17.2)	21
20–60 years:					
Men	33	7.2	1.8	(3.5–11.9)	21
Women	26	4.6	1.6	(2.1–8.8)	21
Europeans					
Men	20	7.5	2.6	(3.2–13.9)	22
Women	21	3.7	1.6	(1.1–6.5)	22
Africans					
Men	21	3.5	1.8	(0.6–7.6)	22
Women	20	2.3	0.9	(0.8–4.6)	22
Indians					
Men	21	4.7	1.3	(2.9–7.9)	22
Women	20	3.3	1.7	(1.3–6.1)	22

↓See text on next page	Eccrine sweat (heat sweat), unless otherwise stated	SI unit	Mean	s	(Extreme range)	Other units	Mean	s	(Extreme range)	Reference
Physicochemical data										
Relative density		...	–	–	(1.001–1.008)	...	...	...	...	1
Dynamic viscosity (30 °C)	8 subjects	10⁻³ Pa s	0.93	–	(0.8–1.1)	cP	0.93	–	(0.8–1.1)	28
Surface tension (37–38 °C)		10⁻³ N m⁻¹	–	–	(69–70)	dyn cm⁻¹	–	–	(69–70)	29
↓ Osmolarity	7 young women	mmol/L	–	–	(83.5–170)	mosm/L	–	–	(83.5–170)	16
	6 young men (work sweat)	mmol/L	150	40	–	mosm/L	150	40	–	27
↓ pH	8 men	...	...	...	...	–	5.82	0.68	–	61
	8 men (pilocarpine sweat)	...	...	...	...	–	6.78	0.60	–	61

↓See text below, on next page and on page after next	Eccrine sweat (heat sweat), unless otherwise stated	Amount of substance				Mass				Refer-ence
		Unit	Mean	s	(Extreme range)	Unit	Mean	s	(Extreme range)	
Water.........	....	mol/L	–	–	(55–55.2)	g/L	–	–	(990–995)	4
Dry mass.......	....	...	...	...	...	g/L	–	–	(3–10)	1
Inorganic substances										
↓ Bicarbonate....	....	...	...	...	...	...	...	...	...	...
↓ Chloride	....	...	...	...	...	...	...	...	...	...
↓ Phosphorus	4 children.............	μmol/L	147	–	(105–180)	mg/L	4.6	–	(3.3–5.6)	43
	4 men................	μmol/L	7.7	–	(3.9–14)	mg/L	0.24	–	(0.12–0.43)	44
Sulfate.........	....	mmol/L	–	–	(0.07–2.0)	mg/L	–	–	(7–190)	1
Bromide	....	μmol/L	–	–	(2.28–6.28)	μg/L	–	–	(182–502)	45
Fluoride	....	μmol/L	–	–	(11–95)	mg/L	–	–	(0.2–1.8)	46
↓ Iodine	....	nmol/L	75	–	(43–96)	μg/L	9.5	–	(5.4–12.2)	47
↓ Potassium	....	...	...	...	...	...	...	...	...	...
↓ Sodium	....	...	...	...	...	...	...	...	...	...
↓ Na/K quotient .	Newborn, 1st day (pilocarpine sweat)	...	3.0	–	–	...	...	...	...	23
	79 adults, unrestricted diet..................	...	5.23	2.09	–	...	...	...	...	53
	79 adults, low-salt diet ...	...	3.31	2.21	–	...	...	...	...	53
↓ Calcium	26 children, 2–13 years (pilocarpine sweat)	mmol/L	0.44	0.18	(0.16–0.84)	mg/L	17.6	7.2	(6.4–33.7)	55
	11 adults................	mmol/L	0.73	0.11	(0.18–1.34)	mg/L	29	4.4	(7.2–53.7)	78
↓ Magnesium	26 children, 2–13 years (pilocarpine sweat)	mmol/L	0.08	0.03	(0.04–0.17)	mg/L	1.9	0.7	(1.0–4.1)	55
	11 adults................	mmol/L	0.13	0.025	(0.07–0.32)	mg/L	3.2	0.61	(1.7–7.8)	78
Iron...........	22 young men (sweat of high cell content)	μmol/L	7.38	2.24	–	μg/L	412	125	–	57
	22 young men (sweat free of cells)...............	μmol/L	5.34	1.52	–	μg/L	298	85	–	57
Nickel	5 men	μmol/L	0.83	–	(0.56–1.4)	μg/L	49	–	(33–81)	58
Zinc	10 subjects	μmol/L	17.6	4.6	–	mg/L	1.15	0.30	–	59
↓ Trace elements	....	...	...	...	...	...	...	...	...	...

Osmolarity. Eccrine sweat is hypotonic relative to the plasma (see introductory text on preceding page). Osmolarity – almost identical with osmolality – varies with the flow according to the changes in concentration of the osmotically active constituents: at a low rate of sweating lactate, and at a high rate sodium and chloride in particular contribute largely to the osmolarity[28]. In cystic fibrosis, osmolarity is increased so that the sweat is approximately isotonic with the extracellular fluid[28].

pH. At a low rate of sweating, eccrine sweat is acid as a result of the high rate of lactic acid secretion; with increasing flow it turns alkaline owing to bicarbonate secretion[28,30] (Fig. 1). Apocrine sweat, because of its higher ammonia content, is somewhat less acidic than eccrine sweat.

Bicarbonate. The concentration increases with the flow from 0 to more than 35 mmol/L[30,31] (Fig. 2). It is increased in cystic fibrosis[30].

Chloride. See Table 1 for normal values. The chloride concentration changes with age, roughly paralleling the sodium concentration (Table 1). A small increase in concentration at an increased flow has been described by some authors[24,28,32]; the connection is uncertain in view of the individual variations[79]. The chloride concentration is increased in cystic fibrosis; most authors recommend for purposes of diagnosis that the upper limit of normal for children and young adults be set at 60–70 mmol/L[33–35]. When the

chloride concentration is measured directly on the skin, the characteristics of the measuring electrode have to be taken into account[36–38].

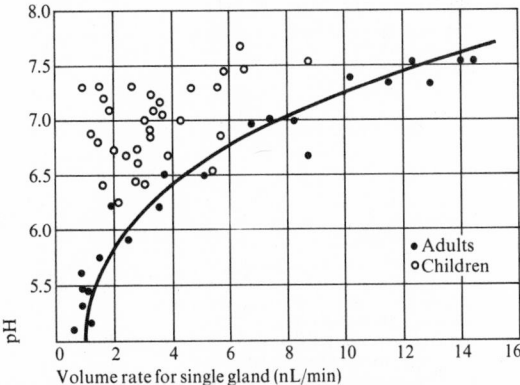

Fig. 1. pH of sweat in relation to flow (determinations on single gland)[30,31].

Phosphorus. The data vary considerably[1,8].

Iodine. Increased in cystic fibrosis[48].

Potassium. See Tables 1 and 2 for normal values. The potassium concentration in sweat declines during the first postnatal days[23]. It

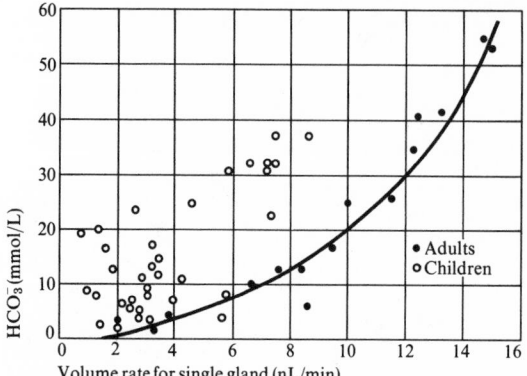

Fig. 2. Bicarbonate concentration in sweat in relation to flow (determinations on single gland)[30,31].

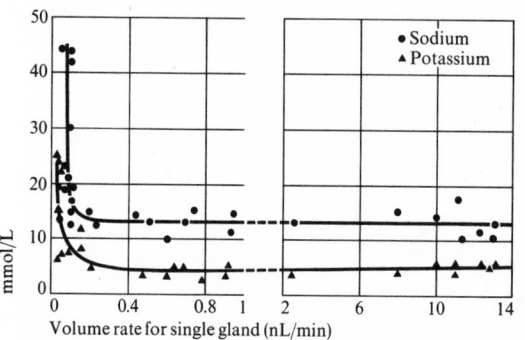

Fig. 3. Sodium and potassium concentrations in sweat of children in relation to flow (determination in sweat from single gland)[51].

is higher upon pharmacologic stimulation than upon heat stimulation[49]. The rate of sweating seems not to affect the potassium concentration except for elevated values at low rates (Fig. 3)[13,18,21,24, 28,50,51]. The potassium concentration reflects mineralocorticoid activity; consequently, it is increased on a low-salt diet, for example[52]. In cystic fibrosis the potassium concentration shows a less characteristic increase than the chloride or sodium concentration[21,28,34,40,43].

Sodium. See Tables 1 and 2 for normal values. The sodium concentration decreases during the first postnatal days[23], is low in childhood, and increases at approximately the time of puberty[21]. There have been divergent reports concerning the effect of the flow rate. Many authors observed an increase in sodium concentration at an increased flow[13,14,18,24,26,28,50,52]. According to KAISER[51], the sodium concentration is low in a wide range of rates of sweating, and is high only at a low rate (see Fig. 3). In cystic fibrosis the sodium concentration is increased. For children and young adults, 70–80 mmol/L has been recommended as a diagnostically useful upper limit of the normal range[33–35]. Adaptation to heat leads to a decrease of the sodium concentration in sweat[26]. The sodium concentration reflects mineralocorticoid activity; therefore, it is reduced on a low-salt diet and in the presence of a hyperfunctioning adrenal cortex, and increased in case of adrenocortical hypofunction[25,52,53].

Na/K quotient. The quotient reflects mineralocorticoid activity and may be utilized for identification of hypokalemic hypertension[53,54].

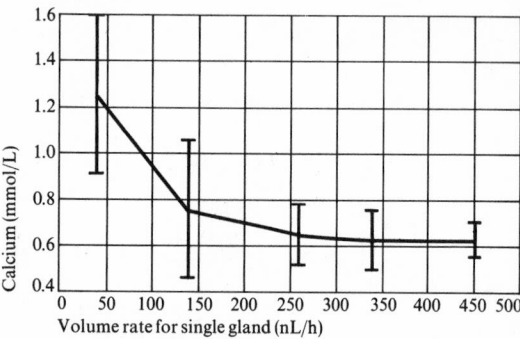

Fig. 4. Calcium concentration in sweat of children (means and standard deviations) in relation to flow (determination in sweat of single gland)[56].

Table 1 *Electrolyte concentration in pilocarpine sweat*

Age	Num-ber	Chloride		Sodium		Potassium		Refer-ence
		Mean	s	Mean	s	Mean	s	
		mmol/L						
Newborn, 1st day	100	39	12.5	36	13	8	3	39
Children, 5 weeks to 1 year	43	12.3	4.9	14.5	4.7	11.2	3.4	40
Children, 1–10 years	107	15.3	8.1	19.5	8.1	9.6	2.8	40
Children, 10–16 years	17	19.9	9.2	29.2	11.6	8.5	2.4	40
Adults, 17–50 years	63	29.7	17.7	46.8	21.5	8.6	2.9	40
Adults, >50 years	65.31	38.9	12.7	60.0	7.5	–	–	41
Cystic fibrosis, 8 months to 17 years	40	111.3	16.7	104.4	16.5	16.5	8.1	40

Table 2 *Electrolyte concentration in pilocarpine sweat, measured in sweat from single gland*

Age	Num-ber	Sodium		Potassium		Refer-ence
		Mean	s	Mean	s	
		mmol/L				
Newborn, 3–16 hours	9	55	–	17.5	–	23
Newborn, 4th day	9	22	–	7.5	–	23
Children, 0–6 months	140	21.2	12.1	14.5	6.5	42
Children, >1 year	141	26.0	13.4	11.1	5.1	42

Table 3 *Excretion of trace elements in sweat[60]*

	μmol/d	mg/d
Iron	9.0	0.5
Copper	25.0	1.59
Zinc	77.7	5.08
Manganese	1.77	0.097
Cobalt	0.29	0.017
Chromium	1.13	0.059
Molybdenum	0.64	0.061
Selenium	4.3	0.34

↓See text below and on next page	Eccrine sweat (heat sweat), unless otherwise stated	Amount				Mass				Reference
		Unit	Mean	s	(Extreme range)	Unit	Mean	s	(Extreme range)	
Organic substances										
↓ **Total nitrogen**	....	mmol/L	–	–	(16–30)	mg/L	–	–	(230–400)	7
↓ **Urea**	13 adults...............	mmol/L	19.6	–	(11.8–33.1)	g/L	1.18	–	(0.71–1.99)	80
↓ **Creatinine**	4 children..............	µmol/L	41	–	(19–74)	mg/L	4.6	–	(2.1–8.4)	43
↓ **Ammonia**	8 adults..............	mmol/L	3.02	0.82	–	mg/L	51.5	14.0	–	61
	8 adults (pilocarpine sweat)...............	mmol/L	2.33	0.76	–	mg/L	39.7	13.0	–	61
↓ **Amino acids** ..	6 children.............(a)	...	...	...	...	g/L	2.65	–	(1.3–5.1)	43
	18 children (pilocarpine sweat).............(a)	...	...	...	...	g/L	1.40	0.87	–	43
	4 men	...	...	...	...	g/L	1.38	–	(0.54–2.59)	63
	2 adults (forehead).......	mmol/L	1.2	–	–	...	...	...	...	64
	7 men (work sweat, forehead).............	mmol/L	3.6	–	–	...	...	...	...	64
	151 adults (pilocarpine sweat)...............	...	...	...	...	g/L	0.476	0.102	–	62
Uric acid......	16 children	µmol/L	12.0	6.9	–	mg/L	2.02	1.16	–	67
↓ **Urocanic acid**.	....	...	...	...	...	...	...	...	...	...
↓ **Acetylcholine** .	13 children	nmol/L	40	–	(12–120)	µg/L	6.5	–	(2–20)	69
Histamine	14 men	nmol/L	121	–	(85–180)	µg/L	13.5	–	(9.5–20.0)	81
↓ **Glucose**.......	6 children..............	µmol/L	–	–	(11–330)	mg/L	–	–	(2–60)	28
	19 adults...............	µmol/L	390	–	(150–940)	mg/L	70	–	(27–170)	75
Short-chain fatty acids										
Acetic acid....	15 adults...............	µmol/L	128	110	(59–415)	mg/L	7.69	6.62	(3.57–24.9)	83
Propionic acid	15 adults...............	µmol/L	3.5	1.5	(1.2–7.4)	mg/L	0.26	0.11	(0.09–0.55)	83
Isobutyric acid	15 adults...............	µmol/L	0.8	0.7	(trace–2.8)	mg/L	0.07	0.06	(trace–0.25)	83
Butyric acid...	15 adults...............	µmol/L	2.4	1.4	(0.5–6.0)	mg/L	0.21	0.12	(0.04–0.53)	83
Isovaleric acid	15 adults...............	µmol/L	1.1	1.1	(0.2–4.5)	mg/L	0.11	0.11	(0.02–0.46)	83
Caproic acid ..	15 adults...............	µmol/L	0.9	0.8	(0.2–3.5)	mg/L	0.10	0.09	(0.02–0.41)	83
↓ **Pyruvic acid** ..	....	µmol/L	–	–	(100–790)	mg/L	–	–	(9–70)	1
↓ **Lactic acid**....	6 children..............	mmol/L	25.5	–	(14–42)	g/L	2.30	–	(1.3–3.8)	43
	18 children (pilocarpine sweat)................	mmol/L	16.3	5.8	–	g/L	1.47	0.52	–	43
	11 adults...............	mmol/L	6.84	0.90	(5.26–13.2)	g/L	0.616	0.081	(0.474–1.19)	78
Prostaglandins (as PGE₂).....	14 adults...............	nmol/L	1.76	1.22	(0.6–4.3)	µg/L	0.62	0.43	(0.2–1.5)	84
↓ **Protein**										
Total protein..	12 adults ....(a)	...	...	...	...	mg/L	77.3	–	(60–115)	80
IgG..........	19 children, < 12 years...	...	...	...	...	mg/L	–	–	(0–17)	80
	23 adults...............	...	...	...	...	mg/L	7	–	(0–20)	80
IgA	19 children, < 12 years...	...	...	...	...	mg/L	–	–	(0–8.8)	80
	23 adults...............	...	...	...	...	mg/L	–	–	(0–15)	80
IgE	11 adults...............	...	...	...	...	µg/L	–	–	(0–3.9)	82
↓ **Enzymes**	....	...	...	...	...	...	...	...	...	...

Calcium. The concentration in sweat decreases with increasing flow (Fig.4)[28,32,56].

Magnesium. The rate of sweating seems to have no effect on the magnesium concentration[32].

Trace elements. See Table 3 (page 110) for datas regarding daily excretion.

Total nitrogen. See Table 4. The nitrogen concentration decreases with increasing flow[27], notably owing to the decreasing urea concentration. The values for daily excretion of nitrogen in sweat increase with increasing protein intake[85].

Urea. At a low rate of sweating the urea concentration in sweat amounts to approximately 4 times the concentration in serum; at a high rate it is close to the serum level[1,28].

Table 4 *Nitrogen distribution (extreme values from the literature[1])*

	mmol/L	mg/L
Total nitrogen	12–140	170–1960
Urea nitrogen	4–110	50–1500
Ammonia nitrogen	0.7–25	10–350
Amino acid nitrogen	0.7–7	10–100

Creatinine. The creatinine concentration decreases with increasing flow; at a low rate of sweating the concentration is higher than in the serum, and at a high rate lower than in the serum[28].

Ammonia. The ammonia concentration in sweat varies widely (literature data between 0.7 mmol/L and 25 mmol/L[1]), partly owing to the varying decomposition of urea by bacteria. It amounts to 25 to 200 times the ammonia concentration in the serum[1].

Amino acids. (a) Calculated as leucine. – The highest concentration is that of serine (about 10 times higher than in serum); the concentrations in sweat of most of the other amino acids are lower than those in the serum[64,65]. Work sweat contains a higher concentration of amino acids than does thermal sweat[64]. The amino acid patterns of sweat samples from different body sites are nearly identical[66].

Urocanic acid. This enters sweat through elution of the epidermis[68].

Acetylcholine. Increased tenfold in cystic fibrosis.

Glucose. Enzymatically determined values. – The glucose concentration in sweat is independent of the flow[28] and of the blood glucose level[75].

Pyruvic acid. The concentration in sweat is about 10 times higher than that in serum.

Lactic acid. Lactic acid results from the anaerobic glucose and glycogen metabolism of the sweat glands[77]. The concentration in the sweat exceeds that in serum approximately 4 to 40 times. The sweat of men contains more lactic acid than that of women[76]. As the flow increases, the lactic acid concentration decreases[1,28], namely, from about 40 mmol/L at a low rate to values below 20 mmol/L at a high rate[28].

Protein. (a) Determined after FOLIN-CIOCALTEU. – The major portion of the protein seems to consist of glycoproteins[70,71]. The various protein assay methods give widely varying results[70]. Up to 16 different plasma proteins have been detected in sweat immunologically[70,72]; Zn-α_2-glycoprotein is present in high concentrations[73]. IgM is not detectable[80].

Enzymes. Sweat contains α-amylase[86], alkaline phosphatase[74] as well as renin-like activity[87].

References

[1] SCHWARTZ, I. L., in COMAR and BRONNER (Eds.), *Mineral Metabolism*, volume 1, part A, Academic Press, New York, 1960, page 346.
[2] BLANK et al., in MONTAGNA et al. (Eds.), *Advances in Biology of Skin*, volume 3, Pergamon, Oxford, 1962, page 97.
[3] STÜTTGEN, G., *Die normale und pathologische Physiologie der Haut*, Fischer, Stuttgart, 1965, page 268.
[4] SCHAAF, F., in FLASCHENTRÄGER and LEHNARTZ (Eds.), *Physiologische Chemie*, volume II/2b, Springer, Berlin, 1957, page 302.
[5] CREMER and FÜHR, in LANG et al. (Eds.), *Hoppe-Seyler/Thierfelder Handbuch der physiologisch- und pathologisch-chemischen Analyse*, 10th ed., volume 5, Springer, Berlin, 1953, page 603; MONTAGNA, W., *The Structure and Function of Skin*, Academic Press, New York, 1956.
[6] ROTHMAN, S., *Physiology and Biochemistry of the Skin*, University of Chicago Press, Chicago, 1954.
[7] ROBINSON and ROBINSON, *Physiol. Rev.*, **34**, 202 (1954).
[8] KUNO, Y., *Human Perspiration*, Thomas, Springfield, 1956.
[9] LOBITZ and DOBSON, *Ann. Rev. Med.*, **12**, 289 (1961).
[10] RANDALL, W. C., in ALTMAN and DITTMER (Eds.), *Biology Data Book*, 2nd ed., volume 3, Federation of American Societies for Experimental Biology, Bethesda (Md.), 1974, page 1493.
[11] SHWACHMAN, H., *Pediatrics*, **30**, 167 (1962).
[12] GIBSON and COOKE, *Pediatrics*, **23**, 545 (1959).
[13] SCHWARTZ and THAYSEN, *J. clin. Invest.*, **35**, 114 (1956).
[14] CAGE and DOBSON, *J. clin. Invest.*, **44**, 1270 (1965); BROWN and DOBSON, *J. appl. Physiol.*, **23**, 97 (1967).
[15] SCHULZ et al., *Pflügers Arch. ges. Physiol.*, **284**, 360 (1965).
[16] MANGOS, J., *Amer. J. Physiol.*, **224**, 1235 (1973).
[17] SLEGERS, J. F., *Dermatologica (Basel)*, **127**, 242 (1963).
[18] EMRICH et al., *Klin. Wschr.*, **48**, 966 (1970).
[19] HURLEY and SHELLEY, *The Human Apocrine Sweat Gland in Health and Disease*, Thomas, Springfield, 1960.
[20] HERRMANN et al., *Biochemie der Haut*, Thieme, Stuttgart, 1973.
[21] LOBECK and HUEBNER, *Pediatrics*, **30**, 172 (1962).
[22] MCCANCE and PUROHIT, *Nature*, **221**, 378 (1969).
[23] KAISER and DRACK, *Helv. paediat. Acta*, **26**, 551 (1971).
[24] CAGE et al., *J. appl. Physiol.*, **29**, 687 (1970).
[25] COLLINS and WEINER, *Physiol. Rev.*, **48**, 785 (1968); GONZALEZ et al., *J. appl. Physiol.*, **36**, 419 (1974).
[26] ALLAN and WILSON, *J. appl. Physiol.*, **30**, 708 (1971).
[27] COSTA et al., *Amer. J. clin. Nutr.*, **22**, 52 (1969).
[28] EMRICH et al., *Pediat. Res.*, **2**, 464 (1968).
[29] RANDALL and CALMAN, *J. invest. Derm.*, **23**, 113 (1954).
[30] KAISER and DRACK, *Europ. J. clin. Invest.*, **4**, 261 (1974).
[31] KAISER et al., *Pflügers Arch. ges. Physiol.*, **349**, 63 (1974).
[32] VELLAR and ASKEVOLD, *Scand. J. clin. Lab. Invest.*, **22**, 65 (1968).
[33] VINK, C. L., in DE REUCK and CAMERON (Eds.), *Ciba Foundation Symposium on the Exocrine Pancreas*, Churchill, London, 1962, page 310.
[34] di SANT'AGNESE and GIBSON, in MONTAGNA et al. (Eds.), *Advances in Biology of Skin*, volume 3, Pergamon, Oxford, 1962, page 229; Report of the committee for a study for evaluation of testing for cystic fibrosis, *J. Pediat.*, **88**, 711 (1976).
[35] KOCH et al., *Internist (Berl.)*, **1**, 35 (1960); SIEGENTHALER and DE HALLER, *Helv. med. Acta*, **32**, 1 (1965).
[36] KOPITO and SHWACHMAN, *Pediatrics*, **43**, 794 (1969).
[37] GÜRSON et al., *Helv. paediat. Acta*, **28**, 165 (1973); FONTAINE and FARRIAUX, *Nouv. Presse méd.*, **2**, 380 (1973).
[38] ROTTER and KAISER, *Z. Kinderheilk.*, **120**, 135 (1975); BRAY et al., *Clin. chim. Acta*, **77**, 69 (1977).
[39] STUR, O., *Öst. Z. Kinderheilk.*, **6**, 347 (1961).
[40] SHWACHMAN et al., *Pediatrics*, **32**, 85 (1963).
[41] DE HALLER et al., *Schweiz. med. Wschr.*, **92**, 1493 (1962).
[42] KAISER, D., personal communication, 1975.
[43] CLARKE et al., *Amer. J. Dis. Child.*, **101**, 490 (1961).
[44] MITCHELL and HAMILTON, *J. biol. Chem.*, **178**, 345 (1949).
[45] CORNBLEET, T., *J. invest. Derm.*, **1**, 399 (1938).
[46] MCCLURE et al., *J. industr. Hyg.*, **27**, 159 (1945).
[47] SPECTOR et al., *J. biol. Chem.*, **161**, 137 (1945).
[48] BRODKEY and GIBBS, *J. appl. Physiol.*, **15**, 501 (1960).
[49] SATO et al., *J. invest. Derm.*, **55**, 433 (1970).
[50] COLLINS, K. J., *Clin. Sci.*, **30**, 207 (1966).
[51] KAISER, D., in *13th International Congress of Pediatrics*, Verlag der Wiener Medizinischen Akademie, Vienna 1971, page 537.
[52] GRANDCHAMP et al., *Helv. med. Acta*, **34**, 367 (1967/68).
[53] ROSSET, G., *Schweiz. med. Wschr.*, **103**, 439 (1973).
[54] GRANDCHAMP et al., *Helv. med. Acta*, **35**, 55 (1969/70).
[55] PAUNIER et al., *Pediatrics*, **52**, 446 (1973).
[56] HÄNGGELI, C. A., *Helv. paediat. Acta*, **28**, 611 (1973).
[57] VELLAR, O. D., *Scand. J. clin. Lab. Invest.*, **21**, 157 (1968).
[58] HORAK and SUNDERMAN, *Clin. Chem.*, **19**, 429 (1973).
[59] PRASAD et al., *J. Lab. clin. Med.*, **62**, 84 (1963).
[60] CONSOLAZIO et al., quoted by SCHROEDER and NASON, *Clin. Chem.*, **17**, 461 (1971).
[61] BRUSILOW and GORDES, *Amer. J. Physiol.*, **214**, 513 (1968).
[62] COLTMAN et al., *Amer. J. clin. Nutr.*, **18**, 373 (1966).
[63] BOSSE and PASCHER, *Klin. Wschr.*, **42**, 1196 (1964).
[64] LIAPPIS and HUNGERLAND, *Amer. J. clin. Nutr.*, **25**, 661 (1972).
[65] HADORN et al., *Nature*, **215**, 416 (1967).
[66] HUNGERLAND and LIAPPIS, *Klin. Wschr.*, **50**, 973 (1972).
[67] DANTON and NYHAN, *Proc. Soc. exp. Biol. (N. Y.)*, **121**, 270 (1966).
[68] BRUSILOW and IKAI, *Science*, **160**, 1257 (1968).
[69] EYERMAN et al., *Nature*, **192**, 77 (1961).
[70] VANFRAECHEM and POORTMANS, *Rev. franç. Etud. clin. biol.*, **13**, 383 (1968).
[71] JIRKA and KOTAS, *Clin. chim. Acta*, **2**, 292 (1957).
[72] PAGE and REMINGTON, *J. Lab. clin. Med.*, **63**, 634 (1967).
[73] POORTMANS and SCHMID, *J. Lab. clin. Med.*, **71**, 807 (1968).
[74] LOEWENTHAL and POLITZER, *Nature*, **195**, 902 (1962).
[75] MÄHR et al., *Med. Klin.*, **63**, 209 (1968).
[76] THURMON and OTTENSTEIN, *J. invest. Derm.*, **18**, 333 (1952).
[77] WOLFE et al., *J. clin. Invest.*, **49**, 1880 (1970).
[78] BENSON et al., *J. invest. Derm.*, **63**, 287 (1974).
[79] YOUSEF and DILL, *J. appl. Physiol.*, **36**, 82 (1974).
[80] CABAU et al., *C. R. Acad. Sci. (Paris)*, **275D**, 297 (1972).
[81] GARDEN, J. W., *J. appl. Physiol.*, **21**, 631 (1966).
[82] FÖRSTRÖM et al., *J. invest. Derm.*, **64**, 156 (1975).
[83] PERRY et al., *Clin. chim. Acta*, **29**, 369 (1970).
[84] FÖRSTRÖM et al., *Prostaglandins*, **7**, 459 (1974).
[85] WEINER et al., *Brit. J. Nutr.*, **27**, 543 (1972); HOWAT et al., *Amer. J. clin. Nutr.*, **28**, 879 (1975).
[86] NIKOLAJEK and EMRICH, *Europ. J. pediat.*, **122**, 289 (1976).
[87] EMRICH and DAHLHEIM, *Klin. Wschr.*, **55**, 291 (1977).

Sebum is a secretion product of the sebaceous glands, which generally occur as appendages of the hair follicles[1]. The number of sebaceous glands thus varies considerably with the body site[2]: 900/cm² on the scalp but only 50/cm² on the forearm. Lipids account for about 95% of the sebum; its melting point is 35°C[3]. However, the fat on the skin surface originates not only from the sebaceous glands but also in part from the stratum corneum cells of the epidermis: of the 150–300 μg/cm² on the forehead, for example, 3–6% are of epidermal origin[4].

Various factors, notably endocrine ones[3–7], age[3,7], and nutrition[3,8] affect sebum secretion. It is low in children (Fig. 1), increased in pregnant women[6], and declines in states of food deprivation[9]. Diurnal variations have also been observed[6]. Sebum formation is increased by testosterone and dehydroepiandrosterone[3–7] as well as by thyroxine[6], and inhibited by estrogens[3,6,7]. Pituitary hormones have either an indirect (increase by TSH) or direct effect (increase by MSH)[6]. In most acne patients sebum secretion is found to be increased[6,7,10].

The sebum lipids (Table 1) consist of a hydrolyzable component (triglycerides and wax esters) and a nonhydrolyzable component (mainly squalene)[2,9,11]. No free fatty acids are found in the

sebaceous glands; they form on the skin by hydrolysis[2,12]. In 5 subjects the secretion of squalene varied between 125 mg/d and 475 mg/d[14]. The fatty-acid composition is extremely complex (Table 2). More than 200 different fatty acids have been identified[2]. *Trans*-3-methyl-2-hexenoic acid has been found only in the sebum of schizophrenics[13].

Table 1 *Skin lipid pattern in adults[2]*

	Sebum	Epi-dermis	Surface lipids
	%		
Squalene	12	<0.5	10
Sterol esters	<1	10	2.5
Sterols, non-esterified	0	20	1.5
Wax esters	23	0	22
Triglycerides	60	10	25
Di- and monoglycerides	0	10	10
Fatty acids, non-esterified	0	10	25
Glycolipids and phospholipids	0	30	0
Unidentified	5	10	4

References

[1] MONTAGNA, W., *J. invest. Derm.*, **62**, 120 (1974).
[2] NICOLAIDES, N., *Science*, **186**, 19 (1974).
[3] HERRMANN et al., *Biochemie der Haut*, Thieme, Stuttgart, 1973.
[4] STRAUSS et al., *Ann. Rev. med.*, **26**, 27 (1975).
[5] STRAUSS, J. S., *New Engl. J. Med.*, **291**, 46 (1974).
[6] SHUSTER and THODY, *J. invest. Derm.*, **62**, 172 (1974).
[7] POCHI and STRAUSS, *J. invest. Derm.*, **62**, 191 (1974).
[8] DOWNING et al., *Amer. J. clin. Nutr.*, **25**, 365 (1972).
[9] DOWNING and STRAUSS, *J. invest. Derm.*, **62**, 228, (1974).
[10] STRAUSS et al., *J. invest. Derm.*, **62**, 321 (1974).
[11] NIKKARI, T., *J. invest. Derm.*, **62**, 257 (1974).
[12] SHALITA, A. R., *J. invest. Derm.*, **62**, 332 (1974).
[13] SMITH et al., *Science*, **166**, 398 (1969).
[14] NIKKARI et al., *J. Lipid Res.*, **15**, 563 (1974).

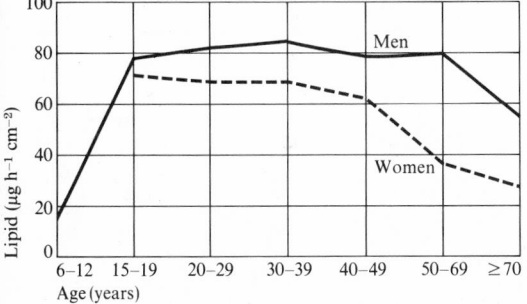

Fig. 1. Sebum secretion in relation to sex and age[7].

Table 2 *Fatty acid pattern of skin lipids[2]*

Type of fatty acids	Saturated		Monoenes		Dienes	
	Range	%	Range	%	Range	%
Unbranched, even number of C atoms	C_{10}–C_{30}	35.8	C_{14}–C_{24}	36.4	C_{16}–C_{22}	2.8
Unbranched, odd number of C atoms	C_{11}–C_{27}	5.4	C_{15}–C_{25}	3.9	C_{17}–C_{19}	0.1
Iso-	C_{12}–C_{28}	4.0	C_{14}–C_{26}	5.3		
Anteiso-	C_{11}–C_{27}	1.4	C_{15}–C_{25}	1.3		
Monomethyl (branched)	C_{11}–C_{26}	2.6	C_{17}–C_{25}	0.2		
Dimethyl (branched)	C_{13}–C_{24}	0.8	?			
		50.0		47.1		2.9

Saliva is formed by the salivary glands localized in the oral cavity and adjacent areas. They are the 2 parotid, submandibular, and sublingual glands as well as the labial and lingual glands and the small isolated mucous glands on the anterior surface of the soft palate, on the hard palate, along the margins of the tongue and at the root of the tongue[1]. More than half of the resting saliva originates from the submandibular glands, and more than half of maximally stimulated saliva from the parotid glands; the proportion of sublingual saliva and of saliva from the small salivary glands amounts to 10%[2]. The composition of the particular secretions varies, and there may also be differences on different sides[3-5]. The following factors can influence the concentration of a substance in a given saliva fraction: flow (Fig. 1, Tables 1 and 2), time of day[8-10], age[11], sex and hormonal conditions (in women, e.g. influence of cycle[12], use of oral contraceptives[13]), and the plasma concentration of the substance (e.g. urea[14,74]).

The term 'resting saliva' commonly refers to saliva that is collected from fasting individuals in the morning without any special stimulation. Saliva flow can be inhibited pharmacologically (e.g. by atropine)[16]. It can be stimulated pharmacologically (e.g. by pilocarpine), by chewing (e.g. of wax), and through the sense of taste (e.g. by fruit candy or citric acid). Not all individuals respond equally to various stimulants[17].

The concentrations of certain saliva constituents can vary with the duration of stimulation (Fig. 1)[6,15].

Appearance

Parotid saliva: thin liquid, not ropy.
Submandibular saliva: clear, rather thin liquid, slightly ropy, slightly frothy but turbid in cystic fibrosis.
Oral mucus: thick, very tenacious, ropy, rich in formed elements.
Mixed saliva: colorless, transparent or translucent, slightly ropy, of low viscosity and insipid taste.

Flow

The daily output of saliva is estimated at 500–1500 mL[1,5,18]. Factors affecting the flow are age, sex, time of day, time of year, nutritional state, and emotional state (Tables 3 and 4, Figs. 2 and 3). In addition, the size of the salivary gland probably plays a role[24]. Volume rates up to 10 mL/min have been measured following stimulation[23].

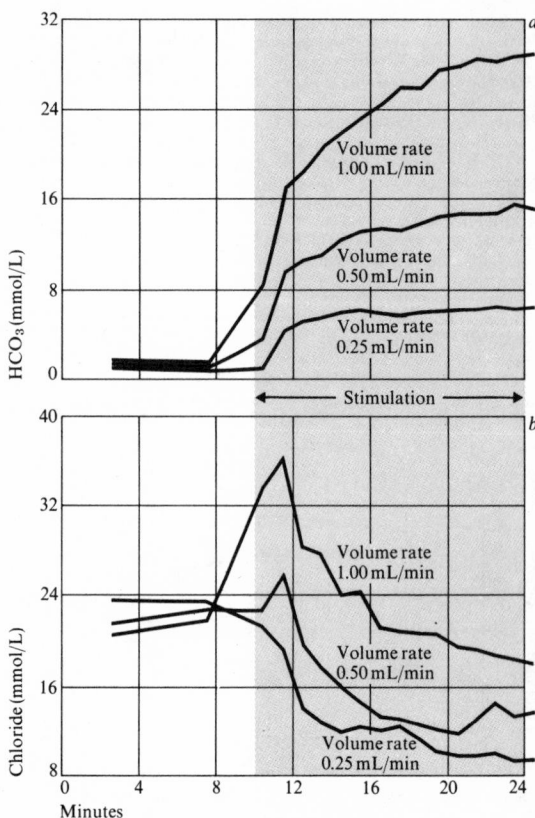

Fig. 1. Effect of flow and duration of stimulation on bicarbonate (*a*) and chloride concentration (*b*) of parotid saliva[6].

Table 1   *Composition of parotid saliva according to flow[7]*

| | Unit | Volume rate | | | | | | | | | |
| | | 0.1 mL/min | | 0.5 mL/min | | 1.0 mL/min | | 2.0 mL/min | | 3.0 mL/min | |
		Mean	s	Mean	s	Mean	s	Mean	s	Mean	s
pH	–	5.8	–	–	–	–	–	–	–	7.8	–
CO_2 pressure	kPa	4.7	0.3	–	–	–	–	–	–	5.2	0.4
	mmHg	35	2	–	–	–	–	–	–	39	3
Bicarbonate	mmol/L	4.6	0.96	19.6	3.91	34.0	4.43	51.0	7.57	59.0	5.71
Sodium	mmol/L	2.5	0.45	19.4	2.12	41.4	4.40	74.6	5.10	83.9	7.38
Potassium	mmol/L	18.5	1.22	16.3	1.74	13.3	1.29	13.0	0.87	12.8	0.83
Calcium	mmol/L	0.9	0.11	1.2	0.16	1.3	0.16	1.4	0.17	1.5	0.25
Magnesium	μmol/L	110	25	50	15	35	15	30	10	30	5

Table 2   *Composition of submandibular saliva according to flow[15]*

| | Unit | Volume rate | | | | | | | |
| | | 0.26 mL/min | | 1.0 mL/min | | 2.0 mL/min | | 3.0 mL/min | |
		Mean	s	Mean	s	Mean	s	Mean	s
pH	–	6.47	–	7.26	–	7.44	–	7.62	–
Bicarbonate	mmol/L	2.2	–	14.3	–	22.4	–	35.5	–
Chloride	mmol/L	11.9	2.3	20.6	10.6	25.2	7.0	32.2	10.2
Phosphate	mmol/L	3.6	0.7	2.06	0.27	1.77	0.29	1.57	0.32
Sodium	mmol/L	2.6	2.7	22.3	15.6	31.1	8.7	54.8	11.5
Potassium	mmol/L	14.4	2.2	14.4	2.5	13.7	2.1	13.7	3.6
Calcium	mmol/L	1.56	0.45	1.66	0.42	1.96	0.23	2.13	0.26
Magnesium	μmol/L	70.4	28.2	34.8	13.1	32.3	12.5	36.0	12.2
Protein	g/L	0.96	0.40	1.47	0.64	2.39	1.30	3.44	1.32

Saliva flow is *pathologically* reduced (xerostomia) under the action of certain drugs, in organic brain disease, neuroses and endogenous depression, in diseases of the salivary glands (particularly in Sjögren's syndrome), and in diseases interfering with water metabolism (e.g. diabetes insipidus)[4]. Saliva flow is pathologically increased (sialorrhea) in stomatitis, in cutting of teeth, and in some neurologic diseases (e.g. epilepsy)[4].

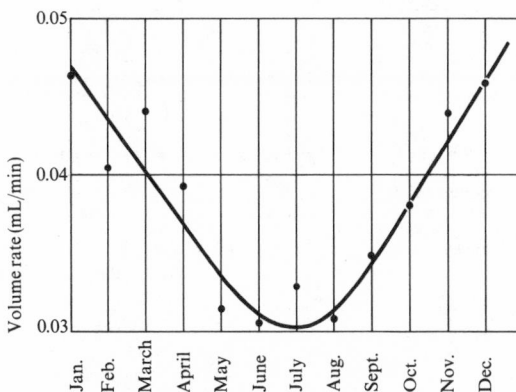

Fig. 3. Flow of parotid saliva over the course of a year[16].

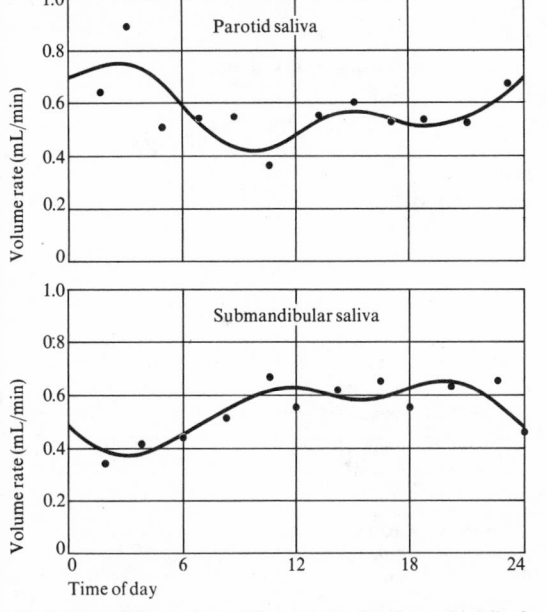

Fig. 2. Diurnal fluctuations of flow of stimulated parotid saliva[8] and submandibular saliva[9] in 1 subject (individual values and fitted curve based on Fourier analysis).

Table 3 *Flow of unstimulated saliva*

		Mean	(Extreme range)	Reference
		μL/min		
Total saliva	Newborn	–	(10–100)	19
	Infants	–	(40–400)	19
	Adults	~350	–	2
Parotid saliva*	75 men	102	s 107	20
	73 women	57	s 53	20
Submandibular saliva*	75 men	134	s 107	20
	73 women	108	s 93	20
Sublingual saliva	1 adult	–	(~2–5)	21
Labial saliva	10 subjects	5.9	s 2.5	22

* Applies to 1 gland.

Table 4 *Flow of parotid saliva in relation to age, sex and stimulation[4]*

Sex	Age	Unstimulated			Chewing gum with fruit flavor			Lemon juice		
		Mean	s	(Extreme range)	Mean	s	(Extreme range)	Mean	s	(Extreme range)
		mL/min								
18 men	<20 years	0.061	0.030	(0.02–0.12)	0.66	0.25	(0.36–1.07)	1.49	0.38	(0.60–2.10)
8 women........................	<20 years	0.083	0.057	(0.04–0.16)	0.46	0.20	(0.27–0.80)	1.99	0.14	(1.25–2.50)
20 men	21–40 years	0.104	0.036	(0.06–0.20)	0.47	0.13	(0.32–0.85)	1.73	0.40	(0.85–2.99)
20 women......................	21–40 years	0.09	0.05	(0.01–0.19)	0.50	0.22	(0.09–1.04)	1.76	0.40	(1.03–2.70)
27 men	41–60 years	0.078	0.10	(0.01–0.31)	0.59	0.42	(0.15–1.76)	1.68	0.57	(0.85–3.20)
31 women......................	41–60 years	0.064	0.06	(0.01–0.34)	0.52	0.28	(0.13–1.15)	1.36	0.67	(0.50–3.02)
14 men	>61 years	0.084	0.07	(0.03–0.20)	0.50	0.30	(0.15–1.26)	1.58	0.60	(0.90–2.76)
31 women......................	>61 years	0.06	0.11	(0.01–0.5)	0.43	0.17	(0.14–0.83)	1.15	0.45	(0.47–2.20)

↓See text on page after next		Flow	Subjects	Unit	Mean	s	(Extreme range)	Reference
Physicochemical data and inorganic substances								
Water..............	Total saliva	Unstimulated....	....	g/L	994	–	–	18
↓ **Dry mass**............	Total saliva	Unstimulated....	....	g/L	6	–	(3–8)	5, 18
	Parotid saliva	0.064 mL/min ...	20 men	g/L	6.6	3.0	–	16
		0.94 mL/min	318 men......	g/L	9.2	2.6	–	16
Relative density	Total saliva	Unstimulated....	....	...	–	–	(1.002–1.012)	5
	Parotid saliva	0.058 mL/min ...	20 men	...	1.0034	0.0009	–	16
		0.94 mL/min	384 men......	...	1.0061	0.0030	–	16

↓See text on next page		Flow	Subjects	Unit	Mean	s	(Extreme range)	Reference
Dynamic viscosity ...	Parotid saliva	0.054 mL/min ...	20 men	10^{-3} Pa s	1.085	0.037	–	16
		0.94 mL/min	384 men......	10^{-3} Pa s	1.20	0.10	–	16
Surface tension	Total saliva	Unstimulated....	....	dyn cm^{-1}	–	–	(15.2–26.0)	5
Freezing-point depression	Total saliva	No data.........	....	K	–	–	(0.07–0.34)	1
Osmolality	Parotid saliva	0.053 mL/min ...	20 men	mmol/kg	48.6	15.8	–	16
		1.02 mL/min	314 men......	mmol/kg	127.2	35.0	–	16
↓pH	Total saliva	Unstimulated....	315 children..	...	7.32	0.46	–	25
			15 adults	...	6.4	–	(5.8–7.1)	26
	Parotid saliva	0.049 mL/min ...	20 men	...	5.82	0.45	–	16
		1.02 mL/min	368 men......	...	7.67	0.18	–	16
	Submandibular saliva	0.26 mL/min	15 adults	...	6.73	0.45	–	9
		0.62 mL/min	31 subjects ...	...	7.42	0.25	(7.14–7.79)	30
	Sublingual saliva	0.16 mL/min	10 subjects ...	...	7.40	0.28	(7.05–7.85)	30
	Labial saliva.........	....	....	...	∼7.0	–	–	27
↓Bicarbonate.........	Total saliva	Unstimulated....	....	mmol/L	–	–	(2–13)	5
		2.15 mL/min	30 adults	mmol/L	13.92	4.01	(6.7–22.1)	23
	Parotid saliva	0.044 mL/min ...	20 men	mmol/L	0.77	0.92	–	16
		0.88 mL/min	368 men......	mmol/L	29.8	9.2	–	16
	Submandibular saliva	0.62 mL/min	31 subjects ...	mmol/L	15.7	7.4	(3.4–35.0)	30
	Sublingual saliva	0.16 mL/min	10 subjects ...	mmol/L	10.9	3.6	(4.5–16.5)	30
	Labial saliva.........	....	....	mmol/L	–	–	(<3)	27
↓Chloride	Total saliva	Unstimulated....	431 children..	mmol/L	16.25	4.63	(6.5–42.9)	32
		Unstimulated....	9 adults	mmol/L	17	–	–	26
		2.15 mL/min	30 adults	mmol/L	22.65	7.52	(11.2–44.7)	23
	Parotid saliva	0.052 mL/min ...	20 men	mmol/L	18.5	3.8	–	16
		0.92 mL/min	292 men......	mmol/L	33.3	13.4	–	16
	Submandibular saliva	0.26 mL/min	15 adults	mmol/L	12.0	4.6	–	9
		0.62 mL/min	31 subjects ...	mmol/L	26.0	9.5	(10.0–42.4)	30
	Sublingual saliva	Unstimulated....	3 adults	mmol/L	–	–	(25–73)	26
		0.16 mL/min	10 subjects ...	mmol/L	26.2	9.6	(11.6–37.6)	30
	Labial saliva.........	Unstimulated....	10 adults	mmol/L	31.4	14.0	(16.0–54.3)	27
		Stimulated	20 adults	mmol/L	56.5	29.7	(19.0–110)	27
↓Phosphate								
– total..............	Total saliva	Unstimulated....	120 subjects ..	mmol/L	6.58	1.35	–	35
– organic...........	Total saliva	Unstimulated....	50 subjects ...	mmol/L	1.77	1.25	–	35
– inorganic..........	Total saliva	Unstimulated....	180 subjects ..	mmol/L	4.81	1.10	–	35
		2.15 mL/min	30 adults	mmol/L	3.63	0.83	(1.89–5.53)	23
	Parotid saliva	0.34 mL/min	20 men	mmol/L	10.3	2.29	–	16
		0.83 mL/min	100 men......	mmol/L	3.1	0.50	–	16
	Submandibular saliva	0.26 mL/min	15 adults	mmol/L	5.63	1.92	–	9
		0.62 mL/min	31 subjects ...	mmol/L	2.8	1.5	(1.3–8.0)	30
	Sublingual saliva	0.16 mL/min	10 subjects ...	mmol/L	2.3	0.4	(1.4–2.8)	30
	Labial saliva.........	Unstimulated....	10 adults	mmol/L	0.62	0.23	(0.25–1.07)	27
		Stimulated	15 adults	mmol/L	0.45	0.11	(0.21–0.61)	27
↓Fluoride	Total saliva ......(a)	Stimulated	....	μmol/L	–	–	(<2.6)	40
	(b)	Stimulated	6 men	μmol/L	–	–	(<1.0)	41
	Parotid saliva	0.37 mL/min	25 men	μmol/L	1.05	0.26	–	16
		0.90 mL/min	25 men	μmol/L	1.05	0.26	–	16
Bromide	Total saliva	Unstimulated....	10 subjects ...	μmol/L	5	–	(2.5–13)	42
↓Iodine								
– total	Total saliva	Unstimulated....	22 subjects ...	μmol/L	0.80	0.40	(0.28–1.89)	43
	Parotid saliva	0.30 mL/min	87 men	μmol/L	1.62	1.10	–	16
		0.86 mL/min	87 men	μmol/L	0.72	0.29	–	16
– organic...........	Parotid saliva	0.30 mL/min	87 men	μmol/L	0.42	0.24	–	16
		0.86 mL/min	87 men	μmol/L	0.20	0.09	–	16

↓See text below		Flow	Subjects	Unit	Mean	s	(Extreme range)	Refer-ence
Thiocyanate	Total saliva	Unstimulated	37 nonsmokers	mmol/L	1.95	1.24	(0.41–6.55)	48
		Unstimulated	23 smokers	mmol/L	5.53	2.57	(1.2–12.2)	48
	Parotid saliva	0.15 mL/min	79 men	mmol/L	0.94	0.56	–	16
		0.43 mL/min	79 men	mmol/L	0.55	0.31	–	16
↓**Nitrate**	Total saliva	Unstimulated	....	μmol/L	–	–	(0.11–0.63)	49
↓**Potassium**	Total saliva	Unstimulated	9 adults	mmol/L	20.7	–	(14–41)	26
		2.15 mL/min	30 adults	mmol/L	16.44	3.26	(11.4–23.0)	23
	Parotid saliva	0.10 mL/min	75 men	mmol/L	26.48	6.40	–	50
		0.057 mL/min ...	75 women	mmol/L	33.8	12.33	–	50
		0.052 mL/min ...	20 men	mmol/L	27.7	6.24	–	16
		0.97 mL/min	192 men........	mmol/L	16.0	2.65	–	16
	Submandibular saliva	0.26 mL/min	15 adults	mmol/L	13.9	3.9	–	9
		0.62 mL/min	31 subjects	mmol/L	13.1	3.0	(4.9–18.6)	30
	Sublingual saliva	0.16 mL/min	10 subjects	mmol/L	13.2	2.0	(9.8–17.3)	30
	Labial saliva.........	Unstimulated	18 adults	mmol/L	19.3	4.9	(10.0–29.4)	27
		Stimulated.......	25 adults	mmol/L	17.3	3.9	(10.7–24.9)	27

Dry mass. About 20% of the solids are suspended and 80% dissolved; about one-third are inorganic and two-thirds organic substances.

pH. In association with the increasing bicarbonate concentration, the pH increases with increasing flow (Tables 1 and 2). Values up to about 7.8[7] are reached in the parotid saliva of adults, and values about 8.0 in that of children[28]. The pH is lowered in pregnant women[29] (mean value 6.5 as compared with 7.0 in nonpregnant women)[29].

Bicarbonate. The bicarbonate concentration increases with increasing flow (Tables 1 and 2 and Fig. 4). In parotid saliva, values of 50 mmol/L or more are reached after a volume rate of 2.0 mL/min[7,31]. This increase is not seen in children with cystic fibrosis[28].

Chloride. The chloride concentration increases at a high volume rate in parotid saliva (starting from a minimum at an average flow, see Fig. 4)[6,31] as well as in submandibular saliva (Table 2)[15], reaching values around 40 mmol/L. The chloride concentration in labial saliva approaches that in the serum with increasing flow. No differences in the salivary chloride concentration have been observed between the sexes[33]. No characteristic change in the chloride concentration seems to occur in cystic fibrosis[34].

Phosphate. About 70% of the total phosphate in the total saliva[35] and the submandibular saliva[9] is inorganic phosphate. The organic phosphate is for the most part acid-soluble and contains phosphoethanolamine[36] as well as adenosine phosphates, sugar phosphates and phosphoglyceric acid[37]; the acid-insoluble fraction contains traces of phospholipids[35].

With increasing flow, the concentration of inorganic phosphate decreases in all saliva fractions. Unstimulated parotid saliva contains 7.8 mmol/L of dihydrogen phosphate and 1 mmol/L of monohydrogen phosphate[7]. By contrast, only monohydrogen phosphate is found in stimulated parotid saliva, because of its high pH, and this in a concentration of about 3.0 mmol/L[7]. The phosphate concentration is increased in the submandibular saliva in cystic fibrosis[38], and in the total saliva in primary hyperparathyroidism[39].

Fluoride. Values cited determined (a) colorimetrically, (b) by means of fluoride electrode. – The concentration in the saliva increases after oral intake (drinking water, NaF) or topical application of fluoride[40,41].

Iodine. In man, the iodine excreted in the saliva consists mostly of iodide[44]. The iodide concentration in the saliva is 6 to 40 times higher than that in the serum[45]. Iodide is concentrated in the parotid, submandibular and labial glands, not in the sublingual glands[44]. At increasing flow the iodide concentration decreases[46,47] (Fig. 5).

Nitrate. Nitrate in the oral cavity can be reduced to nitrite by bacteria.

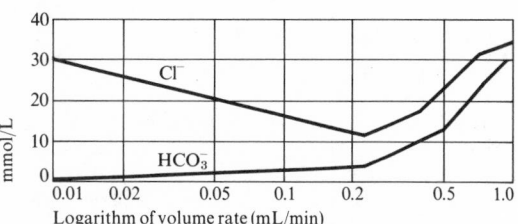

Fig. 4. Chloride and bicarbonate concentrations of parotid saliva in relation to flow[16].

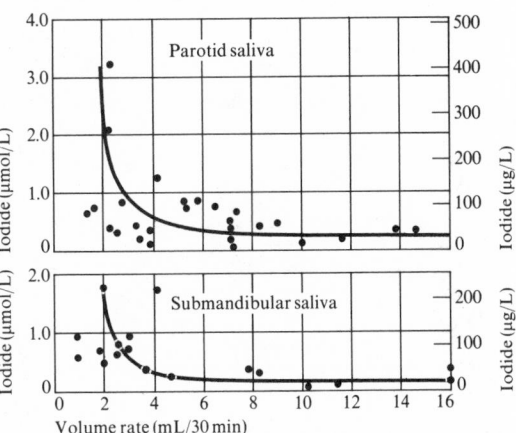

Fig. 5. Iodide concentrations in parotid and submandibular saliva in relation to flow[47].

Potassium. In all saliva fractions the potassium concentration is higher before stimulation than after stimulation (Tables 1 and 2 and Fig. 6)[22,28,31]. It appears to be higher in the saliva of young children than in the saliva of adults[51]. In adults, it does not change with age[50,52]. The potassium concentration is *increased,* at least in individual fractions, in primary hyperaldosteronism[53], in Bartter's syndrome[54], and possibly in digitalis intoxication[55,56].

Sodium. The sodium concentration increases with increasing flow rate in all saliva fractions (Tables 1 and 2 and Fig. 6)[22,28,31]. In the saliva of young children the sodium concentration seems to be higher than in the saliva of adults[51]. In adults it is independent of sex and age[50,52]. An increased sodium concentration in the secretion of the small salivary glands is characteristic of cystic fibrosis[22].

↑↓See text on page 117 and below		Flow	Subjects	Unit	Mean	s	(Extreme range)	Reference
↑ **Sodium**	Total saliva	Unstimulated	9 adults	mmol/L	14.4	–	(5.2–24.4)	[26]
		2.15 mL/min	30 adults	mmol/L	29.30	16.11	(10.0–75.0)	[23]
	Parotid saliva	0.10 mL/min	75 men	mmol/L	5.14	3.17	–	[50]
		0.057 mL/min	75 women	mmol/L	5.47	3.48	–	[50]
		0.052 mL/min	20 men	mmol/L	2.05	1.38	–	[16]
		0.97 mL/min	192 men	mmol/L	54.9	16.9	–	[16]
	Submandibular saliva	0.26 mL/min	15 adults	mmol/L	3.30	3.66	–	[9]
		0.62 mL/min	31 subjects	mmol/L	29.8	14.2	(7.4–58.3)	[30]
	Sublingual saliva	0.16 mL/min	10 subjects	mmol/L	32.7	10.4	(21.6–55.0)	[30]
	Labial saliva	Unstimulated	20 adults	mmol/L	13.9	12.0	(2.6–37.5)	[27]
		Stimulated	27 adults	mmol/L	37.3	22.7	(11.0–97.7)	[27]
↓ **Na/K quotient**				...	...	...	...	...
↓ **Calcium**	Total saliva	Unstimulated	34 adults	mmol/L	1.55	0.35	(0.69–2.46)	[60]
		Stimulated	46 adults	mmol/L	1.46	0.31	(0.94–2.27)	[60]
	Parotid saliva	0.068 mL/min	20 men	mmol/L	0.86	0.28	–	[16]
		0.83 mL/min	100 men	mmol/L	0.82	0.55	–	[16]
	Submandibular saliva	0.26 mL/min	15 adults	mmol/L	0.81	0.39	–	[9]
		0.62 mL/min	31 subjects	mmol/L	2.2	0.4	(1.6–3.7)	[30]
	Sublingual saliva	0.16 mL/min	10 subjects	mmol/L	2.1	0.4	(1.7–3.0)	[30]
	Labial saliva	Unstimulated	17 adults	mmol/L	2.29	0.47	(1.60–3.20)	[27]
		Stimulated	19 adults	mmol/L	2.03	0.38	(1.64–2.48)	[27]
↓ **Magnesium**	Total saliva	Unstimulated	34 adults	mmol/L	0.20	0.079	(0.065–0.38)	[68]
		Stimulated	61 adults	mmol/L	0.15	0.016	(0.083–0.34)	[68]
	Parotid saliva	0.068 mL/min	20 men	mmol/L	0.09	0.04	–	[16]
		0.83 mL/min	100 men	mmol/L	0.021	0.012	–	[16]
	Labial saliva	Unstimulated	18 adults	mmol/L	0.65	0.25	(0.41–1.22)	[27]
		Stimulated	20 adults	mmol/L	0.54	0.14	(0.38–0.80)	[27]
Iron	Parotid saliva	1.03 mL/min	77 adults	µmol/L	6.61	–	2.94–14.9	[69]
Copper	Total saliva	Unstimulated	30 subjects	µmol/L	4.99	2.38	(0.8–12)	[70]
	Parotid saliva	1.03 mL/min	49 adults	µmol/L	<0.65	–	<0.31–1.92	[69]
Zinc	Parotid saliva	Stimulated	34 subjects	µmol/L	0.78	0.21	(0.41–1.3)	[71]
		1.03 mL/min	103 adults	µmol/L	2.20	–	(0.80–6.09)	[69]
Selenium	Total saliva	Stimulated	26 children, 11–12 years	nmol/L	39	13	(14–66)	[72]
Lead	Total saliva	Stimulated	12 subjects	µmol/L	0.54	–	(0.14–1.11)	[73]

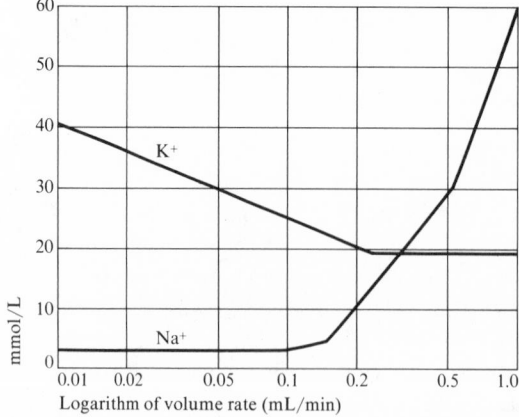

Fig. 6. Potassium and sodium concentrations in parotid saliva in relation to flow[16].

Na/K quotient. The quotient increases with increasing flow as a result of the increasing sodium concentration and a tendency to a decreasing potassium concentration (Fig. 7). The quotient provides clues to the mineralocorticoid activity of the adrenal cortex: it is reduced after administration of desoxycorticosterone[57], in primary hyperaldosteronism[58], in Bartter's syndrome[54], and in hypertension with renin suppression[59].

Calcium. Twenty-eight percent of the calcium in parotid saliva and 23% in submandibular saliva is not dialyzable[61]. In parotid saliva (Table 1)[28,62] and in submandibular saliva (Table 2) the calcium concentration increases slightly with increasing flow; by contrast, it decreases in the secretion of the small salivary glands[22]. Near term, the calcium concentration in the submandibular saliva is reduced[63]. Total saliva values in children are identical to those in adults[60]. In cystic fibrosis, the calcium concentration in the submandibular saliva is increased[38,64,65], which causes clouding of the saliva due to a precipitated calcium-protein complex[65,66]. In digitalis intoxication[55,56,67] and primary hyperparathyroidism[39] the calcium concentration in the total saliva is increased.

Magnesium. The magnesium concentration in all saliva fractions decreases with increasing flow (Tables 1 and 2)[22]. The total saliva values in children are identical to those in adults[68]. In cystic fibrosis, the magnesium concentration in the secretion of the small salivary glands tends to be reduced[22].

↓See text below			Flow	Subjects	Unit	Mean	s	95% range (extreme range in brackets)	Reference
Organic substances									
Total nitrogen	Total saliva		Unstimulated	7 subjects	mmol/L	42.9	–	(14–76)	26
	Parotid saliva		Unstimulated	47 subjects	mmol/L	41.9	15.9	–	26
			0.42 mL/min	100 men	mmol/L	32.7	13.4	–	16
			1.09 mL/min	100 men	mmol/L	49.7	21.2	–	16
	Submandibular saliva		Unstimulated	23 subjects	mmol/L	19.1	5.9	–	26
			0.26 mL/min	15 adults	mmol/L	25.9	14.4	–	9
Nonprotein nitrogen	Parotid saliva		0.42 mL/min	100 men	mmol/L	11.1	2.9	–	16
			1.09 mL/min	100 men	mmol/L	8.2	2.4	–	16
↓ Urea	Total saliva		Unstimulated		mmol/L	3.33	–	(2.40–12.5)	5
	Parotid saliva		0.31 mL/min	418 men	mmol/L	3.2	0.87	–	16
			0.88 mL/min	418 men	mmol/L	2.7	0.65	–	16
			0.40 mL/min	44 children	mmol/L	1.1	0.41	(0.40–2.0)	38
	Submandibular saliva		0.30 mL/min	18 children	mmol/L	0.85	0.35	(0.30–1.6)	38
	Labial saliva				mmol/L	4.7	–		27
Creatinine	Parotid saliva		0.42 mL/min	100 men	µmol/L	13	4	–	16
			1.09 mL/min	100 men	µmol/L	11	4	–	16
↓ Ammonia	Parotid saliva		0.28 mL/min	72 men	µmol/L	120	82	–	16
			0.93 mL/min	72 men	µmol/L	35	18	–	16
			0.40 mL/min	44 children	µmol/L	400	220*	–	38
↓ Amino acids	Total saliva		Unstimulated	5 subjects	mmol/L	0.74	–	–	76
Choline	Total saliva		Stimulated	2 subjects	mmol/L	–	–	(0.04–0.3)	77
Histamine	Total saliva		Unstimulated	24 subjects	µmol/L	1.3	–	(1.0–1.6)	78
↓ Uric acid	Parotid saliva		0.051 mL/min	20 men	µmol/L	550	190	–	16
			0.99 mL/min	314 men	µmol/L	170	50	–	16
			0.40 mL/min	44 children	µmol/L	89	48	(12–300)	38
	Submandibular saliva		0.30 mL/min	10 children	µmol/L	89	18	(71–120)	38
			Unstimulated	4 adults	µmol/L	196	–	(125–240)	79
			Stimulated	4 adults	µmol/L	77	–	(59–89)	79
Cyclic adenosine monophosphate	Parotid saliva		Unstimulated	6 subjects	nmol/L	10	–	–	80
			Stimulated	6 subjects	nmol/L	3.6	1.3	–	80

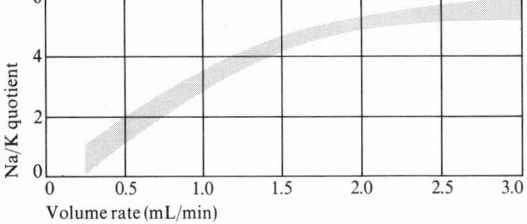

Fig. 7. Ratio of sodium to potassium concentration in parotid saliva in relation to flow[54].

Table 5   *Amino acids in total saliva (means of 5 specimens)[76]*

	µmol/L		µmol/L
Alanine	32	Isoleucine	6
α-Aminobutyric acid	trace	Leucine	8
δ-Aminovaleric acid	131	Lysine	32
Arginine	10	Phenylalanine	12
Aspartic acid	26	Proline	88
Citrulline	13	Serine	5
Glutamine	6	Taurine	71
Glutamic acid	37	Threonine	5
Glycine	144	Tyrosine	15
Histidine	18	Valine	80

Urea. The concentration in parotid saliva increases with increasing blood urea levels[14,74]. In parotid and submandibular saliva it decreases with increasing flow[75]. In both fractions the urea concentration is increased in cystic fibrosis[38].

Ammonia. The divergent values cited in the literature are probably due to the instability of urea[18]. With increasing flow, the ammonia concentration in parotid and submandibular saliva declines[75].

Amino acids. They have to be determined in saliva collected under sterile conditions since amino acids are formed and consumed by bacterial metabolism (see Table 5 for the concentrations of individual amino acids). Among ninhydrin-positive substances, phosphoethanolamine has the highest concentration[36].

Uric acid. With increasing flow the uric acid concentration in parotid and submandibular saliva decreases[75,79]. The concentration in parotid saliva is increased in cystic fibrosis[38].

↓See text below and on next page		Flow	Subjects	Unit	Mean	s	(Extreme range)	Reference
↓ Carbohydrates								
– total	Parotid saliva	Stimulated	8 adults	mg/L	245	57.7	(154–334)	[81]
	Submandibular saliva	0.26 mL/min	15 adults	mg/L	83.9	34.8	–	[9]
		Stimulated	8 adults	mg/L	104	54	(40–192)	[82]
– protein-bound	Parotid saliva	Stimulated	8 adults	mg/L	213	57.5	(132–304)	[81]
	Submandibular saliva	Stimulated	8 adults	mg/L	90	49	(20–160)	[82]
– non-protein-bound	Parotid saliva	Stimulated	8 adults	mg/L	32	5.8	(22–49)	[81]
	Submandibular saliva	Stimulated	8 adults	mg/L	14	10	(0–40)	[82]
↓ Glucose, free	Total saliva	Unstimulated	18 subjects	µmol/L	15	–	(0–56)	[85]
	Parotid saliva	0.058 mL/min	20 men	µmol/L	45	17	–	[16]
		0.62 mL/min	106 men	µmol/L	8.3	3.3	–	[16]
		0.35–1.0 mL/min	6 adults	µmol/L	–	–	(5.6–39)	[84]
↓ Lactic acid	Total saliva	Stimulated		mmol/L	–	–	(0.11–0.56)	[18]
	Parotid saliva	0.35–1.0 mL/min	6 adults	mmol/L	–	–	(0.2–0.48)	[84]
↓ Pyruvic acid	Parotid saliva	0.35–1.0 mL/min	6 adults	mmol/L	–	–	(0.01–0.07)	[84]
Citric acid	Total saliva	Stimulated		mmol/L	–	–	(0–0.1)	[5]
↓ Lipids	Parotid saliva		10 specimens	mg/L	28	15	–	[87]
	Submandibular saliva		16 specimens	mg/L	20	13	–	[87]
↓ Protein								
Total protein	Total saliva	Unstimulated		g/L	–	–	(1.4–6.4)	[5]
	Parotid saliva	0.10 mL/min	75 men	g/L	2.28	1.66	–	[20]
		0.057 mL/min	73 women	g/L	3.14	2.04	–	[20]
		0.065 mL/min	20 men	g/L	2.53	0.84	–	[16]
		0.95 mL/min	534 men	g/L	3.19	1.23	–	[16]
	Submandibular saliva	0.13 mL/min	75 men	g/L	0.90	0.61	–	[20]
		0.11 mL/min	73 women	g/L	0.93	0.57	–	[20]
		0.26 mL/min	15 adults	g/L	1.14	0.58	–	[9]
	Labial saliva	Unstimulated	21 subjects	g/L	2.96	1.02	(1.45–5.60)	[27]
		Stimulated	21 subjects	g/L	2.58	0.72	(1.45–3.55)	[27]
Albumin	Parotid saliva	0.8 mL/min	20 adults	mg/L	7	5	–	[88]
	Submandibular saliva	0.7 mL/min	20 adults	mg/L	11	8	–	[88]
		1.09 mL/min	10 subjects, 12–28 years	mg/L	3.9	–	(1.3–11.8)	[89]
Zn-α_2-glycoprotein	Total saliva	Unstimulated		mg/L	20	–		[90]
β_2-Microglobulin	Parotid saliva	Stimulated	17 patients	mg/L	0.95	0.91	–	[94]
↓ IgA	Total saliva	Unstimulated	12 adults	mg/L	65	38	(22–150)	[91]
	Parotid saliva	Stimulated	12 adults	mg/L	54	18	(21–83)	[91]
		0.33 mL/min	50 men	mg/L	126	54.9	–	[16]
		0.68 mL/min	50 men	mg/L	59	20	–	[16]
		0.8 mL/min	20 adults	mg/L	24.4	16.3	–	[88]
		No data	10 subjects	mg/L	71.9	11.1	–	[92]
		Stimulated	17 men	mg/L	62	–	(25–170)	[93]
	Labial saliva	Stimulated	17 men	mg/L	194	–	(20–470)	[93]
Secretory component	Parotid saliva	No data	10 subjects	µg/L	218	205	–	[92]
IgG	Total saliva	Unstimulated	12 adults	mg/L	8	5	(3–18)	[91]
	Parotid saliva	Stimulated	12 adults	mg/L	5	4	(0–15)	[91]
		Stimulated	4 men	mg/L	–	–	(<3)	[93]
	Labial saliva	Stimulated	4 men	mg/L	–	–	(<3–12)	[93]
IgM	Total saliva	Unstimulated	12 adults	mg/L	5	3	(1–12)	[91]
	Parotid saliva	Stimulated	12 adults	mg/L	7	4	(2–16)	[91]

Carbohydrates. Of the carbohydrates in the parotid and submandibular saliva, 86% are non-dialyzable[81, 82] and are constituents of glycoproteins and mucins. The mucins are contained mostly in submandibular and sublingual saliva; they determine the viscosity of the saliva. The mucins in the saliva of secretors have blood-group-specific properties. Table 6 lists the protein-bound carbohydrates.

Glucose. Both in parotid and in submandibular saliva, free carbohydrates are present only in low concentrations of about 30 µmol/L (5 mg/L)[75]. Presumably, they represent glucose almost exclusively. In hyperglycemia, the glucose concentration in the saliva may be elevated; however, no correlation between the glucose concentration in the saliva and that in the blood has been demonstrated[85].

↓See text below and on next page		Flow	Subjects	Unit	Mean	s	(Extreme range)	Refer-ence
↓ Enzymes								
↓ α-Amylase	Total saliva	Unstimulated	16 men	g/L	0.38	0.32	–	[102]
	Parotid saliva	Unstimulated	16 men	g/L	1.03	0.44	–	[102]
		Stimulated	11 men	g/L	0.95	0.50	–	[102]
	Submandibular saliva	Unstimulated	16 men	g/L	0.25	0.24	–	[102]
	Sublingual saliva	Unstimulated	16 men	g/L	0.26	0.32	–	[102]
↓ Lysozyme	Total saliva	Unstimulated ...	12 adults	mg/L	275	140	(130–660)	[91]
	Parotid saliva	Stimulated	12 adults	mg/L	71	27	(38–116)	[91]
		Stimulated	20 children ...	mg/L	23	–	(0–59)	[38]
	Submandibular saliva	Stimulated	15 children ...	mg/L	31	–	(3–100)	[38]
Deoxyribonucleases	Parotid saliva	Unstimulated	8 men	μg/L	~1.2	–	–	[104]
↓ Vitamins								
Ascorbic acid	Parotid saliva	Stimulated	37 adults	μmol/L	5.2	5.3	(0–24)	[114]
	Submandibular and sublingual saliva ..	Stimulated	37 adults	μmol/L	4.0	3.2	(0–12)	[114]
↓ Hormones								
Free 17-hydroxy-corticosteroids	Parotid saliva	0.33 mL/min	50 men	μg/L	24.8	10.8	–	[16]
		0.96 mL/min	50 men	μg/L	20.6	7.4	–	[16]
17α-Hydroxyproges-terone	Total saliva	Unstimulated	32 children ...	pmol/L	527	353	(90–1520)	[116]

Table 6 *Protein-bound carbohydrates in saliva*

	Unit	Parotid saliva					Submandibular saliva				
		22 children[83]			45 adults[75]		25 children[38]			45 adults[75]	
		Mean	s	(Extreme range)	Mean	s	Mean	s	(Extreme range)	Mean	s
Protein	g/L	1.65	0.75	(0.63–3.21)	2.18	0.73	1.82	0.75	(0.39–3.65)	1.08	0.40
Hexosamine*	mg/L	99	59	(20–223)	132	58	86	46	(26–209)	75	35
Fucose	mg/L	89	54	(33–244)	108	51	61	29	(17–137)	68	35
Hexose◇	mg/L	195	100	(73–441)	195	73	142	66	(50–380)	137	56
Sialic acid	mg/L	12.4	8.1	(3.5–21.1)	26	8	25	11	(11–60)	23	14

* Parotid saliva: 85% glucosamine and 15% galactosamine. ◇ Parotid saliva: mainly mannose and galactose.

Lactic acid. The concentration is increased after ingestion of fructose, lactose and sucrose[86].

Pyruvic acid. The concentration is increased after ingestion of fructose and sucrose[86].

Lipids. The lipid concentration in cell-free saliva is very low. Triglycerides, phospholipids, cholesterol and free fatty acids have been detected. Among fatty acids, eicosapentaenoic acid accounts for approximately 40%[87].

Protein. Because of the complex composition of salivary proteins the assay method needs to be taken into account when evaluating concentration data. With increasing flow, the protein concentration in parotid[6, 28] and submandibular saliva[15] increases. It is higher in the parotid saliva of women than in the parotid saliva of men and increases with age in both sexes[20]. The protein concentration in the total saliva[95] and in parotid saliva[103] increases during pregnancy and, particularly, in the first few postpartum days.

The proteins are composed of saliva-specific glycoproteins and mucins, plasma proteins as well as proteins of leukocytes, epithelial cells and bacteria. In the parotid saliva, amylase is the most important protein component (30–40% of total protein as against 25% in submandibular saliva). Electrophoresis yields a varying number of protein bands, depending on the carrier medium: with separation on polyacrylamide gel, up to 36 fractions have been found in parotid saliva[96], and up to 21 in submandibular saliva[97].

Among the proteins detected by immunologic methods are prealbumin, albumin, a β₁-glycoprotein, a β₂-glycoprotein, a transferrin, a vitamin B₁₂ transport protein, IgG, IgA and the enzymes amylase, esterase, and lysozyme in parotid saliva[98], and pre-albumin, albumin, α₁-antitrypsin, transferrin, IgG, IgA, IgM and amylase in submandibular saliva[89]. Some salivary proteins show a genetically determined polymorphism[99].

IgA. IgA is made up of 70–80% secretory IgA and of 10% normal IgA; the remaining 10–20% represent dimeric and trimeric secretory IgA[100]. Approximately one-third of the IgA stems from the small salivary glands[93]. The protein is lacking in the saliva of the newborn; its concentration generally reaches adult levels at puberty[101].

Enzymes. Enzymes should be assayed in pure catheterized saliva inasmuch as the total saliva always contains dead epithelial cells, bacteria and leukocytes, which are in turn rich in various enzymes. The glycolytic and proteolytic enzymes, most glucosidases as well as lactic dehydrogenase are contained almost exclusively in the salivary sediment[75, 105–107]. Amylase is secreted mainly by the parotid gland, and kininogenin (kallikrein) by the submandibular gland[108]. The concentrations of alkaline phosphatase[109], lysozyme and a nonspecific esterase are higher in submandibular saliva than in parotid saliva[75]. β-N-Acetylglucosaminidase and α-fucosidase[107] as well as acid phosphatase, cholinesterase and ribonuclease are present in both saliva fractions in similar concentrations[75].

Amylase. Amylase can be separated into as many as 7 isoenzymes by electrophoresis on polyacrylamide gel[110–112]. The amylase activity in the saliva of the newborn is low; it reaches adult levels toward the end of the first year (Fig. 8). In children with cystic fibrosis the activity in the submandibular saliva is increased[38].

Lysozyme. In children with cystic fibrosis the lysozyme concentration in the submandibular saliva is increased[38].

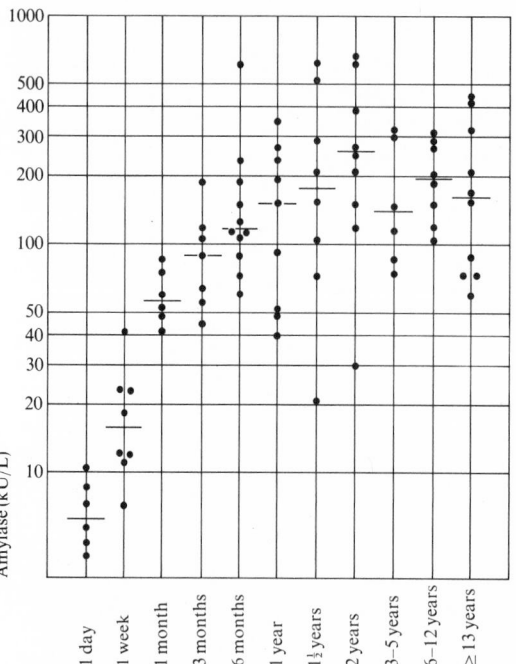

Fig. 8. Amylase activity in stimulated saliva in relation to age[113].

Vitamins. Most of the vitamins in saliva probably originate from the sediment; thus, no folic acid was found in saliva taken directly from the parotid gland[115].

Hormones. The concentration of steroid hormones – cortisol, 17α-hydroxyprogesterone, progesterone, testosterone – is low in saliva compared to plasma[117]. The cortisol concentration shows a circadian rhythm[118], the concentrations of 17α-hydroxyprogesterone and progesterone change during the menstrual cycle[117].

References

[1] HINSBERG and SCHMID, in LANG et al. (Eds.), *Hoppe-Seyler/Thierfelder Handbuch der physiologisch- und pathologisch-chemischen Analyse,* 10th ed., volume 5, Springer, Berlin, 1953, page 357; KRZYWANEK and FLASCHENTRÄGER, in FLASCHENTRÄGER and LEHNARTZ (Eds.), *Physiologische Chemie,* volume 2/Ia, Springer, Berlin, 1954, page 2.
[2] KERR, A. C., *The Physiological Regulation of Salivary Secretions in Man,* Pergamon, Oxford, 1961, page 9; SCHNEYER, L. H., *J. appl. Physiol.,* **9**, 79 (1956); DAWES and WOOD, *Arch. oral Biol.,* **18**, 337 (1973).
[3] RAUCH, S., *Die Speicheldrüse des Menschen,* Thieme, Stuttgart, 1959.
[4] MASON and CHISHOLM, *Salivary Glands in Health and Disease,* Saunders, London, 1975.
[5] AFONSKY, D., *Saliva and Its Relation to Oral Health,* University of Alabama Press, Drawer (Ala.), 1961.
[6] DAWES, C., *Arch. oral Biol.,* **14**, 277 (1968).
[7] KREUSSER et al., *Europ. J. clin. Invest.,* **2**, 398 (1972).
[8] FERGUSON et al., *Arch. oral Biol.,* **18**, 1155 (1973).
[9] FERGUSON and FORT, *Arch. oral Biol.,* **19**, 47 (1974).
[10] DAWES, C., *J. Physiol. (Lond.),* **220**, 529 (1972); *Int. J. Chronobiol.,* **2**, 253 (1974), and *J. Physiol. (Lond.),* **244**, 535 (1975).
[11] GUTMAN and BEN-ARYEH, *Int. J. oral Surg.,* **3**, 314 (1974).
[12] PUSKULIAN, C., *J. dent. Res.,* **51**, 1212 (1972).
[13] MAGNUSSON et al., *Arch. oral Biol.,* **20**, 119 (1975).
[14] DAHLBERG et al., *J. appl. Physiol.,* **23**, 100 (1967).
[15] DAWES, C., *Arch. oral Biol.,* **19**, 887 (1974).
[16] SHANNON et al., *Saliva: Composition and Secretion,* Karger, Basle, 1974.
[17] ERICSON, S., *Arch. oral Biol.,* **14**, 591 (1969).
[18] EASTOE, J. E., in LONG et al. (Eds.), *Biochemists' Handbook,* Spon, London, 1961, page 907.
[19] PRADER et al., *Helv. paediat. Acta,* **10**, 29 (1955).
[20] VOGT and SEMMANN, *Z. Laryng. Rhinol.,* **49**, 611 (1970).
[21] KNAUF and FRÖMTER, *Pflügers Arch. ges. Physiol.,* **316**, 213 (1970).
[22] WIESMANN et al., *Lancet,* **2**, 510 (1972).
[23] DREIZEN et al., *Arch. oral Biol.,* **13**, 229 (1968).
[24] ERICSON, S., *Arch. oral Biol.,* **16**, 9 (1971).
[25] TURNER et al., *J. dent. Res.,* **33**, 55 (1954).
[26] KÖSTLIN and RAUCH, *Helv. med. Acta,* **24**, 600 (1957).
[27] DAWES and WOOD, *Arch. oral Biol.,* **18**, 343 (1973).
[28] KAISER et al., *Helv. paediat. Acta,* **29**, 145 (1974).
[29] ROSENTHAL et al., *J. dent. Res.,* **38**, 883 (1959).

[30] CHAUNCEY et al., *J. dent. Res.,* **45**, 1230 (1966).
[31] THAYSEN et al., *Amer. J. Physiol.,* **178**, 155 (1954).
[32] ANDERS, J. T., *J. appl. Physiol.,* **8**, 659 (1956).
[33] SHANNON and PRIGMORE. *Proc. Soc. exp. Biol. (N. Y.),* **97**, 825 (1958).
[34] KAISER et al., *Amer. J. Dis. Child.,* **92**, 369 (1956).
[35] EGGERS-LURA, H., *J. dent. Res.,* **26**, 203 (1947).
[36] ROSE and KERR, *Quart. J. exp. Physiol.,* **43**, 160 (1958).
[37] BRAMSTEDT and NAUJOKS, *Dtsch. zahnärztl. Z.,* **17**, 867 (1962).
[38] MANDEL et al., *Amer. J. Dis. Child.,* **113**, 431 (1967).
[39] WEINBERGER et al., *Clin. chim. Acta,* **50**, 5 (1974).
[40] ERICSSON, Y., *Caries Res.,* **3**, 159 (1969).
[41] BÜTTNER et al., *Dtsch. med. Wschr.,* **98**, 751 (1973).
[42] VITTE, G., *C. R. Soc. Biol. (Paris),* **124**, 1227 (1937).
[43] BRUGER et al., *J. Lab. clin. Med.,* **26**, 1942 (1941).
[44] COHEN and MYANT, *J. Physiol. (Lond.),* **145**, 595 (1959); CHISHOLM et al., *Arch. oral Biol.,* **16**, 1245 (1971).
[45] MASON et al., *J. oral Med.,* **21**, 66 (1966).
[46] FERGUSON et al., *Canad. J. Biochem.,* **35**, 333 (1957); FITTING, W., *Klin. Wschr.,* **42**, 1203 (1964).
[47] MASON et al., *Arch. oral Biol.,* **11**, 235 (1966).
[48] TOPI and ZANE, *Gazz. int. Med. Chir.,* **64**, 512 (1959).
[49] TANNENBAUM et al., *J. nat. Cancer Inst.,* **53**, 79 (1974).
[50] VOGT and ZAHL, *Arch. klin. exp. Ohr.-, Nas. -u. Kehlk. -Heilk.,* **203**, 310 (1973).
[51] HUNGERLAND et al., *Klin. Wschr.,* **33**, 44 (1955).
[52] GRAD, B., *J. Geront.,* **9**, 276 (1954).
[53] WOTMAN et al., *Arch. intern. Med.,* **126**, 428 (1970).
[54] HEIDLAND et al., *Klin. Wschr.,* **50**, 959 (1972).
[55] WOTMAN et al., *New Engl. J. Med.,* **285**, 871 (1971).
[56] CLARA, F., *Méd. et Hyg. (Genève),* **30**, 970 (1972).
[57] WHITE et al., *J. clin. Invest.,* **34**, 246 (1955).
[58] CRANE et al., *J. Lab. clin. Med.,* **61**, 51 (1963).
[59] ADLIN et al., *Circulation,* **39**, 685 (1969).
[60] GOW, B. S., *J. dent. Res.,* **44**, 885 (1965).
[61] MANDEL et al., *Proc. Soc. exp. Biol. (N. Y.),* **115**, 959 (1964).
[62] CHAUNCEY et al., *Proc. Soc. exp. Biol. (N. Y.),* **97**, 539 (1958).
[63] MARDER et al., *Amer. J. Obstet. Gynec.,* **112**, 233 (1972).
[64] CHERNICK and BARBERO, *Ann. N. Y. Acad. Sci.,* **106**, 698 (1963).
[65] GUGLER et al., *J. Pediat.,* **71**, 585 (1967).
[66] BOAT et al., *Pediat. Res.,* **8**, 531 (1974).
[67] BOLTE et al., *Verh. dtsch. Ges. inn. Med.,* **79**, 1047 (1973); AVISSAR et al., *Arch. intern. Med.,* **135**, 1029 (1975).
[68] GOW, B. S., *J. dent. Res.,* **44**, 890 (1965).
[69] SKURK et al., *Laryngol. Rhinol.,* **53**, 863 (1974).
[70] DE JORGE et al., *Clin. chim. Acta,* **9**, 148 (1964).
[71] HENKIN et al., *J. Lab. clin. Med.,* **86**, 175 (1975).
[72] HADJIMARKOS and SHEARER, *Amer. J. clin. Nutr.,* **24**, 1210 (1971).
[73] FUNG et al., *Clin. chim. Acta,* **61**, 423 (1975).
[74] KOPSTEIN and WRONG, *Clin. Sci.,* **52**, 9 (1977).
[75] MANDEL and ELLISON, *Ann. N. Y. Acad. Sci.,* **131**, 802 (1965).
[76] DREYFUS et al., *Experientia (Basel),* **24**, 447 (1968).
[77] EAGLE, E., *J. Lab. clin. Med.,* **27**, 103 (1941).
[78] SANDERS, S. G., *J. oral Surg.,* **13**, 193 (1955).
[79] MASON et al., *J. dent. Res.,* **45**, 1439 (1966).
[80] SCHMID et al., *Dtsch. med. Wschr.,* **100**, 1435 (1975).
[81] DANIELS and NEWBRUN, *Arch. oral Biol.,* **11**, 1171 (1966).
[82] NEWBRUN, E., *Arch. oral Biol.,* **12**, 1289 (1967).
[83] MANDEL et al., *Amer. J. Dis. Child.,* **110**, 646 (1965).
[84] KELSAY et al., *Arch. oral Biol.,* **17**, 439 (1972).
[85] MÄHR et al., *Med. Klin.,* **63**, 209 (1968).
[86] KELSAY et al., *J. Nutr.,* **102**, 661 (1972).
[87] MANDEL and EISENSTEIN, *Arch. oral Biol.,* **14**, 231 (1969).
[88] ZENGO et al., *Arch. oral Biol.,* **16**, 557 (1971).
[89] GUGLER et al., *J. Pediat.,* **73**, 548 (1968).
[90] POORTMANS and SCHMID, *J. Lab. clin. Med.,* **71**, 807 (1968).
[91] VIRELLA et al., *Clin. Chem.,* **24**, 1421 (1978).
[92] STROBER et al., *New Engl. J. Med.,* **294**, 351 (1976).
[93] CRAWFORD et al., *Science,* **190**, 1206 (1975).
[94] MICHALSKI et al., *New Engl. J. Med.,* **293**, 1228 (1975).
[95] DONAT, S., *Zbl. Gynäk,* **97**, 1641 (1975).
[96] SMITH et al., *Proc. Soc. exp. Biol. (N. Y.),* **151**, 535 (1976).
[97] CALDWELL and PIGMAN, *Arch. Biochem.,* **110**, 91 (1965).
[98] CARLIER et al., *Clin. chim. Acta,* **47**, 249 (1973).
[99] TAN and TENG, *Hum. Hered.,* **29**, 69 (1979).
[100] TOMASI, T. B., *New Engl. J. Med.,* **287**, 500 (1972).
[101] SOUTH et al., *Amer. J. Med.,* **44**, 168 (1968).
[102] SCHNEYER, L. H., *J. appl., Physiol.,* **9**, 453 (1956).
[103] DONAT et al., *Zbl. Gynäk.,* **99**, 1564 (1977).
[104] ZÖLLNER et al., *Enzyme,* **19**, 60 (1975).
[105] TONZETICH and FRIEDMAN, *Ann. N. Y. Acad. Sci.,* **131**, 815 (1965).
[106] EICHEL et al., *Ann. N. Y. Acad. Sci.,* **131**, 851 (1965).
[107] MENGUY et al., *Proc. Soc. exp. Biol. (N. Y.),* **134**, 1020 (1970).
[108] BHOOLA et al., *New Engl. J. Med.,* **281**, 277 (1969).
[109] CORNISH and POSEN, *Clin. chim. Acta,* **20**, 387 (1968).
[110] WOLF and TAYLOR, *Nature,* **213**, 1128 (1967).
[111] KAUFFMAN et al., *Arch. Biochem.,* **137**, 325 (1970).
[112] SKURK et al., *Arch. oral Biol.,* **20**, 429 (1975).
[113] ROSSITER et al., *Acta paediat. scand.,* **63**, 389 (1974).
[114] MÄKILÄ and KIRVESKARI, *Arch. oral Biol.,* **14**, 1285 (1969).
[115] MÄKILÄ and KIRVESKARI, *Int. Z. Vitaminforsch.,* **37**, 487 (1967).
[116] WALKER et al., *Clin. Chem.,* **25**, 542 (1979).
[117] RIAD-FAHMY et al., *Postgrad. med. J.,* **56**, suppl. 1, 75 (1980).
[118] WALKER et al., *Clin. Chem.,* **24**, 1460 (1978).

Owing to the difficulty of collecting pure gastric juice the exact composition of this body fluid is not known for certain. The use of a gastric tube or even a gastric fistula yields not pure gastric juice but simply the gastric contents, almost always containing saliva, food remnants and occasionally also bile, pancreatic juice and intestinal contents. If food residues remain in the gastric contents 12 hours after the last intake of food, this is indicative of a disturbance of emptying[1]. Unless otherwise stated, the following values apply to unstimulated gastric juice obtained from fasting subjects by means of permanent intubation.

The gastric juice consists of a mixture of the various secretions of the cells of the gastric mucosa.

In the cardiac area of the stomach the glands are lined by mucus-producing cells only. In the area of the fundus the glands are lined by 3 types of cells. The glands are covered by columnar epithelial cells which contain and secrete mucus and an alkaline fluid. The chief cells, containing and secreting pepsinogen, line the lower half of the glandular tubules. The parietal (so-called because of their location) or oxyntic cells (so-called because they produce hydrochloric acid) are usually crowded away from the lumen, to which they are connected by capillaries. The glands in the pyloric area are composed of cells resembling chief cells. The gastric juice may be formally divided into 2 components: the parietal-cell secretion and the secretion of the other cells (nonparietal secretion)[2-4].

The calculated or experimentally determined ion composition of the 2 formal gastric-juice components is shown in Table 1. Nothing definite is known about the magnitude of the sodium concentration in the parietal secretion. The composition of a gastric-juice specimen is determined by the relative proportions of the 2 gastric-juice components.

The strongest stimulation of acid and pepsin secretion is produced via the vagus nerve (e.g. in sham feeding). In man, vagal stimulation can be accomplished through hypoglycemia, which can be brought about by administration of insulin or 2-deoxy-D-glucose.

The acid secretion of the parietal cells is regulated by the interaction of a wide variety of nervous and hormonal stimuli (Fig. 1). Stimulants likely to have physiological roles in regulation are acetylcholine, gastrin and histamine[10]. Acetylcholine is released by vagal and intramucosal reflex stimulation, acting directly on the parietal cell. Gastrin is released by peptides and free amino acids in the stomach and possibly also by acetylcholine. Factors influencing histamine release are not well defined, but studies with H_2-receptor antagonists have confirmed the important role of histamine in acid secretion[147, 148]. Studies with isolated parietal cells point to separate receptors for histamine, gastrin and acetylcholine in these cells. The action of histamine appears to be mediated through increased production of CAM[146].

The composition of the gastric juice has been described in detail[3, 11-14]; in addition, the diagnostic aspects of gastric-juice analyses have been discussed[15-18].

Appearance

Pure fistula juice is a clear to slightly turbid, nearly colorless liquid of slightly sour taste and odor. The fasting stomach contents are slightly cloudy, mucous and show greenish discoloration from bile reflux. Under normal conditions, the fasting contents of the unstimulated stomach do not include free hydrochloric acid.

Table 1 *Composition of parietal and nonparietal secretion*

	Parietal secretion			Nonparietal secretion	
	MAKH-LOUF et al.[5]	HOBSLEY and SILEN[6]	HOBS-LEY[9]	MAKH-LOUF et al.[5]	GARDHAM and HOBSLEY[7]
	mmol/L				
H+	148	143	134	0	0
HCO₃⁻	0	0	0	25	13
Na+	0	0	9◊	138	128
K+	16	16	17	5	13
Cl⁻	164	169	160	120	132
Ca²⁺	< 0.1*	–	–	1.6*	–

* Values taken from MOORE and MAKHLOUF[8]. ◊ Estimated.

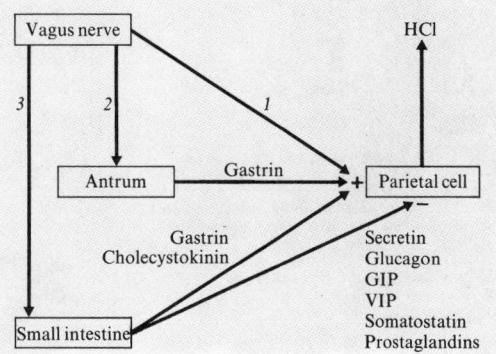

Fig. 1. Action of nervous and hormonal stimuli on HCl secretion by parietal cells[145]. 'Cephalic' (*1*), 'gastric' (*2*) and 'intestinal' (*3*) phases according to the terminology formerly in use. + Stimulation of acid secretion. − Inhibition of acid secretion. *GIP* 'gastric inhibitory polypeptide'. *VIP* 'vasoactive intestinal peptide'.

Traces of fresh blood may be due to an injury from intubation. Pathological blood in the fasting contents is generally dark brown and comparable to coffee grounds in appearance.

Volume

Tables 2 and 3 present the normal values of the intragastric fasting volume and of the flow of gastric juice. Concerning the basal secretion data, it should be borne in mind that measurements are very difficult to accomplish in the absence of any stimulation. Parietal secretion begins within the very first hours after birth.

Table 2 *Intragastric fasting volume and flow of gastric juice*

		Intragastric fasting volume			Volume rate			
	Number	Mean	s	(Extreme range)	Mean	s	(Extreme range)	Reference
		mL			mL/min			
Newborn, unstimulated	154	2.65	2.05	(0.4–12.3)	–	–	–	19
Infants, unstimulated	3	2.4	0.7	(1.0–3.5)	–	–	–	20
Children (mean age 9 years), unstimulated	59	8.8	8.2	(0.4–[80])	–	–	–	20
Adults, aspiration during night	16	–	–	–	0.56	–	(0.23–1.0)	21
Adults, unstimulated	7	24	5	–	0.9	0.2	–	149
Adults, continuous intravenous infusion of pentagastrin	7	95	16	–	5.0	0.6	–	149
Patients with Zollinger-Ellison syndrome	3	42	6	–	8.2	1.0	–	149
Patients with Zollinger-Ellison syndrome, continuous intravenous infusion of metiamide	3	10	0.4	–	1.3	0.4	–	149

Gastric-juice output in the adult is 2–3 L/d, or about 35 mL/d to 1 kg of body mass[13]. There is *hyposecretion* in the absence of parietal secretion (pernicious anemia, atrophic gastritis) and frequently in diabetics[28] and in patients with stomach cancer[29] or cirrhosis[30]. *Hypersecretion* occurs in patients with duodenal ulcers[29,31,32] (especially during the night[32]) and in cases of the Zollinger-Ellison syndrome[33–35].

Table 3　*Basal and maximal flow of gastric juice*

Subjects	Basal*		Maximal stimulation*						Stimulation (dose for 1 kg of body mass)	Reference
	BVO		MVO		PVO		PHR			
	Mean	(Extreme range)	Mean	(Extreme range)	Mean	(Extreme range)	Mean	s		
	mL/h									
30 adults..............	79.7	s 37.9	–	–	–	–	194	52	24 µg/h histamine dihydrochloride by continuous intravenous infusion	25
17 adults.............	96.6	s 25.8	190	–	216	s 35.1	–	–	6 µg pentagastrin subcutaneous	26
39 men	68.5	s 28.2	–	–	–	–	210	51.3	2 mg betazole intramuscular	27
38 women	58.6	s 28.2	–	–	–	–	157	41.5	2 mg betazole intramuscular	27
5 children, 6–10 days........	–	–	–	–	10.6	(3.2–20.4)	–	–	6 µg pentagastrin subcutaneous	36
5 children, 9–11 weeks	–	–	–	–	19.8	(8–33.2)	–	–	6 µg pentagastrin subcutaneous	36
5 children, 6–7 months	–	–	–	–	32.4	(16.6–43.0)	–	–	6 µg pentagastrin subcutaneous	36
5 children, 10–15 months	–	–	–	–	65.7	(61.2–69.2)	–	–	6 µg pentagastrin subcutaneous	36
14 children, 1–2 years	29	(10–48)	46	(25–93)	–	–	–	–	40 µg acid histamine phosphate subcutaneous	23
20 children, 2–12 years: – values for 1 kg of body mass................	1.82	s 0.60	3.85	s 0.83	4.57	s 0.87	–	–	6 µg pentagastrin subcutaneous	24

* *Abbreviations and definitions for gastric-juice volume[24,27]:*
BVO (basal volume output): gastric-juice volume during 1 hour under basal conditions (unstimulated, fasting).
MVO (maximal volume output): gastric-juice secretion during 1 hour after maximal stimulation.

PVO (peak volume output): gastric-juice volume after maximal stimulation in the following 15-minute portions or in the 20-minute portion with the highest secretion values, converted to 1 hour.
PHR (peak hour response): gastric-juice volume after maximal stimulation in the 4 following 15-minute portions with the highest acid secretion.

↓See text below and on following pages	Fasting values, unstimulated (basal secretion), unless otherwise stated	SI unit	Mean	s	(Extreme range)	Other units	Mean	s	(Extreme range)	Reference
Physicochemical data										
Relative density	....	...	–	–	(1.004–1.010)	...	...	...	...	13
Freezing-point depression	....	K	0.47	–	–	°C	0.47	–	–	13
↓ **Osmolality**	....	mmol/kg	–	–	(171–276)	mosm/kg	–	–	(171–276)	21
	15 adults, stimulated .... (a)	mmol/kg	282	22	(262–306)	mosm/kg	282	22	(262–306)	22
↓ **pH**	....	...	...	...	...	...	...	...	...	...
		Amount of substance				Mass				
		Unit	Mean	s	(Extreme range)	Unit	Mean	s	(Extreme range)	
↓ **Acidity**	15 adults, stimulated (continuous intravenous infusion of betazole).........	mmol/min	0.58	0.16	(0.39–0.88)	...	...	...	...	22
Water	....	mmol/L	55.2	–	–	g/L	994	–	–	11
Dry mass	....	...	...	...	...	g/L	5.6	–	–	11

Osmolality. (a) Continuous intravenous infusion of betazole. – Compared with the serum, the osmolality of nonparietal secretion is slightly hypotonic, and that of parietal secretion isotonic. The osmolality of the basal secretion amounts to about two-thirds of that of the serum and approaches the serum values as the rate of secretion increases[22]. Mixing of the acid-containing parietal secretion with the bicarbonate-containing nonparietal secretion gives volatile CO_2; gastric juice of low acid content is frequently hypotonic for this reason[21].

pH (see Table 4a). The extreme values are theoretically 0.9 (parietal secretion) and 7.7 (nonparietal secretion). Contamination of the gastric juice with saliva or intestinal contents results in increase of the pH. Approximately neutral values in the stomach contents of newborn infants are suggestive of swallowed amniotic fluid[37]. See literature on intragastric measurement of pH by endoradiosonde[38]; however, this does not permit a quantitative analysis of the gastric juice.

Acidity

On the basis of the electrometrically determined hydrogen ion activity a_{H^+}, the hydrogen ion concentration is calculated by means of the activity coefficient γ_{HCl} (Table 5)[39]. *Titratable acidity*

Table 4a *pH of gastric juice*

Subjects	Basal			Stimulated*			Reference
	Mean	s	(Extreme range)	Mean	s	(Extreme range)	
5 children, 6–10 days..	4.6	–	(3.4–6.9)	3.1	–	(2.0–3.9)	36
5 children, 9–11 weeks	4.0	–	(2.6–6.4)	1.7	–	(1.3–1.9)	36
5 children, 6–7 months	2.4	–	(1.5–3.2)	1.3	–	(1.3–1.4)	36
5 children, 10–15 months.......................................	2.0	–	(1.7–2.2)	1.3	–	(1.25–1.6)	36
25 men...	1.92	1.28	–	–	–	–	28
12 women..	2.59	2.08	–	–	–	–	28

* Stimulation: 6 µg pentagastrin to 1 kg of body mass.

Table 4b *Hydrogen and chloride ion concentrations in gastric juice (mmol/L)*

Subjects	H+				Cl−				Stimulation (dose for 1 kg of body mass)	Reference
	Basal		Stimulated		Basal		Stimulated			
	Mean	s	Mean	s	Mean	s	Mean	s		
9 children, 6½–14 years.....	16	–	88	–	95	–	142	–	6 µg pentagastrin subcutaneous	44
15 adults..................	30	24	121	12	97	20	147	13	2 mg/h betazole by continuous intravenous infusion	22
12 adults..................	26.9	9.8	97.6	8.2	104	9.0	129	5.3	6 µg pentagastrin subcutaneous	26
30 and 23 adults...........	39.9	17.7	102	20.3	107	25.1	140	25.1	24 µg histamine dihydrochloride hourly by continuous intravenous infusion	25

Table 5 *Determination of hydrogen ion concentration in gastric juice from pH values measured with glass electrode at 25 °C*[39]

pH	a_{H^+}	Na + K												
		0 mmol/L		20 mmol/L		40 mmol/L		50 mmol/L		60 mmol/L		80 mmol/L		100 mmol/L	
		γ_{HCl}	c_{H^+}	γ_{HCl}	c_{H^+}	γ_{HCl}	c_{H^+}	γ_{HCl}	c_{H^+}	γ_{HCl}	c_{H^+}	γ_{HCl}	c_{H^+}	γ_{HCl}	c_{H^+}
14.0.........	0.00	1.000	0.00	0.873	0.00	0.837	0.00	0.827	0.00	0.816	0.00	0.800	0.00	0.788	0.00
5.0..........	0.01	–	–	0.873	0.01	0.837	0.01	0.827	0.01	0.816	0.01	0.800	0.01	0.788	0.01
4.0..........	0.10	–	–	0.873	0.11	0.837	0.12	0.827	0.12	0.816	0.12	0.800	0.12	0.788	0.13
3.5..........	0.32	–	–	0.872	0.37	0.837	0.38	0.827	0.39	0.816	0.39	0.800	0.40	0.788	0.41
3.0..........	1.00	0.966	1.04	0.871	1.15	0.836	1.20	0.826	1.21	0.815	1.23	0.800	1.25	0.788	1.27
2.9..........	1.26	0.961	1.31	0.870	1.45	0.836	1.51	0.826	1.52	0.815	1.55	0.800	1.58	0.788	1.60
2.8..........	1.58	0.955	1.65	0.870	1.82	0.836	1.89	0.825	1.92	0.815	1.94	0.799	1.98	0.788	2.00
2.7..........	2.00	0.950	2.10	0.868	2.30	0.835	2.40	0.825	2.42	0.815	2.45	0.799	2.50	0.788	2.54
2.6..........	2.51	0.947	2.65	0.867	2.90	0.834	3.01	0.824	3.05	0.814	3.08	0.799	3.14	0.787	3.19
2.5..........	3.16	0.944	3.35	0.865	3.65	0.834	3.79	0.824	3.83	0.814	3.88	0.798	3.96	0.787	4.02
2.4..........	3.98	0.935	4.26	0.864	4.61	0.833	4.78	0.823	4.84	0.813	4.90	0.797	4.99	0.786	5.06
2.3..........	5.01	0.928	5.40	0.862	5.81	0.831	6.03	0.821	6.10	0.812	6.17	0.796	6.29	0.786	6.37
2.2..........	6.31	0.921	6.85	0.859	7.34	0.830	7.60	0.821	7.68	0.811	7.78	0.795	7.94	0.785	8.04
2.1..........	7.94	0.912	8.71	0.855	9.29	0.828	9.59	0.819	9.69	0.809	9.81	0.794	10.0	0.784	10.1
2.0..........	10.00	0.902	11.1	0.853	11.7	0.826	12.1	0.817	12.2	0.807	12.4	0.793	12.6	0.783	12.8
1.9..........	12.59	0.893	14.1	0.848	14.8	0.823	15.3	0.815	15.4	0.805	15.6	0.791	15.9	0.781	16.1
1.8..........	15.85	0.882	18.0	0.842	18.8	0.820	19.3	0.812	19.5	0.803	19.7	0.790	20.1	0.780	20.3
1.7..........	19.95	0.871	22.9	0.837	23.8	0.816	24.4	0.808	24.7	0.799	25.0	0.788	25.3	0.778	25.6
1.6..........	25.12	0.860	29.2	0.831	30.2	0.811	31.0	0.804	31.2	0.796	31.6	0.786	32.0	0.776	32.4
1.5..........	31.62	0.847	37.3	0.823	38.4	0.806	39.2	0.799	39.6	0.792	39.9	0.782	40.4	0.772	41.0
1.4..........	39.81	0.834	47.7	0.816	48.8	0.800	49.8	0.794	50.1	0.788	50.5	0.778	51.2	0.770	51.7
1.3..........	50.12	0.822	61.0	0.806	62.2	0.792	63.3	0.788	63.6	0.783	64.0	0.776	64.6	0.768	65.3
1.2..........	63.10	0.809	78.0	0.796	79.3	0.785	80.4	0.783	80.6	0.777	81.2	0.771	81.8	0.764	82.6
1.1..........	79.43	0.796	99.8	0.786	101.0	0.779	102.0	0.776	102.4	0.772	102.9	0.767	103.6		
1.0..........	100.0	0.784	127.6	0.778	128.5	0.772	129.5	0.771	129.7	0.767	130.4				
0.95.........	112.2	0.779	144.0	0.774	145.0										
0.90.........	125.9	0.774	162.7												
0.85.........	141.3	0.769	183.7												

a_{H^+}: hydrogen ion activity. γ_{HCl}: activity coefficient. c_{H^+}: hydrogen ion concentration.

is determinable by titration up to the end point of pH 7.0 or 7.4 (phenolsulfonphthalein) or 8.3 (phenolphthalein). This value is equivalent to the so-called total acidity. Values such as 'clinical unit', 'free acid' (titration to end point of pH 2.5–3.5), and 'bound acid' (difference between 'total acidity' and 'free acid') are no longer in use[40]. *Undissociated acid* is the difference in acidity upon titration to the end points of ph 7.0 and 8.3[41].

The hydrogen ion concentration increases with the flow (Fig.2) and reaches the calculated value for parietal secretion at a high flow. The acidity of the gastric juice in the basal state and after

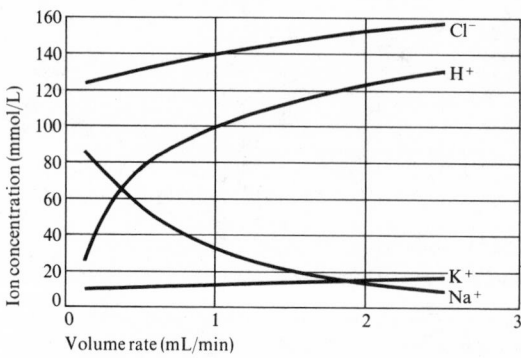

Fig. 2. Electrolyte concentration in gastric juice as a function of flow. Measurements made in a young man upon intravenous stimulation with histamine[42].

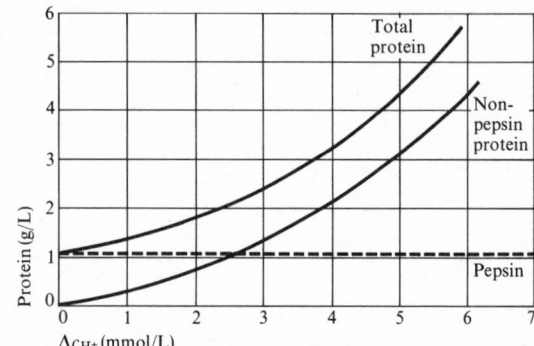

Fig. 3. Relation between protein concentration and undissociated acid (Δc_{H^+}) in gastric juice[41].

Table 6   *Basal and 'maximal' acid secretion*

Subjects	Basal secretion*		'Maximal' secretion							Stimulation (dose for 1 kg of body mass)	Reference
	BAO		MAO		PAO		PHR				
	Mean	(Extreme range)	Mean	(Extreme range)	Mean	(Extreme range)	Mean	s			
	mmol/h										
30 adults	3.0	s 1.3	–	–	–	–	19.7	4.5		24 µg/h histamine dihydro-chloride by continuous intra-venous infusion	25
17 adults	3.2	s 1.8	16.7	s 4.4	–	–	–	–		6 µg pentagastrin subcutaneous	26
39 men	2.53	s 1.87	17.9	s 5.0	–	–	23.0	6.7		2 mg betazole intramuscular	27
38 women	1.63	s 1.23	12.8	s 4.5	–	–	16.6	5.4		2 mg betazole intramuscular	27
11 adults	–	–	–	–	–	–	28.3	8.6		0.04 IU/h of insulin by continuous intravenous infusion	43
5 children, 6–10 days	0.103	(0.05–0.12)	0.163	(0.09–0.26)	0.24	(0.12–0.34)	–	–		6 µg pentagastrin subcutaneous	36
5 children, 9–11 weeks	0.149	(0.05–0.30)	0.56	(0.39–0.84)	0.75	(0.63–0.97)	–	–		6 µg pentagastrin subcutaneous	36
5 children, 6–7 months	0.193	(0.07–0.4)	2.08	(1.33–2.8)	3.05	(1.54–3.84)	–	–		6 µg pentagastrin subcutaneous	36
5 children, 10–15 months	0.322	(0.08–0.48)	3.93	(3.25–4.39)	5.48	(3.84–6.26)	–	–		6 µg pentagastrin subcutaneous	36
14 children, 1–2 years	0.26	(0.00–1.32)	1.94	(0.37–3.73)	–	–	–	–		40 µg acid histamine phosphate subcutaneous	23
20 children, 2–12 years: – values for 1 m² body surface	1.90	s 0.99	9.25	s 2.35	11.7	s 2.31	–	–		6 µg pentagastrin subcutaneous	24
– values for 1 kg of body mass	0.077	s 0.042	0.372	s 0.089	0.472	s 0.087	–	–		6 µg pentagastrin subcutaneous	24

* Abbreviations and definitions for rate of acid secretion[15, 17, 27]:
BAO (basal acid output), *MBAO* (morning basal acid output): acid secretion under basal conditions (unstimulated, fasting) during 1 hour.
FHR (first-hour response), *MAO* (maximal acid output), *MSR* (maximal secretory response): acid secretion during 1 hour after maximal stimulation.

PAO (peak acid output): acid volumes after maximal stimulation in 2 successive 15-minute portions or in 20-minute portion with the highest acid values, converted to 1 hour.
PHR (peak hour response): acid volumes after maximal stimulation in 4 successive 15-minute portions with the highest acid values.

stimulation by drugs at the customary dose levels is shown in Table 4b. The maximum titratable acidity amounts to 150 mmol/L[43]. The hydrogen ion concentration is several mmol/L lower than the titratable acidity; the undissociated acid amounts to several mmol/L, depending on the protein concentration in the gastric juice[41] (Fig. 3).

Acid secretion. Values of basal and 'maximal' acid secretion obtained with different stimulants are shown in Table 6. Maximal acid secretion is attainable by stimulation using the subcutaneous, intramuscular or intravenous route. Continuing stimulation by continuous infusion is more likely to produce higher acid secretion than a single subcutaneous dose. 'Maximal' refers to that dose of a

drug which, when doubled, causes no further significant increase of the rate of secretion[18, 55]. At the usual doses, this so-called maximal secretion rate amounts to approximately 70–90% of the theoretical maximum[18, 58]. Use of a combination of several stimulants may under some circumstances cause greater acid secretion than use of a single substance[60]. In patients with a considerably increased mass of parietal cells, e.g. in ulcer patients, the usual dose may not be sufficient for maximal stimulation of acid secretion[59]. Generally speaking, the effects of the individual stimulants are quite comparable[53, 58, 61–63] – as is true of the effect of a test meal[64] – even though maximal stimulation may be produced at different times, depending on the substance and the route of ad-

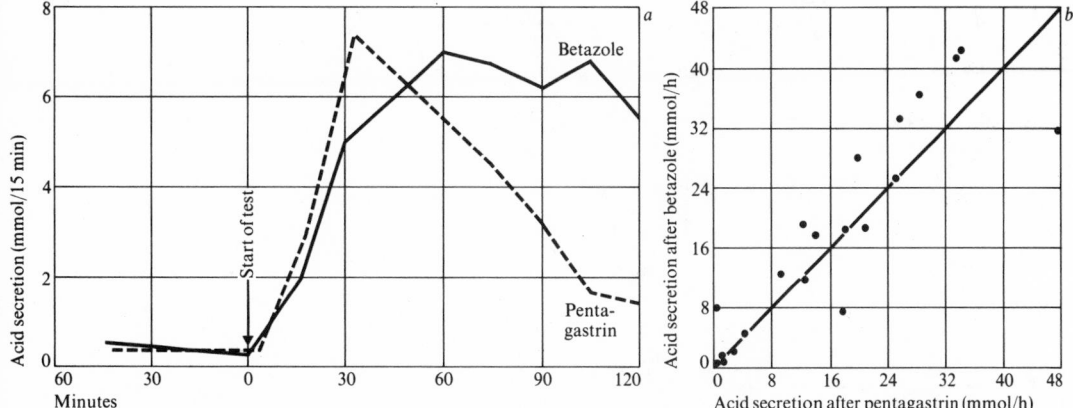

Fig. 4. a Acid secretion after stimulation with betazole (1.5 mg/kg) and with pentagastrin (6 µg/kg). Mean of 20 studies. *b* Comparison of the peak acid output after stimulation with betazole ($\bar{x}$ 32.6 mmol/h, s 5.8 mmol/h) and with pentagastrin ($\bar{x}$ 29.0 mmol/h, s 5.4 mmol/h) in men with various gastrointestinal diseases[61].

ministration (Fig. 4). Stimulation sets in within 30–45 minutes after intravenous infusion of pentagastrin[152]. Except when the insulin test is specifically indicated, pentagastrin is to be given preference because of its insignificant side effects[65].

Physiological variations in acid secretion. Strictly basal conditions are difficult to produce in the examination. The lowest basal secretion values are found during sleep; the acid secretion occasionally decreases to less than 0.1 mmol in 20-minute portions[45, 144]. Mechanical, psychic and chemical stimuli, sleeplessness, noise, and anxiety stimulate acid secretion[46–48]. Basal secretion in an individual varies considerably[49, 50] and changes in the course of the day (Fig. 5)[51]. It is higher in men than in women and tends to diminish with advanced age[21, 27, 28]. In the newborn, acid secretion is demonstrable within the very first hours after birth[52]. 'Maximal' acid secretion in one and the same individual is significantly more consistent than the basal (aside from spontaneous changes in a few cases[53]). It is a measure of the total number of parietal cells (parietal cell mass)[54], which is estimated at 1.09×10^9 in men, and at 0.82×10^9 in women. The highest rate of acid secretion at all possible is not known exactly; estimates range up to 32–35 mmol/h relative to 10^9 parietal cells[55]. In relation to body mass, the sex differences in the 'maximal' acid secretion rate disappear almost entirely[27, 56]. But the meaning of this finding is doubtful, since the dose of a stimulant is calculated in relation to body mass rather than to parietal cell mass: in a person with an average parietal cell mass who is underweight the dosage would then be submaximal[57].

Evaluation of acid secretion[15–17]. The study of *basal* secretion has for its sole purpose the detection of a Zollinger-Ellison syndrome. As a result of the increased release of gastrin from the pancreatic tumor the basal secretion rate exceeds 15 mmol/h and increases only slightly upon stimulation so that the ratio of basal to maximal acid secretion is over 0.6[35, 71]. A single examination can yield a false negative result since tumor activity varies widely. The determination of '*maximal*' acid secretion permits detection of achlorhydria, which is characteristic of idiopathic pernicious anemia, for example, or of hypersecretion of hydrogen ions. The diagnosis of achlorhydria presupposes that pH 8.3 is taken as the titration end point so that undissociated acid may be determined as well[41]. An examination for *hypersecretion* of a maximally acidified stomach juice aids differentiation between a benign and a malignant gastric tumor although no final conclusion can be drawn in the individual case. In cases of benign ulcer, acid secretion is increased[68, 69] (Table 7) because of the increased parietal cell mass[67]; however, the values overlap the normal range. Aside from exceptional cases[70], lack of acid secretion virtually precludes a benign ulcer and arouses suspicion of a carcinoma. On the other hand, hypersecretion of hydrogen ions does not rule out a carcinoma since the maximal acid secretion rate is above 20 mmol/h in 5% or more of the cases[66]. *Insulin test* (Hollander test): In the presence of an intact vagus nerve acid secretion can be stimulated by central vagal stimulation. Such a stimulation is obtained via hypoglycemia by administration of insulin, tolbutamide or 2-deoxy-D-glucose[72, 73]. The test is made to determine whether or not a vagotomy is complete[74].

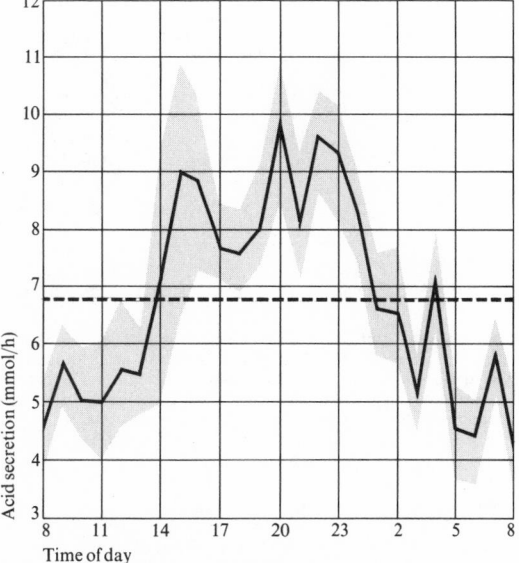

Fig. 5. Hourly basal acid secretion during the course of the day ($\bar{x} \pm 1\ s_{\bar{x}}$ of 8 examinations in 1 subject). The dashed horizontal line indicates the average hourly acid secretion in 24 hours[51].

Table 7
'*Maximal*' acid secretion (peak acid output) in stomach diseases[68]

	Men			Women		
	Number	Mean	(Extreme range)	Number	Mean	(Extreme range)
		mmol/h			mmol/h	
Control subjects....	16	27.6	s 8.0 (14.7–42.0)	19	23.3	s 8.9 (5.0–36.8)
Duodenal ulcer.......	53	37.9	s 11.6 (13.6–68.3)	18	30.2	s 12.3 (14.7–65.5)
Stomach cancer	7	8.5	(0.0–37.0)	4	8.7	(0.0–15.0)

Stimulation: 6 µg of pentagastrin to 1 kg of body mass.

↓See text below and on next page	Fasting values, unstimulated (basal secretion) unless otherwise stated	Amount of substance				Mass				Reference
		Unit	Mean	s	(Extreme range)	Unit	Mean	s	(Extreme range)	
Inorganic substances										
↓**Bicarbonate**......	....	...	...	...	...	...	...	...	...	...
↓**Chloride**	15 adults, stimulated .. (a)	mmol/min	0.71	0.18	(0.46–1.04)	mg/min	25	6.4	(16–37)	22
↓**Phosphate** (as P) .	19 adults, stimulated .. (a)	mmol/L	0.87	0.15	–	mg/L	27	4.7	–	75
Fluoride	....	µmol/L	–	–	(20–40)	mg/L	–	–	(0.4–0.7)	77
↓**Bromide**	....	µmol/L	–	–	(8–110)	mg/L	–	–	(0.6–9.0)	78
↓**Iodide**............	....	...	...	...	...	...	...	...	...	...
↓**Thiocyanate**	....	...	...	...	...	...	...	...	...	...
Nitrite	18 subjects.............	µmol/L	1.7	2.1	...	...	...	...	...	150
↓**Potassium**	15 adults, stimulated .. (a)	µmol/min	37	13	(25–64)	mg/min	1.4	0.5	(1.0–2.5)	22
↓**Sodium**	15 adults, stimulated .. (a)	µmol/min	73	41	(22–310)	mg/min	1.7	0.9	(0.5–7.1)	22
↓**Calcium**.........	15 adults, stimulated.. (a)	µmol/min	0.6	1.1	(0–3.7)	µg/min	24	44	(0–148)	22
↓**Magnesium**	15 adults, stimulated .. (a)	µmol/min	0.6	0.6	(0–2.1)	µg/min	15	15	(0–51)	22
↓**Iron**.............	26 subjects..............	µmol/L	52	–	–	mg/L	2.9	–	–	81
Iron-binding capacity..........	18 children, 4–36 months..	mmol/L	2.77	0.97	–	mg/L	155	54	–	82
	24 children, 4–13 years....	mmol/L	2.63	1.38	–	mg/L	147	77	–	82
	11 adults, stimulated .. (a)	mmol/L	2.75	–	(0–3.94)	mg/L	154	–	(0–220)	83
Copper..........	46 subjects..............	µmol/L	6.1	3.1	(1.5–13)	mg/L	0.39	0.20	(0.10–0.85)	85

Bicarbonate. Contained only in nonparietal secretion (see Table 1, page 123).

Chloride. (a) Continuous intravenous infusion of betazole. – See Table 4b (page 125) for chloride concentration in unstimulated and stimulated gastric juice. The chloride concentration increases with the flow (Fig.2, page 126); when this is high, the chloride values approach the theoretical concentration in the parietal secretion (Table 1, page 123). Concentrations below 120 mmol/L are indicative of contamination of the gastric juice with saliva or duodenal contents.

Phosphate. (a) Submaximal stimulation with histamine. – At least 95% of the total phosphorus is present as inorganic phosphate[76], which is probably contained only in nonparietal secretion (P concentration about 2.2 mmol/L)[3]. The phosphate concentration varies inversely to the acid concentration and decreases to as little as 0.2 mmol/L in strongly acid gastric juice[76].

Bromide. Compared with chloride, bromide is preferentially secreted by the parietal cells. The ratio of bromide to chloride concentration in the gastric juice is approximately one and a half times as great as the ratio in the plasma[21].

Iodide. At low plasma levels of iodide the ratio of iodide to chloride concentration in the gastric juice is about 15 times the ratio in the plasma; it drops as far as 1 at high plasma iodide levels[21].

Thiocyanate. If the gastric juice contains thiocyanate, it is probably contaminated with saliva[79].

Potassium. (a) Continuous intravenous infusion of betazole. – See Table 8 for potassium concentration in unstimulated and stimulated gastric juice. The potassium concentration is largely independent of the flow rate. A brief rise of the potassium concentration after stimulation suggests that intracellular potassium is being mobilized[21]. Values above 20 mmol/L point to contamination with saliva.

Sodium. (a) Continuous intravenous infusion of betazole. – See Table 8 for sodium concentration in unstimulated and stimulated gastric juice. The sodium concentration varies with the flow in the opposite sense to the hydrogen ion concentration (Fig.2) and approaches the theoretical sodium concentration in the parietal secretion at a high flow (Table 1). A small portion of the sodium comes from diffusion through the mucosa, which can increase considerably after an injury, e.g. from acetylsalicylic acid[21].

Table 8   *Cation concentrations in gastric juice (means and s)*

Subjects	Na⁺		K⁺		Ca²⁺		Mg²⁺		Stimulation (dose for 1 kg of body mass)	Reference
	Basal	Stimulated	Basal	Stimulated	Basal	Stimulated	Basal	Stimulated		
	mmol/L									
9 children, 6½–14 years................	51	27	11.7	15.1	1.23	0.58	–	–	6 µg pentagastrin subcutaneous	44
15 adults...............................	58	15	8.4	7.8	1.0	0.15	0.47	0.13	2 mg/h betazole by continuous	22
	s 13	s 7	s 1.7	s 0.4	s 0.4	s 0.25	s 0.17	s 0.06	intravenous infusion	
12 adults...............................	59.7	25.0	14.2	17.9	–	–	–	–	6 µg pentagastrin subcutaneous	26
	s 6.6	s 4.4	s 2.3	s 1.6	–	–	–	–		
23 adults...............................	50.8	18.9	14.0	16.9	–	–	–	–	24 µg/h of histamine dihydro-	25
	s 14.6	s 10.9	s 3.6	s 3.4	–	–	–	–	chloride by continuous intravenous infusion	

↓See text below	Fasting values, unstimulated (basal secretion) unless otherwise stated	Amount of substance				Mass				Reference
		Unit	Mean	s	(Extreme range)	Unit	Mean	s	(Extreme range)	
Organic substances										
Total nitrogen....	21 subjects...............	mmol/L	53.7	–	–	mg/L	752	–	–	87
	6 young men.............	mmol/L	–	–	(65–156)	mg/L	–	–	(910–2180)	31
Nonprotein nitrogen.........	21 subjects...............	mmol/L	29.6	–	–	mg/L	415	–	–	87
	10 subjects...............	mmol/L	–	–	(11–23)	mg/L	–	–	(150–320)	88
Peptide nitrogen .	10 subjects...............	mmol/L	–	–	(2.7–5.0)	mg/L	–	–	(38–70)	88
↓ Amino-acid nitrogen	10 subjects...............	mmol/L	–	–	(1.1–5.4)	mg/L	–	–	(16–75)	88
↓ Ammonia	26 subjects...............	mmol/L	1.02	0.61	–	mg/L	17.3	10.4	–	91
↓ Urea............	9 subjects	µmol/L	193	105	–	mg/L	11.6	6.3	–	94
	7 subjects, stimulated . (a)	µmol/L	137	105	–	mg/L	8.2	6.3	–	94
Creatinine	20 subjects...............	µmol/L	19	–	(9–48)	mg/L	2.1	–	(1.0–5.4)	86
Histamine		µmol/L	–	–	(0.06–0.43)	µg/L	–	–	(7–48)	96
↓ Uric acid.........	13 subjects...............	µmol/L	61	34	–	mg/L	10.3	5.7	–	94
	12 subjects, stimulated (a)	µmol/L	43	41	–	mg/L	7.3	6.9	–	94
↓ Porphyrins		...	...	...	...	...	...	...	...	...
↓ Cyclic adenosine monophosphate ..		nmol/L	12.3	–	–	µg/L	4.0	–	–	151
	Stimulated...............	nmol/L	8.5	–	–	µg/L	2.8	–	–	151
Cyclic guanosine monophosphate ..		nmol/L	2.2	–	–	µg/L	0.8	–	–	151
	Stimulated...............	nmol/L	0.6	–	–	µg/L	0.2	–	–	151
↓ Nondialyzable material.......		...	...	...	...	...	...	...	...	...
↓ Protein										
Total protein.....	13 subjects............ (a)	...	...	...	...	g/L	2.8	0.3	–	102
Albumin.........		...	...	...	...	g/L	–	–	(< 0.2)	1
Acid α₁-glyco-protein...........	41 adults................	...	...	...	...	mg/L	1.04	0.8	(0.04–4.1)	103
IgG	65 subjects, stimulated (b)	...	...	...	...	g/L	–	–	(0.10–2.0)	104
IgA	65 subjects, stimulated (b)	...	...	...	...	g/L	–	–	(0.10–2.0)	104
IgM.............	65 subjects, stimulated (b)	...	...	...	...	g/L	–	–	(0–0.35)	104

Calcium. (a) Continuous intravenous infusion of betazole. – See Table 8 for the calcium concentration in unstimulated and stimulated gastric juice. Calcium probably originates mostly from nonparietal secretion (Table 1). The parietal cells secrete the small amounts of calcium that are bound to pepsin. 99% of the calcium in the acid-containing gastric juice is ionized[6].

Magnesium. (a) Continuous intravenous infusion of betazole. – See Table 8 for the magnesium concentration in unstimulated and stimulated gastric juice. Apart from a brief rise following stimulation, the magnesium concentration decreases with increasing flow[80]. Magnesium seems therefore to originate mainly from nonparietal secretion and, like calcium, to be subject to a mobilization effect.

Iron. (a) Maximal stimulation with histamine. – In alkaline gastric juice, iron remains in solution owing to complexation with a glycoprotein[84].

Amino-acid nitrogen. See Table 9 for amino-acid concentrations in gastric juice. Amino-acid secretion is increased in patients with atrophic gastritis or pernicious anemia, and lowered in patients with duodenal ulcers[90].

Ammonia. The stimulation of acid secretion does not significantly affect the ammonia concentration[91]. It amounts to about 18 times the blood level of ammonium. The ammonium concentration is increased in hyperammonemia and in hyperuricemia[92,93].

Urea. (a) Submaximal stimulation with histamine. – For the nonparietal secretion a concentration of 5.3 mmol/L has been calculated – a value which conforms to the serum urea level[95]. Urea is unlikely to be contained in the parietal secretion. The urea concentration in the gastric juice is increased in hyperuricemia[92,93].

Uric acid. (a) Submaximal stimulation with histamine. – The uric acid concentration decreases as the hydrogen ion concentration increases[97].

Porphyrins. Small quantities of porphyrins (protoporphyrin besides traces of coproporphyrin) are detectable in an order of magnitude of 1 nmol/L[98].

Cyclic adenosine monophosphate. Only the nonparietal secretion appears to contain some cyclic adenosine monophosphate[99].

Nondialyzable material. This consists of a soluble and an insoluble fraction; the latter forms part of the gastric mucus. Approximately one-half of the material is protein, and the other half is made up of carbohydrates (Table 10). It is a mixture of various proteins, glycoproteins and mucopolysaccharides[108].

Protein. (a) Determined by the biuret reaction. (b) Values of patients with achlorhydria after stimulation with pentagastrin. The

Table 9   *Amino-acid concentrations in gastric juice[89]*

	Basal secretion of normal acidity (15 subjects)	Basal secretion of high acidity (10 subjects)
	μmol/L	
Alanine	300	210
Arginine	190	210
Aspartic acid...............	130	170
Cystine	75	150
Glutamic acid..............	140	160
Glycine	170	210
Histidine...................	84	130
Isoleucine	53	110
Leucine....................	140	170
Lysine	96	120
Methionine	60	100
Phenylalanine	48	110
Proline	280	220
Serine......................	150	220
Threonine	150	130
Tryptophan	93	69
Tyrosine	55	61
Valine	200	180

IgA value includes IgA and secretory IgA. – In stimulated gastric juice pepsin accounts for the major portion of the protein (Table 11). The parietal secretion contains only small amounts of 'nonpepsin' protein[110], including the 'intrinsic factor' and other proteins binding vitamin B_{12}. For the nonparietal secretion, calculation yields a 'nonpepsin' protein concentration of 4.1 g/L[110]. Plasma proteins pass into gastric juice at a rate of about 2.5 g/d[110]; however, they also enter the stomach with the blood[111]. In an acidic environment they are rapidly broken down to low-molecular peptides. A number of plasma proteins have been identified by immunoelectrophoresis[111]. In various stomach diseases the albumin concentration is increased, while the globulin concentration tends to be reduced[111]. The concentration of α_1-glycoprotein is considerably elevated in stomach cancer[103].

Mucins. This term covers all viscous substances that are secreted by the parietal cells and other mucous cells[108]. Mucins (Table 12) represent a mixture of inadequately characterized mucopolysaccharides and variously sulfated glycoproteins, some of which have the properties of blood group antigens[108,112]. The gastric mucus (mostly sulfated glycoproteins) presumably protects the mucosa against mechanical and proteolytic effects. The secretion of sialic-acid-containing mucins is diminished in ulcer patients[153].

Intrinsic factor (IF). (a) Calculated from values in Table 13 on the premise that 1 mg of IF binds 25 μg of vitamin B_{12}. – IF is a

Table 10   *Composition of total nondialyzable material in gastric juice and gastric mucus*

	Gastric juice		Gastric mucus	
	Basal	Stimulated	Basal	Stimulated
	Mass fraction (as percent)			
Protein..........................	48.9	50.5	38.4	35.1
Total carbohydrates.............	41.7	37.7	52.9	55.7
Hexoses.........................	20.5	19.6	27.5	29.9
Hexosamine	15.0	12.5	19.0	18.8
Sialic acid......................	3.1	3.2	2.6	2.9
Fucose.........................	6.2	5.3	7.5	8.2

Table 11
Protein and pepsin in gastric juice of 10 subjects (means and s)[107]

	Stimulation (dose for 1 kg of body mass)	Volume	Protein		Pepsin *	
		mL/h	g/L	mg/h	g/L	mg/h
Basal	....	93	2.0	187 s 52	0.87	81 s 43
Stimulated	24 μg/h histamine dihydrochloride by continuous intravenous infusion	218	1.8	385 s 75	1.25	273 s 100
	0.15 U insulin intravenous	202	2.3	464 s 86	1.68	339 s 95

* Determined by hydrolysis of hemoglobin at pH 1.7 and 35.5 °C with hog pepsin as standard (1 pepsin unit is equivalent to 63 mg of standard).

Table 12   *Fractions of mucins in gastric juice[105]*

	g/L
Undissolved substances	1.4
Trichloroacetic acid precipitate........................	1.0
Dissolved mucoprotein................................	0.5
Dissolved mucoproteose	1.2

sialic-acid-containing glycoprotein with a carbohydrate content of 12%[114]. IF is contained in the parietal secretion; its concentration increases proportionally to the acid concentration after stimulation[115]. However, the maximal IF secretion begins earlier than the

↑↓See text above and on next page	Fasting values, unstimulated (basal secretion) unless otherwise stated	Amount of substance				Mass				Reference
		Unit	Mean	s	(Extreme range)	Unit	Mean	s	(Extreme range)	
↑ **Mucins**										
Sulfated glycoproteins........	....	...	...	...	...	g/L	0.2	–	–	106
↑ Intrinsic factor .	....	...	...	...	...	mg/L	~ 1	–	–	–
↓ Gastrone........	....	...	...	...	...	...	...	...	...	...
↓ **Enzymes**	....	...	...	...	...	...	...	...	...	...
↓ **Carbohydrates, bound**										
Hexoses........	16 subjects	mmol/L	1.78	–	–	mg/L	321	–	–	140
Hexosamine ...	10 subjects	mmol/L	1.83	–	–	mg/L	327	–	–	140
Sialic acid......	13 subjects	mmol/L	0.24	–	–	mg/L	73	–	–	140
Glucuronic acid	12 subjects	mmol/L	0.10	–	–	mg/L	20	–	–	140
Fucose.........	15 subjects	mmol/L	0.84	–	–	mg/L	138	–	–	140

Table 13 *Intrinsic factor (IF) in gastric juice of children and adults*

Subjects	IF concentration (bound vitamin B_{12})				IF secretion (bound vitamin B_{12})				Stimulation (dose for 1 kg of body mass)	Reference
	Basal		Stimulated		Basal		Stimulated			
	Mean	(Extreme range)	Mean	(Extreme range)	Mean	(Extreme range)	Mean	(Extreme range)		
	µg/L				µg/L					
14 children (1–2 years)........	–	–	–	–	0.95	(0.11–2.00)	2.21	(1.05–3.83)	40 µg acid histamine phosphate subcutaneous	23
21 men...........	28.1	s 25.7 (0–84)	68.8	s 36.2 (25–135)	2.10	s 2.67 (0–9.24)	13.0	s 9.36 (1.20–31.1)	6 µg pentagastrin subcutaneous	113
7 women.........	30.4	s 12.9 (18–56)	79.0	s 19.2 (52–130)	1.14	s 0.50 (0.63–2.04)	10.8	s 3.90 (4.58–15.1)	6 µg pentagastrin subcutaneous	113

maximal acid secretion and lasts less long than the latter[114,116]. The amount of IF secreted in 24 hours is able to bind 50–200 µg of vitamin B_{12}, that is, 10 to 50 times the amount of vitamin B_{12} that is needed for the daily supply of vitamin B_{12}[117]. IF secretion is low in the newborn; however, relative to body mass, it approaches IF secretion in adults at the age of 2–3 months[118]. IF secretion is markedly reduced in atrophy of the gastric mucosa and in the presence of IF antibodies[114,119]. In pernicious anemia, the hourly secretion of IF always corresponds to less than 0.25 µg of bound vitamin B_{12}[114,116].

Gastrone. This glycoprotein, which is probably secreted with the gastric mucus, inhibits the secretion of acid[21].

Enzymes. The protein in the gastric juice consists in large part of enzymes, with proteolytic enzymes predominating. Enzymes detected in gastric juice are indicated in Table 14.

Table 14 *Enzymes in gastric juice*

EC-number	Name of enzyme	Reference
1.1.1.27	Lactate dehydrogenase	133–135
1.1.1.41	Isocitrate dehydrogenase	135
1.2.4.2	Oxoglutarate dehydrogenase	135
2.6.1.1	Aspartate aminotransferase	135
2.6.1.2	Alanine aminotransferase	135
3.1.1.1	Carboxylesterase	130
3.1.1.3	Triacylglycerol lipase	128,129,136
3.1.27.5	Ribonuclease I	135
3.2.1.17	Lysozyme	137
3.2.1.31	β-D-Glucuronidase	131–133,135
3.4.11.1	Aminopeptidase	135
3.4.23.1	Pepsin A	120,121,138,139
3.4.23.3	Pepsin C	120,121,138,139
3.5.1.5	Urease	93
4.1.2.13	Fructose-bisphosphate aldolase	135
5.3.1.9	Glucosephosphate isomerase	135

Table 15 *Basal and stimulated pepsin secretion*[124]

Subjects	Basal		Stimulated	
	Mean	(Extreme range)	Mean	(Extreme range)
	mg/h			
18 children, 9–30 months........	9.0	(1.1–14.8)	12.5	(2.2–26.0)
12 adults..............	33.3	(12.2–68.2)	80.9	(32.4–153)

Stimulation: 40 µg of acid histamine phosphate to 1 kg of body mass. Pepsin assay: Hydrolysis of bovine plasma at pH 1.9 and 37 °C with crystalline pepsin as standard.

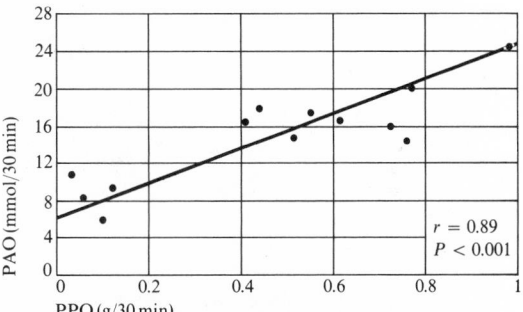

Fig. 6. Correlation between PAO (peak acid output) after stimulation with pentagastrin and PPO (peak pepsin output) after stimulation with insulin in normal subjects[122].

Pepsinogen and pepsin: 5 different pepsinogens occur exclusively in the fundus mucosa; 2 others also occur in the mucosa of the antrum and the proximal duodenum[120]. In the acid environment of the stomach contents the pepsinogens are converted to proteolytic pepsins. As many as 11 different pepsins have been demonstrated in the gastric juice[120]. The nomenclature of the individual pepsinogen is confusing[120,121,139]. According to SAMLOFF[120], the pepsinogens of the fundus mucosa are designated as Pepsinogen Group I, and the two other pepsinogens as Group II. The proteolytic enzyme named gastricsin seems to originate from Pepsinogen Group II[121]. Various methods are available for the determination of *proteolytic activity*. They give different results, depending on the substrate, pH, temperature and standard. *Pepsin secretion* in the gastric juice is closely linked to acid secretion (Fig.6); however, after stimulation pepsin secretion peaks earlier than acid secretion[107,109]. Stimulation by vagal irritation (insulin, 2-deoxy-D-glucose) activates pepsin secretion to a higher degree than does stimulation with histamine or gastrin[107,123]. The normal values of proteolytic activity are shown in Tables 11 and 15. Pepsin secretion in the newborn is low; at the age of 2–3 months it amounts – in relation to body mass – to approximately one-half of that in adults[118]. Pepsin secretion is reduced in atrophy of the gastric mucosa and in the presence of gastric carcinoma[29,125] although the changes in the pepsin pattern as yet defy unequivocal interpretation[126,127].

Nonproteolytic enzymes: The 5 isoenzymes of lactate dehydrogenase that are present in the serum are also found in gastric juice[111]. The lipase of the gastric juice differs in its properties from that of pancreatic juice and is more of a nonspecific esterase[139,140]. A stomach-specific carboxylesterase has been immunologically detected in the gastric juice[130]. The markedly elevated activities of lactate dehydrogenase and β-D-glucuronidase in atrophic gastritis with intestinal metaplasia and in patients with stomach cancer are of diagnostic significance[131,133].

Carbohydrates, bound. The carbohydrates are contained for the most part in the mucin fraction (see preceding page). The hexose is galactose, and the hexosamines are glucosamine and galactosamine[112].

↓See text below	Fasting values, unstimulated (basal secretion) unless otherwise stated	Amount of substance				Mass				Reference
		Unit	Mean	s	(Extreme range)	Unit	Mean	s	(Extreme range)	
↓ **Lactic acid**	17 subjects	μmol/L	311	205	–	mg/L	28.0	18.5	–	94
	14 subjects, stimulated (a)	μmol/L	285	139	–	mg/L	25.7	12.5	–	94
↓ **Pyruvic acid**	17 subjects	μmol/L	75	39	–	mg/L	6.6	3.4	–	94
	15 subjects, stimulated (a)	μmol/L	159	224	–	mg/L	14.0	19.7	–	94
↓ **Citric acid**	20 subjects	μmol/L	255	181	–	mg/L	48.9	34.8	–	94
	17 subjects, stimulated (a)	μmol/L	175	142	–	mg/L	33.6	27.3	–	94
↓ **Lipids**			...	...	...	...	...	...	...	...
↓ **Prostaglandins**										
PGA$_2$	28 samples	nmol/L	0.461	0.37	–	ng/L	154	125	–	100
PGE$_2$	28 samples	nmol/L	1.26	0.73	–	ng/L	444	259	–	100
Vitamin B$_{12}$	40 subjects	nmol/L	–	–	(0.04–2.2)	μg/L	–	–	(0.06–3.0)	143
Ascorbic acid		μmol/L	–	–	(8.5–85)	mg/L	–	–	(1.5–15.0)	13

Lactic acid. (a) Submaximal stimulation with histamine. – In one study, 56% of the values in patients with stomach cancer were above 1.1 mmol/L; this was not the case in a normal subject[141].

Pyruvic acid. (a) Submaximal stimulation with histamine.

Citric acid. (a) Submaximal stimulation with histamine.

Lipids. Gastric juice appears to contain small quantities of lipids[142].

Prostaglandins. Some specimens additionally contain PGF$_2$. The prostaglandin concentration does not change significantly upon stimulation[100].

References

[1] DEMLING, L., in SCHWIEGK, H. (Ed.), *Handbuch der inneren Medizin,* 5th ed., volume 3, part 2, Springer, Berlin, 1974, page 57.
[2] HOLLANDER, F., *Fed. Proc.,* **11**, 706 (1952).
[3] HUNT, J. N., *Physiol. Rev.,* **39**, 491 (1959).
[4] OTTENJANN et al., *Digestion,* **1**, 81 (1968).
[5] MAKHLOUF et al., *Gastroenterology,* **51**, 149 (1966).
[6] HOBSLEY and SILEN, *Clin. Sci.,* **39**, 61 (1970).
[7] GARDHAM and HOBSLEY, *Clin. Sci.,* **39**, 77 (1970).
[8] MOORE and MAKHLOUF, *Gastroenterology,* **55**, 465 (1968).
[9] HOBSLEY, M., *Clin. Sci.,* **47**, 131 (1974).
[10] SOLL and WALSH, *Ann. Rev. Physiol.,* **41**, 35 (1979).
[11] KRZYWANEK and FLASCHENTRÄGER, in FLASCHENTRÄGER and LEHNARTZ (Eds.), *Physiologische Chemie,* volume II/Ia, Springer, Berlin, 1954, page 2.
[12] HINSBERG and BRUNS, in LANG et al. (Eds.), *Hoppe-Seyler/Thierfelder Handbuch der physiologisch- und pathologisch-chemischen Analyse,* 10th ed., volume 5, Springer, Berlin, 1953, page 372.
[13] LEACH, A. A., in LONG et al. (Eds.), *Biochemists' Handbook,* Spon, London, 1961, page 911.
[14] LIEBOWITZ et al., FRAZER et al., in ALTMAN and DITTMER (Eds.), *Metabolism,* Federation of American Societies for Experimental Biology, Bethesda (Md.), 1968, page 247.
[15] KAY, A. W., *Gastroenterology,* **53**, 834 (1967).
[16] SUN et al., *Amer. J. Gastroent.,* **67**, 338 (1977).
[17] BARON, J. H., *Clinical Tests of Gastric Secretion: History, Methodology and Interpretation,* Oxford University Press, New York, 1979.
[18] CLASSEN and DOMSCHKE, in SCHWIEGK, H. (Ed.), *Handbuch der inneren Medizin,* 5th ed., volume 3, part 2, Springer, Berlin, 1974, page 161.
[19] THOMSON, J., *Arch. Dis. Childh.,* **26**, 558 (1951).
[20] WOLMAN, I. J., *Amer. J. Dis. Child.,* **71**, 394 (1946).
[21] DAVENPORT, H. W., *Physiology of the Digestive Tract,* 3rd ed., Year Book Medical Publishers, Chicago, 1971.
[22] MERTZ et al., *Klin. Wschr.,* **46**, 85 (1968).
[23] RØDBRO et al., *Scand. J. Gastroent.,* **2**, 209 (1967).
[24] FIEBER et al., *Z. Kinderheilk.,* **120**, 199 (1975).
[25] SCHMIDT et al., *Dtsch. med. Wschr.,* **95**, 1878 (1970).
[26] OTTENJANN et al., *Dtsch. med. Wschr.,* **93**, 2269 (1968).
[27] FEIFEL et al., *Klin. Wschr.,* **50**, 413 (1972).
[28] DOTEVALL, G., *Acta med. scand.,* **170**, 59 (1961).
[29] HIRSCHOWITZ, B. I., *Amer. J. dig. Dis.,* **6**, 199 (1961).
[30] SCOBIE and SUMMERSKILL, *Gut,* **5**, 422 (1964).
[31] IHRE, B., *Acta med. scand.,* suppl. 95, 1 (1938).
[32] DRAGSTEDT, L. R., *Ann. N. Y. Acad. Sci.,* **99**, 190 (1962).
[33] ZOLLINGER and ELLIOTT, in *Proceedings of the World Congress of Gastroenterology,* volume 1, Williams & Wilkins, Baltimore, 1959, page 419; ZOLLINGER and MOORE, *J. Amer. med. Ass.,* **204**, 361 (1968).
[34] BUCHTA and KAPLAN, *Pediatrics,* **47**, 594 (1971).
[35] LEWIN et al., *Brit. med. J.,* **2**, 139 (1973).
[36] BECKER et al., *Dtsch. med. Wschr.,* **101**, 1800 (1976).
[37] AVERY et al., *Pediatrics,* **37**, 1005 (1966).
[38] DEMLING et al., in DEMLING and BACHMANN (Eds.), *Biotelemetrie,* Thieme, Stuttgart, 1970, page 266; NOELLER, H. G., *Dtsch. med. Wschr.,* **85**, 1707 (1960); OTTENJANN, R., *Med. Klin.,* **58**, 1999 (1963); DEYHLE et al., *Dtsch. med. Wschr.,* **94**, 2274 (1969).
[39] MOORE, E. W., *Gastroenterology,* **54**, 501 (1968).
[40] MOORE, E. W., *Ann. N. Y. Acad. Sci.,* **140**, 866 (1967).
[41] MAKHLOUF et al., *Gastroenterology,* **58**, 345 (1970).
[42] NORDGREN, B., *Acta physiol. scand.,* **58**, suppl. 202, 1 (1963).
[43] CARTER et al., *Brit. med. J.,* **2**, 202 (1972).
[44] STOLL et al., *Helv. paediat. Acta,* **25**, 234 (1970).
[45] STACHER et al., *Gastroenterology,* **68**, 1449 (1975).
[46] CRAWSHAW et al., *Lancet,* **2**, 66 (1968).
[47] BERNER et al., *Z. Gastroent.,* **9**, 256 (1971).
[48] STUTZER and BERGER, *Med. Klin.,* **67**, 48 (1972).
[49] BARON, J. H., *Lancet,* **2**, 547 (1970).
[50] WHITE and JUNIPER, *Amer. J. dig. Dis.,* **18**, 7 (1973).
[51] MOORE and ENGLERT, *Nature,* **226**, 1261 (1970).
[52] MONTES-GALLO and SAARI, *Ann. Paediat. Fenn.,* **6**, 185 (1960).
[53] DESAI et al., *Digestion,* **7**, 227 (1972).
[54] CARD and MARKS, *Clin. Sci.,* **19**, 147 (1960).
[55] MERTZ, D. P., *Med. Klin.,* **64**, 237 (1969).
[56] BARON, J. H., *Gut,* **10**, 637 (1969).
[57] DESAI et al., *Gastroenterology,* **59**, 701 (1970).
[58] MAKHLOUF, G. M., *Gastroenterology,* **55**, 423 (1968).
[59] DESAI et al., *Postgrad. med. J.,* **48**, 83 (1972).
[60] KONTUREK and OLEKSY, *Gastroenterology,* **53**, 912 (1967).
[61] ISENBERG et al., *J. Amer. med. Ass.,* **206**, 2897 (1968).
[62] A multicentre study, *Lancet,* **1**, 341 (1969).
[63] KONZ et al., *Z. Gastroent.,* **9**, 413 (1971).
[64] RUNE, S. J., *Gut,* **7**, 344 (1966).
[65] KOCH, H., *Dtsch. med. Wschr.,* **98**, 938 (1973).
[66] BERNDT, H., in SCHWIEGK, H. (Ed.), *Handbuch der inneren Medizin,* 5th ed., volume 3, part 2, Springer, Berlin, 1974, page 871.
[67] COX, A. J., *Arch. Path.,* **54**, 407 (1952).
[68] PEDERSEN, S. A., *Digestion,* **3**, 81 (1970).
[69] ISENBERG et al., *J. clin. Invest.,* **55**, 330 (1975).
[70] ISENBERG et al., *New Engl. J. Med.,* **285**, 620 (1971).
[71] KAYE et al., *Gastroenterology,* **58**, 476 (1970).
[72] ISENBERG, J. I., *Gastroenterology,* **63**, 701 (1972).
[73] STALDER et al., *Gastroenterology,* **63**, 552 (1972).
[74] KENNEDY, T., *Med. Clin. N. Amer.,* **58**, 1231 (1974).
[75] DEMAND et al., *Gastroenterology,* **72**, 258 (1968).
[76] HOESCH, K., *Dtsch. Arch. klin. Med.,* **165**, 201 (1929).
[77] GOLDEMBERG and SCHRAIBER, *Rev. Soc. argent. Biol.,* **11**, 111 (1935).
[78] CORNBLEET, T., *J. invest. Derm.,* **1**, 399 (1938).
[79] TEICHMANN, W., *Dtsch. Z. Verdau.- u. Stoffwechselkr.,* **13**, 203 (1953).
[80] AAGAARD and CHRISTIANSEN, *Gastroenterology,* **59**, 46 (1970).
[81] KIMURA et al., *Acta haemat. jap.,* **31**, 199 (1968).
[82] RUSSO et al., *Lancet,* **1**, 258 (1969).
[83] WYNTER and WILLIAMS, *Lancet,* **2**, 534 (1968).
[84] RUDZKI and DELLER, *Digestion* **8**, 35 (1973); RUDZKI et al., *Digestion,* **8**, 53 (1973).
[85] GOLLAN et al., *Clin. Biochem.,* **4**, 42 (1971).
[86] JONES and BURNETT, *Clin. Chem.,* **20**, 1204 (1974).
[87] NORPOTH, L., *Klin. Wschr.,* **26**, 406 (1948).
[88] NAGL, F., *Z. klin. Med.,* **151**, 429 (1954).
[89] MÜTING, D., *Naturwissenschaften,* **41**, 580 (1954).
[90] HEATHCOTE and WASHINGTON, *Nature,* **207**, 941 (1965); DUNZENDORFER, U., *Münch. med. Wschr.,* **118**, 1495 (1976).

[91] SUMMERSKILL et al., *Gut,* **7**, 497 (1966).
[92] LIEBER and LEFÈVRE, *J. clin. Invest.,* **38**, 1271 (1959).
[93] RAPPOPORT and KERN, *J. Lab. clin. Med.,* **61**, 550 (1963).
[94] PIPER et al., *Gastroenterology,* **53**, 42 (1967).
[95] KAESS, H., *Klin. Wschr.,* **48**, 1245 (1970).
[96] FAREDIN et al., *Gastroenterologia (Basel),* **79**, 185 (1953).
[97] MERTZ, D. P., *Pflügers Arch. ges. Physiol.,* **316**, 132 (1970).
[98] DOSS and FILIPPINI, *Dtsch. med. Wschr.,* **94**, 2392 (1969).
[99] LEVINE, R. A., *J. clin. Invest.,* **53**, 45a (1974).
[100] PESKAR et al., *Clin. chim. Acta,* **55**, 21 (1974).
[101] KUHN and WEICKER, *Z. klin. Chem.,* **8**, 80 (1970).
[102] BERG, G., *Bibl. gastroent. (Basel),* **5**, 195 (1962).
[103] LUDWIG et al., *Clin. chim. Acta,* **64**, 253 (1975).
[104] MCCLELLAND et al., *Gastroenterology,* **60**, 509 (1971).
[105] KENT, P. W., *Gastroenterology,* **43**, 292 (1962).
[106] LAMBERT and ANDRÉ, *Digestion,* **5**, 116 (1972).
[107] SCHMIDT et al., *Dtsch. med. Wschr.,* **95**, 2011 (1970).
[108] GLASS, G. B., *Advanc. clin. Chem.,* **7**, 235 (1964); GLASS, G. B., *Ann. N. Y. Acad. Sci.,* **140**, 804 (1967).
[109] MAKHLOUF et al., *Gastroenterology,* **52**, 787 (1967).
[110] MAKHLOUF et al., *Gastroenterology,* **55**, 457 (1968).
[111] FAULK et al., *J. Lab. clin. Med.,* **77**, 228 (1971).
[112] SCHRAGER and OATES, *Gut,* **12**, 559 (1971).
[113] KANAGHINIS et al., *Amer. J. dig. Dis.,* **18**, 85 (1973).
[114] GRÄSBECK, R., *Progr. Hemat.,* **6**, 233 (1969).
[115] LAWRIE and ANDERSON, *Lancet,* **1**, 68 (1967).
[116] IRVINE et al., *Lancet,* **2**, 184 (1968).
[117] ALLEN, R. H., *Progr. Hemat.,* **9**, 57 (1975).
[118] AGUNOD et al., *Amer. J. dig. Dis.,* **14**, 400 (1969).
[119] ROSE and CHANARIN, *Brit. med. J.,* **1**, 468 (1969).
[120] SAMLOFF, I. M., *Gastroenterology,* **60**, 586 (1971).
[121] MAGEE, D. F., *Med. Clin. N. Amer.,* **58**, 1277 (1974).
[122] ELDER and SMITH, *Lancet,* **1**, 1000 (1975).
[123] DUKE et al., *Lancet,* **2**, 871 (1965).
[124] RØDBRO et al., *Scand. J. Gastroent.,* **2**, 257 (1967).
[125] TAYLOR, W. H., *Physiol. Rev.,* **42**, 519 (1962).
[126] TAYLOR, W. H., *Nature,* **227**, 76 (1970).
[127] AGUNOD and GLASS, *Amer. J. dig. Dis.,* **17**, 814 (1972).
[128] COHEN et al., *Gastroenterology,* **60**, 1 (1971).
[129] SZAFRAN et al., *Gastroenterology,* **64**, 140 (1973).
[130] RAPP, W., *Clin. chim. Acta,* **36**, 5 (1972).
[131] PIPER et al., *Gastroenterology,* **51**, 172 (1966).
[132] RUSSELL et al., *Gastroenterology,* **58**, 352 (1970).
[133] SIMON and FIGUS, *Digestion,* **7**, 174 (1972).
[134] SMYRNIOTIS et al., *Amer. J. dig. Dis.,* **7**, 712 (1962).
[135] PIPER et al., *Gastroenterology,* **45**, 614 (1963); *Amer. J. dig. Dis.,* **8**, 701 (1963).
[136] SCHØNHEYDER and VOLQVARTZ, *Acta physiol. scand.,* **11**, 349 (1946); BANK et al., *Gut,* **5**, 480 (1964).
[137] LOBSTEIN and FOGELSON, *Amer. J. dig. Dis.,* **18**, 282 (1951).
[138] TANG and WOLF, *Gastroenterology,* **44**, 908 (1963).
[139] BUCHS, S., *Dtsch. med. Wschr.,* **96**, 511 (1971).
[140] RICHMOND et al., *Gastroenterology,* **29**, 1017 (1955).
[141] PIPER et al., *Gastroenterology,* **58**, 766 (1970).
[142] HOROWITZ, M. I., *Ann. N. Y. Acad. Sci.,* **106**, 278 (1963).
[143] PENDL and FRANZ, *Acta haemat. (Basel),* **13**, 207 (1955).
[144] ORR et al., *Arch. intern. Med.,* **136**, 655 (1976).
[145] ESTLER, C. J., *Med. Welt (Stuttg.),* **25**, 487 (1974); PHILLIP and CLASSEN, *Med. Welt (Stuttg.),* **25**, 495 (1974); IVEY, K. J., *Amer. J. Med.,* **58**, 389 (1975).
[146] DOUSA and DOZOIS, *Gastroenterology,* **73**, 904 (1977).
[147] BLACK et al., *Nature,* **236**, 385 (1972); BLACK, J. W., *Klin. Wschr.,* **54**, 911 (1976).
[148] FELDMAN and RICHARDSON, *Advanc. intern. Med.,* **23**, 1 (1978).
[149] DUBOIS et al., *J. clin. Invest.,* **59**, 255 (1977).
[150] RUDDELL et al., *Lancet,* **2**, 1037 (1976).
[151] SCHWARTZEL et al., *Analyt. Biochem.,* **78**, 395 (1977).
[152] SCHMIDT et al., *Klin. Wschr.,* **50**, 744 (1972).
[153] DOMSCHKE et al., *Med. Welt (Stuttg.),* **25**, 493 (1974).

The pancreatic juice probably arises from two different types of cells: one type, presumably the epithelial cells of the ducts, secretes a very watery juice rich in bicarbonate, whereas the other type, the epithelial cells of the acini, produces a viscous secretion rich in enzymes and proenzymes. The secretion of pancreatic juice is mediated by hormonal and nervous factors[1]: various stimuli, notably acid in the duodenum, activate the release of secretin, whereas peptones and amino acids in the duodenum activate the release of pancreozymin (identical with cholecystokinin). Secretin stimulates above all the secretion of water and bicarbonate, while the neurotransmitter acetylcholine and pancreozymin are the physiological stimulants of enzyme secretion from the acini. The secretagogues of enzyme secretion act by involving calcium ions as intracellular messenger and probably cyclic GMP as modulator[7,8].

There is a physiologic feedback mechanism[71] linking the secretion of secretin and bicarbonate: secretin stimulates the secretion of bicarbonate in the duodenum; bicarbonate neutralizes gastric acid, whereby the elevated duodenal pH brings the secretin production to a standstill. The acid-mediated secretin release appears to be impaired in patients suffering from duodenal ulcers[72].

The composition of pancreatic juice is mainly known from the analysis of juices secured by fistulization, or from the study of duodenal content collected with a two-way tube that simultaneously serves to siphon off gastric juice. More recently, techniques were developed [2-5] to collect pure pancreatic juice by endoscopic retrograde cannulation of the main pancreatic duct.

In terms of its ionic composition, the nonstimulated pancreatic juice is similar to plasma[1]. The sum of the bicarbonate and chloride concentrations is constant, at some 154 mmol/kg water[6]. With incipient secretin-mediated stimulation bicarbonate concentration increases with a corresponding decrease of chloride concentration, whereas sodium and potassium levels remain essentially unchanged[6]. Some 95% of the bicarbonate is apparently derived from plasma. CO_2 penetrates the pancreatic cells where it reacts with carbonate dehydratase to form bicarbonate, which is secreted along with water into the lumen of the pancreas, while an equivalent quantity of hydrogen ions simultaneously enters the plasma[7,8]. The digestive proenzymes are synthesized on polysomes bound to the endoplasmatic reticulum, whereas nonexportable proteins are synthesized on polysomes free in the cell sap[7]. In the Golgi complex concentration of exportable proteins occurs resulting in the formation of zymogen granules. Then these granules move to the cell apex where fusion and fission of limiting membranes occur. The storage products are finally extruded into the ductal lumen.

Pancreas tests. To test the excretory function, the pancreatic juice is analyzed after stimulation with secretin and/or pancreozy-

min intravenously, in a single injection or by slow infusion[9]. Cerulein may also be used in lieu of pancreozymin[10,11]. The preferred practice in the United States is to inject pancreozymin ahead of secretin; in Europe, the reverse sequence is more common.

The published normal values are difficult to compare, being conditioned by such factors as the origin of the hormone preparations, which vary in purity and activity[12,13], the dosage (ordinarily limited to submaximal stimulation[14]), and the sampling technique (different collection periods and allowance for losses[15-17]). Maximal stimulation is reportedly achieved by continuous infusions of hormonal preparations[13,14], but according to other authors peak secretory output depends on simultaneous parenteral and enteral stimulation with intraduodenal infusions of bovine bile[18] or amino acids[19]. A simpler technique for the determination of enzyme secretion involves stimulation by a test meal (the Lundh test)[20-22]. In calculating the normal range, allowance should be made for the logarithmic distribution of values[13,18,23].

For further data on the composition of pancreatic juice, see the literature[24-26].

Appearance

Thin, colorless watery fluid, clear to slightly opalescent, similar in appearance to saliva.

Volume

Under basal conditions, secretion, if detectable at all[4], is very limited[1] (see Table 1). As a rule, a copious flow of pancreatic juice sets in within minutes after the ingestion of a meal, and continues for perhaps three hours. With a normal eating and sleeping rhythm, the daily output of pancreatic juice has been estimated at

Table 1   *Flow (volume rate) of pancreatic juice*

	Number	Mean	s	(Extreme range)	Reference
			mL/min		
Basal	–	–	–	(<0.1)	27
Under maximal intravenous stimulation with secretin + pancreozymin..............	–	–	–	(4–14)	13
Under intravenous secretin stimulation (measured within the duct)	14	8.02	3.46	–	5

Table 2   *Flow and bicarbonate secretion after intravenous stimulation*

Subjects	Flow rate				Bicarbonate secretion				Stimulant (dose per kg of body mass if not otherwise stated) and collection period	Reference
	Units	Mean	s	Lower limit of norm	Units	Mean	s	Lower limit of norm		
47 adults without pancreatic disease	–	–	–	–	mmol/L	76	7	54	2 U secretin Vitrum; 60 min collection	30
	mL/h	176	69	98	mmol/h	13.5	6.8	6.2		
– values related to body mass	mL h⁻¹ kg⁻¹	2.68	0.82	1.80	mmol h⁻¹ kg⁻¹	0.20	0.067	0.11		
41 men without gastro-intestinal disease	–	–	–	–	mmol/L	110*	11.8*	–	1 U secretin Lilly; 80 min collection	31
	mL/h	173	60	–	mmol/h	15.5	6.19	–		
– values related to body mass	mL h⁻¹ kg⁻¹	2.67	0.92	–	mmol h⁻¹ kg⁻¹	0.24	0.09	–		
62 women without gastro-intestinal disease	–	–	–	–	mmol/L	107*	10*	–	1 U secretin Lilly; 80 min collection	31
	mL/h	159	42	–	mmol/h	13.7	8.4	–		
– values related to body mass	mL h⁻¹ kg⁻¹	2.9	0.8	–	mmol h⁻¹ kg⁻¹	0.25	0.17	–		
20 adults without gastro-intestinal disease	–	–	–	–	mmol/L	91*	13*	65*	75 U (total amount) pan-creozymin Vitrum; 10 min later, 1 U secretin Vitrum; 60 min collection	32
	mL/h	181	57	70	mmol/h	13.9	5.0	4		
– values related to body mass	mL h⁻¹ kg⁻¹	2.9	0.9	1.1	mmol h⁻¹ kg⁻¹	0.22	0.08	0.06		
27 children (6 weeks to 13 years)	mL h⁻¹ kg⁻¹	4.7	1.8		mmol h⁻¹ kg⁻¹	0.23	0.10	–	2 U pancreozymin Boots; 20 min later, 2 U secretin Boots; 50 min collection	29
– values related to body mass										

U: units.   * Peak levels in 10-minute collection period.

700–2500 mL[27] or 17–20 mL for 1 kg of body mass[25]. As much as 3300 mL of juice in 1 day was measured in fistulized subjects[27]. Tables 1 and 2 show the flow after stimulation with secretin or pancreozymin + secretin. Under these conditions, the flow in the newborn is quite low[28], but within the first months of life it matches the flow in adults, when related to the body mass[28, 29]. In children, the volume rate per unit of body mass is not age-related[29].

↓See text on next page	Duodenal content in adults unless otherwise stated	SI unit	Mean	s	(Extreme range)	Other units	Mean	s	(Extreme range)	Reference
Physico-chemical data										
Secretory pressure ...	Basal, intraductal	kPa	2.18	0.72	(0.94–3.63)	mmH₂O	222	73	(96–370)	74
	Stimulated, intraductal	kPa	3.82	1.07	–	mmH₂O	390	109	–	33
Relative density	....	...	–	–	(1.008–1.011)	...	...	...	...	34–36
Dynamic viscosity ...	Stimulated, intraductal, 20 subjects	mPa s	1.0	–	–	cP	1.0	–	–	75
Freezing-point depression	....	K	–	–	(0.55–0.63)	°C	–	–	(0.55–0.63)	35, 36
Osmolality..........	....	mmol/kg	–	–	(300–340)	mosm/kg	–	–	(300–340)	35, 36
	Maximum stimulation	mmol/kg	–	–	(300–315)	mosm/kg	–	–	(300–315)	14
↓pH.................	Basal ....(a)	...	...	...	...	...	–	–	(7.0–7.7)	–
	Stimulated, 15 subjects	...	...	...	...	...	7.7	0.31	–	37
	Fistular juice	...	...	...	...	...	–	–	(7.5–8.8)	38, 39

		Amount of substance				Mass				
		Unit	Mean	s	(Extreme range)	Unit	Mean	s	(Extreme range)	
Water..............	Fistular juice	mol/L	54.8	–	–	g/L	987	–	–	34
↓Dry mass..........	Fistular juice	...	...	...	...	g/L	13.0	–	(7.5–15.7)	40
Inorganic substances										
↓Bicarbonate	Basal	mmol/L	–	–	(10–45)	...	...	...	...	14
	Maximum stimulation, 30 subjects	mmol/L	85	11	–	...	...	...	...	13
	Stimulated, intraductal, 12 subjects	mmol/L	84.5	10.7	–	...	...	...	...	5
↓Chloride	Basal	mmol/L	–	–	(75–135)	g/L	–	–	(2.66–4.79)	14
	Maximum stimulation, 30 subjects	mmol/L	56	11	–	g/L	2.0	0.4	–	13
	Stimulated, intraductal, 12 subjects	mmol/L	50.8	8.7	–	g/L	1.80	0.31	–	5
Phosphate (as P)	In terms of water................	mmol/kg	0.8	0.4	–	mg/kg	25	12.5	–	6
↓Potassium	Basal, 38 subjects	mmol/L	7.6	1.7	–	mg/L	300	66	–	41
	Fistular juice	mmol/L	–	–	(4.1–5.5)	mg/L	–	–	(160–215)	39
↓Sodium	Basal, 38 subjects	mmol/L	125	14	–	g/L	2.87	0.32	–	41
	Fistular juice, 3 subjects	mmol/L	138	–	–	g/L	3.17	–	–	38
↓Magnesium	Basal, 27 subjects	mmol/L	0.33	0.69	–	mg/L	8	17	–	23
↓Calcium	Basal, 27 subjects	mmol/L	0.60	0.80	–	mg/L	24	32	–	23
	Fistular juice, 3 subjects	mmol/L	–	–	(1.1–1.6)	mg/L	–	–	(44–64)	38
Copper..............	Fistular juice	–	trace	–	–	–	trace	–	–	24
↓Zinc	Basal	µmol/L	18.5	–	(0–35.5)	mg/L	1.21	–	(0–2.32)	43
Organic substances										
Total nitrogen	Fistular juice	mmol/L	–	–	(54–70)	g/L	–	–	(0.76–0.98)	24
Non-protein nitrogen	Fistular juice, 3 subjects	mmol/L	10	–	–	g/L	0.14	–	–	38
Urea..............	Fistular juice, 3 subjects	mmol/L	1.78	–	–	mg/L	107	–	–	38
Creatinine	Fistular juice	–	trace	–	–	–	trace	–	–	39
Uric acid...........	Fistular juice, 3 subjects	µmol/L	12	–	–	mg/L	2	–	–	38

↓See text below	Duodenal content in adults unless otherwise stated	SI unit	Mean	s	(Extreme range)	Other units	Mean	s	(Extreme range)	Reference
↓ Cyclic adenosine monophosphate	1 intraductal sample	nmol/L	1.75	–	–	µg/L	0.6	–	–	73
Cyclic guanosine monophosphate	1 intraductal sample	nmol/L	1.15	–	–	µg/L	0.4	–	–	73
↓ Protein	Basal, 10 children................	...	...	...	...	g/L	6.6	–	(2.6–13.0)	44
	Basal, 3 subjects	...	...	...	...	g/L	–	–	(4.8–5.3)	45
	Fistular juice, 3 subjects	...	...	...	...	g/L	–	–	(1.9–3.4)	38
	Maximal stimulated, intraductal 9 subjects......................	...	...	...	...	g/L	7.8	2.7	–	77
↓ Enzymes	....	...	...	...	...	...	...	...	...	...
Reducing substances (as glucose)	Fistular juice, 1 subject	mmol/L	–	–	(0.47–1.0)	mg/L	–	–	(85–180)	39
Lipids..............	Fistular juice	...	...	...	...	mg/L	5.2	–	–	25

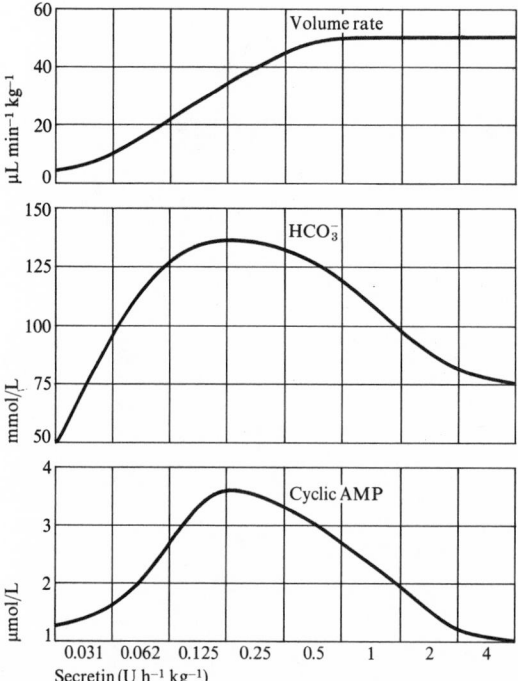

Fig. 1. Effect of secretin dosage (intravenous infusion, 7 subjects) on flow, bicarbonate concentration, and cyclic AMP in pancreatic juice[70].

pH. (a) Calculated from basal bicarbonate concentration, assuming a CO_2 pressure in pancreatic juice of 5.3 kPa[1]. The pH is a function of the bicarbonate concentration and will therefore rise under stimulation.

Dry mass. Some 50–60% are inorganic substances.

Bicarbonate. With increasing secretion rate, the bicarbonate concentration rises to a maximum of some 140 mmol/L[2,6,14] (Fig. 1). At a high flow, the concentration of bicarbonate declines[13,14] (Fig. 2). Maximal bicarbonate secretion is in the order of 0.9–1.2 mmol/min[2,14]. Table 2 recapitulates the results of secretin and secretin/pancreozymin tests. For an evaluation of the results, see Table 5.

Chloride. At increasing flow, the chloride concentration changes inversely to the bicarbonate concentration[6] (Fig. 2).

Potassium and sodium. No significant concentration changes under stimulation[2,41].

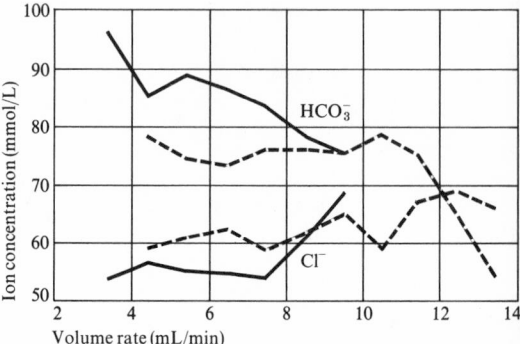

Fig. 2. Bicarbonate and chloride concentration in relation to flow under secretin stimulation (solid lines) and under secretin + pancreozymin (broken lines)[13].

Magnesium. After secretin stimulation, the magnesium concentration is somewhat lower[23,41,42].

Calcium. After secretin stimulation, the calcium concentration is depressed (approximately 0.25–0.5 mmol/L)[23,41,42,69]. After pancreozymin or acetylcholine stimulation, the concentration of calcium rises in parallel with the enzyme protein concentration (1 molecule of amylase contains 1 calcium atom)[69].

Zinc. Zinc is a constituent of carboxypeptidase A. The concentration declines under secretin stimulation[43].

Cyclic adenosine monophosphate. Under stimulation, the concentration changes parallel the bicarbonate concentration (see Fig. 1).

Protein. The bulk of pancreatic-juice proteins are enzymes and their precursors; the balance are mucoproteins and plasma proteins. As many as 20 fractions can be demonstrated by electrophoresis and immunologic tests[46–49]. The following plasma proteins have been identified, the numbers in brackets denoting the relative composition of total protein[50]: albumin (1.3%), IgG (0.23%), IgA (0.18%); in many specimens IgM and IgD[51] were present along with acid α_1-glycoprotein and traces of transferrin[44] and lactoferrin[76]. For protein secretion after stimulation with secretin and pancreozymin, see Table 3.

Enzymes. Pancreatic juice contains amylase, lipase and two ribonucleases as well as the following enzyme precursors: two procarboxypeptidases A, proelastase, two trypsinogens and several chymotrypsinogens[48,49]. Proteolytic enzymes are released from the precursors in the small intestine only, under the influence of enterokinase[53]. In addition, pancreatic juice contains a trypsin inhibitor[54] and very low activities of disaccharidases (maltase, saccharase, cellobiase, lactase)[55]. In nonstimulated pancreatic juice, enzyme activity varies within such broad limits as to be of no

Table 3   *Pancreatic excretion of protein after intravenous stimulation*

Substance	Method or substrate	Subjects	Units	Mean	Extreme range or lower limit of norm	Stimulant (dose per kg of body mass if not otherwise stated) and collection period	Reference
Protein	FOLIN	26 men without pancreatic disease	g/h	2.56	(1.23–4.98) 1.50	1.5 U/h secretin Vitrum + 1.5 U pancreozymin Vitrum; 30 min later, 4.5 U pancreozymin; 15 min collection	52
Protein	LOWRY	10 children (9 months to 13 years) – values related to body mass	mg/h mg h⁻¹ kg⁻¹	– –	(170–496) (10.1–35.6)	2 U pancreozymin Boots; 20 min later, 2 U secretin Boots; 50 min collection	44
Trypsin	p-Toluene-sulfo-nyl-L-arginine methyl ester	20 adults without gastro-intestinal disease – values related to body mass	mg/L mg/h mg h⁻¹ kg⁻¹	422* 40.1 0.65	210* 22 0.34	75 U (total amount) pancreozymin Vitrum; 10 min later, 1 U secretin Vitrum; 70 min collection	32
Trypsin	N-Benzoyl-L-arginine ethyl ester	25 children (6 weeks to 13 years) – values related to body mass	mg h⁻¹ kg⁻¹	0.95	(0.26–2.6)	2 U pancreozymin Boots; 20 min later, 2 U secretin Boots; 50 min collection	29
Chymotrypsin	L-Tyrosine ethyl ester	26 children (6 weeks to 13 years) – values related to body mass	mg h⁻¹ kg⁻¹	1.03	(0.3–2.28)	2 U pancreozymin Boots; 20 min later, 2 U secretin Boots; 50 min collection	29

U: units.   * Peak levels during 10-minute collection period.

Table 4   *Pancreatic enzyme secretion in 25 adults[59]*

Enzyme	Substrate	Mean	95% range
		U/min (25 °C)	
Chymotrypsin	L-Tyrosine ethyl ester	34	13.8–86
	N-Benzoyl-L-tyrosine ethyl ester	66	28.4–154
Trypsin	Nα-Benzoyl-L-arginine-ethyl ester	31	16.3–61
	p-Toluene-sulfonyl-L-arginine methyl ester	136	55.5–335
Carboxypeptidase A	N-Carbo-β-naphthoxy-L-phenylalanine	0.21	0.077–0.57
	Hippuryl-L-phenylala-nine	8.5	4.9–14.9
Carboxypeptidase B	Hippuryl-L-arginine	61	23.9–157
α-Amylase	Starch	850	400–1780
Lipase	Olive oil, triolein	1650	780–3500

Stimulation with 1 U pancreozymin (Gastrointestinal Hormone Laboratory) per kg of body mass.

diagnostic use. Under stimulation, the activity range is more circumscribed (see also Tables 3 and 4 for normal values). Enzymes may be detected in pancreatic juice right from birth[28]. For trypsin and chymotrypsin secretion in small children, see NIESSEN et al.[56].

Diagnostic value of pancreatic function tests

For purposes of diagnosing a pancreatic disease, the determination of excretory pancreatic function surpasses the determination of serum lipase, serum or urinary amylase, and stool tests[60–63], but it is technically more cumbersome. A number of authors prefer to interpret maximal bicarbonate concentration[37,64,65]; others judge the secretion rate of bicarbonate[66] and yet others still relying on enzyme secretion (notably trypsin)[18,20,37,59]. Table 5 summarizes the findings in the most important diseases of the pancreas. In addition, there have been reports of isolated enzyme defects (trypsinogen[53], lipase[67]).

Enzyme secretions can also be measured by the radio-selenium test, based on the uptake of radioactive ⁷⁵Se-selenium methionine by the pancreatic enzyme proteins after intravenous injection[57,58].

References

[1] DAVENPORT, H. W., *Physiology of the Digestive Tract,* 3rd ed., Year Book Medical Publishers, Chicago, 1971.

[2] COTTON et al., *Gastroenterology, 66,* 678 (1974), and *Gut, 15,* 838 (1974).

[3] HATFIELD et al., *Gut, 15,* 305 (1974).

[4] GREGG et al., *Gastroenterology, 68,* 904 (1975).

[5] KAWANISHI et al., *Gastroenterology, 68,* 1033 (1975).

[6] JANOWITZ and DREILING, in DE REUCK and CAMERON (Eds.), *The Endocrine Pancreas,* Ciba Foundation Symposium, Churchill, London, 1962, page 115.

[7] WEBSTER et al., *Gastroenterology, 73,* 1434 (1977).

[8] SCRATCHERD and CASE, *Gut, 14,* 592 (1973).

[9] SUN, D. C., *Progr. clin. Path., 3,* 337 (1970).

[10] ROBBERECHT et al., *Gastroenterology, 69,* 374 (1975).

[11] RIBET and VAYSSE, *Amer. J. dig. Dis., 20,* 1097 (1975); GULLO et al., *Digestion, 14,* 97 (1976).

[12] STENING et al., *Gastroenterology, 55,* 687 (1968).

[13] VAYSSE et al., *Amer. J. dig. Dis., 19,* 887 (1974).

[14] WORMSLEY, K. G., *Gastroenterology, 54,* 197 (1968).

[15] LAGERLÖF et al., *Gastroenterology, 52,* 67 (1967).

[16] TYMPNER et al., *Scand. J. Gastroent., 9,* 377 (1974).

[17] TYMPNER et al., *Dtsch. med. Wschr., 99,* 1611 (1974).

[18] OTTE et al., *Klin. Wschr., 51,* 915 (1973).

[19] GO et al., *Gastroenterology, 58,* 321 (1970).

[20] LUNDH, G., *Gastroenterology, 42,* 275 (1962); BERGSTRÖM and LUNDH, *Scand. J. Gastroent., 5,* 533 (1970).

[21] JAMES, O., *Gut, 14,* 582 (1973).

[22] MOTTALEB et al., *Gut, 14,* 835 (1973).

[23] BALTZER et al., *Klin. Wschr., 52,* 74 (1974).

[24] KRZYWANEK and FLASCHENTRÄGER, in FLASCHENTRÄGER and LEHNARTZ (Eds.), *Physiologische Chemie,* volume II/1a, Springer Berlin, 1954, page 155.

[25] LEACH, A. A., in LONG et al. (Eds.), *Biochemists' Handbook,* Spon, London 1961, page 914; HINSBERG and BRUNS, in LANG et al. (Eds.), *Hoppe-Seyler/ Thierfelder Handbuch der physiologisch- und pathologisch-chemischen Analyse,* 10th ed., volume 5, Springer, Berlin, 1953, page 389.

[26] LIEBOWITZ and ELLIS as well as FRAZER et al., in ALTMAN and DITTMER (Eds.), *Metabolism,* Federation of American Societies for Experimental Biology, Bethesda (Md.), 1968, page 259.

[27] ELMSLIE et al., *Ann. Surg., 160,* 937 (1964).

[28] ZOPPI et al., *Pediat. Res., 6,* 880 (1972).

[29] HADORN et al., *J. Pediat., 73,* 39 (1968).

[30] HARTLEY et al., *Amer. J. dig. Dis., 11,* 27 (1966).

[31] ROSENBERG et al., *Gastroenterology, 50,* 191 (1966).

[32] CHOI et al., *Gastroenterology, 53,* 397 (1967).

[33] GREGG and SHARMA, *Gastroenterology, 68,* 906 (1975).

[34] GLAESSNER, K., *Hoppe-Seylers Z. physiol. Chem., 40,* 465 (1903/04).

[35] LUCKHARDT et al., *Amer. J. Physiol., 63,* 397 (1923).

[36] MANGEOT et al., *Ann. Méd., 54,* 604 (1953).

[37] GYR et al., *Amer. J. dig. Dis., 20,* 506 (1975).

[38] MILLER and WIPER, *Ann. Surg., 120,* 852 (1944).

[39] KOGUT et al., *J. clin. Invest., 15,* 393 (1936).

[40] VERSCHURE, J. C., *Clin. chim. Acta, 4,* 38 (1959).

[41] GOEBELL et al., *Klin. Wschr., 48,* 1330 (1970).

[42] NIMMO et al., *Gut, 11,* 163 (1970).

Table 5   *Results of the secretin–pancreozymin test in diseases of the pancreas*[59]

	Volume of secretion	Bicarbonate concentration	Bicarbonate secretion	Enzyme secretion	Additional findings
Chronic recurrent pancreatitis	Normal or ↓	Usually ↓	Usually ↓	Sometimes irregularly (initial stages?), sometimes uniformly ↓	Lipase, amylase in blood
Chronic calcifying pancreatitis	↓	Strongly ↓, usually ∼ plasma	Strongly ↓	Extremely and uniformly ↓ ($^1/_{10}$–$^1/_{100}$ of the lower limit of normal)	X-ray findings
Pseudocyst following acute pancreatitis	Normal or ↓ (depending on where the cyst is located)	Usually ↓	Usually ↓	Sometimes irregularly, sometimes uniformly ↓	X-ray findings
Stenosing papillitis, mobile papillary calculus	↓	↓	↓	Sometimes irregularly, sometimes uniformly ↓	Frequently pain in response to secretin and pancreozymin
Carcinoma of the pancreas....	Normal or ↓ (depending on the extent to which the duct is constricted)	Usually normal, sometimes ↓	Usually ↓	Usually uniformly ↓	Lipase, amylase in blood
Status post partial resection of the pancreas	Usually ↓	Usually normal	Usually ↓	Depends on the type of resection	–
Status post cholecystectomy ...	Usually normal	Usually normal	Usually normal	Usually normal	–
Hemochromatosis	↑	Usually normal	↑	In upper range of normal	Iron in serum
Primary hyperparathyroidism .	Usually normal	Usually normal	Usually normal	Sometimes irregularly, sometimes uniformly ↓	Calcium and phosphate metabolism
Cystic fibrosis[29, 68]	↓	Strongly ↓	Strongly ↓	Sometimes normal, sometimes irregularly or uniformly ↓	Sweat findings

[43] SULLIVAN et al., *Gastroenterology*, **48**, 438 (1965).
[44] ZOPPI et al., *Helv. paediat. Acta*, **23**, 577 (1968).
[45] BARTELHEIMER et al., *Klin. Wschr.*, **33**, 160 (1955).
[46] SILBERBERG and HADORN, *Biochim. biophys. Acta(Amst.)*, **167**, 616 (1968).
[47] KNAUFF and ADAMS, *Clin. chim. Acta.*, **19**, 19 (1968).
[48] CLEMENTE et al., *Europ. J. Biochem.*, **31**, 186 (1972).
[49] ALLAN and WHITE, *Biochem. Med.*, **12**, 166 (1975).
[50] CLEMENTE et al., *Clin. chim. Acta*, **33**, 317 (1971).
[51] BRASHER et al., *Amer. J. dig. Dis.*, **20**, 454 (1975).
[52] HANSCOM et al., *Ann. intern. Med.*, **66**, 721 (1967).
[53] HADORN, B., *Med. Clin. N. Amer.*, **58**, 1319 (1974).
[54] KELLER and ALLAN, *J. biol. Chem.*, **242**, 281 (1967).
[55] BÖHMER and ROMMEL, *Klin. Wschr.*, **48**, 1226 (1970).
[56] NIESSEN et al., *Klin. Wschr.*, **52**, 796 (1974).
[57] YOUNGS et al., *Quart. J. Med.*, **42**, 597 (1973).
[58] SHICHIRI et al., *Amer. J. dig. Dis.*, **20**, 460 (1975).
[59] RICK, W., *Internist (Berl.)*, **11**, 110 (1970).
[60] CHEY et al., *J. Amer. med. Ass.*, **201**, 347 (1967).
[61] HANSCOM, D. H., *Med. Clin. N. Amer.*, **52**, 1483 (1968).

[62] BROOKS, F. P., *New Engl. J. Med.*, **286**, 300 (1972).
[63] SCHMIDT and LANKISCH, *Med. Klin.*, **70**, 1227 (1975).
[64] DREILING and JANOWITZ, in DE REUCK and CAMERON (Eds.), *The Exocrine Pancreas*, Ciba Foundation Symposium, Churchill, London, 1962, page 225.
[65] DREILING et al., *Pancreatic Inflammatory Disease*, Harper, New York, 1964.
[66] PASCAL et al., *Amer. J. dig. Dis.*, **13**, 213 (1968).
[67] BALZER, E., *Z. Gastroent.*, **5**, 239 (1967).
[68] HADORN et al., *Canad. med. Ass. J.*, **98**, 377 (1968).
[69] GOEBELL, H., *Acta hepato-gastroenterol. (Stuttg.)*, **23**, 151 (1976).
[70] DOMSCHKE et al., *Gastroenterology*, **70**, 533 (1976).
[71] RAYFORD et al., *New. Engl. J. Med.*, **294**, 1093 (1976).
[72] BLOOM and WARD, *Brit. med. J.*, **1**, 126 (1975).
[73] SCHWARTZEL et al., *Analyt. Biochem.*, **78**, 395 (1977).
[74] WEISS et al., *Med. Klin.*, **72**, 519 (1977).
[75] TYMPNER and RÖSCH, *Klin. Wschr.*, **56**, 421 (1978).
[76] FIGARELLA et al., *Lancet*, **1**, 1105 (1978).
[77] SAHEL and SARLES, *Dig. Dis.*, **24**, 897 (1979).
[78] SCHULZ and STOLZE, *Ann. Rev. Physiol.*, **42**, 127 (1980).

Lipid particles consisting of linoleyllecithin, cholesterol and the sodium salts of the bile acids are formed[1-4] in the microsomes of the hepatocytes. These particles are probably transported into the biliary canaliculi by means of a carrier protein and are accompanied, owing to osmotic filtration, by electrolytes and water (about 14 mL of water to 1 mmol of bile acid)[4]. In addition to this bile flow due to bile acids, there is a flow independent of bile acids which may be related to an active transport of inorganic ions[2,4].

The composition of the primary bile is modified in the bile ducts, in which both secretion (stimulated by secretin) and absorption take place[4]. Water and electrolytes are absorbed in the gallbladder[5,6] so that a concentrated solution, mostly of the sodium salt of the bile acid, is produced[5,6] (Fig. 1). However, the gallbladder wall is also permeable to lipids and secretes mucopolysaccharides besides; for this reason the composition of the gallbladder bile differs considerably from that of the hepatic bile[5,6]. In adults the gallbladder capacity ranges from 14 mL to 60 mL[22]. Determination of the gallbladder volume in the fasting state by ultrasonography gave values of 4–24 mL in nonpregnant women and 15–36 mL in late pregnancy[14].

The outflow of bile from the gallbladder into the small intestine is made possible by the action of cholecystokinin, which is released from the intestinal wall upon the appearance of fat or amino acids in the small bowel[6].

Pure hepatic bile can be collected via a biliary fistula, and pure gallbladder bile by puncture. Duodenal drainage in a fasting individual yields a yellow to light-brown fluid (Fraction A) composed of hepatic bile, pancreatic and duodenal secretions. After injection of magnesium sulfate or sorbitol solution through the duodenal tube, or after intravenous administration of cholecystokinin, a viscous, dark-brown fluid (Fraction B) is aspirated which consists of gallbladder bile mixed with duodenal contents. Fluid collected hereafter (Fraction C) closely resembles Fraction A.

Reference may be made to the summary presentations on the composition of the bile[7,8,17].

Appearance

Hepatic bile: golden-yellow, orange-yellow.
Gallbladder bile: brownish-black, brownish-green.

Volume

Volume rates of hepatic bile are given in Tables 1 and 2. The daily production of bile amounts to approximately 600 mL[4]; this is consistent with values obtained in 100 patients by means of T-tube drainage (extreme value 1600 mL). The output of bile is lower during the night than during the day; it is increased after meals[7,12,13].

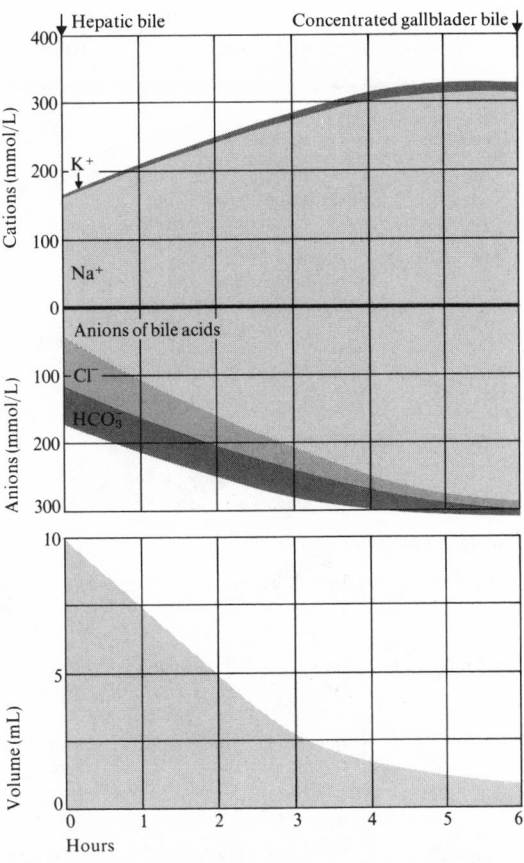

Fig. 1. Changes in volume and ion concentration due to reabsorption of water, chloride and bicarbonate during concentration of hepatic bile in the rabbit gallbladder[9].

Table 1 *Basal flow of hepatic bile in adults*

	Number	Mean	s	(Extreme range)	Reference
		mL/min			
Total flow..................	10	0.36	0.05	(0.27–0.43)	10
Bile acid-dependent flow...	5	0.21	–	–	11
Bile acid-independent flow.	5	0.20	–	–	11

Table 2 *Flow and composition of hepatic bile[10]*

	Volume rate		Bicarbonate		Taurocholate	
	Mean	s	Mean	s	Mean	s
	mL/min		mmol/L			
Basal values	0.35	0.058	25.5	9.8	26.8	12.7
Peak values after administration of secretin	1.19	0.77	46.3	18.0	8.5	3.4

	Material	SI unit	Mean	s	(Extreme range)	Other units	Mean	s	(Extreme range)	Reference
Physicochemical data										
Relative density (37 °C)	Hepatic bile, 11 samples	...	–	–	(0.9950–1.008)	...	...	...	...	15
	Gallbladder bile, 6 samples .	...	–	–	(1.008–1.034)	...	...	...	...	15
Surface tension (37 °C)	Hepatic bile, 11 samples	10^{-3} N m^{-1}	42.6	–	(39.6–44.0)	dyn cm^{-1}	42.6	–	(39.6–44.0)	15
	Gallbladder bile, 6 samples .	10^{-3} N m^{-1}	42.0	–	(40.8–44.2)	dyn cm^{-1}	42.0	–	(40.8–44.2)	15
Relative viscosity	Hepatic bile, 16 adults	...	1.27	0.24	(1.07–1.75)	...	...	...	...	16
	Gallbladder bile, 11 adults..	...	2.85	1.63	(1.31–5.42)	...	...	...	...	16

↓See text below and on page after next	Material	SI unit	Mean	s	(Extreme range)	Other units	Mean	s	(Extreme range)	Reference
Freezing-point depression	Hepatic bile	K	–	–	(0.56–0.61)	°C	–	–	(0.56–0.61)	7
↓ **Osmolality**	Hepatic bile, 16 adults	mmol/kg	284	17	(260–322)	mosm/kg	284	17	(260–322)	16
	Gallbladder bile, 8 adults	mmol/kg	281	10	(265–299)	mosm/kg	281	10	(265–299)	16
	Gallbladder bile, 20 adults	mmol/kg	349	40	–	mosm/kg	349	40	–	23
↓ **pH**	Hepatic bile	...	...	...	...	–	7.15	–	(6.5–8.6)	17,18
	Gallbladder bile	...	...	...	...	–	6.89	–	(6.1–8.6)	17,18
	Gallbladder bile, 20 adults	...	...	...	...	–	7.00	0.89	–	23

		Amount of substance				Mass				
		Unit	Mean	s	(Extreme range)	Unit	Mean	s	(Extreme range)	
↓ **Dry mass**	Hepatic bile, 16 adults	...	...	...	...	g/L	20	9	(8–34)	16
	Hepatic bile, 13 subjects	...	...	...	...	g/L	33.9	9.0	(25.0–55.6)	19
	Gallbladder bile, 11 adults	...	...	...	...	g/L	136	60	(70–248)	16
	Gallbladder bile, 10 adults	...	...	...	...	g/L	85.1	49.4	(12–153)	20

Inorganic substances

	Material	SI unit	Mean	s	(Extreme range)	Other units	Mean	s	(Extreme range)	Reference
↓ **Bicarbonate**	Hepatic bile	mmol/L	30	–	–	...	...	...	...	18
	Hepatic bile, 10 subjects	mmol/L	24.5	8.2	(18–46)	...	...	...	...	10
	Gallbladder bile	mmol/L	19	–	–	...	...	...	...	18
Chloride	Hepatic bile, 10 subjects	mmol/L	105	11	(83–117)	g/L	3.72	0.39	(2.9–4.15)	10
	Gallbladder bile, 20 adults	mmol/L	66.2	33.2	–	g/L	2.35	1.18	–	23
↓ **Phosphorus**										
– total	Hepatic bile, 8 subjects	mmol/L	4.78	–	(2.91–7.20)	mg/L	148	–	(90–223)	24
	Gallbladder bile	mmol/L	45	–	–	g/L	1.4	–	–	24
– inorganic	Hepatic bile	mmol/L	0.90	–	–	mg/L	28	–	–	30
	Hepatic bile	mmol/L	–	–	(0.17–0.90)	mg/L	–	–	(5.3–27.9)	106
Potassium	Hepatic bile, 16 adults	mmol/L	4.8	0.5	(4.0–6.2)	mg/L	188	20	(156–242)	16
	Hepatic bile, 10 subjects	mmol/L	4.7	0.6	(3.6–5.8)	mg/L	183	23	(141–227)	10
	Gallbladder bile, 11 adults	mmol/L	12.8	3.7	(8.2–19.6)	mg/L	500	145	(321–766)	16
	Gallbladder bile, 20 adults	mmol/L	24.6	6.0	–	mg/L	962	235	–	23
Sodium	Hepatic bile, 16 adults	mmol/L	146	8	(132–158)	g/L	3.36	0.18	(3.04–3.63)	16
	Hepatic bile, 10 subjects	mmol/L	149	5	(144–159)	g/L	3.43	0.12	(3.31–3.66)	10
	Gallbladder bile, 11 adults	mmol/L	209	34	(156–264)	g/L	4.81	0.78	(3.59–6.07)	16
	Gallbladder bile, 20 adults	mmol/L	179	32	–	g/L	4.12	0.74	–	23
Calcium	Hepatic bile, 4 subjects	mmol/L	–	–	(1.3–2.4)	mg/L	–	–	(52–96)	25
	Hepatic bile	mmol/L	2.6	–	(1.05–5.6)	mg/L	104	–	(42–224)	107
	Gallbladder bile, 20 adults	mmol/L	3.7	2.5	–	mg/L	150	100	–	23
	Gallbladder bile, 8 subjects	mmol/L	10.8	4.1	(3.1–17.2)	mg/L	430	160	(120–690)	26
Magnesium	Hepatic bile, 4 subjects	mmol/L	–	–	(0.7–1.5)	mg/L	–	–	(17–36)	25
↓ **Iron**	Hepatic bile	µmol/L	–	–	(7–56)	mg/L	–	–	(0.4–3.1)	7
	Hepatic bile, 16 adults	µmol/L	15	11	(2.1–44)	mg/L	0.83	0.61	(0.12–2.44)	28
↓ **Copper**	Hepatic bile, 6 subjects	µmol/L	25.3	–	(4.2–100)	mg/L	1.61	–	(0.27–6.36)	30
	Hepatic bile, 6 subjects	µmol/L	5.8	3.3	–	mg/L	0.37	0.21	–	31
	Gallbladder bile, 36 men	µmol/L	87.2	51.8	–	mg/L	5.54	3.29	–	31
↓ **Manganese**	Hepatic bile, 6 subjects	µmol/L	0.38	0.53	–	µg/L	21	29	–	31
	Gallbladder bile, 36 men	µmol/L	0.20	0.11	–	µg/L	11	6	–	31
Zinc	Gallbladder bile	µmol/L	5.4	–	–	mg/L	0.35	–	–	96

Osmolality. Bile is approximately isotonic with the serum; however, the osmolality may reach 400 mmol/kg in the secretin test[27]. The osmolality does not change significantly on concentration of the hepatic bile in the gallbladder since the sodium salts of the bile-acids form osmotically inactive micelles (osmotic coefficient 0.45)[6].

pH. The fact that the pH of gallbladder bile is lower than that of hepatic bile is probably due to secretion of H^+ into the lumen[6].

Dry mass. The gallbladder contains almost exclusively organic substances. The lipids account for 90% (bile acids 40–70%, phospholipids 20–25%, cholesterol 3–5%), bilirubin for 2%, and proteins for 5% of the dry mass[20,21].

Bicarbonate. Similarly to pancreatic juice, the concentration in the hepatic bile increases with increasing flow rate (Table 2, page 139)[10,22].

↓See text on next page	Material	Amount of substance				Mass				Refer-ence
		Unit	Mean	s	(Extreme range)	Unit	Mean	s	(Extreme range)	
Organic substances										
↓ **Total nitrogen** ..	Hepatic bile, 16 adults	mmol/L	51	22	(17–104)	g/L	0.72	0.31	(0.24–1.45)	16
	Hepatic bile, 8 subjects......	mmol/L	55	–	(49–66)	g/L	0.77	–	(0.68–0.92)	24
	Gallbladder bile, 9 adults ...	mmol/L	249	104	(134–430)	g/L	3.49	1.45	(1.88–6.00)	16
	Gallbladder bile	mmol/L	350	–	–	g/L	4.9	–	–	24
	Gallbladder bile, 5 subjects .	mmol/L	200	–	(114–236)	g/L	2.8	–	(1.6–3.3)	34
↓ **Nonprotein nitrogen**	Hepatic bile, 1 subject	mmol/L	33	–	–	g/L	0.46	–	–	36
	Gallbladder bile, 2 subjects .	mmol/L	–	–	(49–67)	g/L	–	–	(0.68–0.94)	36
	Gallbladder bile, 5 subjects .	mmol/L	190	–	–	g/L	2.7	–	–	34
Peptide nitrogen	Hepatic bile, 1 subject	mmol/L	10	–	–	mg/L	140	–	–	36
	Gallbladder bile, 2 subjects .	mmol/L	–	–	(2.8–19.3)	mg/L	–	–	(39–270)	36
↓ **Amino acid nitrogen**	Hepatic bile, 1 subject	mmol/L	3.9	–	–	mg/L	54	–	–	36
	Gallbladder bile, 2 subjects .	mmol/L	–	–	(4.3–15.4)	mg/L	–	–	(60–216)	36
↓ **Urea**	Hepatic bile	mmol/L	3.93	–	–	mg/L	236	–	–	36
	Gallbladder bile	mmol/L	–	–	(3.3–7.5)	mg/L	–	–	(200–450)	36
↓ **Choline**	Hepatic bile, 8 subjects......	mmol/L	4.7	1.45	(2.9–7.3)	g/L	0.57	0.175	(0.35–0.89)	24
	Gallbladder bile	mmol/L	45	–	–	g/L	5.5	–	–	24
Spermidine......	Gallbladder bile, 2 samples .	µmol/L	100	–	–	mg/L	15	–	–	101
Spermine	Gallbladder bile, 2 samples .	µmol/L	79	–	–	mg/L	16	–	–	101
Uric acid........	Hepatic bile	mmol/L	0.26	–	–	mg/L	44	–	–	39
Cyclic adenosine monophosphate .	Hepatic bile	nmol/L	169	109	–	µg/L	56	36	–	100
	Hepatic bile	nmol/L	84	12	–	µg/L	28	4.0	–	102
Cyclic guanosine monophosphate .	Hepatic bile	nmol/L	6.0	0.5	–	µg/L	2.1	0.2	–	102
↓ **Bilirubin**	Hepatic bile, 16 adults	mmol/L	1.11	0.22	(0.21–2.31)	g/L	0.65	0.13	(0.12–1.35)	16
	Hepatic bile, 8 subjects......	mmol/L	0.56	–	(0.44–0.70)	g/L	0.33	–	(0.26–0.41)	24
	Gallbladder bile, 11 adults ..	mmol/L	5.03	3.32	(0.62–10.8)	g/L	2.94	1.94	(0.36–6.30)	16
	Gallbladder bile, 10 subjects	mmol/L	3.56	2.46	(0.31–9.41)	g/L	2.08	1.44	(0.18–5.50)	20
	Gallbladder bile, 20 adults ..	mmol/L	4.00	2.33	–	g/L	2.34	1.36	–	23
↓ **Porphyrins**	Gallbladder bile	µmol/L	0.15	–	–	mg/L	0.10	–	–	44
↓ **Protein**										
Total protein....	Hepatic bile, 8 subjects......	...	...	...	...	g/L	1.8	–	(1.4–2.7)	24
	Hepatic bile, 6 subjects......	...	...	...	...	g/L	7	2	–	31
	Gallbladder bile	...	...	...	...	g/L	4.5	–	–	24
	Gallbladder bile, 36 men....	...	...	...	...	g/L	18	10	–	31
	Gallbladder bile, 20 adults ..	...	...	...	...	g/L	26.7	18.2	–	23
Albumin........	Hepatic bile, 37 adults	...	...	...	...	mg/L	634	83.5	(101–198)	46
Acid α_1-glyco-protein..........	Hepatic bile, 37 adults	...	...	...	...	mg/L	54.7	7.0	(10.7–207)	46
α_1-Antitrypsin ..	Gallbladder bile, 6 children .	...	...	...	...	mg/L	∼200	–	–	47
α_2-Macroglobulin	Hepatic bile, 21 adults	...	...	...	...	mg/L	44.5	6.7	(4.8–119)	46
IgG	Hepatic bile, 36 adults	...	...	...	...	mg/L	166	26.7	(10.4–771)	46
IgA	Hepatic bile, 37 adults	...	...	...	...	mg/L	98.8	13.4	(19.9–413)	46
↓ **Enzymes**	....	...	...	...	...	...	...	...	...	...
↓ **Carbohydrates** – total...........	Hepatic bile, 3 subjects......	...	...	...	...	g/L	–	–	(0.35–0.91)	24
	Gallbladder bile	...	...	...	...	g/L	2.4	–	–	24
Hexosamine – bound.........	Hepatic bile, 16 adults	...	...	...	...	mg/L	57	49	(5–160)	16
	Gallbladder bile, 11 adults ..	...	...	...	...	mg/L	83	53	(30–180)	16

↓See text on next page	Material	Amount of substance				Mass				Reference
		Unit	Mean	s	(Extreme range)	Unit	Mean	s	(Extreme range)	
↓ **Lactic acid**........	Hepatic bile, 24 subjects	mmol/L	2.0	7.4	(0.1–16.2)	g/L	0.18	0.67	(0.01–1.46)	65
	Gallbladder bile, 23 subjects .	mmol/L	3.0	7.9	(0.3–32.3)	g/L	0.27	0.71	(0.30–2.91)	65
Pyruvic acid	Hepatic bile, 23 subjects	mmol/L	–	–	(0–0.20)	mg/L	–	–	(0–18)	65
	Gallbladder bile, 20 subjects .	mmol/L	–	–	(0–0.75)	mg/L	–	–	(0–66)	65
Malic acid	Hepatic bile, 23 subjects	mmol/L	–	–	(0–0.08)	mg/L	–	–	(0–11)	65
	Gallbladder bile, 20 subjects .	mmol/L	–	–	(0–0.50)	mg/L	–	–	(0–67)	65
↓ **Oxalacetic acid** ...	Hepatic bile, 23 subjects	mmol/L	–	–	(0–0.08)	mg/L	–	–	(0–11)	65
	Gallbladder bile, 20 subjects .	mmol/L	–	–	(0–0.08)	mg/L	–	–	(0–11)	65
α-Oxoglutaric acid..............	Hepatic bile, 21 subjects	mmol/L	–	–	(0–0.19)	mg/L	–	–	(0–28)	65
	Gallbladder bile, 21 subjects .	mmol/L	–	–	(0–0.75)	mg/L	–	–	(0–110)	65
Lipids										
↓ **Total lipids**	Gallbladder bile, 10 subjects .	...	...	...	...	g/L	77.3	45.1	(12–144)	20
Triglycerides*.....	Gallbladder bile, 10 subjects .	–	0	–	–	–	0	–	–	20
Diglycerides*	Gallbladder bile, 10 subjects .	mmol/L	0.10	–	(0–0.21)	g/L	0.06	–	(0–0.13)	20
Monoglycerides*..	Gallbladder bile, 10 subjects .	mmol/L	0.34	–	(0–1.1)	g/L	0.12	–	(0–0.41)	20
Free fatty acids* ..	Gallbladder bile, 10 subjects .	mmol/L	0.96	0.92	(0.04–3.2)	g/L	0.27	0.26	(0.01–0.90)	20

* Factors for conversion of mmol to g: triglycerides 0.885; diglycerides 0.621; monoglycerides 0.357; free fatty acids 0.282.

Phosphorus. The major portion of the phosphorus is contained in phospholipids.

Iron. Only about 20% of the iron appearing in bile is likely to originate from the plasma[29].

Copper. This is present in non-dialyzable form. Bile has a high capacity for binding copper[32]. Biliary copper excretion is reduced in Wilson's disease[33].

Manganese. Present in non-dialyzable form.

Total nitrogen. The total nitrogen concentration of the gallbladder bile varies widely owing to its variable bilirubin and protein contents. About 40% of the nitrogen in the gallbladder bile is dialyzable[35].

Nonprotein nitrogen. The principal substances of this fraction are bilirubin, choline (component of phospholipids), urea, and amino acids (mainly glycine and taurine as constituents of the bile-acid conjugates).

Amino-acid nitrogen. Besides the amino acids bound to the bile acids, several free amino acids are demonstrable in the bile (mainly glycine)[37].

Urea. The urea concentration in the hepatic bile roughly parallels that in the blood[38].

Choline. Choline is a constituent of the phospholipids.

Bilirubin. 70–80% of the bilirubin in the gallbladder bile and more than 90% of the bilirubin in the hepatic bile is present as bilirubin diglucuronide; the rest consists of bilirubin monoglucuronide and small amounts of conjugates with glucose and xylose[40] as well as with sulfate[41]. Besides bilirubin, small amounts of other bile pigments are found in the bile[7,42]. About two-thirds of the bilirubin appears to be present in the form of a macromolecular aggregate forming a micellar solution[43]. At most 1% of the total bilirubin in normal bile is present in free form[103]. Calcium-bilirubin gallstones such as occur in the Far East could be caused by liberation of bilirubin from the conjugates through action of glucuronidase[21].

Porphyrins. The ratio of total coproporphyrin to protoporphyrin is approximately 10:1; there seems to be no uroporphyrin[45]. 80 to 90% of the coproporphyrin is in the form of coproporphyrin I[45].

Protein. Data on the protein concentration vary considerably[48]. The proteins originate for the most part from the plasma, and to a lesser extent from the liver and the gallbladder[46,49–51].

Table 3 *Enzymes in bile*

EC-number	Name of enzyme	Reference
1.1.1.27	Lactate dehydrogenase	51,52
1.1.1.30	3-Hydroxybutyrate dehydrogenase	51
1.1.1.37	Malate dehydrogenase	51,52
1.1.1.49	Glucose-6-phosphate dehydrogenase	48
1.4.1.3	Glutamate dehydrogenase	48
1.16.3.1	Ferroxidase (ceruloplasmin)	48
2.1.3.3	Ornithine carbamoyltransferase	48
2.6.1.1	Aspartate aminotransferase	51,52
2.6.1.2	Alanine aminotransferase	51,52
2.7.3.2	Creatine kinase	51
3.1.1.8	Cholinesterase	48
3.1.3.1	Alkaline phosphatase	48,52,53,56,57
3.2.1.17	Lysozyme	58
3.2.1.31	β-D-Glucuronidase	59
3.4.11.1	Aminopeptidase	52
3.4.22.12	γ-Glutamyl hydrolase (glutamate carboxypeptidase)	60
4.1.2.13	Fructose-bisphosphate aldolase	52

Enzymes. A number of enzymes including ceruloplasmin have been detected in the bile (Table 3). Their activities vary greatly[48,51]; they are generally higher in the gallbladder bile than in the hepatic bile. The activity level of cholinesterase is lower than that in the serum, whereas the activities of most other enzymes are substantially higher[48,51,52]. Alkaline phosphatase appears to form in the liver; however, the enzyme in the bile is not identical with the liver-specific isoenzyme in the serum[53].

Carbohydrates. Bile contains carbohydrates (glucuronic acid, small quantities of glucose and xylose) in the form of bilirubin conjugates and in the form of glycoproteins and mucopolysaccharides. At a normal plasma glucose level there is hardly any free glucose in the bile[61]. The individual carbohydrate-containing proteins have not been completely identified[50,62–64]. Glycoproteins from the plasma are found in the hepatic bile, probably in addition to glycoproteins from the bile ducts; pathological bile contains, in addition, liver-specific sulfated glycoproteins or peptides[63,64]. In

↓See text below, on next page and on page after next	Material	Amount of substance				Mass				Reference
		Unit	Mean	s	(Extreme range)	Unit	Mean	s	(Extreme range)	
↓**Cholesterol**	Hepatic bile, children	mmol/L	–	–	(0.52–0.57)	g/L	–	–	(0.20–0.22)	67
	Hepatic bile, 8 subjects	mmol/L	3.6	–	(2.1–5.4)	g/L	1.4	–	(0.8–2.1)	24
	Hepatic bile	mmol/L	4.63	–	(1.2–16)	g/L	1.79	–	(0.45–6)	26
	Gallbladder bile, children ...	mmol/L	–	–	(2.0–2.1)	g/L	–	–	(0.78–0.81)	67
	Gallbladder bile, 10 subjects .	mmol/L	10.1	6.33	(1.3–22)	g/L	3.90	2.45	(0.5–8.5)	20
	Gallbladder bile, 11 subjects .	mmol/L	10.4	3.70	(5.7–18)	g/L	4.02	1.43	(2.2–7)	26
	Gallbladder bile, 14 subjects .	mmol/L	10.4	5.48	(4.9–21.0)	g/L	4.02	2.12	(1.9–8.1)	68
↓**Phospholipids***	Hepatic bile, 8 subjects.......	mmol/L	3.2	–	(1.3–5.6)	g/L	2.5	–	(1.0–4.3)	24
	Gallbladder bile, 10 subjects .	mmol/L	26.2	19.9	(2.6–62.3)	g/L	20.3	15.4	(2.0–48.2)	20
	Gallbladder bile, 14 subjects .	mmol/L	33.3	16.5	(12.5–67.5)	g/L	25.8	12.8	(9.7–52.2)	68
↓**Bile acids**										
– total*	Hepatic bile, 8 subjects.......	mmol/L	25	–	(16–35)	g/L	10	–	(6.5–14)	24
	Hepatic bile	mmol/L	13	–	–	g/L	5.1	–	–	26
	Gallbladder bile, 10 subjects .	mmol/L	94.8	51.5	(17.8–160)	g/L	37.9	20.6	(7.1–64)	20
	Gallbladder bile, 11 subjects .	mmol/L	75.3	32.3	(14–118)	g/L	30.1	12.9	(5.6–47)	26
Cholic acid	Gallbladder bile, 10 subjects .	mmol/L	44.8	30.4	(5.9–94.0)	g/L	18.3	12.4	(2.4–38.4)	20
Chenodeoxycholic acid..............	Gallbladder bile, 10 subjects .	mmol/L	29.3	12.5	(7.6–50.7)	g/L	11.5	4.9	(3.0–19.9)	20
Deoxycholic acid..	Gallbladder bile, 10 subjects .	mmol/L	17.1	11.0	(3.8–36.7)	g/L	6.7	4.3	(1.5–14.4)	20
Lithocholic acid...	Gallbladder bile, 10 subjects .	mmol/L	4.0	3.7	(0.5–13.3)	g/L	1.5	1.4	(0.2–5.0)	20
↓**Steroid hormones**										
Dehydroepian-drosterone	Hepatic bile, men	µmol/L	–	–	(0.38–5.15)	mg/L	–	–	(0.11–1.49)	84
	Hepatic bile, women	µmol/L	–	–	(0.21–2.35)	mg/L	–	–	(0.06–0.68)	84
Vitamins										
Folic acid	Duodenal contents, 8 subjects	nmol/L	75	–	(18–150)	µg/L	33	–	(8–65)	54
Vitamin B$_{12}$	Hepatic bile	nmol/L	–	–	(2–7)	µg/L	–	–	(3–10)	55

*Factors for conversion of mmol to g: phospholipids 0.774; free bile acids 0.4.

Table 4 *Lipid pattern of bile (means and s)*

	Cholesterol	Phospholipid	Bile acids	Reference
	As percent of total lipid			
Bile from duodenum				
Adults	7.2	20.6	72.2	66
Young children	5.0	14.7	80.3	98
Gallbladder bile				
25 adults...........	6.0	20.4	73.5	85
	s 1.3	s 3.6	s 3.9	
Men	8.0	20.6	71.3	97
Women	7.4	20.4	72.2	97
Post-mortem	9.1	29.0	61.9	68

Table 5 *Phospholipid pattern of bile[73]*

	Phospholipid P (mg/L)				Individual phospholipids as percent of total phospholipids			
	Liver bile*		Gallbladder bile◊		Liver bile*		Gallbladder bile◊	
	Mean	s	Mean	s	Mean	s	Mean	s
Lysolecithin ..	0.4	0.8	2.1	2.2	0.2	0.5	0.2	0.2
Sphingomyelin	0.6	1.0	1.7	1.5	0.4	0.8	0.2	0.2
Lecithin	156	101	1116	576	97.7	1.6	97.9	0.7
Cephalin	3.0	3.6	19.9	10.7	1.4	1.1	1.6	0.7

* 9 subjects with uncomplicated gallstones and peptic ulcers.
◊ 11 subjects with uncomplicated gallstones and peptic ulcers.

gallbladder bile, a group of bile-specific mucopolysaccharides accounts for 70–90% of the total carbohydrate content[50].

Lactic acid. The value given is the geometric mean.

Oxalacetic acid. Present above the detection limit in a few samples only.

Total lipids. In native bile, lipids are organized in the form of a lipoprotein carrying albumin as apoprotein[99]. The major portion of the lipids is made up of bile acids (Table 4). Data on the lipid pattern of gallbladder bile in different ethnic groups have been compiled by OVIEDO et al.[23]. The fatty-acid pattern is determined by the structure of the lecithin[20]. The 3 predominant fatty acids (relative to total fatty acids) are: palmitic acid (46%), oleic acid (11%), and linoleic acid (28%)[66].

Cholesterol. Cholesterol is present almost exclusively in free form; only about 4% is esterified (gallbladder bile)[69]. The nonesterified cholesterol remains in solution through formation of a complex with the mixed micelles from the sodium salts of the bile acids and lecithin[21,70,71]. See page 145 for calculus formation.

Phospholipids. More than 90% of the phospholipids are lecithins, the remainder being composed of cephalins, sphingomyelins and lysolecithins (Table 5)[72,73]. The secretion of the phospholipids is induced by bile acids[11], with which they form a micellar complex (see page 145).

Bile acids. Cholic acid (a trihydroxycholanic acid) and chenodeoxycholic acid (a dihydroxycholanic acid) together account for about 60–90% of the total bile acids (Fig.2)[21,77]. They are formed

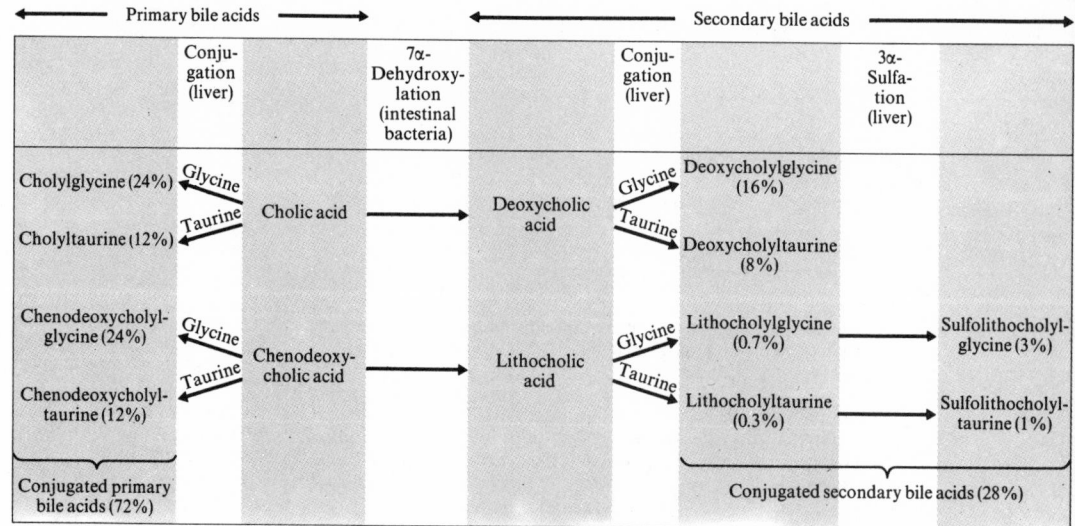

Fig. 2. Bile acid metabolism and relative proportions of individual components to total conjugated bile acids[77].

Table 6   *Bile acids in bile of children and adults*

	Age or sex	Num-ber	Bile acids*			Glycine/taurine ratio		Cholic acid/ chenodeoxycholic acid/ deoxycholic acid ratio	Refer-ence
			Mean	(Extreme range)		Mean	(Extreme range)		
			mmol/L						
Hepatic bile (fraction A)	1–4 days	13	10.7	(4.6–26.7)		0.47	(0.21–0.86)	2.5 : 1 : –†	74
	5–7 days	17	11.3	(2.0–29.2)		0.95	(0.34–2.30)	2.5 : 1 : –†	74
	7–12 months	8	8.8	(2.2–19.7)		2.4	(1.4–3.1)	1.1 : 1 : –◊	74
	4–10 years	3	3.4	(2.4–5.2)		1.7	(1.3–2.4)	2.0 : 1 : 0.9	74
	20 years	19	8.1	(2.8–20.0)		3.1	(1.9–5.0)	1.2 : 1 : 0.6	74
Gallbladder bile	Over 20 years	4	121	(31.5–222)		3.0	(1.0–6.6)	1.0 : 1 : 0.5	75
	Men	20	99.5	s24.5		3.9	–	1.6 : 1 : 0.3	76
	Women	20	145	s44.7		2.4	–	0.7 : 1 : 0.3	76

* 1 mmol is equivalent to 0.4 g of free bile acids.
† Secondary bile acids are lacking because the intestine is not yet colonized by bacteria possessing 7α-hydroxylase[108].
◊ In young children, the proportion of deoxycholic acid is small, and urso-deoxycholic acid is present in approximately the same amount[98].

Table 7   *Kinetics of bile acids in adults (means from different studies)[77]*

Bile acid	Pool		'Fractional turnover rate'	Synthesis or input	
	µmol kg⁻¹	mg	d⁻¹	µmol d⁻¹ kg⁻¹	mg d⁻¹
	μmol kg^{-1}	mg	d^{-1}	μmol d^{-1} kg^{-1}	mg d^{-1}
Cholic acid	12.0–14.2	600–1000	0.32	3.8–4.6	192–320
Chenodeoxycholic acid	10.0–11.4	500–800	0.20	2.0–2.3	100–160
Deoxycholic acid..................................	4.0–5.7	200–400	0.20	0.8–1.1	40–80
Lithocholic acid...................................	0.8–1.1	40–80	1.0	0.8–1.1	40–80
Total	26.8–32.4	1340–2280			

in the liver from cholesterol (primary bile acids). In the intestine, the primary bile acids are converted by bacterial action to deoxycholic acid (a dihydroxycholanic acid) and lithocholic acid (a monohydroxycholanic acid) which, after absorption in the intestine, also appear in the bile via the liver (secondary bile acids). In addition, the bile contains small quantities of trihydroxycoprostanic acid (an intermediate product of cholic acid formation) and allocholic acid (a by-product of cholic acid formation). (See EL-LIOTT and HYDE[78] for further details and literature on bile-acid synthesis). The bile acids are conjugated with glycine and taurine in the liver; except in the neonatal period, the glycine conjugates predominate in the bile[79] (Table 6); only a few percent are uncon-

jugated[75]. The lithocholic acid conjugates are for the most part sulfated in the liver (Fig. 2). The bile acids are conjugated predominantly with taurine[79] (Table 6). In the form of the anions, they form a micellar complex with lecithin and cholesterol (see page 145 for calculus formation). A healthy adult on a normal diet synthesizes daily approximately 1 mmol of cholic acid and 0.5 mmol of chenodeoxycholic acid[77]. The daily secretion of bile acids amounts to 30–60 mmol[77]. This high rate of secretion becomes possible only because of the fact that the relatively small pool of bile acids passes through the enterohepatic circulation 6–10 times per day[80]. The bile-acid kinetics (Table 7) are determined by active absorption in the ileum, transport to the liver via the portal blood,

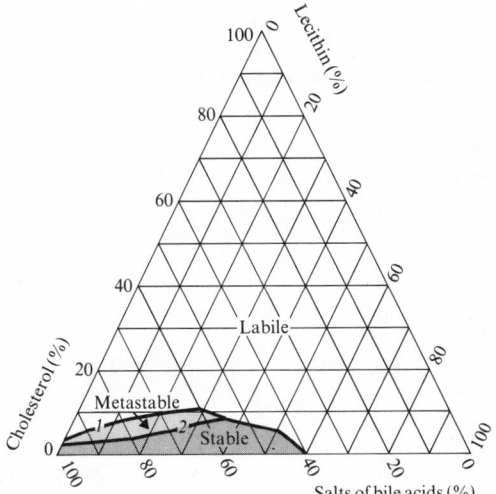

Fig. 3. The composition of gallbladder bile in terms of cholesterol, lecithin and salts of bile acids plotted on triangular coordinates (*1* ADMIRAND and SMALL[85]; *2* HOLZBACH et al.[97]). If the molar relation of the bile lipids falls in the labile range, cholesterol crystals rapidly form; if it falls in the metastable range, the formation of cholesterol crystals proceeds more slowly; if it falls in the stable range, cholesterol crystals do not generally form.

extraction by the liver parenchyma cells, and secretion against a concentration gradient into the biliary ductules[2,81]. In the newborn, the rate of bile-acid synthesis and the bile-acid pool are reduced in relation to body surface[82].

Steroid hormones. Many metabolites of the steroid hormones are excreted with the bile[83]: 31 different neutral steroids and several estrogens have been identified. About 13 mg of neutral steroids daily are excreted by men, and about 6.5 mg daily by women. The estriol concentration in the bile increases markedly in the late phase of pregnancy. The steroid hormones – like the bile acids – enter the enterohepatic circulation.

Formation of cholesterol gallstones

90% of gallstones analyzed in the USA contain cholesterol[3,89]. Of these, 10% are practically pure cholesterol stones which, containing no calcium, are not detectable by x-rays. 80% of the stones contain more than 70% of cholesterol in addition to bile pigments, bile acids, calcium salts and a protein matrix. The remaining 10% are pigment stones.

In normal bile, nonesterified cholesterol remains in solution by forming a complex with the mixed micelles from the salts of the bile acids and lecithin[21,70,71]. These mixed micelles are able to take up only a certain amount of cholesterol. If the cholesterol concentration exceeds the binding capacity of the mixed micelles, the bile is supersaturated with cholesterol and potentially lithogenous[85–89] (Fig. 3).

Cholesterol supersaturation can be caused by an absolute increase in cholesterol secretion, as occurs in obese patients[90,104], or by reduced secretion of bile-acid salts or reduction of the bile-acid pool[91,104]. The composition of the bile changes in the course of the day[87,92,93]. Between meals, the bile-acid pool is retained in the gallbladder, and secretion of bile-acid salts and, consequently, phospholipid secretion as well, decreases. However, since there appears to be no change in cholesterol secretion, gallstones may form during such periods even in normal individuals[3]. The danger of stone formation increases with a high-cholesterol diet[94] and with the use of oral contraceptives[95]. In women, the greater susceptibility to stone formation may be related to the fluctuations in bile composition during the course of the cycle[105].

Cholesterol crystals can be precipitated from supersaturated bile, with bile pigments, bacteria, mucoproteins or refluxed intestinal contents serving as crystal nuclei. Whether or not the microcrystals grow into calculi depends on the equilibrium between the growth of the microcrystals and their dissolution or their passage into the intestine.

References

[1] PREISIG et al., *Rev. franç. Etud. clin. biol.,* **14**, 151 (1969).
[2] WHEELER, H. O., *Arch. intern. Med.,* **130**, 533 (1972).
[3] SWELL et al., *Med. Clin. N. Amer.,* **58**, 1449 (1974).
[4] ERLINGER and DHUMEAUX, *Gastroenterology, 66*, 281 (1974); JAVITT, N. B., *New Engl. J. Med., 295,* 1464 and 1511 (1976).
[5] WHEELER, H. O., *Amer. J. Med.,* **51**, 588 (1971).
[6] BANFIELD, W. J., *Gastroenterology, 69*, 770 (1975).
[7] STARY, Z., in FLASCHENTRÄGER and LEHNARTZ (Eds.), *Physiologische Chemie,* volume II/2a, Springer, Berlin, 1956, page 527.
[8] SOBOTKA, H., *Physiological Chemistry of the Bile,* Baillière, London, 1937; HINSBERG and BRUNS, in LANG et al. (Eds.), *Hoppe-Seyler/Thierfelder Handbuch der physiologisch- und pathologisch-chemischen Analyse,* 10th ed., volume 5, Springer, Berlin, 1953, page 390; POPPER and SCHAFFNER, *Liver: Structure and Function,* McGraw-Hill, New York, 1957, page 80; KÜHN, H. A., in BÜCHNER et al. (Eds.), *Handbuch der allgemeinen Pathologie,* volume 5, part 2, Springer, Berlin, 1959, page 390; LATHE, G. H., in LONG et al. (Eds.), *Biochemists' Handbook,* Spon, London, 1961, page 917; LIEBOWITZ and ELLIS as well as FRAZER et al., in ALTMAN and DITTMER (Eds.), *Metabolism,* Federation of American Societies for Experimental Biology, Bethesda (Md.), 1968, page 253.
[9] DIETSCHY, J. M., *Gastroenterology, 47*, 395 (1964).
[10] WAITMAN et al., *Gastroenterology, 56*, 286 (1969).
[11] SCHERSTÉN et al., *Europ. J. clin. Invest.,* **1**, 242 (1971).
[12] MOLLOWITZ, G., *Langenbecks Arch. klin. Chir.,* **291**, 359 (1959).
[13] BRUNNER et al., *Proc. Mayo Clin.,* **49**, 851 (1974).
[14] BRAVERMAN, D. Z., *New Engl. J. Med.,* **302**, 362 (1980).
[15] DePALMA et al., *J. Amer. med. Ass.,* **195**, 943 (1966).
[16] BOUCHIER et al., *Gastroenterology, 49*, 343 (1965).
[17] RITTER, U., in BARTELHEIMER, H. (Ed.), *Klinische Funktionsdiagnostik,* Thieme, Stuttgart, 1973, page 220.
[18] DIETRICH and ANDERS, *Hoppe-Seylers Z. physiol. Chem.,* **309**, 60 (1957).
[19] MIHAESCU and MIHAESCU, *Nature,* **186**, 394 (1960).
[20] NAKAYAMA, F., *J. Lab. clin. Med.,* **69**, 594 (1967).
[21] BOUCHIER and FRESTON, *Lancet,* **1**, 340 (1968); SOLOWAY et al., *Gastroenterology, 72,* 167 (1977).
[22] DAVENPORT, H. W., *Physiology of the Digestive Tract,* 3rd ed., Year Book Medical Publishers, Chicago, 1971, page 129.
[23] OVIEDO et al., *Arch. Path.,* **101**, 208 (1977).
[24] POLONOVSKI and BOURRILLON, *Bull. Soc. Chim. biol. (Paris),* **34**, 703 (1952).
[25] THUREBORN, E., *Acta chir. scand.,* suppl. 303 (1962).
[26] ARIANOFF, A. A., *Acta gastro-ent. belg.,* **29**, 733 (1966).
[27] WHEELER, H. O., *Med. Clin. N. Amer.,* **47**, 607 (1963).
[28] GREEN, in *Amer. J. Med.,* **45**, 336 (1968).
[29] BOTHWELL, T. H., in HALLBERG et al. (Eds.), *Iron Deficiency,* Colloquia Geigy, Academic Press, London, 1970, page 151.
[30] LEWIS, K. O., *Gut,* **14**, 221 (1973).
[31] MILLER et al., *J. nucl. Med.,* **8**, 891 (1967).
[32] GOLLAN et al., *Amer. J. clin. Nutr.,* **24**, 1025 (1971).
[33] STERNLIEB et al., *Gastroenterology, 64*, 99 (1973).
[34] RUSSELL et al., *Clin. chim. Acta,* **10**, 210 (1964).
[35] GILES et al., *J. Lab. clin. Med.,* **55**, 38 (1960).
[36] NAGL, F., *Z. klin. Med.,* **151**, 429 (1954).
[37] PAPPO et al., *Acta gastro-ent. belg.,* **29**, 949 (1966).
[38] WRONG, O. M., *Sci. Basis Med.,* 192 (1971).
[39] SORENSEN, L. B., *Metabolism,* **8**, 687 (1959).
[40] BILLING, B. H., *Advanc. clin. Chem.,* **2**, 267 (1959); HOFFMAN et al., *J. clin. Invest.,* **39**, 132 (1960); SCHACHTER, D., *Med. Clin. N. Amer.,* **47**, 621 (1963); KUENZLE et al., *J. Lab. clin. Med.,* **67**, 294 (1966); FEVERY et al., *J. clin. Invest.,* **51**, 2482 (1972).
[41] NOIR et al., *Biochim. biophys. Acta(Amst.),* **222**, 15 (1970).
[42] WITH, T. K., *Biologie der Gallenfarbstoffe,* Thieme, Stuttgart, 1960.
[43] BOUCHIER and COOPERBAND, *Clin. chim. Acta,* **15**, 291 (1967).
[44] BRUGSCH, J., *Z. ges. inn. Med.,* **7**, 321 (1952).
[45] AZIZ and WATSON, *Clin. chim. Acta,* **26**, 525 (1969).
[46] DIVE and HEREMANS, *Europ. J. clin. Invest.,* **4**, 235 (1974).
[47] KYAW-MYINT et al., *Clin. chim. Acta,* **59**, 51 (1975).
[48] LORENTZ and JASPERS, *Klin. Wschr.,* **48**, 215 (1970).
[49] HARDWICKE et al., *Clin. Sci.,* **26**, 509 (1964); YOON et al., *J. Lab. clin. Med.,* **67**, 640 (1966); ENGLERT, E., *Clin. chim. Acta,* **29**, 319 (1970); GIRARD and DE KALBERMATTEN, *Schweiz. med. Wschr.,* **100**, 336 (1970).
[50] SCHRAGER et al., *Digestion,* **6**, 338 (1972).
[51] LORENTZ et al., *Klin. Wschr.,* **48**, 218 (1970).
[52] LORENTZ, K., *Klin. Wschr.,* **41**, 18 (1963).
[53] PRICE et al., *J. clin. Path.,* **25**, 149 (1972).
[54] BAKER et al., *Lancet,* **1**, 685 (1965).
[55] GRÄSBECK, R., *Advanc. clin. Chem.,* **3**, 299 (1960).
[56] ALLEN and SPELLBERG, *Arch. intern. Med.,* **120**, 667 (1967).
[57] OHLEN and LEY, *Klin. Wschr.,* **48**, 1056 (1970).
[58] HANKIEWICZ and SWIERCZEK, *Clin. chim. Acta,* **57**, 205 (1974).
[59] LUND and JACOBSEN, *J. Pediat.,* **85**, 262 (1964); LUND and PETERSEN, *J. Pediat.,* **85**, 268 (1974).
[60] BERNSTEIN and GUTSTEIN, *New Engl. J. Med.,* **281**, 565 (1969).
[61] SCHEIN et al., *Gastroenterology, 54*, 1094 (1968); GUZELIAN and BOYER, *J. clin. Invest.,* **53**, 526 (1974).
[62] CLAUSEN and GÜTTLER, in PEETERS, H. (Ed.), *Protides of the Biological Fluids,* Proceedings of the 11th Colloquium, Brügge 1963, Elsevier, Amsterdam, 1964, page 323.
[63] MATSUSHIRO et al., *Clin. chim. Acta,* **30**, 645 (1970).
[64] BOUCHIER and CLAMP, *Clin. chim. Acta,* **35**, 219 (1971).
[65] ADLUNG, J., *Klin. Wschr.,* **47**, 385 (1969).
[66] DAM et al., *Z. Ernährungsw.,* **10**, 160 (1971).

[67] KOSTIN, O. S., quoted from *Gastroenterology,* **40**, 836 (1961).
[68] BRÜHL, W., *Schweiz. med. Wschr.,* **102**, 1766 (1972).
[69] NAKAYAMA and JOHNSTON, *J. Lab. clin. Med.,* **59**, 364 (1962).
[70] SMALL, D. M., *Advanc. intern. Med.,* **16**, 243 (1970).
[71] CAREY and SMALL, *Arch. intern. Med.,* **130**, 506 (1972).
[72] PHILLIPS, G. B., *Biochim. biophys. Acta(Amst.),* **41**, 361 (1960); SPITZER et al., *Nature,* **204**, 288 (1964).
[73] GOTTFRIES et al., *Scand. J. clin. Lab. Invest.,* **21**, 168 (1968).
[74] ENCRANTZ and SJÖVALL, *Clin. chim. Acta,* **4**, 793 (1959).
[75] SJÖVALL, J., *Clin. chim. Acta,* **5**, 33 (1960).
[76] FISHER and YOUSEF, *Canad. med. Ass. J.,* **109**, 190 (1973).
[77] FROMM and HOFMANN, *Ergebn. inn. Med. Kinderheilk.,* **37**, 143 (1975); HOFMANN, A. F., *Advanc. intern. Med.,* **21**, 501 (1976).
[78] ELLIOTT and HYDE, *Amer. J. Med.,* **51**, 568 (1971).
[79] GARBUTT et al., *Amer. J. clin. Nutr.,* **24**, 218 (1971).
[80] DIETSCHY, J. M., *Arch. intern. Med.,* **130**, 473 (1972).
[81] KRAG and PHILLIPS, *J. clin. Invest.,* **53**, 1686 (1974); ACCATINO and SIMON, *J. clin. Invest.,* **57**, 496 (1976).
[82] WATKINS et al., *New Engl. J. Med.,* **288**, 431 (1973).
[83] TAYLOR, W., *Vitam. and Horm.,* **29**, 201 (1971).
[84] LAATIKAINEN, T., quoted from *Vitam. and Horm.,* **29**, 201 (1971).
[85] ADMIRAND and SMALL, *J. clin. Invest.,* **47**, 1043 (1968).
[86] REDINGER and SMALL, *Arch. intern. Med.,* **130**, 618 (1972); REDINGER, R. N., *Schweiz. med. Wschr.,* **104**, 1673 (1974).

[87] SMALLWOOD et al., *Brit. med. J.,* **4**, 263 (1972).
[88] MACKAY et al., *Gut,* **13**, 759 (1972); HELLER and BOUCHIER, *Gut,* **14**, 83 (1973).
[89] GOLDSTEIN and SCHOENFIELD, *Advanc. intern. Med.,* **20**, 89 (1975); CONLEY and GOLDSTEIN, *Med. Clin. N. Amer.,* **59**, 1025 (1975).
[90] BENNION and GRUNDY, *J. clin. Invest.,* **56**, 996 (1975).
[91] GREGORY et al., *Amer. J. dig. Dis.,* **19**, 268 (1974).
[92] DAM, H., *Amer. J. Med.,* **51**, 596 (1971).
[93] METZGER et al., *New Engl. J. Med.,* **288**, 333 (1973).
[94] DENBESTEN et al., *Surgery,* **73**, 266 (1973).
[95] BENNION et al., *New Engl. J. Med.,* **294**, 189 (1976).
[96] SULLIVAN et al., *Gastroenterology,* **48**, 438 (1965).
[97] HOLZBACH et al., *J. clin. Invest.,* **52**, 1467 (1973).
[98] VON BERGMANN et al., *Clin. chim. Acta,* **64**, 241 (1975).
[99] MANZATO et al., *J. clin. Invest.,* **57**, 1248 (1976).
[100] LEVINE and HALL, *Gastroenterology,* **70**, 537 (1976).
[101] McEVOY and HARTLEY, *Pediat. Res.,* **9**, 721 (1975).
[102] SCHWARTZEL et al., *Analyt. Biochem.,* **78**, 395 (1977).
[103] BOONYAPISIT et al., *J. Lab. clin. Med.,* **88**, 857 (1976).
[104] SHAFFER and SMALL, *J. clin. Invest.,* **59**, 828 (1977).
[105] LOW-BEER et al., *Brit. med. J.,* **1**, 1568 (1977).
[106] SUTOR and WILKIE, *Clin. chim. Acta,* **77**, 31 (1977).
[107] SUTOR and WILKIE, *Clin. chim. Acta,* **79**, 119 (1977).
[108] NIESSEN, K. H., *Mschr. Kinderheilk.,* **127**, 29 (1979).

The intestinal juice (succus entericus) or intestinal fluid in the fasting state is not so much an intestinal secretion as the result of an equilibrium between ingoing and outgoing fluid in the intestine[1]. Older studies about the composition of the contents of various segments of the intestine have been summarized in the literature[2]. More recent data on the electrolyte composition have been obtained by perfusion of individual small-bowel segments with solutions of varying ion concentration[1]. Thus, the potassium and sodium concentrations in the intestinal fluid hardly differ from those in the serum; the bicarbonate concentration is low in the jejunum and high in the ileum, and the chloride concentration varies inversely with the bicarbonate concentration. A rapid exchange of water and electrolytes also takes place in the large intestine; whether or not calcium is secreted by the colon in man: in certain animal species it has been established that calcium is secreted by the colon, but whether this is also the case in man is not known with certainty[3].

Appreciable quantities of serum proteins pass into the intestinal fluid (about 2 mg/min in a small-bowel segment 5 cm long)[4], in addition to which the intestinal wall seems to secrete secretory IgA and IgM[10]. The mucins in the intestinal fluid originate from goblet cells, and the enzymes have been reported to be released from desquamated cells[1].

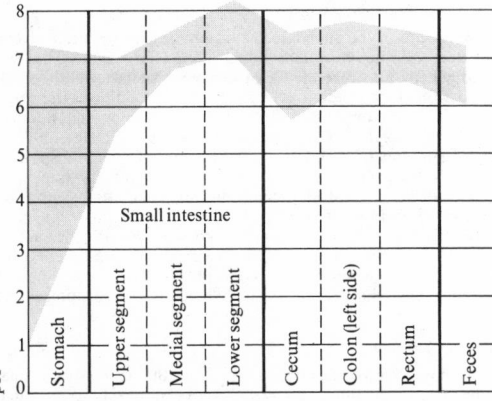

Fig. 1. pH profile of intestinal contents (measurement with radiotelemetry capsule; range of 9 subjects)[6].

	Intestinal segment	Subjects	Unit	Mean	s	(Extreme range)	Reference
Flow	Jejunum	Men	mL/min	2.16	1.32	–	7
	Ileum	Men	mL/min	0.67	–	–	7
pH (Fig. 1)			...	...	...	...	...
Osmolality	Jejunum	7 subjects	mmol/kg	285	10	–	8
	Ileum	9 subjects	mmol/kg	292	12	–	8
Bicarbonate	Jejunum	7 subjects	mmol/L	8.2	5	–	8
	Ileum	9 subjects	mmol/L	30	11	–	8
Chloride	Jejunum	7 subjects	mmol/L	135	8	–	8
	Ileum	9 subjects	mmol/L	125	12	–	8
Potassium	Jejunum	7 subjects	mmol/L	4.8	0.5	–	8
	Ileum	9 subjects	mmol/L	4.9	1.5	–	8
Sodium	Jejunum	7 subjects	mmol/L	142	7	–	8
	Ileum	9 subjects	mmol/L	140	6	–	8
Calcium	Proximal ileum	2 subjects	mmol/L	4.2	–	(0.5–11.5)	3
Magnesium	Proximal ileum	2 subjects	mmol/L	2.8	–	(0.5–6.5)	3
Protein	Jejunum	5 subjects	g/L	–	–	(0.95–3.2)	5
Immunoglobulins							
IgG	Jejunum	12 subjects	mg/L	12	19	–	9
IgA	Jejunum	12 subjects	mg/L	230	220	–	9
IgM	Jejunum	12 subjects	mg/L	15	32	–	9
IgE	Jejunum	12 subjects	10^3IU/L	27	24	–	9

References

[1] HENDRIX and BAYLESS, *Ann. Rev. Physiol.,* **32**, 139 (1970).
[2] SUNDERMAN and BOERNER, *Normal Values in Clinical Medicine,* Saunders, Philadelphia, 1950, page 243; HINSBERG and BRUNS, in LANG et al. (Eds.), *Hoppe-Seyler/Thierfelder Handbuch der physiologisch- und pathologisch-chemischen Analyse,* 10th ed., volume 5, Springer, Berlin, 1953, page 383; ALTMAN and DITTMER (Eds.), *Metabolism,* Federation of American Societies for Experimental Biology, Bethesda (Md.), 1968, page 261.
[3] PHILLIPS and GILLER, *J. Lab. clin. Med.,* **81**, 733 (1973).
[4] DA COSTA, L. R., *J. Nutr.,* **101**, 431 (1971).
[5] BULL et al., *Gastroenterology,* **60**, 370 (1971).
[6] MELDRUM et al., *Brit. med. J.,* **2**, 104 (1972).
[7] WHALEN et al., *Gastroenterology,* **51**, 975 (1966).
[8] BANWELL et al., *J. clin. Invest.,* **50**, 890 (1971).
[9] JONES et al., *Digestion,* **14**, 12 (1976).
[10] BRANDTZAEG and BAKLIEN, in *Immunology of the Gut,* Ciba Foundation Symposium, NS 46, Elsevier, Amsterdam, 1977, page 77.

Oral ¹⁴C-cholylglycine test

A portion of the cholylglycine originating in the bile is deconjugated in the ileum by the action of a bacterial enzyme. The liberated glycine is oxidized to CO_2 by enzymes of bacteria, the small-bowel mucosa and the liver. Under normal conditions the conjugated bile acids are absorbed so rapidly in the ileum that administration of cholyl-1-(¹⁴C)-glycine is followed by the release of only small amounts of $^{14}CO_2$, as shown by analysis of the respiratory air[1,2]. In the event of bacterial overgrowth in the proximal small intestine (in the blind-loop syndrome, intestinal fistulas, etc.) or in case of bile-acid malabsorption (in resection of ileum, etc.), on the other hand, the $^{14}CO_2$ content of the respiratory air is increased[1-6] (Fig.1). By determining the fecal excretion of the labelled bile acid – which is increased in malabsorption – it is possible to decide whether bacterial overgrowth or bile-acid malabsorption is present[1,5].

Oral xylose test

Monosaccharides are transported from the lumen of the small intestine into the interstitium by an active transport mechanism of the brush border[7]. This transport mechanism may be disturbed if there has been damage to the intestinal mucosa. The oral xylose test has been introduced for the purpose of detecting such a disturbance[8-10]. D-Xylose is absorbed almost entirely in the upper segment of the small intestine and to a small extent only in the ileum[11], namely, with the aid of a transport mechanism comparable to that for D-glucose[12]. In contradistinction to D-glucose absorption, however, D-xylose absorption is not subject to effects of the gastrointestinal hormones. A total of approximately 60% of an oral test dose is absorbed[11]. About 40% of a parenterally administered dose is excreted via the kidneys, and about 60% is probably metabolized in the course of glucuronic acid-xylose metabolism[13,14].

The maximum blood level of xylose is reached approximately 75 minutes after oral administration (Fig.2). It is reached later in young children than in older children and adults (Fig.3). After a challenge with 25 g of D-xylose, 25–30% is excreted in the urine within the first 5 hours, and another 5% in the next 19 hours[11,3].

Test procedure: A specific quantity of D-xylose is orally administered to the fasting patient with a certain volume of water. The customary test parameters are the 1-hour and 2-hour blood values

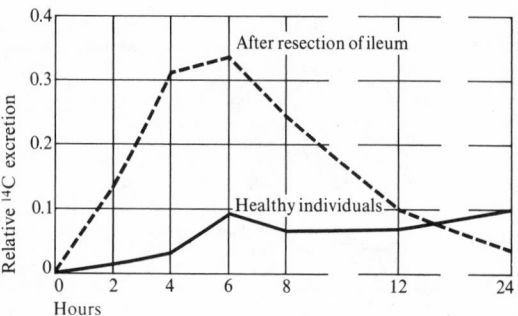

Fig.1. Time course of relative excretion of ¹⁴C in percent of the dose administered, referred to mmol CO_2 in the expired air and multiplied by kg of body mass to correct for endogenous CO_2 formation (means in 18 healthy individuals and 19 individuals with bile-acid malabsorption secondary to resection of ileum)[1].

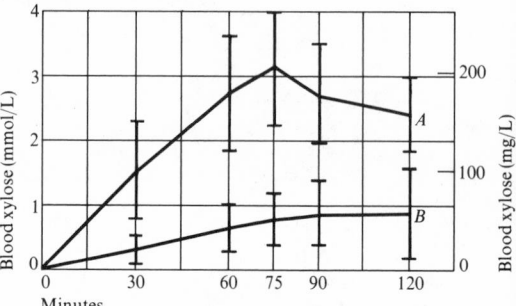

Fig.2. Xylose concentration in blood after oral load with 100 mmol (15 g) of D-xylose[15]. *A* 30 patients without celiac disease (mean $\pm$ s). *B* 17 patients with celiac disease (mean $\pm$ s).

Table 1 *Normal values for the oral xylose test*

		Test dose*	Amount of substance				Mass				Reference
			Unit	Mean	s	(Extreme range)	Unit	Mean	s	(Extreme range)	
Blood	*1-hour values*										
	75 children, <30 kg	5 g	mmol/L	2.5	–	(1.5–4.1)	mg/L	370	–	(220–620)	17
	26 children, 8 months to 16 years	5 g	mmol/L	2.06	0.66	(1.05–3.73)	mg/L	310	99	(158–560)	18
	30 children, 6 weeks to 16 years	0.4 g/kg	mmol/L	2.74	0.49	(1.91–3.78)	mg/L	412	74	(286–568)	19
	2-hour values										
	29 children, 6 weeks to 16 years	0.4 g/kg	mmol/L	2.02	0.57	(0.84–2.98)	mg/L	304	86	(126–448)	19
	23 subjects..............	25 g	mmol/L	2.4	1.1	(1.0–5.1)	mg/L	360	160	(150–760)	20
	1 subject	25 g	mmol/L	4.22	–	–	mg/L	634	–	–	21
Urine	*5-hour excretion*										
	29 subjects.............	5 g	mmol	11	1.7	–	g	1.7	0.25	–	13
	114 subjects............	25 g	mmol	38	9.3	(22–61)	g	5.7	1.4	(3.3–9.2)	13
	25 subjects.............	25 g	mmol	43	8	(27–55)	g	6.5	1.2	(4.1–8.2)	20
	14 subjects.............	25 g	mmol	47.9	7.6	(39–64)	g	7.19	1.14	(5.8–9.6)	21
	10 subjects.............	25 g	mmol	45.0	5.9	(37–55)	g	6.76	0.88	(5.6–8.2)	22
	40 young adults........	25 g	mmol	45	7.5	–	g	6.7	1.12	–	23
	36 subjects, 70–89 years .	25 g	mmol	36	9.6	(16–63)	g	5.4	1.44	(2.4–9.5)	23
	37 subjects, <61 years ..	25 g	mmol	37.0	10.1	(15.7–56.6)	g	5.55	1.52	(2.36–8.50)	9
	9 subjects, >61 years ...	25 g	mmol	20.2	5.2	(15.3–30.0)	g	3.04	0.78	(2.30–4.50)	9
	11 subjects.............	25 g	mmol	52	6.7	(43–63)	g	7.8	1.0	(6.4–9.4)	11
	24-hour excretion										
	11 subjects.............	25 g	mmol	59	8	(52–68)	g	8.9	1.2	(7.8–10.2)	11

* 1 g is equivalent to 6.66 mmol of D-xylose.

Table 2 *Activities of lysosomal enzymes in small-bowel mucosa at 37°C (relative to protein)*

| Small-bowel segment | α-Glucosidase | | β-Glucosidase | | β-Glucuronidase | | Acid β-galactosidase | | Aryl sulfatase | | β-N-Acetylglucosaminidase | | Acid phosphatase | | Reference |
	Mean	(Extreme range)	Mean	(Extreme range)	Mean	(Extreme range)	Mean	(Extreme range)	Mean	(Extreme range)	Mean	(Extreme range)	Mean	(Extreme range)	
							U/g								
22 fetuses, 10–24 weeks	Medial jejunum	1.69	(0.85–2.82)	3.19	(1.00–5.98)	2.47	(0.87–5.27)	4.83	(2.40–6.82)	1.23	(0.75–2.16)	145	(57–375)	31	(18–52)	31
9 fetuses, 17–24 weeks	20–40 cm from pylorus	1.33	(0.82–2.67)	1.46	(0.43–2.00)	2.00	(1.45–3.14)	5.29	(2.51–6.82)	0.94	(0.35–1.93)	108	(57–235)	30	(25–42)	31
1 premature infant, gestation 28 weeks	Jejunum	1.67	–	6.20	–	1.56	–	3.28	–	0.77	–	69	–	47	–	31
1 newborn, gestation 39 weeks	Jejunum	1.34	–	4.92	–	2.14	–	–	–	–	–	62	–	33	–	31
19 adults	Level of M.suspensorius duodeni (oral biopsy)	–	–	–	–	–	–	3.6	(3.0–4.7)	–	–	–	–	–	–	32

Table 3 *Activities of brush-border enzymes in small-bowel mucosa at 37°C (relative to protein)*

| Small-bowel segment | 'Lactase' | | | 'Saccharase' | | | 'Maltase' | | | 'Isomaltase' | | | Alkaline phosphatase | | | Reference |
	Mean	s	(Extreme range)	Mean	s	(Extreme range)	Mean	s	(Extreme range)	Mean	s	(Extreme range)	Mean	s	(Extreme range)	
								U/g								
22 fetuses, 10–24 weeks	Medial jejunum	6.98	3.06	(2.7–13.6)	64.8	30.7	(15.7–127)	146	50.7	(37.6–250)	11.2	3.91	(2.0–21.2)	–	–	–	31
9 fetuses, 17–24 weeks	20–40 cm from pylorus	5.40	2.69	(2.6–11.7)	59.7	22.8	(13.8–94.3)	141	43.0	(53.1–207)	11.0	4.0	(2.3–16.4)	–	–	–	31
1 premature infant, gestation 28 weeks	Jejunum	57.3	–	–	81.6	–	–	147	–	–	17.7	–	–	–	–	–	31
1 newborn, gestation 39 weeks	Jejunum	32.0	–	–	41.1	–	–	143	–	–	10.3	–	–	–	–	–	31
25 children, 2–11 months	Proximal jejunum (oral biopsy)	29.9	11.2	(17.0–64.7)	55.5	19.3	(30.0–105)	183	65.6	(104–315)	13.0	5.4	(4.8–25.1)	–	–	–	31
117 children	Jejunum (oral biopsy)	55.8	21.9	–	102	30.3	–	309	95.2	–	102	28.4	–	429	180	–	33
17 subjects, 1–22 years	Duodenum or upper jejunum (oral biopsy)	23.8	–	(4.9–61)	70	–	(11–250)	253	–	(31–1020)	75	–	(8–280)	–	–	–	34
19 adults	Level of M.suspensorius duodeni (oral biopsy)	29	8.4	(16–49)	49	14.9	(28–80)	179	46.5	(114–274)	64	18.7	(36–93)	–	–	–	32
22 adults	Upper jejunum (oral biopsy)	44	22	(9–98)	87	29	(26–138)	266	70	(111–420)	97	30	(25–183)	802	617	(201–2540)	35
38 men	Jejunum (oral biopsy)	49	–	(1–149)	104	–	(21–247)	335	–	(52–816)	–	–	–	–	–	–	36
22 adults	Duodenum or upper jejunum (oral biopsy)	38	–	(13–85)	61	–	(27–119)	228	–	(84–410)	15	–	(8–28)	–	–	–	37

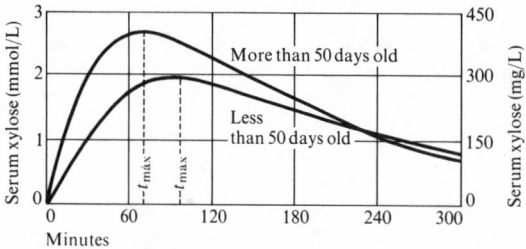

Fig. 3. Xylose concentration in serum of children after oral load with 3.3 mmol (0.5 g) of D-xylose to 1 kg of body mass (t_{max}: time of maximum concentration)[16].

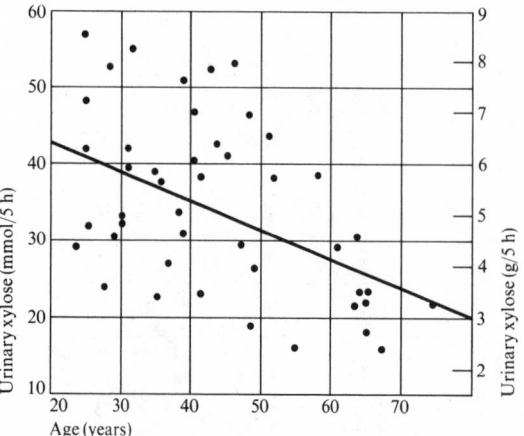

Fig. 4. Xylose excretion in urine after oral load with 167 mmol (25 g) of D-xylose in relation to age (values of 46 subjects)[9].

and excretion in the 5-hour urine (Table 1). In adults, xylose excretion declines with increasing age (Fig. 4), probably owing to the decreasing number of functional nephrons. The reduced xylose excretion observed in the tropics[24] may also be related to an altered renal function[25]. In children, determination of blood levels of xylose is preferred to determination of urinary excretion since the latter is subject in part to unknown factors that vary with the age[26].

The informative value of the test is limited since both the blood xylose concentration and excretion in the urine can be normal in the presence of a damaged small-bowel mucosa[15,27]. The test is useless in the presence of restricted renal function, inadequate urine output, delayed gastric emptying and colonization of the intestine with xylose-converting bacteria. In the opinion of some authors, oral folic-acid loading[28] or oral vitamin-A loading[29] is a more sensitive test for the detection of small-bowel damage.

Enzymes of small-bowel mucosa

The small-bowel mucosa contains brush-bound enzymes (disaccharidases, dipeptidases, enteropeptidase, alkaline phosphatase),

lysosomal enzymes (acid phosphatase, β-N-acetyl-D-glucosaminidase), mitochondrial enzymes (dehydrogenases) as well as several others (adenosine triphosphatase, adenylate cyclase)[30]. The activity of the disaccharidases is low in the duodenum, increases toward the jejunum, and decreases in the ileum[38]; by contrast, the activity of enteropeptidase (enterokinase) is highest in the duodenum[42]. The activities of many of the enzymes in the small-bowel mucosa are already well developed in the early fetal stage (Tables 2 and 3). Lactase activity reaches a maximum shortly before birth[31,39]; the activity usually decreases after birth but in some individuals it remains undiminished into adulthood[40]. The enteropeptidase activity is considerably lower in the fetal stage than during the first few postnatal years[42]. For detection of a hereditary lactase or saccharase-isomaltase deficiency causing diarrhea, determination of the activities of these enzymes in oral biopsy material is helpful[41].

References

[1] FROMM and HOFMANN, *Lancet,* **2,** 621 (1971).
[2] SHERR et al., *New Engl. J. Med.,* **285,** 656 (1971).
[3] PARKIN et al., *Lancet,* **2,** 777 (1972).
[4] JAMES et al., *Brit. med. J.,* **3,** 191 (1973).
[5] PEDERSEN et al., *Scand. J. Gastroent.,* **8,** 665 (1973); ARNFRED et al., *Scand. J. Gastroent.,* **9,** 325 (1974).
[6] CASPARY and REIMOLD, *Dtsch. med. Wschr.,* **101,** 353 (1976).
[7] CRANE, R. K., in *Handbook of Physiology,* section 6; Alimentary Canal, volume 3, American Physiological Society, Washington (D.C.), 1968, page 1323; RIECKEN, E. O., *Verh. dtsch. Ges. inn. Med.,* **81,** 764 (1975).
[8] HELMER and FOUTS, *J. clin. Invest.,* **16,** 343 (1937).
[9] TEXTER et al., *Med. Clin. N. Amer.,* **48,** 117 (1964).
[10] REINER and CHEUNG, *Stand. Meth. clin. Chem.,* **5,** 257 (1965).
[11] FORDTRAN et al., *New Engl. J. Med.,* **267,** 274 (1962).
[12] SCHEDL et al., *J. clin. Invest.,* **43,** 1232 (1964).
[13] BUTTERWORTH et al., *New Engl. J. Med.,* **261,** 157 (1959).
[14] WYNGAARDEN et al., *J. clin. Invest.,* **36,** 1395 (1957).
[15] STEVENS et al., *J. clin. Path.,* **30,** 76 (1977).
[16] HEIMANN et al., *Europ. J. Pediat.,* **124,** 285 (1977).
[17] ROLLES et al., *Lancet,* **2,** 1043 (1973).
[18] SCHAAD et al., *Helv. paediat. Acta,* **30,** 331 (1975).
[19] LANZKOWSKY et al., *J. Amer. med. Ass.,* **186,** 517 (1963).
[20] BENSON et al., *New Engl. J. Med.,* **256,** 335 (1957).
[21] MERIAN, P., *Helv. med. Acta,* **29,** 579 (1962).
[22] CHRISTIANSEN et al., *Amer. J. Med.,* **27,** 443 (1959).
[23] DRUBE, H. C., *Klin. Wschr.,* **40,** 518 (1962).
[24] KEUSCH et al., *J. Lab. clin. Med.,* **75,** 558 (1970); KEUSCH et al., *Amer. J. clin. Nutr.,* **25,** 1067 (1972).
[25] AUNG-THAN-BATU et al., *Clin. chim. Acta,* **32,** 145 (1971).
[26] MEEUWISSE and DANO, *Acta paediat. scand.,* **54,** 33 (1965).
[27] SLADEN and KUMAR, *Brit. med. J.,* **3,** 223 (1973).
[28] CHANARIN and BENNETT, *Brit. med. J.,* **1,** 985 (1962).
[29] SCHMIDT et al., *Med. Klin.,* **70,** 1745 (1975).
[30] LORENZ-MEYER and RIECKEN, *Med. Klin.,* **71,** 7 (1976).
[31] ANTONOWICZ et al., *Gastroenterology,* **67,** 51 (1974).
[32] ASP et al., *Scand. J. Gastroent.,* **10,** 647 (1975).
[33] LÜCKING, T., *Europ. J. Pediat.,* **121,** 263 (1976).
[34] SHMERLING et al., *Helv. paediat. Acta,* **19,** 507 (1964).
[35] DUNPHY et al., *Gastroenterology,* **49,** 12 (1965).
[36] SHEEHY and ANDERSON, *Lancet,* **2,** 1 (1965).
[37] WELSH et al., *Arch. intern. Med.,* **117,** 488 (1966).
[38] SEMENZA, G., in *Handbook of Physiology,* section 6: Alimentary Canal, volume 5, American Physiological Society, Washington (D.C.), 1968, page 2543.
[39] AURICCHIO et al., *Pediatrics,* **35,** 944 (1965).
[40] LEBENTHAL et al., *Gastroenterology,* **67,** 1107 (1974); *Amer. J. clin. Nutr.,* **595** (1975); WELSH et al., *Gastroenterology,* **75,** 847 (1978).
[41] PRADER and AURICCHIO, *Ann. Rev. Med.,* **16,** 345 (1965); HOLZEL, A., in SCHWIEGK, H. (Ed.), *Handbuch der inneren Medizin,* 5th ed., volume 7, part 1, Springer, Berlin, 1974, page 87.
[42] ANTONOWICZ and LEBENTHAL, *Gastroenterology,* **72,** 1299 (1977).

Intestinal gases are produced by aerophagia and by the enzymatic degradation of food constituents[1,2]. They diffuse from the intestine into the blood to an extent depending on their partial pressure, until pressure equilibration, and are for the most part exhaled. Approximately 100 mL of gas is present in the intestinal tract[1]. The volume of gas expelled daily through the anus is 400–2000 mL[1,2]. The volume of flatus can increase considerably upon ingestion of large quantities of fermentable foods: after the ingestion of beans[3], for example, it may increase from 15 mL/h to 176 mL/h. The composition of the intestinal gases varies over a wide range, depending mainly on the food ingested (see Table 1).

Hydrogen is produced solely by the metabolism of the intestinal flora with carbohydrate as the main substrate. 99% of the hydrogen is formed in the colon. No hydrogen formation is demonstrable during the first 12 hours after birth. The amount of hydrogen that is exhaled is commensurate to the amount formed in the intestine. A test for the detection of carbohydrate malabsorption is based on this fact[5].

Methane is formed exclusively in the colon, namely by anaerobic bacteria. No methane is formed in the newborn; its formation sets in gradually and reaches its final value at the age of 8 years. Methane is not formed in all individuals. The possession of a methane-producing microflora appears to be an environmentally acquired familial trait.

Carbon dioxide is formed, on one hand, upon neutralization of the bicarbonate-rich secretions of the digestive tract by gastric acid and by amino acids and fatty acids released by hydrolysis and, on the other hand, by action of bacteria on food components. The volume of carbon dioxide in the intestine is a function of its production and absorption.

Nitrogen originates mainly from swallowed air. It can diffuse from the blood into the intestinal lumen; intraluminal production cannot be ruled out.

The oxygen in the intestine is rapidly consumed by the bacteria so that the oxygen tension in the rectum amounts to no more than 0.4–0.5 kPa.

Table 1
Volume and composition of intestinal gases in 11 subjects[4]

	Mean	(Extreme range)	Mean	(Extreme range)
	mL		Volume fraction as percent	
Total amount	90	(30–200)	–	–
Nitrogen	64	(11–177)	64	(26–88)
Carbon dioxide	9.7	(5.8–14.0)	14.0	(5.5–27.0)
Hydrogen	14.0	(0.07–32.0)	19.0	(0.17–49.0)
Methane*	2.0	(0–17.0)	3.2	(0–20.0)
Oxygen	0.6	(0.05–1.3)	0.7	(0.1–1.8)

* Detected in only 4 subjects.

Odor-generating gases such as ammonia, hydrogen sulfide, indole, skatole, volatile amines and fatty acids account for less than 1% of the total gas volume. After absorption, they are eliminated with the respiratory air, which appears to contain about 250 different substances[6].

References

[1] HAFTER, E., *Schweiz. med. Wschr., 98*, 1049 (1968).
[2] LEVITT and BOND, *Gastroenterology, 59*, 921 (1970); LEVITT and ENGEL, *Advanc. intern. Med., 20*, 151 (1975).
[3] STEGGERDA, F. R., *Ann. N. Y. Acad. Sci., 150*, 57 (1968).
[4] LEVITT, M. D., *New Engl. J. Med., 284*, 1394 (1971).
[5] BARR et al., *Pediatrics, 62*, 393 (1978); HEPNER, G. W., *Advanc. intern. Med., 23*, 25 (1978).
[6] PAULING et al., *Proc. nat. Acad. Sci. (Wash.), 68*, 2374 (1971).

Feces

The feces are a very complex mixture of food residues, secreta of the gastrointestinal tract, desquamated cells of the intestinal wall, and constituents of the intestinal flora. In contrast to the feces after ingestion of food, the feces produced after fasting, about which data from only a few older studies are available[1], are devoid of food residues. Meconium, the infant's intestinal contents at birth, also contains no bacteria.

Unless indicated otherwise, the data presented in this section refer to the feces of adults receiving a Western European diet. Fecal composition has been discussed in detail by KRZYWANEK and FLASCHENTRÄGER[1] as well as by HINSBERG et al.[2]; a tabular summary has been supplied by VAN PILSUM[3].

For many diagnostic purposes, notably for the interpretation of fat excretion, the examination of individual stool specimens is hardly sufficient; it becomes necessary to collect the stools of 3 to 5 days[4,5].

Appearance

Meconium: Soft, sticky, homogeneous mass, odorless and colored greenish-brown to black.

Infant stools: Golden-yellow with breast-feeding (bilirubin); after prolonged standing green (biliverdin), brown in infants fed cow's milk (stercobilin).

Adult stools: Brown (stercobilin, bilifuscin, mesobilifuscin). Darkening due to oxidation in the air; darker with animal diet of low bulkage, lighter in color with high-bulkage vegetable diet. Black from plant juices (raspberries), charcoal, iron (iron sulfide); pitch-black at high hematin content (black pudding; hemorrhages in stomach and in upper intestinal segments). Light-gray with fat-containing stools (not because of fat content but owing to degradation products of biliary pigments[6]).

Odor

The meconium is generally odorless. The odor of the feces is due to volatile products of protein putrefaction.

Mass

Both the daily stool mass and transit time are affected by the composition of the diet (see Tables 2 and 3)[134,135]. After ingestion of a diet low in indigestible carbohydrates ('low in fiber content') the stool mass is small and the transit time prolonged; the reverse

Table 1   *Number of stools*

	Age	d⁻¹	Reference
Children	1st day*	3–4	13
	1st week	4–5	13
	2nd week	3–4	13
	3–6 weeks	2–3	13
	7–13 weeks	1–2	13
115 men		~1	9

* Of 500 normal newborns, 69% had their first stool within 12 hours, and 94% had it within 24 hours[14].

Table 2   *Stool mass at various ages*

	Unit	Mean	s	(Extreme range)	Reference
Meconium	g	–	–	(70–90)	7
84 children, 8–96 days	g/d	83	42	–	137
44 children, 2 months to 6 years	g/d	–	–	(6.6–54.1)	8
115 men, balanced European diet	g/d	124	40.2	(35–224)	9

is true for a diet of 'high fiber content'. After prolonged fasting[11] the stool mass decreases to 9.5–22 g/d. In adults on the customary Western European diet, daily mass in excess of 200 g is pathological[6]. It may range up to 1000 g or more (extreme values of 6000 g have been recorded) in cases of chronic pancreatic insufficiency, celiac disease, regional enteritis, and small-bowel resection[6,12]. For elimination in cholera, see the text on 'Water' on next page

Table 3   *Mouth-to-anus transit time and daily stool mass in relation to diet[134]*

		Transit time*		Stool mass	
		Mean	(Extreme range)	Mean	(Extreme range)
		h		g/d	
Diet of high fiber content	500 children	34	(20–48)	275	(150–350)
	24 vegetarians	42	(18–97)	225	(71–488)
Mixed diet	500 children	45	(24–59)	165	(120–260)
	13 adults	44	(23–64)	155	
European diet	9 children	76	(35–120)	110	(71–142)
	15 adults	83	(44–144)	104	(39–223)

*The mouth-to-anus transit time was determined as the time within which 20 out of 25 ingested plastic cubes appear in the feces.

↓See text below and on next page		SI unit	Mean	s	95% range (extreme range in brackets)	Other units	Mean	s	95% range (extreme range in brackets)	Reference
Physicochemical data										
↓ **Relative density** (d_4^{25})	33 subjects....................	...	1.09	–	–	...	...	...	...	15
↓ **Osmolality**	Relative to water in dialyzate ..	mmol/kg	357	–	284–430	mosm/kg	357	–	284–430	18
↓ **pH**	Meconium....................	...	...	...	...	...	6.1	–	(5.7–6.4)	26
	Infants, breast-fed	...	...	...	...	...	5.1	–	(4.0–7.0)	17
	Infants, fed cow's milk	...	...	...	...	...	6.5	–	(5.0–7.5)	17
	28 adults	...	...	...	...	...	7.15	0.65	–	27
	....	...	...	...	...	...	6.96	–	5.92–8.00 (5.6–9.4)	18
↓ **Energy**	....	MJ/d	0.58	–	<0.89	kcal/d	139	–	<213	25
	Relative to dry mass	MJ/kg	21.5	–	(17.6–25.1)	kcal/kg	5150	–	(4210–5990)	25

		Amount of substance				Mass				
		Unit	Mean	s	(Extreme range)	Unit	Mean	s	(Extreme range)	
↓ **Water**	Meconium, 12 newborn	mol/kg	43.0	1.7	–	g/kg	774	31	–	16
	21 infants, breast-fed	mol/kg	48.3	–	(42.2–54.9)	g/kg	870	–	(760–990)	17
	31 infants, fed cow's milk	mol/kg	41.1	–	(21.1–51.1)	g/kg	740	–	(380–920)	17
	44 children, 2 months to 6 years	mol/kg	–	–	(34.6–47.6)	g/kg	–	–	(623–857)	8
	20 adults	mol/kg	42.7	2.8	(38.8–47.7)	g/kg	770	50	(700–860)	10
	20 adults	mol/d	4.26	1.96	(1.9–8.7)	g/d	76.8	35.3	(34–157)	10
↓ **Dry mass**	Meconium....................	...	...	...	...	g/kg	276	–	–	23
	84 children, 8–96 days	...	...	...	...	g/d	10.5	4.2	–	137
	44 children, 2 months to 6 years	...	...	...	...	g/d	–	–	(2.0–12.9)	8
	24 adults	...	...	...	...	g/d	34.0	16.2	–	24
	7 adults....................	...	...	...	...	g/d	21	5	–	21
Ash	Relative to dry mass:									
	– meconium	...	...	...	...	g/kg	40	–	–	23
	– adults....................	...	...	...	...	g/kg	200	–	–	1

Relative density. Determined after removal of intestinal gases. Gas-containing stools have relative density values below 1.00.

Osmolality. Osmolality is determined primarily by the following ions (in parentheses, values for dialyzate in mmol/L[18]): cations: potassium (80), sodium (26), ammonium (15), and a portion of calcium (12.5) and magnesium (21); anions: bicarbonate (30), chloride (17), organic acids (172) and a portion of phosphate (2) and sulfate (1.5)[28–30].

pH. The pH depends on the diet, the rapidity of intestinal transit, intestinal flora, etc.

↓See text below		Amount of substance				Mass				Refer-ence
		Unit	Mean	s	95% range (extreme range in brackets)	Unit	Mean	s	95% range (extreme range in brackets)	
↓ Inorganic substances										
Bicarbonate....	....	mmol/kg	<30	–	–	...	...	...	...	29
↓ Chloride	Adults ingesting 50–150 mmol/d	mmol/d	–	–	(0.5–3.0)	mg/d	–	–	(18–106)	31
↓ Phosphorus	Meconium, 12 newborn.........	mmol/kg	5.28	1.45	–	mg/kg	164	45		16
	Adults ingesting 25–50 mmol/d.	mmol/d	–	–	(10–25)	mg/d	–	–	(310–770)	31
Fluoride	Mean intake 231 µmol/d	µmol/d	15	–	(10–23)	mg/d	0.29	–	(0.19–0.43)	32
Iodine..........	7 subjects.....................	nmol/d	–	–	(79–450)	µg/d	–	–	(10–57)	33
	Intake of 790 nmol/d...........	nmol/d	129	–	–	µg/d	16.4	–	–	34
	Intake of 4700 nmol/d..........	nmol/d	183	–	–	µg/d	23.2	–	–	34
↓ Potassium	Meconium, 12 newborn.........	mmol/kg	31.4	9.8	–	g/kg	1.23	0.38	–	16
	Adults ingesting 50–75 mmol/d.	mmol/d	–	–	(5–15)	g/d	–	–	(0.2–0.6)	31
	7 adults......................	mmol/d	11.3	4.1	–	g/d	0.44	0.16	–	21
Sodium	Meconium, 12 newborn.........	mmol/kg	136	23	–	g/kg	3.13	0.53	–	16
	Adults ingesting 50–150 mmol/d	mmol/d	–	–	(0.5–5.0)	g/d	–	–	(0.01–0.11)	31
	7 adults......................	mmol/d	6.5	3	–	g/d	0.15	0.07	–	21
↓ Calcium........	Meconium, 12 newborn.........	mmol/kg	11.6	4.18	–	g/kg	0.47	0.17	–	16
	Adults ingesting 10–40 mmol/d.	mmol/d	–	–	(7.5–33)	g/d	–	–	(0.30–1.32)	31
	Intake of 21.3 mmol/d.........	mmol/d	16.7	–	–	g/d	0.67	–	–	36
– of endogenous origin........	10 adults	mmol/d	3.4	1.5	(2.3–5.5)	g/d	0.14	0.06	(0.09–0.22)	37
Magnesium	Meconium, 12 newborn.........	mmol/kg	19.6	5.25	–	g/kg	0.48	0.13	–	16
	– Adults:									
	– intake of 10–20 mmol/d	mmol/d	–	–	(5–15)	g/d	–	–	(0.12–0.36)	31
	– intake of 9 mmol/d	mmol/d	5	–	–	g/d	0.12	–	–	38
Iron...........	Meconium, 6 newborn..........	µmol/kg	301	–	(215–485)	mg/kg	16.8	–	(12.0–27.1)	39
	Adults ingesting 125 µmol/d....	µmol/d	–	–	(100–120)	mg/d	–	–	(5.7–6.7)	40
	9 women ingesting 410 µmol/d .	µmol/d	344	–	–	mg/d	19.2	–	–	41
Copper........	Meconium, 6 newborn..........	µmol/kg	270	–	(150–390)	mg/kg	17.0	–	(9.5–24.7)	39
	Adults........................	µmol/d	30.8	20.9	–	mg/d	1.96	1.33	–	42
	Intake of 58 µmol/d	µmol/d	57.3	–	–	mg/d	3.64	–	–	43
Manganese	Adults........................	µmol/d	67.2	41.9	–	mg/d	3.69	2.30	–	42
	101 men......................	µmol/d	75	–	(<255)	mg/d	4.1	–	(<14)	44
	Intake of 55 µmol/d	µmol/d	52.1	–	–	mg/d	2.86	–	–	45
Zinc	Meconium, 6 newborn..........	µmol/kg	994	–	(593–1790)	mg/kg	65.0	–	(38.8–117)	39
	Adults........................	µmol/d	–	–	(78–158)	mg/d	–	–	(5.1–10.3)	46
	Intake of 193 µmol/d..........	µmol/d	162	–	–	mg/d	10.6	–	–	47
Lead..........	Children, 2 years	µmol/d	0.63	–	<0.87	mg/d	0.13	–	<0.18	48
	Adults ingesting 1.7 µmol/d	µmol/d	1.5	–	–	mg/d	0.32	–	–	49
Cadmium	Intake of 2.0 µmol/d...........	µmol/d	1.4	–	–	mg/d	0.16	–	–	47
Chromium	Mean intake of 1.2 µmol/d	µmol/d	1.2	–	(0.6–1.9)	mg/d	0.06	–	(0.03–0.10)	50

Energy. Values relative to dry mass above 25 MJ/kg are pathological and indicative of reduced food utilization.

Water. The upper limit of normal for fecal excretion of water is approximately 150 g/d for adults[18]. Large volumes are excreted in diarrhea – up to 10–20 L/d in cases of Asiatic cholera[19]. In congenital chloride diarrhea, a high rate of water excretion persists throughout life: infants 300 mL/d; about 3 L/d in one adult[20].

Dry mass. In the adult[1,11,21,22], 14–30% or more of the fecal solids consist of dead bacteria and 25–40% of food residues (cellulose, muscle fiber, etc.); about one-third are inorganic substances, one-third nitrogenous substances, one-sixth lipids, and one-sixth cellulose and like substances.

Inorganic substances. Sodium, chloride and bicarbonate as well as iodine are mainly of endogenous origin. The concentrations of these components are therefore little affected by the composition of the diet. By contrast, calcium, magnesium and, above all, the trace elements originate mostly from the food.

Chloride. An excess of chloride over sodium and potassium is excreted in chloride diarrhea (chloride concentrations up to 169 mmol/L; normally, 16 mmol/L)[20].

Phosphorus. The major portion of the phosphorus is present as calcium phosphate, and a small portion as solute phosphate ions[29,30].

Potassium. Potassium excretion is increased in primary hyperaldosteronism[35].

Calcium. The excretion of endogenous calcium is considerably increased in steatorrhea.

↓See text on next page		Amount of substance			95% range (extreme range in brackets)	Mass			95% range (extreme range in brackets)	Reference
		Unit	Mean	s		Unit	Mean	s		
Cobalt	Mean intake 5.1 µmol/d	µmol/d	0.68	–	(0.39–1.02)	µg/d	40	–	(23–60)	51
Molybdenum...	Mean intake 3.49 µmol/d	µmol/d	1.30	–	(0.94–2.0)	mg/d	0.125	–	(0.09–0.19)	52
Nickel	10 adults	µmol/d	4.4	–	(1.4–9.2)	mg/d	0.26	–	(0.08–0.54)	53
Selenium	Intake of 0.8–1.9 µmol/d	µmol/d	–	–	(0.10–0.38)	µg/d	–	–	(8–30)	54
Titanium	Intake of 6.3 µmol/d..........	µmol/d	6.1	–	–	mg/d	0.29	–	–	55
Vanadium......	Intake of 39 µmol/d	µmol/d	39	–	–	mg/d	2.0	–	–	56
Tin	Intake of 8–340 µmol/d.......	µmol/d	34	–	(8–340)	mg/d	4.0	–	(1–40)	57

Nitrogenous substances

↓See text on next page		Unit	Mean	s	95% range	Unit	Mean	s	95% range	Reference
↓ **Nitrogen**	Meconium	mol/kg	1.4	–	–	g/kg	19	–	–	23
	Children, 0–1 year	mmol/d	40	15	(17–67)	g/d	0.56	0.21	(0.24–0.94)	58
	Children, 1–4 years	mmol/d	46	17	(14–93)	g/d	0.64	0.24	(0.20–1.3)	58
	Children, 4–10 years..........	mmol/d	48	16	(24–103)	g/d	0.67	0.22	(0.34–1.45)	58
	Children, >10 years..........	mmol/d	64	21	(39–84)	g/d	0.89	0.30	(0.55–1.17)	58
	24 adults	mmol/d	128	14	(64–200)	g/d	1.8	0.2	(0.9–2.8)	24
	83 young men at minimal protein intake	mmol/d	45.2	11.0	–	g/d	0.633	0.154	–	59
↓ **Ammonia**	....	mmol/kg	–	–	(14.7–51.9)	mg/kg	–	–	(251–884)	60
	Dialyzate, 83 subjects..........	mmol/L	11.2	–	2.9–44	mg/L	191	–	(49–750)	18
↓ **Urea**...........		...	...	...	...	...	...	...	...	...
↓ **Amino acids** ...		...	...	...	...	...	...	...	...	...
↓ **Amines**		...	...	...	...	...	...	...	...	...
↓ **Porphyrins**										
Coproporphyrin	24 adults	µmol/d	0.645	0.313	–	mg/d	0.422	0.205	–	65
	Relative to dry mass: – 100 subjects.................	µmol/kg	4.6	4.6	–	mg/kg	3	3	–	66
Protoporphyrin	24 adults	µmol/d	1.70	1.01	–	mg/d	0.955	0.567	–	65
	Relative to dry mass: – 100 subjects.................	µmol/kg	27	21	–	mg/kg	15	12	–	66
↓ **Bilirubin**	Meconium....................	mmol/kg	1.00	–	(0.43–1.74)	mg/kg	585	–	(252–1020)	68
	Adults......................	µmol/d	–	–	(9–34)	mg/d	–	–	(5–20)	69
↓ **Urobilinogen**...	Men........................	µmol/d	170	–	(96–337)	mg/d	101	–	(57–200)	71
	Women......................	µmol/d	67	–	(135–253)	mg/d	40	–	(80–150)	71
	8 men	µmol/d	277	} –	(79–466)	mg/d	164	} –	(47–276)	72
	5 women	µmol/d	138			mg/d	82			
↓ **Purine base nitrogen**	....	mmol/d	–	–	(4.6–5.2)	mg/d	–	–	(64–73)	73
↓ **Protein**	Meconium, 35 specimens	...	...	...	...	g/kg	96.4	–	(56–164)	133
↓ **Enzymes**										
Trypsin	22 infants....................	...	...	...	...	mg/kg	152	–	(37–730)	132
	54 children	...	...	...	...	mg/kg	219	–	(80–742)	79
	100 adults	...	...	...	...	mg/kg	124	–	>30 (6–650)	80
Chymotrypsin..	22 infants....................	...	...	...	...	mg/kg	411	–	(67–1092)	132
	54 children	...	...	...	...	mg/kg	351	–	(75–839)	79
	100 adults	...	...	...	...	mg/kg	290	–	>120 (39–1265)	80
Lysozyme......	Infants, breast-fed	...	...	...	...	mg/kg	~170	–	–	81
	Infants, fed cow's milk	...	...	...	...	mg/kg	~10	–	–	81
	Adults.......................	...	...	...	...	–	–	–	0	81

↓See text below and on next page		Amount of substance				Mass				Reference
		Unit	Mean	s	(Extreme range)	Unit	Mean	s	(Extreme range)	
Non-nitrogenous substances										
↓ **Carbohydrates** .	Children, < 1 year..............	...	...	...	...	g/kg	–	–	(<8)	85
	Adults......................	...	...	...	...	–	–	–	0	85
↓ **Organic acids** ..	....	mmol/kg	150	–	(100–400)	...	...	...	...	29
	Filtrate, 20 subjects............	mmol/d	13.1	5.4	(4.3–21)	...	...	...	...	10
Lactic acid.....	11 children	mmol/d	1.78	–	(0.05–4.11)	mg/d	160	–	(4.5–370)	90
	28 adults	mmol/d	0.36	0.24	–	mg/d	32.4	22	–	91
	Filtrate, 20 subjects...........	mmol/d	0.62	0.76	(0.007–2.80)	mg/d	55.8	68.5	(0.63–252)	10
↓ **Lipids**										
↓ **Total fat**	....	...	...	...	...	...	...	...	...	

Nitrogen. The fecal nitrogen stems from mucus and the epithelial cells of the intestinal wall, the digestive fluids, bacteria, and the food. 17% of the nitrogen is contained in the bacterial fraction; about 47% is water-soluble[21]. Nitrogen excretion is increased in steatorrhea.

Ammonia. NH_3 is formed mainly by bacterial degradation of endogenous urea, and also of proteins and amino acids (mostly glutamine).

Urea. Normally not detectable in feces. Concentrations ranging up to 5% of the blood urea level have been found in cases of uremia[18].

Amino acids. Free amino acids – a small proportion of the total nitrogen – have been detected in children[61,62]. Glutamic acid reaches the highest concentration (8.2 mmol/kg)[62]. There is increased excretion of free amino acids in cystic fibrosis[63].

Amines. Various amines have been detected in the feces of children, notably tyramine and tryptamine[64].

Porphyrins. Feces also contain deuteroporphyrin and mesoporphyrin[65]. The porphyrin content of the feces is often increased in idiopathic steatorrhea[65] and in most forms of porphyria[67].

Bilirubin. The bilirubin content of the meconium decreases as the plasma concentration of bilirubin increases (values given refer to a plasma bilirubin level of less than 50 mg/L). Toward the end of the first postnatal year, as soon as the intestinal flora has developed, the bilirubin content of the infantile feces conforms to the adult value[70]. When the intestinal flora is disturbed by broad-spectrum antibiotics, adults, too, excrete larger amounts of bilirubin.

Urobilinogen. Various colorless and colored degradation products of bilirubin (predominantly stercobilinogen and stercobilin) are determined as urobilinogen. Urobilinogen is rarely found in the feces of infants in the first week after birth; it is found in small, variable amounts during the first postnatal year[69].

Purine bases. Besides purine bases, small amounts of uric acid are found in the feces and in the meconium[1].

Protein. Glycopeptides and mucopolysaccharides, some of them related to blood-group-specific substances, predominate in the meconium[74]. The plasma proteins in the meconium originate for the most part from swallowed amniotic fluid; pre-albumin, albumin, IgG, α_2-macroglobulin and transferrin have been detected[75]; IgA has also been found in the meconium[76]. The albumin content of the meconium is greatly increased in cystic fibrosis[77]; a concentration relative to dry mass of 20 mg/g and higher is demonstrable by means of test strips[78].

Enzymes. The fecal enzymes originate from the gastrointestinal juices, the intestinal-wall cells, and bacteria. Trypsin and chymotrypsin come from pancreatic juice. In newborn and very young infants, chymotryptic activity predominates, while tryptic activity is preponderant later[131]. The activities of these enzymes in the feces are reduced in moderately severe to severe pancreatic insufficiency[80,82,83] including cystic fibrosis[79,84]. By contrast, the

Table 4   *Disaccharidases in meconium (relative to protein)[133]*

	Number	Mean	(Extreme range)
		U/g	
Maltase........................	31	33.9	(0–93)
Lactase	30	0.13	(0–4)
Saccharase	31	3.9	(0–29.3)

U ≡ μmol min⁻¹.

Table 5   *Fecal lipid fractions*

Lipid fraction	27 adults[99]			10 newborn[105]	
	Mean	s	%*	g/d	%*
	g/d				
Total lipids.....................	4.20	6.10	–	3.10	–
Free sterols	1.62	2.50	39	0.51	16.4
Sterol esters...................	0.51	1.12	13	0.35	11.3
Triglycerides...................	0.49	1.30	11	–	–
Free fatty acids	1.35	3.0	31	–	–
Phospholipids..................	0.23	0.24	6	–	–

* Mass fraction of total lipids.

activity of the disaccharidases in the meconium is increased in cystic fibrosis (Table 4)[133].

Carbohydrates. Only indigestible dietary polysaccharides, such as cellulose and hemicellulose, are found in the feces of normal adults. Small quantities of glucose, galactose and/or lactose are frequently detectable in the stools of infants[85–87].

Organic acids. The organic acids account for about 75% of the anions in the dialyzate[18,88]. They are formed by bacterial degradation of unabsorbed carbohydrates and are neutralized by bicarbonate from intestinal secreta. High concentrations of organic acids are associated with a low fecal pH and increased water excretion[10,18]. Approximate composition of organic acid fraction (total concentration in dialyzate 172 mmol/L, of which 53% identified)[89]: formate 1.6 mmol/L; acetate 46 mmol/L; propionate 17 mmol/L; butyrate 15 mmol/L; isobutyrate 1.6 mmol/L; valerate 1.7 mmol/L; isovalerate 2.2 mmol/L; succinate 4.2 mmol/L; lactate 0.6 mmol/L; fumarate 0.8 mmol/L.

Lipids. Under normal circumstances – except in infants – about 98% of the fat ingested with the food is absorbed[94]. Approximately one-half of the fecal fat is of endogenous origin and probably originates mostly from desquamated intestinal-wall cells[94]. About 15% of the fecal lipids are contained in the bacterial fraction[21]. The composition of fecal fat is normally only slightly affected by the

↓See text below		Amount of substance				Mass				Reference
		Unit	Mean	s	(Extreme range)	Unit	Mean	s	(Extreme range)	
↓ **Fatty acids**.....	....	...	...	...	...	...	...	...	...	...
↓ **Phospholipids**..	On butter-containing diet.......	μmol/d	–	–	(43–217)	mg/d	–	–	(33–168)	110
	On fat-free diet	μmol/d	–	–	(68–258)	mg/d	–	–	(53–200)	110
↓ **Sterols**........	13 adults	...	...	...	...	mg/d	889	306	–	111
↓ **Neutral sterols**.	5 children, < 1½ years	...	...	...	...	mg/d	139	85	–	92
	5 children, 4 years	...	...	...	...	mg/d	278	121	–	92
	5 men	...	...	...	...	mg/d	719	472	–	92
	13 adults	...	...	...	...	mg/d	651	238	–	111
↓ **Bile acids***.....	18 children, 4 months to 5 years	μmol/d	275	115	–	mg/d	110	46	–	117
	5 children, < 1½ years	μmol/d	84	95	–	mg/d	34	38	–	92
	5 children, 4 years	μmol/d	118	95	–	mg/d	47	38	–	92
	5 men	μmol/d	733	385	–	mg/d	293	154	–	92
	13 adults	μmol/d	595	225	–	mg/d	238	90	–	111
	11 subjects.....................	μmol/d	490	–	(245–880)	mg/d	196	–	(98–352)	112

* 1 μmol is equivalent to 0.4 mg of free bile acids.

Table 6   *Fecal fat excretion (method of van de Kamer)*

	Mean	Normal range	Reference
		g/d	
84 children, 8–96 days..................	4.0	s 2.3	137
11 children, 0–1 year	2.3	< 4.3	58
29 children, 1–4 years	1.72	< 3.0	58
26 children, 4–10 years	1.79	< 3.1	58
5 children, 10 years	2.38	< 4.9	58
14 adults..............................	5.54	< 10.9	107
24 adults..............................	4.0	< 7.2	24
13 adults..............................	2.4	< 4.6	111
		$g\,d^{-1}\,kg^{-1}$	
Relative to body mass:			
– infants	–	< 2	93
– 10 infants, 11–22 days (breast-fed)....	0.37	0.15–0.59	106
– 10 infants, 11–22 days (cow's milk) ...	0.73	0.35–1.11	106

Table 7   *Fatty acid pattern of lipid fractions in adults[99]*

Fatty acid		Free fatty acids	Triglyceride fatty acids	Sterol ester fatty acids
		Mass fraction as percent		
$C_{12:0}$	Lauric acid	0.6	1.1	2.7
$C_{14:0}$	Myristic acid......................	2.2	4.8	5.0
$C_{16:0}$	Palmitic acid......................	32.3	29.7	27.5
$C_{16:1}$	Palmitoleic acid...................	1.8	2.3	8.2
$C_{18:0}$	Stearic acid.......................	35.4	24.1	23.9
$C_{18:1}$	Oleic acid.........................	16.5	22.5	11.7
$C_{18:2}$	Linoleic acid......................	4.0	5.8	9.4
$C_{20:0}$	Arachidic acid	5.6	6.9	7.0
	Other fatty acids*	1.6	2.8	4.6

* About 1% are hydroxyfatty acids, which are formed by bacterial action on unsaturated fatty acids[108,109].

lipid pattern of the diet because the lipids in the colon are altered by bacteria, particularly through hydrogenation of unsaturated fatty acids[95]. However, short-chain fatty acids are absorbed better than long-chain ones[96]. Separation of the fecal lipids into the individual substances requires considerable technical effort – column chromatography, thin-layer chromatography, gas chromatography[97–99] – which reveals the following distribution of fractions[97]: free fatty acids (41.9%), partly present in the form of soaps; di- and triglycerides (15.9%); phospholipids (6.3%); free sterols (28.7%); sterol esters (7.2%). Values obtained by a simplified technique are presented in Table 5.

Total fat. The indicated limit values as well as the values in Table 6 refer to the method of VAN DE KAMER[100] in which fat content is determined as fatty acids and sterols are not taken into account. Gravimetrically determined values are about 1–1.5 g/d, or 25%, higher[4,101]. In fat-free diets, about 2 g/d of fat is excreted in the feces[102]. Obese individuals excreted 0.55–1.93 g/d after an extended period of fasting[103]. The fat content of the feces is increased in various forms of malabsorption, at an unduly rapid intestinal transit of the food, in biliary and pancreatic diseases, and in cases of obstruction of lymph flow from the intestine. In chronic pancreatitis[5] fat excretion may be in excess of 60 g/d. Steatorrhea can be diagnosed far better by determining the fat content of the 24-hour stools than by determining it in the fecal dry mass[6]. Microscopic examination for undigested food constituents is of no diagnostic value[6,104].

Fatty acids. See Table 7 regarding the fatty-acid pattern of the lipid fractions. Free fatty acids account for 30–50% of total fat in adults[97,99], and for more than 50% in infants[105].

Phospholipids (Table 5) probably originate for the most part from intestinal bacteria. Phosphatidylglycerol, phosphatidylethanolamine, phosphatidylcholine and phosphatidylinositol have been detected[110].

Sterols. The sterols can be divided into two main fractions, neutral sterols and bile acids. The quantity and pattern of the sterols are affected by diet composition and by the bacterial flora in the intestine[113,114]. Steroidal hormones, too, are excreted in the feces, particularly so pregnanediol during pregnancy (about 20 mg/d) and in the meconium[115].

Neutral sterols. The neutral sterols are present in both free and esterified form (Table 5). They are a complex mixture of animal and vegetable sterols (Table 8) which are metabolized by the intestinal bacteria. In infants, coprosterol, formed from cholesterol by bacterial action, is almost entirely absent[116].

Bile acids. Action by intestinal bacteria results in formation of a highly complex mixture of isomers of cholanic acid substituted with 1–3 hydroxy or keto groups[118]. Large amounts of bile acids are excreted after ileal resection (up to 4 g/d[120]) and in certain cases of cystic fibrosis[117,119]. The excretion of bile acids is reduced in cirrhosis of the liver[111].

↓See text below		Amount of substance				Mass				Refer-ence
		Unit	Mean	s	(Extreme range)	Unit	Mean	s	(Extreme range)	
Vitamins										
↓ **Thiamine**	Relative to dry mass:									
	– Meconium, 15 newborn	μmol/kg	1.02	0.34	–	mg/kg	0.27	0.09	–	121
	– 20 infants, breast-fed	μmol/kg	61.4	11.7	–	mg/kg	16.3	3.1	–	121
	– 20 infants, fed cow's milk	μmol/kg	39.2	8.3	–	mg/kg	10.4	2.2	–	121
Vitamin B₆	Infants	μmol/d	–	–	(0.89–1.8)	mg/d	–	–	(0.15–0.30)	122
	Adults........................	μmol/d	–	–	(4.1–5.3)	mg/d	–	–	(0.7–0.9)	122
Vitamin B₁₂		nmol/d	~7	–	–	μg/d	~10	–	–	123
Ascorbic acid ..		μmol/d	–	–	(<60)	mg/d	–	–	(<10)	124
↓ **Bacteria**										
	Infants	...	...	...	...	10¹²/kg	–	–	(1–100)	125
	Adults........................	...	...	...	...	10¹²/kg	–	–	(10–100)	114 126
	Relative to dry mass:									
	– 33 adults....................	...	...	...	...	10¹²/kg	800	–	(100–2200)	128
↓ **Blood**										
	10 adults .... (a)	...	...	...	...	mL/d	1.27	–	(0.28–2.14)	129
	71 adults .... (b)	...	...	...	...	mL/d	1.69	1.24	–	130

Table 8   *Sterol patterns*

Sterol	Adults[99]		Infants[105]	
	Free sterols	Sterol ester sterols	Free sterols	Sterol ester sterols
	Mass fraction as percent			
Coprosterol	68.2	61.6	1.9	4.0
Cholesterol + cholestanol	15.8	20.8	87.1	75.4
7-Dehydrocholesterol + 7-choles-tenone	4.8	3.3	2.6	5.1
Phytosterols........................	10.2	13.2	8.4	15.5
Unknown sterols	1.0	1.1	–	–

Thiamine. Thiamine in the meconium appears to originate from swallowed amniotic fluid.

Bacteria. It has been estimated that up to 500 species of bacteria can occur in a stool specimen[127,128]. In the adult, 1–10%[114,125–128], and in the infant about 0.1%, are aerobic bacteria[125]. Among anaerobic bacteria, bifidus bacteria predominate in infants[125], while bifidus bacteria and bacteroides are present in approximately equal numbers in adults[114,126,128]. Methane-producing bacteria have been found in 40% of stool specimens[128].

Blood. Determined by (a) means of labeled chromium; (b) chemically. – Methods for detecting occult blood loss should have a sensitivity of 2.5–4.5 mL/d. Leukocytes are not normally found in the feces; when present, they are suggestive of damage to the intestinal mucosa[136].

References

1 KRZYWANEK and FLASCHENTRÄGER, in FLASCHENTRÄGER and LEHNARTZ (Eds.), *Physiologische Chemie*, volume II/2b, Springer, Berlin, 1957, page 202.
2 HINSBERG et al., in LANG et al. (Eds.), *Hoppe-Seyler/Thierfelder Handbuch der physiologisch- und pathologisch-chemischen Analyse*, 10th ed., volume 5, Springer, Berlin, 1953, page 401.
3 VAN PILSUM, J., in ALTMAN and DITTMER (Eds.), *Biology Data Book*, 2nd ed., volume 3, Federation of American Societies for Experimental Biology, Bethesda (Md.), 1974, page 1489.
4 WYBENGA and INKPEN, in HENRY et al. (Eds.), *Clinical Chemistry*, 2nd ed., Harper & Row, New York, 1974, page 1421.
5 RAFFENSPERGER et al., *Arch. intern. Med.*, **119**, 573 (1967).
6 HAEMMERLI and AMMANN, *Schweiz. med. Wschr.*, **93**, 1517 (1963).
7 ADAM, A., in BROCK, J. (Ed.), *Biologische Daten für den Kinderarzt*, 2nd ed., volume 1, Springer, Berlin, 1954, page 598.
8 ANDERSEN, D. H., *Amer. J. Dis. Child.*, **69**, 141 (1945).
9 RENDTORFF and KASHGARIAN, *Dis. Colon Rect.*, **10**, 222 (1967).
10 BUSTOS FERNÁNDEZ et al., *New Engl. J. Med.*, **284**, 295 (1971).
11 HARRISON, G. A., *Chemical Methods in Clinical Medicine*, 4th ed., Churchill, London, 1957, page 507.
12 FORDTRAN and DIETSCHY, *Gastroenterology*, **50**, 263 (1966).
13 GONCE and LEWIS, *Amer. J. Dis. Child.*, **80**, 274 (1950).
14 SHERRY and KRAMER, *J. Pediat.*, **46**, 158 (1955).
15 LEVITT and DUANE, *New Engl. J. Med.*, **286**, 973 (1972).
16 WIDDOWSON et al., *Lancet*, **2**, 373 (1962).
17 BULLEN and WILLIS, *Brit. med. J.*, **3**, 338 (1971).
18 WRONG, O. M., *Sci. Basis Med.*, 192 (1971).
19 PHILLIPS and SUMMERSKILL, in MAXWELL and KLEEMAN (Eds.), *Clinical Disorders of Fluid and Electrolyte Metabolism*, 2nd ed., McGraw-Hill, New York, 1972, page 897.
20 BREMER and HEINISCH, *Mschr. Kinderheilk.*, **121**, 403 (1973).
21 TRÉMOLIÈRES et al., *Nutr. et Dieta (Basel)*, **3**, 281 (1961).
22 RÜEDI, W. F., *Schweiz. med. Wschr.*, **93**, 1065 (1963).
23 BUCHANAN and RAPOPORT, *Pediatrics*, **9**, 304 (1952).
24 PIMPARKAR et al., *Amer. J. Med.*, **30**, 910 and 927 (1961).
25 WOLF, F., *Bibl. gastroent. (Basel)*, **5**, 293 (1962).
26 NORTON and SHOHL, *Amer. J. Dis. Child.*, **32**, 183 (1926).
27 KERN et al., *J. Lab. clin. Med.*, **64**, 874 (1964).
28 GOIFFON et al., *Gastroenterologia (Basel)*, **96**, 223 (1961).
29 GOIFFON et al., *Gastroenterologia (Basel)*, **96**, 312 (1961).
30 GOIFFON et al., *Gastroenterologia (Basel)*, **96**, 326 (1961).
31 BERGER, E. Y., in COMAR and BRONNER (Eds.), *Mineral Metabolism*, volume 1, part A, Academic Press, New York, 1960, page 249.
32 SPENCER et al., *Amer. J. Med.*, **49**, 807 (1970).
33 VAN MIDDLESWORTH, L., in ASTWOOD, E. B. (Ed.), *Clinical Endocrinology*, volume 1, Grune & Stratton, New York, 1960, page 103.
34 HARRISON, M. T., *Postgrad. med. J.*, **44**, 69 (1968).
35 SHIELDS et al., *Brit. med. J.*, **1**, 93 (1968).
36 SCHROEDER et al., *J. chron. Dis.*, **25**, 491 (1972).
37 MELVIN et al., *Quart. J. Med.*, **39**, 83 (1970).
38 SCHROEDER et al., *J. chron. Dis.*, **21**, 815 (1968/69).
39 CAVELL and WIDDOWSON, *Arch. Dis. Childh.*, **39**, 496 (1964).
40 JOHNSTON et al., *J. Nutr.*, **38**, 479 (1949).
41 WHITE and GYNNE, *J. Amer. diet. Ass.*, **59**, 27 (1971).
42 KEHOE et al., *J. Nutr.*, **19**, 579 (1940).
43 SCHROEDER et al., *J. chron. Dis.*, **19**, 1007 (1966).
44 HORIUCHI et al., *Osaka Cy med. J.*, **13**, 151 (1967).
45 SCHROEDER et al., *J. chron. Dis.*, **19**, 545 (1966).
46 VALLEE, B. L., *Physiol. Rev.*, **39**, 443 (1959).
47 SCHROEDER et al., *J. chron. Dis.*, **20**, 179 (1967).
48 BARLTROP and KILLALA, *Lancet*, **2**, 1017 (1967).
49 SCHROEDER and BALASSA, *J. chron. Dis.*, **14**, 408 (1961).
50 SCHROEDER et al., *J. chron. Dis.*, **15**, 941 (1962).

[51] SCHROEDER et al., *J. chron. Dis.,* **20**, 869 (1967).
[52] SCHROEDER et al., *J. chron. Dis.,* **23**, 481 (1970).
[53] HORAK and SUNDERMAN, *Clin. Chem.,* **19**, 429 (1973).
[54] SCHROEDER et al., *J. chron. Dis.,* **23**, 227 (1970).
[55] SCHROEDER et al., *J. chron. Dis.,* **16**, 55 (1963).
[56] SCHROEDER et al., *J. chron. Dis.,* **16**, 1047 (1963).
[57] SCHROEDER et al., *J. chron. Dis.,* **17**, 483 (1964).
[58] SHMERLING et al., *Pediatrics,* **46**, 690 (1970).
[59] SCRIMSHAW et al., *J. Nutr.,* **102**, 1595 (1972).
[60] ROBINSON, C. S., *J. biol. Chem.,* **52**, 445 (1922).
[61] HOOFT et al., *Ann. paediat. (Basel),* **205**, 73 (1965).
[62] HOOFT et al., *Helv. paediat. Acta,* **23**, 334 (1968).
[63] GIBBONS et al., *Lancet,* **1**, 877 (1967).
[64] BERIO et al., *Minerva pediat.,* **23**, 660 (1971).
[65] ENGLAND et al., *Clin. Sci.,* **22**, 447 (1962).
[66] WETTERBERG et al., *Scand. J. clin. Lab. Invest.,* **22**, 131 (1968).
[67] LEVERE and KAPPAS, *Advanc. clin. Chem.,* **11**, 133 (1968).
[68] FASHENA, G. J., *Amer. J. Dis. Child.,* **76**, 196 (1948).
[69] WITH, T. K., *Biologie der Gallenfarbstoffe,* Thieme, Stuttgart, 1960, page 277.
[70] SCHACHTER, D., *Med. Clin. N. Amer..* **47**, 621 (1963).
[71] BALIKOV, B., *Clin. Chem.,* **3**, 145 (1957); *Stand. Meth. clin. Chem.,* **2**, 192 (1958).
[72] BLOOMER et al., *Clin. chim. Acta,* **29**, 463 (1970).
[73] MENDEL and LYMAN, *J. biol. Chem.,* **8**, 115 (1910/11).
[74] RAPOPORT and BUCHANAN, *Science,* **112**, 150 (1950); FRASER and CLAMP, *Clin. chim. Acta,* **59**, 301 (1975); HARRIES, J. T., *Brit. med. Bull.,* **34**, 75 (1978).
[75] BARANDUN et al., *Schweiz. med. Wschr.,* **92**, 316 and 353 (1962); DE MURALT and ROULET, in PEETERS, H. (Ed.), *Protides of the Biological Fluids,* Proceedings of the 11th Colloquium, Brügge 1963, Elsevier, Amsterdam, 1964, page 216.
[76] RULE et al., *Pediatrics,* **48**, 601 (1971).
[77] GREEN and SHWACHMAN, *Pediatrics,* **41**, 989 (1968); RULE et al., *Pediatrics,* **45**, 847 (1970).
[78] STEPHAN et al., *Pediatrics,* **55**, 35 (1975).
[79] BARBERO et al., *Amer. J. Dis. Child.,* **112**, 536 (1966).
[80] AMMANN, R., *Schweiz. med. Wschr.,* **98**, 744 (1968); *Schweiz. med. Wschr.,* **99**, 504 (1969); AMMANN et al., *Amer. J. dig. Dis.,* **13**, 123 (1968).
[81] BRAUN, O. H., *Dtsch. med. Wschr.,* **94**, 1458 (1969).
[82] HAVERBACK et al., *Amer. J. dig. Dis.,* **7**, 972 (1962).
[83] SCHNEIDER et al., *Dtsch. med. Wschr.,* **99**, 1449 (1974); LÖFFLER et al., *Med. Klin.,* **70**, 1755 (1975).
[84] BONIN et al., *J. Pediat.,* **83**, 594 (1973).
[85] GRYBOSKI et al., *Gastroenterology,* **47**, 26 (1964).
[86] DAVIDSON and MULLINGER, *Pediatrics,* **46**, 632 (1970).
[87] SIMAR and FARRIAUX, *Ann. Pédiat.,* **19**, 873 (1972).
[88] FORDTRAN, J. S., *New Engl. J. Med.,* **284**, 329 (1971).
[89] RUBINSTEIN et al., *Clin. Sci.,* **37**, 549 (1969).
[90] HOOFT et al., *Ann. paediat. (Basel),* **205**, 73 (1965).
[91] KERN et al., *J. Lab. clin. Med.,* **64**, 874 (1964).
[92] HUANG et al., *Amer. J. clin. Nutr.,* **29**, 1196 (1976).
[93] FOMON et al., *Amer. J. clin. Nutr.,* **23**, 1299 (1970).

[94] Leading Article, *Lancet,* **2**, 627 (1969).
[95] WIGGINS et al., *Gut,* **10**, 400 (1969).
[96] BERG and ALTENBURG, *Med. u. Ernähr.,* **12**, 6 (1971).
[97] BÖHLE and STARCK, *Med. u. Ernähr.,* **8**, 81 (1967).
[98] THOMPSON et al., *J. Lab. clin. Med.,* **73**, 512 (1969).
[99] ERB et al., *Klin. Wschr.,* **48**, 303 (1970).
[100] VAN DE KAMER et al., *J. biol. Chem.,* **177**, 347 (1949).
[101] KELLEHER et al., *Clin. chim. Acta,* **30**, 267 (1970).
[102] LEWIS and PARTIN, *J. Lab. clin. Med.,* **44**, 91 (1954).
[103] ERB et al., *Z. klin. Chem.,* **8**, 498 (1970).
[104] CREUTZFELDT, W., *Verh. dtsch. Ges. inn. Med.,* **70**, 781 (1964).
[105] BÖHLE et al., *Klin. Wschr.,* **48**, 800 (1970).
[106] SOUTHGATE and BARRETT, *Brit. J. Nutr.,* **20**, 363 (1966).
[107] BERNDT et al., *Dtsch. med. Wschr.,* **88**, 225 (1963).
[108] GIARDINI et al., *New Engl. J. Med.,* **286**, 1059 (1972).
[109] SOONG et al., *Gastroenterology,* **63**, 748 (1972).
[110] ALI and KUKSIS, *Canad. J. Biochem.,* **45**, 703 (1967).
[111] MIETTINEN, T. A., *Helv. med. Acta,* **37**, 113 (1973).
[112] SHELTAWY and LOSOWSKY, *Clin. chim. Acta,* **64**, 127 (1975).
[113] MOORE et al., *J. clin. Invest.,* **47**, 1517 (1968).
[114] HILL and ARIES, *J. Path.,* **104**, 129 (1971); HILL et al., *Lancet,* **1**, 95 (1971); CROWTHER et al., *Gut,* **14**, 790 (1973).
[115] TAYLOR, W., *Vitam. and Horm.,* **29**, 201 (1971).
[116] GUSTAFSSON and WERNER, *Acta physiol. scand.,* **73**, 305 (1968).
[117] WEBER et al., *New Engl. J. Med.,* **289**, 1001 (1973).
[118] ENEROTH et al., *J. Lipid Res.,* **7**, 524 (1966); EVRARD and JANSSEN, *J. Lipid Res.,* **9**, 226 (1968).
[119] GOODCHILD et al., *Arch. Dis. Childh.,* **50**, 769 (1975).
[120] WOODBURY and KERN, *J. clin. Invest.,* **50**, 2531 (1971).
[121] KUSAKA, T., *Tokushima J. exp. Med.,* **15**, 93 (1968).
[122] VILTER, R. W., in WOHL and GOODHART (Eds.), *Modern Nutrition in Health and Disease,* 3rd ed., Lea & Febiger, Philadelphia, 1964, page 400.
[123] CALLENDER and SPRAY, *Lancet,* **1**, 1391 (1951).
[124] VILTER, R. W., in WOHL and GOODHART (Eds.), *Modern Nutrition in Health and Disease,* 3rd ed., Lea & Febiger, Philadelphia, 1964, page 433.
[125] MATA et al., *Amer. J. clin. Nutr.,* **25**, 1380 (1972).
[126] SCHMIDT, F., *Schweiz. med. Wschr.,* **98**, 532 (1968).
[127] MOORE and HOLDEMAN, *Amer. J. clin. Nutr.,* **25**, 1306 (1972); *Amer. J. clin. Nutr.,* **27**, 1450 (1974).
[128] FINEGOLD et al., *Amer. J. clin. Nutr.,* **27**, 1456 (1974).
[129] ROCHE et al., *J. clin. Invest.,* **36**, 1183 (1957).
[130] EBAUGH and BEEKEN, *J. Lab. clin. Med.,* **53**, 777 (1959).
[131] SÄLZER et al., *Europ. J. Pediat.,* **121**, 279 (1976).
[132] ROBINSON et al., *Clin. chim. Acta,* **62**, 225 (1975).
[133] ANTONOWICZ et al., *Pediatrics,* **56**, 782 (1975).
[134] BURKITT et al., *J. Amer. med. Ass.,* **229**, 1068 (1974).
[135] BALASEGARAM and BURKITT, *Lancet,* **1**, 152 (1976); CUMMINGS et al., *Amer. J. clin. Nutr.,* **29**, 1468 (1976); SPILLER et al., *Amer. J. clin. Nutr.,* **30**, 659 (1977); GLOBER et al., *Lancet,* **2**, 110 (1977).
[136] Leading Article, *Brit. med. J.,* **4**, 62 (1972).
[137] MACLEAN et al., *J. Pediat.,* **92**, 562 (1978).

Synovial fluid consists of a serum ultrafiltrate and a secretion containing mucopolysaccharides which is produced by the cells of the synovial membrane. Normal synovial fluid values have been compiled by ROPES and BAUER[1] and also by DITTMER[2].

Because of the difficulty of collecting sufficient fluid from non-diseased joints for examination, normal values of many constituents are not fully known. For diagnostic purposes[1,3,4] it is usually sufficient to consider the differences between the composition of the fluids in degenerative joint diseases and in inflammatory joint diseases. The examination may give clues as to inflammatory activity and can be of help in the differential diagnosis of joint diseases.

Unless otherwise indicated, the data presented below refer to fluid from the knee joint. However, the composition of the fluid of one joint is by no means representative of that of other joints of an individual.

↓See text below	Material	SI unit	Mean	s	(Extreme range)	Other units	Mean	s	(Extreme range)	Reference
Physical data										
↓ **Volume**	In 1 knee joint	mL	1.1	–	(0.13–4.00)	...	...	...	...	2
Relative density .... (d_{20}^{20})	25 subjects post mortem	...	–	–	(1.0081–1.015)	...	...	...	...	7
↓ **Relative viscosity** (37 °C)...............	....	...	–	–	(>300)	...	...	...	...	8
↓ **Limiting viscosity number**										
– at shear rate of 500 s⁻¹	....	10^{-3} m³ g⁻¹	5.23	–	(4.5–6.0)	cm³ g⁻¹	5230	–	(4500–6000)	9
– at shear rate of 1300 s⁻¹	....	10^{-3} m³ g⁻¹	4.36	–	(3.8–4.9)	cm³ g⁻¹	4360	–	(3800–4900)	9
↓ **Osmolarity**............	6 adults	mmol/L	296	–	(292–300)	mosm/L	296	–	(292–300)	17
↓ **pH**......................	....	...	...	...	...	–	7.434	–	(7.31–7.64)	19
↓ **CO₂ pressure**.........	....	kPa	–	–	(4.7–7.3)	mmHg	–	–	(35–55)	–
↓ **O₂ pressure**	....						...	...	...	...

		Amount of substance				Mass			
		Unit	Mean	s	(Extreme range)	Unit	Mean	s	(Extreme range)	
Water.................	25 subjects post mortem	mol/kg	–	–	(53.3–54.8)	g/kg	–	–	(960–988)	7
Dry mass...............			...	...	...	g/kg	34	–	(12–48)	2
Inorganic substances										
↓ **Carbon dioxide**........	....	mmol/L	–	–	(19.3–30.6)	[Vol%]	–	–	(43.0–68.2)]	24
↓ **Chloride**	....	mmol/L	107.4	–	(87–138)	g/L	3.81	–	(3.08–4.89)	15

Volume. The upper limit of the normal range is difficult to define. Effusions of 2–6 mL could be externally palpated on the knee joint in some subjects in the absence of a joint disease[5,6]. In the presence of joint diseases, volumes of 10–30 mL and occasionally more can be found.

Viscosity. The synovial fluid has thixotropic properties; its viscosity decreases at increasing shear rate[9–11]. The rheological properties are determined by the concentration of hyaluronic acid, its molecular size and form as well as by its association with protein and other constituents of synovial fluid[9,12–14]. The viscosity may be lowered in pathological effusions[8,9,15,16].

Osmolarity. Technique employed: measurement of vapor pressure. Higher values are obtained by freezing-point measurements[18]. The osmolarity is identical with that of the plasma[17]. Values found in the presence of joint diseases fell within the specified range[17].

pH. Measured in vivo. Reduced in inflammatory joint diseases (down to 6.7[117]) in connection with the increased lactate concentration[20,21].

CO₂ pressure. Results of measurements at normal pH values of synovial fluid. At reduced pH the CO₂ pressure increases, reaching values between 5 and 20 kPa in various joint diseases[20–22].

O₂ pressure (Table 1). Low values are found especially at increased lactate concentrations[21,22]. In rheumatoid arthritis they

Table 1 *O₂ pressure in joint diseases*[22]

	kPa		mmHg	
	Mean	s	Mean	s
Rheumatoid arthritis...............	3.53	2.57	26.5	19.3
Osteoarthritis	5.72	2.01	42.9	15.1
Traumatic effusions	8.40	2.56	63.0	19.2

extend down to 0 – the arterial blood supply cannot keep pace with the intensified metabolism of the inflamed joint[22,23].

Carbon dioxide. According to Donnan's equilibrium, the bicarbonate concentration is higher than in the serum[1].

Chloride. Concentrations are higher than in serum, in accordance with Donnan's equilibrium[1].

Phosphate, inorganic. The concentration conforms to that in the serum[1]; this is true also in joint diseases including chondrocalcinosis[25–27].

Pyrophosphate, inorganic. The concentration conforms roughly to that in the serum except in chondrocalcinosis, in which the val-

↑↓See text on page 159 and below	Material	Amount of substance				Mass				Reference
		Unit	Mean	s	(Extreme range)	Unit	Mean	s	(Extreme range)	
↑**Phosphate**	....	...	...	...	...	...	...	...	...	...
↑**Pyrophosphate**	....	...	...	...		...	...	...	...	...
↓**Sulfate**	....	...	...	...		...	...	...	...	...
↓**Potassium**	10 subjects	mmol/L	4.0	0.25	–	mg/L	156	10	–	31
↓**Sodium**	10 subjects	mmol/L	136	1.63	–	g/L	3.13	0.037	–	31
↓**Calcium**	25 subjects post mortem	mmol/L	–	–	(1.2–2.4)	mg/L	–	–	(48–96)	7
↓**Magnesium**	....	...	...	...		...	...	...	...	...
↓**Iron**	50 subjects post mortem	µmol/kg	5.19	5.12	–	µg/kg	290	286	–	32
↓**Copper**	50 subjects post mortem	µmol/kg	4.33	2.58	–	µg/kg	275	164	–	32
↓**Zinc**	24 subjects post mortem	µmol/kg	2.69	3.32	–	µg/kg	176	217	–	32
Nitrogenous substances										
↓**Total nitrogen**	25 subjects post mortem	mmol/L	–	–	(60–286)	g/L	–	–	(0.84–4.0)	7
↓**Nonprotein nitrogen** ..	....	mmol/L	–	–	(16–31)	g/L	–	–	(0.22–0.43)	24
Urea	....	mmol/L	2.5	–	–	mg/L	150	–	–	38
↓**Uric acid**	....	mmol/L	0.23	–	–	mg/L	39	–	–	38
↓**Amino acids**	....	...	...	...	...	...	...	...	...	...
↓**Deoxyribonucleic acid**	....	...	...	...	...	...	...	...	...	...
↓**Protein**	....	...	...	...	...	...	...	...	...	...

ues are 2 to 10 times higher[25–27]. In chondrocalcinosis, calcium pyrophosphate crystals may form in the synovial fluid[27–29].

Sulfate. The concentration of inorganic sulfate conforms to that in the serum but tends to be *increased* in traumatic degenerative arthritis and *decreased* in rheumatoid arthritis[30].

Potassium. Concentrations are lower than in the serum, in keeping with Donnan's equilibrium[1]. No characteristic change in joint diseases[15].

Sodium. Concentrations are lower than in the serum, in keeping with Donnan's equilibrium[1]. No characteristic change in joint diseases[15].

Calcium. Calcium concentrations are lower than in the serum, in keeping with Donnan's equilibrium. In some cases of chondrocalcinosis the calcium concentration was low; in other joint diseases it apparently does not change[25, 26].

Magnesium. Concentrations are lower than in the serum, in keeping with Donnan's equilibrium.

Iron. Hemosiderin deposits have been found in the synovial tissue in rheumatoid arthritis (due to intra-articular hemorrhage)[33].

Copper. Increased concentrations are found in inflammatory joint diseases and are primarily a reflection of the increased ceruloplasmin concentration[34, 35].

Zinc. In contrast to inflammatory joint diseases, the zinc values are normal in degenerative and traumatic joint lesions[36, 37].

Total nitrogen. This is increased in joint diseases owing to increased protein concentration.

Nonprotein nitrogen. This amounts to approximately 10% of total nitrogen.

Uric acid. The uric-acid concentration of the joint fluid roughly conforms to that in the serum. In gout, uric-acid crystals are almost invariably found in the synovial fluid of the affected joint[39].

Amino acids. In 14 patients with various joint diseases, the amino-acid concentration varied between 2.14 mmol/L and 3.70 mmol/L, while the ratio between the amino-acid concentrations in the synovial fluid and the plasma ranged from 1.50 to 0.82[40]. The concentration of total hydroxyproline approximates to that in the serum[113].

Deoxyribonucleic acid. In cell damage due to various causes, deoxyribonucleic acid can pass into the synovial fluid[41].

Protein. See Table 2 for normal values. Except for a few proteins that are present in extremely low concentrations, the proteins originate from the serum. The protein concentration is frequently increased in joint diseases[8, 15, 35, 49, 50], with changes in the proportions of the individual fractions (Table 3a).

Proteins of low-molecular mass pass through the synovialis more readily than proteins of high-molecular mass notably glycoproteins[51, 52]. As the severity of an inflammation increases, so does the permeability of the synovialis for plasma proteins, and the concentration of certain α_2-glycoproteins, particularly α_2-macroglobulin[45, 52, 53] and haptoglobin[44, 51, 54, 55], increases considerably (Table 4).

The increase in the concentrations of the immunoglobulins in joint inflammations appears to be due in part to their formation in the synovial tissue[52, 56, 57]. Lactoferrin, which is present in the joint fluid in increased amounts in inflammations, seems to originate solely from the neutrophil granulocytes[58, 116]; the β_2-microglobulin seems to stem partly from lymphocytes[59], and in inflammatory joint diseases its concentration in the synovial fluid is higher than in plasma[119].

Fibrinogen and fibrinogen–fibrin degradation products (FFDP) are not detectable in normal synovial fluid, but traces of plasminogen are[53, 60]. Fibrinogen and large amounts of FFDP are, however, found in the synovial fluid in inflammatory joint diseases[53].

The activities of the first four components of the complement system (Fig. 1) in the synovial fluid are reduced in some inflamed joints; these are changes suggestive of activation of the complement system in the synovial fluid by an immune complex[61, 62].

Table 2 *Proteins in synovial fluid*

	Method	Subjects	Unit	Mean	s	95% range (extreme range in brackets)	Reference
Total protein	Literature review	Postmortem specimens	g/L	–	–	(9–36)	–
	Biuret reaction	8 men	g/L	12	–	(5–18)	42
	Protein N × 6.25	13 specimens	g/L	13.1	–	(10.4–15.8)	9
Albumin	Total protein × 0.6	13 specimens	g/L	8	–	(6–10)	9
α_1-Antitrypsin	Radial immunodiffusion	5 subjects	g/L	0.78	0.17	–	43
Ceruloplasmin	*p*-Phenylenediamine oxidation	6 subjects	mg/L	43	16	–	35
Haptoglobin	No data	12 subjects	g/L	0.09	–	–	44
α_2-Macroglobulin	Radial immunodiffusion	11 men	g/L	0.31	0.21	–	45
Lactoferrin	Radioimmuno assay	9 subjects	mg/L	0.44	0.33	–	116
IgG	Radial immunodiffusion	32 postmortem specimens	g/L	2.62	–	1.47–4.62	46
IgA	Radial immunodiffusion	32 postmortem specimens	g/L	0.84	–	0.62–1.15	46
IgM	Radial immunodiffusion	32 postmortem specimens	g/L	0.14	–	0.09–0.22	46
IgE	Radioimmuno assay	7 subjects post mortem	μg/L	14	–	(3.7–46)	47

Table 3a *Protein fractions in synovial fluid[48]*

		Volume in knee joint mL	Biuret reaction Protein g/L	Albumin	α_1-Globulin	α_2-Globulin	β-Globulin	γ-Globulin	$\dfrac{\alpha_1\text{-Globulin}}{\alpha_2\text{-Globulin}}$	19S	7S	4S	1S
				Fraction as percent (Paper electrophoresis at pH 8.6)						Fraction as percent (Ultracentrifuge)			
Synovial fluid	Normal	0.2–0.4	18	63	7	7	9	14	1.0	–	–	–	3
	Post mortem	7	18	50	9	7	12	23	1.3	2	12	83	3
	Traumatic	10	26	55	5	8	11	21	0.7	3	8	88	1
	Rheumatoid arthritis	–	45	45	5	10	14	26	0.5	4	24	72	0
Serum	Normal	–	70	49	6	12	17	16	0.5	2	12	86	0

Table 3b *Synovial fluid immunoglobulins and complement components in joint diseases[118]*

	Rheumatoid arthritis Number	Mean g/L	s	Osteoarthritis Number	Mean g/L	s
IgG	34	8.03	2.98	37	5.72	2.36
IgM	35	0.98	0.54	38	0.66	0.43
IgA	33	1.29	0.60	38	0.97	0.48
C4	33	0.10	0.05	25	0.15	0.07
C3	38	0.31	0.17	42	0.34	0.14
Factor B	39	0.11	0.05	41	0.08	0.04

Table 4 *Ratio between concentrations of individual proteins in synovial fluid and in serum*

	Control subjects	Rheumatoid arthritis	Reference
Albumin	0.43	0.57	51
Acid α_1-glycoprotein	0.23	0.71	52
Ceruloplasmin	0.16	0.53	52
Haptoglobin	0.03	0.38	51
α_2-Macroglobulin	0.03	0.35	52
Transferrin	0.24	0.66	52
IgG	0.13	0.83	52
IgM	0.05	0.51	52
IgE	0.22	0.52	47

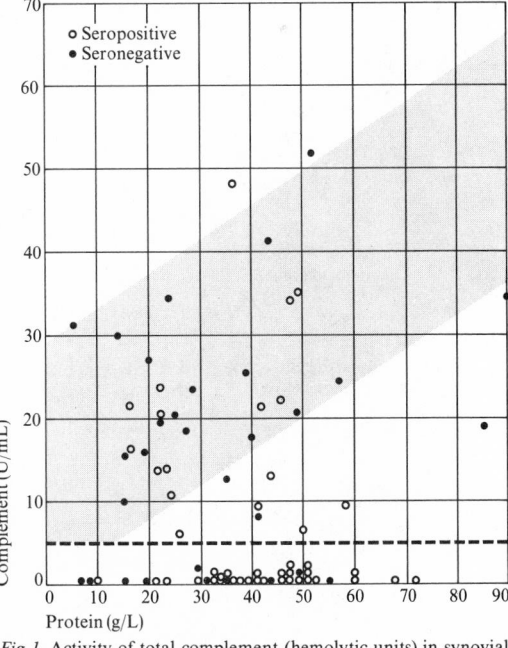

Fig. 1. Activity of total complement (hemolytic units) in synovial fluid in rheumatoid arthritis. The shaded area represents the 90% confidence range for values in traumatic or degenerative joint diseases; the broken line designates the detection limit for complement activity[114].

↓See text below and on next page	Material	Amount of substance				Mass				Refer- ence
		Unit	Mean	s	(Extreme range)	Unit	Mean	s	(Extreme range)	
↓ **Enzymes**	....	...	...	...	...	...	...	...	...	...
Nitrogen-free substances										
↓ **Carbohydrates, protein-bound**										
Hexosamine	13 specimens .... (a)	mmol/L	0.84	–	(0.06–1.5)	g/L	0.15	–	(0.01–0.27)	9
Sialic acid.............	13 specimens .... (a)	mmol/L	0.32	–	(0.22–0.48)	g/L	0.10	–	(0.07–0.15)	9
	10 specimens	mmol/L	0.91	0.22	–	g/L	0.28	0.07	–	63
↓ **Glycosaminoglycans** ...	12 men......................	...	...	...	...	g/L	2.50	0.41	–	64
Hyaluronic acid........	12 men	...	...	...	...	g/L	2.19	0.33	–	64
	13 specimens .... (a)	...	...	...	...	g/L	2.26	–	(1.45–2.94)	9
	In 1 knee joint........... (a)	...	...	...	...	mg	2.03	–	(0.59–5.88)	9
Chondroitin-4-sulfate ..	12 men	...	...	...	...	mg/L	42	6.2	–	64
↓ **Glucose**............	....	...	...	...	...	...	...	...	...	...
↓ **Lactic acid**............	....	...	...	...	...	...	...	...	...	...
↓ **Pyruvic acid**............	....	...	...	...	...	...	...	...	...	...
↓ **Ascorbic acid**	....	...	...	...	...	...	...	...	...	...
↓ **Lipids**										
↓ **Sediment**										

Table 5 *Hydrolytic enzymes in synovial fluid (U/L)*

	Control subjects	Rheumatoid arthritis	Refer- ence
Acid phosphatase	1.6	5.4	88
Dipeptidyl peptidase (cathepsin C)...................	2.5	6.2	88
β-D-Glucuronidase.............	<0.25	7.8 (0.6–33)	89
β-D-Galactosidase	<0.17	1.6 (0.2–5.5)	89
β-N-Acetyl-D-glucosaminidase .	12.2 (8.0–16)	63 (13–267)	89

Enzymes. Many enzymes have been detected in the synovial fluid (Table 6); they originate from the serum, the synovial cells, the rheumatoid granulation tissue, and the white blood cells[77–83, 85, 88]. In normal synovial fluid their activity is generally lower than in the serum. In inflammatory joint diseases individual enzymes may reach high activities; this is true especially of enzymes of lysosomal origin (acid phosphatases, glycoside hydrolases; Table 5) and of lactate dehydrogenase (according to Jasani et al.[81], 10 times the serum value, for example). In chondrocalcinosis, the activity of inorganic pyrophosphatase appears to be reduced[86]; whether this is also true of alkaline phosphatase has not been established[25, 26, 87].

Carbohydrates, protein-bound. (a) Pooled specimens of 71 joints and 3 individual specimens. – The concentrations of hexosamine and sialic acid are increased in rheumatoid arthritis[9].

Table 6 *Enzymes in synovial fluid*

EC-number	Name of enzyme	Reference	EC-number	Name of enzyme	Reference
1.1.1.27	Lactate dehydrogenase	77,80,81,83, 84,90,91,112	3.2.1.20	α-D-Glucosidase	78
(1.1.1.27)	α-Hydroxybutyrate dehydrogenase	112	3.2.1.23	β-D-Galactosidase	78,89
1.1.1.37	Malate dehydrogenase	77,92	3.2.1.24	α-D-Mannosidase	78,101
1.1.1.41	Isocitrate dehydrogenase (NAD+)	92	3.2.1.25	β-D-Mannosidase	99
1.2.1.12	Glyceraldehyde-phosphate dehydrogenase	77	3.2.1.30	β-N-Acetyl-D-glucosaminidase	78,89,95
1.4.1.2	Glutamate dehydrogenase	77	3.2.1.31	β-D-Glucuronidase	78,89,91,95
1.6.4.2	Glutathione reductase	92	3.4.11.1	Aminopeptidase (cytosol)	91
1.14.11.2	Proline,2-oxoglutarate dioxygenase	115	3.4.11.4	Tripeptide aminopeptidase	91
2.6.1.1	Aspartate aminotransferase	77,81,92	3.4.14.1	Dipeptidyl peptidase I	88
2.6.1.2	Alanine aminotransferase	77,81,92	3.4.21.1	Chymotrypsin	91
2.7.1.1	Hexokinase	77	3.4.21.4	Trypsin	91
2.7.1.40	Pyruvate kinase	77	3.4.21.11	Elastase	112
2.7.5.1	Phosphoglucomutase	77	3.4.22.1	Cathepsin B	82,88,95
3.1.3.1	Alkaline phosphatase	25,26,79,87	3.4.24.3	*Clostridium histolyticum* collagenase	98,100
3.1.3.2	Acid phosphatase	81,85,88,91, 93,95,112	3.5.1.26	4-N-(2-β-D-Glucosaminyl)-L-asparaginase	78
			3.5.3.1	Arginase	91
3.1.3.5	5′-Nucleotidase	94	3.6.1.1	Inorganic pyrophosphatase	86
3.1.6.1	Arylsulfatase	78	4.1.2.13	Fructose-bisphosphate aldolase	77,92
3.2.1.17	Lysozyme	96,97,116	5.3.1.1	Triosephosphate isomerase	77
			5.3.1.9	Glucosephosphate isomerase	77,92

Table 7   *Synovial fluid lipids in joint diseases*[75]

	Rheumatoid arthritis			Osteoarthritis			Gout		
	Number	Mean	(Extreme range)	Number	Mean	(Extreme range)	Number	Mean	(Extreme range)
		mmol/L			mmol/L			mmol/L	
Triglycerides.........................	54	0.74	(0.23–1.19)	38	0.24	(0.14–0.75)	–	1.56	(1.15–2.61)
Cholesterol	54	2.48	(1.19–3.47)	38	2.19	(1.04–4.07)	–	1.89	(1.06–2.59)

Table 8   *Synovial fluid in joint diseases*[76]

	Normal	Not inflamed	Inflamed	Septic	Hemorrhagic
Volume (mL)	<3.5	>3.5	>3.5	>3.5	>3.5
Appearance......................	Clear, color-less	Straw-colored, clear	Cloudy, yellow	Cloudy, yellow	Bloody
Viscosity......................	High	High	Low	Low	Variable
Fibrin clot	Absent	Usually absent	Present	Present	Usually absent
Mucin clot*	Strong	Strong	Friable	Friable	Variable
Nucleated cells (μL^{-1})	<200	200–5000	2000–100000	20000–200000	200–10000
Of which polymorphonuclear leukocytes (%)	<25	<25	>50	>75	<50
Difference between glucose concentration of blood and synovial fluid (mg/L)................	<100	<100	>250	>250	<250
Culture	Negative	Negative	Negative	Often positive	Negative

* After addition of acetic acid.

Glycosaminoglycans. (a) Pooled specimens of 71 joints and 3 individual specimens. – Hyaluronic acid accounts for about 98% of the glycosaminoglycans; about 2% are chondroitin sulfate[64]. In joint diseases the hyaluronate concentration is usually decreased[8,9,15,49,50], but the total amount is increased because of the increased fluid volume in the affected joint[9]. Hyaluronic acid is a polymer of N-acetylglucosamine and glucuronic acid and is in polar linkage to protein in the synovial fluid. In normal joint fluid, the hyaluronate contains approximately 2% of protein[65,66]; in pathological effusions it contains 5–10%, possibly owing to association with IgG[50,67]. In the normal fluid the relative molecular mass of the hyaluronic acid[9] amounts to 6 to 11×10^6; in rheumatoid arthritis it amounts to 1 to 2×10^6. The reduced degree of polymerization of the hyaluronic acid entails a lower limiting viscosity number and accounts for the pathological result of the mucin test (Table 8)[9,16,68].

Glucose. Depending on the degree of glycolysis, the glucose concentration in normal synovial fluid is up to 10% lower than that in the serum. Low values are found in inflammatory joint diseases as a result of glycolysis by the leukocytes, and in septic joint diseases owing to glucose consumption by bacteria (Table 8).

Lactic acid. The lactate concentration of the synovial fluid normally conforms to that in the serum: in joint fluid with a pH above 7.3 it is below 2 mmol/L[20,21]. In inflamed synovial tissue lactate formation is greatly increased and the lactate concentration in the synovial fluid is consequently increased also[1,21,69].

Pyruvic acid. Concentrations of about 0.1–0.2 mmol/L have been measured in various joint diseases[21].

Ascorbic acid. Values of 8.5–65.9 μmol/L have been found in rheumatoid arthritis[70].

Lipids. Knowledge of normal values is inadequate. See Table 7 for values in joint diseases. Lipids originate from the synovial tissue, particularly so in diseased joints[71], when the concentration is increased to about 10 times the normal level[72,73]. Extreme values of 9–19 g/L have been found in patients with filariasis following passage of lymph into the joint[74].

Sediment. Cell count: mean value 63/μL (extreme range 13–180/μL); 63% are mononuclear phagocytes, 25% are lymphocytes, 6.5% polymorphonuclear leukocytes, and 4% synovial cells[102]. The cells originate partly from peripheral blood and partly from synovial tissue[4]. Erythrocytes are normally found only after traumatic aspiration. In joint diseases, the number and type of the cells provide clues to the age of the effusion and the activity of the inflammation (Table 8)[4,103,104]. In rheumatoid arthritis and occasionally

in other joint diseases as well, so-called 'ragocytes' are found in the synovial fluid[105] (RA cells[106]); they probably are leukocytes that have phagocytized immune complexes[107–109]. The detection of crystals is of pathological significance[4,110]. They occur in synovial fluid in free or phagocytized form. Urate crystals, usually in the form of short, rounded rods, are found in gout, and sharply angular rods or rhomboids of calcium pyrophosphate dihydrate in chondrocalcinosis. In rheumatoid arthritis, cholesterol crystals are detectable at times, and crystals of steroids may be found following their intra-articular injection. Collagen fibrils have been detected in the sediment in various joint diseases[111].

References

[1] ROPES and BAUER, *Synovial Fluid Changes in Joint Disease,* Harvard University Press, Cambridge (Mass.), 1953.

[2] DITTMER, D. S. (Ed.), *Blood and Other Body Fluids,* Biological Handbooks, Federation of American Societies for Experimental Biology, Washington (D.C.), 1961, page 329.

[3] GATTER and McCARTY, *Rheumatism,* **20**, 2 (1964); SCHMID and OGATA, *Med. Clin. N. Amer.,* **49**, 165 (1965); HOLLANDER et al., *Med. Clin. N. Amer.,* **50**, 1281 (1966).

[4] GREILING and KLEESIEK, *Clinico-pathological Investigation of Synovial Fluid,* Documenta Geigy - Folia rheumatologica, Basle, 1978.

[5] BOLZAN et al., *Arthr. and Rheum.,* **15**, 253 (1972).

[6] HUNDER, G. G., *Arthr. and Rheum.,* **15**, 645 (1972).

[7] HORIYE, K., *Virchows Arch. path. Anat.,* **251**, 649 (1924).

[8] SUNDBLAD, L., *Acta Soc. Med. upsalien.,* **58**, 113 (1953).

[9] BALAZS et al., *Arthr. and Rheum.,* **10**, 357 (1967).

[10] WALKER et al., *Nature,* **225**, 956 (1970).

[11] DINTENFASS, L., *Fed. Proc.,* **25**, 1054 (1966).

[12] BALAZS et al., *Arthr. and Rheum.,* **10**, 264 (1967).

[13] LINN and RADIN, *Arthr. and Rheum.,* **11**, 674 (1968).

[14] Leading Article, *Lancet,* **1**, 609 (1969).

[15] MÄKINEN, P., *Ann. Med. exp. Fenn.,* **36**, suppl. 7 (1958).

[16] CASTOR et al., *Arthr. and Rheum.,* **9**, 783 (1966).

[17] OLSON et al., *Arthr. and Rheum.,* **10**, 180 (1967).

[18] LIPSON and JOHNSON, *Arthr. and Rheum.,* **10**, 294 (1967).

[19] CUMMINGS and NORDBY, *Arthr. and Rheum.,* **9**, 47 (1966).

[20] FALCHUK et al., *Amer. J. Med.,* **49**, 223 (1970).

[21] TREUHAFT and McCARTY, *Arthr. and Rheum.,* **14**, 475 (1971); McCARTY, D. J., *Arthr. and Rheum.,* **17**, 289 (1974).

[22] LUND-OLESEN, K., *Arthr. and Rheum.,* **13**, 769 (1970).

[23] GOETZL et al., *J. clin. Invest.,* **50**, 1167 (1971).

[24] CAJORI et al., *Arch. intern. Med.,* **37**, 92 (1924).

[25] RUSSEL et al., *Lancet,* **2**, 899 (1970).

[26] McCARTY et al., *J. Lab. clin. Med.,* **78**, 216 (1971).

[27] SILCOX and McCARTY, *J. Lab. clin. Med.,* **83**, 518 (1974).

[28] McCARTY et al., *Ann. intern. Med.,* **56**, 711 (1962); KOHN et al., *Ann. intern. Med.,* **56**, 738 (1962).

[29] SKINNER and COHEN, *Arch. intern. Med.,* **123**, 636 (1969).

[30] CHRISMAN et al., *J. Bone Jt Surg.,* **40A**, 457 (1958).

[31] YIELDING et al., *Proc. Soc. exp. Biol. (N.Y.),* **85**, 665 (1954).

[32] NIEDERMEIER and GRIGGS, *J.chron. Dis.*, **23**, 527 (1971).

[33] SENATOR and MUIRDEN, *Ann.rheum. Dis.*, **27**, 49 (1968).

[34] BONEBRAKE et al., *Arthr. and Rheum.*, **11**, 95 (1968).

[35] NIEDERMEIER, W., *Ann.rheum. Dis.*, **24**, 544 (1965).

[36] BONEBRAKE et al., *Arthr. and Rheum.*, **9**, 849 (1966).

[37] BONEBRAKE et al., *Proc. Mayo Clin.*, **47**, 746 (1972).

[38] SOUTEYRAND-BOULENGER and AMOUROUX, *Nouv. Presse méd.*, **1**, 469 (1972).

[39] McCARTY, D. J., *Ann. Rev. Med.*, **21**, 357 (1970); SPILBERG, I., *Arthr. and Rheum.*, **18**, 129 (1975).

[40] LIDSKY, M. D., *Arthr. and Rheum.*, **11**, 830 (1968).

[41] HUGHES et al., *Arthr. and Rheum.*, **14**, 259 (1971).

[42] PEKIN and ZVAIFLER, *J.clin. Invest.*, **43**, 1372 (1964).

[43] SWEDLUND et al., *Arthr. and Rheum.*, **12**, 337 (1969).

[44] NETTELBLADT and SUNDBLAD, *Acta rheum.scand.*, **11**, 11 (1965).

[45] LADD and CASSIDY, *Arthr. and Rheum.*, **12**, 309 (1969).

[46] HRNČÍŘ et al., *Ann.rheum. Dis.*, **31**, 325 (1972).

[47] HUNDER and GLEICH, *Arthr. and Rheum.*, **17**, 955 (1974).

[48] BINETTE and SCHMID, *Arthr. and Rheum.*, **8**, 14 (1965).

[49] SEPPÄLÄ, P., *Scand.J.clin. Lab.Invest.*, **16**, suppl. 79 (1964).

[50] HAMERMAN and SANDSON, *J.clin. Invest.*, **42**, 1882 (1963).

[51] SUNDBLAD et al., *Nature*, **192**, 1192 (1961).

[52] KUSHNER and SOMERVILLE, *Arthr. and Rheum.*, **14**, 560 (1971).

[53] GORMSEN et al., *Arthr. and Rheum.*, **14**, 503 (1971).

[54] NIEDERMEIER et al., *Arthr. and Rheum.*, **8**, 355 (1965).

[55] CHAMPION and HOWARD, *Arthr. and Rheum.*, **14**, 374 (1971).

[56] SLIWINSKI and ZVAIFLER, *J. Lab.clin. Med.*, **76**, 304 (1970).

[57] GEILER, G., in MÜLLER et al. (Eds.), *Rheumatoid Arthritis,* Academic Press, London, 1971, page 317.

[58] DECOTEAU et al., *Arthr. and Rheum.*, **15**, 324 (1972); BENNETT et al., *Arthr. and Rheum.*, **16**, 186 (1973).

[59] TALAL et al., *Science*, **187**, 1196 (1975).

[60] CAUGHEY and HIGHTON, *Ann.rheum. Dis.*, **26**, 297 (1967).

[61] RUDDY and AUSTEN, *Arthr. and Rheum.*, **13**, 713 (1970); SVARTMAN et al., *J.clin. Invest.*, **56**, 111 (1975).

[62] ZVAIFLER, N. J., *Arthr. and Rheum.*, **17**, 297 (1974).

[63] PIGMAN et al., *Arthr. and Rheum.*, **1**, 151 (1958).

[64] KOFOED et al., *Experientia (Basel),* **29**, 680 (1973).

[65] SANDSON and HAMERMAN, *J.clin. Invest.*, **41**, 1817 (1962).

[66] SANDSON, J., *Arthr. and Rheum.*, **11**, 838 (1968).

[67] HOW et al., *Biochim.biophys.Acta(Amst.),* **194**, 81 (1969).

[68] DECKER et al., *Clin. Chem.*, **5**, 465 (1959).

[69] GREILING et al., *Klin. Wschr.*, **42**, 427 (1964).

[70] ABRAMS and SANDSON, *Ann.rheum. Dis.*, **23**, 295 (1964).

[71] BLAND et al., *Arthr. and Rheum.*, **11**, 469 (1968).

[72] CHUNG et al., *Arthr. and Rheum.*, **5**, 176 (1962).

[73] BOLE, G. G., *Arthr. and Rheum.*, **5**, 589 (1962).

[74] DAS and SEN, *Brit. med.J.*, **2**, 27 (1968).

[75] VAN WERSCH et al., in MÜLLER et al. (Eds.), *Purine Metabolism in Man – II,* Plenum Press, New York, 1977, page 619.

[76] GATTER and McCARTY, *Rheumatism*, **20**, 2 (1964); SCHMID and OGATA, *Med.Clin. N.Amer.*, **49**, 165 (1965); HOLLANDER et al., *Med.Clin. N.Amer.*, **50**, 1281 (1966).

[77] GREILING et al., *Enzymologia*, **30**, 135 (1966).

[78] EBERHARD et al., *Z. Rheumaforsch.*, **31**, 105 (1972).

[79] DABICH and NEUHAUS, *Proc. Soc.exp. Biol.(N. Y.),* **123**, 548 (1966).

[80] VEYS and WIEME, *Ann.rheum. Dis.*, **27**, 569 (1968).

[81] JASANI et al., *Ann.rheum. Dis.*, **28**, 497 (1969).

[82] LEMPERG and LUNDGREN, *Clin.chim.Acta*, **43**, 321 (1973).

[83] LINDY et al., *Clin.chim.Acta*, **35**, 377 (1971).

[84] GØTZE and ROSSEL, *Scand.J. Rheum.*, **1**, 171 (1972).

[85] BECKMAN et al., *Acta rheum. scand.*, **17**, 47 (1971).

[86] GOOD and STARKWEATHER, *Arthr. and Rheum.*, **12**, 298 (1969).

[87] YARON et al., *Ann.intern. Med.*, **73**, 751 (1970).

[88] KALLIOMÄKI and VANHA-PERTTULA, *Scand.J. Rheum.*, **1**, 21 (1972).

[89] BARTHOLOMEW, B. A., *Scand.J. Rheum.*, **1**, 69 (1972).

[90] VESELL et al., *J.clin. Invest.*, **41**, 2012 (1962).

[91] HAWTHORN and LAPOUSSE, *Méd. et Hyg. (Genève)*, **30**, 599 (1972).

[92] WEST et al., *J. Lab.clin. Med.*, **62**, 175 (1963).

[93] LEHMAN et al., *J.BoneJt Surg.*, **46A**, 1732 (1964).

[94] KENDALL et al., *Lancet*, **2**, 1012 (1971); FARR et al., *Ann.rheum. Dis.*, **32**, 326 (1973).

[95] FALLET et al., in MÜLLER et al. (Eds.), *Rheumatoid Arthritis,* Academic Press, London, 1971, page 177.

[96] PRUZANSKI et al., *Arthr. and Rheum.*, **13**, 389 (1970).

[97] OKA and SEPPÄLÄ, *Acta rheum. scand.*, **16**, 223 (1970).

[98] STOJAN et al., in MÜLLER et al. (Eds.), *Rheumatoid Arthritis,* Academic Press, London, 1971, page 169.

[99] BARTHOLOMEW and PERRY, *Arthr. and Rheum.*, **13**, 304 (1970); *Scand.J. Rheum.*, **2**, 151 (1973).

[100] HARRIS et al., *J.clin. Invest.*, **48**, 2104 (1969).

[101] BARTHOLOMEW and PERRY, *Acta rheum.scand.*, **16**, 304 (1970).

[102] COGGESHALL et al., *Anat. Rec.*, **77**, 129 (1940).

[103] VOJTÍŠEK, O., *Z. Rheumaforsch.*, **21**, 114 (1962).

[104] TAKASUGI and HOLLINGSWORTH, *Arthr. and Rheum.*, **10**, 495 (1967).

[105] DELBARRE et al., *Presse méd.*, **72**, 2129 (1964).

[106] HOLLANDER et al., *Ann.intern. Med.*, **62**, 271 (1965).

[107] BARNHART et al., *Ann.rheum. Dis.*, **26**, 281 (1967).

[108] BIERTHER and STREIT, *Dtsch.med. Wschr.*, **97**, 453 (1972).

[109] BRITTON and SCHUR, *Arthr. and Rheum.*, **14**, 87 (1971).

[110] SOLNICA et al., *Sem. Hôp. Paris*, **43**, 2573 (1967).

[111] KITRIDOU et al., *Arthr. and Rheum.*, **12**, 580 (1969).

[112] BUNEAUX et al., *Rev. Rhum.*, **42**, 97 (1975).

[113] WIZE et al., *Scand.J. Rheum.*, **4**, 65 (1975).

[114] BUNCH et al., *Proc. Mayo Clin.*, **49**, 715 (1974).

[115] TUDERMAN and KIVIRIKKO, *Europ.J.clin. Invest.*, **7**, 295 (1977).

[116] BENNETT and SKOSEY, *Arthr. and Rheum.*, **20**, 84 (1977).

[117] WARD and STEIGBIGEL, *Amer.J. Med.*, **64**, 933 (1978).

[118] STOJAN and HASLER, *Schweiz.med. Wschr.*, **108**, 1165 (1978).

[119] MANICOURT et al., *Ann.rheum. Dis.*, **39**, 207 (1980).

The cerebrospinal fluid (CSF) fills the ventricles of the brain, as inner fluid, and surrounds the brain and bone marrow in the subarachnoid space as outer fluid[1]. It is a secretion product of various central nervous structures – primarily the choroid plexus but also the ependymal lining of the ventricles of the brain and, possibly, of the cerebral subarachnoid space – and it assumes its final composition as a result of material exchange with the blood and adjacent brain tissues[1-3]. However, since secretion predominates in the ventricles, and absorption in the subarachnoid space, a flow from the ventricles into the subarachnoid space is produced. From the intracerebral spaces, the fluid circulates through several openings in the roof of the fourth ventricle into the subarachnoid space. In the area of the pacchionian granulations and along the cerebral nerves as well as via spinal nerve root pockets the fluid finally enters the venous blood stream and the lymphatic channels.

Cerebrospinal fluid is generally collected from the lumbar subarachnoid space (lumbar CSF) and less frequently from the cisterna magna (suboccipital CSF, cisternal CSF). Ventricular CSF is obtained by puncture of the lateral ventricles. Regarding the technique of CSF collection, see BISCHOFF[4] and JANZEN[5], for example. Unless otherwise stated, the data presented below refer to lumbar

CSF of adults. In view of ethical reservations about the removal of CSF from completely normal subjects, the normal values generally are retrospectively assessed results from probably healthy individuals.

Only values from specimens collected at identical puncture sites are comparable. The choice of the puncture site can be critical for diagnosis[6].

Pathological processes in the area of the central nervous system can be, but need not be, detectable by the composition of the cerebrospinal fluid. Pathological CSF findings are the more likely to be made the closer the localization of the disease process to the CSF space[3].

For details the reader is referred to the specialized literature[7-11].

Appearance

The fluid is usually clear and colorless. Colored or turbid CSF is pathological except in the event of a hemorrhage due to puncture. A white blood cell count of about 200/μL and higher results in turbidity.

Red coloration (erythrochromia) is seen if the fluid has become mixed with blood in the course of puncture or not more than 5 to 6 hours before (red blood cell count >30/μL).

The fluid is yellow (xanthochromic) if blood has been present for more than 6 hours before the puncture, or if the permeability of the meningeal barrier for pigments such as bilirubin and carotene is increased (as in meningitis or blockage of CSF circulation).

Brown coloration results from melanosarcoma of the central nervous system or the meninges.

Volume and rate of production (Table 1)

In the adult, about 35 mL of the CSF is found in the ventricles, 25 mL in the subarachnoid space and in the cisterns, and 75 mL in the spinal canal.

Beginning at a CSF pressure of 0.7 kPa, CSF reabsorption increases linearly with the pressure: at a pressure of approximately 1.2 kPa the rate of production equals the rate of reabsorption. In the presence of hydrocephalus reabsorption of the CSF may be disturbed or the rate of production increased.

Table 1   *Spinal fluid volume and rate of production*

		Mean	(Extreme range)	Reference
			mL	
Volume	Infants.........	–	(40–60)	10
	Young children	–	(60–100)	10
	Older children .	–	(80–120)	10
	Adults	135	(100–160)	10
		mL/min		
Rate of production .	....	0.35	–	12

↓See text below	Lumbar CSF unless otherwise stated	SI unit	Mean	*s*	95% range (extreme range in brackets)	Other units	Mean	*s*	(Extreme range)	Reference
Physicochemical data										
↓ **Pressure**	Children .... (a)	kPa	–	–	(0.40–1.00)	mmHg	–	–	(3.0–7.5)	10
	Adults............. (a)	kPa	–	–	(0.60–1.80)	mmHg	–	–	(4.5–13.5)	10
	15 adults:									
	– initial pressure.... (b)	kPa	1.41	0.30	(0.9–2.0)	cmH$_2$O / mmHg	14.4 / 10.6	3.1 / 2.3	(9–20) / (7–15)	13
	– final pressure ..... (b)	kPa	0.82	0.37	(0.05–1.3)	cmH$_2$O / mmHg	8.4 / 6.2	3.8 / 2.8	(0.5–13) / (0.4–9.6)	13
Refractive index	....	–	–	–	(1.33494–1.33510)	...	...	...	...	16
↓ **Surface tension** (20 °C)	....	10^{-3} N m^{-1}	61.5	0.75	–	dyn cm^{-1}	61.5	0.75	–	17
Relative viscosity (38 °C)	....	...	–	–	(1.020–1.027)	...	...	...	...	18
Specific conductivity (18 °C)	....	S cm^{-1}	0.01190	–	–	...	...	...	...	19
Relative density (d_4^{25})	150 subjects	...	1.0040	0.0004	1.0032–1.0048	...	...	...	...	20

Pressure. Measured (a) with open manometer, (b) by isometric technique (final pressure after removal of an average of 14 mL of CSF). – As a rule, measurements of CSF pressure are taken with the subject recumbent, lying on his side, in either the lumbar or both lumbar and suboccipital regions. With the subject in a horizontal, relaxed position, the spinal fluid pressures in the lateral and the abdominal positions are approximately equal. Changes in the position of the head, abdominal-wall tension and in the angle of inclination of the head cause pressure changes of 50–100% relative

to resting pressure. Coughing, voluntary compression of the abdomen, or compression of the jugular veins is associated with sharp, short-lived pressure rises of 100–150% – a phenomenon which may be evaluated to test for a hydrostatic block (Queckenstedt test)[14]. The value obtained varies with the heart rate and the respiratory rate. Inhalation of CO_2 and alkalosis cause a rise in pressure; inhalation of O_2 and hyperventilation cause the pressure to drop[15].

Surface tension. Measured with torsion balance.

↓See text on next page	Lumbar CSF unless otherwise stated	SI unit	Mean	s	(Extreme range)	Other units	Mean	s	(Extreme range)	Reference
Freezing-point depression	47 subjects	K	0.569	–	(0.540–0.603)	°C	0.569	–	(0.540–0.603)	21
Osmolality	47 subjects	mmol/kg	306	–	(290–324)	mosm/kg	306	–	(290–324)	21
	36 subjects	mmol/kg	292	6	(279–302)	mosm/kg	292	6	(279–302)	22
↓ pH		...	...	...	...	...	...	...	...	...
↓ CO₂ pressure		...	...	...	...	...	...	...	...	...
↓ O₂ pressure		...	...	...	...	...	...	...	...	...

		Amount of substance				Mass				
		Unit	Mean	s	95% range (extreme range in brackets)	Unit	Mean	s	95% range (extreme range in brackets)	
↓ Dry mass	28 subjects	...	...	...	...	g/kg	10.8	–	(8.5–17.0)	21

Inorganic substances

↓ Bicarbonate		...	...	...	...	...	...	...	...	...
↓ Chloride	37 subjects	mmol/L	123.3	2.5	–	g/L	4.37	0.089	–	36
	100 subjects	mmol/L	125	3.0	119–131	g/L	4.43	0.11	4.21–4.65	37
Phosphorus										
– total		µmol/L	–	–	(442–694)	mg/L	–	–	(13.7–21.5)	40
↓ – inorganic	70 subjects	µmol/L	520	74	(371–668)	mg/L	16.1	2.3	(11.5–20.7)	41
	47 subjects	µmol/L	433	74	(542–649)	mg/L	13.4	2.3	(7.3–20.1)	49
↓ Lipid phosphorus		µmol/L	7.1	1.3	–	mg/L	0.22	0.04	–	42
Sulfur										
↓ – inorganic		...	...	...	...	...	...	...	...	...
↓ Fluoride		µmol/L	5	–	–	mg/L	0.1	–	–	44
↓ Bromide		µmol/L	29	–	(18–48)	mg/L	2.3	–	(1.4–3.8)	45
↓ Iodine		nmol/L	16	–	–	µg/L	2	–	–	47
Thiocyanate		µmol/L	–	–	(5.2–50)	mg/L	–	–	(0.3–2.9)	7
↓ Potassium	37 subjects	mmol/L	2.84	0.17	–	mg/L	111	6.6	–	36
	102 subjects	mmol/L	2.96	0.17	2.62–3.30	mg/L	116	6.6	103–129	37
	15 subjects	mmol/L	2.8	0.2	–	mg/L	109	7.8	–	223
	Suboccipital CSF, 15 subjects	mmol/L	2.5	0.2	–	mg/L	98	7.8	–	223
↓ Sodium	37 subjects	mmol/L	147.0	2.6	–	g/L	3.38	0.060	–	36
	102 subjects	mmol/L	145	3.9	137–153	g/L	3.33	0.090	3.15–3.51	37
	15 subjects	mmol/L	145	3.6	–	g/L	3.33	0.082	–	223
	Suboccipital CSF, 15 subjects	mmol/L	146	2.5	–	g/L	3.36	0.057	–	223
↓ Calcium	37 subjects	mmol/L	1.32	0.12	–	mg/L	52.9	4.8	–	36
	50 subjects	mmol/L	1.19	0.08	1.02–1.34	mg/L	47.7	3.2	41.3–54.1	37
Magnesium	37 subjects	mmol/L	1.12	0.07	–	mg/L	27.2	1.7	–	36
	81 subjects	mmol/L	0.89	0.17	0.55–1.23	mg/L	21.6	4.1	13.4–29.8	37
	11 subjects	mmol/L	1.12	0.09	–	mg/L	27.2	2.2	–	59
↓ Iron	23 subjects	µmol/L	0.8	0.4	(0.3–1.5)	µg/L	45	22	(17–84)	54
↓ Copper	30 children (a)	µmol/L	–	–	(0.28–0.24)	µg/L	–	–	(18–27)	55
	15 subjects (b)	µmol/L	0.25	0.06	–	µg/L	16	4	–	56
Manganese		nmol/L	–	–	(15–27)	µg/L	–	–	(0.83–1.50)	58
↓ Zinc	30 children	µmol/L	–	–	(0.37–0.61)	µg/L	–	–	(24–40)	55
	2 subjects	µmol/L	–	–	(0.35; 0.92)	µg/L	–	–	(23; 60)	59

Nitrogenous substances

Total nitrogen		mmol/L	13.2	–	(11.2–15.7)	mg/L	185	–	(157–220)	7
↓ Nonprotein nitrogen		mmol/L	–	–	(7.9–14.3)	mg/L	–	–	(110–200)	7

↓See text below	Lumbar CSF unless otherwise stated	Amount of substance				Mass				Reference
		Unit	Mean	s	95% range (extreme range in brackets)	Unit	Mean	s	95% range (extreme range in brackets)	
↓ **Urea**	106 subjects	mmol/L	4.16	–	(2.30–6.06)	mg/L	250	–	(138–364)	60
	37 subjects	mmol/L	4.10	1.12	–	mg/L	246	67	–	36
↓ **Creatinine**	37 subjects	μmol/L	64.8	27.6	–	mg/L	7.33	3.12	–	36
	10 specimens	μmol/L	–	–	(57.5–92.8)	mg/L	–	–	(6.5–10.5)	61
Guanidinosuccinic acid	....	μmol/L	–	–	<8.6	mg/L	–	–	<1.5	63

Table 2 *Characteristic values of acid–base status*

	Number	pH		CO_2 pressure				CO_2		HCO_3^-		Reference
		Mean	s	Mean	s	Mean	s	Mean	s	Mean	s	
				kPa		mmHg		mmol/L				
Lumbar CSF....................	–	7.311	0.026	6.39	0.76	47.9	5.7	–	–	22.9	2.3	23
	23	7.317	0.025	6.12	0.57	45.9	4.3	–	–	21.8	1.6	24
Suboccipital CSF	15	7.349	0.011	6.03	0.38	45.2	2.84	25.1	1.25	23.6	1.17	25
	6	7.328	0.018	5.72	0.39	42.9	2.9	–	–	22.1	1.9	26

Table 3 *Oxygen pressure*

	Number	O_2 pressure				Reference
		Mean	s	Mean	s	
		kPa		mmHg		
Lumbar CSF........	8 newborn	4.35	0.23	32.6	1.7	35
	23	8.39	0.99	62.9	7.4	24
	15	4.91	0.81	36.8	6.1	29
Suboccipital CSF ...	15	6.28	0.60	47.1	4.5	29

pH, CO_2 pressure. See Table 2. Different measurement temperatures need to be taken into consideration when comparing normal values. The pH of lumbar CSF is lower and its CO_2 pressure higher than that of suboccipital CSF[26,28,29]. Other normal values have been cited by LOESCHCKE[27]. The carbon dioxide–bicarbonate system is almost exclusively responsible for the buffering effect of the spinal fluid. The constants of the system have been given by MITCHELL et al.[30]. SIGGAARD-ANDERSEN's nomogram has been revised for CSF[31]. In disturbances of the acid–base metabolism, the pH of the CSF is usually changed less than that of the blood, probably owing to the nearly complete independence of the CSF bicarbonate concentration from the serum bicarbonate concentration. In metabolic alkalosis and acidosis the CSF pH is fairly constant; the same is true in acute respiratory disorders[32,33]. In chronic respiratory acidosis, on the other hand, the CSF pH has been found to decrease concomitantly with the blood pH[34].

O_2 pressure. See Table 3. The oxygen pressure is lower in the lumbar than in the suboccipital CSF. In adults the oxygen tension in the CSF declines with increasing age[29].

Dry mass. Mostly sodium chloride.

Bicarbonate. See Table 2.

Chloride. The chloride concentrations of cistern and lumbar CSF are virtually equal[38]. The CSF/serum ratio of chloride concentrations is 1.20[36]. Reduced concentrations may occur in meningitis[38].

Phosphorus, inorganic. Upon passage from cistern CSF to lumbar CSF the phosphate concentration slightly increases[38]. It is elevated in inflammatory diseases of the central nervous system (particularly in meningitis), in some cases of epilepsy and of cerebrovascular diseases[38].

Lipid phosphorus. The mean values cited in the literature range from 4.8 μmol/L to 8.1 μmol/L[42].

Sulfur, inorganic. Mean concentration in individuals with neurologic diseases[43]: 190 μmol/L.

Fluoride. The concentration is approximately one-half of that in the serum.

Bromide. The bromide concentration in ventricular CSF is lower than that in lumbar CSF[46]. The CSF/serum ratio of bromide concentrations is normally below 0.5 and increases to as much as 1.1 in tuberculous meningitis[52].

Iodine. Small amounts of iodine are present as iodide; the major portion is in the form of thyroxine[48]. The CSF level of iodine amounts to approximately 2% of the serum level of iodine.

Potassium. The CSF/serum ratio of potassium concentrations is 0.72[36]. The potassium concentration of the fluid increases slightly upon transition from cistern to lumbar CSF[38]; it is fairly constant and largely independent of changes in the serum level[33,50]. In infants, the concentration tends to be lower than in adults[51].

Sodium. The CSF/serum ratio of sodium concentrations is 1.05[36]. The sodium concentration in the CSF varies commensurately with that in the serum.

Calcium. The CSF/serum ratio of calcium concentrations is 0.52[39] to 0.56[36] (total) and approximately 0.73 (ionized)[39]. The calcium concentration in the CSF is fairly constant and largely independent of changes in the serum level[33,50].

Magnesium. The CSF/serum ratio of magnesium concentrations is 1.35[36]. The magnesium concentrations of cistern and lumbar CSF are nearly identical[38]. Changes in the serum level of magnesium have little effect on the CSF[33]. The concentration in the CSF of children seems to conform to that of adults at all ages[53]. Elevated values may be found in epilepsy[38].

Iron. The iron concentration is higher than would be expected on the basis of the transferrin concentration.

Copper. Values determined (a) by atomic absorption, (b) by neutron activation. – In patients with neurologic diseases, the copper concentration varied between 0.15 μmol/L and 4.40 μmol/L (averaging 6% of serum copper)[57].

Zinc. In patients with neurologic diseases the level varied between 0.15 μmol/L and 5.35 μmol/L (averaging 8% of serum zinc)[57].

Nonprotein nitrogen. The CSF contains small amounts of protein only. The nonprotein nitrogen consists predominantly of urea and amino acids.

Urea. The CSF/serum ratio of urea concentrations is 0.91[36]. The urea concentration is increased in diseases associated with nitrogen retention.

Creatinine. The CSF/serum ratio of creatinine concentrations is 0.80[36].

↓See text below and on next page	Lumbar CSF unless otherwise stated	Amount of substance				Mass				Reference
		Unit	Mean	s	95% range (extreme range in brackets)	Unit	Mean	s	95% range (extreme range in brackets)	
↓**Ammonia**	15 subjects .... (a)	µmol/L	15.5	5.93	–	mg/L	0.264	0.101	–	64
	20 subjects .... (b)	µmol/L	11.9	1.76	–	mg/L	0.202	0.030	–	65
α-**Amino nitrogen** ...	8 children, <5 years....	mmol/L	0.78	0.12	(0.66–0.81)	mg/L	10.9	1.7	(9.2–11.4)	67
	42 adults	mmol/L	0.88	0.08	(0.69–1.05)	mg/L	12.3	1.1	(9.6–14.7)	67
	Ventricular CSF, 8 adults	mmol/L	0.81	0.09	(0.69–0.97)	mg/L	11.3	1.3	(9.7–13.6)	67
↓**Amino acids**........	10 subjects	mmol/L	1.76	0.34	...	...	...	...	...	232
Choline	22 specimens	µmol/L	8.3	1.7	(7–13)	mg/L	1.0	0.2	(0.8–1.6)	246
↓**Acetylcholine**	16 subjects	nmol/L	103	33	–	µg/L	16.8	5.4	–	77
↓**Polyamines**		...	...	...	...	...	...	...	...	...
Histamine		nmol/L	87	–	(18–270)	µg/L	9.7	–	(2–30)	78
3,4-Dihydroxyphenyl-acetic acid (Dopa) ..	10 subjects	nmol/L	2.9	0.5	–	ng/L	490	80	–	247
↓**Catecholamines**										
Norepinephrine.....		nmol/L	1.4	–	–	ng/L	240	–	–	248
Epinephrine		nmol/L	0.24	–	–	ng/L	44	–	–	249
↓**Serotonin**	48 subjects	nmol/L	5.90	1.08	3.74–8.06	µg/L	1.04	0.19	0.66–1.42	79
↓**Indoxylsulfuric acid** .	50 subjects	µmol/L	4.7	0.9	2.9–6.5	mg/L	1.0	0.2	0.6–1.4	94
↓**Bilirubin**	34 newborn......... (a)	µmol/L	4.1	1.7	–	mg/L	2.4	1.0	–	95
	Adults.................	µmol/L	–	–	(<0.2)	mg/L	–	–	(<0.1)	96
↓**Porphyrins**		...	...	...	...	...	...	...	...	...
Uric acid............	61 men	µmol/L	22	7.7	6.6–37	mg/L	3.7	1.3	1.1–6.3	99
	57 women	µmol/L	16	5.9	4.2–28	mg/L	2.7	1.0	0.7–4.7	99
Hypoxanthine + xanthine		...	...	...	...	mg/L	1.3	0.6		100
	35 subjects	...	...	...	...	mg/L	0.97	–	(0.25–1.50)	99
↓**Cyclic adenosine monophosphate**	22 children	nmol/L	22.4	2.8	–	µg/L	7.37	0.92	–	237
	23 subjects	nmol/L	21	8	–	µg/L	6.9	2.6	–	101
	14 subjects	nmol/L	8.7	8.3	–	µg/L	2.9	2.7	–	238
↓**Cyclic guanosine monophosphate**	23 subjects	nmol/L	2.4	0.5	–	µg/L	0.83	0.17	–	101
	14 subjects	nmol/L	3.4	4.0	–	µg/L	1.2	1.4	–	238
	16 subjects	nmol/L	1.94	0.68	–	µg/L	0.67	0.23	–	239

Ammonia. Values determined (a) by microdiffusion; (b) enzymatically. – The concentration is increased in hepatic coma[66].

Amino acids. Column chromatography according to STEIN and MOORE yields 35 ninhydrin-positive substances[68]. At least 32 different amino acids have been determined quantitatively[229]. Normal values are given in Tables 4 and 5. The concentration in the CSF amounts for most amino acids to 5–25% of that in the plasma. Glutamine is present in an approximately equal concentration, cystine and proline are present in extremely low concentrations, and phosphoethanolamine in a higher concentration. γ-Aminobutyric acid and its derivatives are detectable in the CSF but not in the plasma. In meningitis[67] and uremia[72] the α-amino acid concentration is increased. The changes in concentration of the individual amino acids do not always parallel pathological changes in the plasma concentrations[71]. Glutamine derivatives and α-oxoglutaramate are present in increased amounts in hepatic coma[66,71,73]. The high taurine values in bacterial meningitis are due to the presence of leukocytes[227]. In untreated phenylketonuria the homocarnosine concentration is increased[71]. The tryptophan concentration is reduced in manic-depressive patients[74].

Acetylcholine. Increased in epilepsy.

Polyamines. Putrescine, spermidine and spermine concentrations have been determined in the CSF of children with leukemia[233].

Catecholamines. Metabolites of dopamine and norepinephrine are 4-hydroxy-3-methoxyphenylacetic acid (homovanillic acid) (Table 6) as well as small amounts of 3-hydroxy-4-methoxyphenylacetic acid (*iso*-homovanillic acid)[87] and 4-hydroxy-3-methoxymandelic acid (vanillinemandelic acid)[88]. To what extent the amine metabolism in the spinal cord contributes to the concentration of these substances in the CSF is not known precisely[82]. The concentration of homovanillic acid is decreased in patients with Parkinson's disease[80,82,83,89] and also in some patients with epilepsy[84,90] and atrophy of the brain[84]. It was increased in one case of herpes zoster oticus[91]. There is uncertainty regarding the changes in concentration of these metabolites in psychic diseases. The concentration of homovanillic acid appear to be decreased in manic-depressive patients, particularly so in the depressive phase[92]. The concentration of 4-hydroxy-3-methoxyphenylglycol tends to be increased in the manic phase[85] and decreased in depressive patients[93]. Also the concentration of epinephrine seems to be decreased in depressive patients during illness[249].

Serotonin. Metabolites of serotonin in the central nervous system are 5-hydroxyindoleethanol[235] and 5-hydroxyindoleacetic acid (Table 6).

Indoxylsulfuric acid. Increased in renal insufficiency.

Table 4 *Amino acids in CSF and CSF/serum ratio of amino acid concentrations*

	32 boys[234] (1–24 months)		20 girls[234] (1–24 months)		48 boys[234] (2–14 years)		49 girls[234] (2–14 years)		19 subjects[69] (19–64 years)		20 subjects[69] (55–78 years)		43 subjects[70] (14–86 years)		CSF/Serum
	Mean	s	Mean	s	Mean	s	Mean	s	Mean	s	Mean	s	Mean	s	
	µmol/L														
Alanine	18.1	12.5	19.6	9.4	13.5	9.0	14.5	7.5	23.2	5.1	30.9	7.0	30.0	6.5	0.08
α-Aminobutyric acid	–	–	–	–	–	–	–	–	2.5	0.4	3.1	1.0	3.7	2.0	0.17
Arginine	15.6	7.8	11.5	6.6	12.4	5.2	12.4	6.1	18.3	3.2	19.0	2.9	19.7	4.3	0.23
Asparagine									5.4	1.4	4.9	1.7	8.5	2.5	0.15
Aspartic acid	7.14	2.65	5.94	1.22	4.96	1.59	5.01	1.28	0.6	0.3	–	–	0.3	0.3	0.15
Ethanolamine	–	–	–	–	–	–	–	–	14.1	3.0	20.5	5.7	15.4	4.8	–
Citrulline	12.2	12.9	5.20	8.60	5.05	6.29	7.46	8.11	1.5	0.5	2.0	0.9	2.1	0.8	0.06
Cystine	–	–	–	–	–	–	–	–	0.1	0.1	0.1	0.1	0.1	0.2	–
Glutamine	504	152	484	129	438	119	467	81	444	84	501	51	602	119	1.0
Glutamic acid	–	–	–	–	–	–	–	–	11.3	6.4	21.2	16.0	1.8	0.7	0.08
Glycine	3.71	2.66	5.37	3.39	3.53	2.39	3.69	2.05	4.7	1.5	7.6	2.9	6.4	1.7	0.03
Histidine	17.1	7.0	14.3	4.5	11.6	4.4	12.4	3.5	11.9	1.7	13.2	3.1	12.7	2.7	0.14
Isoleucine	5.56	2.74	4.30	1.75	4.17	2.10	3.84	1.91	3.9	1.0	5.0	1.4	4.8	1.5	0.08
Leucine	12.7	3.9	12.2	3.4	10.7	4.1	10.6	3.4	10.1	2.1	12.9	3.8	12.9	3.5	0.11
Lysine	24.2	8.6	16.2	4.5	17.2	8.0	17.6	7.1	21.7	3.7	25.4	5.6	27.5	5.1	0.15
Methionine	–	–	–	–	–	–	–	–	1.9	0.7	3.1	0.9	3.0	0.9	0.15
Nε-Methyllysine	–	–	–	–	–	–	–	–	–	–	–	–	1.5	2.0	0.21
Ornithine	7.19	3.56	5.58	2.58	5.73	3.29	5.90	3.46	3.7	1.0	4.2	0.8	5.5	1.9	0.10
Phenylalanine	12.1	4.5	10.1	3.3	10.0	4.1	10.2	4.2	6.5	1.2	8.2	2.8	8.7	3.5	0.17
Phosphoethanolamine	–	–	–	–	–	–	–	–	6.0	1.1	4.7	1.0	4.9	1.6	2.5
Phosphoserine*	–	–	–	–	–	–	–	–	–	–	–	–	4.2	1.7	0.58
Proline	–	–	–	–	–	–	–	–	trace	–	–	–	0	–	–
Serine	36.9	9.4	35.8	7.8	24.9	6.4	27.9	6.5	24.5	4.4	24.9	4.1	26.8	6.0	0.25
Taurine	8.66	3.53	8.60	4.08	7.15	4.10	8.22	5.69	6.8	1.7	7.5	1.7	6.6	1.7	0.12
Threonine	21.5	8.4	20.4	8.3	15.1	6.6	16.8	7.0	27.7	4.7	27.3	9.2	31.4	8.3	0.22
Tryptophan	1.39	1.34	0.95	0.80	1.18	1.15	0.96	0.83	1.3	0.4	1.4	0.8	1.0	0.7	0.03
Tyrosine	12.5	5.6	9.78	4.63	7.56	2.73	7.33	2.80	6.4	1.5	7.2	1.6	8.0	2.1	0.15
Valine	13.1	8.7	17.7	10.2	14.7	9.2	13.3	7.9	15.0	2.8	18.8	4.8	18.1	4.7	0.08

* Values of 37 subjects[36]

Table 5 *γ-Aminobutyric acid and its derivatives in the CSF*

	Subjects	Mean	s	(Extreme range)	Reference
		µmol/L			
γ-Aminobutyric acid	40 subjects	0.233	0.075	–	62
γ-Aminobutyrylhistidine (homocarnosine)	Children	7.9	2.6	–	75
	19 subjects, 19–64 years	2.7	2.5	–	69
	20 subjects, 55–78 years	0.6	0.6	–	69
2-(γ-Aminobutyryl)lysin	16 children, ½–6 years	0.11	–	(0–0.35)	76
	8 children, 8–14 years	0.04	–	(0–0.35)	76
	24 subjects, 15–65 years	0.32	–	(0–1.10)	76

Table 6 *Metabolites of serotonin and catecholamines in CSF*

5-Hydroxyindoleacetic acid					4-Hydroxy-3-methoxy-phenylacetic acid					4-Hydroxy-3-methoxy-phenylglycol				
Number	Mean	s	(Extreme range)	Reference	Number	Mean	s	(Extreme range)	Reference	Number	Mean	s	(Extreme range)	Reference
	nmol/L					nmol/L					nmol/L			
19	152	–	(78–288)	81	19	99	–	(16–274)	81	24	87	–	(54–130)	85
29	143	45	–	82	29	123	71	–	82	29	66	38	–	82
21	99	21	–	83	11	290	203	–	83	49	–	–	(33–107)	86
18	162	67	–	84	25	290	165	–	84	43	76	–	(43–231)	236

Bilirubin. (a) Corresponding serum concentration 115 µmol/L. As the serum concentration increases, so does the CSF concentration (correlation coefficient 0.58[95]). The CSF bilirubin is present mostly in unconjugated form[95, 97].

Porphyrins. Uroporphyrin and heptacarboxyporphyrin have been demonstrated in the CSF in chronic hepatic porphyria[98].

Cyclic adenosine monophosphate. There is no concentration difference in children and in adults[101]. Values of about 50 nmol/L have been observed in acute meningitis[224].

Cyclic guanosine monophosphate. Concentrations in children and adults do not differ[101]. High values have been found when pressure in the ventricular fluid was abnormally elevated[101].

Protein

Total protein concentration (Table 7). The origin of the CSF and the method employed need to be taken into consideration in assessing the values[3, 11, 144–146]. By comparison with the serum, the CSF contains little protein. The CSF/serum ratio of protein concentrations is 4×10^{-3}. In the neonatal period and particularly in premature infants, the protein concentration in the CSF is increased[95, 147–149]. The lowest values are found in children (Fig. 1). In old age, there is a tendency toward elevated CSF protein values[103, 144, 177].

Protein fractions. The CSF proteins can be electrophoretically separated into several fractions on paper[151], on cellulose acetate[152–154], on agar gel[155–157], or on polyacrylamide gel[158–160]. More than 60 components have been detected in separation on polyacrylamide[160]; however, not all these components also occur in the serum, particularly with a pathological CSF. The normal values of the CSF protein fractions obtained by the different separation techniques (Table 8) are comparable with one another only under certain conditions[3, 157]. The pattern of the protein fractions appears to be much the same in the individual CSF spaces[150].

Individual proteins. More than 30 proteins are demonstrable by means of immunoelectrophoresis[9, 167]. Some published normal values are presented in Table 11; additional normal values are given in papers by SCHULLER et al.[168]. See NERENBERG and PRASAD[228] concerning the concentrations of radioimmunologically

Table 7 *Total protein concentration in CSF*

	Precipitation with sulfosalicylic acid[150]			Cu-folin differential method[144]		
	Number	Mean	s	Number	Mean	Normal range
		mg/L			mg/L	
Lumbar CSF.......	21	313	95	98	297	180–413
Suboccipital CSF ..	13	183	43	25	250	140–360
Ventricular CSF ...	7	171	99	–	–	–

Table 8 *Protein fractions in lumbar CSF of adults*

Electrophoresis on	Number	Total protein	Prealbumin		Albumin		α_1-Globulin		α_2-Globulin		β_1-Globulin		τ-Globulin		γ-Globulin		Reference
			Mean	95% range	Mean	95% range	Mean	95% range	Mean	95% range	Mean	95% range	Mean	95% range	Mean	95% range	
		mg/L							Fraction as percent								
Celluloseacetate	140	356	5.2	2.5–7.9	62.7	53.0–72.4	3.6	1.1–6.1	5.0	2.7–7.3	8.8	6.2–11.5	6.1	2.8–9.3	8.6	4.0–13.2	153
	>1000	–	–	1.4–5.4	–	48.0–62.0	–	8.5–9.0	–	6.2–9.6	–	8.0–11.5	–	4.2–7.3	–	7.0–12.6	154
Agar gel	53	301 (s 58)	6.0	3.5–8.4	64.3	55.8–73.0	6.2	3.6–8.8	8.4	5.3–11.6	5.9	4.0–7.8	3.5	2.0–4.9	5.1	2.3–8.0	157

Table 9 *Proteins in the CSF of adults*

		Number	Mean	s	(Extreme range)	Reference
				mg/L		
Prealbumin.............................	Immunoelectrophoresis................	40	17.3	6.6	–	161
Albumin..............................	Immunoelectrophoresis................	52	155	39	–	161
Acid α_1-glycoprotein................	Immunoelectrophoresis................	37	3.6	1.4	–	161
	Radial immunodiffusion.............	48	3.67	1.9	–	162
	Radial immunodiffusion.............	174	1.85	0.74	–	170
α-Antitrypsin........................	Radial immunodiffusion.............	38	7.0	3.0	–	250
α-Microglobulin......................	Radioimmunoassay....................	21	42.3	16.8	(13–84)	251
Ceruloplasmin.........................	Immunoelectrophoresis................	26	0.97	0.37	–	161
	Radial immunodiffusion.............	174	0.88	0.21	–	170
α_2HS-glycoprotein..................	Immunoelectrophoresis................	24	1.7	0.6	–	161
Haptoglobin...........................	Radial immunodiffusion.............	48	2.24	1.5	–	162
α_2-Macroglobulin....................	Radial immunodiffusion.............	174	4.64	1.84	–	170
Plasminogen...........................	Immunoelectrophoresis................	6	0.25	–	–	161
β-Lipoprotein........................	Immunoelectrophoresis................	6	0.59	–	–	161
C 3 component (β_1C-globulin)..............	Immunoelectrophoresis................	29	4.48	1.56	–	163
C 4 component (β_1E-globulin)..............	Radial immunodiffusion.............	25	6.4	3.8	–	164
	Immunoelectrophoresis................	16	3.25	1.28	(1.61–5.41)	240
Transferrin..................................	Immunoelectrophoresis................	30	14.4	4.4	–	161
	Radial immunodiffusion.............	15	17	4	(11–23)	54
	Radial immunodiffusion.............	174	8.42	3.5	–	170
Fibrinogen.............................	Immunoelectrophoresis................	6	0.65	–	–	161
β-Trace protein	Radial immunodiffusion.............	5	23	11	–	166
β_2-Microglobulin	Radioimmunoassay	23*	1.1	0.5	(0.1–1.9)	241
γ-Trace protein	Enzyme immunoassay	30	5.8	2.2	(3.2–12.5)	245
IgG	Radial immunodiffusion.............	48	17.6	2.06	–	162
	Radial immunodiffusion.............	20	15	6.5	–	165
	Radial immunodiffusion.............	174	13.9	6.6	–	170
IgA	Radial immunodiffusion.............	48	2.26	0.95	–	162
	Radial immunodiffusion.............	20	1.9	0.73	–	165

* Children.

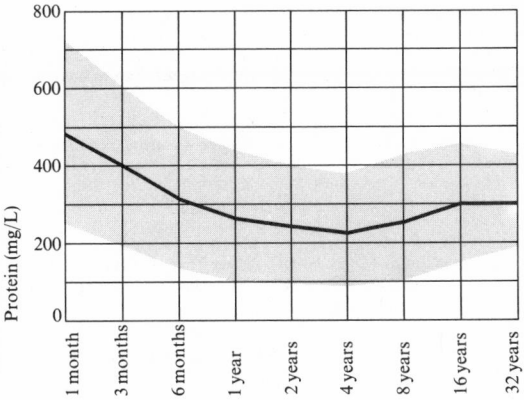

Fig. 1. Means and 95% limit values of lumbar CSF protein concentration in relation to age[146].

Table 10   *Concentrations of IgG and albumin in CSF of children[230]*

	IgG		Albumin		IgG/Albumin ratio	
	Mean	s	Mean	s	Mean	s
	mg/L					
27 boys, 1–24 months	7.5	10.7	136	70.2	0.0471	0.0591
13 girls, 1–24 months	2.2	3.0	92.5	36.9	0.0201	0.0229
31 boys, 2–14 years..	8.0	6.7	103	24.4	0.0703	0.0563
34 girls, 2–14 years..	8.9	6.1	107	28.9	0.0808	0.0558

Table 11   *Concentrations of IgG and albumin in CSF of adults[177]*

Age	Number	IgG		Albumin		IgG/Albumin ratio	
		Mean	s	Mean	s	Mean	s
		mg/L					
17–30 years	21	17	4	170	46	0.107	0.026
31–40 years	18	21	7	179	50	0.116	0.018
41–50 years	22	24	8	204	57	0.116	0.023
51–60 years	21	27	9	242	76	0.114	0.022
61–77 years	11	26	9	238	73	0.107	0.019

Table 12   *IgG/total protein ratio in CSF*

	Number	Mean	Normal range	s	Reference
Children	–	–	<0.082	–	178
	17	–	0.035–0.087	–	180
Adults	39	–	0.035–0.108	–	180
	93	0.053	–	0.013	177

determined immunoglobulins[228]; see COHEN et al.[244] regarding the radioimmunoassay of the basic myelin protein.

Aside from prealbumin, the concentrations of the proteins in the CSF when compared with those in the serum are the lower the higher the relative molecular mass[169] or the hydrodynamic volume[161]. IgM is not detectable in normal CSF[165, 242]. On the other hand, CSF-specific proteins such as the β-trace protein and the γ-trace protein are detectable in the serum only in traces or not at all[169].

Pathological changes in CSF proteins. An increase of the protein concentration is diagnostic, the rare phenomenon of a decrease is

Table 13
Increase of protein in CSF (according to Bischoff[4], updated)

Protein concentration	Disorder
++++ (>3.0 g/L)	Blocked CSF Hypertensive dehydration[184] Melanoma of central nervous system[106] Mycoses of central nervous system[106] Purulent meningitis
+++	Guillain-Barré syndrome Auditory nerve neurinoma Aliquorrhea Idiopathic or diabetic polyneuritis
++	Tuberculous meningitis Parasitic infestation of CNS Neurosyphilis Subdural hematoma
+ (<1.0 g/L)	Brain tumor (variable) Tabes dorsalis Viral meningoencephalitis Vicinity of intervertebral disc prolapse

Table 14   *Increase of γ-globulin in CSF*

	Disorder
Oligoclonal	Untreated neurosyphilis Subacute sclerosing panencephalitis Multiple sclerosis Retrobulbar neuritis Trypanosomiasis
Monoclonal	γ-Plasmacytoma (due to transudation)

not[3]. An extreme increase may manifest itself in spontaneous coagulation of the frequently xanthochromic spinal fluid. Diseases that may be associated with an increased protein concentration are listed in Table 12.

With the use of electrophoresis, 3 characteristic pathological distribution patterns besides the normal type are distinguishable[171]: the γ-globulin type, the transudative plasma type (without increase of cell count), and the transudative type with concomitant increase of cell count. The γ-globulin type is indicative of a central inflammatory disease and is characterized by an excessive accumulation of proteins in the γ-globulin region; an isolated increase of specific IgG types may occur (oligoclonal Ig production)[172, 173]. In the case of the plasma type, a permeability disturbance of the blood/CSF barrier leads to transudation of plasma proteins.

A permeability disturbance of the blood/CSF barrier is discernible by determination of the CSF/serum ratio of albumin concentrations[178]. Determination of the immunoglobulin or IgG concentration in the CSF is used for the detection of multiple sclerosis, but this concentration has to be interpreted in relation to the protein concentration in the CSF[11, 174]. CSF immunoglobulin/CSF protein[170, 175, 176], CSF IgG/CSF protein[179–181], and CSF IgG/CSF albumin[179, 182] represent comparable concentration ratios. In the 'IgG index', the concentration ratios in the CSF are compared with the corresponding concentration ratios in the serum[179, 183]; increased 'IgG index' values have been found in 88% of patients with multiple sclerosis[179].

Enzymes

So far approximately 30 enzymes have been demonstrated in the CSF[9, 11]. Literature references to several of them are given in Table 15.

In choosing the method of determination, it should be borne in mind that the enzymes in the CSF are less stable than those in the serum[185]. The activity in the CSF is generally lower than that in the serum, and changes of activity in the serum are not reflected in the CSF activity. The activity of glycerol-3-phosphate dehydrogenase in the CSF is four times as high as that in the serum[231]. Lysozyme, on the other hand, is not normally detectable in the CSF[203, 241]; if it is, it presumably stems from cells or blood[204].

Table 15
Enzymes in CSF and CSF/serum ratio of enzyme activity

EC-number	Name of enzyme	CSF/Serum	Reference
1.1.1.14	L-Iditol dehydrogenase	0.5–1	193
1.1.1.27	Lactate dehydrogenase	0.1–0.5	188–196
1.1.1.37	Malate dehydrogenase	0.5–1	185, 194
2.1.3.3	Ornithine carbamoyltransferase	<0.1	197
2.3.1.6	Choline acetyltransferase	≥1	198
2.6.1.1	Aspartate aminotransferase	0.5–1	185, 186, 188, 189, 192, 193, 199
2.6.1.2	Alanine aminotransferase	0.5–1	192, 193, 199
2.7.3.2	Creatine kinase	<0.1	192, 200, 201
3.1.1.8	Cholinesterase	<0.01	190, 198
3.1.3.2	Acid phosphatase	<0.1	202
3.1.6.1	Arylsulfatase	<0.1	202
3.4.11.1	Aminopeptidase (cytosol) (leucine aminopeptidase)	<0.1	205
3.5.4.4	Adenosine deaminase	<0.1	206
4.1.2.13	Fructose-bisphosphate aldolase	<0.1	194
5.3.1.6	Ribosephosphate isomerase	<0.1	207
5.3.1.9	Glucosephosphate isomerase	0.1–0.5	207

Normal values of CSF enzymes (Table 16). These are not sufficiently well known. For diagnostic evaluation, knowledge of a possible age dependence would be necessary. In the first postnatal week lactate dehydrogenase activity is higher than in later childhood[186,187]. With advanced age, the activity of lactate dehydrogenase and aspartate aminotransferase appears to increase[188,189].

Pathological changes in CSF enzymes. Disturbances in the permeability of the blood/brain and blood/CSF barriers can lead to transudation of enzymes from the serum and the brain parenchyma into the CSF. The diagnostic significance of an enzyme assay is low. Changes in lactate dehydrogenase activity have been studied most. It is increased for example in bacterial meningitis[187], in glioblastomas[190], in CNS metastases[191], and in eclampsia[192]. In malignant effusions, the activity of the isoenzyme LDH V in particular is increased[190].

Table 16   *Reference limits (upper limit of normal range) for CSF enzymes at 37 °C[185]*

	Activity	
	µmol s⁻¹	U/L
Lactate dehydrogenase	0.67	40
Malate dehydrogenase	1.42	85
Aspartate aminotransferase	0.23	13.5

↓See text on next page	Lumbar CSF unless otherwise stated	Amount of substance				Mass				Reference
		Unit	Mean	s	(Extreme range)	Unit	Mean	s	(Extreme range)	
Nitrogen-free substances										
↓ **Glucose**	....	...	...	...	...	...	...	...	...	...
Galactose	12 subjects	µmol/L	166	99	–	mg/L	29.9	17.8	–	114
Fructose	3 specimens	µmol/L	–	–	(220–260)	mg/L	–	–	(40–47)	119
Mannose	3 specimens	µmol/L	–	–	(56–72)	mg/L	–	–	(10–13)	119
↓ **Sialic acid**										
– total	28 subjects	µmol/L	38.8	18.4	–	mg/L	12.0	5.7	–	117
– free	28 subjects	µmol/L	11.9	7.1	–	mg/L	3.7	2.2	–	117
Polyols (polyhydric alcohols)										
Glycerol	3 specimens	µmol/L	–	–	(11–16)	mg/L	–	–	(1.0–1.5)	119
Erythritol	3 specimens	µmol/L	–	–	(29–45)	mg/L	–	–	(3.5–5.5)	119
Ribitol	3 specimens	µmol/L	–	–	(20–23)	mg/L	–	–	(3.0–3.5)	119
Arabitol	12 subjects	µmol/L	19.0	6.3	–	mg/L	2.89	0.96	–	118
Mannitol	12 subjects	µmol/L	4.8	2.0	–	mg/L	0.87	0.36	–	118
↓ Sorbitol	12 subjects	µmol/L	17.2	4.6	–	mg/L	3.13	0.84	–	118
	3 specimens	µmol/L	–	–	(19–38)	mg/L	–	–	(3.5–7)	119
↓ Myoinositol	12 subjects	µmol/L	174	31	–	mg/L	31.3	5.6	–	118
	3 specimens	µmol/L	–	–	(200–270)	mg/L	–	–	(36–49)	119
1,5-Anhydrosorbitol	65 adults	µmol/L	–	–	(11–95)	mg/L	–	–	(1.8–16)	122
	3 specimens	µmol/L	–	–	(146–323)	mg/L	–	–	(24–53)	119
Short-chain fatty acids										
Acetic acid	21 subjects	µmol/L	116	55	(19–210)	mg/L	6.99	3.33	(1.14–12.6)	123
Propionic acid	21 subjects	µmol/L	2.8	3.2	(trace–13)	mg/L	0.21	0.24	(trace–0.94)	123
Isobutyric acid	21 subjects	µmol/L	–	–	(0–3.6)	mg/L	–	–	(0–0.32)	123
Butyric acid	21 subjects	µmol/L	–	–	(0–2.8)	mg/L	–	–	(0–0.25)	123
Isovaleric acid	21 subjects	µmol/L	–	–	(0–2.7)	mg/L	–	–	(0–0.28)	123
Caproic acid	21 subjects	µmol/L	–	–	(0–trace)	mg/L	–	–	(0–trace)	123

↓See text below and on next page	Lumbar CSF unless otherwise stated	Amount of substance				Mass				Reference
		Unit	Mean	s	95% range (extreme range in brackets)	Unit	Mean	s	95% range (extreme range in brackets)	
↓ Lactic acid........	25 children .... (a)	mmol/L	1.59	0.33	–	mg/L	143	30	–	124
	23 subjects .... (a)	mmol/L	1.62	0.19	–	mg/L	146	17	–	24
	81 men .... (b)	mmol/L	1.34	0.37	0.60–2.08	mg/L	120	33	54–186	103
	133 women .... (b)	mmol/L	1.20	0.25	0.70–1.70	mg/L	108	23	62–154	103
	15 subjects .... (a)	mmol/L	1.63	0.34	–	mg/L	147	31	–	223
	Suboccipital CSF, 15 subjects .... (a)	mmol/L	1.45	0.27	–	mg/L	131	24	–	223
↓ Pyruvic acid.......	10 children .... (a)	mmol/L	0.136	0.029	(0.085–0.184)	mg/L	12.0	2.6	(7.5–16.2)	126
	23 subjects .... (b)	mmol/L	0.115	0.017	–	mg/L	10.1	1.5	–	24
↓ α-Oxoglutaric acid.	10 children .... (a)	µmol/L	2.1	0.7	(1.4–2.7)	mg/L	0.3	0.1	(0.2–0.4)	126
	15 subjects .... (b)	µmol/L	8.9	3.4	–	mg/L	1.3	0.5	–	112
Oxalacetic acid		µmol/L	–	–	(6.1–8.3)	mg/L	–	–	(0.8–1.1)	127
Succinic acid		µmol/L	–	–	(24–33)	mg/L	–	–	(2.8–3.9)	128
↓ Citric acid	15 subjects	µmol/L	176	50	–	mg/L	33.9	9.6	–	112
↓ Ketone bodies (as acetone)	16 subjects	µmol/L	117	65	–	mg/L	6.8	3.8	–	130
↓ Acetoacetic acid ...	11 subjects	µmol/L	26.2	12.3	(15.8–53.5)	mg/L	2.67	1.26	(1.61–5.46)	131
↓ β-Hydroxybutyric acid...............	11 subjects	µmol/L	46.4	23.9	(23.7–94.1)	mg/L	4.83	2.49	(2.47–9.80)	131

Glucose (Table 17). About 90% of the reducing substances in the CSF are glucose. The glucose concentration of the CSF is about two-thirds of the serum concentration. Newborn infants with a low serum glucose level may also be expected to have a low CSF glucose level. In childhood, the CSF glucose level does not change[102]; after age 50 there is a tendency toward lower values[103]. *Pathological variations:* In diabetes mellitus, the CSF glucose level is elevated at the same time as the serum level but with treatment it decreases more slowly than the latter[104]. Low values in relation to the serum level may be encountered in bacterial meningitis (meningococci, pneumococci, tubercle bacilli)[105, 106, 116], fungal meningitis (cryptococcosis, histoplasmosis)[106], viral meningoencephalitis (mumps, herpes simplex, lymphocytic choriomeningitis)[107, 108, 116], meningeal carcinoma[109, 116], and sarcoidosis of the central nervous system[106, 110].

Sialic acid. Sialic acid is a component of the cerebral gangliosides. Increased values are found in some patients with pneumococcal meningitis.

Sorbitol. The concentration is increased in diabetes mellitus.

Myoinositol. This is a component of the phosphoinositides, which are rapidly metabolized in the brain. The CSF/serum ratio of myoinositol concentrations is ~3. See GARCIA-BUÑUEL[120] regarding the concentration in neurologic diseases. Low values may be found in acute bacterial meningitis, and high values in diabetes[121].

Lactic acid. Values determined (a) enzymatically, (b) colorimetrically. The lactate concentration in the CSF is higher than that in the blood[125]. High CSF lactate values are found in cerebrovascular diseases[125], lactacidosis[125] and in bacterial or tuberculous meningitis[125, 129], while they are only slightly increased in viral meningitis.

Pyruvic acid. Values determined (a) by paper chromatography, (b) enzymatically.

α-Oxoglutaric acid. Values determined (a) by paper chromatography, (b) enzymatically. The CSF/serum ratio of α-oxoglutaric acid concentrations is ~0.80.

Citric acid. The CSF/serum ratio of citric acid concentrations is ~2. In adults the concentrations increase with increasing age[112]. Uncharacteristic increases are seen in some neurologic diseases[112].

Ketone bodies. Determined colorimetrically (CSF sampled 4 to 14 hours after meal).

Table 17 *Glucose concentration in CSF*

	Material	Method	Number	Mean	95% range	s	Mean	95% range	s	Reference
				mmol/L			mg/L			
Children, 1 month to 16 years	Lumbar CSF	Glucose oxidase/peroxidase	335	3.16	1.78–4.54	0.69	570	320–820	125	102
Adults	Lumbar CSF	Glucose oxidase/peroxidase	100	3.41	2.69–4.13	0.36	615	487–743	64	111
	Lumbar CSF	Folin-Wu	30	3.72	–	0.53	670	–	95	111
	Lumbar CSF	Somogyi-Nelson	15	3.24	–	0.31	583	–	56	112
	Lumbar CSF	o-Toluidine	128	3.35	2.53–4.17	0.41	603	455–751	74	115
	Lumbar CSF	Neocuproin (AutoAnalyzer)	29	3.66	–	0.39	660	–	70	113
	Lumbar CSF	Hexokinase/glucose-6-phosphate dehydrogenase	29	3.50	–	0.22	630	–	40	113
	Lumbar CSF	Hexokinase/glucose-6-phosphate dehydrogenase	15	3.82	–	0.72	688	–	129	29
	Suboccipital CSF	Hexokinase/glucose-6-phosphate dehydrogenase	15	3.83	–	0.63	690	–	113	29

↓See text below and on next page	Lumbar CSF unless otherwise stated	Amount of substance				Mass				Reference
		Unit	Mean	s	95% range (extreme range in brackets)	Unit	Mean	s	95% range (extreme range in brackets)	
Lipids										
↓ **Total lipids**.........	138 young adults	...	...	...	...	mg/L	12.5	2.43	7.66–17.4	133
Neutral fat*........ (triglycerides)	138 young adults	µmol/L	4.71	2.73	0–10.2	mg/L	4.17	2.42	0–9.01	133
↓ **Cholesterol**	138 young adults	µmol/L	10.2	2.30	5.6–14.8	mg/L	3.95	0.88	2.19–5.71	133
	41 subjects	µmol/L	12.0	4.0	4.0–20.0	mg/L	4.63	1.54	1.55–7.71	134
↓ **Phospholipids***......	138 young adults	µmol/L	5.21	0.90	3.41–7.01	mg/L	4.03	0.70	2.63–5.43	133
	41 subjects	µmol/L	7.09	2.20	2.69–11.5	mg/L	5.49	1.70	2.09–8.89	134
↓ **Fatty acids*** – total............		µmol/L	26.1	–	–	mg/L	7.36	–	–	136
	17 subjects	µmol/L	70	14	–	mg/L	20	4	–	135
– free		µmol/L	3.5	–	–	mg/L	1.0	–	–	136
↓ **Cerebrosides**........		µmol/L	0.87	–	–	...	...	...	...	140
Prostaglandins										
PGE.............	19 subjects	nmol/L	1.31	2.09	–	ng/L	460	737	–	225
PGF.............	19 subjects	nmol/L	1.98	1.88	–	ng/L	701	667	–	225
Vitamins										
↓ **Thiamine**	45 subjects .... (a)	nmol/L	–	–	(49–64)	µg/L	–	–	(13–17)	208
	36 subjects .... (b)	nmol/L	15	–	(11–45)	µg/L	4	–	(3–12)	209
↓ **Vitamin B$_6$**.........		nmol/L	–	–	(0–4.4)	µg/L	–	–	(0–0.75)	208
Nicotinic acid.......		µmol/L	–	–	(0.8–4)	mg/L	–	–	(0.1–0.5)	7
↓ **Folic acid**	30 subjects .... (a)	nmol/L	53.5	24.9	(28.5–152)	µg/L	23.6	11.0	(12.6–67)	210
	23 adults .... (b)	nmol/L	71.6	–	(34–122)	µg/L	31.6	–	(15–54)	211
	62 subjects .... (b)	nmol/L	–	–	45–113	µg/L	–	–	20–50	212
Biopterin	27 specimens	nmol/L	1.7	0.89	(1.1–3.0)	µg/L	0.4	0.21	(0.25–0.7)	214
	19 specimens	nmol/L	8.0	2.4	–	µg/L	1.9	0.57	–	243
↓ **Vitamin B$_{12}$**	62 subjects	pmol/L	13	5.7	(6–26)	ng/L	17.8	7.7	(8.0–35.6)	212 215
	15 subjects	pmol/L	16	5.7	–	ng/L	21.3	7.7	5.9–36.7	216
↓ **Pantothenic acid**	103 subjects	µmol/L	2.37	–	(0.46–7.8)	mg/L	0.52	–	(0.10–1.7)	208
↓ **Ascorbic acid**		µmol/L	–	–	(17–119)	mg/L	–	–	(3–21)	7

* Factors for conversion of µmol into mg: triglycerides, 0.885; phospholipids, 0.774; fatty acids, 0.282.

Acetoacetic acid, β-hydroxybutyric acid. Determined enzymatically. The CSF/serum ratio of acetoacetic acid and β-hydroxybutyric acid concentrations is 0.6–0.8. The CSF concentrations are increased in states of food deprivation[132] and in diabetic acidosis[104], concurrently with the serum concentrations.

Total lipids. Compared with the serum, the lipid concentration in the CSF is very low (Table 18).

Table 18
Lipids in CSF and CSF/serum ratio of lipid concentrations[141]

	Concentration in CSF*	$\dfrac{\text{CSF}}{\text{Serum}}$
Total lipids........................	20.3 mg/L	2.9×10^{-3}
Total cholesterol	10.4 µmol/L	2.0×10^{-3}
Free cholesterol...................	5.0 µmol/L	3.2×10^{-3}
Cholesterol esters.................	5.3 µmol/L	1.5×10^{-3}
Phospholipids.....................	9.23 µmol/L	3.2×10^{-3}

* CSF of presumably normal composition.

Cholesterol. Cholesterol – approximately half esterified[138] – is normally the only sterol in the CSF. The cholesterol values increase with increasing protein concentration[138]. After administration of triparanol, desmosterol is detectable in the CSF; values above 0.25 µmol/L are indicative of a brain tumor[137]. Cholesterol determination has not proved important for clinical purposes thus far[172].

Phospholipids. The phospholipid level rises with increasing protein concentration[139]. It is higher in adults than in children, and the proportions of the individual fractions change according to age[142, 143] (Table 19). Changes of the phospholipid pattern in neurologic diseases are not clinically evaluable[172].

Fatty acids. The individual lipid fractions have different fatty-acid patterns[143]. The cholesterol esters are rich in unsaturated fatty acids – particularly in oleic acid (36%) and linoleic acid (16%). In the phospholipids, palmitic acid (33%) predominates, while the linoleic acid content is small (4%). Triglycerides are rich in oleic acid (39%) and likewise have a low linoleic-acid content (5%).

Cerebrosides. The carbohydrate is almost exclusively galactose. The bases are (C$_{18}$)-4-sphingenin and (C$_{18}$)-sphinganin.

↓See text below	Lumbar CSF unless otherwise stated	SI unit	Mean	s	95% range (extreme range in brackets)	Other unit	Mean	s	(Extreme range)	Refer-ence
Cells										
↓ **Cell count**										
Erythrocytes	Newborn, 0–14 days....	µL⁻¹	120	–	(0–675)	. . .	. . .	. . .	. . .	147
Leukocytes	Newborn, 0–14 days....	µL⁻¹	7.5	–	(0–15)	. . .	. . .	. . .	. . .	147
	10 children, 1st month ..	µL⁻¹	5	–	1–25	. . .	. . .	. . .	. . .	102
	319 children, 2nd month to 16 years	µL⁻¹	1	–	0–7	. . .	. . .	. . .	. . .	102
	60 adults	µL⁻¹	1.1	–	0–5.3	. . .	. . .	. . .	. . .	218
	Suboccipital CSF, 20 adults............	µL⁻¹	0.9	–	0–3.6	. . .	. . .	. . .	. . .	218
	Ventricular CSF........	µL⁻¹	–	–	(0–1)	. . .	. . .	. . .	. . .	219
↓ **Electrophoretic mobility**............	....	. . .	. . .	. . .	. . .	µms⁻¹ V⁻¹ cm	–	–	(0.95–1.05)	222

Thiamine. Values determined with (a) *Ochromonas malhamensis,* (b) *Ochromonas danica.* – Thiamine is present in the CSF both in free form and in phosphorylated form[7].

Vitamin B₆. Determined with *Tetrahymena pyriformis.*

Folic acid. Values determined (a) with *Lactobacillus casei,* and (b) by the aseptic technique using *Lactobacillus casei.*
The CSF/serum ratio of folate concentrations is 2.5–4.0[210–212]. According to some authors[210,211] but not all[213], low values are found in subjects using anticonvulsants.

Vitamin B₁₂. Determined by radioimmunoassay. The CSF/serum ratio of vitamin B₁₂ concentrations is 0.05[212,215,217]. In pernicious anemia and megaloblastic anemia due to anticonvulsant therapy the concentration in the CSF is low[212,215].

Pantothenic acid. Determined with *Lactobacillus plantarum;* present mainly in bound form.

Ascorbic acid. Present in reduced form.

Cell count. The cell count is increased in the first month after birth[102,147], particularly in premature infants[148]. Beginning with the second month and until adulthood, no differences are apparent[102]. See Table 20 regarding the proportions of the different cell forms; 0–3% are ependymal and epithelial cells from the choroid plexus[3,4,220]. The lymphocytes are almost exclusively of the T type[226]. The cell count is increased in all inflammatory processes of the central nervous system and its membranes, most markedly so – with neutrophil granulocytes predominating – in acute bacterial meningitis[4,106]. Depending on the nature of the disease, reticular cells with enlarged nuclei and abundant metaplasia, macrophages, plasma cells and tumor cells may occur in the CSF. See literature for details[3,4,106,219,220].

Electrophoretic mobility of cells toward anode. This roughly equals the mobility of the blood lymphocytes. Reduced cell mobility is encountered in bacterial meningitis, while heightened cell mobility is seen in progressive paralysis and encephalomyelitis.

Table 19   *Concentrations and fractions of CSF phospholipids in relation to age[142]*

Age	Lipid phosphorus				Lysoleci-thin	Sphingo-myelin*	Lecithin	Cephalin°	Unknown†
	Mean	(Extreme range)	Mean	(Extreme range)					
	µmol/L		µg/L		Mass fraction of lipid phosphorus as percent				
0–1 year	3.45	(3.23–3.58)	107	(100–111)	5.8	5.8	63.1	1.3	24.0
1–2 years...........................	2.91	(2.32–3.62)	90	(72–112)	5.4	10.7	69.6	3.5	13.9
2–4 years...........................	3.13	(2.65–3.78)	97	(82–117)	7.9	13.0	60.5	5.9	12.6
4–8 years	3.81	(3.55–4.04)	118	(110–125)	5.0	10.0	60.5	7.9	16.5
8–14 years	3.91	(3.84–3.97)	121	(119–123)	11.7	13.6	52.5	6.5	16.0
Adults	6.94	(5.46–8.78)	215	(169–272)	14.2	6.7	49.8	11.7	17.5

* According to other authors[42,141,143] the sphingomyelin proportion is approximately 20%.
† This fraction probably contains the phosphatide acids.

° Cephalin (phosphatidylethanolamine) including phosphatidylserine and phosphatidylinositol; however, the former compound represents the major portion of this fraction[42]. 2% of the CSF phospholipids are lysocephalin[42].

Table 20   *Distribution of cell forms in CSF of normal subjects and of patients with CNS diseases[221]*

	Num-ber	Total cell count		Small lympho-cytes		Large lympho-cytes		Mono-cytes		Reticulo-mono-cytes		Granulo-cytes		Macro-phago-cytes	
		Mean	s	Mean	s	Mean	s	Mean	s	Mean	s	Mean	s	Mean	s
		µL⁻¹		Number fraction as percent											
Normal newborn, < 1 month	6	10.2	8.45	9	10	10	6	13	8	60	15	3	5	5	4
Normal older subjects, 4–75 years	34	2.59	1.73	18	14	45	18	6	6	31	13	1	1	0	–
Acute CNS disease.......................	34	34.3	64.8	23	19	38	20	7	6	27	15	2	3	1	3
Chronic CNS disease....................	17	3.47	3.48	20	19	28	19	8	7	39	17	0	–	0	2

References

[1] THORN, L., *Dtsch. med. Wschr.*, **98**, 2253 (1973).

[2] CSERR, H. F., *Physiol. Rev.*, **51**, 273 (1971).

[3] DELANK, H. W., *Nervenarzt*, **43**, 57 (1972).

[4] BISCHOFF, A., *Schweiz. med. Wschr.*, **99**, 1381 (1969).

[5] JANZEN, R., in BARTELHEIMER, H. (Ed.), *Klinische Funktionsdiagnostik*, 4th ed., Thieme, Stuttgart, 1973, page 596.

[6] BALZEREIT, F., *Dtsch. med. Wschr.*, **93**, 963 (1968).

[7] HINSBERG and GEINITZ, in LANG et al. (Eds.), *Hoppe-Seyler/Thierfelder Handbuch der physiologisch- und pathologisch-chemischen Analyse*, 10th ed., volume 5, Springer, Berlin, 1953, page 300.

[8] HINSBERG, K., in FLASCHENTRÄGER and LEHNARTZ (Eds.), *Physiologische Chemie*, volume II/1a, Springer, Berlin, 1954, page 564; WOLSTENHOLME and O'CONNOR (Eds.), *The Cerebrospinal Fluid*, Ciba Foundation Symposium, Churchill, London, 1958; BOWSHER, D., *Cerebrospinal Fluid Dynamics in Health and Disease*, American Lecture Series No. 413, Thomas, Springfield, 1960; HENLY, A. A., in LONG et al. (Eds.), *Biochemists' Handbook*, Spon, London, 1961, page 892; DAVSON, H., *Physiology of the Cerebrospinal Fluid*, Churchill, London, 1967; DAVSON, H., *Ergebn. Physiol.*, **52**, 20 (1963).

[9] BAUER and HABECK, *Internist (Berl.)*, **4**, 535 (1963).

[10] LUPS and HAAN, *The Cerebrospinal Fluid*, Elsevier, Amsterdam, 1954.

[11] MCALPINE et al., *Multiple Sclerosis*, 2nd ed., Churchill, Livingstone, Edinburgh, 1972.

[12] CUTLER et al., *Neurology(Minneap.)*, **23**, 1 (1973).

[13] GILLAND, O., *New Engl. J. Med.*, **280**, 904 (1969).

[14] SCHMIDT-VANDERHEYDEN, W., *Nervenarzt*, **45**, 153 (1974).

[15] RICH et al., *Circulat. Res.*, **1**, 389 (1953).

[16] HALLMANN, L., *Klinische Chemie und Mikroskopie*, 10th ed., Thieme, Stuttgart, 1966.

[17] KÜNZEL, O., *Ergebn. inn. Med. Kinderheilk.*, **60**, 565 (1941).

[18] LEVINSON, A., *Cerebrospinal Fluid in Health and in Disease*, 2nd ed., Mosby, St. Louis, 1923.

[19] TESCHLER, L., *Dtsch. Z. Nervenheilk.*, **103**, 87 (1928).

[20] WOLMAN et al., *Techn. Bull. Reg. med. Technol.*, **7**, 33 (1946); DAVIS and KING, *Anesthesiology*, **15**, 666 (1954).

[21] FREMONT-SMITH et al., *Arch. Neurol. Psychiat. (Chic.)*, **25**, 1271 (1931).

[22] FORMAN and CHANGUS, *Clin. Chem.*, **14**, 38 (1968).

[23] POSNER and PLUM, *New Engl. J. Med.*, **277**, 605 (1967).

[24] SCHNABERTH et al., *Nervenarzt*, **44**, 199 (1973); *Med. Welt(Stuttg.)*, **26**, 1666 (1975).

[25] SCHWAB, M., *Klin. Wschr.*, **40**, 765 (1962).

[26] PLUM and PRICE, *New Engl. J. Med.*, **289**, 1346 (1973).

[27] LOESCHCKE, H. H., *Klin. Wschr.*, **50**, 581 (1972).

[28] VAN HEIJST et al., *Pflügers Arch. ges. Physiol.*, **287**, 242 (1966).

[29] GÄNSHIRT, H., *Klin. Wschr.*, **46**, 771 (1968).

[30] MITCHELL et al., *J. appl. Physiol.*, **20**, 27 (1965).

[31] KIENLE, G., *Klin. Wschr.*, **47**, 545 (1969).

[32] MITCHELL et al., *J. appl. Physiol.*, **20**, 443 (1965).

[33] LEUSEN, I., *Physiol. Rev.*, **52**, 1 (1972).

[34] RONCORONI et al., *Amer. Rev. resp. Dis.*, **102**, 790 (1970).

[35] ROTMAN and STERN, *Neurology(Minneap.)*, **23**, 1292 (1973).

[36] MCGALE et al., *J. Neurochem.*, **29**, 291 (1977).

[37] PIRKE et al., *Z. klin. Chem.*, **10**, 462 (1972).

[38] BREYER and KANIG, *Neurology(Minneap.)*, **20**, 247 (1970).

[39] MOORE and BLUM, *J. clin. Invest.*, **47**, 70a (1968).

[40] TROPP et al., *Biochem. Z.*, **290**, 320 (1937).

[41] FRIEDMAN and LEVINSON, *Arch. Neurol. Psychiat. (Chic.)*, **74**, 424 (1955).

[42] KUNZ and RUMPL, *Z. Neurol.*, **203**, 259 (1972).

[43] WATCHORN and McCANCE, *Biochem. J.*, **29**, 2291 (1935).

[44] SINGER et al., *J. dent. Res.*, **46**, 455 (1967).

[45] CUMINGS and LASCELLES also HAMILTON, P. B., in ALTMAN and DITTMER (Eds.), *Biology Data Book*, 2nd ed., volume 3, Federation of American Societies for Experimental Biology, Bethesda (Md.), 1974, page 1976.

[46] SMITH et al., *J. Neurol. Neurosurg. Psychiat.*, **18**, 237 (1955).

[47] GILDEA and MAN, *Arch. Neurol. Psychiat. (Chic.)*, **49**, 93 (1943).

[48] ALPERS and RALL, *J. clin. Endocr.*, **15**, 1482 (1955).

[49] KUONEN, E., *Cholinesterase, alkalische Phosphatase und anorganisches Phosphat im Liquor cerebrospinalis*, Dissertation, Basle, 1975.

[50] PRILL, A., *Dtsch. med. Wschr.*, **94**, 1743 (1969).

[51] GIUSTI, M., *Riv. Clin. pediat.*, **56**, 49 (1955).

[52] CROOK et al., *Brit. med. J.*, **1**, 704 (1960).

[53] SETHI and AGARWAL, *Indian J. Pediat.*, **36**, 120 (1969).

[54] BLEIJENBERG et al., *Clin. chim. Acta*, **31**, 277 (1971).

[55] KOTLAREK and BERG, *Mschr. Kinderheilk.*, **126**, 719 (1978).

[56] KJELLIN, K., *J. Neurochem.*, **10**, 89 (1963).

[57] MERET and HENKIN, *Clin. Chem.*, **17**, 369 (1971).

[58] COTZIAS and PAPAVASILIOU, *Nature*, **195**, 823 (1962).

[59] WOODBURY et al., *Neurology (Minneap.)*, **18**, 700 (1968).

[60] STRAUBE and HOFMANN, *Klin. Wschr.*, **13**, 1377 (1934).

[61] KRSTULOVIC et al., *Clin. chim. Acta*, **99**, 189 (1979).

[62] HARE et al., *Lancet*, **2**, 534 (1979).

[63] STEIN et al., *New Engl. J. Med.*, **280**, 926 (1969).

[64] SCHWAB and DAMMASCHKE, *Klin. Wschr.*, **40**, 184 (1962).

[65] MÜTING et al., *Clin. chim. Acta*, **19**, 391 (1968).

[66] VERGARA et al., *Science*, **183**, 81 (1974).

[67] WILLIAMS and MATTHEWS, *J. clin. Path.*, **18**, 771 (1965).

[68] PERRY and JONES, *J. clin. Invest.*, **40**, 1363 (1961).

[69] GJESSING et al., *Europ. Neurol.*, **12**, 33 (1974).

[70] PERRY et al., *J. Neurochem.*, **24**, 587 (1975).

[71] VAN SANDE et al., *J. Neurochem.*, **17**, 125 (1970).

[72] MÜTING and DISHUK, *Proc. Soc. exp. Biol. (N. Y.)*, **126**, 754 (1967).

[73] HOURANI et al., *Arch. intern. Med.*, **127**, 1033 (1971); GLASGOW and DHIENSIRI, *Clin. Chem.*, **20**, 642 (1974).

[74] COPPEN et al., *Lancet*, **1**, 1393 (1972).

[75] GJESSING and SJAASTAD, *Lancet*, **2**, 1028 (1974).

[76] VAN REGEMORTER et al., *Clin. chim. Acta*, **38**, 59 (1972).

[77] DUVOISIN and DETTBARN, *Neurology(Minneap.)*, **17**, 1077 (1967).

[78] JACKSON and ROSE, *J. Lab. clin. Med.*, **34**, 250 (1949).

[79] SINGH et al., *Nature*, **206**, 206 (1965).

[80] PARKES et al., *Lancet*, **1**, 1083 (1971).

[81] WILK et al., *Nature*, **235**, 440 (1972).

[82] POST et al., *Science*, **179**, 897 (1973).

[83] MAWDSLEY et al., *Clin. Pharmacol. Ther.*, **13**, 575 (1972).

[84] PAPESCHI et al., *Neurology(Minneap.)*, **22**, 1151 (1972).

[85] SHOPSIN et al., *Arch. gen. Psychiat.*, **28**, 230 (1973).

[86] O'KEEFFE and BROOKSBANK, *Clin. Chem.*, **19**, 1031 (1973).

[87] EBINGER and ADRIAENSSENS, *Clin. chim. Acta*, **48**, 427 (1973).

[88] KAROUM et al., *Clin. chim. Acta*, **62**, 451 (1975).

[89] RINNE and SONNINEN, *Neurology(Minneap.)*, **22**, 62 (1972).

[90] SHAYWITZ et al., *Neurology(Minneap.)*, **25**, 72 (1975).

[91] JOHANSSON and ROOS, *New Engl. J. Med.*, **285**, 637 (1971).

[92] PAPESCHI and McCLURE, *Arch. gen. Psychiat.*, **25**, 354 (1971); MENDELS et al., *Science*, **175**, 1380 (1972).

[93] POST et al., *Science*, **179**, 1002 (1973).

[94] MÜTING, D., *Clin. chim. Acta*, **12**, 551 (1965).

[95] NASRALLA et al., *J. clin. Invest.*, **37**, 1403 (1958).

[96] BERMAN et al., *J. Lab. clin. Med.*, **44**, 273 (1954).

[97] STEMPFEL and ZETTERSTRÖM, *Pediatrics*, **16**, 184 (1955).

[98] FILIPPINI and SIMMLER, *Dtsch. med. Wschr.*, **98**, 513 (1973).

[99] PRAETORIUS et al., *Scand. J. clin. Lab. Invest.*, **9**, 133 (1957).

[100] ROSENBLOOM et al., *J. clin. Invest.*, **46**, 1110 (1967).

[101] RUDMAN et al., *J. clin. Endocr.*, **42**, 1088 (1976).

[102] AMMON and RICHTERICH, *Schweiz. med. Wschr.*, **100**, 1317 (1970).

[103] PRYCE et al., *Clin. Chem.*, **16**, 562 (1970).

[104] OHMAN et al., *New Engl. J. Med.*, **284**, 283 (1971).

[105] MENKES, J. H., *Pediatrics*, **44**, 1 (1969).

[106] DUFRESNE, J. J., *Praktische Zytologie des Liquors*, CIBA-GEIGY AG, Basle, 1973.

[107] WILFERT, C. M., *New Engl. J. Med.*, **280**, 855 (1969).

[108] Case records of the Massachusetts General Hospital, *New Engl. J. Med.*, **284**, 1023 (1971).

[109] FISHMAN, R. A., *Trans. Amer. neurol. Ass.*, **88**, 114 (1963).

[110] GAINES et al., *Arch. intern. Med.*, **125**, 333 (1970).

[111] MARKS, V., *Clin. chim. Acta*, **4**, 395 (1959).

[112] HAERER, A. F., *Neurology(Minneap.)*, **21**, 1059 (1971).

[113] GREENAWALD et al., *Amer. J. clin. Path.*, **59**, 518 (1973).

[114] ROMMEL and BURKHARDT, *Klin. Wschr.*, **46**, 1311 (1968).

[115] SCHMUCKLE, U., *Zum Glucosegehalt des Liquor cerebrospinalis bei neurologischen Erkrankungen*, thesis, Basle, 1978.

[116] SILVER and TODD, *Pediatrics*, **58**, 67 (1976).

[117] O'TOOLE et al., *J. clin. Invest.*, **50**, 979 (1971).

[118] PITKÄNEN and SERVO, *Clin. chim. Acta*, **44**, 437 (1973).

[119] SMITH et al., *Clin. Chem.*, **24**, 545 (1978).

[120] GARCIA-BUÑUEL and GARCIA-BUÑUEL, *Neurology(Minneap.)*, **15**, 348 (1965).

[121] LEWIN et al., *Clin. chim. Acta*, **45**, 361 (1973).

[122] PITKÄNEN, E., *Clin. chim. Acta*, **48**, 159 (1973).

[123] PERRY et al., *Clin. chim. Acta*, **29**, 369 (1970).

[124] BLAND et al., *Amer. J. Dis. Child.*, **128**, 151 (1974).

[125] KÖNIGSHAUSEN et al., *Dtsch. med. Wschr.*, **103**, 999 (1978).

[126] SINGH and GUPTA, *Indian J. med. Res.*, **60**, 1342 (1972).

[127] GRÜNDIG, E., *Clin. chim. Acta*, **7**, 498 (1962).

[128] THUNBERG, T., *Acta med. scand.*, suppl. 90, 122 (1938).

[129] CONTRONI et al., *J. Pediat.*, **91**, 379 (1977).

[130] GÖSCHKE et al., *Clin. chim. Acta*, **28**, 359 (1970).

[131] SCHMIDT and SCHWARTZ, personal communication.

[132] OWEN et al., *Metabolism*, **23**, 7 (1974).

[133] TOURTELLOTTE, W. W., *Med. Clin. N. Amer.*, **47**, 1619 (1963).

[134] SHIN, Y. S., *Analyt. Biochem.*, **5**, 369 (1963).

[135] FARSTAD, M., *Scand. J. clin. Lab. Invest.*, **16**, 554 (1964).

[136] ELLRINGMANN, U., quoted from SCHRAPPE, O., *Klin. Wschr.*, **50**, 158 (1972).

[137] PAOLETTI et al., *Neurology(Minneap.)*, **19**, 190 (1969).

[138] PEDERSEN, H. E., *Acta neurol. scand.*, **49**, 626 (1973).

[139] PEDERSEN, H. E., *Acta neurol. scand.*, **49**, 639 (1973).

[140] NAGAI and KANFER, *J. Lipid Res.*, **12**, 143 (1971).

[141] SCHRAPPE, O., *Klin. Wschr.*, **50**, 158 (1972).

[142] SASTRY and STANCER, *Clin. chim. Acta*, **22**, 301 (1968).

[143] ILLINGWORTH and GLOVER, *J. Neurochem.*, **18**, 769 (1971).

[144] JUNG et al., *Klin. Wschr.*, **51**, 810 (1973).

[145] FRIEDMAN, H. S., *Stand. Meth. clin. Chem.*, **5**, 223 (1965).

[146] MAURER and RIEDER, *Schweiz. med. Wschr.*, **108**, 1854 (1978).

[147] WIDELL, S., *Acta paediat. (Uppsala)* **47**, suppl. 115 (1958).

[148] GYLLENSWÄRD and MALMSTRÖM, *Acta paediat. (Uppsala)* **51**, suppl. 135, 54 (1962).

[149] PILIERO and LENDING, *Amer. J. Dis. Child.*, **97**, 785 (1959).

[150] GOLDSTEIN et al., *Med. Clin. N. Amer.*, **44**, 1053 (1960).

[151] SCHEIFFARTH et al., *Papierelektrophorese in Klinik und Praxis*, Urban & Schwarzenberg, Munich, 1962, page 78.

[152] KAPLAN, A., *Amer. J. med. Sci.*, **253**, 549 (1967).

[153] MERTIN et al., *Z. klin. Chem.*, **9**, 337 (1971).

[154] HORDYNSKY, W. E., *Amer. J. clin. Path.*, **57**, 251 (1972).

[155] LOWENTHAL, A., *Agar Gel Electrophoresis in Neurology*, Elsevier, Amsterdam, 1964.

156 LAURELL, C. B., *Scand. J. clin. Lab. Invest.,* 29, suppl. 124, 71 (1972).
157 RIEDER et al., *Z. klin. Chem.,* 10, 379 (1972).
158 FELGENHAUER et al., *Klin. Wschr.,* 45, 371 (1967).
159 DELANK, H. W., *Klin. Wschr.,* 46, 779 (1968).
160 WRIGHT, G. L., *Clin. Chem.,* 17, 430 (1971).
161 FELGENHAUER, K., *Klin. Wschr.,* 52, 1158 (1974).
162 GOTTESLEBEN and BAUER, *Germ. med. Mth.,* 12, 331 (1967).
163 PROPP et al., *J. Lab. clin. Med.,* 82, 154 (1973).
164 PETZ et al., *Medicine (Baltimore),* 50, 259 (1971).
165 GLASNER and WENIG, *Klin. Wschr.,* 51, 806 (1973).
166 ERICSSON et al., *Neurology (Minneap.),* 19, 606 (1969).
167 DENCKER and SWAHN, *Nature,* 194, 288 (1962).
168 SCHULLER et al., *Clin. chim. Acta,* 30, 73 (1970); 33, 5 (1971); 39, 233 (1972); 42, 5 (1972); SCHULLER and TÖMPE, *Clin. chim. Acta,* 44, 287 (1973).
169 LINK et al., *Z. Neurol.,* 203, 119 (1972).
170 LAMOUREUX et al., *Neurology (Minneap.),* 25, 537 (1975).
171 RIEDER and WÜTHRICH, *Schweiz. med. Wschr.,* 105, 166 (1975); GRAUNE et al., *Schweiz. med. Wschr.,* 106, 1602 (1976).
172 THOMPSON, E. J., *Brit. med. Bull.,* 33, 28 (1977).
173 LINK, H., *Ann. clin. Res.,* 5, 330 (1973); SCHMIDT et al., *Europ. Neurol.,* 15, 241 (1977).
174 POSER, C. M., *Med. Clin. N. Amer.,* 56, 1343 (1972).
175 YAHR et al., *Ann. N. Y. Acad. Sci.,* 58, 613 (1954).
176 ACKERMANN et al., *Europ. Neurol.,* 13, 131 (1975).
177 TIBBLING et al., *Scand. J. clin. Lab. Invest.,* 37, 385 (1977).
178 LINK and TIBBLING, *Scand. J. clin. Lab. Invest.,* 37, 391 (1977).
179 LINK and TIBBLING, *Scand. J. clin. Lab. Invest.,* 37, 397 (1977).
180 SAVORY and HEINTGES, *Neurology (Minneap.),* 23, 953 (1973).
181 ANSARI et al., *Neurology (Minneap.),* 25, 688 (1975).
182 TOURTELLOTTE et al., *Arch. Neurol. (Chic.),* 25, 345 (1971).
183 DELPECH and LICHTBLAU, *Clin. chim. Acta,* 37, 15 (1972).
184 GOEL and LINDSAY, *Brit. med. J.,* 1, 571 (1972).
185 SHARPE et al., *Clin. Chem.,* 19, 240 (1973).
186 LENDING et al., *Amer. J. Obstet. Gynec.,* 85, 41 (1963).
187 NECHES and PLATT, *Pediatrics,* 41, 1097 (1968).
188 HAIN and NUTTER, *Arch. Neurol. (Chic.),* 2, 331 (1960).
189 SPOLTER and THOMPSON, *Neurology (Minneap.),* 12, 53 (1962).
190 HELLER and OLDENKOTT, *Dtsch. med. Wschr.,* 96, 1222 (1971).
191 DAVIES-JONES, G. A., *J. neurol. Sci.,* 11, 583 (1970).
192 MORRISON et al., *Amer. J. Obstet. Gynec.,* 110, 619 (1971).
193 VERREY, F., *Enzymol. biol. clin. (Basel),* 2, 233 (1962/63).
194 CONCONI et al., *Acta vitamin. (Milano),* 15, 197 (1961).
195 VAN DER HELM et al., *Clin. chim. Acta,* 8, 193 (1963).
196 DITTMANN, J., *Dtsch. Z. Nervenheilk.,* 192, 310 (1968).
197 WEBER, H., *Klin. Wschr.,* 41, 37 (1963).
198 JOHNSON and DOMINO, *Arch. Neurol.,* 35, 421 (1971).
199 WRÓBLEWSKI, F., *Advanc. clin. Chem.,* 1, 313 (1958).
200 FRICK, E., *Klin. Wschr.,* 45, 973 (1967); LISAK and GRAIG, *J. Amer. med. Ass.,* 199, 750 (1967); SHERWIN et al., *Neurology (Minneap.),* 19, 993 (1969); KATZ and LIEBMAN, *Amer. J. Dis. Child.,* 120, 543 (1970).
201 VALE et al., *Arch. Neurol. (Chic.),* 30, 103 (1974).
202 YATES et al., *Clin. chim. Acta,* 47, 397 (1973).

203 GROSSGEBAUER et al., *Klin. Wschr.,* 46, 1127 (1968); NEWMAN et al., *Lancet,* 2, 756 (1974).
204 DI LORENZO and PALMA, *Lancet,* 1, 1077 (1976); GROSSOWICZ et al., *Clin. Chem.,* 25, 484 (1979).
205 GREEN and PERRY, *Neurology (Minneap.),* 13, 924 (1963).
206 KLUGE et al., *Klin. Wschr.,* 47, 1268 (1969).
207 BRUNS et al., *Clin. chim. Acta,* 1, 63 (1956).
208 BAKER and SOBOTKA, *Advanc. clin. Chem.,* 5, 173 (1962).
209 BAKER et al., *Amer. J. clin. Nutr.,* 14, 197 (1964).
210 WELLS and CASEY, *Brit. med. J.,* 3, 834 (1967).
211 REYNOLDS et al., *Nature,* 240, 155 (1972).
212 FRENKEL et al., *J. Lab. clin. Med.,* 81, 105 (1973).
213 WECKMAN and LEHTOVAARA, *Lancet,* 1, 207 (1969).
214 BAKER et al., *Amer. J. clin. Nutr.,* 27, 1247 (1974).
215 FRENKEL et al., *Amer. J. clin. Path.,* 55, 58 (1971).
216 BREUEL et al., *Dtsch. med. Wschr.,* 99, 581 (1974).
217 SCHRUMPF and BJELKE, *Acta neurol. scand.,* 46, 243 (1970).
218 RIEDER, H. P., unpublished observation.
219 SAYK, J., *Cytologie der Cerebrospinalflüssigkeit,* Fischer, Jena, 1960, page 24.
220 BISCHOFF, A., *Dtsch. med. Wschr.,* 96, 1881 (1971).
221 DYKEN, P. R., *Neurology (Minneap.),* 25, 210 (1975).
222 SACHTLEBEN and KRÄMER, *Dtsch. med. Wschr.,* 92, 69 (1967).
223 KALIN et al., *New Engl. J. Med.,* 293, 1013 (1975).
224 HEIKKINEN et al., *Z. Kinderheilk.,* 120, 243 (1975).
225 PHILIPP-DORMSTON and SIEGERT, *Klin. Wschr.,* 53, 1167 (1975).
226 MANCONI et al., *New Engl. J. Med.,* 294, 49 (1976).
227 ZAKARIYA et al., *Clin. Chem.,* 25, 1368 (1979).
228 NERENBERG and PRASAD, *J. Lab. clin. Med.,* 86, 887 (1975).
229 LAKKE and TEELKEN, *Neurology (Minneap.),* 26, 489 (1976).
230 LIAPPIS and JÄKEL, *Klin. Pädiat.,* 188, 267 (1976).
231 GUMIŃSKI, T., *Clin. chim. Acta,* 71, 61 (1976).
232 RECORD et al., *Europ. J. clin. Invest.,* 6, 387 (1976).
233 RENNERT et al., *Clin. chim. Acta,* 75, 365 (1977).
234 LIAPPIS et al., *Klin. Pädiat.,* 189, 155 (1977).
235 TAKAHASHI et al., *Clin. chim. Acta,* 84, 55 (1978).
236 MURRAY et al., *Clin. chim. Acta,* 79, 63 (1977).
237 MYLLYLÄ et al., *Z. Kinderheilk.,* 118, 259 (1975).
238 GOLDBERG, M. L., *Clin. Chem.,* 23, 576 (1977).
239 TRABUCCHI et al., *Arch. Neurol.,* 34, 12 (1977).
240 COVA et al., *J. Lab. clin. Med.,* 89, 615 (1977).
241 GEKLE et al., *Klin. Wschr.,* 55, 189 (1977).
242 WEISNER et al., *Nervenarzt,* 46, 532 (1975).
243 LEEMING et al., *J. clin. Path.,* 29, 444 (1976).
244 COHEN et al., *New Engl. J. Med.,* 295, 1455 (1976).
245 LÖFBERG and GRUBB, *Scand. J. clin. Lab. Invest.,* 39, 619 (1979).
246 BAKER et al., *Amer. J. clin. Nutr.,* 31, 532 (1978).
247 ZÜRCHER and DA PRADA, *J. Neurochem.,* 33, 631 (1979).
248 POST et al., *Amer. J. Psychiat.,* 135, 907 (1978).
249 CHRISTENSEN et al., *Lancet,* 2, 722 (1980).
250 GALVEZ et al., *Clin. chim. Acta,* 91, 191 (1979).
251 TAKAGI et al., *J. clin. Path.,* 33, 786 (1980).

The intraocular fluids are the aqueous humor and the vitreous humor. Both in chemical composition and in function, the aqueous humor resembles fairly closely the cerebrospinal fluid[1]. It protects the retina against heat damage and drying and makes certain that the intraocular pressure remains constant – the precondition for a sharp image. In addition, the aqueous humor is important for the nutrition of the lens and the cornea since these two organs contain no blood vessels.

The aqueous humor is produced in the ciliary body of the lateral wall of the posterior chamber of the eye[1-3]. There is some evidence that the aqueous humor is primarily an ultrafiltrate of the plasma; according to another line of reasoning[3,4] the formation of the aqueous humor is related to an active transport of Na^+, Cl^- and possibly HCO_3^-. Through special mechanisms it concentrates ascorbic acid, amino acids and perhaps glucose so that it can function as a nutritive material in the anterior chamber[3]. Outflow of

the aqueous humor takes place mostly at the lateral angle of the anterior chamber through the pores of the canal of Schlemm, from which it is diverted via the episcleral veins. The canal of Schlemm is preceded by a spongelike structure – the trabecular meshwork – which traps and phagocytizes degradation products of the lenticular and corneal tissues. A small portion of the aqueous humor – perhaps 5–20% in man – passes through the anterior chamber along the fascicle of the ciliary muscle into the supraciliary and suprachoroid space and onward through the sclera[3].

The composition of the aqueous humor of the normal human eye is not sufficiently well known, particularly because of the difficulty of recovering it. Most of the data have been obtained in postmortem studies or by puncture of cataractous eyes. The composition changes on the way from the site of formation to the outflow site. The data presented below apply to the fluid in the anterior chamber of the eye.

↓See text on next page	Cataract patients unless otherwise stated	SI unit	Mean	s	(Extreme range)	Other units	Mean	s	(Extreme range)	Reference
Physicochemical data										
Mass	Normal eye, 23 specimens	...	...	...	...	mg	193	–	(110–303)	6
↓ **Flow**	Normal eye, young adults	...	...	...	...	µL/min	–	–	(2–8)	7
Relative density .	Normal eye, 23 specimens	...	1.0059	–	(1.0051–1.0068)	...	...	...	...	6
Relative viscosity (22 °C)	No data..............	...	–	–	(1.025–1.10)	...	...	...	...	2
Surface tension (37 °C)	No data..............	$10^{-3} N m^{-1}$	60.4	–	–	dyn cm^{-1}	60.4	–	–	8
Freezing-point depression	Normal lens, 4 specimens	K	0.564	–	(0.560–0.567)	°C	0.564	–	(0.560–0.567)	9
Osmolality	Normal lens, 4 specimens	mmol/kg	303	–	(301–305)	mosm/kg	303	–	(301–305)	9
O_2 pressure	16 subjects..............	kPa	7.96	–	(7.1–9.1)	mmHg	59.7	–	(53–68)	10
	Normal eye, 32 specimens	kPa	6.4	–	(4.5–8.0)	mmHg	48	–	(34–60)	11
CO_2 pressure....	16 subjects..............	kPa	5.15	–	(4.67–5.93)	mmHg	38.6	–	(35.0–44.5)	10
	Normal eye, 32 specimens	kPa	4.9	–	(4.4–5.7)	mmHg	37	–	(33–43)	11
pH.............	16 subjects..............	...	...	...	...	–	7.38	–	(7.31–7.42)	10
	Normal eye, 32 specimens	...	...	...	...	–	7.32	–	(7.15–7.41)	11

		Amount of substance				Mass				
		Unit	Mean	s	(Extreme range)	Unit	Mean	s	(Extreme range)	
Inorganic substances										
Bicarbonate	Relative to water:									
	– 22 subjects	mmol/kg	21.5	–	(17.3–22.5)	...	...	...	...	12
	– 22 subjects	mmol/kg	20.7	1.99	(17.4–24.4)	...	...	...	...	5
	– Clear lens, 22 subjects..	mmol/kg	19.6	1.40	(16.0–22.0)	...	...	...	...	5
Chloride	Normal eye, 29 subjects..	mmol/L	107	–	(55–130)	g/L	3.79	–	(1.9–4.6)	13
	Relative to water:									
	– 22 subjects	mmol/kg	126	–	(118–132)	g/kg	4.47	–	(4.18–4.68)	12
	– 15 subjects	mmol/kg	128	22.4	(99–158)	g/kg	4.54	0.79	(3.51–5.64)	5
	– Clear lens, 17 subjects..	mmol/kg	134	22.4	(92–160)	g/kg	4.75	0.79	(3.26–5.67)	5
Phosphorus										
– inorganic......	4 subjects	mmol/L	0.62	–	(0.55–0.68)	mg/L	19.2	–	(17–21)	14
Potassium	Normal eye, 29 subjects..	mmol/L	3.2	–	–	mg/L	125	–	–	13
Sodium	Normal eye, 29 subjects..	mmol/L	111	–	(60–155)	g/L	2.55	–	(1.38–3.56)	13
	Relative to water:									
	– 12 adults	mmol/kg	163	13.1	(136–184)	g/kg	3.75	0.30	(3.01–4.23)	15

↓See text below	Cataract patients unless otherwise stated	Amount of substance				Mass				Reference
		Unit	Mean	s	(Extreme range)	Unit	Mean	s	(Extreme range)	
Copper.........	Normal eye, 5 specimens	µmol/L	–	–	(2.5–3.1)	µg/L	–	–	(160–200)	16
Zinc	Relative to solids: – 9 subjects	mmol/kg	1.59	–	(0.9–2.8)	mg/kg	104	–	(60–180)	17
Nitrogenous substances										
Urea...........	13 specimens	mmol/L	4.51	1.32	–	mg/L	271	79	–	18
Uric acid.......	2 subjects................	µmol/L	–	–	(65–270)	mg/L	–	–	(11–45)	14
↓**Amino acids**	....	...	...	...	...	...	...	...	...	...
↓**Protein**	....	...	...	...	...	...	...	...	...	...
↓**Enzymes**	....	...	...	...	...	...	...	...	...	...

Flow. The flow of the aqueous humor from the anterior chamber into the episcleral veins is a codeterminant of the intraocular pressure:

$$P_{io} = P_v + R \times \dot{V}$$

(P_{io} = intraocular pressure [in Pa]; P_v = pressure in episcleral veins [in Pa]; R = resistance in outflow system [in Pa min µL^{-1}]; $\dot{V}$ = volume rate in outflow system [in µL min^{-1}].)
At a volume rate of 2 µL min^{-1}, the calculated intraocular pressure is 2.1 kPa (16 mmHg)[3].

Amino acids (Table 1). Some amino acids (e.g. lysine) are present in the aqueous humor in a higher concentration than in the plasma[18,19]. After administration of acetazolamide, the amino-acid concentration increases by about 50%[18].

Protein. The protein concentration in the aqueous humor (Table 2) is only about 1% of the concentration in the plasma[38]. Proteins with a high relative molecular mass, such as α_2-macroglobulin and β-lipoprotein, cannot pass the blood-aqueous barrier[38]. Secretory IgA is likewise undetectable in the aqueous humor[38]. The concentrations of IgG and IgA increase with increasing age[37].

Enzymes. The activities of lactate dehydrogenase[26,27], aspartate aminotransferase and alanine aminotransferase[28] in the aqueous humor amount to only fractions of those in the plasma except in the presence of intraocular tumors, when the activity ratio increases to more than 1. There is no relation between the activity of cholinesterase in the plasma and that in the aqueous humor; how-

Table 1   *Free amino acids in aqueous humor (8 subjects)[19]*

	Mean	s		Mean	s
	µmol/L			µmol/L	
Alanine	294	66.1	Lysine	155	23.5
α-Aminobutyric acid	31.4	7.8	Methionine ..	44.4	9.9
Arginine	133	26.0	Ornithine	25.3	4.6
Asparagine	49.2	11.5	Phenylalanine	119	14.0
Aspartic acid........	1.0	1.5	Proline........	16.0	5.3
Citrulline	9.8	4.8	Serine........	179	38.1
Glutamine	717	134	Taurine	39.1	11.3
Glutamic acid.......	12.0	3.4	Threonine ...	152	41.4
Glycine	16.7	3.5	Tryptophan ..	31.9	10.0
Histidine............	77.9	12.7	Tyrosine	123	16.5
Isoleucine...........	79.8	16.9	Valine	388	84.5
Leucine	192	39.6			

Table 2   *Proteins in aqueous humor*

	Material	Method	Unit	Mean	s	(Extreme range)	Reference
Total protein.............	Normal eye, 36 specimens	After LOWRY	g/L	0.45	–	(0.2–0.9)	13
	12 specimens of cataract patients	After LOWRY	g/L	–	–	(0.3–0.5)	20
	5 specimens of cataract patients .	Turbidimetry	g/L	0.25	0.06	–	21
Prealbumin	50 postmortem specimens	Radial immunodiffusion .	mg/L	17	8	–	22
Albumin.................	50 postmortem specimens	Radial immunodiffusion .	g/L	0.66	–	(0.20–1.20)	23
Acid α_1-glycoprotein	50 postmortem specimens	Radial immunodiffusion .	mg/L	55	–	(15–130)	23
α_1-Antitrypsin	142 postmortem specimens	Radial immunodiffusion .	mg/L	118	–	(40–170)	24
Retinol-binding protein ..	50 postmortem specimens	Radial immunodiffusion .	mg/L	0.5	0.3	–	22
Gc globulin	50 postmortem specimens	Radial immunodiffusion .	mg/L	8	3	–	22
Ceruloplasmin	Postmortem specimens	Radial immunodiffusion .	mg/L	3	–	(2–8)	24
Haptoglobin	50 postmortem specimens	Radial immunodiffusion .	mg/L	19	–	(0–60)	23
Hemopexin	50 postmortem specimens	Radial immunodiffusion .	mg/L	11	–	(6–31)	23
C3 component	50 postmortem specimens	Radial immunodiffusion .	mg/L	10	–	(0–20)	23
C4 component	50 postmortem specimens	Radial immunodiffusion .	mg/L	10	4	–	22
Transferrin..............	50 postmortem specimens	Radial immunodiffusion .	mg/L	59	–	(22–150)	23
IgG	⎫	Radial immunodiffusion .	mg/L	136	–	(50–220)	25
IgA	⎬ 232 postmortem specimens ... ⎨	Radial immunodiffusion .	mg/L	40	–	(10–130)	25
IgM.....................	⎭	Radial immunodiffusion .	mg/L	39	–	(0–80)	25

↓See text below	Cataract patients unless otherwise stated	Amount of substance				Mass				Reference
		Unit	Mean	s	(Extreme range)	Unit	Mean	s	(Extreme range)	
Carbohydrates and metabolites										
↓ Glucose.........	23 adults	mmol/L	–	–	(3.64–4.77)	mg/L	–	–	(655–860)	30
	Relative to water:									
	– 15 subjects	mmol/kg	2.42	0.80	(1.31–4.04)	mg/kg	436	144	(236–728)	5
	– Clear lens, 14 subjects...	mmol/kg	2.06	–	(1.04–3.66)	mg/kg	371	–	(187–659)	5
Carbohydrates, protein-bound										
Hexose	Clear lens, 5 subjects......	mmol/L	370	–	(350–420)	mg/L	67	–	(63–75)	31
Hexosamine	5 specimens	µmol/kg	89	–	(83–102)	mg/kg	16.0	–	(14.9–18.3)	32
Lactic acid......	Relative to water:									
	– 20 subjects	mmol/kg	4.69	0.90	(3.50–6.28)	mg/kg	422	81	(315–566)	5
	– Clear lens, 17 subjects...	mmol/kg	4.28	1.30	(1.78–6.66)	mg/kg	386	117	(160–600)	5
Citric acid	25 men	µmol/L	131	23	–	mg/L	25.2	4.44	–	33
	28 women	µmol/L	136	27	–	mg/L	26.1	5.16	–	33
Vitamins and metabolites										
Nicotinamide ...	1 normal eye..............	nmol	40	–	–	µg	5	–	–	34
Trigonelline	1 normal eye..............	nmol	70	–	–	µg	10	–	–	34
Trigonellinamide	1 normal eye..............	nmol	150	–	–	µg	21	–	–	34
Vitamin B_{12}.....	16 adults	pmol/L	22.1	–	(9–44)	ng/L	29.9	–	(12–60)	35
↓ Ascorbic acid ...	Normal eye...............	mmol/L	–	–	(0.68–1.53)	mg/L	–	–	(120–270)	36
	Normal eye, 22 subjects...	mmol/L	0.81	–	(0.57–1.48)	mg/L	143	–	(100–260)	13
	Relative to water:									
	– 15 subjects	mmol/kg	1.26	0.40	(0.58–2.10)	mg/L	222	70	(102–370)	5
	– Clear lens, 15 subjects...	mmol/kg	1.06	0.31	(0.61–1.60)	mg/L	187	55	(107–282)	5

ever, the enzyme is not demonstrable in the aqueous humor of patients with open-angle glaucoma[29].

Glucose. At high blood-glucose levels the glucose concentration in the aqueous humor is increased[5].

Ascorbic acid. The ascorbic-acid concentration in the aqueous humor amounts to approximately 20–30 times the concentration in the plasma[5].

References

[1] RINTELEN, F., *Augenheilkunde,* 2nd ed., Karger, Basle, 1969.
[2] AMSLER et al., *L'humeur aqueuse et ses fonctions,* Masson, Paris, 1955.
[3] BILL, A., *Physiol. Rev., 55,* 383 (1975)
[4] Editorial, *Invest. Ophthal., 13,* 479 (1974).
[5] DE BERARDINIS et al., *Exp. Eye Res., 4,* 179 (1965).
[6] WUNDERLY et al., *Experientia (Basel), 10,* 432 (1954).
[7] HOLM and KRAKAU, *Acta ophthal.(Kbh.), 46,* 558 (1968).
[8] MAGITOT, A., *Ann. Physiol. Physicochim. biol., 2,* 363 (1926).
[9] DIETER, W., *Arch. Augenheilk., 96,* 179 (1925).
[10] THIEL, H. J., *Albrecht v. Graefes Arch. klin. exp. Ophthal., 174,* 127 (1967).
[11] BEC and ARNE, *Arch. Ophtal.(Paris), 36,* 227 (1976).
[12] BECKER, B., *Arch. Ophthal., 57,* 793 (1957).
[13] BESSIÈRE et al., *Arch. Ophtal.(Paris), 32,* 227 (1972).
[14] WALKER, A. M., *J. biol. Chem., 101,* 269 (1933).
[15] CAGIANUT, B., *Docum. ophthal.(Den Haag), 11,* 173 (1957).

[16] GERHARD and CALME, *Bull. Soc. Ophtal. Fr., 64,* 929 (1964).
[17] GALIN et al., *Invest. Ophthal., 1,* 142 (1962).
[18] HANNA and SANCHEZ, *Ophthal. Res., 3,* 283 (1972).
[19] DURHAM, D. G., *Trans. Amer. ophthal. Soc., 68,* 462 (1970); DURHAM et al., *Clin. Chem., 17,* 285 (1971).
[20] PERETZ and TOMASI, *Arch. Ophthal., 65,* 20 (1961).
[21] DERNOUCHAMPS et al., *Bull. Soc. belge Ophtal., 159,* 544 (1971).
[22] SCHMUT and ZIRM, *Albrecht v. Graefes Arch. klin. exp. Ophthal., 197,* 209 (1975).
[23] SCHMUT and ZIRM, *Albrecht v. Graefes Arch. klin. exp. Ophthal., 190,* 63 (1974).
[24] ZIRM and SCHMUT, *Albrecht v. Graefes Arch. klin. exp. Ophthal., 194,* 125 (1975).
[25] SCHMUT and ZIRM, *Klin. Mbl. Augenheilk., 164,* 368 (1974).
[26] JORDANO et al., *Ophthalmologica(Basel), 157,* 223 (1969).
[27] SWARTZ et al., *Amer. J. Ophthal., 78,* 612 (1974).
[28] CHILARIS et al., *Ann. Ophthal., 4,* 580 (1972).
[29] GENOVESI and GASPA, *Ophthalmologica(Basel), 162,* 60 (1971).
[30] POHJOLA, S., *Acta ophthal.(Kbh.),* suppl. 88 (1966).
[31] CARDIA and CORIGLIONE, *G. ital. Ofial., 15,* 24 (1962).
[32] MEYER et al., *Amer. J. Ophthal., 21,* 1083 (1938).
[33] GRÖNVALL, H., *Acta ophthal.(Kbh.),* suppl.14 (1937).
[34] CIUSA et al., *Exp. Eye Res., 3,* 169 (1964).
[35] PHILLIPS et al., *Nature, 217,* 67 (1968).
[36] KRONFELD, P. C., *Trans. Amer. ophthal. Soc., 50,* 347 (1952).
[37] ZIRM and SCHMUT, *Albrecht v. Graefes Arch. klin. exp. Ophthal., 188,* 239 (1973).
[38] ZIRM and SCHMUT, *Wien. klin. Wschr., 88,* 343 (1976).

The lacrimal fluid serves to cleanse the conjunctival sac as well as to moisten and nourish the cornea[1,2]. In addition, it improves the optical properties of the corneal surface by equalizing level differentials due to the epithelial cells.

The wetting fluid of the cornea (about 4 μm thick[3]) is composed of 3 layers[4]. The innermost layer surmounts the corneal epithelium and contains mucins and/or glycoproteins that promote wetting of the cornea. The middle layer, which is the thickest, is a watery fluid, the lacrimal fluid per se. The outermost layer is of an oily consistency.

The wetting fluid originates from several types of glands[2,5]. The actual lacrimal fluid is formed by the lacrimal gland (glandula lacrimalis) and the accessory lacrimal glands (Krause's glands and glands of Wolfring). The lacrimal gland localized in the fossa sacci lacrimalis of the os frontale in the outer upper angle of the orbit is made up of a group of tubulo-alveolar glands. It is divided by the tendon of the M. levator palpebrae superioris into 2 segments, the larger of which (the orbital) has also been called the actual 'lacrimal gland'[2]. The gland tubes of the larger segment traverse the smaller segment and join the gland tubes of the smaller segment to form 10–12 macroscopically visible excretory ducts which pass above the lateral eyelid margin into the conjunctival sac. Opening and closing of the lid distributes the lacrimal fluid over the lid. Only the lacrimal gland is capable of reflex secretion; the stimuli are probably transmitted via (efferent) parasympathetic nerves. The accessory glands, on the other hand, provide for continuous fluid secretion in the resting state. The sebaceous glands of the lid represent the most important of the 3 types of glands from which the oleaginous secretion originates[6].

The composition of the secretions of the individual glands is known only in part. The following data refer almost entirely to the mixed fluid in the conjunctival sac. It may be assumed, however, that after irritation – mechanical, chemical (e.g. with onions, bromoacetone, bromotoluene, ammonia, pharmacologic (e.g. with pilocarpine) or by light – we are dealing largely with actual lacrimal fluid. Pure lacrimal fluid can be extracted from the excretory ducts. The secretion of the palpebral sebaceous glands can be obtained by expression.

After pharmacologic suppression of reflex secretion, the electrolyte concentration in the fluid of the conjunctival sac differs somewhat from that which is present after stimulation of lacrimation (Table 1). However, in contrast to saliva, for example, no change in the electrolyte concentration with increasing flow has been observed[8]. By comparison with the serum, the tears are slightly hypertonic owing to the higher potassium concentration.

Details of tear composition may be found in the literature reviews[1,9].

Appearance

Pure lacrimal fluid is water-white and colorless. The fluid in the conjunctival sac is slightly clouded from the oily secretions and epithelial desquamation. The tears may occasionally be mixed – for a wide variety of reasons – with blood[10].

Volume

The volume produced per day is difficult to estimate[2]. A portion of the tears evaporates, and another portion passes through the lacrimal ducts into the lacrimal sac and further through the nasolacrimal duct into the inferior nasal concha. It can be inferred from the data in Table 2 that no more than 1 g is formed per day, with lacrimation occurring, for all practical purposes, only during waking hours. Lacrimation sets in within the first few days after birth in most children[15]. It is most profuse in children and young adults and then declines with increasing age[16,17]. The outflow and formation of tears mutually regulate one another[12,18].

A semiquantitative determination of lacrimal flow is made possible by Schirmer's test[2,14]. The stimulus is contact of a piece of filter paper with the walls of the conjunctival sac in the area of the lower lid; tear production is measured by the size of the wetted zone on the paper. A strip of a standardized paper grade 5 mm wide and 35 mm long which protrudes from the conjunctival sac a distance of 30 mm will normally show a wetted zone 15 mm long in 5 minutes; a value of less than 5 mm is generally considered clearly abnormal[2].

Hypersecretion (hyperlacrimia) is liable to result from irritation in various local diseases of the eye. It may also be of nervous origin or occur in connection with diseases of the thyroid. To be distinguished from genuine hypersecretion is overflowing of tears due to obstruction of the lacrimal passages[2].

Hyposecretion (hypolacrimia) is found in many individuals at an advanced age without any perceived symptoms of dryness[2]. Hyposecretion is common in Sjögren's syndrome (keratoconjunctivitis sicca)[19] and is even in childhood characteristic of familial dysautonomia[20]. Hyposecretion is also found in various neurologic lesions, in trachoma, and after removal of all or part of the lacrimal gland[2].

Protein

The protein concentration in the tears (Table 3) is about 10% of that in the plasma. Up to 14 components have been detected by electrophoresis on acrylamide gel[42]. Some of the protein components originate from the plasma; others are formed locally[43]. A high content of a specific prealbumin (lacrimal prealbumin) is

Table 1 *Electrolytes in tears of children[7]*

Electrolyte	Number	Reflex lacrimation suppressed (proxymetacaine)	Lacrimation stimulated (onion)
		mmol/L	
Chloride	9	130	112
Potassium	9	8	13.5
Sodium	9	86	98
Calcium:			
– without corneal desquamation	7	0.45	0.35
– with corneal desquamation	3	2.5	0.9

Table 2 *Tear volume in conjunctival sac and rate of production*

Method		Tear volume in conjunctival sac				Rate of production			Reference
		Unit	Mean	s	(Extreme range)	Unit	Mean	(Extreme range)	
50 eyes	Isotope dilution	μL	7	–	–	μL/min	0.6	–	11
37 adults, 20–89 years	Fluorescein dilution	μL	7.0	2.0	(4.0–13)	μL/min	1.2	(0.5–2.2)	12
17 adults	Fluorescein dilution	μL	6.5	1.8	(3.4–10.7)	μL/min	–	(0.6–1.1)	13
25 children, ½–11 years	Fluorescein dilution:								
– unstimulated		...	...	...	...	mg/h	84	(43–208)	14
– pilocarpine-stimulated		...	...	...	...	mg/h	438	(278–669)	14
25 adults, ages 26–77 years	Fluorescein dilution:								
– unstimulated		...	...	...	...	mg/h	38	(18–56)	14
– pilocarpine-stimulated		...	...	...	...	mg/h	261	(216–486)	14

Secretion in conjunctival sac after stimulation unless otherwise stated		SI unit	Mean	s	(Extreme range)	Other units	Mean	s	(Extreme range)	Reference
Physicochemical data										
Relative density	No data	...	–	–	(1.004–1.005)	...	...	...	...	21
Refractive index	No data	...	–	–	(1.336–1.337)	...	...	...	...	21
Surface tension										
– at 32 °C	6 adults	10^{-3} N m^{-1}	46.2	–	–	dyn cm^{-1}	46.2	–	–	22
– at 30 °C	43 men	10^{-3} N m^{-1}	–	–	(40–50)	dyn cm^{-1}	–	–	(40–50)	18
Relative viscosity	No data	...	–	–	(1.26–1.32)	...	...	...	...	21
Freezing-point depression	10 adults	K	0.570	–	(0.551–0.584)	°C	0.570	–	(0.551–0.584)	23
	53 subjects, 14–87 years	K	0.604	–	(0.572–0.642)	°C	0.604	–	(0.572–0.642)	24
Osmolality	50 adults	mmol/kg	320	–	(304–332)	mosm/kg	320	–	(304–332)	25
	10 adults	mmol/kg	308	–	(297–315)	mosm/kg	308	–	(297–315)	23
	53 subjects, 14–87 years	mmol/kg	326	–	(309–347)	mosm/kg	326	–	(309–347)	24
pH	50 adults	...	...	...	...	–	7.4	–	(7.3–7.5)	25
	50 subjects	...	...	...	...	–	7.85	–	(7.50–8.20)	26
	From excretory ducts: – 50 subjects	...	...	...	...	–	7.48	–	(7.20–7.80)	26
Dry mass	215 subjects	...	...	...	...	g/L	18.7	–	–	27
	32 subjects	...	...	...	...	g/L	18.4	–	–	28
		Amount of substance				**Mass**				
		Unit	Mean	s	(Extreme range)	Unit	Mean	s	(Extreme range)	
Inorganic substances										
Bicarbonate	6 adults	mmol/L	26	–	(20–40)	...	...	...	...	25
Chloride	32 children	mmol/L	135	16.6	–	g/L	4.79	0.59	–	29
	42 specimens	mmol/L	128	5.2	–	g/L	4.54	0.18	–	8
	32 subjects	mmol/L	–	–	(110–135)	g/L	–	–	(3.90–4.79)	28
Phosphorus										
– organic	No data	mmol/L	8.1	–	(0.11–10.3)	mg/L	250	–	(35–320)	21
Potassium	32 children	mmol/L	29	3.1	–	g/L	1.13	0.12	–	29
	42 specimens	mmol/L	16.2	4.8	–	g/L	0.63	0.19	–	8
	No data	mmol/L	–	–	(31–36)	g/L	–	–	(1.2–1.4)	2
Sodium	32 children	mmol/L	142	16.8	–	g/L	3.27	0.39	–	29
	42 specimens	mmol/L	146	10	–	g/L	3.36	0.23	–	8
Calcium	59 subjects, 13–52 years	mmol/L	0.57	–	(0.35–0.77)	mg/L	22.9	–	(14.2–31.0)	30
Nitrogenous substances										
Total nitrogen	Adults	mmol/L	113	–	–	g/L	1.58	–	–	31
Nonprotein nitrogen	Adults	mmol/L	36	–	–	g/L	0.51	–	–	31
Urea	Adults	mmol/L	5	–	–	g/L	0.3	–	–	31
	36 specimens	mmol/L	–	–	(5.5–23)	g/L	–	–	(0.33–1.4)	8
Ammonia	Adults	mmol/L	3	–	–	mg/L	50	–	–	31
Amino acids, free	No data	...	...	...	...	mg/L	~50	–	–	21

characteristic of tears[36,44], as is the high content of lysozyme (see next page). Lacrimal prealbumin together with a small amount of serum albumin makes up the total albumin fraction. The concentration of (secretory) IgA in tears, unlike that in the plasma, is higher than the concentration of IgG[34]. Of complement factors, traces of C4 have been demonstrated in tears[45]. The protein composition of the tears of newborn infants differs from that of adults[46].

Table 3 *Proteins in tears*

	Subjects	Method	Unit	Mean	s	(Extreme range)	Reference
Total protein..............	27 children	After LOWRY............	g/L	7.3	0.5	–	33
	12 subjects.............	Biuret reaction	g/L	8.0	–	–	32
	25 subjects.............	After LOWRY............	g/L	8.1	2.25	(4.3–12.2)	34
Total albumin..............			g/L	3.94	–	–	2
Total globulin..............			g/L	2.75	–	–	2
Albumin....................	Children............	Radial immunodiffusion .	g/L	0.37	0.03	–	31
α_1-Antitrypsin	43 subjects............	Electroimmunodiffusion .	mg/L	15	–	–	35
α_1-Antichymotrypsin........	43 subjects............	Electroimmunodiffusion .	mg/L	14	–	–	35
Inter-α-trypsin inhibitor......	43 subjects............	Electroimmunodiffusion .	mg/L	5	–	–	35
Ceruloplasmin..............	30 specimens	Radial immunodiffusion .	mg/L	40	–	–	36
Transferrin.................	30 specimens	Radial immunodiffusion .	mg/L	100	–	–	36
IgG	27 children	Radial immunodiffusion .	mg/L	48	47	–	33
	74 subjects............	Radial immunodiffusion .	mg/L	141	–	(40–620)	34
	50 subjects............	Radial immunodiffusion .	mg/L	<10	–	–	37
IgA	27 children	Radial immunodiffusion .	mg/L	64	47	–	33
	66 subjects............	Radial immunodiffusion .	mg/L	171	–	(40–800)	34
	50 subjects............	Radial immunodiffusion .	mg/L	246	148	–	37
IgM	61 subjects............	Radial immunodiffusion .	mg/L	–	–	(0–trace)	34
IgE	22 children	Radial immunodiffusion .	µg/L	250	–	(60–700)	34
	10 adults	Radial immunodiffusion .	µg/L	61	–	–	38
Lysozyme...................	306 subjects	Agarose gel diffusion.....	g/L	1.7	–	(1.0–2.8)	39
('human lacrimal lysozyme')	60 subjects............	Spectrophotometry.......	g/L	1.5	0.39	–	40
	5 subjects..............	Agarose gel diffusion.....	g/L	1.27	0.06	–	41

Enzymes

Literature references to enzymes detected in tears are given in Table 4. Determination of β-N-acetyl-D-hexosaminidase-A and α-D-galactosidase-A activity in the tears has assumed importance in the diagnosis of heterozygosity in cases of Tay-Sachs[61–63] and Fabry's disease[59,60]. In both diseases heterozygotes have about one-half of the normal enzyme activity in the tears (Table 5), whereas it is virtually absent in homozygotes.

The activity of *lactate dehydrogenase* in the tears is higher than that in the plasma[47]. In contrast to the latter, LDH V is the predominant isoenzyme in the tears[47], suggesting local formation of lactate dehydrogenase[48].

The isoenzyme pattern of *amylase* in tears differs from that in saliva and urine[51]. The enzyme probably is a secretion product of the lacrimal gland.

Lysozyme (determinable by lysis of dead cells of *Micrococcus lysodeikticus*) constitutes a portion of the bactericidal activity of tears (determinable by inhibition of growth of *Micrococcus lysodeikticus*)[54]. The nonlysozymal factor appears to be B-lysine[57]. The lysozyme concentration is highest in the tears of children and decreases with increasing age[53,55,56]. It is lowered in patients with keratoconjunctivitis sicca[56].

Table 4 *Enzymes in tears*

EC number	Name of enzyme	Reference
1.1.1.27	Lactate dehydrogenase	47,48
1.1.1.37	Malate dehydrogenase	48
2.6.1.1	Aspartate aminotransferase	49
2.6.1.2	Alanine aminotransferase	49
2.7.1.40	Pyruvate kinase	48
3.1.3.1	Alkaline phosphatase	49
3.1.3.2	Acid phosphatase	49
3.2.1.1	α-Amylase	48,50,51
3.2.1.17	Lysozyme	21,36,39–41,46,48,51–58
3.2.1.22	α-D-Galactosidase	59,60
3.2.1.23	β-D-Galactosidase	77
3.2.1.52	β-N-Acetyl-D-hexosaminidase	59–63
4.2.1.13	L-Serine dehydratase	64

Table 5 *α-D-Galactosidase and β-N-acetyl-D-hexosaminidase activity (37°C) in tears*

	Normal subjects					Heterozygotes*					Reference
	Number	Unit	Mean	s	(Extreme range)	Number	Unit	Mean	s	(Extreme range)	
α-D-Galactosidase, total....................	58	U/L	2.37	0.96	(1.42–4.48)	13	U/L	1.08	0.26	(0.48–1.35)	59
α-D-Galactosidase B	58	U/L	0.24	0.10	(0.07–0.47)	13	U/L	0.22	0.06	(0.11–0.36)	59
β-N-Acetyl-D-hexosaminidase, total........	58	U/L	21.0	8.9	(6.0–48.2)	–	–	–	–	–	59
	80	U/L	76.3	99.1	(17.3–156)	–	–	–	–	–	61
	200	U/L	149	–	(50.3–317)	–	–	–	–	–	63
β-N-Acetyl-D-hexosaminidase B	58	U/L	10.2	5.0	(2.6–28.2)	–	–	–	–	–	59
β-N-Acetyl-D-hexosaminidase A	92	%°	51	–	(38–82)	13	%°	–	–	(13–39)	61
	200	%°	48.0	–	(34–65)	15	%°	26.4	–	(18–32)	63

* Values for α-D-galactosidase in Fabry's disease; for β-N-acetyl-D-hexosaminidase in Tay-Sachs disease.

° As percent of total β-N-acetyl-D-hexosaminidase activity.

↓See text below	Secretion in conjunctival sac after stimulation unless otherwise stated	Amount of substance				Mass				Reference
		Unit	Mean	s	(Extreme range)	Unit	Mean	s	(Extreme range)	
Carbohydrates and metabolites										
↓ Glucose............	23 children, 6–38 months	μmol/L	1200	–	(0–2500)	mg/L	220	–	(0–450)	65
	12 subjects	μmol/L	140	–	(60–280)	mg/L	26	–	(10–50)	28
	50 specimens	μmol/L	230	170	–	mg/L	41	31	–	66
	43 adults	μmol/kg	206	177	–	mg/kg	37.1	31.9	–	67
Carbohydrates, protein-bound										
Hexoses	7 subjects	mmol/L	2.56	–	(2.36–3.11)	mg/L	462	–	(425–560)	70
	12 subjects	mmol/L	2.81	–	–	mg/L	506	–	–	32
Hexosamine	12 subjects	mmol/L	2.50	–	–	mg/L	448	–	–	32
N-Acetylneuraminic acid................	12 subjects	mmol/L	1.19	0.21	–	mg/L	369	64	–	32
Pyruvic acid	16 subjects	μmol/L	470	–	(120–990)	mg/L	41	–	(11–87)	64
Citric acid	2 adults	μmol/L	–	–	(26–36)	mg/L	–	–	(5–7)	71
↓ Ketone bodies......	....	...	...	...	...	...	...	...	...	...
Ascorbic acid	No data	μmol/L	–	–	(0–970)	mg/L	–	–	(0–140)	73
↓ Lipids										
Cholesterol	2 subjects	mmol/L	0.4	–	(0.2–0.8)	mg/L	150	–	(80–310)	74
	16 subjects	mmol/L	0.44	0.097	(0.27–0.62)	mg/L	171	3.7	(106–240)	75

Glucose. The glucose concentration in tears is higher after stimulation than in the basal secretion[68,69]. It increases as the blood glucose level increases[66] so that the tears give positive results on glucose test strips at high blood glucose levels[68,69].

Ketone bodies. The concentration of ketone bodies in the tears amounts to approximately one-half of that in the plasma[72].

Lipids. Lipids in tears probably are for the most part secretions of the palpebral sebaceous glands. These secretions are of similar composition as the sebum and consist of complex mixtures of waxes and of free and esterified cholesterol[76].

References

[1] SÜLLMANN, H., in FLASCHENTRÄGER and LEHNARTZ (Eds.), *Physiologische Chemie,* volume II/2a, Springer, Berlin, 1956, page 864.
[2] VEIRS, E. R., *Lacrimal Disorders,* Mosby, St. Louis, 1976.
[3] NORN, M. S., *Acta ophthal.(Kbh.),* **44**, 212 (1966).
[4] BRAUNINGER et al., *Amer. J. Ophthal.,* **73**, 132 (1972).
[5] JONES, L. T., *Int. Ophthal. Clin.,* **13**, 3 (1973).
[6] ANDREWS, J. S., *Int. Ophthal. Clin.,* **13**, 23 (1973).
[7] BOTELHO et al., *J. Pediat.,* **83**, 601 (1973).
[8] THAYSEN and THORN, *Amer. J. Physiol.,* **178**, 160 (1954).
[9] LEOPOLD and HARRIS, in ALTMAN and DITTMER (Eds.), *Biological Data Book,* 2nd ed., volume 3, Federation of American Societies for Experimental Biology, Bethesda (Md.), 1974, page 2032.
[10] SIGGERS, D. C., *Brit. med. J.,* **4**, 177 (1970); BANTA et al., *Amer. J. Ophthal.,* **75**, 726 (1973).
[11] SØRENSEN, T., *Acta ophthal.(Kbh.),* suppl. 125, 43 (1975).
[12] MISHIMA et al., *Invest. Ophthal.,* **5**, 264 (1966).
[13] SCHERZ et al., *Albrecht v. Graefes Arch. klin. exp. Ophthal.,* **192**, 141 (1974).
[14] KIRCHNER, C., *Klin. Mbl. Augenheilk.,* **144**, 412 (1964).
[15] PENBHARKKUL and KARELITZ, *J. Pediat.,* **61**, 859 (1962); APT and CULLEN, *J. Amer. med. Ass.,* **189**, 951 (1964).
[16] NORN, M. S., *Acta ophthal.(Kbh.),* **43**, 567 (1965).
[17] BRANDT and FRITSCHE, *Acta ophthal.(Kbh.),* **45**, 166 (1967).
[18] FRANÇOIS and NEETENS, *Amer. J. Ophthal.,* **76**, 351 (1973).
[19] BLOCH et al., *Medicine(Baltimore),* **44**, 187 (1965).
[20] BRUNT and McKUSICK, *Medicine(Baltimore),* **49**, 343 (1970).
[21] LIOTET and COCHET, *Arch. Ophtal.(Paris)* **27**, 251 (1967).
[22] MILLER, D., *Arch. Ophthal.,* **82**, 368 (1969).
[23] KROGH et al., *Acta physiol. scand.,* **10**, 88 (1945).
[24] MASTMAN et al., *Arch. Ophthal.,* **65**, 509 (1961).
[25] GROVE-RASMUSSEN et al., *Acta pharm. int.(Kbh.),* **2**, 343 (1951/53).
[26] MATTHÄUS, W., *Klin. Mbl. Augenheilk.,* **141**, 899 (1962).
[27] SMOLENS et al., *Amer. J. Ophthal.,* **32**, part 2, 153 (1949).
[28] GIARDINI and ROBERTS, *Brit. J. Ophthal.,* **34**, 737 (1950).

[29] DI SANT'AGNESE et al., *Pediatrics,* **22**, 507 (1958).
[30] UOTILA et al., *Invest. Ophthal.,* **11**, 258 (1972).
[31] WATSON et al., *Amer. J. clin. Nutr.,* **30**, 599 (1977).
[32] CABEZAS et al., *Biochim. biophys. Acta(Amst.),* **83**, 318 (1964).
[33] McMURRAY et al., *Amer. J. clin. Nutr.,* **30**, 1944 (1977).
[34] McCLELLAN et al., *Amer. J. Ophthal.,* **76**, 89 (1973).
[35] ZIRM et al., *Albrecht v. Graefes Arch. klin. exp. Ophthal.,* **198**, 89 (1976).
[36] SAPSE et al., *Bull. Soc. franç. Ophtal.,* **80**, 236 (1967).
[37] SEN et al., *Brit. J. Ophthal.,* **60**, 302 (1976).
[38] ALLANSMITH et al., *Amer. J. Ophthal.,* **81**, 506 (1976).
[39] SAPSE et al., *Amer. J. Ophthal.,* **66**, 76 (1968).
[40] RONEN et al., *Invest. Ophthal.,* **14**, 479 (1975).
[41] HANKIEWICZ and SVIERCZEK, *Clin. chim. Acta,* **57**, 205 (1974).
[42] SAPSE et al., *Arch. Ophthal.,* **81**, 815 (1969).
[43] JOSEPHSON and LOCKWOOD, *J. Immunol.,* **93**, 532 (1964).
[44] BONAVIDA et al., *Nature,* **221**, 375 (1969).
[45] CHANDLER et al., *Invest. Ophthal.,* **13**, 151 (1974).
[46] ALLERHAND et al., *J. Pediat.,* **62**, 85 (1963).
[47] KAHÁN and OTTOVAY, *Albrecht v. Graefes Arch. klin. exp. Ophthal.,* **194**, 267 (1975).
[48] VAN HAERINGEN and GLASIUS, *Exp. Eye Res.,* **19**, 135 (1974).
[49] LIOTET, S., *Ann. Oculist.(Paris),* **200**, 526 (1967).
[50] LIOTET, S., *Ann. Oculist.(Paris),* **200**, 1258 (1967).
[51] VAN HAERINGEN and GLASIUS, *Exp. Eye Res.,* **21**, 395 (1975).
[52] BONAVIDA, M., *J. Lab. clin. Med.,* **70**, 951 (1967).
[53] BONAVIDA and SAPSE, *Amer. J. Ophthal.,* **66**, 70 (1968).
[54] FRIEDLAND et al., *Amer. J. Ophthal.,* **74**, 52 (1972).
[55] PIETSCH and PEARLMAN, *Arch. Ophthal.,* **90**, 94 (1973).
[56] MACKIE and SEAL, *Brit. J. Ophthal.,* **60**, 70 (1976).
[57] FORD et al., *Amer. J. Ophthal.,* **81**, 30 (1976).
[58] JANKE et al., *Klin. Mbl. Augenheilk.,* **163**, 366 (1973).
[59] JOHNSON et al., *Clin. chim. Acta,* **63**, 81 (1975).
[60] DEL MONTE et al., *New Engl. J. Med.,* **290**, 57 (1974).
[61] SINGER et al., *Lancet,* **2**, 1116 (1973).
[62] CARMODY et al., *New Engl. J. Med.,* **289**, 1072 (1973).
[63] GOLDBERG et al., *Clin. chim. Acta,* **77**, 43 (1977).
[64] KAHÁN and ERDEI, *Ophthalmologica(Basel),* **164**, 71 (1972).
[65] HULL and MORROW, *Amer. med. Ass.,* **234**, 1052 (1975).
[66] GASSET et al., *Amer. J. Ophthal.,* **65**, 414 (1968).
[67] REIM et al., *Ophthalmologica(Basel),* **154**, 39 (1967).
[68] BERGER, W., *Schweiz. med. Wschr.,* **102**, 1008 (1972).
[69] BERGER, W., *Dtsch. med. Wschr.,* **98**, 2252 (1973).
[70] CORIGLIONE et al., *G. ital. Oftal.,* **12**, 820 (1959).
[71] GRÖNVALL, H., *Acta ophthal.(Kbh.),* suppl. 14 (1937).
[72] BERGER, W., *Dtsch. med. Wschr.,* **98**, 2355 (1973).
[73] KRONFELD, P. C., *Trans. Amer. ophthal. Soc.,* **50**, 347 (1952).
[74] VAN HAERINGEN and GLASIUS, *Exp. Eye Res.,* **20**, 271 (1975).
[75] HILL and TERRY, *Arch. Ophthal.,* **56**, 155 (1976).
[76] ANDREWS, J. S., *Exp. Eye Res.,* **10**, 223 (1970).
[77] TSUBOYAMA et al., *Clin. chim. Acta,* **80**, 237 (1977).

The ejaculum (total sperm) is a suspension of spermatozoa in a fluid medium, the seminal fluid. It consists of various secretions of the accessory reproductive organs, namely, of the secretions of testes, epididymides, vas deferens, seminal vesicles, prostate and Cowper's and Littre's glands. The composition of the total sperm depends on the proportions of these individual secretions; the proportions of the 3 main secretions in the ejaculate can be estimated from the contents of acid phosphatase (characteristic of prostatic secretion), spermatozoa (characteristic of testicular and epididymal secretions), and of fructose (characteristic of seminal vesicle secretion)[1-4].

Upon ejaculation, a few drops of the secretion of Cowper's and Littre's glands are expelled first, generally followed initially by prostatic secretion free of spermatozoa, then by the spermatozoa-containing middle portion, and finally by the highly viscous secretion of the seminal vesicles[5]. Deviations from this course may be caused e.g. by reflex spasms in segments of the genital tract[6].

Ejaculation is immediately followed by a coagulation in that a proteinase from the prostate (clotting enzyme) acts on the fibrino-gen-like protein from the seminal vesicles. Within 5–20 minutes after the ejaculation, the initially gelatinous-viscous sperm becomes liquefied as a result of proteolytic degradation of the coagulation product, which involves a plasmin-like enzyme from the prostate gland; in addition, the clot fragments are hydrolyzed to tripeptides, dipeptides and free amino acids under the action of a chymotrypsin-like enzyme as well as of dipeptidases and amino-peptidases[7].

Sperm can be collected most readily by masturbation; other means are coitus interruptus or use of a spermicide-free condom. None of these methods, however, is entirely physiological so that the method of collection should be taken into account when interpreting the sperm data. It may happen, for example, that sperm collected by masturbation contains no spermatozoa, whereas sperm discharged during coitus contains a large number of spermatozoa; yet the reverse is also possible[6]. The individual secretions do not completely mix during ejaculation and care should be taken therefore to collect all of the ejaculate. If the ejaculate is collected fractionally (split ejaculation), on the other hand, the origin of a substance may be inferred from its concentration in the individual fractions[8-10] (Fig.1).

Not only the study of the spermatozoa but study of the seminal fluid, too, is very important for the detection of disorders of male fertility[6, 11, 12].

Appearance

Fresh ejaculate has a milky turbidity, is slightly opalescent and permeated with glassy, sticky fibers and with sago- and tapioca-like granules. Yellow pigments (flavines) are occasionally found in the seminal-vesicle secretion.

Volume

The volume of the total ejaculum is indicated in Table 1. These values were obtained after at least 3 days of abstinence. – The volume varies considerably in one and the same individual. It decreases with repeated coitus; after prolonged abstinence it may reach 13 mL. 13–33% of the ejaculate originates from the prostate, 46–80% from the seminal vesicles, and about 10% from the epididymides[1, 15]. The proportions of prostatic secretion and seminal-vesicle secretion in the total ejaculate volume are fairly constant in the same individual and independent of changes in volume or of the frequency of ejaculation[16]. Increased values (multisemia) are probably due to venous or lymphogenous congestions in the genital tract; reduced values (parvisemia) are probably attributable to a decrease in prostatic and/or seminal-vesicle secretion[6].

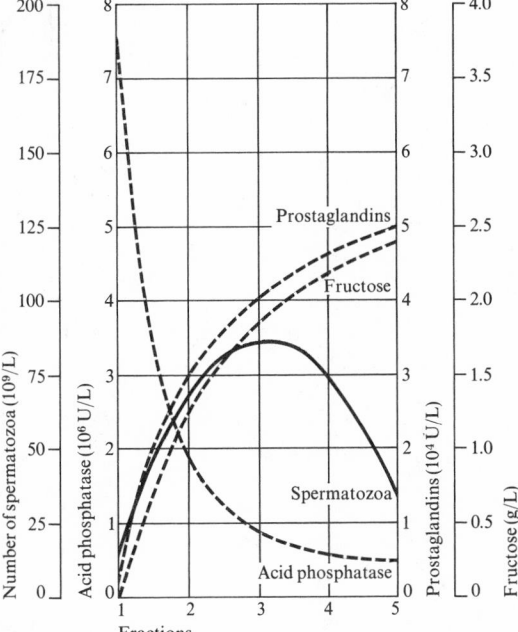

Fig.1. Distribution of spermatozoa, acid phosphatase, prostaglandins and fructose in fractionated ejaculate[8].

Table 1 *Volume of total ejaculate*

Number	Mean	s	95% Limits	(Extreme range)	Reference
			mL		
1000 specimens	3.4	1.6	0.2–6.6	–	13
1300 specimens	3.2	1.4	–	(0.1–11)	14

↓See text below	Material	Number	SI unit	Mean	s	(Extreme range)	Other units	Mean	s	(Extreme range)	Reference
Physicochemical data											
↓**Relative density**	Total ejaculate	6	...	1.035	–	(1.031–1.039)	...	...	...	...	17
	Prostatic secretion......	14	...	1.022	–	(1.018–1.027)	...	...	...	...	17
	Seminal vesicle secretion	2	...	1.037	–	(1.036–1.038)	...	...	...	...	17
↓**Relative viscosity**											
– at 20°C	Total ejaculate	1	...	6.46	–	(6.40–6.55)	...	...	...	...	20

Relative density. The relative density of the total ejaculate is dependent on the content of spermatozoa.

Relative viscosity. The relative viscosity of the total ejaculate depends largely on the content of spermatozoa; that of the prostatic secretion is low and that of the seminal vesicle secretion high. The secretions of Cowper's and Littre's glands are characterized by spinnbarkeit[5].

↓See text on next page	Material	Number	SI unit	Mean	s	(Extreme range)	Other units	Mean	s	(Extreme range)	Reference
Dynamic viscosity											
– at 23°C	Total ejaculate, 1st hour	65	10^{-3} Pa s	14.1	8.1	(3.5–54.5)	cP	14.1	8.1	(3.5–54.5)	21
– at 23°C	Total ejaculate, 2nd hour	28	10^{-3} Pa s	9.3	2.77	(4.4–14.2)	cP	9.3	2.77	(4.4–14.2)	21
–	Total ejaculate, 2nd hour	1111	10^{-3} Pa s	3.92	2.00	(1.3–23.3)	cP	3.92	2.00	(1.3–23.3)	22
↓ Freezing-point depression	....	...	...	...	...	...	...	...	...	...	...
↓ Osmolality	....	...	...	...	...	...	...	...	...*	...	...
Surface tension											
– at 20°C	Total ejaculate, 1st hour	1	10^{-3} N m^{-1}	66	–	–	dyn cm^{-1}	66	–	–	20
– at 15°C	Total ejaculate	–	10^{-3} N m^{-1}	–	–	(52–59.5)	dyn cm^{-1}	–	–	(52–59.5)	23
Specific conductivity											
– at 20°C	Total ejaculate	4	S cm^{-1}	–	–	(0.0088–0.0108)	...	...	...	...	20
↓ pH	Total ejaculate	16	...	...	...	...	–	7.60	0.16	–	30
		9	...	...	...	...	–	7.19	–	(6.9–7.36)	17
	Prostatic secretion	3	...	...	...	...	–	6.45	–	(6.33–6.6)	17
	Seminal vesicle secretion	2	...	...	...	...	–	7.29	–	(7.29–7.32)	17

			Amount of substance				Mass				
			Unit	Mean	s	(Extreme range)	Unit	Mean	s	(Extreme range)	
Water	Total ejaculate	13	mol/L	51.0	–	(49.5–52.4)	g/L	918	–	(891–944)	17
	Prostatic secretion	5	mol/L	51.7	–	(51.4–51.9)	g/L	932	–	(927–936)	17
	Seminal vesicle secretion	2	mol/L	49.4	–	(48.8–49.9)	g/L	890	–	(880–900)	17
	Spermatozoa	3	mol/kg	46.1	–	(45.6–46.8)	g/kg	830	–	(822–844)	24
↓ Dry mass	Spermatozoa	–	...	...	...	...	g/L	176	–	–	25
Inorganic substances											
Carbon dioxide .	Total ejaculate	7	mmol/L	24	–	(19.2–33.2)	[Vol%]	53.5	–	(42.8–74.0)]	17
	Prostatic secretion	3	mmol/L	4.2	–	(3.1–5.4)	[Vol%]	9.4	–	(6.9–12.0)]	17
	Spermatozoa	2	mmol/kg	10.5	–	–	...	...	...	...	24
Chloride	Total ejaculate	31	mmol/L	42.8	–	(28.3–57.3)	g/L	1.52	–	(1.00–2.03)	17
	Prostatic secretion	8	mmol/L	38.1	–	(34.8–46.1)	g/L	1.35	–	(1.23–1.63)	17
	Spermatozoa	3	mmol/kg	33	–	–	g/kg	1.17	–	–	24
↓ Phosphorus											
– total	Total ejaculate	–	mmol/L	36.1	–	–	g/L	1.12	–	–	3
	Spermatozoa	2	mmol/kg	50	–	(47–52)	g/kg	1.6	–	(1.5–1.6)	24
– acid-soluble ...	Total ejaculate	–	mmol/L	18.3	–	(8.9–30.2)	mg/L	570	–	(275–935)	3
		8	mmol/L	23.8	–	(17.2–32.3)	mg/L	738	–	(533–1000)	27
	Prostatic secretion	16	mmol/L	1.09	–	(0.65–1.77)	mg/L	34	–	(20–55)	27
	Seminal vesicle secretion	7	mmol/L	14.7	–	(9.65–19.8)	mg/L	456	–	(300–615)	27
– inorganic	Total ejaculate	–	mmol/L	3.5	–	–	mg/L	110	–	–	3
Lipid phosphorus	Total ejaculate	–	mmol/L	2	–	–	mg/L	60	–	–	3
↓ Potassium	Total ejaculate	12	mmol/L	22.9	–	(17–27.4)	g/L	0.895	–	(0.66–1.07)	17
	Prostatic secretion	6	mmol/L	48.3	–	(28.7–61.4)	g/L	1.89	–	(1.12–2.40)	17
	Seminal vesicle secretion	2	mmol/L	17.8	–	(14.3–21.2)	g/L	0.696	–	(0.559–0.829)	17
	Seminal fluid	53	mmol/L	20.5	5.4	–	g/L	0.80	0.21	–	28
		11	mmol/kg	23.2	9.2	–	g/kg	0.91	0.36	–	29
	Spermatozoa	11	mmol/kg	43.7	26.6	–	g/kg	1.71	1.04	–	29
		3	mmol/kg	35	–	(29–39)	g/kg	1.4	–	(1.1–1.5)	24

↓See text below	Material	Number	Amount of substance				Mass				Reference
			Unit	Mean	s	(Extreme range)	Unit	Mean	s	(Extreme range)	
Sodium	Total ejaculate	14	mmol/L	117	–	(100–133)	g/L	2.69	–	(2.30–3.06)	17
	Prostatic secretion.......	5	mmol/L	153	–	(149–158)	g/L	3.52	–	(3.43–3.63)	17
	Seminal vesicle secretion	1	mmol/L	103	–	–	g/L	2.37	–	–	17
	Seminal fluid...........	53	mmol/L	129	17	–	g/L	2.97	0.39	–	28
		11	mmol/kg	112	14	–	g/kg	2.58	0.32	–	29
	Spermatozoa............	11	mmol/kg	88	13	–	g/kg	2.02	0.31	–	29
		3	mmol/kg	110	–	(101–125)	g/kg	2.53	–	(2.32–2.86)	24
↓**Calcium**	Total ejaculate	3	mmol/L	6.22	–	(5.3–7.15)	mg/L	249	–	(212–287)	17
	Prostatic secretion.......	3	mmol/L	30.2	–	(28.7–32.7)	g/L	1.21	–	(1.15–1.31)	17
	Seminal fluid...........	53	mmol/L	8.0	3.0	–	mg/L	320	120	–	28
		11	mmol/kg	7.04	2.71	–	mg/kg	282	109	–	29
	Spermatozoa............	11	mmol/kg	8.78	2.25	–	mg/kg	352	90	–	29
↓**Magnesium**	Prostatic secretion.......	7	mmol/L	6.2	–	(3.0–9.6)	mg/L	150	–	(74–233)	9
	Seminal vesicle secretion	7	mmol/L	1.1	–	(0.4–1.8)	mg/L	27	–	(9–43)	9
	Seminal fluid...........	53	mmol/L	4.7	1.75	–	mg/L	114	43	–	28
		775	mmol/L	4.4	–	(0.53–17.7)	mg/L	108	–	(13–429)	32
		11	mmol/kg	3.7	1.6	–	mg/kg	90	40	–	29
	Spermatozoa............	11	mmol/kg	6.3	2.5	–	mg/kg	153	60	–	29
		85	μmol/10^9	1.51	–	(0.08–5.18)	μg/10^9	36.7	–	(2.0–126)	33
↓**Zinc**	Total ejaculate	18	mmol/L	2.29	–	(1.24–3.58)	mg/L	150	–	(81–234)	35
		39	mmol/L	2.98	–	–	mg/L	195	–	–	36
	Prostatic secretion.......	7	mmol/L	4.53	–	(1.54–7.49)	mg/L	296	–	(101–490)	9
	Seminal vesicle secretion	7	mmol/L	0.67	–	(0.20–1.42)	mg/L	44	–	(13–93)	9
	Seminal fluid...........	809	mmol/L	2.03	–	(0.02–9.50)	mg/L	133	–	(1–621)	37
	Spermatozoa............	91	mmol/10^9	0.84	–	(0.07–3.01)	μg/10^9	55.3	–	(4.6–197)	33
Copper..........	Total ejaculate	39	μmol/L	8.2	–	–	mg/L	0.52	–	–	36

Nitrogenous substances

Total nitrogen ..	Total ejaculate	34	mmol/L	652	–	(400–878)	g/L	9.13	–	(5.60–12.3)	17
	Prostatic secretion.......	14	mmol/L	297	–	(210–365)	g/L	4.16	–	(2.95–5.11)	17
	Seminal vesicle secretion	3	mmol/L	914	–	(878–956)	g/L	12.8	–	(12.3–13.4)	17
	Seminal fluid...........	13	mmol/L	500	200	(260–710)	g/L	7.0	2.8	(3.6–10)	34

Freezing-point depression and osmolality. At body temperature this increases rapidly, within a few hours, owing to enzymatic hydrolysis of proteins and peptides as well as of phosphorylated choline derivatives[18–20] (Fig. 2).

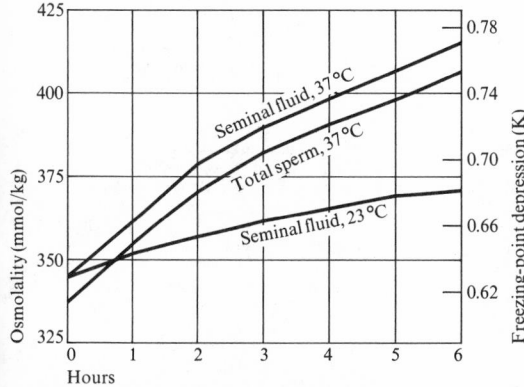

Fig. 2. Osmolality and freezing-point depression of total sperm and seminal fluid in relation to incubation time[18].

pH. Sperm specimens become more alkaline (pH 7.6–8.0) on prolonged standing as a result of escape of CO_2. A pH below 6.7 suggests the absence of seminal-vesicle secretion[31].

Dry mass. About 10% of the dry mass in the total ejaculate consists of inorganic substances; 90% is organic[26].

Phosphorus. The acid-soluble phosphorus of the seminal fluid is present mainly in the form of phosphorylcholine and glycerylphosphorylcholine.

Potassium. The potassium in the seminal fluid stems for the most part from the prostatic secretion; its concentration is increased in cystic fibrosis[34].

Calcium. The calcium in the seminal fluid stems for the most part from the prostatic secretion; its concentration is increased in cystic fibrosis[34].

Magnesium. The magnesium in the seminal fluid stems for the most part from the prostatic secretion[32]; its concentration is increased in cystic fibrosis[34].

Zinc. The prostatic secretion and the spermatozoa are the body fluid and the organ, respectively, with the highest zinc content[38]. The zinc in the seminal fluid comes almost exclusively from the prostatic secretion[37,39] and is bound to glycoproteins[40]. The concentration in the seminal fluid is increased in cystic fibrosis[34], and decreased in prostatitis[35].

↓See text below	Material	Num-ber	Amount of substance				Mass				Refer-ence
			Unit	Mean	s	(Extreme range)	Unit	Mean	s	(Extreme range)	
Nonprotein nitrogen	Total ejaculate	12	mmol/L	69	–	(52–93)	g/L	0.96	–	(0.73–1.30)	17
	Prostatic secretion.......	6	mmol/L	39	–	(21–43)	g/L	0.54	–	(0.30–0.60)	17
	Seminal vesicle secretion	1	mmol/L	71	–	–	g/L	0.99	–	–	17
↓**Ammonia**	Total ejaculate	–	mmol/L	1.2	–	–	mg/L	20	–	–	1
Urea............	Prostatic secretion.......	33	mmol/L	4.2	–	–	mg/L	250	–	–	62
	Seminal fluid............	–	mmol/L	12	–	–	mg/L	720	–	–	41
Creatine	Seminal fluid............	–	mmol/L	1.3	–	–	mg/L	170	–	–	42
↓**Amino acids**	Seminal fluid.........(a)	10	...	...	...	...	g/L	12.6	–	–	43
Ergothioneine ..	Seminal fluid............	–	µmol/L	65	–	–	mg/L	15	–	–	45
Glutathione	Seminal fluid............	–	mmol/L	1	–	–	mg/L	300	–	–	46
↓**Choline** (free)...	Total ejaculate	–	mmol/L	5.8	–	–	g/L	0.70	–	–	47
↓**Phosphoryl-choline**.........	Total ejaculate	4	mmol/L	14	–	(13–17)	g/L	3.06	–	(2.86–3.80)	48
↓**Glycerylphos-phorylcholine** ...	Total ejaculate	4	mmol/L	2.6	–	(2.1–3.5)	mg/L	660	–	(540–900)	48
	Seminal fluid............	24	mmol/L	0.845	0.110	–	mg/L	217	28	–	49
	Spermatozoa...........	7	µmol/10^9	0.933	0.07	–	µg/10^9	240	18	–	49
↓**Carnitine**											
– total (as car-nitine HCl) ...	Seminal fluid............	12	mmol/L	1.34	–	(0.58–2.71)	mg/L	264	–	(115–535)	50
– free	Seminal fluid............	20	mmol/L	0.319	0.024	–	mg/L	51.4	3.87	–	49
	Spermatozoa...........	8	µmol/10^9	0.853	0.106	–	µg/10^9	137.5	17.1	–	49
↓**Polyamines**											
Putrescine	Seminal fluid............	44	µmol/L	230	73	–	mg/L	20	6.4	–	51
Spermidine	Seminal fluid............	43	µmol/L	113	52	–	mg/L	16	7.6	–	51
		62	µmol/L	213	–	(100–340)	mg/L	31	–	(15–50)	52
Spermine	Seminal fluid............	42	mmol/L	3.04	0.24	–	mg/L	615	49	–	51
		62	mmol/L	1.35	–	(0.28–7.00)	mg/L	273	–	(56–1418)	52
Uric acid........	Total ejaculate	–	mmol/L	0.36	–	–	mg/L	60	–	–	3
Cyclic adenosine monophosphate .	Total ejaculate	27	µmol/L	22.5	9.4	(15–35)	mg/L	7.4	3.1	(4.9–12)	54
	Seminal fluid............	27	µmol/L	21.7	10.8	–	mg/L	7.1	3.6	–	54
Cyclic guanosine monophosphate .	Total ejaculate	11	nmol/L	26.1	14.9	–	µg/L	9.0	5.1	–	54

Ammonia. Increases upon prolonged incubation at 37 °C owing to progressive proteolysis.

Amino acids. (a) The value shown is the sum of 19 free and pep-tide-bound amino acids determined by column chromatography (4–6 hours after ejaculation). At this time all the amino acids are present in significantly higher concentrations than in the plasma. – 24 different amino acids have been identified by thin-layer chro-matography[44].

Choline. The value shown was determined 2 minutes after ejac-ulation. – 6 hours after ejaculation the concentration rises to more than 160 mmol/L since choline is released from phosphorylcho-line under the action of acid phosphatase.

Phosphorylcholine. This compound is hydrolyzed within 1 hour of ejaculation, forming phosphate and choline[133].

Glycerylphosphorylcholine. This compound is synthesized mainly by the epididymis and, unlike phosphorylcholine, it is very stable to the action of hydrolyzing enzymes[133].

Carnitine. More than 94% of the free carnitine originates from the epididymis[134].

Polyamines. These originate from the prostatic secretion. The primary polyamine is putrescine, which is formed from arginine in the prostate. The spermine concentration in the seminal fluid can range up to 17 mmol/L, a value higher than those in all other body fluids or organs[53].

Protein. The major portion of the protein stems from the semi-nal vesicle[31]. The sperm quality has no appreciable effect on the protein concentration[55, 56, 61, 64]. After ejaculation, the proteins are gradually broken down under the action of proteolytic enzymes and peptide hydrolases so that the protein concentration drops to one-half after 6 days at room temperature[57].

The seminal-fluid proteins can be separated into 8–15 fractions by electrophoresis on polyacrylamide gel[65–67]. Immunoelectro-phoresis separates them into 5 principal groups with a total of 12 components, 6 of which are specific for the seminal fluid[68–70]. The plasma proteins enter the seminal fluid via the prostate[10,71], and presumably there is also some local formation of IgA[71]. The zinc-containing glycoproteins[40] and lysozyme[72] also appear to originate from the prostatic secretion. Other proteins, on the other hand, such as the secretory IgA[58] and lactoferrin[10,73] are primarily com-ponents of the seminal-vesicle secretion. Other proteins identified in the seminal fluid are α_2-macroglobulin[72], β_2-microglobulin[67], a post-γ-globulin[67], 2 low-molecular sperm-specific proteinase in-hibitors, one of which inhibits the spermatozoal proteinase acro-sine[60] and a lectin-like hemagglutinin[136].

↑↓See text on previous page and below	Material	Number	Method	Unit	Mean	s	(Extreme range)	Reference
↑ Protein								
Total protein....	Total ejaculate	12	(Total N – nonprotein) × 6.25	g/L	45.0	–	(32.9–68.5)	17
		11	Gravimetry	g/L	58.0	–	(43.0–77.4)	17
	Prostatic secretion.......	6	(Total N – nonprotein) × 6.25	g/L	21.7	–	(16.6–29.3)	17
		2	Gravimetry	g/L	25.5	–	(24.6–26.4)	17
	Seminal vesicle secretion	1	(Total N – nonprotein) × 6.25	g/L	77.8	–	–	17
		1	Gravimetry	g/L	90.4	–	–	17
	Seminal fluid............	13	After LOWRY...................	g/L	48.2	16.2	(27.0–74.7)	34
		20	After LOWRY...................	g/L	42	11	(21–66)	55
		140	After LOWRY...................	g/L	51	23	(32–99)	61
	Seminal fluid (10–27 °C):							
	– 1 hour................	8	Biuret reaction......................	g/L	37.6	–	(32.7–46.7)	57
	– 24 hours.............	4	Biuret reaction......................	g/L	26.8	–	(26.3–27.4)	57
Albumin.......	Total ejaculate	9	Radial immunodiffusion	mg/L	630	230	–	10
	Seminal fluid............	41	Radial immunodiffusion	mg/L	660	960	–	58
α_1-Antitrypsin ..	Seminal fluid............	12	Radial immunodiffusion	mg/L	86	16	(72–120)	59
		129	Radial immunodiffusion	mg/L	97.7	52.4	(5–275)	60
α_1-Antichymo-trypsin..........	Seminal fluid............	129	Radial immunodiffusion	mg/L	32.8	35.1	(0–145)	60
β-Trace protein .	Total ejaculate	140	Radial immunodiffusion	mg/L	49	35	(6–180)	61
Transferrin	Total ejaculate	10	Radial immunodiffusion	mg/L	70	50	–	10
Lactoferrin	Total ejaculate	9	Radial immunodiffusion	g/L	1.18	0.74	–	10
IgG.............	Total ejaculate	10	Radial immunodiffusion	mg/L	90	30	–	10
	Prostatic secretion.......	33	Radial immunodiffusion	mg/L	380	–	(160–860)	62
	Seminal fluid...........	41	Radial immunodiffusion	mg/L	51	38	–	58
IgA	Total ejaculate	10	Radial immunodiffusion	mg/L	30	10	–	10
	Prostatic secretion.......	33	Radial immunodiffusion	mg/L	120	–	(0–27)	62
	Seminal fluid...........	41	Radial immunodiffusion	mg/L	30	19	–	58
Secretory IgA ...	Seminal fluid...........	41	Radial immunodiffusion	g/L	1.16	0.51	–	58
IgM.............	Prostatic secretion.......	33	Radial immunodiffusion	g/L	140	–	(0–490)	62
	Seminal fluid...........	41	Radial immunodiffusion	mg/L	9	19	–	58
Lysozyme.......	Seminal fluid...........	10	Agarose gel diffusion.................	mg/L	13.4	5.4	–	63

			SI unit	Mean	s	(Extreme range)	Other units	Mean	s	(Extreme range)	
↓ Enzymes											
Lactate dehydrogenase (25 °C)....	Seminal fluid...........	18	µmol s⁻¹/L	35	–	(12–65)	kU/L	2.1	–	(0.7–3.9)	56
Amine oxidase (37 °C)	Seminal fluid...........	58	nmol s⁻¹/L	116	97	–	U/L	7.0	5.8	–	51
Acid phosphatase (37 °C)...........	Total ejaculate	39	mmol s⁻¹/L	13.1	–	–	kU/L	786	–	–	36
		25	mmol s⁻¹/L	5.0	2.7	(2.0–10.2)	kU/L	300	160	(120–612)	76
	Prostatic secretion:										
	– Boys, 11 years	–	mmol s⁻¹/L	0.15	–	–	kU/L	9	–	–	77
	– Boys, 16 years	–	mmol s⁻¹/L	25.7	–	–	kU/L	1540	–	–	77
	– Men, 20–40 years......	–	mmol s⁻¹/L	42.7	–	–	kU/L	2560	–	–	78
	– Men, 40–100 years.....	–	mmol s⁻¹/L	11.0	–	–	kU/L	660	–	–	78
	Seminal fluid...........	10	mmol s⁻¹/L	6.2	–	(1.6–12.5)	kU/L	370	–	(96–750)	75

Some sperm specimens contain antibodies (probably of the IgA type) which are capable of agglutinating spermatozoa and significant with respect to male infertility[74].

Enzymes. The seminal fluid contains a number of enzymes (see Table 2), certain of which also occur in spermatozoa (page 195). Besides the 5 isoenzymes of lactate dehydrogenase that are present in the plasma, sperm contains another isoenzyme (LDH X)[56,66] which originates from the spermatozoa and is therefore not detectable in sperm after vasectomy[98]. The acid phosphatase[8,31] and the lysozyme[63] come almost exclusively from the prostate. On the other hand, lactate dehydrogenase[31], aspartate aminotransferase[31], and adenosylmethionine decarboxylase[97] are present in higher concentrations in the seminal-vesicle secretion than in the prostatic secretion.

The sperm possesses a high proteolytic activity, which is responsible for the liquefaction of the sperm following ejaculation[7,99]. The enzymes that determine this activity, however, have not been adequately identified. One of the proteolytic enzymes is active at acid pH values; a second one resembles chymotrypsin[100]. In addition, the sperm contains one or more plasminogen activators which are detectable by virtue of their ability to split arginine esters[99]. A major portion of the proteolytic activity in the sperm appears to originate from the prostatic secretion[101].

Table 2 *Enzymes in sperm*

EC number	Name of enzyme	Reference	EC number	Name of enzyme	Reference
1.1.1.27	Lactate dehydrogenase	56,79,80,82	3.2.1.17	Lysozyme	63
1.1.1.37	Malate dehydrogenase	79	3.2.1.20	α-D-Glucosidase	92
1.1.1.41	Isocitrate dehydrogenase	79,83	3.2.1.23	β-D-Galactosidase	93
1.4.3.6	Amine oxidase (diamine oxidase)	51,84	3.2.1.24	α-D-Mannosidase	93
1.6.4.2	Glutathione reductase	79	3.2.1.25	β-D-Mannosidase	93
2.3.2.2	γ-Glutamyltransferase	85	3.2.1.30	β-N-Acetyl-D-glucosaminidase	93
2.5.1.16	Aminopropyltransferase (Spermidine synthase)	51	3.2.1.31	β-D-Glucuronidase	93
2.6.1.1	Aspartate aminotransferase	16,80,83,86	3.2.1.33	Amylo-1,6-glucosidase	94
2.6.1.2	Alanine aminotransferase	80,83,86	3.2.1.76	L-Iduronidase	95
2.7.3.2	Creatine kinase	87	3.4.11.1	Aminopeptidase (cytosol)	80,83
3.1.3.1	Alkaline phosphatase	55,80,88–90	3.6.1.9	Nucleotide pyrophosphatase	135
3.1.3.2	Acid phosphatase	11,16,34,36,55,75,77,78,80,89,90	4.1.1.17	Ornithine decarboxylase	96
3.1.4.1	Phosphodiesterase I	135	4.1.1.50	Adenosylmethionine decarboxylase	51,97
3.2.1.1	α-Amylase	91	4.2.1.2	Fumarate hydratase	84
			5.3.1.9	Glucosephosphate isomerase	81,82

↓See text below and on next page	Material	Number	Amount of substance				Mass				Reference
			Unit	Mean	s	(Extreme range)	Unit	Mean	s	(Extreme range)	
↓ Carbohydrates and metabolites											
↓ Glucose.........	Total ejaculate	5	mmol/L	0.30	0.21	(0.12–0.55)	mg/L	54	38	(2.2–99)	106
	Seminal fluid............	185	mmol/L	0.40	0.52	(0–5.50)	mg/L	72.4	93.9	(0–990)	107
↓ Fructose	Total ejaculate	5	mmol/L	13.2	8.4	(5.4–26.0)	g/L	2.38	1.51	(0.97–1.68)	106
	Seminal vesicle secretion	21	mmol/L	26.4	–	(9.3–45.5)	g/L	4.76	–	(1.68–8.19)	1
	Seminal fluid............	50	mmol/L	17.8	5.5	–	g/L	3.20	0.99	–	107
		11	mmol/L	16.1	–	(7.9–34.4)	g/L	2.90	–	(1.42–6.20)	79
		61	mmol/L	12.3	–	(4.7–35.3)	g/L	2.22	–	(0.84–6.36)	108
		20	mmol/L	14.2	–	(1.6–28.8)	g/L	2.56	–	(0.28–5.19)	109
↓ Carbohydrates, protein-bound											
Sialic acid	Seminal fluid............	10	mmol/L	3.31	–	(1.75–4.85)	g/L	1.02	–	(0.54–1.50)	16
		20	mmol/L	4.43	0.91	(3.39–6.82)	g/L	1.37	0.28	(1.05–2.11)	55
		13	mmol/L	2.59	1.16	(1.23–4.56)	g/L	0.80	0.36	(0.38–1.41)	34
Fucose..........	Seminal fluid............	13	mmol/L	2.7	0.4	(2.2–3.2)	g/L	0.45	0.07	(0.36–0.52)	34
↓ Myoinositol.....	Seminal fluid.........(a)	20	mmol/L	3.6	–	(1.4–8.3)	g/L	0.64	–	(0.26–1.50)	109
	(b)	25	mmol/L	2.7	–	(0.58–10.9)	g/L	0.48	–	(0.106–1.97)	112
Sorbitol........	Seminal fluid............	3	mmol/L	0.5	–	–	g/L	0.1	–	–	113
↓ Lactic acid......	Total ejaculate	–	mmol/L	–	–	(2.2–5.6)	mg/L	–	–	(200–500)	1
↓ Pyruvic acid	Seminal fluid............	11	mmol/L	3.2	–	(1.5–4.9)	mg/L	280	–	(130–430)	79
		5	mmol/L	1.45	0.79	(0.90–2.77)	mg/L	128	70	(79–243)	106
↓ Citric acid	Total ejaculate	10	mmol/L	19.6	–	(5.0–74.4)	g/L	3.76	–	(0.96–14.3)	3
		13	mmol/L	18	14	(6.2–30)	g/L	3.4	2.7	(1.2–5.8)	34
	Prostatic secretion.......	–	mmol/L	–	–	(25–140)	g/L	–	–	(4.80–26.9)	3
	Seminal vesicle secretion	–	mmol/L	–	–	(0.8–1.1)	g/L	–	–	(0.15–0.22)	3
	Seminal fluid............	20	mmol/L	26.5	8.4	(18.2–35.0)	g/L	5.10	1.61	(3.49–6.72)	114

Carbohydrates. The carbohydrates of the seminal fluid can be separated into a dialyzable and a non-dialyzable fraction (Table 3). The dialyzable fraction contains free sugars (fructose, glucose, traces of galactose, ribose and fucose), polyhydric alcohols (myoinositol, sorbitol), and a polysaccharide[102] composed of mannose, fucose and an amino sugar. The non-dialyzable fraction has not been fully identified. Two glycopeptides with a relative molecular mass of 10000[103] have been isolated in addition to Blood Group A substance from the sperm of secretors[104]. The major portion of the non-dialyzable fraction presumably consists of glycoproteins of high sialic-acid content made up of at least 6 compo-

nents[105]. Contrary to earlier reports, glycogen is not a significant constituent of sperm[102].

Glucose. Besides fructose, glucose is the most important source of energy for the spermatozoa[106].

Fructose. Fructose is formed almost entirely in the seminal vesicles[1,8,10]. Its formation depends on sufficient androgenic activity[4,81,90]. Fructose is the most important energy source of the spermatozoa[106,110]. Determination of the fructose concentration in the seminal fluid provides clues to the secretory function of the seminal vesicles and, indirectly, to testosterone secretion[110]. Fruc-

↓See text below	Material	Num-ber	Amount of substance				Mass				Refer-ence
			Unit	Mean	s	(Extreme range)	Unit	Mean	s	(Extreme range)	
↓ Lipids											
Total lipids	Prostatic secretion.......	10	...	...	...	...	g/L	2.86	–	(2.60–3.10)	[115]
	Seminal fluid............	10	...	...	...	...	g/L	1.86	–	(1.67–2.06)	[115]
Phospholipids...	Prostatic secretion.......	10	mmol/L	2.33	–	(1.86–2.91)	g/L	1.80	–	(1.44–2.25)	[115]
	Seminal fluid............	10	mmol/L	1.09	–	(0.62–1.72)	g/L	0.84	–	(0.48–1.33)	[115]
Cholesterol	Total ejaculate	39	mmol/L	1.65	–	–	g/L	0.64	–	–	[36]
	Prostatic secretion.......	10	mmol/L	2.07	–	(1.60–2.71)	g/L	0.80	–	(0.62–1.05)	[115]
		6	mmol/L	1.50	–	(0.67–1.96)	g/L	0.58	–	(0.26–0.76)	[116]
	Seminal fluid............	10	mmol/L	2.66	–	(1.81–3.10)	g/L	1.03	–	(0.70–1.20)	[115]
		184	mmol/L	1.2	–	(0.41–2.4)	g/L	0.45	–	(0.16–0.94)	[116]
		9	mmol/L	1.0	–	(0.78–1.8)	g/L	0.39	–	(0.30–0.69)	[16]
↓ Prostaglandins											
PGE$_1$	Seminal fluid............	6	µmol/L	71	–	(54–85)	mg/L	25	–	(19–30)	[117]
PGE$_2$	Seminal fluid............	6	µmol/L	65	–	(43–85)	mg/L	23	–	(15–30)	[117]
19-OH-PGE$_1$ ...	Total ejaculate	6	µmol/L	270	130	–	mg/L	100	47	–	[118]
19-OH-PGE$_2$ ...	Total ejaculate	6	µmol/L	260	120	–	mg/L	96	43	–	[118]
Vitamins											
Vitamin B$_{12}$	Seminal fluid............	18	nmol/L	–	–	(0.22–0.44)	µg/L	–	–	(0.30–0.60)	[121]
Ascorbic acid ...	Total ejaculate	10	µmol/L	240	–	(100–410)	mg/L	43	–	(18–72)	[122]
		72	µmol/L	200	79	–	mg/L	35	14	–	[123]

* 1 mmol is equivalent to 0.774 g.

tose is largely absent in the sperm before puberty and after castration. In adults the fructose concentration decreases with increasing age (15 mmol/L at ages 20–30; 8 mmol/L at ages 61–70)[12,81,110]. The low fructose concentration in the sperm of individuals with cystic fibrosis suggests that it represents for the most part prostatic secretion[34].

Carbohydrates, protein-bound. Except for traces, fucose and sialic acid are present exclusively in the form of glycopeptides, mucopolysaccharides and glycoproteins (see also Table 3). Equal sialic acid concentrations are found in prostatic secretion and in seminal-vesicle secretion[111].

Myoinositol. The values shown were determined (a) microbiologically, and (b) by gas chromatography. – The myoinositol concentration in the seminal fluid is about 100 times as great as that in the plasma. Myoinositol originates mostly from prostatic secretion[81,112]. The formation of myoinositol, like that of acid phosphatase and fructose, appears to be influenced by androgenic activity[81].

Lactic acid and pyruvic acid. Lactic acid and pyruvic acid are metabolites produced by the anaerobic metabolism of the spermatozoa. Their concentrations have to be evaluated in connection with the incubation time after ejaculation.

Citric acid. Citric acid is derived almost exclusively from the prostate[1,3], in which it is formed under the action of testosterone[81]. After castration its concentration in the prostatic secretion gradually decreases. The high citric-acid concentration in the sperm of individuals with cystic fibrosis suggests that it represents mainly prostatic secretion[34].

Lipids. The lipids originate for the most part from the prostate and are contained in part in the lipid granules of the secretion[115]. Sphingomyelin is the compound predominating in the seminal fluid (Table 4), whereas phosphatidylcholine is preponderant in the plasma.

Prostaglandins. The prostaglandins of the sperm are for the most part assignable to the E series. Previously found prostaglandins of the A and B series[119] were most probably artifacts[120]. The prostaglandins are more likely to originate from the seminal vesicles than from the prostate[8,53].

Table 3   *Distribution of nitrogen and carbohydrates*[102]

	Dialyz-able	Non-dialyz-able
	g/L	
Nitrogen.......................	3.2	4.1
Fructose	2.7	trace
Orcinol-reactive carbohydrates..............	4.7	3.9
Hexosamines	3.6	1.9
Sialic acid..................................	trace	0.9

Table 4
Distribution of phospholipids in seminal fluid and spermatozoa[130]

	Seminal fluid			Spermatozoa		
	Mean	s	Mean	Mean	s	Mean
	µmol/L		mol%	nmol/10^9		mol%
Lipid phosphorus	390	56	–	1973	269	–
Phospholipids						
Phosphatidylethanol-amine (cephalin)..........	33.2	5.1	8.5	426	64	21.6
Ethanolamine plasmal-ogen	48.0	6.9	12.3	185	49	9.4
Phosphatidylcholine (lecithin)....................	30.4	6.0	7.8	568	39	28.8
Choline plasmalogen.......	3.1	1.8	0.8	53	20	2.7
Sphingomyelin.............	172	13.9	44.0	422	59	21.4
Phosphatidylserine.........	43.7	6.0	11.2	93	20	4.7
Phosphatidylinositol	6.6	4.2	1.7	37	61	1.9
Cardiolipin	3.1	4.2	0.8	32	20	1.6
Other phospholipids	50.3	19.9	12.9	156	93	7.9

↓See text below	Material	Number	Amount of substance				Mass				Reference
			Unit	Mean	s	95% range	Unit	Mean	s	95% range (extreme range in brackets)	
↓ Hormones											
Pregnenolone											
– free	Seminal fluid............	24	nmol/L	2.27	–	1.80–2.87	ng/L	718	–	570–908	[124]
– sulfate	Seminal fluid............	24	nmol/L	30.3	–	23.6–38.9	µg/L	12.0	–	9.36–15.4	[124]
Dehydroepian-drosterone											
– free	Seminal fluid............	24	nmol/L	7.49	–	4.92–11.5	µg/L	2.17	–	1.43–3.33	[124]
– sulfate	Seminal fluid............	24	nmol/L	1190	–	955–1490	µg/L	441	–	353–552	[124]
Androstenedione											
– free	Seminal fluid............	20	nmol/L	0.981	–	0.294–3.26*	ng/L	281	–	84.3–935*	[125]
Testosterone											
– free	Seminal fluid............	24	nmol/L	0.420	–	0.347–0.510	ng/L	121	–	100–147	[124]
– sulfate	Seminal fluid............	17	nmol/L	1.52	–	1.15–1.99	ng/L	560	–	423–733	[124]
– glucuronide ...	Seminal fluid............	24	nmol/L	38.8	–	29.7–50.6	µg/L	18.0	–	13.8–23.5	[124]
Dihydrotesto-sterone											
– free	Seminal fluid............	17	nmol/L	1.56	–	1.25–1.94	ng/L	453	–	363–563	[124]
– sulfate	Seminal fluid............	17	nmol/L	4.37	–	3.29–5.85	µg/L	1.62	–	1.22–2.17	[124]
Estradiol (free)..	Seminal fluid............	20	pmol/L	45.5	–	24.6–84.1*	ng/L	12.4	–	6.69–22.9*	[125]
Luteinizing hormone	Seminal fluid............	28	...	...	...	...	IU/L	372	71.4	–	[127]
		20	...	...	...	...	IU/L	41.1	13.9	–	[128]
Follicle-stimu-lating hormone..	Seminal fluid............	20	...	...	...	...	IU/L	9.6	4.1	–	[128]
Prolactin	In 1 ejaculate:										
	– seminal fluid	15	...	...	...	...	ng	165	104		[129]
Cells (for spermatozoa see pages 194–196)											
↓ Leukocytes	Total ejaculate	53	...	...	...	...	10⁹/L	0.33	–	(0.1–1)	[131]

*90% range with 90% confidence limits.

Hormones. After ejaculation, the conjugated steroidal hormones are hydrolyzed by action of glucosidases and sulfatases so that the concentration of steroidal hormones gradually increases[126].

Leukocytes. White blood cell counts up to 2×10^9/L may be considered normal. Values above 5×10^9/L are certain to be pathological[132].

References

[1] LUNDQUIST, F., *Acta physiol. scand.,* **19**, suppl. 66, 7 (1949).
[2] DOEPFMER, R., in JADASSOHN, J. (Ed.), *Handbuch der Haut- und Geschlechts-krankheiten,* supplementary volume, volume 6, part 3, Springer, Berlin, 1960, page 281.
[3] MANN, T., *The Biochemistry of Semen and of the Male Reproductive Tract,* Methuen, London, 1964.
[4] MANN, T., in *Handbook of Physiology,* section 7: Endocrinology, volume 5, American Physiological Society, Washington (D.C.), 1975, page 461.
[5] OETTLE, A. G., *Fertil. and Steril.,* **5**, 227 (1954).
[6] HORNSTEIN, O. P., *Verh. dtsch. Ges. inn. Med.,* **76**, 311 (1970).
[7] SCHILL, W. B., *Hautarzt,* **26**, 514 (1975).
[8] ELIASSON, R., *Fertil. and Steril.,* **19**, 344 (1968).
[9] LINDHOLMER and ELIASSON, *Int. J. Fertil.,* **19**, 45 (1974).
[10] TAUBER et al., *J. Reprod. Fertil.,* **43**, 249 (1975).
[11] ELIASSON, R., *Andrologie,* **3**, 49 (1971).
[12] SCHIRREN, C., *Praktische Andrologie,* Hartmann, Berlin, 1971.
[13] MacLEOD, J., *Fertil. and Steril.,* **2**, 115 (1951).
[14] NAGHMA-E-REHAN et al., *Fertil. and Steril.,* **26**, 492 (1975).
[15] JUNKMANN, K., in FLASCHENTRÄGER and LEHNARTZ (Eds.), *Physiologische Chemie,* volume II/2b, Springer, Berlin, 1954, page 563.
[16] ELIASSON, R., *J. Reprod. Fertil.,* **9**, 331 (1965).
[17] HUGGINS et al., *Amer. J. Physiol.,* **136**, 467 (1942).
[18] HOFMANN and KARLAS, *Arch. derm. Forsch.,* **246**, 35 (1973).
[19] LORD ROTHSCHILD, *J. nat. med. Ass. (N.Y.),* **52**, 6 (1960).
[20] ZAGAMI, V., *Arch. Sci. biol. (Bologna),* **25**, 208 (1939).
[21] HORNSTEIN and HOFMANN, in HASEGAWA et al. (Eds.), *Fertility and Sterility,* Proceedings of the 7th World Congress, Tokyo and Kyoto, Excerpta Medica, Amsterdam, 1973, page 236.
[22] TJIOE and OENTOENG, *Fertil. and Steril.,* **19**, 562 (1968).
[23] SHEDLOVSKY et al., *Proceedings of the 2nd Conference on Biology of the Spermatozoa,* National Committee on Maternal Health, New York, 1940.
[24] KEITEL and JONES, *J. Lab. clin. Med.,* **47**, 917 (1956).
[25] MAWSON and FISCHER, *Biochem. J.,* **55**, 696 (1953).
[26] WEISMAN, A. I., *Spermatozoa and Sterility,* Hoeber, New York, 1941.
[27] HUGGINS and JOHNSON, *Amer. J. Physiol.,* **103**, 574 (1933).
[28] BONDANI et al., *Fertil. and Steril.,* **24**, 150 (1973).
[29] QUINN et al., *J. Reprod. Fertil.,* **10**, 379 (1965).
[30] RABOCH and ŠKACHOVÁ, *Fertil. and Steril.,* **16**, 252 (1965).
[31] MOLNAR et al., *Fertil. and Steril.,* **22**, 480 (1971).
[32] ELIASSON and LINDHOLMER, *Invest. Urol.,* **9**, 286 (1972).
[33] LINDHOLMER and ELIASSON, *Int. J. Fertil.,* **17**, 153 (1972).
[34] RULE et al., *Fertil. and Steril.,* **21**, 515 (1970).
[35] MARMAR et al., *Fertil. and Steril.,* **26**, 1057 (1975).
[36] STANKOVIĆ and MIKAC-DEVIĆ, *Clin. chim. Acta,* **70**, 123 (1976).
[37] ELIASSON and LINDHOLMER, *Andrologie,* **3**, 147 (1971).
[38] MACKENZIE et al., *Nature,* **193**, 72 (1962).
[39] JANICK et al., *Fertil. and Steril.,* **22**, 573 (1971).
[40] HERRMANN, W. P., *Andrologia,* **7**, 329 (1975).
[41] GOLDBLATT, M. W., *Biochem. J.,* **29**, 1346 (1935).
[42] WHITE and GRIFFITHS, *Aust. J. exp. Biol. med. Sci.,* **36**, 97 (1958).

[43] Krampitz and Doepfmer, *Nature,* **194**, 684 (1962).
[44] Keller and Pataki, *Helv. chim. Acta,* **46**, 1687 (1963).
[45] Haag and MacLeod, *J. appl. Physiol.,* **14**, 27 (1959).
[46] Infantellina, F., *Boll. Soc. ital. Biol. sper.,* **20**, 322 (1945).
[47] Kahane and Lévy, *Bull. Soc. Chim. biol. (Paris),* **19**, 959 (1937).
[48] Dawson et al., *Biochem. J.,* **65**, 627 (1957).
[49] Frenkel et al., *Fertil. and Steril.,* **25**, 84 (1974).
[50] Lewin et al., *Fertil. and Steril.,* **27**, 9 (1976).
[51] Jänne et al., *Clin. chim. Acta,* **48**, 393 (1973).
[52] Fair et al., *Fertil. and Steril.,* **23**, 38 (1972).
[53] Mann, T., *J. Reprod. Fertil.,* **37**, 179 (1974).
[54] Beck et al., *Fertil. and Steril.,* **27**, 403 (1976).
[55] Nun et al., *Fertil. and Steril.,* **23**, 357 (1972).
[56] Rotbøl et al., Clin. chim. Acta, **25**, 147 (1969).
[57] Quinlivan, W. L., *Fertil. and Steril.,* **23**, 163 (1972).
[58] Uehling, D. T., *Fertil. and Steril.,* **22**, 769 (1971).
[59] Schumacher, G. F., *J. reprod. Med.,* **5**, 13 (1970).
[60] Schill, W. B., *Andrologia,* **8**, 359 (1976).
[61] Olsson, J. E., *J. Reprod. Fertil.,* **42**, 149 (1975).
[62] Gray et al., *Clin. chim. Acta,* **57**, 163 (1974).
[63] Hankiewicz and Swierczek, *Clin. chim. Acta,* **57**, 205 (1974).
[64] Moon and Bunge, *Fertil. and Steril.,* **21**, 220 (1970).
[65] Davajan and Kunitake, *Fertil. and Steril.,* **19**, 623 (1968).
[66] Walkar and Master, *Clin. chim. Acta,* **39**, 433 (1972).
[67] Colle et al., *Clin. chim. Acta,* **67**, 93 (1976).
[68] Li and Shulman, *Int. J. Fertil.,* **16**, 87 (1971).
[69] Li and Beling, *Fertil. and Steril.,* **24**, 134 (1973).
[70] Li et al., *Fertil. and Steril.,* **27**, 702 (1976).
[71] Hekman and Rümke, in Miescher and Müller-Eberhard (Eds.), *Text-book of Immunopathology,* 2nd ed., volume 2, Grune & Stratton, New York, 1976, page 947.
[72] Mroueh and Adham, *Clin. chim. Acta,* **28**, 259 (1970).
[73] Quinlivan and Sullivan, *Fertil. and Steril.,* **23**, 873 (1972).
[74] Husted and Hjort, *Int. J. Fertil.,* **20**, 97 (1975).
[75] Gutman and Gutman, *Endocrinology,* **28**, 115 (1941).
[76] Schumann et al., *Amer. J. clin. Path.,* **66**, 944 (1976).
[77] Kirk et al., *J. clin. Endocr.,* **12**, 338 (1952).
[78] Kirk, E., *J. Geront.,* **3**, 98 (1948).
[79] Rhodes and Williams-Ashman, *Med. exp. (Basel)* **3**, 123 (1960).
[80] Ishibe et al., *Fertil. and Steril.,* **22**, 774 (1971).
[81] Kimmig et al., *Internist (Berl.),* **8**, 25 (1967).
[82] Gregoire and Moran, *Fertil. and Steril.,* **23**, 708 (1972).
[83] Gregoire and Moran, *Fertil. and Steril.,* **24**, 208 (1973).
[84] Crabbe, M. J., *Lancet,* **2**, 1295 (1976).
[85] Rosalki and Rowe, *Lancet,* **1**, 323 (1973).
[86] Searcy et al., *Lancet,* **1**, 1413 (1962); Kipping, D., *Z. Haut- u. Geschl.-Kr.,* **45**, 201 (1970).
[87] Lehmann and Griffiths, *Lancet,* **2**, 498 (1963).
[88] Moon and Bunge, *Fertil. and Steril.,* **19**, 766 (1968).

[89] Kipping, D., *Clin. chim. Acta,* **33**, 409 (1971).
[90] Roy and Taneja, *Andrologia,* **7**, 195 (1975).
[91] Moon and Bunge, *Fertil. and Steril.,* **19**, 977 (1968).
[92] Sheth and Rao, *Experientia (Basel),* **18**, 370 (1962).
[93] Conchie and Mann, *Nature,* **179**, 1190 (1957).
[94] Sheth et al., *J. Reprod. Fertil.,* **22**, 77 (1970).
[95] Herd and Hayhome, *Lancet,* **2**, 206 (1976).
[96] Sheth et al., *Clin. chim. Acta,* **46**, 351 (1973).
[97] Thakur et al., *Clin. chim. Acta,* **55**, 377 (1974).
[98] Prasad et al., *Fertil. and Steril.,* **27**, 832 (1976).
[99] Suominen and Niemi, *Scand. J. clin. Lab. Invest.,* **25**, suppl. 113, 52 (1970).
[100] Lundquist et al., *Biochem. J.,* **59**, 69 (1955).
[101] Suominen et al., *J. Reprod. Fertil.,* **27**, 153 (1971).
[102] Mann and Rottenberg, *J. Endocr.,* **34**, 257 (1966).
[103] Scacciati de Cerezo, J. M., *Int. J. Fertil.,* **19**, 211 (1974).
[104] Uhlenbruck et al., *Arch. derm. Forsch.,* **246**, 47 (1973).
[105] Herrmann and Uhlenbruck, *Z. klin. Chem.,* **10**, 363 (1972).
[106] Peterson and Freund, *Fertil. and Steril.,* **22**, 639 (1971).
[107] Eliasson, R., *J. Reprod. Fertil.,* **9**, 325 (1965).
[108] Moon and Bunge, *Fertil. and Steril.,* **19**, 186 (1968).
[109] Nixon, D. A., *J. Reprod. Fertil.,* **8**, 419 (1964).
[110] Schill, W. B., *Med. Klin.,* **71**, 1031 (1976).
[111] Eliasson, R., *Nature,* **203**, 980 (1964).
[112] Lewin and Beer, *Fertil. and Steril.,* **24**, 666 (1973).
[113] King and Mann, *Proc. roy. Soc. B,* **151**, 226 (1959).
[114] Dondero et al., *Fertil. and Steril.,* **23**, 168 (1972).
[115] Scott, W. W., *J. Urol. (Baltimore),* **53**, 712 (1945).
[116] Moon and Bunge, *Fertil. and Steril.,* **21**, 80 (1970).
[117] Bygdeman and Samuelsson, *Clin. chim. Acta,* **13**, 465 (1966).
[118] Kelly et al., *Nature,* **260**, 544 (1976).
[119] Bygdeman et al., *Clin. chim. Acta,* **26**, 373 (1969).
[120] Jonsson et al., *Science,* **187**, 1093 (1975); Cooper and Kelly, *Prosta-glandins,* **10**, 506 (1975).
[121] Watson, A. A., *Lancet,* **2**, 644 (1962).
[122] Koets and Michelson, *Fertil. and Steril.,* **7**, 15 (1956).
[123] Vaishwanar and Deshkar, *Amer. J. Obstet. Gynec.,* **95**, 1080 (1966).
[124] Purvis et al., *Clin. Endocr.,* **5**, 253 (1976).
[125] Purvis et al., *Clin. Endocr.,* **4**, 247 (1975).
[126] Purvis et al., *Fertil. and Steril.,* **27**, 929 (1976).
[127] Sheth et al., *Fertil. and Steril.,* **27**, 933 (1976).
[128] Schoenfeld et al., *Fertil. and Steril.,* **29**, 69 (1978).
[129] Sheth et al., *Fertil. and Steril.,* **26**, 905 (1975).
[130] Poulos and White, *J. Reprod. Fertil.,* **35**, 265 (1973).
[131] Svendsen, M., *J. Path. Bact.,* **60**, 131 (1948).
[132] Morton, R. S., *Brit. J. vener. Dis.,* **44**, 72 (1968).
[133] Arrata et al., *Fertil. and Steril.,* **30**, 329 (1978).
[134] Wetterauer and Heite, *Andrologia,* **10**, 203 (1978).
[135] Haugen and Skrede, *Clin. Chem.,* **23**, 1531 (1977).
[136] Mahadevan et al., *Fertil. and Steril.,* **34**, 490 (1980).

The spermatozoa formed in the testicles migrate into the epididymis, where they are stored and subject to a maturation process. The spermatozoa require between 1 and 21 days (average of 12 days) to pass from the testicles into the ejaculate[1]. Up to 75% of the spermatozoa of a normal ejaculate originate in the epididymis[1]. Following bilateral vasectomy, no spermatozoa remain demonstrable in the ejaculate after 6–15 ejaculations[1,2]. The volume fraction of spermatozoa in the total ejaculate (10 μL spermatozoa in 1 mL of ejaculate) amounts to approximately 0.01[3]. The frequency of ejaculation independently affects the expulsion of spermatozoa and the release of prostatic or seminal-vesicle secretions[1].

Number of spermatozoa

Table 1 presents the normal values of fertile men who have begotten 2–10 children after 3 to 15 days of continence. In view of the wide range (Fig. 1) possible physiological variations are difficult to detect[1,5].

The relations between the number of spermatozoa and fertility have not been exactly defined in man. In cases of hypospermia (20–40 million spermatozoa in 1 mL) fertility is not restricted[7], and even in oligospermia (fewer than 20 million spermatozoa in 1 mL) there is a chance, if a smaller one, of fertility (see also Fig. 1). Considering spermatozoal motility, SANTOMAURO et al.[6] came to the conclusion that approximately 90% of men with a spermatozoal number of less than 10 million in 1 mL, with a proportion of motile spermatozoa of less than 40%, and with a total of fewer than 10 million motile spermatozoa in the ejaculate are infertile. Even in the presence of polyspermia, however, reduced fertility is to be expected[5].

Morphology

More than half of the spermatozoa are X spermatozoa[1]. The proportion of Y spermatozoa, which is determinable by fluorescence of the long arm of the Y chromosome after staining with quinacrine, amounts, according to various studies, to 36–49%; however, the Y spermatozoa predominate in some sperm specimens[10]. Owing to the higher DNA content of the X spermatozoa their head radius is approximately 1% larger than that of the Y spermatozoa, which may account for their lower motility[11].

The division of the spermatozoa into morphologically normal and pathological forms[19] is based on subjective criteria so that data of the kind given in Table 2 are of limited validity. The proportion of abnormal forms increases with increasing age[13]. In a normal ejaculate at least 60% of the spermatozoa should be morphologically normal[7]; if more than 50% of the spermatozoa are morphologically abnormal, the chances of fertility are reduced. Round-headed spermatozoa without acrosomes are not fertilizable (cause of a form of infertility that is probably hereditary)[14].

Motility

The in-vitro motility of spermatozoa is usually determined according to subjective criteria with the aid of the phase-contrast microscope[19]. Table 3 compares a frequently employed subjective classification with objective motility data obtained by a photographic technique. A classification of 'very good' according to HARVEY[20] corresponds to motility of the class '4 – to 4'[9]. In vitro, the motility is temperature-dependent (sometimes considerably higher at 37 °C than at room temperature)[9]. Results of motility determination by means of a counting chamber are shown in Table 4. This method, developed by BAKER et al.[22] and HYNIE[23], yields a mean motility value for all spermatozoa contained in a

Table 1 *Sperm quality in relation to age*[4]

Age	Number	Ejaculate volume Mean	Ejaculate volume s	Number of spermatozoa Mean	Number of spermatozoa s	Motile spermatozoa Mean	Motile spermatozoa s	Motility* Mean
		mL		10^6/mL		%		
< 25 years	39	3.20	1.53	· 70	46	63	16	3.25
26–30 years	173	2.70	1.37	73	47	65	26	3.03
31–35 years	262	3.37	1.57	83	51	63	30	3.07
36–40 years	316	3.20	1.51	80	59	65	20	3.04
41–45 years	271	3.34	1.47	78	74	66	17	3.08
> 45 years	239	2.97	1.23	81	53	62	19	2.88

* According to classification of MACLEOD[8,9]

Table 2 *Form of spermatozoa*

	Mean	(Extreme range)
		%
Oval (normal) forms	89.8	(66–99)
Tapering forms	3.6	(0–24)
Round forms	1.6	(0–9)
Duplicate forms	1.8	(0–11)
Giant and pinhead forms	0.6	(0–8)
Amorphous group	2.1	(0–12)

Table 3 *Subjective and objective evaluation of spermatozoal motility (88 measurements at 24–27 °C)*[9]

Subjective classification	Objectively measured motility Mean	Objectively measured motility (Extreme range)	Frequency
	μm s⁻¹		%
2	–	–	–
2 to 2 +	15.8	(15.3–16.3)	2.3
2 +	–	–	–
2 + to 3 –	20.0	(17.0–21.9)	6.8
3 –	28.3	(25.3–30.0)	4.5
3 – to 3	29.6	(25.1–33.3)	12.5
3	34.3	(30.0–39.1)	22.3
3 to 3 +	37.1	(32.3–42.0)	21.6
3 + to 4 –	40.6	(36.8–44.0)	20.5
4 –	44.6	(42.9–45.9)	4.5
4 – to 4	47.7	(46.6–48.8)	2.3
4	52.9	(50.2–55.6)	2.3

Table 4 *Frequency distribution of mean forward movement of all spermatozoa contained in a sample (500 samples with normospermia)*[21]

Mean forward movement	1 h	3 h	5 h
	after ejaculation		
	%		
100–46 μm s⁻¹	26.6	22.8	10.8
45–23 μm s⁻¹	43.6	43.4	27.2
22–10 μm s⁻¹	29.0	28.8	44.0
9.9–4.6 μm s⁻¹	0.8	3.4	12.2
4.5–2.3 μm s⁻¹	0	1.6	2.6
2.2–1.0 μm s⁻¹	0	0	2.8
< 1 μm s⁻¹	0	0	0.4

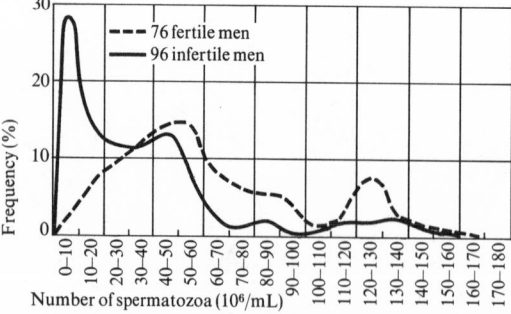

Fig. 1. Frequency distribution of numbers of spermatozoa in 76 fertile and 96 infertile men[6].

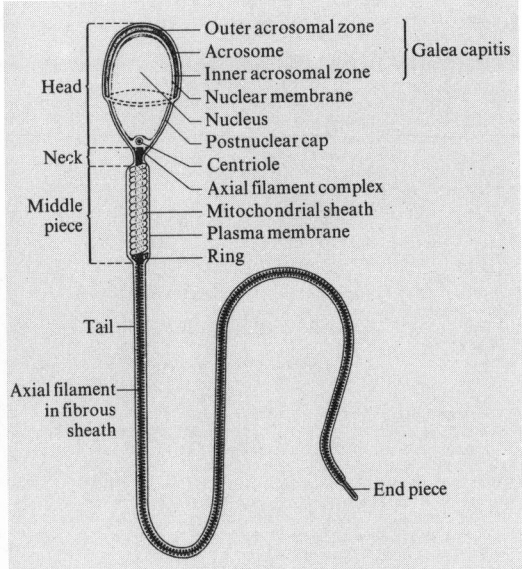

Fig. 2. Schematic representation of a spermatozoon[18].

Labels (from figure):
- Outer acrosomal zone
- Acrosome
- Inner acrosomal zone — Galea capitis
- Nuclear membrane
- Head
- Nucleus
- Postnuclear cap
- Neck — Centriole
- Axial filament complex
- Middle piece — Mitochondrial sheath
- Plasma membrane
- Ring
- Tail
- Axial filament in fibrous sheath
- End piece

Table 5   *Spermatozoal dimensions*

	Unit	Mean	(Extreme range)	Reference
Whole spermatozoon				
Volume	µm³	17.4	s 1.46	15
Mass	pg	37	–	16
Head				
Length	µm	4.4	(3.3–6.2)	16
Width	µm	3.2	–	16
Thickness	µm	2.0	–	16
Volume	µm³	6.4	–	16
Middle piece				
Length	µm	4.0	–	16
Diameter	µm	1.0	–	16
Volume	µm³	3.1	–	16
Tail				
Length	µm	–	(40–60)	16
Diameter	µm	–	(0.4–0.7)	16
Volume	µm³	–	(4.5–6.8)	16
Tail end				
Length	µm	–	(6–10)	16
Diameter	µm	0.2	–	16
Volume	µm³	0.16	–	16
Wave frequency	s⁻¹	15	–	17

Table 6   *Deoxyribonucleic acid in 1 spermatozoon[33]*

	Number	Mean	s
		pg	
Normospermia	13	1.35	0.29
Oligospermia	13	2.86	0.41

Table 7   *Acrosin activity in spermatozoa[48]*

Measurement conditions	Number	Mean	s	(Extreme range)
		mU/10⁶		
Substrate: N-benzoyl-L-arginine ethylester, 25 °C, pH 8.0	7	6.5	1.5	(4.4–8.9)

Table 8   *Mean activity of enzymes of glycolysis in spermatozoal homogenate at 37 °C[39]*

EC Number	Name of enzyme	Relative to protein	Relative to number of spermatozoa
		U/g	U/10⁹
1.1.1.8	Glycerol-3-phosphate dehydrogenase	1.7	0.06
1.1.1.27	Lactate dehydrogenase	818	27.3
1.1.1.44	Phosphogluconate dehydrogenase (decarboxylating)	10.7	0.36
1.1.1.49	Glucose-6-phosphate dehydrogenase	9.2	0.31
1.2.1.12	Glyceraldehyde-phosphate dehydrogenase	94.7	3.15
2.7.1.1	Hexokinase	23.2	0.77
2.7.1.11	6-Phosphofructokinase	29.2	0.97
2.7.1.40	Pyruvate kinase	433	14.4
2.7.2.3	Phosphoglycerate kinase	675	22.5
2.7.5.3	Phosphoglyceromutase	180	5.99
4.1.2.13	Fructose bisphosphate aldolase	91.3	3.04
4.2.1.11	Enolase	119	3.95
5.3.1.9	Glucosephosphate isomerase	375	12.5

sample, regardless of the proportion of motile spermatozoa. Details of motility, e.g. wave frequency (Table 5), are detectable by kinephotomicrography[17].

The proportion of highly motile spermatozoa diminishes with increasing age[13]. A high proportion of motile spermatozoa and motility of good quality benefit fertility[6,24]. As studies with suitable staining methods have shown, nonmotile spermatozoa are by no means necessarily dead[25]. A recently demonstrated genetic defect involves the cilia of all organs and manifests itself in the spermatozoa in immobility of the tail[26].

Following coitus, spermatozoa are detectable in cervical-mucus specimens within 1½–3 minutes after ejaculation[27]. The motility of the spermatozoa is greater and longer-lasting in the ovulatory cervical secretion than in the individual's own seminal fluid[28]. Penetration of the cervical mucus by the spermatozoa is determined by its structure, which consists of a cross-linked meshwork of threadlike molecules. The spermatozoa travel along the micelles[29]. Approximately 2 hours after insemination, spermatozoa are demonstrable in the tubes[30]. Of the many millions of spermatozoa that are deposited in the vagina upon ejaculation, only 1000–5000 reach the ovum[47].

Chemical composition of spermatozoa

The spermatozoal contents of elements and lipids are indicated in the preceding section 'Sperm'. The contents of zinc and calcium are higher in the middle piece than in the head[31]. Spermatozoa contain spermine, but this may be absorbed at the surface only[36].

The head of the spermatozoon contains the nucleus and the acrosome (Fig. 2). The nucleus contains deoxyribonucleoprotein, the deoxyribonucleic acid of which is composed of the nucleotides adenylic acid, guanylic acid, cytidylic acid, thymidylic acid and small amounts of other bases, such as methylcytosine[32]. The deoxyribonucleic acid content is relatively constant (Table 6) and, owing to the chromatin reduction during spermatogenesis, amounts to only one-half the content of the diploid cell. It is 3–4% higher in the X spermatozoa than in the Y spermatozoa[11]. The increased deoxyribonucleic acid content in a group of infertile men with oligospermia (Table 6) suggests a defect in spermatogenesis. The acrosome is a modified lysosome containing a characteristic lipoglycoprotein complex which is associated with a number of enzymes[32]. Lysosomal enzymes detected in the acrosome comprise hyaluronidase, acid phosphatase, arylsulphatase, β-N-acetyl-D-glucosaminidase, phospholipase A and various proteinases. Some of these enzymes, notably a trypsin-like proteinase (acrosin)[34,35,48], are important for fertilization in that they cooperate in breaking open the ovarian cumulus and in the penetration of the pellucid zone[1,32,45]. At the time of ejaculation, most of the acrosin in the spermatozoa is present in an inactive precursor form (proacrosin) and is activated to acrosin during the capacitation process[48].

The middle piece is rich in lipids[32] – particularly plasmalogen and lecithin – and contains the cytochrome system, the various coenzymes including adenosine triphosphate as well as the enzymes of glycolysis and the spermatozoon-specific isoenzyme of lactate dehydrogenase (LDH X)[37].

The fibrils of the axial filament contain adenosine triphosphatase[38], which is needed for the transfer of energy from adenosine triphosphate to the contractile elements and which ensures spermatozoal motility.

Determination of anaerobic fructolysis is relevant to the evaluation of spermatozoal vitality[40]. Normal values of the enzymes of glycolysis are presented in Table 8.

Spermatozoa possess several antigens some of which are segment-specific, while others are common to the head and the tail[41,42,46]. One of the spermatozoon-specific antigens is LDH X[46]. Some of the antigens stem from the secretions of the accessory glands and adhere to the surface of the spermatozoa. The best known is a lactoferrin originating from seminal-vesicle secretions, which has been called scaferrin (from 'sperm-coating antigen' and 'lactoferrin')[43]. A and B Blood Group substances may also be adsorbed on the spermatozoal surface in secretors; furthermore, the spermatozoa appear to contain histocompatibility antigens[41,44].

References

[1] WHO Scientific Group on Reproductive Function in the Human Male, *Wld Hlth Org. techn. Rep. Ser.,* No. 520 (1973).
[2] FREUND and DAVIS, *Fertil. and Steril., 20,* 163 (1969).
[3] LUNDQUIST, F., in LONG, C. (Ed.), *Biochemists' Handbook,* Spon, London, 1961, page 904.
[4] NAGHMA-E-REHAN et al., *Fertil. and Steril., 26,* 492 (1975).
[5] HORNSTEIN, O. P., *Verh. dtsch. Ges. inn. Med., 76,* 311 (1970).
[6] SANTOMAURO et al., *Fertil. and Steril., 23,* 245 (1972).
[7] GÜNTHER and RADTKE, *Zbl. Gynäk., 99,* 257 (1977).
[8] MACLEOD and GOLD, *Fertil. and Steril., 2,* 187 (1951).
[9] JANICK and MACLEOD, *Fertil. and Steril., 21,* 140 (1970).
[10] QUINLIVAN and SULLIVAN, *Fertil. and Steril., 25,* 315 (1974).
[11] ROBERTS, A. M., *Nature, 238,* 223 (1972), GOODALL and ROBERTS, *J. Reprod. Fertil., 48,* 433 (1976).

[12] HOTCHKISS, R. S., *Fertility in Men,* Lippincott, Philadelphia, 1944, page 117.
[13] SCHIRREN et al., *Andrologia, 7,* 117 (1975).
[14] HOLSTEIN et al., *Dtsch. med. Wschr., 98,* 61 (1973).
[15] LAUFER et al., *Fertil. and Steril., 28,* 456 (1977).
[16] VAN DUIJN, C., *J. roy. micr. Soc., 77,* 12 (1957).
[17] ZORGNIOTTI et al., *Med. Radiogr. Photogr., 34,* 44 (1958).
[18] MANN, T., *The Biochemistry of Semen and of the Male Reproductive Tract,* Methuen, London, 1964, page 20.
[19] ELIASSON, R., *Andrologie, 3,* 49 (1971).
[20] HARVEY, C., *J. Reprod. Fertil., 1,* 84 (1960).
[21] BARTÁK, V., *Int. J. Fertil., 16,* 107 (1971).
[22] BAKER et al., *Fertil. and Steril., 8,* 149 (1957).
[23] HYNIE, J., *Int. J. Fertil., 7,* 345 (1962).
[24] MACLEOD and GOLD, *Fertil. and Steril., 4,* 10 (1953).
[25] ELIASSON and TREICHL, *Fertil. and Steril., 22,* 134 (1971).
[26] AFZELIUS, B. A., *Science, 193,* 317 (1976); ELIASSON et al., *New Engl. J. Med., 297,* 1 (1977).
[27] SOBRERO and MACLEOD, *Fertil. and Steril., 13,* 184 (1962).
[28] SHETTLES, L. B., *J. Reprod. Med., 3,* 147 (1969).
[29] MOGHISSI, K. S., *Fertil. and Steril., 23,* 295 (1972); SCHILL, W. B., *Hautarzt, 24,* 469 (1973).
[30] AHLGREN, M., *Migration of Spermatozoa to the Fallopian Tubes and the Abdominal Cavity in Women Including Some Immunological Aspects,* thesis, Lund, 1969.
[31] MAYNARD et al., *J. Reprod. Fertil., 43,* 41 (1975).
[32] MANN, T., in *Handbook of Physiology,* section 7: Endocrinology, volume 5, American Physiological Society, Washington (D.C.), 1975, page 461.
[33] FRAJESE et al., *Fertil. and Steril., 27,* 14 (1976).
[34] FRITZ et al., *Hoppe-Seylers Z. physiol. Chem., 353,* 1943 (1972).
[35] SCHILL, W. B., *Fertil. and Steril., 25,* 703 (1974).
[36] PULKKINEN et al., *J. Reprod. Fertil., 43,* 49 (1975).
[37] ZINKHAM, W. H., *Johns Hopk. med. J., 130,* 1 (1972).
[38] DURR et al., *J. Reprod. Fertil., 31,* 313 (1972).
[39] PETERSON and FREUND, *Fertil. and Steril., 21,* 151 (1970).
[40] KIMMIG et al., *Internist (Berl.), 8,* 25 (1967).
[41] HEKMAN and RÜMKE, in MIESCHER and MÜLLER-EBERHARD (Eds.), *Textbook of Immunopathology,* 2nd ed., volume 2, Grune & Stratton, New York, 1976, page 947.
[42] MANCINI et al., *Fertil. and Steril., 22,* 475 (1971).
[43] LI et al., *Fertil. and Steril., 27,* 702 (1976).
[44] HALIM and FESTENSTEIN, *Lancet, 2,* 1255 (1975).
[45] MCRORIE and WILLIAMS, *Ann. Rev. Biochem., 43,* 777 (1974).
[46] METTLER and SKRABEL, *Med. Welt (Stuttg.), 28,* 556 (1977).
[47] ZANEVELD and TAUBER, *Human Fertilization,* International Workshop 1976, Excerpta Medica, Amsterdam, 1976, page 27.

The data presented in the following compilations were derived from normal uncomplicated pregnancies and are related, wherever possible, to the week of pregnancy. It should be noted, however, that many of the source reports fail to state the reason why an amniocentesis was performed, so that caution is called for in assessing the significance of this information in efforts to ensure that a pregnancy remains normal.

Origin

During the first half of the pregnancy, amniotic fluid volume is more closely related to fetal mass (Fig.1) than to placental mass (Fig.2) or the week of gestation (Fig.3)[1], suggesting that at this stage amniotic fluid is fetal in origin. It probably arises as a dialyzate of fetal plasma, whereby the fetal skin acts as a semipermeable diffusing membrane. This view is supported by the fact that in the first half of pregnancy the concentration of some of the components of amniotic fluid approximates more closely to that of fetal plasma than to that of maternal plasma (Figs.4 and 5)[2], allowing for the differences in their water content.

In the second half of the pregnancy, fetal urine is the main contributor to the volume of amniotic fluid[3], and so the concentration of many constituents is subject to complex interrelations between amniotic fluid, mother and fetus[4].

Amniotic fluid appears to be removed mainly by swallowing by the fetus.

Production rate

No absolute figures are available for the production rate of amniotic fluid under physiologic conditions in the course of pregnancy. After rupture of the membranes at term, drainage of the contents of the sac and insertion of a catheter, a flow of 16–24 mL/h has been recorded in 4 patients[5]. This is equivalent to a production of 400–1000 mL in 24 hours.

The mature fetus of the rhesus monkey produces urine at the rate of 5 mL kg^{-1} h^{-1} and swallows it at about the same rate[6]. If the same is true of the human fetus, assuming a fetal mass of 3 kg, fetal urine would contribute some 400 mL to the daily production of amniotic fluid.

Volume

Measurement of amniotic fluid volume (AFV) obtained from intact amniotic sacs by abdominal hysterotomy between the 8th

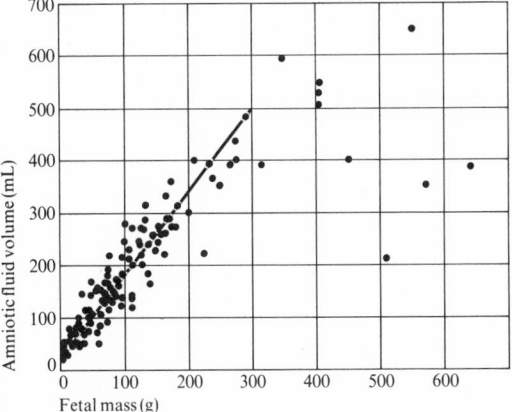

Fig. 1. Correlation between amniotic fluid volume and fetal mass[1].

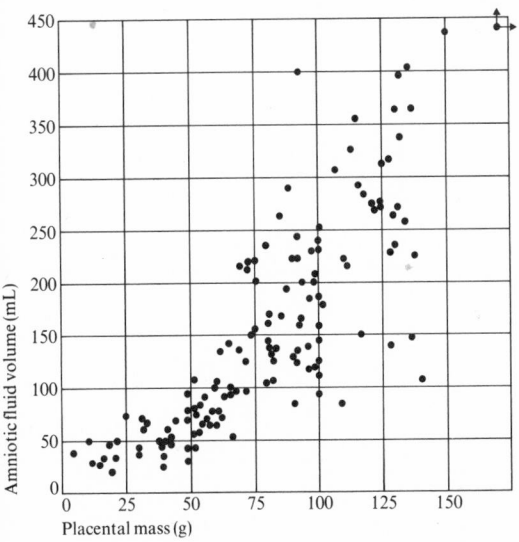

Fig. 2. Correlation between amniotic fluid volume and placental mass[1].

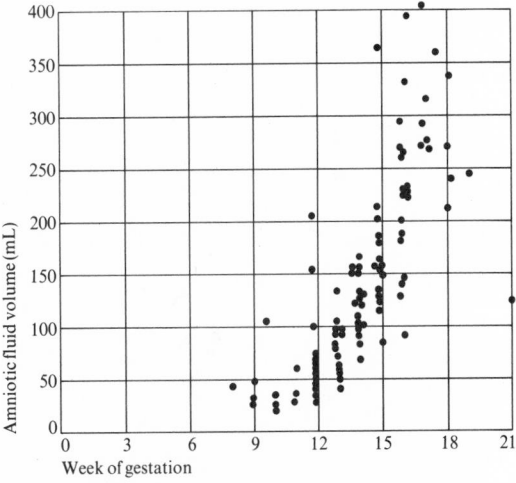

Fig. 3. Correlation between amniotic fluid volume and week of gestation[1].

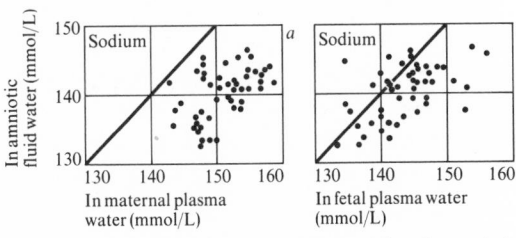

Fig. 4. Correlation between sodium concentrations in amniotic fluid water and maternal plasma water (*a*) and in fetal plasma water (*b*) (48 fetuses of body mass < 300 g²).

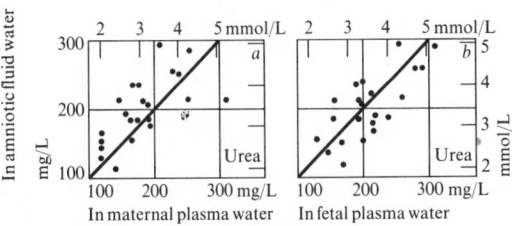

Fig. 5. Correlation between urea concentrations in amniotic fluid water and in maternal plasma water (*a*) and in fetal plasma water (*b*) (22 fetuses of body mass < 300 g²).

* The chapter on Amniotic Fluid, pages 197–212, was prepared in cooperation with T. LIND, Medical Research Council, Human Reproduction Group, Newcastle upon Tyne, UK.

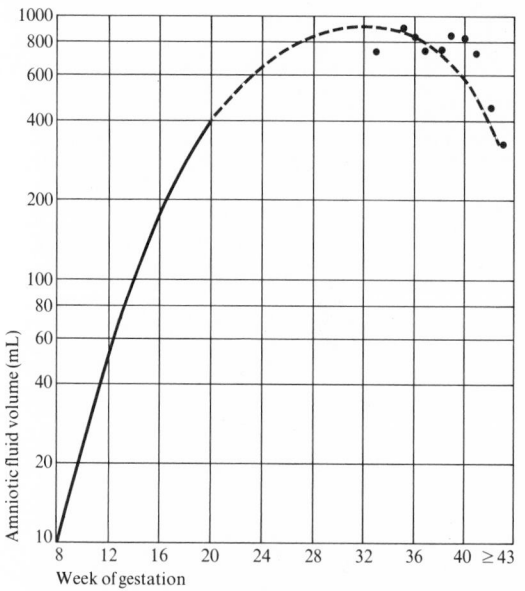

Fig. 6. Volume of amniotic fluid in the course of pregnancy (see text below).

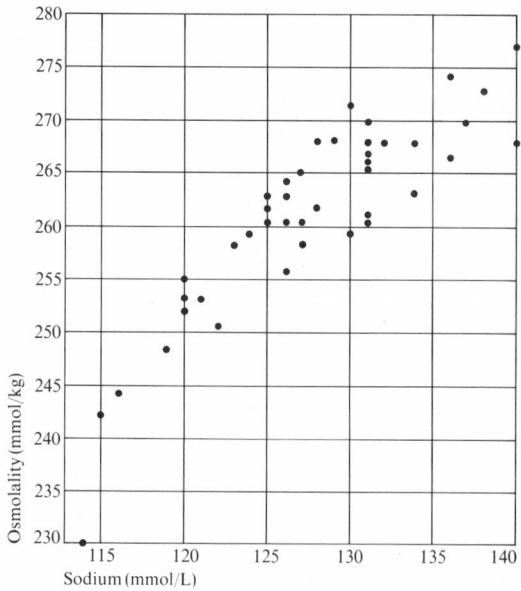

Fig. 7. Correlation between sodium concentration and osmolality of amniotic fluid[19].

and the 20th week of gestation allowed the following equation to be derived[7]:

$$\log AFV = 4.0988 \log A - 6.1612$$
where A is the age in days

The coefficient of correlation in 102 measurements was 0.816 with a 68% coefficient of variance. The graph plotted from these correlations in Figure 6 is in good agreement with data published elsewhere[8,9]. For the second half of pregnancy, data derived from indirect measurements[9-11] vary widely on account of difficulties inherent in the method, so that the curve for this segment of gestation must be viewed as an approximation only.

Oxygen pressure, acid-base balance

Because of difficulties inherent in the methods of measuring oxygen pressure in amniotic fluid[12], published data are not readily comparable (Table 1). Similar difficulties are encountered in measuring parameters of the acid-base balance (Table 1). Despite such difficulties, investigators agree that the pH value and the bicarbonate concentration decline during pregnancy, but the significance of these parameters for the diagnosis of asphyxia is limited[13].

Osmolality, electrolytes

Osmolality decreases from values just below serum osmolality in early pregnancy to low levels towards term (Table 2), an indication of the addition of hypotonic fetal urine. Osmolality is primarily a function of sodium concentration (Fig. 7). In one study of osmolality during labor, it was found to decline from 260 mmol/kg at the start to 247 mmol/kg just before delivery[20].

In the first half of pregnancy, the concentration of sodium, potassium and chloride in amniotic fluid appears to be in balance with the corresponding electrolytes in maternal plasma[17]. From the few available data it may be deduced that in very early pregnancy the concentration of electrolytes in amniotic fluid is closely comparable to that in chorionic fluid[21]. In the second half of pregnancy, sodium and chloride concentrations decline, whereas potassium concentration appears to undergo no change (Table 2). This pattern of electrolyte concentrations applies also to pregnancies in which the fetus is affected by rhesus isoimmunization[17]. In the last stages of pregnancy, electrolyte concentrations vary widely. In one investigation[22], the 90% range was 80–145 mmol/L for sodium, 89–115 mmol/L for chloride and 2.5–5.5 mmol/L for potassium.

The concentrations of calcium, magnesium and phosphate are not as extensively reported as the other electrolytes, and they do not appear to be subject to characteristic changes in the course of

Table 1   *Oxygen pressure, acid-base balance*

Gestational age	Num-ber	O₂ pressure		CO₂ pressure		pH		HCO₃⁻		Refer-ence
		Mean	s	Mean	s	Mean	s	Mean	s	
		kPa				–		mmol/L		
11–14 weeks	20	–	–	7.3	1.5	7.10	0.09	16.7	4.4	[14]
35–40 weeks	20	–	–	7.6	0.8	6.98	0.06	13.1	1.4	[14]
12 weeks	12	1.57	0.46	6.37	0.38	7.32	0.097	23.6	6.0	[15]
13–24 weeks*	154*	1.49	0.50	6.27	0.49	7.17	0.047	16.5*	1.6*	[15]
27–40 weeks*	26*	0.76	0.40	7.17	0.56	7.11	0.051	15.7*	1.8*	[15]
10–25 weeks	15	9.99	4.40	4.47	0.87	7.31	0.254	16.3	2.9	[16]
38–42 weeks	24	7.77	2.47	5.62	1.23	7.13	0.066	13.5	4.9	[16]
≥ 43 weeks	9	5.61	4.44	6.21	1.54	7.08	0.212	13.3	3.4	[16]
Intrauterine death	4	2	–	13.3	–	6.6	–	10	–	[16]

* HCO₃⁻ values: 17–20 weeks for 63 subjects and 37–40 weeks for 35 subjects.

Table 2 *Osmolality, electrolytes*

Gestational age	Num-ber	Osmolality Mean	s	Sodium Mean	s	Potassium Mean	s	Chloride Mean	s	CO$_2$ Mean	s	Refer-ence
		mmol/kg					mmol/L					
10–16 weeks	20–38	–	–	137.1	3.48	4.2	0.38	109.1	3.94	18.6	4.5	[14]
35–40 weeks	20–51	–	–	127.7	6.07	4.7	0.57	104.8	4.80	14.9	1.4	[14]
11–12 weeks	5	281	12.5	134	5.1	3.9	0.18	103	5.8	–	–	[15]
13–16 weeks	15	272	9.7	134	3.9	4.0	0.19	112	3.5	–	–	[15]
17–20 weeks	18	272	7.2	134	3.4	4.0	0.17	111	3.8	–	–	[15]
29–32 weeks	6	269	7.3	131	3.9	4.0	0.12	109	2.9	–	–	[15]
33–36 weeks	29	263	8.2	131	3.8	4.2	0.22	108	3.2	–	–	[15]
37–40 weeks	18	263	9.2	128	4.2	4.2	0.34	106	3.4	–	–	[15]
6–20 weeks	27, 34	276	5.4	136	5.1	–	–	–	–	–	–	[17]
31–32 weeks	32, 38	269	6.7	132	5.6	–	–	–	–	–	–	[17]
33–34 weeks	32, 38	268	9.0	132	4.7	–	–	–	–	–	–	[17]
35–36 weeks	39, 47	264	6.5	131	5.1	–	–	–	–	–	–	[17]
37–38 weeks	12, 18	261	17.3	128	8.4	–	–	–	–	–	–	[17]
≥ 39 weeks	18, 26	259	14.0	125	6.0	–	–	–	–	–	–	[17]
15 weeks	21–25	272.7	3.8	138.5	2.1	3.9	0.3	110.8	1.9	16.3	1.8	[18]
19 weeks	26–60	273.9	3.4	135.8	1.8	3.8	0.2	109.9	2.9	17.4	2.6	[18]
22 weeks	2–4	264.5	8.5	135.3	0.8	3.9	0.1	111.8	2.9	16.0	1.9	[18]
25 weeks	2–8	272.0	4.3	138.4	3.7	4.0	0.1	109.3	2.1	17.7	2.0	[18]
28 weeks	8–10	272.4	6.0	136.0	3.4	4.0	0.1	108.8	1.6	17.0	2.0	[18]
31 weeks	4–5	271.3	4.3	133.2	3.3	4.2	0.3	107.4	3.4	16.6	2.3	[18]
34 weeks	15	264.5	11.0	128.2	6.0	4.5	0.5	103.7	5.7	16.7	2.4	[18]
37 weeks	21–26	256.9	12.3	126.3	7.4	4.5	0.5	104.4	3.7	15.2	4.4	[18]
40 weeks	40–51	255.2	8.9	125.6	6.2	4.3	0.4	102.8	3.9	16.1	3.1	[18]
44 weeks	13–17	251.9	16.0	123.5	6.2	4.3	0.4	101.4	6.3	16.1	2.0	[18]

Table 3 *Calcium, magnesium and trace elements*

Gestational age	Num-ber	Calcium Mean	s	Magnesium Mean	s	Phosphate Mean	s	Iron Mean	s	Copper Mean	s	Zinc Mean	(Extreme range)	Refer-ence
		mmol/L						μmol/L						
10–16 weeks	23–31	1.65	0.36	0.65	0.04	0.99	0.27	–	–	–	–	–	–	[14]
35–40 weeks	19	1.60	0.18	0.50	0.02	0.44	0.19	–	–	–	–	–	–	[14]
11–12 weeks	5	1.80	0.49	0.70	0.22	–	–	–	–	–	–	–	–	[15]
13–16 weeks	15	2.05	0.19	0.75	0.19	–	–	–	–	–	–	–	–	[15]
17–20 weeks	18	1.90	0.21	0.65	0.13	–	–	–	–	–	–	–	–	[15]
29–32 weeks	6	1.85	0.27	0.60	0.07	–	–	–	–	–	–	–	–	[15]
33–36 weeks	29	1.90	0.32	0.55	0.16	–	–	–	–	–	–	–	–	[15]
37–40 weeks	18	1.90	0.34	0.55	0.17	–	–	–	–	–	–	–	–	[15]
11–19 weeks	16–20	1.67	0.12	0.47	0.17	–	–	5.6	3.6	4.9	2.0	–	–	[23]
17–22 weeks	–	–	–	–	–	–	–	–	–	–	–	3.8	(2.3–6.1)	[157]

pregnancy (Table 3). Considerable interindividual variation has been reported toward the end of gestation; thus, in one study[22] the 90% range for calcium was found to be 1.25–3.25 mmol/L and for inorganic phosphorus 0.2–1.3 mmol/kg.

Trace elements

For concentrations of iron, copper and zinc, see Table 3. On average[168], the iodine concentration is 61 nmol/L in mid-pregnancy and 35 nmol/L at term.

Urea, creatinine and uric acid

All studies point to an increased concentration of these substances in the second half of gestation, attributable to the growing proportion of amniotic fluid accounted for by fetal urine

(Table 4)[4]. Under the influence of diuretics, the concentration of uric acid tends to increase[25].

Amino acids

A number of studies are available concerning the concentration of free amino acids in amniotic fluid (see Table 5 for the results of 2 such studies). While the absolute figures tend to vary quite considerably, what all the investigations have in common is that the concentration of amino acids either declines (as in the case of hydroxyproline, tyrosine and valine) or remains substantially unchanged (methionine and serine)[28] as pregnancy progresses. Along with free hydroxyproline, peptide-bound hydroxyproline also occurs and its concentration similarly declines in the course of pregnancy[29].

Table 4 *Urea, creatinine, uric acid*

Gestational age	Number	Urea				Creatinine				Uric acid				Reference
		Mean	s	Mean	s	Mean	s	Mean	s	Mean	s	Mean	s	
		mmol/L		mg/L		µmol/L		mg/L		µmol/L		mg/L		
10–16 weeks	20	3.90	0.68	234	41	–	–	–	–	–	–	–	–	14
35–40 weeks	23	5.56	1.88	334	113	–	–	–	–	–	–	–	–	14
6–20 weeks	35, 28	3.00	0.97	180	58	50	13	5.7	1.5	–	–	–	–	17
31–32 weeks	38	3.50	0.65	210	39	106	21	12	2.4	–	–	–	–	17
33–34 weeks	38, 37	3.50	0.85	210	51	115	23	13	2.6	–	–	–	–	17
35–36 weeks	47, 44	4.00	0.95	240	57	133	25	15	2.8	–	–	–	–	17
37–38 weeks	18, 17	4.80	1.50	290	93	168	44	19	5.0	–	–	–	–	17
≥ 39 weeks	26	5.30	1.30	320	80	177	38	20	4.3	–	–	–	–	17
15 weeks	27–29	3.85	0.96	232	58	70	9	8	1	238	59	40	10	18
19 weeks	58–61	3.89	0.75	234	45	70	9	8	1	250	59	42	10	18
22 weeks	5	3.43	1.46	206	88	70	9	8	1	321	71	54	12	18
25 weeks	11–12	4.04	0.82	242	49	80	18	9	2	339	54	57	9	18
28 weeks	12–13	3.86	0.89	232	54	97	27	11	3	393	95	66	16	18
31 weeks	6–8	4.68	0.79	281	47	124	27	14	3	387	77	65	13	18
34 weeks	19–20	6.18	2.14	371	128	150	35	17	4	547	220	92	37	18
37 weeks	29–31	6.43	1.93	386	116	186	44	21	5	607	196	102	33	18
40 weeks	53–55	6.31	1.64	379	99	194	44	22	5	619	178	104	30	18
44 weeks	16–17	6.89	2.07	414	124	194	35	22	4	547	178	92	30	18
39–42 weeks	31	5.23	1.47	314	88	189	37	21.4	4.2	537	108	90.2	18.2	24

Table 5 *Free amino acids*

	15–20 weeks (N 10)[26]			33–37 weeks (N 5)[26]			41–44 weeks (N 5)[26]			7–18 weeks (N 11)[27]			36–40 weeks (N 16)[27]		
	Mean	s	(Extreme range)	Mean	s	(Extreme range)	Mean	s	(Extreme range)	Mean	s	(Extreme range)	Mean	s	(Extreme range)
	µmol/L									µmol/L					
Alanine	312	79	(169–433)	143	92	(36–230)	126	26	(93–162)	401	83	(310–550)	156	66	(64–344)
Ethanolamine	20	8	(7–33)	13	10	(0–23)	18	16	(0–44)	–	–	–	–	–	–
α-Aminobutyric acid	16	7	(3–25)	6	3	(2–8)	3	2	(1–6)	15	7	(9–28)	7	5	(0–15)
Arginine	43	22	(12–66)	20	13	(3–33)	10	10	(1–26)	63	32	(31–112)	23	12	(11–50)
Aspartic acid	17	15	(7–49)	6	5	(0–12)	7	4	(1–11)	8	6	(0–20)	7	5	(0–18)
Citrulline	23	32	(4–80)	4	–	(trace–4)	1	1	(0–2)	6	6	(0–19)	2	3	(0–10)
Cystathionine	4	4	(1–13)	5	6	(1–12)	4	5	(0–12)	–	–		–	–	
Cysteic acid	9	6	(3–24)	9	6	(3–19)	73	107	(3–229)	–	–		–	–	
½ Cystine	63	15	(46–77)	57	15	(32–73)	34	27	(0–64)	89	26	(62–140)	65	22	(33–121)
Glutamic acid	227	53	(158–301)	76	50	(20–136)	53	18	(27–71)	149	88	(37–361)	48	46	(10–199)
Glycine	124	24	(88–165)	110	64	(35–162)	73	25	(34–100)	164	34	(135–220)	139	28	(94–188)
Histidine	76	26	(26–103)	40	26	(11–70)	20	11	(7–35)	102	23	(77–142)	44	12	(26–67)
Hydroxyproline	42	24	(20–100)	17	12	(0–33)	11	8	(0–20)	–	–		–	–	
Isoleucine	45	9	(34–63)	13	9	(3–21)	9	4	(4–12)	47	20	(21–76)	14	5	(6–23)
Leucine	80	18	(58–119)	24	16	(6–137)	19	9	(8–32)	106	45	(56–163)	26	9	(11–40)
Lysine	239	87	(68–336)	150	109	(41–265)	59	23	(30–95)	319	111	(155–465)	100	30	(46–163)
Methionine	25	8	(18–41)	21	16	(5–40)	5	1	(3–6)	25	8	(17–41)	9	4	(3–17)
Methionine sulfoxide	13	6	(1–25)	20	6	(10–26)	13	16	(1–38)	–	–		–	–	
3-Methylhistidine	1	1	(0–5)	0	–		0	–		–	–		–	–	
Ornithine	38	14	(11–58)	20	11	(6–31)	23	14	(12–41)	51	22	(20–90)	20	9	(9–47)
Phenylalanine	59	8	(49–76)	29	17	(6–48)	21	10	(12–37)	77	20	(48–108)	24	10	(9–48)
Proline	332	94	(180–484)	203	96	(89–281)	102	17	(91–131)	198	55	(150–323)	130	58	(66–280)
Glutamine	⎫ 186	57	(104–301)							50	32	(10–132)	58	32	(27–152)
Serine	⎬			120	72	(65–204)	91	30	(53–124)	235	54	(163–330)	143	54	(72–260)
Threonine	⎭												–	–	
Taurine	83	29	(50–135)	101	17	(78–118)	62	38	(28–110)	124	52	(60–222)	118	46	(62–209)
Tyrosine	51	7	(44–65)	21	11	(9–33)	16	9	(4–29)	64	21	(40–104)	21	8	(8–36)
Valine	194	53	(80–268)	69	38	(19–100)	49	16	(31–74)	200	70	(100–297)	54	22	(19–104)

Glucose and organic acids

In early pregnancy, the concentration of glucose in amniotic fluid mirrors the concentration in fetal and maternal plasma (Table 6). At term, glucose is no longer demonstrable in many specimens of amniotic fluid[22], a sign that the fetal kidney is often capable of complete reabsorption of glucose[35]. In maternal diabe-

Table 6   *Glucose, organic acids*

	Gestational age	Number	Amount of substance				Mass				Reference
			Unit	Mean	s	95% range (Extreme range in brackets)	Unit	Mean	s	95% range (Extreme range in brackets)	
Glucose..................	10–16 weeks .	27	mmol/L	2.67	0.65	–	mg/L	481	118	–	14
	35–40 weeks .	28	mmol/L	1.23	0.64	–	mg/L	222	116	–	14
	15 weeks.....	27	mmol/L	2.60	0.52	–	mg/L	469	93	–	18
	19 weeks.....	58	mmol/L	2.51	0.57	–	mg/L	453	102	–	18
	22 weeks.....	5	mmol/L	2.02	0.49	–	mg/L	364	89	–	18
	25 weeks.....	11	mmol/L	2.19	0.52	–	mg/L	394	94	–	18
	28 weeks.....	13	mmol/L	2.36	0.77	–	mg/L	426	138	–	18
	31 weeks.....	7	mmol/L	2.33	0.68	–	mg/L	420	122	–	18
	34 weeks.....	19	mmol/L	2.76	1.86	–	mg/L	498	335	–	18
	37 weeks.....	31	mmol/L	2.25	0.64	–	mg/L	405	116	–	18
	40 weeks.....	51	mmol/L	1.79	1.19	–	mg/L	322	215	–	18
	44 weeks.....	15	mmol/L	1.45	0.59	–	mg/L	261	107	–	18
Methylmalonic acid......	....	–	µmol/L	–	–	0–0.8	mg/L	–	–	0–0.1	31
Lactic acid	10–16 weeks .	20	mmol/L	9.1	1.5	–	mg/L	820	135	–	14
	35–40 weeks .	20	mmol/L	6.6	1.1	–	mg/L	590	100	–	14
	13–16 weeks .	18	mmol/L	11.0	1.7	–	mg/L	990	150	–	15
	17–20 weeks .	23	mmol/L	9.8	2.4	–	mg/L	880	220	–	15
	33–36 weeks .	25	mmol/L	9.8	1.5	–	mg/L	880	135	–	15
	37–40 weeks .	16	mmol/L	9.1	1.6	–	mg/L	820	140	–	15
	At term	20	mmol/L	8.4	2.4	–	mg/L	760	213	–	32
	15–40 weeks .	22	mmol/L	8.4	–	(5.22–11.2)	mg/L	760	–	(470–1010)	33
Pyruvic acid..............	At term	19	µmol/L	93	45	–	mg/L	8.2	4.0	–	32
2(α)-Hydroxybutyric acid	15–40 weeks .	22	mmol/L	0.05	–	(0.03–0.10)	mg/L	5	–	(3–10)	33
3(β)-Hydroxybutyric acid	15–40 weeks .	22	mmol/L	0.12	–	(0.06–0.24)	mg/L	12	–	(6–25)	33
	At term	53	mmol/L	0.11	0.12	–	mg/L	11	12	–	34
α-Oxoglutaric acid	At term	8	µmol/L	51	23	–	mg/L	7.4	3.3	–	32
Citric acid	19–24 weeks .	7	µmol/L	345	56	(240–400)	mg/L	66.2	10.8	(46–77.2)	30
	28–32 weeks .	9	µmol/L	348	80	(214–446)	mg/L	66.8	15.3	(41.2–85.7)	30
	33–36 weeks .	14	µmol/L	277	68	(160–420)	mg/L	53.2	13.1	(31–80.7)	30
	37–40 weeks .	30	µmol/L	204	83	(57–450)	mg/L	39.2	15.9	(11–87)	30
	41–43 weeks .	22	µmol/L	145	34	(99–200)	mg/L	27.9	6.6	(19–38.5)	30
	At term	9	µmol/L	289	66	–	mg/L	55.5	12.7	–	32
Ketone bodies	At term	17	–	–	–	–	mg/L	8.7	5.9	–	32

Table 7   *Lipids*

	Gestational age	Number	Amount of substance				Mass				Reference
			Unit	Mean	s	(Extreme range)	Unit	Mean	s	(Extreme range)	
Total lipids	8–24 weeks ..	17	–	–	–	–	mg/L	170	87	–	39
	25–34 weeks .	10	–	–	–	–	mg/L	179	113	–	39
	35–39 weeks .	29	–	–	–	–	mg/L	331	167	–	39
	≥ 39 weeks ..	21	–	–	–	–	mg/L	386	197	–	39
	20 weeks.....	7	–	–	–	–	mg/L	40	28	–	40
	38–40 weeks .	41	–	–	–	–	mg/L	408	168	–	40
Cholesterol	9–24 weeks ..	60	µmol/L	506	264	(50–1550)	mg/L	196	102	(20–600)	41
	32–43 weeks .	75	µmol/L	148	107	–	mg/L	57.4	41.6	–	42
Bile acids	28–42 weeks .	18	µmol/L	–	–	(0.9–2.4)	mg/L	–	–	(0.4–1.0)	43

tes mellitus, glucose is increasingly eliminated in fetal urine. As a result, its concentration in amniotic fluid may remain elevated toward the end of gestation, indicating the possibility of neonatal hypoglucosemia[36], should its level exceed 1.7 mmol/L near term.

The extent of variations in the concentrations of the individual organic acids throughout pregnancy is only partly known (Table 6). The lactic-acid concentration tends to decline[37].

Ketone levels have been reported to increase in amniotic fluid during maternal energy deprivation[38].

Lipids

Wide variations have been reported in the total lipid content of amniotic fluid (Table 7). The lipid concentration is higher toward the end of pregnancy than in early stages, due to the elevation of triglyceride levels (Table 8) and higher phospholipid content (Tables 7 and 8) stemming from sharply enhanced synthesis of dipalmitoyl lecithin in the fetus from Week 36 on. Because of extreme variations in cholesterol levels (0–900 µmol/L at the 90% range in one investigation[22]), it is impossible to make any statements as to the changes in the course of pregnancy.

The determination of the concentration of phospholipid phosphorus or phosphatidylcholine (lecithin) has become an important element in judging fetal lung maturity[46–48]. At term, lecithin accounts for some 65% of total phospholipids (Table 9). Where these parameters fail to increase subsequent to the 36th week of gestation, there is the risk of respiratory distress for the newborn. Be-

Table 8   *Lipids[44]*

	26–33 weeks (15 women)		34–40 weeks (11 women)		In labor (22 women)	
	Mean	s	Mean	s	Mean	s
	mg/L					
Total lipids	121.6	–	138.2	–	153.8	–
Monoglycerides.....	2.4	1.2	2.1	0.7	2.3	1.4
Diglycerides	9.7	3.9	8.8	3.3	8.5	3.3
Triglycerides........	6.2	7.0	13.6	8.6	14.3	8.0
Free fatty acids	20.0	10.1	20.9	5.3	22.5	8.4
Free cholesterol.....	15.0	5.4	13.7	3.3	13.7	8.4
Cholesterol esters ...	19.0	12.4	18.3	10.3	21.9	10.8
Phospholipids.......	31.5	22.5	45.0	27.5	51.9	16.4
Hydrocarbons.......	17.7	7.0	15.8	4.6	18.6	9.8

Table 9   *Phospholipids near term*

	9 women[44]		10 women[45]	
	Mean	s	Mean	s
	As percent of total phospholipids			
Phosphatidylethanolamine (cephalin).	4.9	2.1	14.4	4.6
Phosphatidylcholine (lecithin).........	64.8	25.2	64.8	4.0
Sphingomyelin.....................	7.9	3.9	6.0	3.2
Phosphatidylserine.................	6.1	4.2	7.3	2.4
Phosphatidic acid .... }	10.0	7.5	–	–
Cardiolipin				
Phosphatidylinositol	2.2	1.5	–	–
Lysophosphatidylcholine (lysolecithin)	4.1	3.0	2.8	1.6

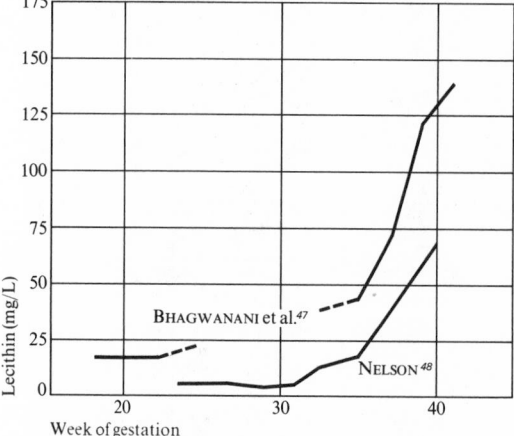

Fig. 8. Lecithin concentration in amniotic fluid without[47] and with acetone precipitation[48] (mean $\pm s$).

Lecithin (mg/L) — Week of gestation. BHAGWANANI et al.[47]   NELSON[48]

Table 10   *Phosphatidylcholine (lecithin), sphingomyelin[40]*

Gestational age	Number	Surface-active lecithin		Sphingo-myelin	
		Mean	s	Mean	s
		mg/L			
12 weeks..................	2	2.8	–	4.2	–
14 weeks..................	6	2.9	1.5	3.9	0.3
16 weeks..................	4	1.9	1.0	5	0.8
18 weeks..................	3	2	–	5	–
20 weeks..................	7	2	0.9	4.9	0.9
22 weeks..................	6	2	0.7	5	0.9
23 weeks..................	2	3	–	6	–
24 weeks..................	9	5	0.3	12	5
25 weeks..................	3	9.7	–	14	–
26 weeks..................	5	11	0.5	16	3
27 weeks..................	2	12	–	15	–
28 weeks..................	9	12	0.8	12.5	5
29 weeks..................	5	15	4	20	6
30 weeks..................	12	26	10	27	5
31 weeks..................	9	29	12	25	10
32 weeks..................	16	30	9	27.5	5
33 weeks..................	14	33	10	27	5
34 weeks..................	18	42	14	21	7
35 weeks..................	24	72	20	19	6
36 weeks..................	23	77	20	18	4
37 weeks..................	19	82	26	14	5
38 weeks..................	21	84	24	12	3
39 weeks (at term)	20	86	33	11	1
40–42 weeks	25	88	30	8	3
≥ 43 weeks	15	128	42	4	2

Table 11   *Fatty-acid composition of lipid fractions during labor (mean of 6 women)[53]*

		Monoglycerides	Diglycerides	Triglycerides	Free fatty acids	Cholesterol esters	Phospholipids
		As percent of total fatty acids					
$C_{12:0}$	Lauric acid	2.2	1.4	2.6	1.7	2.4	0.9
$C_{13:0}$	Tridecanoic acid	1.6	1.1	1.6	0.7	1.6	0.6
$C_{14:0}$	Myristic acid.........	5.5	10.9	10.6	10.3	8.0	9.3
$C_{14:1}$	Myristoleic acid......	2.7	5.4	4.7	3.4	2.4	6.8
$C_{15:0}$	Pentadecanoic acid ..	1.6	1.1	2.6	1.7	4.0	1.2
$C_{16:0}$	Palmitic acid........	41.2	39.8	29.1	51.5	16.0	43.3
$C_{16:1}$	Palmitoleic acid.....	10.9	18.1	26.4	4.8	41.6	8.3
$C_{17:0}$	Heptadecanoic acid ..	trace	trace	trace	1.4	trace	0.6
$C_{17:1}$	Heptadecenoic acid ..	2.8	1.8	2.6	0.8	4.0	0.9
$C_{18:0}$	Stearic acid	9.9	2.2	2.6	6.8	3.2	9.3
$C_{18:1}$	Oleic acid............	9.4	10.9	9.0	6.8	8.0	9.9
$C_{18:2}$	Linoleic acid........	5.5	2.9	2.7	6.5	2.4	3.2
$C_{18:3}$ $C_{20:1}$	Linolenic acid .... cis-Δ^5-Eicosenoic acid }	1.7	1.1	1.1	1.0	–	0.6
$C_{20:0}$	Arachidic acid	2.8	0.7	1.1	3.4	1.6	0.9
$C_{20:4}$	Arachidonic acid.....	–	–	–	0.8	–	3.8
$C_{22:0}$	Behenic acid	1.1	0.8	1.6	1.7	2.4	1.8
$C_{24:0}$	Lignoceric acid	1.1	1.8	1.6	3.5	2.4	3.1
Unsaturated fatty acids		34.1	40.2	46.5	19.7	58.4	29.0
Saturated fatty acids		65.9	59.8	53.4	80.3	41.6	71.0

cause of methodological differences in the determination of phospholipids, published normal levels are not directly comparable (Table 10 and Fig. 8)[13,49]. Thus, for example, lecithin determined after precipitation with acetone (surface-active lecithin) yields lower values than untreated specimens[48]. Some authors judge the lung maturity from the lecithin/sphingomyelin ratio, since the concentration of the latter does not vary materially in the course of pregnancy and may thus be regarded so to speak as a standard. Nevertheless, opinions differ on the clinical significance of any particular ratio[13,50,51].

The accuracy of diagnosing fetal lung maturity can be improved by estimating the phospholipids phosphatidylinositol and phosphatidylglycerol besides the lecithin/sphingomyelin ratio[169]. The appearance of phosphatidylglycerol in amniotic fluid signals the final maturation of lung surfactant[170–172].

Fatty acids. Palmitic acid predominates among the fatty acids of lecithin (Table 11) and its determination in amniotic fluid is as in-

Table 12 *Phosphatidylcholine (lecithin), lecithin/sphingomyelin ratio and palmitic acid before and during labor[52]*

Gestational age	Lecithin				Lecithin/sphingomyelin				Palmitic acid			
	Before labor		During labor		Before labor		During labor		Before labor		During labor	
	Mean	s	Mean	s	Mean	s	Mean	s	Mean	s	Mean	s
	mg/L				mg/mg				µmol/L			
34–35 weeks	43.0	18.3	85.0	6.6	2.55	0.53	4.58	1.04	63	30	172	41
36–37 weeks	86.1	35.7	241	78	6.32	3.18	13.8	4.01	95	55	264	75
38–39 weeks	86.3	57.7	211	103	6.03	2.87	11.4	4.79	106	75	252	151
40–41 weeks	134	69.2	243	125	7.39	2.75	11.8	5.04	129	79	282	147
42–43 weeks	147	37.5	232	108	8.84	5.08	12.1	6.16	193	108	318	187

dicative of fetal lung maturity as the determination of lecithin itself[54, 55]. During labor, the concentration of lecithin increases and with it the concentration of palmitic acid (Table 12).

Additionally, amniotic fluid contains hydrocarbons and long-chain alcohols (Table 8). Both fractions have been separated by gas chromatography[53], but little is known about the significance of either substance. Squalene possibly stemming from fetal skin predominates among the hydrocarbons.

Inasmuch as dipalmitoyl lecithin determines the surfactant system of fetal lung, it is also possible to judge lung maturity by measuring the surface tension of amniotic fluid[54].

Bile acids (Table 7). Cholic acid, chenodeoxycholic acid and 3 β-hydroxy-Δ5-cholenic acid occur in amniotic fluid, the latter apparently of fetal origin. The bile-acid concentration is elevated in duodenal and ileal atresia[158].

Proteins

The proteins of amniotic fluid stem primarily from maternal plasma[56–59]. The total protein concentration rises from low levels in early pregnancy to maximal levels between the 25th and the 30th week, only to decline gradually thereafter[18, 60–62]. The absolute values vary, presumably due in part to different methods of determination (Table 13). By the use of injected ^{125}I or ^{131}I-labelled protein fractions into the intact amniotic sac, the half-life of proteins was determined to be 29 h (s 3 h); the resultant amniotic fluid 'clearance' was calculated as 342 mL/d (s 33 mL/d) and the percentage of protein turned over per day was 63% (s 5%)[65].

These rates appear to apply to all proteins that were investigated, irrespective of relative molecular mass. The major route for the removal of amniotic fluid proteins was fetal swallowing.

Table 14 shows the changes in protein fractions separated by electrophoresis in the course of pregnancy. The prealbumin concentration rises with progressing gestation and this protein appears to be of fetal origin. Other proteins reaching the amniotic fluid with the urine are α-fetoprotein[67] and β2-microglobulin[68]. The concentration of these and other designated proteins is detailed in Tables 15a and 15b. In amniotic fluid as in serum, cortisol[73] and testosterone[74] are bound to specific proteins.

α-Fetoprotein. The determination of this protein is significant for the early prenatal diagnosis of anencephaly and spina bifida[79–83]. In open defects of the neural tube spaces, the α-fetoprotein concentration in amniotic fluid before the 26th week of gestation is almost always above the upper physiologic limit for the corresponding week (Table 16).

In the early stages of pregnancy markedly higher α-fetoprotein concentrations have also been reported in omphalocele[83, 84], congenital nephrosis[85], sacrococcygeal teratoma[86], duodenal atresia[87], intrauterine fetal death[88] and many cases of Turner's syndrome (the X0 karyotype)[89, 90]. The determination of α-fetoprotein levels is less useful for the diagnosis of fetal defects in late pregnancy than in early pregnancy[82].

Fibrinogen–fibrin degradation products. In open defects of the neural tube, high molecular proteins, for example β-lipoprotein, α2-macroglobulin[159], IgM[91] as well as fibrin and products of fibrinogen breakdown[75, 160], may occur in amniotic fluid in elevated concentrations.

Table 13 *Protein, albumin*

Gestational age	Method	Number	Protein		Albumin		Reference
			Mean	s	Mean	s	
			g/L				
10–16 weeks	Biuret reaction	24	3.38	1.78	–	–	14
35–40 weeks	Biuret reaction	33	5.23	3.01	–	–	14
39–40 weeks	Biuret reaction	24	2.26	0.46	–	–	60
13–16 weeks	UV absorption spectrophotometry	12	3.3	1.6	–	–	15
17–20 weeks		29	5.4	1.0	–	–	15
29–32 weeks		1	2.9	–	–	–	15
33–36 weeks		14	2.5	0.5	–	–	15
37–40 weeks		24	2.5	0.6	–	–	15
15 weeks	Automated biuret reaction (protein) Automated bromcresol-green binding (albumin)	29, 26	5	2	3	2	18
19 weeks		61, 58	5	1	3	1	18
22 weeks		5	5	1	3	1	18
25 weeks		12, 11	8	4	5	3	18
28 weeks		13, 11	8	7	6	6	18
31 weeks		7	4	1	2	1	18
34 weeks		19, 12	4	2	2	1	18
37 weeks		29, 16	3	1	2	1	18
40 weeks		51, 34	3	2	1	1	18
44 weeks		17, 14	3	1	2	1	18
16–20 weeks	Automated Folin reaction (protein) Immunoelectrophoresis (albumin)	101	5.09	1.41	2.73	0.84	63
3rd trimester	UV absorption spectrophotometry	19	2.75	0.4	–	–	64
Inception of labor		20	1.95	0.56	–	–	64
Delivery		12	2.96	0.48	–	–	64

Table 14　*Protein fractions (electrophoretic separation)*

Carrier and gestational age	Number	Prealbumin Mean	(Extreme range)	Albumin Mean	(Extreme range)	α_1-Globulin Mean	(Extreme range)	α_2-Globulin Mean	(Extreme range)	β-Globulin Mean	(Extreme range)	γ-Globulin Mean	(Extreme range)	Reference
						As percent of total protein								
Agarose gel														
16–18 weeks	11	2.2	(1–3)	–	(42–61)	–	(8–12)	–	(3–15)	–	(12–15)	–	(7–9)	66
20 weeks	7	4.4	(4–6)	–	(49–60)	–	(9–13)	–	(6–9)	–	(11–16)	–	(6–10)	66
22–34 weeks	9	4.7	(3–6)	–	(40–55)	–	(8–14)	–	(6–13)	–	(13–18)	–	(8–13)	66
36–37 weeks	10	10.5	(6–19)	–	(32–49)	–	(9–15)	–	(6–14)	–	(12–25)	–	(8–13)	66
38–40 weeks	10	17.9	(11–30)	–	(29–40)	–	(10–16)	–	(6–11)	–	(13–22)	–	(7–10)	66
42 weeks	10	6.4	(5–7)	–	(33–66)	–	(8–17)	–	(5–13)	–	(11–23)	–	(2–13)	66
Cellulose acetate														
34–40 weeks	28	–	–	64.8	s3.1	6.8	s1.0	6.5	s0.9	12.3	s2.7	9.6	s1.6	58

Table 15a　*Proteins and related compounds*

	Gestational age	Number	Unit	Mean	s	(Extreme range)	Reference
Albumin	36–40 weeks	19	g/L	1.23	–	(0.7–1.9)	69
Acid α_1-glycoprotein	31–42 weeks	69	mg/L	23	–	(4–65)	70
α_1-Lipoprotein	14–17 weeks	–	mg/L	–	–	(8–16)	164
	23–30 weeks	–	mg/L	–	–	(10–21)	164
	34–38 weeks	–	mg/L	–	–	(3–15)	164
α-Fetoprotein	14 weeks	–	mg/L	15	2.5	–	71
	31–42 weeks	69	mg/L	1.3	–	(0.04–3.5)	70
α_1-Antitrypsin	16–20 weeks	101	mg/L	290	120	(120–780)	63
	31–42 weeks	69	mg/L	132	–	(35–315)	70
	11–42 weeks	47	mg/L	270	288	(50–1600)	62
Thyroxin-binding globulin	At term (delivery)	7	mg/L	2.9	0.8	–	111
Zn-α_2-Glycoprotein	11–38 weeks	96	mg/L	9.8	4.0	–	165
Carcinoembryonic antigen (CEA)	19 weeks	–	µg/L	53	–	–	166
	36 weeks	–	µg/L	25	–	–	166
β-Trace protein	14–33 weeks	70	mg/L	5.7	2.5	(3.0–16.7)	72
β_2-Microglobulin	≤ 36 weeks	13	mg/L	6.3	–	(5.0–10.0)	68
	≥ 37 weeks	7	mg/L	0.87	–	(0.2–1.3)	68
	16–20 weeks	101	mg/L	200	90	(70–560)	63
Transferrin	31–42 weeks	69	mg/L	151	–	(12–325)	70
	36–40 weeks	19	mg/L	150	–	(100–280)	69
IgG	16–20 weeks	101	mg/L	410	160	(130–970)	63
	36–40 weeks	19	mg/L	230	–	(90–400)	69
IgA	16–20 weeks	101	mg/L	–	–	(0–63)	63
Fibrinogen–fibrin degradation products	16–28 weeks	10	mg/L	3.3	1.0	–	75
	28–40 weeks	42	mg/L	3.1	0.8	–	75
	10–24 weeks	35	mg/L	2.37	1.59	–	76
	25–40 weeks	18	mg/L	2.12	1.66	–	76
Mucoproteins	At term (in labor)	24	g/L	1.80	0.203	(1.20–2.09)	77
Glycosaminoglycans	14–22 weeks	123	mg/L	25.2	11.1	6.1–51.4*	78
	22–40 weeks	128	mg/L	17.6	7.2	4.6–35*	78

*95% range.

Table 15b　*Immunoglobulins[167]*

Gestational age	Number	IgG Mean	s	IgD Mean	s	IgA Mean	s	IgA$_1$ Mean	s	IgA$_2$ Mean	s	IgM Mean	s
						mg/L							
11–15 weeks	14	330	260	5	4	28	19	23	20	11	5	3	1
16–20 weeks	98	410	440	7	6	32	18	24	12	12	7	3	4
21–25 weeks	13	360	240	9	8	50	42	29	19	13	8	2	1
26–35 weeks	8	270	110	5	5	32	18	19	10	10	5	2	2
36–40 weeks	28	120	100	3	4	29	19	21	13	5	4	5	4

Table 16 *α-Fetoprotein*[81]

Gestational age	Number	Mean	95 percentile	Gestational age	Number	Mean	95 percentile	Gestational age	Number	Mean	95 percentile	Gestational age	Number	Mean	95 percentile
		mg/L				mg/L				mg/L				mg/L	
15 weeks.	31	18.46	32.81	22 weeks..	18	4.83	13.75	29 weeks..	85	1.86	4.56	36 weeks.	25	0.39	1.19
16 weeks.	38	17.08	32.20	23 weeks..	21	4.66	8.78	30 weeks..	71	1.42	2.93	37 weeks.	12	0.23	1.42
17 weeks.	39	16.02	30.38	24 weeks..	29	3.90	7.98	31 weeks..	86	1.17	2.60	38 weeks.	8	0.29	1.42
18 weeks.	24	13.48	27.60	25 weeks..	37	3.90	9.35	32 weeks..	82	0.99	1.98	39 weeks.	7	0.26	1.42
19 weeks.	23	10.67	27.57	26 weeks..	47	3.15	5.62	33 weeks..	74	0.78	1.82				
20 weeks.	20	7.93	15.90	27 weeks..	78	2.58	5.54	34 weeks..	56	0.57	1.32				
21 weeks.	19	6.27	14.11	28 weeks..	81	2.15	4.78	35 weeks..	45	0.51	1.35				

Enzymes

Normal values (expressed in $U \equiv \mu mol\ min^{-1}$) for different enzymes are compiled in Tables 17 to 23. The activity of most enzymes changes in the course of pregnancy in a pattern roughly parallel to the protein concentration. An exception is amylase, which may reach very high activity levels after the 36th week of pregnancy[99]. This enzyme appears to enter amniotic fluid with fetal urine and saliva[58, 100].

As with α-fetoprotein determination an increased activity of acetylcholinesterase may indicate an open neural-tube defect in the fetus[173]; furthermore this enzyme assay distinguishes between neural-tube problems and congenital nephrosis[174] while α-fetoprotein assay does not.

Determination of the activity of specific enzymes in cells cultured from amniotic fluid is used for the prenatal diagnosis of inborn errors of metabolism. The use of uncultered cells is rather unreliable and the enzyme determination in cell-free amniotic fluid is of value only in a few diseases (Hunter syndrome, Sandhoff disease, Tay–Sachs disease)[92, 93].

Table 17 *Alkaline phosphatase in normal pregnancy and preeclampsia*[153]

Gestational age	Normal			Preeclampsia		
	Number	Mean	s	Number	Mean	s
		U/L			U/L	
33–34 weeks	8	13.3	5.92	–	–	–
35–36 weeks	7	12.1	3.48	7	19.2	9.22
37–38 weeks	15	18.5	9.05	9	30.1	23.8
39–40 weeks	30	16.5	5.37	11	28.4	12.7
41–42 weeks	18	18.2	8.10	–	–	–

Table 18 *Lactate dehydrogenase*[95]

Gestational age	Total LDH			Lactate dehydrogenase isoenzymes											
				LDH I		LDH II		LDH III		LDH IV		LDH V			
	Number	Mean	s	Number	Mean	s	Mean	s	Mean	s	Mean	s	Mean	s	
		U/L			As percent of total activity										
24–32 weeks	26	161	83	16	15	5.9	20	7.8	22	4.1	11	3.8	32	17.1	
33–42 weeks	25	130	63	15	8	5.4	12	5.2	19	6.1	11	6.6	50	17.3	

Table 19 *Enzymes*[18]

Name of enzyme	15 weeks (N 24,25)		19 weeks (N 59,60)		25 weeks (N 8,9)		28 weeks (N 9,10)		31 weeks (N 5)		34 weeks (N 11,15)		37 weeks (N 19–21)		40 weeks (N 48,49)		44 weeks (N 17)	
	Mean	s	Mean	s	Mean	s	Mean	s	Mean	s	Mean	s	Mean	s	Mean	s	Mean	s
	U/L																	
Lactate dehydrogenase.......	83	24	87	52	101	23	199	146	161	64	137	82	135	59	162	118	161	52
α-Hydroxybutyrate dehydrogenase.............	46.2	20.9	49.4	35.6	59.4	20.8	90.0	63.2	58.0	25.8	56.3	36.9	51.0	20.2	63.2	47.8	64.7	23.2
Creatin kinase	0.4	2.0	0	0	1.8	0	0.5	1.5	0	0	0.3	1.2	1.6	3.6	0.3	1.6	0	0
Alkaline phosphatase	16.6	10.1	18.4	12.8	11.7	10.5	45.0	68.3	9.0	4.9	14.0	3.7	20.5	19.9	32.8	56.7	20.0	9.7
Acid phosphatase	1.4	0.8	2.0	1.2	4.2	2.7	6.3	3.8	3.0	0.8	2.5	1.7	2.8	1.8	3.3	2.3	4.0	3.6

Table 20 *Enzymes in last trimester*[94]

EC number	Name of enzyme	Number	Mean	s	(Extreme range)	EC number	Name of enzyme	Number	Mean	s	(Extreme range)
			U/L						U/L		
1.1.1.27	Lactate dehydrogenase	10	239	109	(97–400)	2.6.1.2	Alanine aminotransferase	10	1.6	0.9	(0–2.3)
1.1.1.37	Malate dehydrogenase	10	82.4	28.8	(56.7–132)	3.1.1.8	Cholinesterase	10	32.8	45.8	(0–117)
1.1.1.49	Glucose-6-phosphate dehydrogenase	11	0.8	0.9	(0–2.9)	3.1.3.1	Alkaline phosphatase.....	10	27.2	11.9	(5.0–44.4)
						3.2.1.1	α-Amylase	8	56.0	49.1	(0–137)
2.6.1.1	Aspartate aminotransferase	9	8.6	3.8	(2.6–14.2)	3.4.11.1	Aminopeptidase (cytosol)	11	2.5	1.8	(0.76–5.18)

Table 21   *Lysosomal enzymes*[96]

EC number	Name of enzyme	11–15 weeks	16–20 weeks	21–25 weeks	26–30 weeks	31–35 weeks	36–41 weeks
		U/L					
3.1.3.2	Acid phosphatase	2.84	3.94	4.62	3.75	4.63	4.84
3.2.1.20	α-D-Glucosidase	1.53	1.40	0.51	0.18	0.16	0.21
3.2.1.21	β-D-Glucosidase	0.066	0.043	0.020	0.004	0.002	0.001
3.2.1.22	α-D-Galactosidase	0.005	0.006	0.009	0.008	0.011	0.016
3.2.1.23	β-D-Galactosidase	0.020	0.022	0.018	0.016	0.020	0.029
3.2.1.24	α-D-Mannosidase	0.31	0.34	0.44	0.39	0.28	0.26
3.2.1.30	β-N-Acetyl-D-glucosaminidase	9.94	11.9	16.5	16.0	13.7	12.3
3.2.1.31	β-D-Glucuronidase	0.25	0.38	0.57	0.63	0.44	0.35
3.2.1.51	α-L-Fucosidase	0.87	1.05	1.59	1.45	1.04	1.06
3.2.1.55	α-L-Arabinofuranosidase	0.024	0.018	0.008	0.008	0.006	0.005

Table 22   *Amine oxidase (diamine oxidase)*[97]

Gestational age	Number	Median	(Extreme range)
		U/L	
9–12 weeks	9	0.042	(0.004–0.411)
13–16 weeks	11	0.065	(0.004–0.452)
17–20 weeks	4	0.397	(0.137–0.916)
21–24 weeks	4	2.22	(0.747–7.53)
25–28 weeks	10	5.89	(1.04–11.0)
29–30 weeks	9	5.19	(1.31–15.4)
31–32 weeks	17	6.46	(2.00–15.1)
33–34 weeks	15	6.29	(1.61–14.8)
35–36 weeks	13	4.83	(2.45–12.2)
37–38 weeks	10	5.18	(1.57–11.8)
39–40 weeks	9	3.60	(2.25–6.30)

Table 23a   *Lysozyme*[98]

Gestational age	Number	Mean	s
		mg/L	
14–19 weeks	5	5.1	1.7
20–24 weeks	6	7.2	3.6
25–28 weeks	3	8.0	2.3
28–29 weeks	22	10.8	2.9
33–34 weeks	15	11.6	5.3
34½–36 weeks	21	12.3	4.8
36½–38 weeks	20	14.3	5.7
38½–40 weeks	9	18.9	4.3
40½–44 weeks	6	15.8	4.0

Table 23b   *Acetylcholinesterase*[175]

Gestational age	Number	Mean	s	(Extreme range)
		U/L		
14–24 weeks	101	2.56	1.10	(0.4–5.8)
26–38 weeks	49	0.73	0.64	(0.0–4.2)

Bilirubin and erythroblastosis fetalis

Chemical methods for the determination of bilirubin are not very specific, for which reason such values (Table 24) are at times referred to as 'bilirubinoid' concentrations. Where spectrophotometry is used, the difficulty lies in selecting a wavelength at which hemoglobin and other pigments cause the least interference (Fig.9). One method involves the determination of the difference of absorbance at wavelength 450 nm and the baseline tangent to the absorbance curve. Another method measures the absorbance

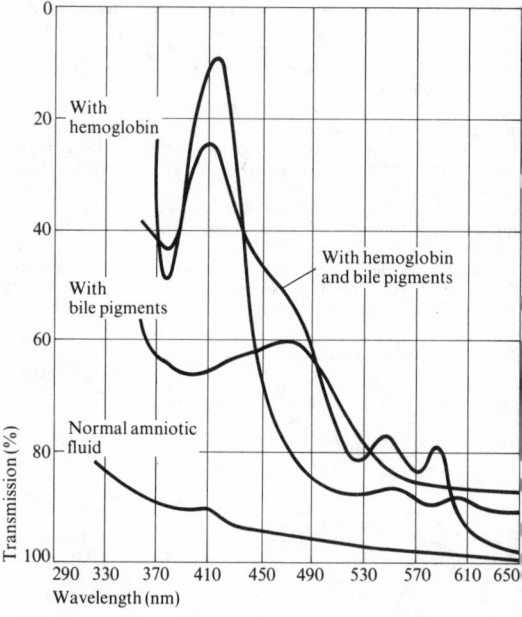

Fig. 9. Spectrograms of different specimens of amniotic fluid[102].

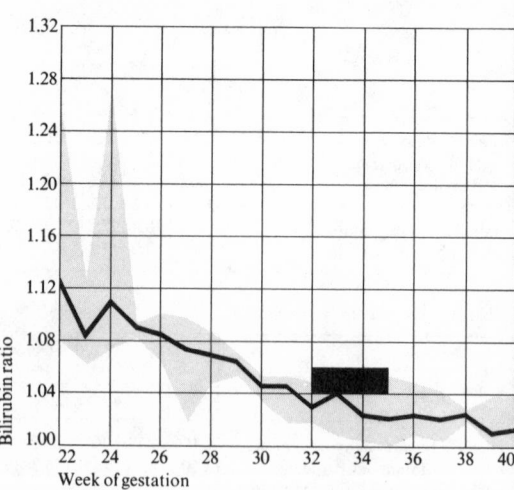

Fig. 10. Bilirubin ratio of normal amniotic fluid (mean and range) from the 22nd week of gestation to term. The black rectangle denotes the area of likely erythroblastosis fetalis[104].

Table 24 *Bilirubinoids ('bilirubin')*

Gestational age	Number	Amount of substance				Mass				Reference
		Unit	Mean	s	(Extreme range)	Unit	Mean	s	(Extreme range)	
16–26 weeks	23	µmol/L	3.35	0.80	(2.1–5.0)	mg/L	1.96	0.47	(1.2–2.9)	[101]
30–34 weeks	25	µmol/L	1.39	0.39	(0.85–2.4)	mg/L	0.816	0.230	(0.5–1.4)	[101]
15 weeks	28	µmol/L	2.2	1.0	–	mg/L	1.3	0.6	–	[18]
22 weeks	3	µmol/L	3.1	1.0	–	mg/L	1.8	0.6	–	[18]
28 weeks	3	µmol/L	1.5	0.5	–	mg/L	0.9	0.3	–	[18]
40 weeks	54	µmol/L	0.7	0.7	–	mg/L	0.4	0.4	–	[18]
9–24 weeks	61	µmol/L	3.9	2.4	(0–17)	mg/L	2.3	1.4	(0–10)	[41]
32–43 weeks	103	µmol/L	3.88	3.13	–	mg/L	2.27	1.83	–	[42]
38–41 weeks	15	µmol/L	0.9	–	(0.5–1.2)	mg/L	0.5	–	(0.3–0.7)	[110]

difference at wavelengths 490 and 520 nm, to compute the corresponding ratio of transmittance (the bilirubin ratio). For a detailed discussion of the processing of specimens and methodology see FAIRWEATHER et al.[103]. Bilirubin concentrations are often elevated in early pregnancy, reaching maximal values between the 20th and the 24th week of gestation and declining thereafter (Fig. 10). At term, the levels are low or below the threshold of detection. Along with free bilirubin, small quantities of conjugated bilirubin may occur in amniotic fluid (of the order of 0.1 mg/L in normal pregnancy)[105]. In addition, biliverdin has been detected in amniotic fluid in the early stages of pregnancy[106].

The determination of bilirubin is of great importance for the prenatal diagnosis and treatment of erythroblastosis fetalis. The evaluation of spectrograms is illustrated in Figure 11. Opinions differ as to the relative merits of chemical methods of bilirubin measurement versus spectrophotometry in pinpointing the hazards to the fetus[102,108,109].

Vitamins

Little is known about the concentration of vitamins in amniotic fluid. Table 25 summarizes the available data for vitamins B.

Table 25 *Vitamins*

	Gestational age	Number	Mean	s	(Extreme range)	Reference
					µg/L	
Thiamine	In labor	10	63	41	(1–170)	[155]
Riboflavin	At term	8	13	7	(4–26)	[156]
Pyridoxine	At term	8	6.1	1.5	(5.4–9.4)	[156]
Vitamin B₁₂	At term	8	121	30	(68–183)	[156]
Folic acid	At term	8	2.3	1.2	(1.1–4.7)	[156]

Hormones

Cyclic adenosine monophosphate (Table 26). The concentration is elevated in the amniotic fluid of women with gestosis[112,113].

Catecholamines. Along with epinephrine and norepinephrine (Table 26), breakdown products of these compounds have also been detected, such as 4-hydroxy-3-methoxyphenylglycol and *p*-hydroxyphenyllactic acid (Fig. 12) as well as – in one specimen[117] – *p*-hydroxyphenylacetic acid (100 µg/L), 4-hydroxy-3-methoxyphenylacetic acid (250 µg/L) and 4-hydroxy-3-methoxymandelic acid (60 µg/L).

5-hydroxyindoleacetic acid is a product of the breakdown of serotonin, occurring in the argentaffin cells of the small intestine. Its concentration in amniotic fluid (Table 26) might possibly be indicative of the degree of maturity of the intestinal tract.

The concentrations of *thyroid hormones* in amniotic fluid are tabulated in Table 26. Up to the 30th week of gestation, the levels of 3,3',5'-triiodothyronine are elevated, whereas 3,3',5-triiodothyronine stays below the threshold of detection[111,116].

In amniotic fluid, *steroid hormones* occur in the free state to a minor extent, the majority being conjugated with sulfate and/or glucuronic acid (Tables 27 and 28). The pattern of steroids in am-

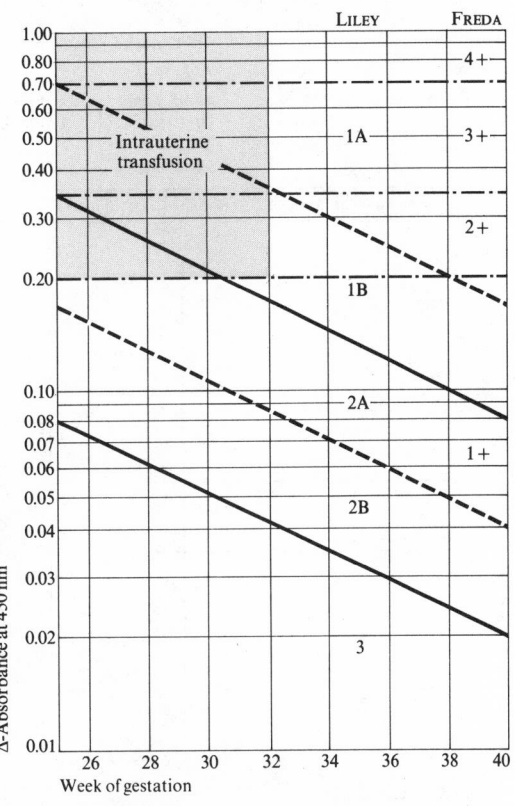

Fig. 11. Schematic interpretation of bilirubin concentration in amniotic fluid relative to the hazard of erythroblastosis fetalis according to spectrophotometric methods of LILEY and FREDA[107].

Method of Liley: 1A (above broken line): condition desperate; immediate delivery or transfusion imperative. *1B* (between broken and solid lines): hemoglobin less than 80 g/L, delivery or transfusion urgent. *2A* (between solid and broken lines): hemoglobin 80–100 g/L; delivery indicated between week 35 and 37. *2B* (between broken and solid lines): hemoglobin 110–139 g/L; delivery indicated between week 37 and 39. *3* (below solid line): anemia unlikely; delivery at term.

Method of Freda: 4+ (above upper horizontal line): fetal death imminent, immediate delivery or transfusion. *3+* (between upper and middle horizontal lines): fetus in jeopardy, death within 3 weeks; delivery or transfusion as soon as possible. *2+* (between middle and lower horizontal lines): fetal survival for at least 7–10 days; repeat test; possible indication for transfusion. *1+* (below lower horizontal line): fetus in no immediate danger of death.

Table 26 *Nonsteroid hormones*

	Gestational age	Number	Amount of substance				Mass				Reference
			Unit	Mean	s	(Extreme range)	Unit	Mean	s	(Extreme range)	
Cyclic adenosine monophosphate	11–20 weeks	}104	nmol/L	8	–	(5–15)	µg/L	2.6	–	(1.6–4.9)	112
	At term.....		nmol/L	25	–	(19–35)	µg/L	8.2	–	(6.3–12)	112
	34–41 weeks	19	nmol/L	19.6	5.5	–	µg/L	6.5	1.8	–	113
Epinephrine	....	22	µmol/L	–	–	(0–76)	mg/L	–	–	(0–14)*	114
Norepinephrine................	....	22	µmol/L	–	–	(0–59)	mg/L	–	–	(0–10)◊	114
5-Hydroxyindoleacetic acid	36–37 weeks	2	nmol/L	–	–	(220–260)	µg/L	–	–	(42–49)	115
	38–39 weeks	8	nmol/L	207	77	(89–310)	µg/L	39.5	14.8	(17–60)	115
	40–41 weeks	21	nmol/L	430	305	(0–940)	µg/L	82.2	58.4	(0–180)	115
	42–43 weeks	12	nmol/L	528	342	(0–1210)	µg/L	101	65.3	(0–232)	115
Thyroxine											
– total.........................	At term......	18	nmol/L	8.2	3.9	(1.8–14)	µg/L	6.4	3.0	(1.4–11)	111
	15–19 weeks	19	nmol/L	5.12	2.02	–	µg/L	3.98	1.57	–	116
	31–35 weeks	7	nmol/L	4.00	1.29	–	µg/L	3.11	1.00	–	116
	36–42 weeks	26	nmol/L	5.66	2.56	–	µg/L	4.40	1.99	–	116
– free	At term......	15	pmol/L	53.1	24.5	(16–77)	ng/L	41.3	19.0	(12.5–60)	111
3,3′,5′-Triiodothyronine	15–19 weeks	21	nmol/L	5.07	2.18	–	µg/L	3.30	1.42	–	116
	20–30 weeks	4	nmol/L	4.96	2.86	–	µg/L	3.23	1.86	–	116
	31–35 weeks	7	nmol/L	1.46	0.12	–	µg/L	0.95	0.08	–	116
	36–42 weeks	23	nmol/L	1.43	0.37	–	µg/L	0.93	0.24	–	116

*No detectable level in 13 samples. ◊ 15 samples below 1 mg/L.

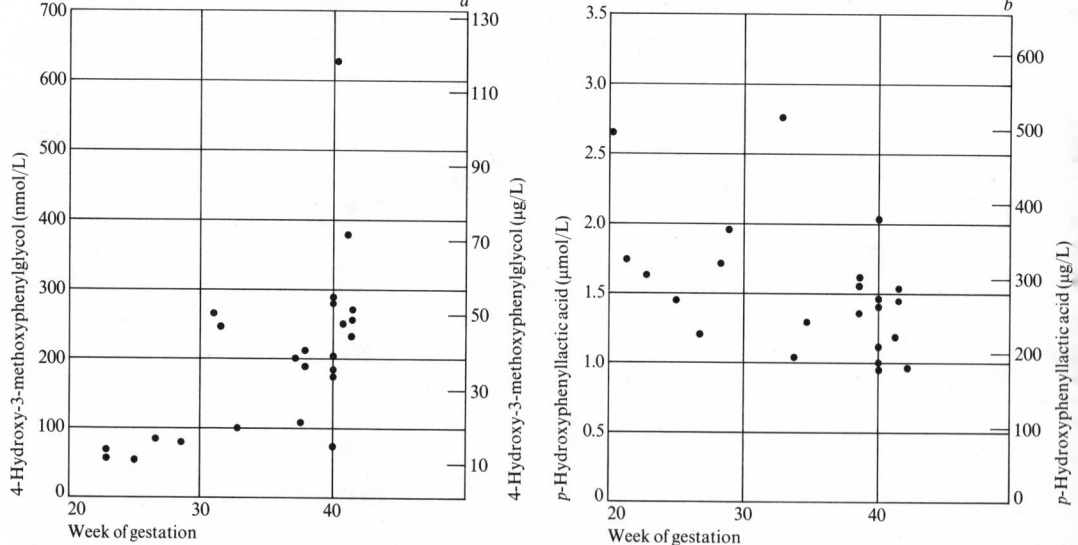

Fig. 12. Correlation between concentration of 4-hydroxy-3-methoxyphenylglycol (*a*) and *p*-hydroxyphenyllactic acid (*b*) in amniotic fluid and gestational age[117].

Table 27 *Free and conjugated 17-oxosteroids and 17-hydroxy-corticosteroids (20 women at term)*[122]

	17-oxosteroids		17-hydroxy-corticosteroids	
	Mean	(Extreme range)	Mean	(Extreme range)
	g/L			
Total.................	120	(42–200)	240	(66.4–472)
Free	12.5	(5.4–32.4)	37.3	(14.3–77.4)
Glucuronide	60.8	(22.9–109)	115	(21.1–282)
Sulfate..............	46.5	(12.2–112)	89.2	(28.2–276)

niotic fluid closely resembles that in the urine of the newborn, an indication that, during the second half of pregnancy at least, amniotic-fluid steroids stem from fetal urine[133]. Thus, steroids synthesized by the fetus and hydroxylated in position 16 occur in amniotic fluid.

The concentration of *estriol*, quantitatively the most important amniotic-fluid steroid, increases in the course of pregnancy (Table 29). Subnormal values suggest intrauterine fetal death[133].

In the course of pregnancy, the *cortisol* concentrations increase moderately at first; only toward the end of pregnancy does the increase become marked (roughly paralleling the rise in lecithin concentrations)[129,130,137,138], a phenomenon linked to fetal lung maturation.

Elevated *pregnanetriol* values have been observed in the adrenogenital syndrome[125,139].

Table 28 *Steroid hormones*

	Gestational age	Num-ber	Amount of substance				Mass				Refer-ence
			Unit	Mean	s	(Extreme range)	Unit	Mean	s	(Extreme range)	
Progesterone...................	At term........	4	nmol/L	165	–	(150–190)	µg/L	52	–	(47–60)	123
	At term........	77	nmol/L	79	–	(17–220)	µg/L	24.8	–	(5.5–68)	161
16α-Hydroxyprogesterone	At term........	4	nmol/L	393	–	(345–445)	µg/L	130	–	(114–147)	123
17α-Hydroxyprogesterone	24–38 weeks	13	nmol/L	2.14	0.59	(1.2–3.0)	ng/L	708	195	(400–1000)	124
Pregnanetriol	At term........	4	nmol/L	92	–	(68–137)	µg/L	31	–	(23–46)	125
Pregnanediol	3rd trimester...	29	nmol/L	512	–	(66–1390)	µg/L	164	–	(21–447)	126
Dehydroepiandrosterone...........	3rd trimester...	14	nmol/L	24	–	(1.7–60)	µg/L	7.0	–	(0.5–17.3)	126
	Before delivery	–	nmol/L	29	–	–	µg/L	8.3	–	–	127
16α-Hydroxypregnenolone..........	Before delivery	–	nmol/L	358	–	–	µg/L	119	–	–	127
16α-Hydroxydehydroepiandrosterone	3rd trimester...	18	µmol/L	1.96	–	(0.25–5.0)	µg/L	600	–	(75–1528)	126
	Before delivery	–	µmol/L	2.61	–	–	µg/L	798	–	–	127
16-Oxoandrostenediol	3rd trimester...	13	µmol/L	0.69	–	(0.07–1.55)	µg/L	211	–	(20–471)	126
	Before delivery	–	µmol/L	1.89	–	–	µg/L	575	–	–	127
Estriol	3rd trimester...	27	µmol/L	2.34	–	(0.85–4.29)	µg/L	674	–	(246–1238)	126
	Before delivery	–	µmol/L	5.45	–	–	µg/L	1573	–	–	127
Estriol-3-sulfate.....................	32–40 weeks	12	nmol/L	312	–	(43–944)	µg/L	115	–	(16–348)	132
Estriol-16-glucuronide	32–40 weeks	20	nmol/L	678	–	(325–1260)	µg/L	315	–	(151–585)	132
Estriol-3-glucuronide	32–40 weeks	12	nmol/L	116	–	(43–295)	µg/L	54	–	(20–137)	132
Estriol-3-sulfate-16-glucuronide	32–40 weeks	20	nmol/L	364	–	(140–586)	µg/L	198	–	(77–319)	132
Estetrol	Before delivery	–	nmol/L	275	–	–	µg/L	83.8	–	–	127
Androstenetriol.....................	Before delivery	–	nmol/L	157	–	–	µg/L	48.0	–	–	127
Testosterone	16–20 weeks...										
	– male fetuses .	55	nmol/L	1.48	0.44	(0.83–2.50)	ng/L	428	128	(240–721)	128
	– female fetuses	41	nmol/L	0.70	0.19	(0.35–1.04)	ng/L	202	54	(100–300)	128
	31–42 weeks...										
	– male fetuses .	21	nmol/L	0.97	0.26	(0.65–1.61)	ng/L	281	74	(192–464)	128
	– female fetuses	10	nmol/L	0.65	0.12	(0.42–0.86)	ng/L	187	36	(121–248)	128
Cortisol											
– total	≤ 20 weeks	8	nmol/L	83	17	–	µg/L	30	6	–	129
	20–34 weeks ..	7	nmol/L	88	11	–	µg/L	31.8	4.0	–	129
	35–40 weeks ..	24	nmol/L	200	51	–	µg/L	72.4	18.6	–	129
	≥ 41 weeks	9	nmol/L	383	99	–	µg/L	139	36	–	129
– free	≤ 20 weeks	26	nmol/L	24	11	–	µg/L	8.6	4.1	–	130
	20–25 weeks...	16	nmol/L	31.5	13	–	µg/L	11.4	4.8	–	130
	30–40 weeks...	36	nmol/L	54.6	21	–	µg/L	19.8	7.5	–	130
	At term........	10	nmol/L	50	–	–	µg/L	18.0	–	–	131
– -sulfate........................	At term........	10	nmol/L	77.1	26.2	(31.2–111)	µg/L	34.1	11.6	(13.8–49.3)	131
Cortisone											
– free	At term........	10	nmol/L	30.5	–	–	µg/L	11.0	–	–	131
– -sulfate........................	At term........	10	nmol/L	60.2	32.5	(15–143)	µg/L	26.5	14.3	(6.6–63.1)	131
Corticosterone											
– free	At term........	10	nmol/L	3.8	–	–	µg/L	1.3	–	–	131
– -sulfate........................	At term........	10	nmol/L	94	22	(49–119)	µg/L	40.0	9.2	(20.7–50.7)	131
11-Dehydrocorticosterone											
– free	At term........	10	nmol/L	3.8	–	–	µg/L	1.3	–	–	131
– -sulfate........................	At term........	10	nmol/L	42.4	–	–	µg/L	18.0	–	–	131
11-Deoxycorticosterone sulfate.......	At term........	10	nmol/L	17	–	–	µg/L	7.0	–	–	131
Tetrahydrocortisol glucuronide.......	At term........	10	nmol/L	42.4	–	–	µg/L	23.0	–	–	131
Tetrahydrocortisone glucuronide.....	At term........	10	nmol/L	228	–	–	µg/L	123	–	–	131
25-Hydroxycholecalciferol	At term........	9	nmol/L	3.0	3.7	–	µg/L	1.2	1.5	–	162

Prostaglandins. Those positively identified are PGE_2 and $PGF_{2\alpha}$ along with a metabolite of the latter (Table 30). This is consistent with the observation that in the intrauterine medium there are greater concentrations of arachidonic acid, the precursor of PGE_2 and $PGF_{2\alpha}$, than of dihomo-γ-linolenic acid, the precursor of PGE_1 and $PGF_{1\alpha}$. Prostaglandin concentrations increase sharply during labor (Fig. 13).

There are wide differences in the reported values of *glycoprotein and polypeptide hormones* (Tables 31–33; Fig. 14), presumably due to methodological differences. Opinions also differ regarding the extent of fluctuations in the course of pregnancy. Proteohormones appear to be subject to the same fluctuations as protein concentrations: low levels during early pregnancy, increasing in the second trimester and declining during the third, coincidentally with the maturation of the renal tubular function[147].

The concentration of *chorionic gonadotropin* in amniotic fluid is higher than in fetal serum, but substantially lower than in maternal serum[64,146].

Table 29 *Estriol*

Gestational age	FENCL et al.[134]			ALEEM et al.[135]			MICHIE and LIVINGSTONE[136]		
	Number	Mean	s	Number	Mean	s	Number	Mean	(Extreme range)
					µg/L				
Up to 20 weeks...	–	–	–	2	285	–	23	21	–
Up to 26 weeks...	9	36.9	14.6	–	–	–	–	–	–
Up to 28 weeks...	5	49.6	17.6	–	–	–	–	–	–
Up to 30 weeks...	7	92.6	37.0	–	–	–	12	89	–
Up to 32 weeks...	7	135.8	37.6	8	397	78	–	–	–
Up to 34 weeks...	6	174.0	57.0	–	–	–	–	–	–
Up to 36 weeks...	10	274.2	104.0	10	571	101	–	–	–
Up to 38 weeks...	12	843.6	306.3	–	–	–	9	198	–
Up to 40 weeks...	24	1254.5	358.3	19	1352	405	–	911	(300–1820)

Table 30 *Prostaglandins*

	Gestational age	Number	Amount of substance				Mass				Reference
			Unit	Mean	s	(Extreme range)	Unit	Mean	s	(Extreme range)	
PGE₂	38–41 weeks.	10	nmol/L	–	–	(<0.6–<1.4)	ng/L	–	–	(<200–<500)	118
	In labor	1	nmol/L	17.6	–	–	ng/L	6200	–	–	118
	33–35 weeks.	4	nmol/L	0.40	0.037	–	ng/L	140	13	–	119
	36 weeks	4	nmol/L	0.90	0.40	–	ng/L	318	142	–	119
	37 weeks	7	nmol/L	0.91	0.35	–	ng/L	322	125	–	119
	38–39 weeks.	6	nmol/L	1.05	0.28	–	ng/L	370	99	–	119
PGF₂α	15–20 weeks.	8	nmol/L	1.83	1.04	–	ng/L	650	370	–	120
	At term	20	nmol/L	4.65	2.65	–	ng/L	1650	940	–	120
	In labor	16	nmol/L	16.7	10.6	–	ng/L	5910	3760	–	120
	33–35 weeks.	4	nmol/L	0.20	0.062	–	ng/L	72	22	–	119
	36 weeks	4	nmol/L	0.24	0.068	–	ng/L	85	24	–	119
	37 weeks	7	nmol/L	0.35	0.21	–	ng/L	123	76	–	119
	38–39 weeks.	6	nmol/L	0.40	0.11	–	ng/L	143	40	–	119
	16–20 weeks.	11	nmol/L	0.09	0.08	–	ng/L	33	27	–	121
	≥36 weeks..	38	nmol/L	0.31	0.21	–	ng/L	110	74	–	121
	At labor.....	8	nmol/L	0.95	0.48	–	ng/L	335	171	–	121
13,14-Dihydroxy-15-oxo-PGF₂α	In term......	–	nmol/L	2.3	0.4	–	µg/L	0.89	0.15	–	152
	At labor.....	–	nmol/L	13.2	8.0	–	µg/L	5.08	3.07	–	152

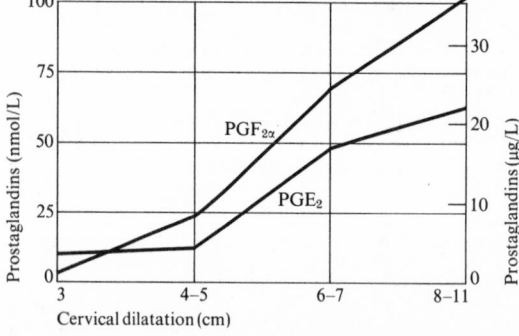

Fig. 13. PGE₂ and PGF₂ concentrations in amniotic fluid during spontaneous labor (37 women)[119].

The concentration of *chorionic somatomammotropin* is low in the first trimester of pregnancy, but rises during later stages[149,150]. At the end of the twentieth week of gestation, it is substantially below the maternal serum levels[143,149]. Elevated values in Rhesus isoimmunization are indicative of fetal jeopardy[149,150].

The *prolactin* concentration in amniotic fluid varies widely[145,147,148]; on average, it is eightfold the concentration in maternal serum[145] and appears to stem from the decidua[154].

Table 31 *Glycoprotein hormones*

	Number	Unit	Mean	s	(Extreme range)	Reference
Chorionic gonadotropin						
3rd trimester	19	IU/L	390	280	–	64
In labor	20	IU/L	450	200	–	64
At term	18	IU/L	731	180	–	142
At term	–	IU/L	380	–	–	144
Chorionic somatomammotropin						
11–13 weeks	10	µg/L	414	528	–	143
14–15 weeks	9	µg/L	458	329	–	143
16–19 weeks	9	µg/L	448	231	–	143
20–23 weeks	6	µg/L	302	87	–	143
24–27 weeks	4	µg/L	573	244	–	143
28–31 weeks	5	µg/L	695	461	–	143
32–35 weeks	9	µg/L	686	373	–	143
36–40 weeks	8	µg/L	443	230	–	143
At term	–	µg/L	547	–	–	144
Prolactin						
12–42 weeks	319	µg/L	408	297	(36–1800)	145

Table 32   *Glycoprotein hormone in relation to fetal sex[146]*

Gestational age	Sex	Chorionic gonadotropin			Luteinizing hormone			Follicle-stimulating hormone		
		Number	Mean µg/L	s	Number	Mean µg/L	s	Number	Mean µg/L	s
8–12 weeks	Male fetuses.....................	17	933	795	15	1.0	0.8	15	<0.1	–
	Female fetuses	6	1139	999	7	1.4	0.8	7	<0.1	–
12–20 weeks	Male fetuses.....................	42	589	415	41	3.5	3.2	41	0.1	0.1
	Female fetuses	31	783	479	31	10.8	6.1	31	0.6	0.6
32 weeks to term	Male fetuses.....................	7	42	34	7	0.6	0.2	5	0.3	0.2
	Female fetuses	20	57	36	20	0.4	0.2	19	0.2	0.04

Table 33   *Polypeptide hormones and prolactin*

	Number	Unit	Mean	s	(Extreme range)	Reference
Insulin						
13–44 weeks	113	mIU/L	–	–	(2–35)	140
Oxytocin						
34–42 weeks	12	ng/L	327	185	(150–800)	141
In labor..........	18	ng/L	756	397	(110–1600)	141

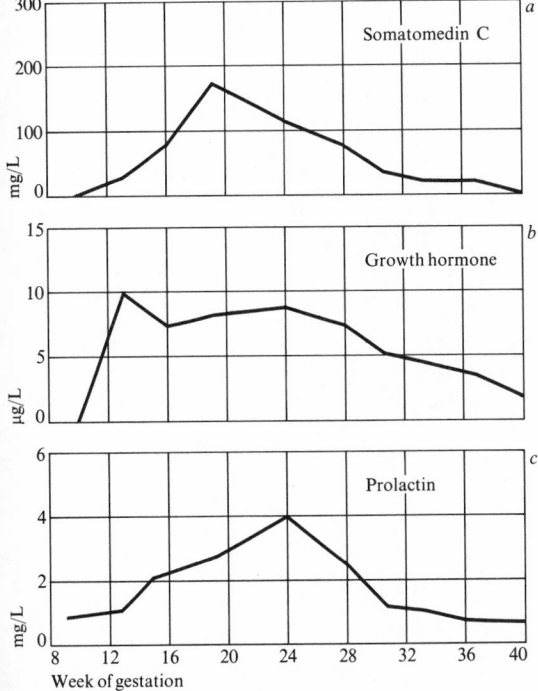

Fig. 14. Correlation between concentration of somatomedin C (*a*), growth hormone (*b*) and prolactin (*c*) in amniotic fluid and gestational age[147].

Insulin appears to originate in part from fetal urine. Its concentration in amniotic fluid corresponds to the mass of the fetus[140].

Determination of gestational age

Some of the amniotic fluid properties correlate closely enough with gestational age to serve as a basis for a realistic estimate. Ac-

cording to LIND et al.[17], a suitable numerical score system may be derived from a combination of cytologic parameters (compare the corresponding color graphs in HYTTEN and LIND[104]), creatinine concentration in amniotic fluid and the difference between the urea concentration in amniotic fluid and in maternal plasma. According to DORAN et al.[151], gestational age may best be projected from cytologic data, as well as from the creatinine concentration and the lecithin/sphingomyelin ratio in amniotic fluid. SCHRÖDER et al.[163] additionally include the glucose concentration in a rating scale.

References

[1] LIND, T., *Brit. J. Hosp. Med.*, **14**, 631 (1975).
[2] LIND et al., *Obstet. Gynaec. Brit. Cwlth*, **79**, 289 (1972).
[3] LIND, T., in FAIRWEATHER and ESKES (Eds.), *Amniotic Fluid: Research and Clinical Application*, Excerpta Medica, Amsterdam, 1973, page 60.
[4] PITKIN, R. M., in NATELSON et al. (Eds.), *Amniotic Fluid,* Wiley, New York, 1974, page 81.
[5] BIGGS and DUNCAN, *J. Obstet. Gynaec. Brit. Cwlth*, **77**, 326 (1970).
[6] CHEZ et al., *Amer. J. Obstet. Gynec.*, **90**, 128 (1964).
[7] BIRKBECK et al., *Ann. hum. Biol.*, **2**, 173 (1975).
[8] WAGNER and FUCHS, *J. Obstet. Gynaec. Brit. Cwlth*, **69**, 131 (1962).
[9] GILLIBRAND, P. N., *J. Obstet. Gynaec. Brit. Cwlth*, **76**, 527 (1969).
[10] ELLIOTT and INMAN, *Lancet*, **2**, 835 (1961).
[11] CHARLES et al., *Amer. J. Obstet. Gynec.*, **93**, 1042 (1965).
[12] BEJAR et al., *Europ. J. Obstet. Gynec.*, **1**, 189 (1971).
[13] BERG, D., *Gynäkologe*, **7**, 4 (1974).
[14] SCHREINER, W. E., *Bibl. gynaec. (Basel)*, **31**, 1 (1964).
[15] JOHNELL and NILSSON, *Acta obstet. gynec. scand.*, **50**, 183 (1971).
[16] MARIANOWSKI and KOZIOROWSKI, *Ginek. pol.*, **41**, 143 (1970).
[17] LIND et al., *J. Obstet. Gynaec. Brit. Cwlth*, **78**, 505 (1971).
[18] BENZIE et al., *Amer. J. Obstet. Gynec.*, **119**, 798 (1974).
[19] LIND et al., *J. Obstet. Gynaec. Brit. Cwlth*, **76**, 673 (1969).
[20] KITTRICH and JANOVSKÝ, *Biol. Neonat. (Basel)*, **18**, 29 (1971).
[21] MCKAY et al., *Amer. J. Obstet. Gynec.*, **69**, 722 (1955).
[22] GIRAUD et al., *J. Gynéc. Obstét. Biol. Reprod.*, **1**, 795 (1972).
[23] NUSBAUM and ZETTNER, *Amer. J. Obstet. Gynec.*, **115**, 219 (1973).
[24] ANDERER and SCHINDLER, *Arch. Gynäk.*, **220**, 65 (1975).
[25] MCALLISTER et al., *Amer. J. Obstet. Gynec.*, **115**, 560 (1973); CARSWELL and SEMPLE, *J. Obstet. Gynaec. Brit. Cwlth*, **81**, 472 (1974).
[26] KANG and SCANLON, *Amer. J. Obstet. Gynec.*, **119**, 603 (1974).
[27] REID et al., *Amer. J. Obstet. Gynec.*, **111**, 251 (1971).
[28] DALLAIRE et al., *J. Obstet. Gynaec. Brit. Cwlth*, **81**, 761 (1974); HEINRICH et al., *Z. Geburtsh. Perinatol.*, **180**, 31 (1976).
[29] SHAH et al., *J. Obstet. Gynec.*, **114**, 250 (1972).
[30] ANTEBY et al., *J. Obstet. Gynaec. Brit. Cwlth*, **80**, 27 (1973).
[31] GOMPERTZ et al., *Pediatrics*, **54**, 511 (1974).
[32] RÄIHÄ, N. C., *Pediatrics*, **32**, 1025 (1963).
[33] NICHOLLS et al., *Clin. chim. Acta*, **69**, 127 (1976).
[34] SMITH and SCANLON, *Amer. J. Obstet. Gynec.*, **115**, 569 (1973).
[35] SPELLACY et al., *Obstet. and Gynec.*, **41**, 323 (1973).
[36] WOOD and SHERLINE, *Amer. J. Obstet. Gynec.*, **122**, 151 (1975).
[37] SCHREINER and SCHMID, in HUNTINGFORD et al. (Eds.), *Perinatal Medicine*, 1st European Congress, Thieme, Stuttgart, 1969, page 20.
[38] KIM and FELIG, *Metabolism*, **21**, 507 (1972).
[39] ROUX et al., *Amer. J. Obstet. Gynec.*, **116**, 633 (1973).
[40] GLUCK and KULOVICH, *Amer. J. Obstet. Gynec.*, **115**, 539 (1973).
[41] WEISBERG, H. F., in NATELSON et al. (Eds.), *Amniotic Fluid,* Wiley, New York, 1974, page 47.
[42] FENNEFROHN, B., *Z. Geburtsh. Perinatol.*, **176**, 233 (1972).
[43] PAUMGARTNER et al., *Schweiz. med. Wschr.*, **107**, 529 (1977).
[44] BIEZENSKI et al., *Amer. J. Obstet. Gynec.*, **102**, 853 (1968).
[45] NELSON, G. H., *Amer. J. Obstet. Gynec.*, **105**, 1072 (1969).
[46] NELSON, G. H., *Amer. J. Obstet. Gynec.*, **112**, 827 (1972).
[47] BHAGWANANI et al., *Lancet*, **1**, 159 (1972).
[48] NELSON, G. H., *Amer. J. Obstet. Gynec.*, **115**, 933 (1973).
[49] ROSENTHAL et al., *Clin. Chem.*, **20**, 486 (1974).

[50] OLSON et al., *Pediat. Res.*, **9**, 65 (1975).
[51] LORENZ et al., *Z. Geburtsh. Perinatol.*, **179**, 101 (1975).
[52] CABERO et al., *Brit. J. Obstet. Gynaec.*, **83**, 452 (1976).
[53] SINGH and ZUSPAN, *Amer. J. Obstet. Gynec.*, **117**, 919 (1973).
[54] KRIEGLSTEINER et al., *Z. Geburtsh. Perinatol.*, **180**, 194 (1976).
[55] MOORE et al., *Brit. J. Obstet. Gynaec.*, **82**, 194 (1975).
[56] RUOSLAHTI et al., *Nature*, **212**, 841 (1966).
[57] SUTCLIFFE and BROCK, *J. Obstet. Gynaec. Brit. Cwlth*, **80**, 721 (1973).
[58] USATEGUI-GOMEZ, M., in NATELSON et al. (Eds.), *Amniotic Fluid*, Wiley, New York, 1974, page 111.
[59] JOHNSON et al., *J. Pediat.*, **84**, 588 (1974).
[60] JONASSON, L. E., *Acta obstet. gynec. scand.*, **51**, 187 (1972).
[61] QUEENAN et al., *Amer. J. Obstet. Gynec.*, **108**, 406 (1970).
[62] SINGER et al., *J. Pediat.*, **88**, 87 (1976).
[63] GOLDSMITH et al., *Lancet*, **1**, 367 (1974).
[64] CROSIGNANI and POLVANI, *J. Obstet. Gynaec. Brit. Cwlth*, **76**, 424 (1969).
[65] GITLIN et al., *Amer. J. Obstet. Gynec.*, **113**, 632 (1972).
[66] TOUCHSTONE et al., *Amer. J. Obstet. Gynec.*, **114**, 58 (1972).
[67] SEPPÄLÄ and RUOSLAHTI, *Amer. J. Obstet. Gynec.*, **114**, 595 (1972).
[68] HALL and ROUX, *Amer. J. Obstet. Gynec.*, **120**, 56 (1974).
[69] NENCIONI et al., *Gynéc. et Obstét.*, **69**, 219 (1970).
[70] BARDOS et al., *Clin. chim. Acta*, **66**, 353 (1976).
[71] SHULMAN et al., *Clin. chim. Acta*, **108**, 151 (1980).
[72] OLSSON et al., *Lancet*, **2**, 347 (1974).
[73] CHALLIS and BENNETT, *Amer. J. Obstet. Gynec.*, **129**, 655 (1977).
[74] CAPUTO and HOSTY, *Amer. J. Obstet. Gynec.*, **113**, 804 (1972).
[75] PURDIE et al., *Lancet*, **1**, 1013 (1975).
[76] WEISS et al., *Lancet*, **1**, 304 (1976).
[77] MUKERJEE and SINHA, *Amer. J. Obstet. Gynec.*, **115**, 858 (1973).
[78] MITRA and BLAU, *Clin. chim. Acta*, **89**, 127 (1978).
[79] BROCK and SUTCLIFFE, *Lancet*, **2**, 197 (1972).
[80] RANDLE and CUMBERBATCH, *J. Obstet. Gynaec. Brit. Cwlth*, **80**, 1054 (1973); MACRI et al., *J. Amer. med. Ass.*, **236**, 1251 (1976).
[81] NEVIN et al., *J. Obstet. Gynaec. Brit. Cwlth*, **81**, 757 (1974).
[82] BROCK, D. J., *Brit. med. Bull.*, **32**, 16 (1976), and *Lancet*, **2**, 345 (1976).
[83] AINBENDER and HIRSCHHORN, *Lancet*, **1**, 597 (1976).
[84] NEVIN and ARMSTRONG, *Brit. J. Obstet. Gynaec.*, **82**, 826 (1975).
[85] KJESSLER et al., *Lancet*, **1**, 432 (1975); SEPPÄLÄ et al., *Lancet*, **2**, 123 (1976); WIGGELINKHUIZEN et al., *J. Pediat.*, **89**, 452 (1976).
[86] SCHMID and MÜHLETHALER, *Hum. Genet.*, **26**, 353 (1975).
[87] WEINBERG et al., *Lancet*, **2**, 496 (1975).
[88] WIŚNIEWSKI et al., *Brit. med. J.*, **3**, 742 (1974).
[89] SELLER et al., *Brit. med. J.*, **2**, 524 (1974).
[90] HUNTER et al., *Lancet*, **1**, 598 (1976).
[91] BROCK, D. J., *Clin. Genet.*, **8**, 297 (1975).
[92] EPSTEIN and GOLBUS, *Ann. Rev. Med.*, **29**, 117 (1978).
[93] MILES and KABACK, *Pediat. Clin. N. Amer.*, **25**, 593, (1978).
[94] GEYER and SCHNEIDER, *Z. klin. Chem.*, **8**, 141 (1970).
[95] MIOTTI et al., *Amer. J. Obstet. Gynec.*, **117**, 1129 (1973).
[96] BUTTERWORTH et al., *Amer. J. Obstet. Gynec.*, **119**, 821 (1974).
[97] WARD et al., *J. Obstet. Gynaec. Brit. Cwlth*, **80**, 525 (1973).
[98] CHERRY et al., *Amer. J. Obstet. Gynec.*, **116**, 639 (1973).
[99] DE CASTRO et al., *Amer. J. Obstet. Gynec.*, **116**, 931 (1973).
[100] WOLF and TAUSSIG, *Obstet. and Gynec.*, **41**, 337 (1973).
[101] MURRAY et al., *Brit. med. J.*, **4**, 387 (1970).
[102] WALKER, W., *Brit. med. J.*, **2**, 220 (1970).
[103] FAIRWEATHER et al., *J. Obstet. Gynaec. Brit. Cwlth*, **79**, 433 (1972).
[104] HYTTEN and LIND, *Diagnostic Indices in Pregnancy*, CIBA-GEIGY Ltd., Basle, 1973, page 107.
[105] KOPECKY, P., *Geburtsh. u. Frauenheilk.*, **30**, 997 (1970).
[106] KRASNER et al., *Z. klin. Chem.*, **109**, 159 (1971).
[107] ROBERTSON, J. G., *Amer. J. Obstet. Gynec.*, **95**, 120 (1966).
[108] BOWMAN and POLLOCK, *Pediatrics*, **35**, 815 (1965).
[109] REIL et al., *Dtsch. med. Wschr.*, **94**, 2602 (1969).
[110] FIKENTSCHER et al., *Dtsch. med. Wschr.*, **94**, 125 (1969).
[111] SACK et al., *J. Pediat.*, **87**, 364 (1975).

[112] DUDENHAUSEN and DUDENHAUSEN, *Z. Geburtsh. Perinatol.*, **180**, 46 (1976).
[113] LING et al., *J. clin. Endocr.*, **39**, 479 (1974).
[114] KOREN et al., *J. Obstet. Gynaec. Brit. Cwlth*, **68**, 438 (1961).
[115] LOOSE and PATERSON, *J. Obstet. Gynaec. Brit. Cwlth*, **73**, 647 (1966).
[116] CHOPRA et al., *New Engl. J. Med.*, **293**, 740 (1975).
[117] ZAMBOTTI et al., *Clin. chim. Acta*, **61**, 247 (1975).
[118] KEIRSE and TURNBULL, *J. Obstet. Gynaec. Brit. Cwlth*, **80**, 970 (1973).
[119] DRAY and FRYDMAN, *Amer. J. Obstet. Gynec.*, **126**, 13 (1976).
[120] KEIRSE et al., *J. Obstet. Gynaec. Brit. Cwlth*, **81**, 131 (1974).
[121] JOHNSON et al., *Acta endocr. (Kbh.)*, **79**, 589 (1975).
[122] WADE and ABRAMOVICH, *Steroids*, **10**, 669 (1967).
[123] FRIEDRICH et al., *Clin. chim. Acta*, **56**, 127 (1974).
[124] FRASIER et al., *J. Pediat.*, **86**, 310 (1975).
[125] JEFFCOATE et al., *Lancet*, **2**, 553 (1965).
[126] SCHINDLER and RATANASOPA, *Acta endocr. (Kbh.)*, **59**, 239 (1968).
[127] SCHINDLER and SIITERI, *J. clin. Endocr.*, **28**, 1189 (1968).
[128] KÜNZIG et al., *Arch. Gynäk.*, **223**, 75 (1977).
[129] FENCL and TULCHINSKY, *New Engl. J. Med.*, **292**, 133 (1975).
[130] TAN et al., *J. clin. Endocr.*, **43**, 412 (1976).
[131] SCHWEITZER et al., *J. clin. Endocr.*, **33**, 605 (1971).
[132] YOUNG et al., *J. clin. Endocr.*, **39**, 842 (1974).
[133] SCHINDLER, A. E., *Fortschr. Geburtsh. Gynäk.*, **46**, 1 (1972).
[134] FENCL et al., *Amer. J. Obstet. Gynec.*, **113**, 367 (1972).
[135] ALEEM et al., *J. Obstet. Gynaec. Brit. Cwlth*, **76**, 200 (1969).
[136] MICHIE and LIVINGSTONE, *Acta endocr. (Kbh.)*, **61**, 329 (1969).
[137] LACOURT et al., *Helv. paediat. Acta*, suppl. 35, 13 (1975).
[138] MURPHY et al., *J. clin. Endocr.*, **40**, 164 (1975); SHARP-CAGEORGE et al., *New Engl. J. Med.*, **296**, 89 (1977).
[139] NICHOLS and GIBSON, *Lancet*, **2**, 1068 (1969).
[140] SPELLACY et al., *Obstet. and Gynec.*, **41**, 323 (1973).
[141] SEPPÄLÄ et al., *Amer. J. Obstet. Gynec.*, **114**, 788 (1972).
[142] MCCARTHY and PENNINGTON, *Amer. J. Obstet. Gynec.*, **89**, 1074 (1964).
[143] BERLE, P., *Acta endocr. (Kbh.)*, **76**, 364 (1974).
[144] CROSIGNANI et al., *J. Obstet. Gynaec. Brit. Cwlth*, **79**, 122 (1972).
[145] BISWAS, S., *Clin. chim. Acta*, **73**, 363 (1976).
[146] CLEMENTS et al., *J. clin. Endocr.*, **42**, 9 (1976).
[147] CHOCHINOV et al., *J. clin. Endocr.*, **42**, 983 (1976).
[148] TYSON et al., *Amer. J. Obstet. Gynec.*, **113**, 14 (1972).
[149] TESCHER et al., *J. Gynéc. Obstét. Biol. Reprod.*, **3**, 1255 (1974).
[150] NIVEN et al., *J. Obstet. Gynaec. Brit. Cwlth*, **81**, 988 (1974).
[151] DORAN et al., *Amer. J. Obstet. Gynec.*, **119**, 829 (1974).
[152] SATOH et al., in *V. International Congress of Endocrinology*, Hamburg 1976, Abstracts, Brühlsche Universitätsdruckerei, Gießen, 1976, page 165.
[153] ROOPNARINESINGH et al., *J. Obstet. Gynaec. Brit. Cwlth*, **79**, 29 (1972).
[154] RIDDICK and KUSMIK, *Amer. J. Obstet. Gynec.*, **127**, 187 (1977).
[155] KUSAKA, T., *Tokushima J. exp. Med.*, **15**, 93 (1968).
[156] CLARKE, H. C., *Int. J. Vit. Nutr. Res.*, **43**, 324 (1973).
[157] SCHLIEVERT et al., *Amer. J. Obstet. Gynec.*, **127**, 603 (1977).
[158] DÉLÈZE et al., *Pediatrics*, **59**, 647 (1977).
[159] BROCK, D. J., *Clin. Genet.*, **8**, 297 (1975).
[160] KIMBALL et al., *Amer. J. Obstet. Gynec.*, **128**, 294 (1977).
[161] ARMSTRONG et al., *Gynecol. Invest.*, **7**, 358 (1976).
[162] KOKOT et al., *Europ. J. clin. Invest.*, **7**, 250 (1977).
[163] SCHRÖDER et al., *Zbl. Gynäk.*, **99**, 205, (1977).
[164] GEBHARDT et al., *Clin. chim. Acta*, **94**, 93 (1979).
[165] JIRKA et al., *Clin. chim. Acta*, **85**, 107 (1978).
[166] GADLER et al., *Acta med. scand.*, **201**, 411 (1977).
[167] CEDERQVIST et al., *Amer. J. Obstet. Gynec.*, **130**, 220 (1978).
[168] ETLING and VIELH, *Nouv. Presse méd.*, **8**, 1647 (1979).
[169] KULOVICH et al., *Amer. J. Obstet. Gynec.*, **135**, 57 (1979).
[170] KULOVICH and GLUCK, *Amer. J. Obstet. Gynec.*, **135**, 64 (1979).
[171] WHITTLE et al., *Brit. med. J.*, **282**, 428 (1981).
[172] BENT et al., *Amer. J. Obstet. Gynec.*, **139**, 259 (1981).
[173] SMITH et al., *Lancet*, **1**, 685 (1979).
[174] BROCK et al., *Lancet*, **1**, 773 (1980).
[175] DALE, G., *Lancet*, **2**, 975 (1980).

Yield

In clinical practice it is usual to estimate the volume of milk produced during a given feed by weighing the baby before and after it is put to the breast ('test-weighing'). Provided the weighing is careful and there are no losses of urine, feces or vomit, this gives a reasonable assessment, and if the breasts are empty after the feed, the difference in body mass corresponds to milk production. Milk left in the breasts may be expressed and measured.

Yield has also been measured by milking the breasts but there is reason to doubt whether either manual or mechanical methods will remove all the milk without disturbing the course of lactation. The suckling of the baby has, for the mother, emotional overtones beyond the mere stimulation of the nipple and areola, and the mechanical replacement of this local stimulus, however ingenious, cannot possibly be an entirely effective substitute. This has been confirmed experimentally[1]. Published estimates of yield must therefore be examined carefully in the light of their method of measurement.

In general, the yield corresponds to the needs of the infant, amounting to about 850 mL per day for a body mass of 5–6 kg.

Composition

It is easy to obtain some milk for chemical analysis, and many published data relate to 'spot' samples taken before, during or after a feed, but it is now recognized that such data have little or no relevance to the overall composition of a day's milk supply. The composition of the milk changes both during a feed[2] and in the course of the day[3]. For example, the fat content of milk rises steadily from beginning to end of a feed[2], and a change from less than 10–60 g/L or more is common. Other major constituents show less dramatic changes, but the lactose content and soluble protein tend to fall as the fat content rises; casein tends to rise.

The diurnal variation in composition mainly concerns the fat content[3,4]. In one study[3] this was usually lowest at 6 a.m., highest at 10 a.m., and somewhat variable during the rest of the day. The extreme differences may commonly be of the order of 25 g/L at

6 a.m. and 40 g/L at 10 a.m. for milk averaging 35 g/L for the whole day.

The differences in composition at different stages of lactation are well known but changes may be rapid in the first two weeks and times must be carefully standardized if valid comparisons are to be made between subjects[4,5].

The collection of a 24-hour milk sample means removing the child from the breast during that time and emptying the breasts, preferably by pump. The administrative difficulties involved have led some workers to leave the child on one breast while sampling the contents of the other. But even this may mislead; the composition of milk from the two breasts is not necessarily the same[6].

There is no escape from the necessity of obtaining complete 24-hour samples from both breasts if misleading measurements are to be avoided. But since this is seldom done, comparisons between milk analyses reported in the literature must be made with the utmost caution.

The composition of breast milk has been described in detail by MACY et al.[7], MACY and KELLY[8] as well as by ALTMAN and DITTMER[9]. A detailed paper on the composition of breast milk samples from England has been published[10].

References

[1] HYTTEN, F. E., *Brit. med. J.,* **1**, 175 (1954).
[2] HYTTEN, F. E., *Brit. med. J.,* **1**, 176 (1954); HALL, B., *Lancet,* **1**, 779 (1975).
[3] HYTTEN, F. E., *Brit. med. J.,* **1**, 179 (1954).
[4] ROLAND and FREIESLEBEN, *Med. u. Ernähr.,* **4**, 11 (1963).
[5] HYTTEN, F. E., *Brit. med. J.,* **1**, 249 (1954).
[6] HYTTEN, F. E., *Proc. Nutr. Soc.,* **15**, vi (1956).
[7] MACY et al., *The Composition of Milks,* National Research Council, Publication 254, Washington (D.C.), 1953.
[8] MACY and KELLY, in KON and COWIE (Eds.), *Milk: The Mammary Gland and Its Secretion,* volume 2, Academic Press, New York, 1961, page 265.
[9] ALTMAN and DITTMER (Eds.), *Metabolism,* Federation of American Societies for Experimental Biology, Bethesda (Md.), 1968.
[10] Department of Health and Social Security, *The Composition of Mature Human Milk,* HMSO, London, 1977.

	Unit	Mature milk (15 days to 15 months post partum)			Reference p. 216	Transitional milk (6th to 10th day post partum)			Reference p. 216	Colostrum (first 5 days post partum)			Reference p. 216	Cow's milk			Reference p. 216
		Mean	s	Extreme range		Mean	s	Extreme range		Mean	s	Extreme range		Mean	s	Extreme range	
Energy	kcal/L	747	93	446–1192	1	735	36	678–830	1	671	–	588–730	1	701	–	587–876	2
	kcal/L	670	–	–	82	620	–	–	82	540	–	–	82	660	–	–	2
	MJ/L	3.13	0.39	1.87–4.99	1	3.08	0.15	2.84–3.47	1	2.81	–	2.46–3.06	1	2.93	–	2.46–3.67	2
	MJ/L	2.80	–	–	82	2.59	–	–	82	2.26	–	–	82	2.76	–	–	82
Relative density	1	1.031	0.002	1.026–1.037	1	1.035	–	1.034–1.036	1	1.034	–	–	38	1.031	–	1.028–1.033	3
Osmolality	mmol/kg	300	12	–	83	–	–	–		–	–	–		288	–	–	83
pH	–	7.01	–	6.4–7.6	4	–	–	–		7.29	0.19	–	32	6.62	–	6.55–6.68	3,5
Water	g/L	897	–	893–901	92	–	–	–		–	–	–		–	–	–	
Dry mass	g/L	129	11	103–175	1	133	8	105–156	1	128	13	100–167	1	124	–	119–142	3
Ash	g/L	2.02	0.18	1.6–2.66	1	2.67	0.32	2.31–3.38	1	3.08	–	2.47–3.50	1	7.15	–	6.81–7.71	6
Minerals																	
Sodium	mg/L	172	45	64–436	1	294	76	192–539	1	501	280	265–1370	1	768	–	392–1390	7
		189	66	80–350	39	536	271	170–1210	39	956	377	330–2240	39	570	110	–	18
Potassium	mg/L	512	85	373–635	1	636	68	528–769	1	745	–	658–870	1	1430	–	380–2870	8
		553	70	425–735	39	692	99	450–910	39	581	120	220–790	39	1420	220	–	18
Calcium	mg/L	344	67	173–609	1	464	95	230–628	1	481	121	242–656	1	1370	–	560–3810	8
		271	30	207–372	39	320	45	166–420	39	261	26	180–364	39	1040	40	–	18
Magnesium	mg/L	35	7	18–57	1	35	6	26–54	1	42	13	31–82	1	130	–	70–220	8
		–	–	–		–	–	–		30	–	–	49	97	22	–	18
Iron	mg/L	0.50	–	0.20–0.80	10	0.59	–	0.29–1.45	40	1.0	–	–	11	0.45	–	0.25–0.75	10
		0.41	0.08	–	76	0.36	0.07	–	76	0.37	0.05	–	76	–	–	–	
Copper	mg/L	0.51	0.046	–	11	1.04	0.073	–	11	1.34	0.112	–	11	0.102	–	–	11
		0.29	0.04	–	76	0.36	0.08	–	76	0.35	0.04	–	76	–	–	–	
Zinc	mg/L	1.18	–	0.17–3.02	8	3.82	–	0.39–5.88	8	5.59	–	0.72–9.81	8	3.9	–	1.7–6.6	84
		3.24	0.29	–	76	5.07	0.14	–	76	8.25	0.17	–	76	3.4	0.3	3.0–4.0	18
Manganese	μg/L	15	–	–	12	–	–	–		–	–	–		20	–	5–67	14
Chromium	μg/L	80	–	–	86	53	–	–	86	–	–	–		50	–	–	86
Cobalt	μg/L	–	–	–		–	–	–		–	–	–		–	–	0.4–1.1	77
Lead	μg/L	26	–	6–58	78	–	–	–		–	–	–		–	–	–	

	Unit	Mature milk (15 days to 15 months post partum)			Reference	Transitional milk (6th to 10th day post partum)			Reference	Colostrum (first 5 days post partum)			Reference	Cow's milk			Reference
		Mean	s	Extreme range		Mean	s	Extreme range		Mean	s	Extreme range		Mean	s	Extreme range	
Phosphorus	mg/L	141	25	68–268	1	198	47	97–317	1	157	47	85–251	1	910	–	560–1120	8
	mg/L	162	30	–	13	155	46	–	13	–	–	–		–	–	–	
Sulfur	mg/L	140	30	50–300	1	200	20	150–230	1	230	–	200–260	1	300	–	240–360	8
Chlorine	mg/L	375	90	88–734	1	457	109	305–721	1	586	–	435–1010	1	1080	–	930–1410	8
Fluorine	µg/L	25	–	4–50	15	–	–	–		–	–	–		30	–	–	15
Iodine	µg/L	61	–	44–93	17	–	–	–		60	–	38–100	16	81	–	42–100	16
Selenium	µg/L	21	–	10–38	41	–	–	–		–	–	–		40	–	5–67	41
	µg/L	14	–	8–19	92	12	–	7–26	9	19	–	9–40	9	5	1.4	4–8	41
Protein																	
Total	g/L	10.6	4.6	7.3–20	1	15.9	9.8	12.7–18.9	1	22.9	12.6	14.6–68.0	–	30.9	–	28.5–34.8	19
	g/L	–	–	9.0–11.0	73	–	–	–		14.1	–	–	73	32.7	1.8	–	18
Casein *	g/L	3.7	0.8	1.4–6.8	1	5.1	–	4.2–5.9	1	–	–	–		25.0	–	23.4–28.1	19
Whey protein **	g/L	7	–	4–10	21	–	–	–		–	–	–		7	–	6–10	21
'Lactalbumin'	g/L	3.6	1.0	1.4–6.0	1	7.8	–	6.9–8.6	1	–	–	–		2.3	–	1.7–2.9	19
'Lactoglobulin'	g/L	–	–	–		–	–	–		–	–	–		2.1	–	1.3–3.8	19
Blood serum proteins◊																	
– Albumin	g/L	0.32	–	0.20–0.47	22	0.37	–	0.26–0.65	22	2.5	–	–	42	0.4	–	–	43
– Immunoglobulins	g/L	0.09	–	0.02–0.27	22	0.36	–	0.01–0.96	22	1.0◊	–	–	42	0.8	–	–	43
Amino acids																	
Total	g/L	12.8	–	9.0–16.0	23	9.4	–	6.0–10.0	23	12.0	–	7.0–40.0	23	33.0	–	27.0–41.0	23
Alanine	g/L	–	–	0.36–0.42	24	–	–	–		–	–	–		0.75	–	–	44
Arginine	g/L	0.43	0.088	0.28–0.64	1	0.63	0.069	0.48–0.73	1	0.74	–	0.62–0.96	1	1.4	–	1.2–1.6	25
Aspartic acid	g/L	–	–	0.89–0.98	24	–	–	–		–	–	–		1.7	–	–	44
Cystine	g/L	–	–	0.23–0.25	24	–	–	–		–	–	–		–	–	–	
Glutamic acid	g/L	–	–	1.89–2.00	24	–	–	–		–	–	–		6.8	–	–	44
Glycine	g/L	–	–	0.23–0.24	24	–	–	–		–	–	–		0.11	–	–	44
Histidine	g/L	0.24	0.041	0.12–0.30	1	0.38	0.046	0.29–0.45	1	0.41	–	0.35–0.46	1	1.2	–	1.1–1.3	25
Isoleucine	g/L	0.61	0.121	0.41–0.92	1	0.97	0.110	0.73–1.21	1	1.01	–	0.88–1.15	1	2.5	–	2.1–2.9	25
Leucine	g/L	0.97	0.174	0.65–1.47	1	1.51	0.219	1.13–1.97	1	1.66	–	1.33–2.14	1	3.6	–	3.2–3.9	25
Lysine	g/L	0.70	0.127	0.36–0.93	1	1.13	0.157	0.88–1.48	1	1.18	–	0.95–1.41	1	2.6	–	2.3–3.1	25
Methionine	g/L	0.12	0.023	0.07–0.16	1	0.24	0.040	0.16–0.34	1	0.25	–	0.19–0.36	1	0.8	–	0.6–0.9	25
Phenylalanine	g/L	0.40	0.069	0.24–0.58	1	0.62	0.062	0.48–0.71	1	0.70	–	0.60–0.84	1	1.8	–	1.5–2.2	25
Proline	g/L	–	–	0.84–0.94	24	–	–	–		–	–	–		2.5	–	–	44
Serine	g/L	–	–	0.47–0.51	24	–	–	–		–	–	–		1.6	–	–	44
Threonine	g/L	0.52	0.085	0.30–0.66	1	0.78	0.079	0.61–0.91	1	0.85	–	0.75–1.04	1	1.7	–	1.3–2.2	25
Tryptophan	g/L	0.19	0.030	0.14–0.26	1	0.28	0.024	0.23–0.32	1	0.32	–	0.25–0.42	1	0.6	–	0.4–0.8	25
Tyrosine	g/L	–	–	0.46–0.52	24	–	–	–		–	–	–		–	–	–	
Valine	g/L	0.73	0.155	0.45–1.14	1	1.05	0.122	0.77–1.36	1	1.17	–	0.98–1.49	1	2.6	–	2.4–2.8	25
Nonprotein nitrogen																	
Total	mg/L	324	57	173–604	1	479	–	425–533	1	–	–	–		281	–	243–323	19
Urea N	mg/L	180	24	127–235	1	111	–	–	1	–	–	–		131	–	61.3–204	19
Uric acid N	mg/L	22	5	13–41	1	–	–	–		–	–	–		7.7	–	3.8–12.3	19
Creatinine N	mg/L	11	2	8–19	1	–	–	–		–	–	–		3.2	–	1.5–4.5	19
Creatine N	mg/L	11	7	2–41	1	–	–	–		–	–	–		11.9	–	7.8–18.0	19
Amino acid N◊◊	mg/L	50	14	28–113	1	44	–	–	1	–	–	40–120	45, 46	48.2	–	37.0–62.3	19
Choline N	mg/L	10.3	2.7	6.2–16.8	1	–	–	–		–	–	–		12	–	5–19	8
Nucleic acids																	
Deoxyribonucleic acid	mg/L	–	–	10.5–22.5	73	–	–	–		8.3	–	–	73	15.1	–	–	73
Ribonucleic acid	mg/L	–	–	215–400	73	–	–	–		111	–	–	73	53.7	–	–	73
Enzymes†																	
Lysozyme	mg/L	390	–	30–3000	47	–	–	–		460	–	90–1020	47	0.13	–	0.00–2.6	47
	mg/L	–	–	–		–	–	–		65	10.2	–	79	–	–	–	
Carbohydrates																	
Lactose	g/L	71	4	49–95	1	64	–	61–67	1	57	–	11–79	26	47	–	45–50	6
	g/L	68	–	–	85	65.7	–	–	85	63	–	–	85	–	–	–	
Oligosaccharides††	g/L	6	–	–	27	–	–	–		–	–	–		–	–	–	
Fucose	g/L	1.3	–	–	27	–	–	–		–	–	–		–	–	–	
Glucosamine	g/L	–	–	0.7–0.8	24	–	–	–		–	–	1.4–4.3	24	0	–	–	24
Galactosamine	g/L	–	–	0.0–0.4	24	–	–	–		–	–	0.04–0.7	24	0	–	–	24
N-Acetylneuraminic acid	g/L	0.63	0.04	–	74	1.01	0.07	–	74	1.27	0.08	–	74	–	–	0.08–0.14	75
Myoinositol	g/L	0.45	–	0.39–0.56	1	–	–	–		–	–	–		0.08	–	0.06–0.12	8
Citric acid	g/L	–	–	0.35–1.25	28	–	–	–		–	–	–		2.54	–	2.15–2.90	31
Fats																	
Total	g/L	45.4	10.0	13.4–82.9	1	35.2	7.3	27.3–51.8	1	29.5	–	24.7–31.8	1	38.0	–	34.0–61.0	3
	g/L	34.5	1.8	–	82	28.2	6.1	–	82	18.7	5.7	–	82	34.7	1.5	–	82
Cholesterol	mg/L	139	25	88–202	46	241	62	126–320	46	280	70	180–345	46	110	–	70–170	29
	mg/L	–	–	118–236	80	–	–	–		–	–	–		–	–	127–159	80
– free, proportion	%	76.1	–	–	46	76.5	–	–	46	79.5	–	–	46	–	–	90–95	48
Lipid phosphorus	mg/L	10.5	0.6	7–14	46	15.5	0.9	11–20	46	12	1	6–17	46	–	–	53–70	30

	Unit	Mature milk (15 days to 15 months post partum)			Reference	Transitional milk (6th to 10th day post partum)			Reference	Colostrum (first 5 days post partum)			Reference	Cow's milk			Reference
		Mean	s	Extreme range		Mean	s	Extreme range		Mean	s	Extreme range		Mean	s	Extreme range	
Vitamins§																	
Vitamin A	mg/L	0.61	0.23	0.15–2.26	1	0.88	0.31	0.58–1.83	1	1.61	0.63	0.75–3.05	1	0.27	–	0.17–0.38	3
Carotene	mg/L	0.25	0.11	0.02–0.77	1	0.38	0.10	0.23–0.63	1	1.37	0.84	0.41–3.85	1	0.37	–	0.12–0.79	3
Vitamin D	µg/L	1.5	–	–	33	–	–	–		–	–	–		1.4	–	–	33
Vitamin D sulfate	µg/L	10	–	–	33	–	–	–		–	–	–		4.4	–	–	33
25-Hydroxyvitamin D	µg/L	0.15	–	–	33	–	–	–		–	–	–		0.25	–	–	33
α-Tocopherol	mg/L	2.4	–	1.0–4.8	34	8.9	≈	4.0–18.5	35	14.8	–	2.8–30.0	36	0.6	–	0.2–1.0	35
	mg/L	3.5	–	2.9–3.9	92	8.2	–	4.4–25.5	9	26.9	–	8.7–60.8	9	1.49	0.43	–	9
Thiamine	mg/L	0.142	0.024	0.081–0.227	1	0.059	0.022	0.023–0.105	1	0.019	0.006	0.009–0.034	1	0.43	–	0.28–0.90	3
Riboflavin	mg/L	0.373	0.087	0.198–0.790	1	0.369	0.053	0.275–0.490	1	0.302	0.087	0.120–0.453	1	1.56	–	1.16–2.02	3
Vitamin B_6	µg/L	239	51	–	50	–	–	–		–	–	–		0.51	–	0.40–0.63	8
	µg/L	59	–	51–72	92	–	–	–		–	–	–		–	–	–	
Nicotinic acid	mg/L	1.83	0.48	0.66–3.30	1	1.75	0.77	0.60–3.60	1	0.75	0.22	0.50–1.45	1	0.74	–	0.50–0.86	37
Folic acid §§														320	–	–	72
– total	µg/L	52	–	61–62	92	–	–	–		–	–	–		55	–	48–71	69
– free	µg/L	14	–	10–19	66	5.7	4.0	–	67	5.0	2.0	–	67				
Vitamin B_{12}	µg/L	0.34	–	0.21–0.46	66	0.10	–	0.04–0.39	70	0.063	0.007	–	71	2.48	–	–	66
Biotin	µg/L	7.6	–	5.2–11.3	92	–	–	–		–	–	–		22	–	14–29	37
Pantothenic acid	mg/L	2.46	0.63	0.86–5.84	1	2.88	0.57	1.35–4.12	1	1.83	0.86	0.29–3.02	1	3.4	–	2.2–5.5	37
Ascorbic acid	mg/L	52	19	0–112	1	71	12	45–90	1	72	18	47–104	1	11	–	3–23	3
Hormones																	
Gonadotropin-releasing hormone	µg/L	107	7.9	–	68	–	–	–		–	–	–		–	–	–	
Sediment																	
Leukocytes	µL⁻¹	–	–	3–167	95	439	–	50–1970	95	2840	–	300–14000	95	–	–	–	

Fatty acid pattern¶ (mass percent of total fatty acids)[82]

	Mature milk		Transitional milk		Colostrum		Cow's milk	
	Mean	s	Mean	s	Mean	s	Mean	s
Saturated fatty acids								
$C_{4:0}$ Butyric acid	–	–	–	–	–	–	3.2	0.11
$C_{6:0}$ Caproic acid	–	–	–	–	–	–	0.6	0.08
$C_{8:0}$ Caprylic acid	0.1	0.05	0.1	0.06	<0.1	–	1.0	0.08
$C_{10:0}$ Capric acid	1.2	0.11	1.1	0.38	0.4	0.21	2.9	0.26
$C_{11:0}$ Undecanoic acid	<0.1	–	<0.1	–	<0.1	–	0.4	0.05
$C_{12:0}$ Lauric acid	4.6	0.55	5.0	1.67	2.3	0.90	4.8	0.38
$C_{13:0}$ Tridecanoic acid	0.1	0	0.1	0.04	0.1	0.05	0.2	0.05
$C_{14:0}$ Myristic acid	6.4	0.51	6.3	1.33	5.3	0.67	11.8	0.47
$C_{15:0}$ Pentadecanoic acid	0.5	0.05	0.4	0.12	0.5	0.03	1.1	0.05
$C_{16:0}$ Palmitic acid	23.4	0.67	21.9	1.64	23.6	0.98	27.4	0.65
$C_{17:0}$ Heptadecanoic acid	0.7	0	0.7	0.09	0.7	0.06	0.8	0.06
$C_{18:0}$ Stearic acid	8.6	0.61	8.5	1.04	8.0	0.25	10.4	0.68
$C_{19:0}$ Nonadecanoic acid	–	–	–	–	–	–	1.0	0.07
$C_{20:0}$ Arachidic acid	0.2	0.06	0.2	0.07	0.2	0.04	0.2	0.11
$C_{21:0}$ Heneicosanoic acid	0.1	0.05	0.1	0.06	<0.1	–	0.2	0.07
$C_{22:0}$ Behenic acid	0.3	0.05	0.4	0.12	0.6	0.16	0.2	0.07
$C_{23:0}$ Tricosanic acid	<0.1	–	0.1	0.05	0.1	0.05	<0.1	–
$C_{24:0}$ Lignoceric acid	<0.1	–	0.1	0.05	0.1	0.03	<0.1	–
Total	47.1	1.39	45.7	3.45	42.8	1.42	67.4	1.19
Unsaturated fatty acids								
$C_{14:1}$ Myristoleic acid	0.7	0.06	0.5	0.13	0.5	0.07	1.8	0.14
$C_{16:1}$ Palmitoleic acid	3.7	0.29	3.7	0.59	3.9	0.36	2.6	0.13
$C_{18:1}$ Oleic acid	33.3	1.66	34.1	2.00	36.1	1.82	22.9	0.99
$C_{18:2}$ Linoleic acid	12.0	1.32	11.6	2.54	10.8	1.06	3.6	0.43
$C_{18:3}$ Linolenic acid	1.8	0.29	2.0	0.29	2.2	0.15	1.1	0.18
$C_{20:polyene}$	0.9	0.11	1.4	0.41	2.0	0.30	0.4	0.10
Monoenoic acids, total	37.9	1.74	38.7	2.34	41.2	1.86	27.4	1.05
Polyenoic acids, total	15.0	1.64	15.6	2.46	16.0	1.36	5.2	0.45
Total	52.9	1.39	54.3	3.45	57.2	1.42	32.6	1.19

* The casein of breast and cow's milk is very heterogeneous, possibly because of varying phosphate and glycosyl-group contents[20].

** Milk-specific proteins of breast milk: α-lactalbumin, lactoferrin (2 g/L to 6 g/L[60]).

◊ Serum proteins beside albumin and immunoglobulins (see table below): Prealbumin (10 mg/L[42]), transferrin (10–50 mg/L[60]), β_2-microglobulin (81 mg/L[51]) and corticosteroid-binding globulin[93].
During the first 3 days of lactation the concentration of immunoglobulins in colostrum is high[61,9]. In addition, a free secretory IgA component is found in early colostrum (1.35 g/L)[81].

Immunoglobulins in colostrum (g/L)[61]:

	Day 1	Day 4
IgG	0.43	0.04
IgA	17.4	1.00
IgM	1.59	0.10

◊◊ Free amino acids account for at most a few percent of total amino acids in breast milk and cow's milk[46,87]. Taurine, available only in free form, is an amino acid important for neonatal nutrition[52,87].

† Enzymes detected in breast milk: Lactate dehydrogenase[53,54], malate dehydrogenase[53,54], glucose-6-phosphate dehydrogenase[55], xanthine oxidase[54], catalase[56], peroxidase[56], aspartate aminotransferase[57], alanine aminotransferase[57], arylesterase[56], lipases[57,58], acetylesterase[56], cholinesterase[56], alkaline phosphatase[56], acid phosphatase[57], amylase[57], β-D-glucuronidase[62], peptide hydrolases[59], inorganic pyrophosphatase[56], adenosine triphosphatase[56], fructose-bisphosphate aldolase[57], glucosephosphate isomerase[57] as well as fucosyl transferases, depending on the Lewis blood group that is present[63].

†† Breast milk contains at least 25 different oligosaccharides[64], notable lacto-N-tetraose (~0.5 g/L[64]) and in persons of the Lewis phenotype Le(a−b+) 2′-fucosidolactose (~0.3 g/L[65]).

§ The concentration of most of the vitamins depends on maternal intake.

§§ Determination with *Lactobacillus casei;* total folic acid after treatment with conjugase.

¶ The fatty acids of milk represent a very complex mixture of at least 140 components[88,89]. Branched-chain and other unusual fatty acids are probably products of the bacterial metabolism in the intestine[89,90]. The fatty-acid pattern of breast milk is affected by the nature of dietary fat and by energy consumption[91]. When energy intake is adequate and the composition of the diet normal, the fatty-acid pattern in the milk is similar to that of the diet; if nutrition is low in energy, the pattern corresponds to that of depot fat. If the diet is low in fat but energy-rich, lauric acid and myristic acid are synthesized in the mammary glands to an increased extent.

References

[1] Macy, I. G., *Amer. J. Dis. Child.*, **78**, 589 (1949).
[2] Kahlenberg and Le Roy Voris, *J. Agric. Res.*, **43**, 749 (1931).
[3] Dahlberg et al., *Sanitary Milk Control and Its Relation to the Sanitary, Nutritive, and Other Qualities of Milk*, National Research Council, Publication 250, Washington (D.C.), 1953.

[4] MODDE et al., *Arch. Gynäk.,* **196**, 343 (1961).
[5] LING et al., in KON and COWIE (Eds.), *Milk: The Mammary Gland and Its Secretion,* volume 2, Academic Press, New York, 1961, page 195.
[6] MEIGS and MARSH, *J. biol. Chem.,* **16**, 147 (1913/14).
[7] JONES and DAVIES, *Biochem. J.,* **29**, 978 (1935).
[8] MACY, I. G. (unpublished), quoted in MACY et al., *The Composition of Milks,* National Research Council, Publication 254, Washington (D.C.), 1953.
[9] MILLAR and SHEPPARD, *N. Z. J. Sci.,* **15**, 3 (1972).
[10] FEUILLEN and PLUMIER, *Acta paediat. (Uppsala),* **41**, 138 (1952).
[11] KLEINBAUM, H., *Z. Kinderheilk.,* **86**, 655 (1962).
[12] McLEOD and ROBINSON, *Brit. J. Nutr.,* **27**, 229 (1972).
[13] BARLTROP and HILLIER, *Acta paediat. scand.,* **63**, 347 (1974).
[14] KIERMEIER and JOHANNSMANN, *Z. Lebensmitt.-Untersuch.,* **118**, 304 (1962).
[15] ERICSSON and RIBELIUS, *Acta paediat. scand.,* **59**, 424 (1970); Editorial, *Brit. med. J.,* **4**, 542 (1970).
[16] MAN and BENOTTI, *Clin. Chem.,* **15**, 1141 (1969).
[17] SOUCI et al. (Eds.), *Die Zusammensetzung der Lebensmittel,* Wissenschaftliche Verlagsgesellschaft, Stuttgart, 1962.
[18] FEELEY et al., *J. Amer. diet. Ass.,* **61**, 505 (1972).
[19] SHAHANI and SOMMER, *J. Dairy Sci.,* **34**, 1010 (1951).
[20] GROVES and GORDON, *Arch. Biochem.,* **140**, 47 (1970).
[21] PLIMMER and LOWNDES, *Biochem. J.,* **31**, 1751 (1937).
[22] SCHWICK et al., *Behringwerk-Mitteilungen,* No. 37, 11 (1959).
[23] ALBRITTON, E. C. (Ed.), *Standard Values in Nutrition and Metabolism,* Saunders, Philadelphia, 1954, page 111.
[24] BIGWOOD, E. J., *Wld Rev. Nutr. Diet.,* **4**, 93 (1963).
[25] SARKAR et al., *J. Dairy Sci.,* **32**, 671 (1949).
[26] WIDDOWS et al., *Biochem. J.,* **29**, 1145 (1935).
[27] MALPRESS and HYTTEN, *Biochem. J.,* **68**, 708 (1958).
[28] JERLOV, E., *Svenska Läk.-Tidn.,* **26**, 785 and 811 (1929), quoted from MACY et al., *The Composition of Milks,* National Research Council, Publication 254, Washington (D.C.), 1953.
[29] NATAF et al., *J. Nutr.,* **36**, 495 (1948).
[30] HESS and HELMAN, *J. biol. Chem.,* **64**, 781 (1925).
[31] FABRIS, A., *Il mondo del latte,* **1951**, 598.
[32] HARRISON and PEAT, *Brit. med. J.,* **4**, 515 (1972).
[33] LE BOULCH et al., *Int. Z. Vitaminforsch.,* **44**, 167 (1974).
[34] HARRIS et al., *J. Nutr.,* **46**, 459 (1952).
[35] ABDERHALDEN, R., *Biochem. Z.,* **318**, 47 (1947).
[36] NEUWEILER, W., *Int. Z. Vitaminforsch.,* **20**, 108 (1948).
[37] LAWRENCE et al., *J. Nutr.,* **32**, 73 (1946).
[38] CASTELLANOS and LIZARRALDE, *Rev. Asoc. argent. Diet.,* **1**, 199 (1943), quoted from MACY et al., *The Composition of Milks,* National Research Council, Publication 254, Washington (D.C.), 1953.
[39] TERHEGGEN, H. G., *Z. Kinderheilk.,* **92**, 193 (1965).
[40] CAVELL and WIDDOWSON, *Arch. Dis. Childh.,* **39**, 496 (1964).
[41] HADJIMARKOS, D. M., *Méd. et Hyg. (Genève),* **24**, 721 (1966); HADJIMARKOS and SHEARER, *Amer. J. clin. Nutr.,* **26**, 583 (1973).
[42] GUGLER and VON MURALT, *Schweiz. med. Wschr.,* **89**, 925 (1959); DE MURALT, G., *Helv. med. Acta,* **29**, suppl. 42, 1 (1962).
[43] BRUNNER et al., *J. Dairy Sci.,* **43**, 901 (1960).
[44] WILLIAMSON, M. B., *J. biol. Chem.,* **156**, 47 (1944).
[45] GHADIMI and PECORA, *Amer. J. clin. Nutr.,* **13**, 75 (1963).
[46] TARJÁN et al., *Nutr. et Dieta (Basel),* **7**, 136 (1965).

[47] CHANDAN et al., *Nature,* **204**, 76 (1964).
[48] DE MAN, J. M., *Z. Ernährungsw.,* **5**, 1 (1964).
[49] HANNA et al., *Pediatrics,* **45**, 216 (1970).
[50] WEST and KIRKSEY, *Amer. J. clin. Nutr.,* **29**, 961 (1976).
[51] ČEJKA et al., *Clin. chim. Acta,* **67**, 71 (1976).
[52] ARMSTRONG and YATES, *Proc. Soc. exp. Biol. (N. Y.),* **113**, 680 (1963).
[53] DEODHAR et al., *Ann. Biochem.,* **23**, 479 (1963).
[54] DEODHAR et al., *Acta paediat. (Uppsala),* **53**, 101 (1964).
[55] SKLAVUNU-ZURUKZOGLU et al., *Helv. paediat. Acta,* **20**, 193 (1965).
[56] HEYNDRICKX, G. V., *Pediatrics,* **31**, 1019 (1963).
[57] HEYNDRICKX, G. V., *Ann. paediat. (Basel),* **198**, 356 (1962).
[58] KARMARKAR et al., *Acta paediat. (Uppsala),* **52**, 554 (1963); TARASSUK et al., *Nature,* **201**, 298 (1964); HERNELL and OLIVECRONA, *J. Lipid Res.,* **15**, 367 (1974); HAMOSH, M., Ciba Found. Symp., NS **70**, 310 (1979).
[59] GRUNDIG and RUMLER, *Klin. Wschr.,* **43**, 1010 (1965).
[60] BULLEN et al., *Brit. med. J.,* **1**, 69 (1972).
[61] AMMANN and STIEHM, *Proc. Soc. exp. Biol. (N. Y.),* **122**, 1098 (1966).
[62] KIERMEIER and GÜLL, *Münch. med. Wschr.,* **110**, 1813 (1968).
[63] SHEN et al., *Proc. nat. Acad. Sci. (Wash.),* **59**, 224 (1968); JARKOVSKY et al., *Biochemistry (Wash.),* **9**, 1123 (1970).
[64] WIEGANDT and EGGE, *Progr. Chem. org. natur. Prod.,* **28**, 404 (1970).
[65] GROLLMAN and GINSBURG, *Biochem. biophys. Res. Commun.,* **28**, 50 (1967).
[66] NICOL and DAVIS, *Med. J. Aust.,* **2**, 212 (1967).
[67] KARLIN, R., *Int. Z. Vitaminforsch.,* **37**, 334 (1967).
[68] SARDA and NAIR, *J. clin. Endocr.,* **52**, 826 (1981).
[69] GHITIS, J., *Amer. J. clin. Nutr.,* **18**, 452 (1966).
[70] JATHAR et al., *Arch. Dis. Childh.,* **45**, 236 (1970).
[71] AITHAL and SIRSI, *Indian J. Physiol. Pharmacol.,* **8**, 189 (1964).
[72] HUSKISSON and RETIEF, *S. Afr. med. J.,* **44**, 362 (1970).
[73] SANGUANSERMSRI et al., *Amer. J. clin. Nutr.,* **27**, 859 (1974).
[74] KHUTETA et al., *Indian J. Pediat.,* **38**, 61 (1971).
[75] LESKOVA and TSOMPANIDOU, *Wien. tierärztl. Mschr.,* **60**, 60 (1973).
[76] NASSI et al., *Minerva pediat.,* **26**, 832 (1974).
[77] UNDERWOOD, E. J., *Nutr. Rev.,* **33**, 65 (1975).
[78] DILLON et al., *Amer. J. Dis. Child.,* **128**, 491 (1974).
[79] HANKIEWICZ and SWIERCZEK, *Clin. chim. Acta,* **57**, 205 (1974).
[80] GLUECK and TSANG, *Amer. J. clin. Nutr.,* **25**, 224 (1972).
[81] HAUPT and BAUDNER, *Behring Inst. Mitt.,* **54**, 9 (1974).
[82] DROESE et al., *Europ. J. Pediat.,* **122**, 57 (1976).
[83] TOMARELLI, R. M., *J. Pediat.,* **88**, 454 (1976).
[84] OSIS et al., *Amer. J. clin. Nutr.,* **25**, 582 (1972).
[85] ROLAND and FREIESLEBEN, *Med. u. Ernähr.,* **4**, 11 (1963).
[86] CARTER et al., *Amer. J. clin. Nutr.,* **21**, 195 (1968).
[87] RASSIN et al., *Pediatrics,* **90**, 177 (1973).
[88] JENSEN et al., *J. Dairy Sci.,* **50**, 119 (1967).
[89] EGGE et al., *Chem. Phys. Lip.,* **8**, 42 (1972).
[90] AGRANOFF and GOLDBERG, *Lancet,* **2**, 1061 (1974).
[91] INSULL et al., *J. clin. Invest.,* **38**, 443 (1959); READ et al., *Amer. J. clin. Nutr.,* **17**, 180 and 184 (1965).
[92] Department of Health and Social Security, *The Composition of Mature Human Milk,* HMSO, London, 1977.
[93] ROSNER et al., *J. clin. Endocr.,* **42**, 1064 (1976).
[94] DONAT, H., *Zbl. Gynäk.,* **98**, 1631 (1976); OGRA and OGRA, *J. Pediat.,* **92**, 546 (1978).
[95] FAITH et al., *Acta paediat. scand.,* **68**, 389 (1979).

Composition of the body and tissues

The human body is a complex structure, made up of many organs and tissues. These contribute different proportions to the body mass at different ages; thus, muscles account for about 25% of the body mass of the newborn and 43% of the body mass of the adult, whereas the brain constitutes 13% of the body mass of the newborn, but only 2% of that of the adult. The composition of each of the component parts of the body changes with age, and the parts do not all mature chemically at the same rate. The composition of the whole body at any age is the resultant of the composition of its tissues and of their contribution to the body mass at that age.

Determination of the composition of the whole body

The composition of the whole body may be determined by direct chemical analysis[1] or by dilution techniques[2]. Chemical analysis can be used only post mortem, whereas dilution methods are applicable in vivo only. Our knowledge of the changes in the composition of the body during prenatal life has been derived from chemical analysis of fetuses and stillborn. During postnatal stages, however, it is extremely difficult to secure suitable material for examination, notably the bodies of healthy individuals. In fact, up to the present time, only 8 bodies of adults who died as a result of an accident have been analyzed chemically, and none of healthy children. Lately it has proved possible to determine certain chemical constituents of the body in vivo, by the method of neutron activation[3]. In addition, it is possible to determine potassium levels by ^{40}K-gamma ray spectrometry in a whole-body counter[4]. On a formal plane, the body may be subdivided into two compartments: the body fat and the fat-free body tissues. The body-fat compartment is free of water, contains no potassium and has a virtually constant density of about 900 kg m^{-3}. The fat-free compartment[5] has a potassium constituent of about 68 mmol kg^{-1} in males (about 10% less in females) and a water content of about 720 g kg^{-1}. By measuring the density of the tissues, whole-body potassium or tissue water, it is possible to calculate the relative proportion of the two compartments, and hence the fat content of the body. Since the procedure is technically quite complex, it is customary in practice to determine body fat by measuring skinfold thickness. Because of the sharp fluctuation of fat content in human tissues, it is best to express all other body constituents in terms of 1 kg of fat-free tissue.

Determination of the composition of tissues

The composition of body tissues is determined by chemical analysis, using material obtained after death, small samples of material obtained by biopsy during life, or occasionally organs removed by surgery. More is known about the composition of separate organs and tissues than about that of the body as a whole. The trace-element composition of hair in particular can be used as a diagnostic tool[9].

Changes in composition during development

The proportion of fat in the human body increases rapidly during the last 2 months of gestation and accounts for about 16% of the body mass of the newborn at full term. One of the characteristic changes that take place during development is a decrease in the proportion of water in the fat-free body tissue and an increase in that of dry mass. The fall in the proportion of total water is due above all to the sharp reduction in the amount of extracellular fluid, more than offsetting the rise in intracellular fluid due to the increase in the proportion of the body occupied by cells. Paralleling these changes there is a decrease in extracellular sodium and chloride, and an increase in the primarily intracellular constituents potassium, phosphorus and nitrogen. This applies to all soft tissues as well as to the body as a whole. Thus, in boys in particular, there is a close correlation between the increase in body potassium and growing height[6].

Growth of the cellular component of organs has been followed by analyzing them for DNA.[7] The amount of DNA in a diploid nucleus is constant for each species and is 6 pg for man. The number of cells in an organ with diploid nuclei can therefore be calculated from the amount of DNA in it, and the ratio of protein to DNA is usually taken as a measure of the size of the average cell. This is true for organs with mononuclear cells. Tissues such as skeletal muscle, with multinucleate fibers, have been studied in a similar way, and the number of nuclei and the average amount of pro-

tein associated with each nucleus determined. The number of muscle fibers in man appears to be complete by the time of birth or soon afterwards and growth of muscle after birth is due entirely to an increase in the size of fibers; at the same time, there is an increase in the number of nuclei contained in them. Growth of the internal organs takes place first by an increase in the number of cells without any increase in their average size; then the cells begin to increase in size as well as to divide. Then cell division ceases, and growth is due entirely to an increase in the size of the cells. Finally this process stops and the growth of the organ is over, except in the spleen where cell division can continue indefinitely and in the liver where it can recommence as necessity arises. The timing of each stage of development differs for each organ and tissue[8].

The proportion of the body mass contributed by the skeleton does not change appreciably between birth and adult life, but the composition of bone alters more after birth than the composition of almost any other tissue. Most of the calcium in the body is in the skeleton and the proportion of calcium in the body more than doubles during postnatal life.

References

[1] WIDDOWSON, E. M., in BROŽEK, J. (Ed.), *Human Body Composition,* Pergamon, Oxford, 1965, page 31.
[2] MOORE et al., *The Body Cell Mass and Its Supporting Environment,* Saunders, Philadelphia, 1963; OLESEN, K. H., in BROŽEK, J. (Ed.), *Human Body Composition,* Pergamon, Oxford, 1965, page 177; EDELMAN and LEIBMAN, *Amer. J. Med.,* **27**, 256 (1959).
[3] COHN and DOMBROWSKI, *J. nucl. Med.,* **12**, 499 (1971); COHN et al., *Amer. J. Med.,* **57**, 683 (1974).
[4] MILLER and REMENCHIK, *Ann. N. Y. Acad. Sci.,* **110**, 175 (1963); ANDERSON, E. C., *Ann. N. Y. Acad. Sci.,* **110**, 189 (1963).
[5] BROŽEK et al., *Ann. N. Y. Acad. Sci.,* **110**, 113 (1963); FORBES and HURSH, *Ann. N. Y. Acad. Sci.,* **110**, 255 (1963); DURNIN and WOMERSLEY, *Brit. J. Nutr.,* **32**, 77 (1974).
[6] FLYNN et al., *Pediat. Res.,* **9**, 834 (1975).
[7] CHEEK, D. B., *Human Growth,* Lea & Febiger, Philadelphia, 1968; WINICK and NOBLE, *Develop. Biol.,* **12**, 451 (1965); WINICK, M., *Pediatrics,* **47**, 969 (1971).
[8] WIDDOWSON et al., *Arch. Dis. Childh.,* **47**, 652 (1972).
[9] MAUGH, T. H., *Science,* **202**, 1271 (1978); RYAN et al., *Clin. Chem.,* **24**, 1966 (1978); HAMBIDGE, K. M., *Pediat. Clin. N. Amer.,* **27**, 855 (1980).

Body composition of fetuses and young children

Age	Body mass	Values per 1 kg fat-free body mass		Values per 1 kg whole body mass		
		Water	Protein*	Water	Protein*	Fat
	kg	g				
Fetuses ◊						
13 weeks	0.03	900	75	898	75	2
17 weeks	0.2	885	81	880	81	5
26 weeks	1.0	870	100	861	99	10
33 weeks	2.0	850	118	799	111	60
40 weeks	3.5	835	135	721	117	136
(or at term)						
Boys†						
4 months......	7.0	817	154	602	113	263
12 months.....	10.5	775	192	590	146	239
24 months.....	13.0	768	198	610	157	206
36 months.....	15.0	759	200	620	163	183
Adults........	–	720	210	–	♂ 157†† ♀ 137††	–

* Protein N × 6.25.
◊ Values based on chemical analysis.
† Based on FOMON's estimates (see references).
†† In vivo by a nuclear technique.

References

WIDDOWSON and DICKERSON, in COMAR and BRONNER (Eds.), *Mineral Metabolism,* volume 2, part A, Academic Press, New York, 1964, page 1; FOMON, S. J., *Infant Nutrition,* 2nd ed., Saunders, Philadelphia, 1974, page 34; WIDDOWSON et al., *Clin. Sci.,* **10**, 113 (1951); WIDDOWSON and SPRAY, *Arch. Dis. Childh.,* **26**, 205 (1951); FORBES et al., *J. biol. Chem.,* **203**, 359 (1953); FORBES et al., *J. biol. Chem.,* **223**, 969 (1956); MCNEILL et al., *Amer. J. clin. Nutr.,* **32**, 1955 (1979).

* This chapter on the 'Composition of the Body' (pages 217–225) has been compiled by E. M. WIDDOWSON, University of Cambridge, Clinical School, Cambridge, UK, and J. W. DICKERSON, Department of Human Nutrition, University of Surrey, Guildford, Surrey, UK.

Proportion of fat in whole body of children aged 13 to 16 (estimates based on measurements of skinfold in 4 locations: biceps, triceps, subscapular and suprailiac)

Sum of skinfold thickness values	Boys	Girls
	Fat as percent of total body mass	
15 mm	9.0	12.5
20 mm	12.5	16.0
25 mm	15.5	19.0
30 mm	17.5	21.5
35 mm	19.5	23.5
40 mm	21.5	25.0
45 mm	23.0	27.0
50 mm	24.0	28.5
55 mm	25.5	29.5
60 mm	26.5	30.5
65 mm	27.5	32.0
70 mm	28.5	33.0
75 mm	29.5	34.0

Reference   DURNIN and RAHAMAN, *Brit. J. Nutr.*, **21**, 681 (1967).

Potassium content of whole body and per 1 kg of body mass, determined by the method of ^{40}K-gamma ray spectrometry

Age	Amount of substance				Mass			
	Mean	s	Mean	s	Mean	s	Mean	s
	mol		mmol/kg		g		g/kg	
Men								
18–25 years	4.051	0.455	56.1	5.5	158.5	17.8	2.18	0.20
25–35 years	4.126	0.402	53.5	4.6	161.4	15.7	2.09	0.19
35–45 years	4.110	0.567	52.7	3.4	160.7	22.2	2.06	0.13
45–55 years	3.775	0.425	49.5	4.2	147.6	16.6	1.94	0.17
55–65 years	3.607	0.433	47.8	3.9	141.0	16.9	1.87	0.16
65–85 years	3.168	0.234	43.4	3.7	123.9	9.2	1.69	0.16
Women								
18–25 years	2.555	0.273	45.6	3.6	99.9	10.7	1.79	0.14
25–35 years	2.626	0.352	46.2	5.9	102.7	13.8	1.81	0.24
35–45 years	2.655	0.351	43.7	5.1	103.6	13.8	1.71	0.20
45–55 years	2.575	0.291	39.1	5.4	100.7	11.4	1.53	0.22
55–65 years	2.403	0.287	38.2	4.5	93.2	10.2	1.49	0.18
65–85 years	2.351	0.200	37.6	4.3	91.9	7.8	1.47	0.18

Reference   NOVAK, L. P., *J. Geront.*, **27**, 438 (1972).

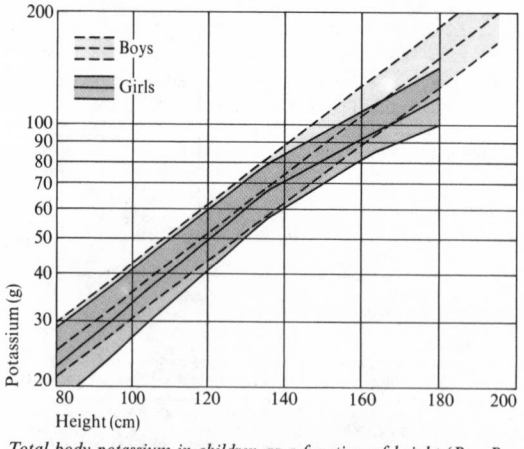

Total body potassium in children as a function of height (P_{16}, P_{50} and P_{84}) (FLYNN et al., *Pediat. Res.*, **6**, 239 [1972]).

Proportion of fat in whole body of adults (estimates based on measurements of skinfold thickness in 4 locations: biceps, triceps, subscapular and suprailiac)

Sum of skinfold thickness values	Men				Women			
	17–29 years	30–39 years	40–49 years	≥ 50 years	16–29 years	30–39 years	40–49 years	≥ 50 years
	Fat as percent of total body mass							
15 mm	4.8	–	–	–	10.5	–	–	–
20 mm	8.1	12.2	12.2	12.6	14.1	17.0	19.8	21.4
25 mm	10.5	14.2	15.0	15.6	16.8	19.4	22.2	24.0
30 mm	12.9	16.2	17.7	18.6	19.5	21.8	24.5	26.6
35 mm	14.7	17.7	19.6	20.8	21.5	23.7	26.4	28.5
40 mm	16.4	19.2	21.4	22.9	23.4	25.5	28.2	30.3
45 mm	17.7	20.4	23.0	24.7	25.0	26.9	29.6	31.9
50 mm	19.0	21.5	24.6	26.5	26.5	28.2	31.0	33.4
55 mm	20.1	22.5	25.9	27.9	27.8	29.4	32.1	34.6
60 mm	21.2	23.5	27.1	29.2	29.1	30.6	33.2	35.7
65 mm	22.2	24.3	28.2	30.4	30.2	31.6	34.1	36.7
70 mm	23.1	25.1	29.3	31.6	31.2	32.5	35.0	37.7
75 mm	24.0	25.9	30.3	32.7	32.2	33.4	35.9	38.7
80 mm	24.8	26.6	31.2	33.8	33.1	34.3	36.7	39.6
85 mm	25.5	27.2	32.1	34.8	34.0	35.1	37.5	40.4
90 mm	26.2	27.8	33.0	35.8	34.8	35.8	38.3	41.2
95 mm	26.9	28.4	33.7	36.6	35.6	36.5	39.0	41.9
100 mm	27.6	29.0	34.4	37.4	36.4	37.2	39.7	42.6
105 mm	28.2	29.6	35.1	38.2	37.1	37.9	40.4	43.3
110 mm	28.8	30.1	35.8	39.0	37.8	38.6	41.0	43.9
115 mm	29.4	30.6	36.4	39.7	38.4	39.1	41.5	44.5
120 mm	30.0	31.1	37.0	40.4	39.0	39.6	42.0	45.1
125 mm	30.5	31.5	37.6	41.1	39.6	40.1	42.5	45.7
130 mm	31.0	31.9	38.2	41.8	40.2	40.6	43.0	46.2
135 mm	31.5	32.3	38.7	42.4	40.8	41.1	43.5	46.7
140 mm	32.0	32.7	39.2	43.0	41.3	41.6	44.0	47.2
145 mm	32.5	33.1	39.7	43.6	41.8	42.1	44.5	47.7
150 mm	32.9	33.5	40.2	44.1	42.3	42.6	45.0	48.2
155 mm	33.3	33.9	40.7	44.6	42.8	43.1	45.4	48.7
160 mm	33.7	34.3	41.2	45.1	43.3	43.6	45.8	49.2
165 mm	34.1	34.6	41.6	45.6	43.7	44.0	46.2	49.6
170 mm	34.5	34.8	42.0	46.1	44.1	44.4	46.6	50.0
175 mm	34.9	–	–	–	44.8	47.0	50.4	
180 mm	35.3	–	–	–	45.2	47.4	50.8	
185 mm	35.6	–	–	–	45.6	47.8	51.2	
190 mm	35.9	–	–	–	45.9	48.2	51.6	
195 mm	–	–	–	–	46.2	48.5	52.0	
200 mm	–	–	–	–	46.5	48.8	52.4	
205 mm	–	–	–	–	–	49.1	52.7	
210 mm	–	–	–	–	–	49.4	53.0	

Reference   DURNIN and WOMERSLEY, *Brit. J. Nutr.*, **32**, 77 (1974).

Annual decrease of whole-body calcium

Age	Men		Women	
	Yearly decrease			
	g	%	g	%
30–39 years	–	–	3.08	0.39
40–49 years	–	–	2.90	0.37
50–54 years	6.44	0.65	2.96	0.36
55–59 years			8.20	1.06
60–69 years	6.50	0.62	7.48	1.07
70–79 years	7.81	0.73	7.01	1.11
80–90 years	7.98	0.79	–	–

Reference   COHN et al., *Metabolism*, **25**, 85 (1976).

Inorganic constituents of the human body, determined by chemical analysis (values per 1 kg of fat-free body mass)

	Body mass	N	Na	K	Cl	Mg	Ca	P	Fe	Cu	Zn	N	Na	K	Cl	Mg	Ca	P	Fe	Cu	Zn
	kg	mol	mmol						µmol			g							mg		
Fetuses																					
13 weeks............	0.03	0.9	110	38	80	4.1	52	68	–	–	–	12	2.5	1.5	2.8	0.10	2.1	2.1	–	–	–
17 weeks............	0.2	0.9	102	42	76	5.8	87	81	1.0	52	300	13	2.3	1.6	2.7	0.14	3.5	2.5	54	3.3	20
26 weeks............	1.0	1.1	94	42	68	8.2	160	130	1.2	54	300	16	2.16	1.6	2.4	0.20	6.3	3.9	65	3.4	20
33 weeks............	2.0	1.4	88	45	62	9.9	200	150	1.5	63	300	19	2.0	1.8	2.2	0.24	7.8	4.8	84	4.0	20
40 weeks............	3.5	1.6	82	53	55	11	240	180	1.7	74	300	22	1.9	2.1	2.0	0.26	9.6	5.6	94	4.7	20
Adults..............	–	2.4	80	69	50	19	560	390	1.3	27	430	34	1.8	2.7	1.8	0.47	22.4	12.0	74	1.7	28

References

WIDDOWSON and DICKERSON, in COMAR and BRONNER (Eds.), *Mineral Metabolism*, volume 2, part A, Academic Press, New York, 1964, page 1; WIDDOWSON et al., *Clin. Sci.,* **10**, 113 (1951); WIDDOWSON and SPRAY, *Arch. Dis. Childh.,* **26**, 205 (1951); FORBES et al., *J. biol. Chem.,* **203**, 359 (1953); FORBES et al., *J. biol. Chem.,* **223**, 969 (1956).

Inorganic constituents of human body, determined by neutron activation (values for whole body)

	Age	Body mass	Na		Cl		K		Ca		P		Ca/K	
			Mean	s	Mean	s	Mean	s	Mean	s	Mean	s	Mean	s
		kg	g											
Men	30–39 years	78.0	83.4	11.2	76.5	11.3	141.2	18.4	1110	15.3	510	16.9	7.92	7.7
	40–49 years	86.0	85.3	12.5	75.2	9.0	142.2	11.9	1077	13.2	473	17.3	7.60	10.1
	50–59 years	75.6	78.2	7.8	72.7	7.4	121.3	15.9	996	15.4	420	19.3	8.24	9.7
	60–69 years	76.1	82.4	8.4	72.7	8.3	128.3	13.1	1055	11.5	435	17.5	8.29	12.6
	70–79 years	70.0	77.6	7.7	74.8	6.5	105.4	19.8	1075	10.8	479	12.1	10.34	8.7
	80–89 years	70.8	81.2	11.0	75.7	11.0	93.7	16.5	1006	19.7	439	10.6	10.75	19.8
Women..........	30–39 years	55.6	59.1	5.1	62.1	4.5	76.6	12.0	785	4.5	402	10.5	10.3	10.7
	40–49 years	63.2	63.4	6.1	61.3	9.0	88.1	11.8	849	8.7	396	10.8	9.70	7.1
	50–59 years	69.0	60.8	7.8	62.6	7.5	81.3	12.9	804	13.2	360	18.0	9.92	8.5
	60–69 years	63.1	58.6	8.6	60.2	8.5	75.3	7.4	701	12.2	346	15.7	9.30	7.9
	70–79 years	57.5	56.8	4.7	57.6	6.7	67.8	7.8	634	15.9	326	17.3	9.64	13.4

References   COHN et al., *Metabolism,* **25**, 85 (1976); ELLIS et al., *Metabolism,* **25**, 645 (1976).

Composition of muscular tissue (values per 1 kg of fat-free tissue)

		As percent of body mass	Water	Total N	Protein*	DNA	Protein/DNA	Na	K	Cl	Mg	Ca	P
			g					mmol					
Skeletal muscle[1]	Fetuses, 13–14 weeks.......	–	907	11.5	75.3[4]	5.00[4]	15.1[4]	101	56.3	76.4	5.85	2.8	36.5
	Fetuses, 20–22 weeks.......	25	887	15.4	86.0[4]	3.47[4]	23.1[4]	90.6	57.6	65.6	5.25	3.65	40.0
	Newborn...................	25	804	20.9	150[4]	1.39[4]	108[4]	60.1	57.7	42.6	7.4	2.15	47.0
	Infants, 4–7 months	–	785	29.6	–	–	–	50.1	89.5	35.5	10.0	1.55	64.9
	Adults	43	792	31.4	160[4]	0.74[4]	216[4]	36.3	92.2	22.1	8.35	1.4	58.8
Heart[2] **Whole heart**	Fetuses, 20–22 weeks.......	0.6	860	14.0	75.9[4]	2.72[4]	27.9[4]	46.1	81.1	41.0	–	–	49.7
	Newborn...................	0.5	841	19.6	112[4]	2.28[4]	49.3[4]	64.2	54.3	45.2	5.45	3.7	47.0
	Infants, 4–7 months	–	830	21.0	–	–	–	59.8	49.3	49.3	5.55	4.1	49.5
	Adults	0.4	827	22.9	–	–	–	57.8	66.5	45.6	6.6	1.3	49.0
Left ventricle	Adults	–	789	–	127[4]	0.70[4]	181[4]	44.7	78.5	38.0	8.5	1.95	63.5
Right ventricle	Adults	–	802	–	–	–	–	47.8	56.2	39.5	8.25	1.9	50.0
Atrium...............	Adults	–	812	–	–	–	–	52.2	35.7	42.2	–	–	30.6
Septum	Adults	–	792	–	–	–	–	40.5	79.0	33.8	–	–	51.8
Myometrium[3]	Non-pregnant.............	–	794	–	–	–	–	87.8	62.6	73.8	6.4	8.3	–
	Early pregnancy...........	–	825	–	–	–	–	93.6	59.0	71.0	4.25	3.55	–
	At term	–	823	–	–	–	–	88.8	62.4	63.2	6.75	8.75	–

*Protein N × 6.25.

References

[1] DICKERSON and WIDDOWSON, *Biochem. J.,* **74**, 247 (1960).
[2] WILKINS and CULLEN, *J. clin. Invest.,* **12**, 1063 (1933); MANGUN et al., *Arch. intern. Med.,* **67**, 320 (1941); ALEXANDER et al., *J. Lab. clin. Med.,* **36**, 796 (1950); CLARKE and MOSHER, *Circulation,* **5**, 907 (1952); WIDDOWSON and DICKERSON, *Biochem. J.,* **77**, 30 (1960).
[3] HAWKINS and NIXON, *J. Obstet. Gynaec. Brit. Emp.,* **65**, 895 (1958).
[4] WIDDOWSON et al., *Arch. Dis. Childh.,* **47**, 652 (1972).

Composition of organs (values per 1 kg of fresh tissue)

		As percent of body mass	Water	Total N	Protein*	DNA	Protein/DNA	Na	K	Cl	Mg	Ca	P
					g					mmol			
Liver[1,4,6]	Fetuses, 13–14 weeks	–	849	20.2	117	9.37	12.5	–	81.8	62.2	–	–	82.5
	Fetuses, 20–22 weeks	4	812	22.1	123	9.47	13.0	54.8	92.9	57.1	7.35	1.15	88.0
	Newborn	5	786	22.6	120	4.22	28.4	59.8	58.7	55.8	5.2	1.5	56.5
	Infants, 4–7 months	4	764	24.4	–	–	–	51.0	66.2	42.8	5.9	2.2	82.5
	Adults	2	711	28.2	146	2.62	55.7	42.5	75.0	38.3	7.6	1.4	86.0
Kidney[4,6]	Fetuses, 20–22 weeks	0.7	884	14.2	62.3	3.78	16.5	68.0	66.5	59.6	4.3	8.7	65.5
	Newborn	1.0	841	19.2	118	4.14	28.6	75.5	56.0	56.4	4.35	3.85	61.0
	Adults	0.5	810	24.5	107	2.41	44.4	82.0	57.0	67.8	4.3	3.5	57.5
Spleen[1,2]	Adults	0.2	790	30.1	–	–	–	–	81.0	–	6.5	2.1	71.0
Lung[3,5,7]	Fetuses, 20–22 weeks	–	888	10.3	–	4.0	–	89.0	71.0	67.5	–	–	56.5
	Newborn	1.7	858	17.0	–	2.4	–	75.6	48.6	62.5	–	–	44.0
	Adults	1.6	787	27.2	–	–	–	75.3	54.7	69.0	2.4	6.25	51.8
Brain[4]	Fetuses, 14 weeks	15.0	914	9.6	–	–	–	97.5	49.6	72.1	–	–	57.0
	Fetuses, 20–22 weeks	13.4	922	8.4	–	–	–	91.7	52.0	72.6	4.2	2.45	52.2
	Newborn	13.4	897	9.3	–	–	–	80.9	58.2	66.1	3.95	2.4	54.0
	Adults	2.3	774	17.1	100	–	–	55.2	84.6	40.5	5.7	2.0	109
Placenta[8,9]	20–40 weeks	–	866	18.5	60◊	3◊	20◊	98	40	–	3.3	6.2	30

* Protein N × 6.25.
◊ These values apply to approximately the 36th week of gestation; thereafter, protein alone continues to rise in parallel with placental growth, but DNA content does not.

References
[1] WIDDOWSON et al., *Clin. Sci.*, **10**, 113 (1951).
[2] FORBES et al., *J. biol. Chem.*, **203**, 359 (1953).
[3] FORBES et al., *J. biol. Chem.*, **223**, 969 (1956).
[4] WIDDOWSON and DICKERSON, *Biochem. J.*, **77**, 30 (1960).
[5] WIDDOWSON and DICKERSON, in COMAR and BRONNER (Eds.), *Mineral Metabolism*, volume 2, part A, Academic Press, New York, 1964, page 1.
[6] WIDDOWSON et al., *Arch. Dis. Childh.*, **47**, 652 (1972).
[7] BRADLEY et al., *J. clin. Invest.*, **55**, 543 (1975).
[8] WIDDOWSON and SPRAY, *Arch. Dis. Childh.*, **26**, 205 (1951).
[9] WINICK et al., *Pediatrics*, **39**, 248 (1967).

Organic constituents of muscular tissue and organs (values per 1 kg of fresh tissue, unless otherwise stated)

		Nonprotein N	Sarcoplasmic protein N	Fibrillar protein N			Collagen N	Carnitine	Glycogen	Total lipids	Cholesterol	Triglycerides
									g			
Skeletal muscle[1]	Fetuses, 14 weeks	1.2	3.6	5.7			0.6*	–	–	–	–	–
	Fetuses, 20–22 weeks	1.7	3.7	8.7			1.8*	–	13[5]	–	–	–
	Newborn	2.4	3.9	10.9			3.8*	–	–	–	–	–
	Infants, 4–7 months	3.2	5.0	17.0			4.6*	–	–	–	–	–
	Adults	3.0	6.7	19.9			1.4*	0.27	2–15[2]	31.0[6]	1.0[6]	14.4[6]
Heart	Fetuses about 20 weeks	–	–	Actomyosin	Myosin	Actotropomyosin	–	–	35–40[5]	–	–	–
	Adults	–	–				–	–	2–15[2]	26.5[6]	1.3[6]	3.5[6]
Uterus Muscle[3]	Non-pregnant	–	–	5	11	4	–	–	–	–	10◊	–
	At term	–	–	13	9	15	–	–	–	–	–	–
Mucous membrane[3]	Proliferative phase	–	–	–	–	–	–	–	3.2	–	–	–
	Early secretory phase	–	–	–	–	–	–	–	11.2	–	–	–
	Secretory phase	–	–	–	–	–	–	–	6.4	–	–	–
Liver	Fetuses about 20 weeks	–	–	–	–	–	–	–	45[5]	–	–	–
	Adults	–	–	–	–	–	–	0.27	10–50[2]	49[4]	3.9[4]	19.4[4]

* Total extracellular protein N.
◊ Values per 1 kg of dry tissue.

References
[1] DICKERSON and WIDDOWSON, *Biochem. J.*, **74**, 247 (1960).
[2] AUERBACH AND DiGEORGE, in VAUGHAN and McKAY (Eds.), *Nelson Textbook of Pediatrics*, 10th ed., Saunders, Philadelphia, 1975, page 407.
[3] CSAPO, A., *Amer. J. Physiol.*, **160**, 46 (1950); NAESLUND and SNELLMAN, *Acta Soc. Med. upsalien.*, **59**, 349 (1954); ARRONET and LATOUR, *J. clin. Endocr.*, **17**, 261 (1957).
[4] KWITEROVICH et al., *J. Lipid Res.*, **11**, 322 (1970).
[5] SHELLEY, H. J., *Brit. med. Bull.*, **17**, 137 (1961).
[6] FLETCHER, R. F., *Lipids*, **7**, 728 (1972).
[7] CHAPOY et al., *New Engl. J. Med.*, **303**, 1389 (1980).

Phospholipids in organs

	Total g per 1 kg of fresh tissue	Phosphatidylethanolamine	Lecithin	Lysolecithin	Sphingomyelin	Phosphatidylinositol	Phosphatidylserine	Cardiolipin
		As percent of phospholipid phosphorus						
Skeletal muscle[1]	7.2	25.2	48.7	7.9	6.8	–	11.4	–
Heart[1]	13.2	26.5	49.2	8.6	6.4	–	8.5	–
Liver[2]	25.1	25.4	42.6	1.3	7.0	6.9	7.5	3.9

References
[1] FLETCHER, R. F., *Lipids*, **7**, 728 (1972).
[2] KWITEROVICH et al., *J. Lipid Res.*, **11**, 322 (1970).

Glycosaminoglycans in organs

	Total g Hexuronic acid per 1 kg fat-free dry mass	Hyaluronic acid	Chondroitin 4-sulfate + chondroitin 6-sulfate	Dermatane sulfate	Heparan sulfate
		As percent of total hexuronic acid			
Brain	0.9	36.0	34.0	8.0	22.0
Liver	0.35		35.0	27.5	42.5
Spleen	0.8		18.0	29.0	53.0

Reference
CONSTANTOPOULOS et al., *J. Neurochem.*, **26**, 901 (1976).

Trace elements in muscular tissue and organs (values per 1 kg of fresh tissue)

		Nonhemoglobin iron mg	Ref.	Cu mg	Ref.	Zn mg	Ref.	Mn mg	Ref.	Cr µg	Ref.	Co µg	Ref.	Mo µg	Ref.	Se mg	Ref.
Muscle	Fetuses	–	–	0.4–1.0	5	–	–	–	–	–	–	–	–	–	–	–	–
	Men	40	10	1.3–2.7	1	54	2	0.09	2	28	3	–	–	29	2	0.24	4
	Women	22	10														
Heart	Adults	–	–	3.4	1	33	2	0.23	2	37	3	17	2	–	–	0.28	4
Liver	Fetuses, 20–22 weeks	200–300	6	63	6	270	6	1.24	6	64	6	129	6	–	–	–	–
	Fetuses, 26 weeks	200–300	6	62	6	246	6	1.38	6	56	6	105	6	–	–	–	–
	Fetuses, 33 weeks	200–300	6	70	6	198	6	1.47	6	58	6	105	6	–	–	–	–
	Fetuses, 40 weeks (or at term)	200–300	6	71	6	118	6	1.53	6	48	6	110	6	–	–	–	–
	Children, 1–13 years	90	7	89*	11	156*	11	–	–	–	–	–	–	–	–	3.2*	11
	Men	250	7	5–10	6	60	6	1.70	6	45	6	52–122	6	925	6	0.54	6
	Women	80	7														
Kidney	Fetuses	–	–	0.5–1.1	5	–	–	–	–	–	–	–	–	–	–	–	–
	Adults	–	–	2–4	1	55	2	0.93	2	24	3	44	2	304	2	1.09	4
Spleen	Fetuses	–	–	0.7–1.3	5	–	–	–	–	–	–	–	–	–	–	–	–
	Adults	–	–	1.2–13	1	21	2	0.22	2	18	3	–	–	42	2	0.34	4
Bone marrow	Men	200	8	1.0–1.4	9	–	–	–	–	–	–	–	–	–	–	–	–
	Women	80	8														
Lungs	Fetuses	–	–	0.3–0.6	5	–	–	–	–	–	–	–	–	–	–	–	–
	Adults	–	–	1.1–3	1	15	2	0.34	2	230	3	–	–	32	2	0.15	4
Pancreas	Fetuses	–	–	1.3–1.7	5	–	–	–	–	–	–	–	–	–	–	–	–
	Adults	–	–	–	–	29	2	1.21	2	38	3	14	2	–	–	0.30	4
Brain◊	Fetuses	–	–	0.3–0.5	5	–	–	–	–	–	–	–	–	–	–	–	–
	Adults	–	–	0.4–5.3	1	14	2	0.34	2	12	3	–	–	32	2	0.13	4
Placenta	20–40 weeks	25–30	12	1.5	6	10	6										

* Values per 1 kg dry tissue.
◊ For specific brain segments, see data reported by SMEYERS-VERBEKE et al., *Clin. chim. Acta*, **51**, 309 (1974), and **68**, 343 (1976), as well as GREINER et al., *Clin. chim. Acta*, **64**, 211 (1975).

References
[1] ADELSTEIN and VALLEE, in COMAR and BRONNER (Eds.), *Mineral Metabolism*, volume 2, part B, Academic Press, New York, 1962, page 371.
[2] UNDERWOOD, E. J., *Trace Elements in Human and Animal Nutrition*, 3rd ed., Academic Press, New York, 1971; TIPTON and COOK, *Hlth Phys.*, **9**, 103 (1963).

[3] SCHROEDER et al., *J. chron. Dis.*, **23**, 123 (1970).
[4] SCHROEDER et al., *J. chron. Dis.*, **23**, 227 (1970).
[5] HORN et al., *Lancet*, **1**, 1236 (1975).
[6] WIDDOWSON and SPRAY, *Arch. Dis. Childh.*, **26**, 205 (1951); WIDDOWSON et al., *Biol. Neonat. (Basel)*, **20**, 360 (1972).
[7] SHAH and BELONJE, *Amer. J. clin. Nutr.*, **29**, 66 (1976).
[8] GALE et al., *J. clin. Invest.*, **42**, 1076 (1963).
[9] LEWIS et al., *J. Lab. clin. Med.*, **88**, 375 (1976).
[10] ROTH et al., *Helv. med. Acta*, **18**, 159 (1951).
[11] LAPIN et al., *J. Pediat.*, **89**, 607 (1976).
[12] SINGLA et al., *Amer. J. clin. Nutr.*, **32**, 1462 (1979).

Free amino acids and related compounds in the brain and muscle (mean and extreme range per 1 kg of fresh tissue)

	Cerebral cortex[1]	Cerebellum[1]	Muscle[2]
Alanine	0.25	0.66	(0.39–4.10)
β-Alanine	0.01	0.01	–
α-Aminobutyric acid	(trace–0.10)	0.02	–
γ-Aminobutyric acid	0.42	0.75	–
γ-Aminobutyryl histidine (homocarnosine)	0.23	0.47	–
2-(γ-aminobutyryl) lysine	0.02	0.04	–
Arginine	0.10	0.11	–
Asparagine	0.06	0.09	–
Aspartic acid	0.96	0.82	(0.09–1.08)
Ethanolamine	0.11	0.99	–
Citrulline	(trace–0.09)	trace	–
Cystathionine	2.02	3.22	–
Cysteine–glutathione disulfide	(trace–0.09)	0.17	–
Cystine	0.01	0.02	–
Glutamine	5.80	6.35	–
Glutamic acid	5.96	7.19	(0.70–12.1)
Glutathione, reduced	(0–0.77)	0.48	–
Glutathione, oxidized	(0.24–1.22)	0.80	–
Glycerophosphoethanolamine	0.60	0.83	–
Glycine	0.40	0.53	(0.15–6.14)
Histidine	0.09	0.10	–
Isoleucine	0.03	0.05	(0.02–0.13)
Leucine	0.07	0.11	(0.04–0.18)
Lysine	0.12	0.24	–
Methionine	0.03	0.05	(0.007–0.12)
Ornithine	0.03	0.08	–
Phenylalanine	0.05	0.05	(0.006–0.19)
Phosphoethanolamine	1.10	1.59	(0.12–1.07)
Proline	0.04	0.16	–
Serine	0.44	0.40	(0.15–3.18)
Taurine	0.93	2.52	(0.53–15.9)
Threonine	0.27	0.28	(0.08–1.16)
Tryptamine*	–	–	–
Tryptophane	0.01	trace	–
Tyrosine	0.06	0.05	(0.01–0.14)
Valine	0.13	0.18	(0.03–0.40)

* Brain[3]: 0.25 mol/kg.

References
[1] PERRY et al., *J. Neurochem.*, **18**, 521 (1971).
[2] ANDO and NYHAN, in NYHAN, W. L. (Ed.), *Heritable Disorders of Amino Acid Metabolism*, Wiley, New York, 1974, page 37.
[3] AXELROD and SAAVEDRA, *Ciba Found. Symp.*, NS22, 51 (1974).

Polyamines in brain and liver (values per 1 kg of fresh tissue)

		Putrescine	Spermidine	Spermine
		μmol		
Brain	Fetuses	429	358	307
	Adults	55	407	221
Liver	Fetuses	216	812	1073
	Adults	65	214	707

Reference STURMAN and GAULL, *Pediat. Res.*, **8**, 231 (1974).

Sterols in the aorta (values per 1 kg of fresh tissue)

	Cholesterol		Campesterol		Stigmasterol		β-Sitosterol	
	Mean	s	Mean	s	Mean	s	Mean	s
	g		mg					
11 infants	0.66	0.36	3.57	4.4	9.2	9.0	8.9	10.1
11 adults	3.44	2.28	14.3	12.9	12.8	11.8	16.0	14.7

Reference MELLIES et al., *J. Lab. clin. Med.*, **88**, 914 (1976).

Lipids in brain and myelin (values per 1 kg of dry tissue)

	Gray matter	White matter	Myelin
	g		
Water	821*	730*	–
Proteolipid protein	32	86	210
Total lipids	318	540	666
Cholesterol	76	150	156
Total phospholipids	221	239	301
Phosphatidylethanolamine	72	81	97
Lecithin	90	68	92
Sphingomyelin	18	43	51
Phosphatidylinositol	7	4	} 58
Phosphatidylserine	32	42	
Total galactolipids	9.2	146	174
Cerebroside	5.0	125	136
Sulfatide	1.4	22	38

* Values per 1 kg of fresh tissue.

References
SUZUKI and SUZUKI, in STANBURY et al. (Eds.), *The Metabolic Basis of Inherited Disease*, 3rd ed., McGraw-Hill, New York, 1972, page 760. For values in fetuses and newborn, see SVENNERHOLM and VANIER, *Brain Res.*, **47**, 457 (1972), as well as CONDE et al., *Pediat. Res.*, **8**, 89 (1974).

Gangliosides in brain segments

Brain segment	Subjects	Total mg N-acetyl-neuraminic acid (NANA) per 1 kg of fresh tissue	Distribution of gangliosides						Reference
			G_{T1}	G_{D1a}	G_{D1b}	G_{M1}	G_{M2}	G_{M3}	
			As percent of total N-acetylneuraminic acid						
Cerebrum, gray matter	6 children, 2–8 years	748	19.0	37.7	16.3	23.2	2.0	1.8	1
Frontal cortex	1 man, 44 years	1002	29.9	22.4	28.3	11.2	1.3	–	2
Caudate nucleus	1 man, 44 years	1010	28.1	27.2	28.3	10.5	1.4	–	2
Corpus callosum	1 man, 44 years	184	30.8	22.7	27.2	13.5	1.2	–	2
Thalamus	1 man, 44 years	708	33.5	14.1	35.3	9.4	1	–	2
Cerebellum	1 man, 44 years	651	42.7	15.0	25.8	6.8	1	–	2

References
[1] YUTAKA et al., *Clin. chim. Acta*, **59**, 283 (1975).
[2] SUZUKI, K., *J. Neurochem.*, **12**, 969 (1965).

For values in fetuses and the newborn, see VANIER et al., *J. Neurochem.*, **18**, 581 (1971).

Cholesterol and deoxyribonucleic acid content in different brain segments (fresh tissue)

Age		Cerebrum				Cerebellum				Brainstem			
		Mass	Water	Choles-terol	DNA-P*	Mass	Water	Choles-terol	DNA-P*	Mass	Water	Choles-terol	DNA-P*
		g	g/kg		µmol	g	g/kg		µmol	g	g/kg		µmol
Fetuses	10–13 weeks.....	0.61–1.95	911	2.88–3.86	7.73–23.5	0.05–0.07	–	3.73	–	0.25–0.53	–	3.48–4.35	2.17–2.38
	16 weeks	11.4	911	3.62	106	0.35	950	3.32	1.90	0.68	914	4.45	2.87
	17 weeks	16.5	908	3.49	159	0.46	–	3.32	2.07	0.81	914	4.86	3.20
	18 weeks	21.7	909	4.10	196	0.59	909	3.30	4.18	0.99	908	4.93	4.02
	19 weeks	31.1	915	4.24	251	1.08	928	3.15	6.50	1.11	914	4.76	4.78
	21 weeks	51.7	894	4.92	348	1.71	908	4.18	9.35	1.34	901	5.96	7.15
	27 weeks	104	915	5.51	393	3.31	913	4.53	19.8	1.58	892	8.05	4.07
	30 weeks	140	897	5.94	474	5.45	887	4.82	37.5	3.05	870	8.59	7.04
	33 weeks	218	904	5.87	651	8.23	898	4.88	55.9	4.41	872	8.33	11.6
	38 weeks	330	887	7.27	698	19.9	887	6.29	198	5.97	874	10.2	13.1
	40 weeks	336	887	7.44	656	21.6	876	6.46	206	5.55	852	12.0	11.6
Children	1 week	402	884	7.32	662	22.8	865	7.11	227	6.41	873	10.8	12.2
	6 weeks	435	881	9.00	717	31.1	866	8.49	349	8.11	855	13.8	16.3–
	13 weeks	522	868	9.83	882	47.8	842	9.78	586	10.8	823	15.6	23.5
	26 weeks	765	851	11.93	1042	78.9	837	11.0	1017	12.7	813	20.1	19.3
	43 weeks	767	830	13.38	1261	96.7	819	13.3	1156	15.8	780	22.5	31.8
	61 weeks	863	822	15.84	1660	110	818	13.0	1467	17.7	776	25.8	38.6
	2 years	996	821	16.10	1317	113	818	14.2	1447	11.4	755	25.9	19.4
Adults	....	1237	793	23.3	2670	145	815	17.1	1343	27.1	746	34.6	55.4

*As deoxyribonucleic acid phosphorus of the whole segment.

References

DOBBING and SANDS, *Arch. Dis. Childh.*, **48**, 757 (1973), as well as personal communication. See also WINICK, M., *Pediat. Res.*, **2**, 352 (1968) and in relation to inorganic constituents WIDDOWSON and DICKERSON, in COMAR and BRONNER (Eds.), *Mineral Metabolism*, volume 2, part A, Academic Press, New York, 1964, page 1.

Fatty acids of subcutaneous adipose tissue of children and adults

		0.2–0.5 years	0.5–1.0 years	1 year	2 years	3 years	4–6 years	7–9 years	10–12 years	Men 15–65 years		
		Federal Republic of Germany[1]									USA[2]	Japan[2]
		g per 1 kg of fresh tissue										
Total fat		652	653	646	663	663	639	649	706	630[3]	–
		As percent of total fatty acids										
Fatty acids												
$C_{10:0}$	Capric acid	0.3	0.2	0.2	0.2	0.2	0.2	0.2	0.1	–	–
$C_{12:0}$	Lauric acid	2.1	1.6	1.8	1.5	1.7	1.7	1.5	1.5	0.41	0.24
$C_{14:0}$	Myristic acid	5.9	6.9	6.7	5.2	5.3	5.2	4.9	4.7	2.97	2.60
$C_{14:1}$	Myristoleic acid................	1.0	1.2	1.0	0.6	0.7	0.6	0.5	0.6	0.48	0.42
$C_{15:0}$	Pentadecylic acid	0.4	0.6	0.6	0.5	0.5	0.4	0.4	0.4	0.34	0.23
$C_{15:?}$		–	–	–	–	–	–	–	–	0.08	0.02
$C_{16:0}$	Palmitic acid....................	28.8	28.4	25.5	23.2	22.8	22.5	22.2	22.2	22.9	21.5
$C_{16:1}$	Palmitoleic acid	8.2	8.3	6.3	5.5	5.1	5.2	5.3	5.7	6.27	8.04
$C_{16:2?}$		–	–	–	–	–	–	–	–	0.45	0.43
$C_{17:0}$	Heptadecanoic acid	0.2	0.3	0.5	0.5	0.5	0.4	0.3	0.4	0.61	0.59
$C_{18:0}$	Stearic acid	3.7	4.7	6.7	8.2	8.2	8.3	7.8	6.7	5.77	3.61
$C_{18:1}$	Oleic acid........................	35.9	37.1	39.3	42.3	41.6	42.6	42.7	42.4	48.2	43.0
$C_{18:2}$	Linoleic acid	11.0	7.8	8.2	8.2	8.7	9.0	10.5	10.7	10.2	16.5
$C_{18:3}$	Linolenic acid	1.1	1.4	1.6	1.6	1.7	1.9	1.9	1.8	0.58	0.97
$C_{20:0}$	Arachidic acid	0.1	<0.1	0.2	0.2	0.2	0.3	0.3	0.2	–	–
$C_{20:Polyen}$	Eicosapolyenic acids	0.4	0.4	0.4	0.8	1.1	0.8	0.7	1.0	trace	trace
$C_{21:0}$	Heneicosanoic acid	–	–	–	–	–	–	–	–	0.65	1.60
$C_{22:0}$	Behenic acid....................	<0.1	<0.1	<0.1	0.2	0.2	0.1	<0.1	0.2	–	–

References
[1] PAPE et al., *Z. Kinderheilk.*, **116**, 269 (1974).
[2] INSULL et al., *J. clin. Invest.*, **48**, 1313 (1969).
[3] GELLHORN and MARKS, *J. clin. Invest.*, **40**, 925 (1961).

Composition of bones and teeth (values per 1 kg of fat-free dry tissue, unless otherwise stated)

		Water*	N	Ca	P	Ca	P	Mg	Na	K	CO₂	Cl	F
			g						mol				
Bones													
Cortex of femur[1]	Fetuses, 14 weeks	–	59.5	189	91	4.72	2.94	–	–	–	–	–	–
	Fetuses, 20–24 weeks	311	52.5	234	105	5.84	3.39	–	–	–	–	–	–
	Newborn	238	50.6	246	108	6.14	3.48	–	–	–	–	–	–
	Infants, 2–4½ weeks	230	52.8	237	108	5.91	3.48	–	–	–	–	–	0.026◊
	Infants, 5–9 months	195	53.1	249	110	6.21	3.55	–	–	–	–	–	–
	Children, 12–24 months	203	52.4	246	111	6.14	3.58	–	–	–	–	–	0.037◊
	Children, 12 years	155	49.2	253	115	6.31	3.71	–	–	–	–	–	–
	Adults, 18–35 years	122	47.4	264	113	6.59	3.65	0.16	0.08–0.26	0.013–0.077	0.7	0.051	0.049–0.142◊
Femur[1] (without epiphysis)	Fetuses, 14 weeks	560	56.9	158	71	3.94	2.29	–	–	–	–	–	–
	Fetuses, 20–24 weeks	546	59.5	191	82	4.77	2.65	–	–	–	–	–	–
	Newborn	488	59.4	236	99	5.89	3.20	–	–	–	–	–	–
	Infants, 2–4½ months	492	67.8	199	97	4.97	3.13	–	–	–	–	–	–
	Infants, 5–9 months	437	68.9	190	86	4.74	2.78	–	–	–	–	–	–
	Children, 12–24 months	397	56.7	183	85	4.57	2.74	–	–	–	–	–	–
	Children, 12 years	307	52.1	272	124	6.79	4.00	–	–	–	–	–	–
	Adults, 18–35 years	227	52.0	251	107	6.26	3.45	–	–	–	–	–	–
Teeth													
Enamel[2]	Adults	30	0.3	360	170	9.0	5.5	0.16	0.31–0.39	0.013–0.077	0.41	0.07	0.005–0.018†
Dentin[2]	Adults	100	34	270	130	6.7	4.2	0.37	0.13	0.018–0.026	0.55	0–0.008	0.013–0.040†

* Values per 1 kg of fat-free tissue.
◊ Values for ribs, levels increasing with fluoridation of tap water.
† Levels increasing with fluoridation of tap water (BRUDEVOLD et al., in WOLSTENHOLME and O'CONNOR [Eds.], *Caries-resistant Teeth,* Ciba Foundation Symposium, Churchill, London, 1965, page 121).

References
[1] EASTOE, J. E., in LONG, G. C. (Ed.), *Biochemists' Handbook,* Spon, London, 1961, page 715; DICKERSON, J. W., *Biochem. J.,* **82**, 56 (1962).
[2] EASTOE, J. E., in LONG, G. C. (Ed.), *Biochemists' Handbook,* Spon, London, 1961, page 720.

Composition of skin, nails and hair (values per 1 kg of fresh tissue)

		As percent of total body mass	Water	N	Ca	P	Ca	P	Mg	Na	K	Cl	F
		%		g						mmol			
Skin[1]	Fetuses, 14 weeks	–	917	11.6	0.09	1.30	2.2	41.8	–	–	23.8	90.6	–
	Fetuses, 20 weeks	13	901	11.9	0.12	0.87	3.05	28.2	1.9	120	36.0	96.0	–
	Newborn	15	828	26.5	0.20	0.98	5.0	31.7	2.35	87.1	45.0	66.9	–
	Infants, 3–5 months	–	675	54.5	0.23	1.08	5.7	34.9	3.7	65.4	43.7	72.3	–
	Adults	7	694	53.0	0.19	0.43	4.75	14.0	1.55	79.3	23.7	71.4	1.6[5]
Epidermis[2]	Adults	–	645	–	0.15	–	3.75	–	7.5	49.6	81.4	–	–
Nails[3]	Newborn	–	–	136	–	–	–	–	–	102	–	–	–
	Adults	–	–	146	0.89	–	22.3	–	4.9	26	–	–	1.5[5]
Hair[4]	Newborn	–	–	–	0.85	–	21.3*	–	3.9◊	75	17	–	–
	Adults	–	41	146	0.21	0.8	5.2	26	–	13	–	–	1.1[5]

* Water-soluble portion 6.0 mmol, water-insoluble portion 15.3 mmol.
◊ Water-soluble portion 1.5 mmol, water-insoluble portion 2.4 mmol.

References
[1] WIDDOWSON and DICKERSON, *Biochem. J.,* **77**, 30 (1960).
[2] SUNTZEFF and CARRUTHERS, *J. biol. Chem.,* **160**, 567 (1945); ZHEUTLIN and FOX, *Arch. Derm.,* **61**, 397 (1950).
[3] JOHNSON et al., *Pediatrics,* **47**, 88 (1971); LOCKARD et al., *Pediatrics,* **49**, 618 (1972); LIM et al., *Clin. chim. Acta,* **42**, 47 (1972).
[4] BAGCHI and GANGULY, *Ann. Biochem.,* **1**, 83 (1941); PERKONS and JERVIS, *J. forens. Sci.,* **7**, 449 (1962); KOPITO et al., *Pediatrics,* **49**, 620 (1972).
[5] CHARNOT, A., quoted after GORDONOFF and MINDER, *Wld Rev. Nutr. Diet.,* **2**, 209 (1960).

Trace elements in nails and hair (median and extreme range per 1 kg of dry tissue)

	Fe	Cu	Zn	Mn	Cr	Se	Pb	Hg
	mg							
Nails								
Men[5]	33 (28–109)	61 (44–102)	153 (132–391)	–	–	–	–	–
Women[5]	29 (14–90)	49 (28–53)	204 (130–360)	–	–	–	–	–
Hair								
Puerperal women[1]	22.1	17.9	136	–	0.12[4]	–	31.5	–
Newborn[1]	30.9	10.9	225	–	0.91[3]	–	13.9	–
Children[2] (0–15 years)	20.8 (2.70–152)	12.1 (1.01–144)	90.5 (10.5–450)	0.56 (0.05–12.0)	0.56 (0.076–4.80)	0.320 (0.025–1.65)	13.5 (2.12–100)	0.672 (0.048–11.3)
Adults[2] (16 years and over)	22.3 (3.60–177)	18.3 (2.22–184)	109 (20.1–313)	0.95 (0.07–11.0)	0.62 (0.06–5.30)	0.303 (0.025–1.58)	12.2 (1.96–155)	0.774 (0.050–14.0)

References
[1] BAUMSLAG et al., *Arch.environm. Hlth*, **29**, 186 (1974).
[2] CREASON et al., *Clin. Chem.*, **21**, 603 (1975).
[3] HAMBIDGE and BAUM, *Amer. J. clin. Nutr.*, **25**, 376 (1972).
[4] MAHALKO and BENNION, *Amer. J. clin. Nutr.*, **29**, 1069 (1976).
[5] HARRISON and TYREE, *Clin. chim. Acta*, **31**, 63 (1971).

Organic constituents of skin, bones and teeth (values per 1 kg of fresh tissue, unless otherwise stated)

		Collagen N	Muco-poly-saccharides
		g	
Skin[1]	Fetuses, 20–22 weeks	2.4	–
	Newborn	16.8	2.9*
	Infants, 4–7 months	39.2	–
	Adults	45.7	2.0*
Bones[2]	Fetuses, 14 weeks	29.2*	–
	Fetuses, 20–24 weeks	40.6*	–
	Newborn	42.0*	–
	Infants, 2–4½ months	44.0*	–
	Infants, 5–9 months	42.7*	–
	Children, 12–24 months	43.7*	2.3◊
	Adults, 18–35 years	41.5*	1.6◊
Teeth			
Enamel[3]	Adults	0.16†	1.0§
Dentin[3]	Adults	30.6–32.4†	2.0–6.0

* Values per 1 kg of fat-free dry tissue.
◊ Values per 1 kg of dry tissue, as glucosamine hydrochloride.
† Values per 1 kg of dry tissue.
§ Value for soluble protein enamel.

References
[1] WIDDOWSON and DICKERSON, *Biochem. J.*, **77**, 30 (1960); LOEWI, G., *Biochim. biophys. Acta*, **52**, 435 (1961).
[2] ROGERS, H. J., *Nature*, **164**, 625 (1949); DICKERSON, J. W., *Biochem. J.*, **82**, 56 (1962).
[3] EASTOE, J. E., in LONG, C. (Ed.), *Biochemists' Handbook*, Spon, London, 1961, page 720.

Trace elements in bones (values per 1 kg of ash, unless otherwise stated)

	Zn[1]	Mn[2]	Al[3]	Sr[4]	Ba[4]	Pb[5]
	mg					
Infants, 0–3 months	–	–	–	79	7	–
Adults	210	2	4*	107	5	29

* Value per 1 kg of dry tissue.

References
[1] SCHROEDER et al., *J. chron. Dis.*, **20**, 179 (1967).
[2] SCHROEDER et al., *J. chron. Dis.*, **19**, 545 (1966).
[3] ALFREY et al., *New Engl. J. Med.*, **294**, 184 (1976).
[4] SOWDEN and STITCH, *Biochem. J.*, **67**, 104 (1957); SCHROEDER et al., *J. chron. Dis.*, **25**, 491 (1972).
[5] CRAWFORD and CLAYTON, *Brit. med. J.*, **2**, 21 (1973).

Trace elements in the skin (values per 1 kg of dry tissue)

	Cu	Zn	Mn
	mg		
Epidermis			
Abdomen	3.9	67	0.45
Foreskin	7.3	132	1.0
Footsole	1.6	49	0.26
Dermis			
Abdomen	1.9	10	0.12
Foreskin	4.2	43	0.31
Footsole	2.8	25	0.28

Reference
MOLOKHIA and PORTNOY, *Brit. J. Derm.*, **82**, 254 (1970).

Body Surface of Children

Nomogram for determination of body surface from height and mass[1]

Height	Body surface	Mass
cm 120 — 47 in	1.10 m²	kg 40.0 — 90 lb

[1] From the formula of Du Bois and Du Bois, *Arch. intern. Med.,* **17**, 863 (1916): $S = M^{0.425} \times H^{0.725} \times 71.84$, or $\log S = \log M \times 0.425 + \log H \times 0.725 + 1.8564$ (S: body surface in cm², M: mass in kg, H: height in cm).

Nomogram for determination of body surface from height and mass[1]

Height	Body surface	Mass

Height		Body surface	Mass	
cm 200	79 in	2.80 m²	kg 150	330 lb
	78	2.70	145	320
195	77		140	310
	76	2.60	135	300
190	75	2.50	130	290
	74			280
185	73	2.40	125	270
	72		120	260
180	71	2.30	115	250
	70	2.20	110	240
175	69			
	68	2.10	105	230
170	67		100	220
	66	2.00	95	210
165	65	1.95		
	64	1.90	90	200
160	63	1.85	85	190
	62	1.80		
155	61	1.75	80	180
	60	1.70		170
150	59	1.65	75	
	58	1.60		160
145	57	1.55	70	150
	56			
140	55	1.50	65	140
	54	1.45		
135	53	1.40	60	130
	52	1.35		
130	51	1.30	55	120
	50			
125	49	1.25	50	110
	48	1.20		105
120	47	1.15	45	100
	46	1.10		95
115	45			90
	44	1.05	40	85
110	43	1.00		80
	42	0.95	35	75
105	41			70
	40	0.90		
cm 100	39 in	0.86 m²	kg 30	66 lb

[1] From the formula of Du Bois and Du Bois, *Arch. intern. Med.,* **17**, 863 (1916): $S = M^{0.425} \times H^{0.725} \times 71.84$, or $\log S = \log M \times 0.425 + \log H \times 0.725 + 1.8564$ (S: body surface in cm², M: mass in kg, H: height in cm).

Table 1   *Energy expenditure at different levels of exertion*[25]

	Men*		Women*	
	kcal/min	kJ/min	kcal/min	kJ/min
Bed-rest..	1.08	4.52	0.90	3.77
Sitting	1.39	5.82	1.15	4.82
Standing...	1.75	7.32	1.37	5.73
Walking (4.9 km/h)..................................	3.7	15.5	3.0	12.6
Walking (4.9 km/h with a 10-kg load)..........	4.0	16.7	3.4	14.2
Office work (sedentary)	1.8	7.5	1.6	6.7
Domestic work (cooking, light cleaning, window-cleaning)	2.1–4.3	8.8–18.0	1.7–3.5	7.1–14.6
Light industry (printing, tailoring, bakery work, electrical industry, chemical industry).....................	2.3–4.1	9.6–17.2	1.9–3.2	7.9–13.4
Building industry	3.2–6.0	13.4–25.1	–	–
Farming (driving tractor, forking, feeding animals, threshing, etc.)...........	2.4–7.8	10.0–32.6	2.4–6.8	10.0–23.0
Forestry	4.1–8.6	17.2–36.0	–	–
Mining...	5.6–6.9	23.4–28.9	–	–
Sports				
light (golf, sailing, billiards, bowls).............	2.5–5.0	10.5–21.0	2.0–4.0	8.3–16.7
moderate (dancing, horse-riding, tennis, swimming)......................	5.0–7.5	21.0–31.5	4.0–6.0	16.7–25.1
heavy (athletics, rowing, soccer)................	≥ 7.5	≥ 31.5	≥ 6.0	≥ 25.0
Armed services (cleaning kit, drill, marching, etc.)	2.7–6.5	11.3–27.2	–	–

* Values refer to a body mass of 65 kg for men and 55 kg for women.

The expenditure of energy may be related to a state of rest or to different degrees of physical exertion (Table 1). Even under conditions of physical and mental rest, energy expenditure is not a precisely definable quantity (Fig. 1). Therefore, for purposes of medical investigation, it is measured under standardized conditions, that is, in the morning, recumbent, fasting and at a neutral temperature, and the quantity so measured is termed 'basal metabolism' or 'energy expenditure at rest'. Basal metabolism denotes the unavoidable thermal loss associated with cellular metabolism and physiologic functions sustained at repose, such as blood circulation, respiration, digestion and involuntary muscle tone. Basal metabolism is above all a function of hepatic metabolism (see Table 2).

Basal metabolism is a function of a number of factors[2, 3], in particular sex, height, mass and composition of the body, age and hormonal balance; fluctuations have been observed according to the time of day, the seasons and climatic influences.

Standard basal metabolic values are commonly expressed in terms of body surface and, in the case of children, body mass[4] (for

methods of determination of body surface, see pages 226 and 227). Inasmuch as the metabolism of adipose tissue is modest compared to that of muscle tissue, it has been suggested that basal metabolism be expressed in terms of fat-free body mass, active cellular mass, muscular mass or similar physical parameters[5].

The discrepancies between the basal metabolism of men and women[6] and the declining rate in advanced age[7] largely disappear when compared to the fat-free body mass (see also Table 3).

In the course of gestation, basal metabolism rises on account of the oxygen consumption of the uterus, placenta and fetus[9].

Table 2   *Contribution of different organs to basal metabolism*[1]

Organ	Organ mass		Oxygen consumption		Contribution to basal metabolism as percent
	Total organ	As percent of body mass	Per unit of organ mass	Per total organ mass	
	kg		mL min⁻¹ kg⁻¹	mL min⁻¹	
(a) Liver	1.5	2.1	44	66	26.4
(b) Brain.........	1.4	2.0	33	46	18.3
(c) Heart	0.3	0.43	94	23	9.2
(d) Kidneys	0.3	0.43	61	18	7.2
Subtotal (a)–(d)..	...	...	...	153	61.1
(e) Skeletal muscle	27.8	39.7	2.3	64	25.6
Total (a)–(e)	...	...	...	217	86.7

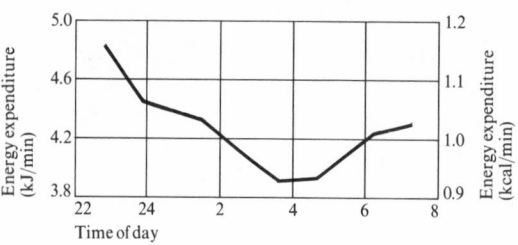

Fig. 1. Energy expenditure of adult during nighttime rest[8].

Table 3   *Provisional standards for energy expenditure of recumbent adults*[8]

Body mass in kg:			45	50	55	60	65	70	75	80	45	50	55	60	65	70	75	80
Fat	Built		Energy expenditure															
%	Men	Women	kcal/min								kJ/min							
5–9	Thin	–	–	0.99	1.06	1.12	1.19	1.26	1.32	1.39	–	4.14	4.44	4.69	4.98	5.27	5.52	5.82
10–14	Average	–	–	0.94	1.01	1.08	1.14	1.21	1.28	1.34	–	3.93	4.23	4.52	4.77	5.06	5.36	5.61
15–19	Plump	Thin	0.82	0.89	0.96	1.03	1.09	1.16	1.23	1.30	3.43	3.73	4.02	4.31	4.56	4.86	5.15	5.44
20–24	Fat	Average	0.78	0.84	0.91	0.98	1.05	1.11	1.18	1.25	3.26	3.52	3.81	4.10	4.39	4.65	4.94	5.23
25–29	–	Plump	–	0.80	0.86	0.93	1.00	1.07	1.13	1.20	–	3.35	3.60	3.89	4.19	4.48	4.73	5.02
>30	–	Fat	–	–	0.81	0.88	0.95	1.02	1.08	1.15	–	–	3.39	3.68	3.98	4.27	4.52	4.81

Table 4 *Standard basal metabolism rates*

	kcal h⁻¹ m⁻²						kJ h⁻¹ m⁻²						
	Men			Women				Men			Women		
Age in years	Standard of DuBois[15]		Standard of Fleisch[13]	Standard of DuBois[15]		Standard of Fleisch[13]	Age in years	Standard of DuBois[15]		Standard of Fleisch[13]	Standard of DuBois[15]		Standard of Fleisch[13]
	Mean*	95% range*	Mean◇	Mean*	95% range*	Mean◇		Mean*	95% range*	Mean◇	Mean*	95% range*	Mean◇
1	–	–	53.0	–	–	53.0	1	–	–	222	–	–	222
2	–	–	52.4	–	–	52.4	2	–	–	219	–	–	219
3	60.1	51.8–68.3	51.3	54.5	47.0–62.0	51.2	3	252	217–286	215	228	197–260	214
4	57.9	49.9–65.9	50.3	53.9	46.5–61.3	49.8	4	242	209–276	211	226	195–257	208
5	56.3	48.5–64.1	49.3	53.0	45.7–60.3	48.4	5	236	203–268	206	222	191–252	203
6	54.0	46.5–61.5	48.3	51.2	44.1–58.3	47.0	6	226	195–257	202	214	185–244	197
7	52.3	45.1–59.5	47.3	49.7	42.8–56.6	45.4	7	219	189–249	198	208	179–237	190
8	50.8	43.8–57.8	46.3	48.0	41.4–54.6	43.8	8	213	183–242	194	201	173–229	183
9	49.5	42.7–56.3	45.2	46.2	39.8–52.6	42.8	9	207	179–236	189	193	167–220	179
10	47.7	41.1–54.3	44.0	44.9	38.7–51.1	42.5	10	200	172–227	184	188	162–214	178
11	46.5	40.1–52.9	43.0	44.1	38.0–50.2	42.0	11	195	168–221	180	185	159–210	176
12	45.3	39.0–51.6	42.5	42.0	36.2–47.8	41.3	12	190	163–216	178	176	152–200	173
13	44.5	38.4–50.6	42.3	40.5	34.9–46.1	40.3	13	186	161–212	177	170	146–193	169
14	43.8	37.8–49.8	42.1	39.2	33.8–44.6	39.2	14	183	158–208	176	164	141–187	164
15	43.7	37.7–49.7	41.8	38.3	33.0–43.6	37.9	15	182	158–208	175	160	138–182	159
16	42.9	37.0–48.8	41.4	37.7	32.5–42.9	36.9	16	180	155–204	173	158	136–180	154
17	41.9	36.1–47.7	40.8	36.2	31.2–41.2	36.3	17	175	151–200	171	152	131–172	152
18	40.5	34.9–46.1	40.0	35.7	30.8–40.6	35.9	18	170	146–193	167	149	129–170	150
19	40.1	34.6–45.6	39.2	35.4	30.5–40.3	35.5	19	168	145–191	164	148	128–169	149
20	39.8	34.3–45.3	38.6	35.3	30.4–40.2	35.3	20	167	144–190	162	148	127–168	148
21	39.4	34.0–44.8	–	35.2	30.3–40.1	–	21	165	142–188	–	147	127–168	–
22	39.2	33.8–44.6	–	35.2	30.3–40.1	–	22	164	141–187	–	147	127–168	–
23	39.0	33.6–44.4	–	35.2	30.3–40.1	–	23	163	141–186	–	147	127–168	–
24	38.7	33.4–44.0	–	35.1	30.3–39.9	–	24	162	140–184	–	147	127–167	–
25	38.4	33.1–43.7	37.5	35.1	30.3–39.9	35.2	25	161	139–183	157	147	127–167	147
26	38.2	32.9–43.5	–	35.0	30.2–39.8	–	26	160	138–182	–	146	126–167	–
27	38.0	32.8–43.2	–	35.0	30.2–39.8	–	27	159	137–181	–	146	126–167	–
28	37.8	32.6–43.0	–	35.0	30.2–39.8	–	28	158	136–180	–	146	126–167	–
29	37.7	32.5–42.9	–	35.0	30.2–39.8	–	29	158	136–180	–	146	126–167	–
30	37.6	32.4–42.8	36.8	35.0	30.2–39.8	35.1	30	157	136–179	154	146	126–167	147
31	37.4	32.2–42.6	–	35.0	30.2–39.8	–	31	157	135–178	–	146	126–167	–
32	37.2	32.1–42.3	–	34.9	30.1–39.7	–	32	156	134–177	–	146	126–166	–
33	37.1	32.0–42.2	–	34.9	30.1–39.7	–	33	155	134–177	–	146	126–166	–
34	37.0	31.9–42.1	–	34.9	30.1–39.7	–	34	155	134–176	–	146	126–166	–
35	36.9	31.8–42.0	36.5	34.8	30.0–39.6	35.0	35	154	133–176	153	146	126–166	146
36	36.8	31.7–41.9	–	34.7	29.9–39.5	–	36	154	133–175	–	145	125–165	–
37	36.7	31.6–41.8	–	34.6	29.8–39.4	–	37	154	132–175	–	145	125–165	–
38	36.7	31.6–41.8	–	34.5	29.7–39.3	–	38	154	132–175	–	144	124–164	–
39	36.6	31.5–41.7	–	34.4	29.7–39.1	–	39	153	132–175	–	144	124–164	–
40	36.5	31.5–41.5	36.3	34.3	29.6–39.0	34.9	40	153	132–174	152	144	124–163	146
45	36.3	31.3–41.3	36.2	33.9	29.2–38.6	34.5	45	152	131–173	152	142	122–162	144
50	36.0	31.0–40.0	35.8	33.4	28.8–38.0	33.9	50	151	130–167	150	140	121–159	142
55	35.4	30.5–40.3	34.9	32.9	28.4–37.4	33.3	55	148	128–169	148	138	119–157	139
60	34.8	30.0–39.6	34.9	32.4	27.9–36.9	32.7	60	146	126–166	146	136	117–154	137
65	34.0	29.3–38.7	34.4	31.8	27.4–36.2	32.2	65	142	123–162	144	133	115–152	135
70	33.1	28.5–37.7	33.8	31.3	27.0–35.6	31.7	70	139	119–158	141	131	113–149	133
≧75	31.8	27.4–36.2	33.2	31.1	26.8–35.4	31.3	≧75	133	115–152	139	130	112–148	131

* Values for 4016 determinations. The standard range was calculated on the basis of a mean coefficient of variation of 6.9. Elaboration based on data of Mayo Foundation Standards by BOOTHBY, BERKSON and DUNN; British

Standards by ROBERTSON and REID, as well as Carnegie Nutrition Laboratory Standards by HARRISON and BENEDICT.
◇ Values derived from 24 different publications.

Commonly known standards of basal metabolism include those of HARRIS and BENEDICT[10], BOOTHBY et al.[11], ROBERTSON and REID[12], as well as FLEISCH[13]. Standard rates for children and adults are shown in Tables 3–5. For details pertaining to the basal metabolism of newborn[16], infants[17] and children[18], see the bibliographic references.

On a pathologic plane, basal metabolism is above all affected by pituitary, thyroid and adrenocortical function: hyperactivity of these glands tends to increase basal metabolism, while hypoactivity leads to declines. A specific form of hypermetabolism, based on interference with mitochondrial respiration, has been reported in 1 subject[19].

Determination of energy expenditure

The calorimetric determination of energy expenditures requires extensive apparatus. For this reason, practical determination is mostly based on oxygen consumption, carbon dioxide liberation and, where greater accuracy is desired, the amount of nitrogen ex-

Table 5 *Standard basal metabolism rates in infants and children*[14]

1 week to 10 months*			11–38 months*						3–16 years				
Body mass	Boys and girls		Body mass	Boys		Girls		Body mass	Boys		Girls		
kg	kcal/h	kJ/h	kg	kcal/h	kJ/h	kcal/h	kJ/h	kg	kcal/h	kJ/h	kcal/h	kJ/h
3.5	8.4	35	9	22.0	92	21.2	89	15	35.8	150	33.3	139
4.0	9.5	40	9.5	22.8	95	22.0	92	20	39.7	166	37.4	157
4.5	10.5	44	10.0	23.6	99	22.8	95	25	43.6	182	41.5	174
5.0	11.6	49	10.5	24.4	102	23.6	99	30	47.5	199	45.5	190
5.5	12.7	53	11.0	25.2	105	24.4	102	35	51.3	215	49.6	208
6.0	13.8	58	11.5	26.0	109	25.2	105	40	55.2	231	53.7	225
6.5	14.9	62	12.0	26.8	112	26.0	109	45	59.1	247	57.8	242
7.0	16.0	67	12.5	27.6	116	26.9	113	50	63.0	264	61.9	259
7.5	17.1	72	13.0	28.4	119	27.7	116	55	66.9	280	66.0	276
8.0	18.2	76	13.5	29.2	122	28.5	119	60	70.8	296	70.0	293
8.5	19.3	81	14.0	30.0	126	29.3	123	65	74.7	313	74.0	310
9.0	20.4	85	14.5	30.8	129	30.1	126	70	78.6	329	78.1	326
9.5	21.4	90	15.0	31.6	132	30.9	129	75	82.5	345	82.2	344
10.0	22.5	94	15.5	32.4	136	31.7	133					
10.5	23.6	99	16.0	33.2	139	32.6	136					
11.0	24.7	103	16.5	34.0	142	33.4	140					

*The values measured on sleeping children aged up to 38 months rest on 'basal' thermal production, including specific dynamic effects of nourishment.

Table 6 *Oxygen consumption, carbon dioxide excretion and energetic value of 1 g of protein, fat and carbohydrates burnt by the body, or nitrogen excreted in urine*[24]

	Oxygen consumption	Carbon dioxide liberation	RQ	kcal/g		kJ/g		kcal/L		kJ/L	
	mL/g			According to RUBNER	According to LOEWY	According to RUBNER	According to LOEWY	Oxygen	Carbon dioxide	Oxygen	Carbon dioxide
Proteins.................	966.3	773.9	0.801	4.10	4.316	17.2	18.06	4.485	5.579	18.77	23.35
Urinary nitrogen (UN)...	5939.0	4757.0	0.801	25.63	26.54	107.3	111.1	4.485	5.579	18.77	23.35
Fats......................	2019.3	1427.3	0.707	9.3	9.461	38.9	39.60	4.686	6.629	19.61	27.75
Carbohydrates	828.8	828.8	1.000	4.1	4.182	17.2	17.50	5.047	5.047	21.12	21.12

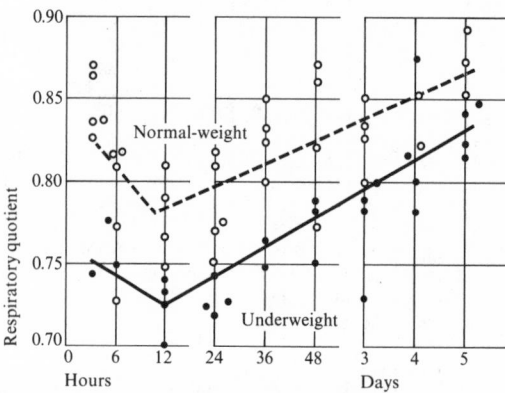

Fig. 2. Respiratory quotient in 8 normal-weight and 6 underweight newborn during the first five days of life. First feeding of milk after 12 hours[16].

creted in the urine. The volume of gases is converted to STPD (standard temperature and pressure, dry).

The numerical relationship between carbon dioxide exhaled ($\dot{V}_{CO_2}$) and oxygen consumed ($\dot{V}_{O_2}$) yields the so-called *respiratory quotient* (RQ):

$$RQ = \frac{\dot{V}_{CO_2}}{\dot{V}_{O_2}}$$

In the combustion of glucose, the volume of carbon dioxide liberated in the process is equal to the oxygen consumption; the res-

piratory quotient is equal to 1 (Table 6). Under basal conditions, the quotient is 0.82 in older children and adults[23]. Moderate exertion has little effect on it, but after one minute of heavy exertion it may rise as high as 1.50[23]. A drop of the respiratory quotient in the first 24 hours (Fig. 2) suggests that more fat is being burnt[20].

The following equations lend themselves to the calculation of energy expenditure, where $\dot{E}$ stands for energy expenditure [in kcal] per unit of time; $\dot{V}_{O_2}$ is the oxygen consumption [in L] per unit of time; $\dot{V}_{CO_2}$ is the carbon dioxide excretion [in L] per unit of time; and $\dot{U}_N$ is the nitrogen excreted in urine [in g] per unit of time:

$$\dot{E} = 4.825 \, \dot{V}_{O_2} \tag{1}$$

(if the determination is limited to oxygen consumption)

$$\dot{E} = 3.941 \, \dot{V}_{O_2} + 1.106 \, \dot{V}_{CO_2} \tag{2a}$$
$$\dot{E} = 3.78 \, \dot{V}_{O_2} + 1.16 \, \dot{V}_{CO_2} \tag{2b}$$

(if both oxygen consumption and carbon dioxide liberation are measured)

$$\dot{E} = 3.941 \, \dot{V}_{O_2} + 1.106 \, \dot{V}_{CO_2} - 2.17 \, \dot{U}_N \tag{3a}$$
$$\dot{E} = 3.78 \, \dot{V}_{O_2} + 1.16 \, \dot{V}_{CO_2} - 2.98 \, \dot{U}_N \tag{3b}$$

(where the protein metabolism is additionally taken into account).

Equation (1)[21] is based on the assumption of an RQ of 0.82. Equations (2a) and (3a)[22] are based on the calorie tables of LOEWY, and equations (2b) and (3b)[23] on those of RUBNER.

References

[1] BROŽEK and GRANDE, cited in KINNEY et al., *Ann. N. Y. Acad. Sci.*, **110**, 711 (1963).
[2] KRAUT and ZIMMERMANN, in FLASCHENTRÄGER and LEHNARTZ (Eds.), *Physiologische Chemie*, volume II/2c, Springer, Berlin, 1959, page 520; TATA, J. R., *Advanc. metab. Disord.*, **1**, 153 (1964); SWIFT and FISHER, in BEATON and McHENRY (Eds.), *Nutrition*, volume 1, Academic Press, New York, 1964, page 181.

[3] SUZUKI, S., *Wld Rev. Nutr. Diet.,* **1**, 103 (1959).

[4] HILL, J. R., in JONXIS et al. (Eds.), *Nutricia Symposium on the Adaptation of the Newborn Infant to Extra-Uterine Life,* Kroese, Leiden, 1964, page 223.

[5] MILLER and BLYTH, *J. appl. Physiol.,* **5**, 311 (1953); MILLER, A. T., *Meth. med. Res.,* **6**, 74 (1954); KINNEY et al., *Ann. N. Y. Acad. Sci.,* **110**, 711 (1963).

[6] LJUNGGREN, H., in BROŽEK, J. (Ed.), *Human Body Composition,* Pergamon Press, Oxford, 1965, page 129.

[7] KEYS et al., *Metabolism,* **22**, 579 (1973).

[8] DURNIN and PASSMORE, *Energy, Work and Leisure,* Heinemann, London, 1967.

[9] HYTTEN and LIND, *Diagnostic Indices in Pregnancy,* CIBA-GEIGY Ltd., Basle, 1973.

[10] HARRIS and BENEDICT, *A Biometric Study of Basal Metabolism in Man,* Publication No. 279 of the Carnegie Institution, Washington, 1919.

[11] BOOTHBY et al., *Amer. J. Physiol.,* **116**, 468 (1936).

[12] ROBERTSON and REID, *Lancet,* **1**, 940 (1952).

[13] FLEISCH, A., *Helv. med. Acta,* **18**, 23 (1951).

[14] JOHNSON, H. L., in ALTMAN and DITTMER (Eds.), *Metabolism,* Federation of American Societies for Experimental Biology, Bethesda (Md.), 1968, page 344.

[15] DUBOIS, E. F., in ALTMAN and DITTMER (Eds.), *Metabolism,* Federation of American Societies for Experimental Biology, Bethesda (Md.), 1968, page 345.

[16] SENTERRE and KARLBERG, *Acta paediat. scand.,* **59**, 653 (1970).

[17] KARLBERG, P., *Acta paediat. (Uppsala),* **41**, suppl. 89 (1952).

[18] SARGENT, D. W., *An Evaluation of Basal Metabolic Data for Children and Youth in the United States,* Home Economics Research Report, No. 14, United States Department of Agriculture, Washington, 1961.

[19] ERNSTER and LUFT, *Advanc. metab. Disord.,* **1**, 95 (1964).

[20] SMITH, C. A., in SMITH and NELSON, *The Physiology of the Newborn Infant,* 4th ed., Thomas, Springfield (Ill.), 1976, page 480.

[21] LUSK, G., *J. biol. Chem.,* **59**, 41 (1924).

[22] WEIR, J. B. DE V., *J. Physiol. (Lond.),* **109**, 1 (1949).

[23] CONSOLAZIO et al., *Physiological Measurements of Metabolic Functions in Man,* McGraw-Hill, New York, 1963, page 315.

[24] According to PETERS and VAN SLYKE, *Quantitative Clinical Chemistry,* 2nd ed., volume 1, Williams & Wilkins, Baltimore, 1946, page 3.

[25] Joint FAO/WHO *ad hoc* Expert Committee on Energy and Protein Requirements, *Wld Hlth Org. techn. Rep. Ser.,* No. 522 (1973).

Dietary standards are used for two primary purposes[1]: to plan diets for individuals or groups of people, and to evaluate the nutritional adequacy of the foods eaten. In view of the largely unknown inter- and intraindividual variations in nutritional requirements it is considered doubtful whether a single list of recommendations could do justice to both these aims[2].

Published recommendations reflect the current state of knowledge in the field of nutritional physiology – without however in every case taking account of the most recent research findings[3]. Interpretations of the results of fundamental research on the minimum, average and optimum dietary requirements differ considerably, with the result that the recommendations made by expert committees in different countries may deviate from one another in some respects[4-6]. Most of the established dietary recommendations (but not energy allowances) are estimates of 'minimal no-risk levels of intake', and they will be above the actual need of practically everyone in the group concerned.

In this chapter, pride of place is given to the recommendations of the Expert Committees of the FAO/WHO[7-12], of the Food and Nutrition Board of the National Research Council, USA[13], and of the Department of Health and Social Security, UK[14].

Energy

In contrast to the allowances of individual nutrients, the energy allowance is established at a level thought to be consonant with good health in average persons in each age group and within a given category. The energy requirement is made up of the basal (resting) metabolic rate, the specific dynamic effect of the food consumed (14–16% of the caloric value of the protein, 5–6% of that of the carbohydrate, and 2–3% of that of the fat[15]), together with the energy expended in bodily activity. The basal (resting) metabolic rate (page 228) depends on the body mass, body height, and age. Provided data for the same degree of bodily activity are compared, there is seen to be a fairly good measure of agreement between the recommendations of the various expert committees. Table 1 shows energy requirements as a function of body mass and degree of bodily activity. These data are based on the energy requirement values for the reference subject, as shown in Table 2[10]. The energy requirements for various kinds of bodily activity are to be found in Table 1 on page 228.

According to the FAO/WHO Expert Committee[10], the energy requirement falls at the rate of 5% per decade between the ages of 40 and 59 years, by 10% during the decade 60–69 years, and by a

Table 1 *Effect of body mass and degree of bodily activity on daily energy requirements (FAO/WHO)[10]*

Body mass	Light activity		Moderately active		Very active		Exceptionally active	
	kcal	MJ	kcal	MJ	kcal	MJ	kcal	MJ
Men								
50 kg......	2100	8.8	2300	9.6	2700	11.3	3100	13.0
55 kg......	2310	9.7	2530	10.6	2970	12.4	3410	14.3
60 kg......	2520	10.5	2760	11.5	3240	13.6	3720	15.6
65 kg......	2700	11.3	3000	12.5	3500	14.6	4000	16.7
70 kg......	2940	12.3	3220	13.5	3780	15.8	4340	18.2
75 kg......	3150	13.2	3450	14.4	4050	16.9	4650	19.5
80 kg......	3360	14.1	3680	15.4	4320	18.1	4960	20.8
Women								
40 kg......	1440	6.0	1600	6.7	1880	7.9	2200	9.2
45 kg......	1620	6.8	1800	7.5	2120	8.9	2480	10.4
50 kg......	1800	7.5	2000	8.4	2350	9.8	2750	11.5
55 kg......	2000	8.4	2200	9.2	2600	10.9	3000	12.6
60 kg......	2160	9.0	2400	10.0	2820	11.8	3300	13.8
65 kg......	2340	9.8	2600	10.9	3055	12.8	3575	15.0
70 kg......	2520	10.5	2800	11.7	3290	13.8	3850	16.1

Table 2 *Energy requirement of reference subjects for various degrees of bodily activity[10]*

Bodily activity	Men (65 kg)		Women (55 kg)	
	kcal/min	kJ/min	kcal/min	kJ/min
Light activity	2.3	9.6	1.7	6.9
Moderately active.........	2.9	12.3	2.1	8.8
Very active................	4.0	16.7	2.9	12.3
Exceptionally active.......	5.0	20.8	3.8	15.6

Table 3 *Recommended daily intakes of energy and nutrients (FAO/WHO)[12]*

Age	Sex	Body mass	Energy		Protein[a]	Vitamin A activity[b]	D[c]	Thiamine	Riboflavin	Niacin	Folic acid[d]	B12	Ascorbic acid	Calcium	Iron[e]
		kg	kcal	MJ	g	µg	µg	mg	mg	mg	µg	µg	mg	g	mg
< 1 year ...		7.3	820	3.4	14	300	10	0.3	0.5	5.4	60	0.3	20	0.5–0.6	5–10
1–3 years...		13.4	1360	5.7	16	250	10	0.5	0.8	9.0	100	0.9	20	0.4–0.5	5–10
4–6 years...		20.2	1830	7.6	20	300	10	0.7	1.1	12.1	100	1.5	20	0.4–0.5	5–10
7–9 years...		28.1	2190	9.2	25	400	2.5	0.9	1.3	14.5	100	1.5	20	0.4–0.5	5–10
10–12 years	Boys	36.9	2600	10.9	30	575	2.5	1.0	1.6	17.2	100	2.0	20	0.6–0.7	5–10
	Girls	38.0	2350	9.8	29	575	2.5	0.9	1.4	15.5	100	2.0	20	0.6–0.7	5–10
13–15 years	Boys	51.3	2900	12.1	37	725	2.5	1.2	1.7	19.1	200	2.0	30	0.6–0.7	9–18
	Girls	49.9	2490	10.4	31	725	2.5	1.0	1.5	16.4	200	2.0	30	0.6–0.7	12–24
16–19 years	Boys	62.9	3070	12.8	38	750	2.5	1.2	1.8	20.3	200	2.0	30	0.5–0.6	5–9
	Girls	54.4	2310	9.7	30	750	2.5	0.9	1.4	15.2	200	2.0	30	0.5–0.6	14–28
Adults	Men (moderately active) ...	65.0	3000	12.6	37	750	2.5	1.2	1.8	19.8	200	2.0	30	0.4–0.5	5–9
	Women (moderately active)	55.0	2200	9.2	29	750	2.5	0.9	1.3	14.5	200	2.0	30	0.4–0.5	14–28
	Pregnancy (2nd half).......	–	+350	+1.5	38	750	10	+0.1	+0.2	+2.3	400	3.0	50	1.0–1.2	*
	Lactation (1st 6 months) ...	–	+550	+2.3	46	1200	10	+0.2	+0.4	+3.7	300	2.5	50	1.0–1.2	*

[a] As egg or milk protein.
[b] As retinol equivalents.
[c] As cholecalciferol.
[d] 'Free' folic acid (pteroylmono-, pteroyldi- and pteroyltriglutamic acids).
[e] On each line the lower value applies when over 25% of calories in the diet come from animal foods, and the higher value when animal foods represent less than 10% of calories.

* For women whose iron intake throughout life has been at the level recommended in this table, the daily intake of iron during pregnancy and lactation should be the same as that recommended for nonpregnant, nonlactating women of childbearing age. For women whose iron status is not satisfactory at the beginning of pregnancy, the requirement is increased, and in the extreme situation of women with no iron stores, the requirement can probably not be met without supplementation.

Table 4 *Recommended daily intakes of energy* and nutrients◊ (Food and Nutrition Board, USA)[13]*

Sex and age category	Body mass kg	Body height cm	Energy kcal	Energy MJ	Protein g	Vitamin A activity[a] µg	D[b] µg	E[c] mg	Thiamine mg	Riboflavin mg	Niacin[d] mg	B6 mg	Folic acid[e] µg	B12 µg	Ascorbic acid mg	Calcium mg	Phosphorus mg	Magnesium mg	Iron mg	Zinc mg	Iodine µg
Infants																					
0–6 months	6	60	f115	f0.48	f2.2	420	10	3	0.3	0.4	6	0.3	30	0.5	35	360	240	50	10	3	40
6–12 months	9	71	f105	f0.44	f2.0	400	10	4	0.5	0.6	8	0.6	45	1.5	35	540	360	70	15	5	50
Children																					
1–3 years...	13	90	1300	5.5	23	400	10	5	0.7	0.8	9	0.9	100	2.0	45	800	800	150	15	10	70
4–6 years...	20	112	1700	7.1	30	500	10	6	0.9	1.0	11	1.3	200	2.5	45	800	800	200	10	10	90
7–10 years .	28	132	2400	10.1	34	700	10	7	1.2	1.4	16	1.6	300	3.0	45	800	800	250	10	10	120
Males																					
11–14 years	45	157	2700	11.3	45	1000	10	8	1.4	1.6	18	1.8	400	3.0	50	1200	1200	350	18	15	150
15–18 years	66	176	2800	11.8	56	1000	10	10	1.4	1.7	18	2.0	400	3.0	60	1200	1200	400	18	15	150
19–22 years	70	177	2900	12.2	56	1000	7.5	10	1.5	1.7	19	2.2	400	3.0	60	800	800	350	10	15	150
23–50 years	70	178	2700	11.3	56	1000	5	10	1.4	1.6	18	2.2	400	3.0	60	800	800	350	10	15	150
≥51 years .	70	178	2400	10.1	56	1000	5	10	1.2	1.4	16	2.2	400	3.0	60	800	800	350	10	15	150
Females																					
11–14 years	46	157	2200	9.2	46	800	10	8	1.1	1.3	15	1.8	400	3.0	50	1200	1200	300	18	15	150
15–18 years	55	163	2100	8.8	46	800	10	8	1.1	1.3	14	2.0	400	3.0	60	1200	1200	300	18	15	150
19–22 years	55	163	2100	8.8	44	800	7.5	8	1.1	1.3	14	2.0	400	3.0	60	800	800	300	18	15	150
23–50 years	55	163	2000	8.4	44	800	5	8	1.0	1.2	13	2.0	400	3.0	60	800	800	300	18	15	150
≥51 years .	55	163	1800	7.6	44	800	5	8	1.0	1.2	13	2.0	400	3.0	60	800	800	300	10	15	150
Pregnant...	–	–	+300	+1.3	+30	+200	+5	+2	+0.4	+0.3	+2	+0.6	+400	+1.0	+20	+400	+400	+150	g	+5	+25
Lactating ..	–	–	+500	+2.1	+20	+400	+5	+3	+0.5	+0.5	+5	+0.5	+100	+1.0	+40	+400	+400	+150	g	+10	+50

* The energy allowances for the young adults are for men and women doing light work. The allowances for the two older age groups represent mean energy needs over these age spans, allowing for a 2-percent decrease in basal (resting) metabolic rate per decade and a reduction in activity of 200 kcal per day for men and women between 51 and 75 years. Energy allowances for children through age 18 are based on median energy intakes of children of these ages followed in longitudinal growth studies.

◊ The allowances are intended to provide for individual variations among most normal persons as they live in the United States under usual environmental stresses. Diets should be based on a variety of common foods in order to provide other nutrients for which human requirements have been less well defined.

[a] Retinol equivalents.

[b] As cholecalciferol. 10 µg cholecalciferol are equal to 400 IU of vitamin D.

[c] α-tocopherol equivalents. See text for calculation of vitamin E activity of the diet as α-tocopherol equivalents.

[d] Niacin equivalents. 1 niacin equivalent is equal to 1 mg of niacin or 60 mg of dietary tryptophan.

[e] The allowances refer to dietary sources as determined by *Lactobacillus casei* assay after treatment with enzymes (conjugases) to make polyglutamyl forms of the vitamin available to the test organism.

[f] Per 1 kg body mass.

[g] During pregnancy, the use of 30–60 mg of supplemental iron is recommended. During lactation, continued supplementation of the mother for 2 to 3 months after parturition is advisable in order to replenish stores depleted by pregnancy.

further 10% over the age of 70. The Food and Nutrition Board, USA[13], proposes a 10% reduction of the energy allowance between the ages of 51 and 75 years and a 20–25% reduction over the age of 75.

The effect of ambient temperature on the energy requirement is less than was formerly supposed. The FAO/WHO Expert Committee[10] sees no reason to make any allowance for climate in calculating the energy requirement. The Food and Nutrition Board, USA[13], considers that the energy cost of work is roughly 5% greater at temperatures below 14 °C and that there is an additional small increase in energy expenditure due to heavy clothing. In men performing heavy work the energy requirement is increased at temperatures of 30 °C and above.

In infants during the first 6 months of life the energy requirement can be calculated from the amount of breast milk necessary for normal growth. The recommended energy allowances for children and adolescents are governed by the individual differences in the rate of growth and development and in the degree of bodily activity. The energy cost of a 9 months' pregnancy is about 335 MJ (80000 kcal). The production of breast milk requires some 3.8 MJ (900 kcal)[13].

Consumption of alcohol must be taken into account in calculating energy allowances. Thus a man weighing 65 kg can oxidize a maximum of 100 g alcohol daily, with a resulting energy gain of 2.9 MJ (700 kcal)[10].

Protein

The recommended desirable protein intakes of the Food and Nutrition Board, USA ('protein allowance')[13], and of the FAO/ WHO ('safe level of protein intake')[10] are based on similar considerations: from assays of the nitrogen balance, an average protein requirement of 0.45 g/d per 1 kg body mass can be derived. This must be increased by 30% to allow for loss of efficiency of the standard reference protein. The allowance of high-quality protein – enough to meet the needs of almost all healthy individuals – is therefore 0.6 g/d per 1 kg body mass. After making a further correction for the 75% efficiency of protein utilization in a mixed diet, the allowance arrived at for the mixed proteins of the US diet is 0.8 g/d per 1 kg body mass[13]. The recommendations of the FAO/WHO on the other hand are for proteins of high biological value (milk protein, egg protein), so that the intakes must be increased when proteins of lower value are consumed (Table 6). The basis for the recommendations in respect of infants is the amount of milk protein necessary to ensure normal growth. In relation to body mass, underweight premature infants have a higher protein requirement[16], though the actual requirement is a matter of discussion[17]. The recommendations for children are likewise based on the amount of protein required for normal growth. The recommendations for pregnant women made by the FAO/WHO differ from those of the Food and Nutrition Board, USA.

The recommended protein intakes are conditional on the energy requirement being met, since otherwise the protein consumed would be used for energy production. On the basis of long-term balance studies, it has recently been suggested that even when energy requirements are adequately met, the recommended protein intakes of the FAO/WHO and of the Food and Nutrition Board, USA, may not be able to guarantee sufficient protein for the needs of all persons[18].

Table 5   *Recommended daily intakes of energy and nutrients (Department of Health and Social Security, UK)[14]*

Sex and age category	Occupational category	Energy kcal	Energy MJ	Protein[a] g	A[b] µg	D[c] µg	Thiamine mg	Riboflavin mg	Niacin[d] mg	Total folic acid[e] µg	Ascorbic acid mg	Calcium mg	Iron mg
Boys													
< 1 year		–	–	–	450	7.5	0.3	0.4	5	50	20	600	6
1 year		1200	5.0	30	300	10	0.5	0.6	7	100	20	600	7
2 years		1400	5.75	35	300	10	0.6	0.7	8	100	20	600	7
3–4 years		1560	6.5	39	300	10	0.6	0.8	9	100	20	600	8
5–6 years		1740	7.25	43	300	f	0.7	0.9	10	200	20	600	10
7–8 years		1980	8.25	49	400	f	0.8	1.0	11	200	20	600	10
9–11 years		2280	9.5	57	575	f	0.9	1.2	14	200	25	700	12
12–14 years		2640	11.0	66	725	f	1.1	1.4	16	300	25	700	12
15–17 years		2880	12.0	72	750	f	1.2	1.7	19	300	30	600	12
Girls													
< 1 year		–	–	–	450	7.5	0.3	0.4	5	50	20	600	6
1 year		1100	4.5	27	300	10	0.4	0.6	7	100	20	600	7
2 years		1300	5.5	32	300	10	0.5	0.7	8	100	20	600	7
3–4 years		1500	6.25	37	300	10	0.6	0.8	9	100	20	600	8
5–6 years		1680	7.0	42	300	f	0.7	0.9	10	200	20	600	10
7–8 years		1900	8.0	47	400	f	0.8	1.0	11	200	20	600	10
9–11 years		2050	8.5	51	575	f	0.8	1.2	14	300	25	700	12[h]
12–14 years		2150	9.0	53	725	f	0.9	1.4	16	300	25	700	12[h]
15–17 years		2150	9.0	53	750	f	0.9	1.7	19	300	30	600	12[h]
Men													
18–34 years	Sedentary	2510	10.5	63	750	f	1.0	1.6	18	300	30	500	10
	Moderately active	2900	12.0	72	750	f	1.2	1.6	18	300	30	500	10
	Very active	3350	14.0	84	750	f	1.3	1.6	18	300	30	500	10
35–64 years	Sedentary	2400	10.0	60	750	f	1.0	1.6	18	300	30	500	10
	Moderately active	2750	11.5	69	750	f	1.1	1.6	18	300	30	500	10
	Very active	3350	14.0	84	750	f	1.3	1.6	18	300	30	500	10
65–74 years	Assuming a sedentary life	2400	10.0	60	750	f	1.0	1.6	18	300	30	500	10
≥ 75 years	Assuming a sedentary life	2150	9.0	54	750	f	0.9	1.6	18	300	30	500	10
Women													
18–54 years	Most occupations	2150	9.0	54	750	f	0.9	1.3	15	300	30	500	12[h]
	Very active	2500	10.5	62	750	f	1.0	1.3	15	300	30	500	12[h]
55–74 years	Assuming a sedentary life	1900	8.0	47	750	f	0.8	1.3	15	300	30	500	10
≥ 75 years	Assuming a sedentary life	1680	7.0	42	750	f	0.7	1.3	15	300	30	500	10
Pregnancy		2400	10.0	60	750	10	1.0	1.6	18	500	60	1200[g]	13
Lactation		2750	11.5	69	1200	10	1.1	1.8	21	400	60	1200	15

[a] Calculated as 10% of the recommended energy intake.
[b] Retinol equivalents.
[c] As cholecalciferol. 10 µg cholecalciferol are equal to 400 IU of vitamin D.
[d] Niacin equivalents. 1 niacin equivalent is equal to 1 mg of niacin or 60 mg of dietary tryptophan.
[e] No information is available on children's requirements of folic acid. Graded amounts should be given between that for infants under 1 year based on the average folic acid content of mature human milk, and the 300 µg daily suggested for adults.
[f] No dietary sources may be necessary for children and adults who are sufficiently exposed to sunlight, but during the winter children and adolescents should receive 10 µg (400 IU) daily by supplementation. Adults with inadequate exposure to sunlight, for example those who are housebound, may also need a supplement of 10 µg daily.
[g] For 3rd trimester only.
[h] This intake may not be sufficient for the 10% of girls and women with large menstrual losses.

Essential amino acids

Nine of the amino acids that are components of the body proteins are essential constituents of the diet. The requirement of methionine can to some extent be covered by cystine, that of phenylalanine to some extent by tyrosine. It is possible that histidine is essential not only for infants but also for adults[19]. For premature infants who cannot convert methionine into cysteine and taurine – or can do this only in inadequate amount – these two amino acids are perhaps also essential[20]. For daily requirements see Table 7.

Adult requirements of essential amino acids are met when the intake contributes about 20% to the nitrogen requirement, but only on condition that the amino acids are present in the diet in balanced amounts[13]. For infants with a protein intake of 2 g/d per 1 kg body mass, 35% of the amino acid intake should consist of essential amino acids[13]. The requirements of children of various ages in respect of essential amino acids are largely unknown, and studies have so far been limited to the 10–12-year-old group[21]. The intake adequate for growth can be regarded as met when the proportion of the total amino-acid intake accounted for by essential amino acids lies between the 37% required by infants and the 15% required by adults[22]. The requirements of essential amino acids during pregnancy and lactation are unknown.

Carbohydrates, fats

There is no specific carbohydrate requirement in the sense that in the long term a diet lacking in carbohydrate is inconsistent with life[15]. Fats are carriers of the fat-soluble vitamins and contain the essential fatty acids. These functions exercised by fats can be fulfilled when the daily diet includes 15–25 g of an appropriate food fat[13]. Desirable intakes of carbohydrates and fats are governed by

Table 6 *Safe levels of daily protein intake (FAO/WHO)[10]*

Age	Sex	Body mass	Protein quality			
			100*	80	70	60
			Protein intake			
		kg	g/kg	g	g	g	g
<3 months .	....	–	2.40	–	–	–	–
3–6 months .	....	–	1.85	–	–	–	–
6–11 months	....	9.0	1.53	14	17	20	23
1–3 years....	....	13.4	1.19	16	20	23	27
4–6 years....	....	20.2	1.01	20	26	29	34
7–9 years....	....	28.1	0.88	25	31	35	41
10–12 years .	Boys ...	36.9	0.81	30	37	43	50
	Girls...	38.0	0.76	29	36	41	48
13–15 years .	Boys ...	51.3	0.72	37	46	53	62
	Girls...	49.9	0.63	31	39	45	52
16–19 years .	Boys ...	62.9	0.60	38	47	54	63
	Girls...	54.4	0.55	30	37	43	50
Adults	Men ...	65.0	0.57	37	46	53	62
	Women	55.0	0.52	29	36	41	48
Pregnancy, 2nd half		–	–	+9	+11	+13	+15
Lactation, 1st 6 months		–	–	+17	+21	+24	+28

* Egg or milk protein.

Table 7 *Daily requirements of essential amino acids in relation to body mass (Food and Nutrition Board, USA)[13]*

Amino acids	Infants (4–6 months)	Children (10–12 years)	Adults*
	mg/kg		
Histidine....................	33	?	?
Isoleucine...................	83	28	12
Leucine.....................	135	42	16
Lysine	99	44	12
Methionine .... }	49	22	10
Cystine			
Phenylalanine .... }	141	22	16
Tyrosine			
Threonine	68	28	8
Tryptophan	21	4	3
Valine	92	25	14

* Minimum requirement + 30% to cover individual variations.

the energy requirement. If 12% of the energy intake is provided by protein, the following desirable distribution of the remaining 88% has been proposed by the US Senate Select Committee on Nutrition and Human Needs[23]: fats 30% (saturated, mono-unsaturated and poly-unsaturated fatty acids 10% each), carbohydrates 58% (simple carbohydrates such as fructose, sucrose and lactose 15%, complex carbohydrates 40–45%). Adults should not consume more than 300 mg/d[23] cholesterol, children not more than 150 mg/d[24]. In breast-fed infants, 7% of the energy requirement is met by protein, 55% by fats and 38% by carbohydrates[16].

Essential fatty acids

The true essential fatty acid is linoleic acid. Arachidonic acid is at least equally active and can be formed from linoleic acid in the animal organism. It has been shown that linoleic acid is not only essential for infants – as has long been known – but also for adults[25,26]. In terms of energy, if signs of essential-fatty-acid deficiency are to be avoided, 1–2% of the total dietary energy must be met by linoleic acid[13]. Since in western countries the diet is now rich in poly-unsaturated fatty acids, about 6% of the total energy is supplied by linoleic acid[27]. In the general population, for groups with a relatively low fat intake, an amount of linoleic acid covering 3% of the energy intake can be regarded as a satisfactory minimum intake[13].

Unlike linoleic acid, there is no direct evidence that man requires linolenic acid, but certain phospholipids of the cerebral cortex, the retina and the spermatozoa contain high proportions of poly-unsaturated fatty acids derived from linolenic acid[28].

Indigestible substances

The diet should contain an adequate amount of indigestible carbohydrates and carbohydrate-like compounds ('dietary fiber')[29], a deficiency of which has been thought to be one of the causes of various 'diseases of civilization' in western countries[30]. These substances comprise cellulose, hemicellulose, lignin and pectin, all of which furnish some protection against intestinal and metabolic disorders. It is not possible to lay down desirable levels of intake of dietary fiber. The intake of crude fiber, which makes up only part of the dietary fiber in the diet, amounts to 4–8 g/d in the United Kingdom[31] and 3–4 g/d on average in the USA[32]. The intake of dietary fiber in a British population ranged from 8 g/d to 32 g/d (mean 19.7 g/d)[33] compared with a mean value of 17g/d in a Danish town population and 31 g/d in a Finnish rural population[34].

Vitamin A

The requirement of vitamin A can be expressed either in international units (IU) or in retinol equivalents[8,13]. 1 IU corresponds to 0.3 µg retinol or 0.6 µg β-carotene. 1 retinol equivalent corresponds to 1 µg retinol, 6 µg β-carotene or 12 µg other carotenes. Retinol equivalents are related to international units in the following way: 1 retinol equivalent corresponds to 3.33 IU retinol or 10 IU β-carotene. Values in retinol equivalents are a truer expression of the bio-availability of the carotenes than those in international units. In the average American diet, retinol and the carotenes contribute to the total vitamin A activity in roughly equal proportions[13].

In men, a retinol intake of 600 µg/d suffices to heal eye and skin injuries and to maintain a plasma vitamin A level of at least 200 µg/L[35]. An intake of 1200 µg/d is necessary if the assumed desirable plasma level of over 300 µg/L is to be reached[35]. The recommendations for infants[13] are based on the average retinol content of breast milk of about 490 µg/L. Only few studies have been made of the vitamin A requirement of children[36], and the recommendations[13] are based largely on estimates. Young children are particularly at risk from vitamin A deficiency, and in some densely populated parts of southern and southeast Asia, Africa and Latin America it is a frequent cause of blindness[37]. There is no advantage in ingesting more than the recommended amount, and in adults toxic signs appear when a retinol intake of over 15000 µg/d is maintained over a long period[38]. It is therefore inadvisable to exceed an intake of 7500 µg retinol per day[13].

Vitamin D

Vitamin D is an unusual nutrient in that most of the body's intake originates not from the diet but from formation of the substance from 7-dehydrocholesterol in the skin under the action of UV radiation. The cholecalciferol (vitamin D_3) formed from 7-dehydrocholesterol plays the role of a prohormone[39] that is converted in the liver and subsequently in the kidneys into the active substances 25-hydroxycholecalciferol and 1,25-dihydroxycholecalciferol. In analogous fashion, ergocalciferol (vitamin D_2) is hydroxylated to 25-hydroxyergocalciferol and 1,25-dihydroxyergocalciferol.

The vitamin D requirements of children up to the age of 6 months have been intensively studied. They are known to be adequately met by a dietary intake of 10 µg/d (400 IU/d) cholecalciferol[9,13,40]. This intake also suffices for older children and adults including pregnant women. In infants and young children, extra dietary vitamin D may be a necessity[12,14]. Normally, the adult requirement is met when the body is adequately exposed to sunlight. Intakes exceeding the body's needs serve no useful purpose, and massive doses may even have a toxic effect[40].

Vitamin E

The requirement can be expressed either in international units (IU) or in mg. 1 mg synthetic dl-α-tocopherol corresponds to 1.1 IU, 1 mg of naturally occurring d-α-tocopherol to 1.49 IU[13,41]. The diet contains a number of other tocopherols with activities varying between 1% and 50% of that of d-α-tocopherol[13]; to calculate the α-tocopherol equivalents of other tocopherols, the number

Table 8 *Estimated safe and adequate daily dietary intakes of selected vitamins (Food and Nutrition Board, USA)*[13]

Age category	Vitamin K	Biotin	Panto-thenic acid
	µg		mg
Infants			
0–6 months	12	35	2
6–12 months	10–20	50	3
Children and adolescents			
1–3 years...........................	15–30	65	3
4–6 years...........................	20–40	85	3–4
7–10 years	30–60	120	4–5
≥ 11 years	50–100	100–200	4–7
Adults.............................	70–140	100–200	4–7

of milligrams of the latter is multiplied by the following factors: 0.5 for β-tocopherol, 0.1 for γ-tocopherol, 0.3 for α-tocotrienol.

Since tocopherols inhibit the peroxidation of poly-unsaturated fatty acids (polyene acids), the requirement of vitamin E is related to the amount of these acids contained in the body's cellular structures[42,43]. The minimum adult requirement of vitamin E when the diet contains the minimum of essential fatty acids is probably not more than 3–4 mg/d of *d*-α-tocopherol equivalents (4.5–6 IU/d)[13]. The desirable tocopherol intakes recommended by the Food and Nutrition Board, USA, are simply statements of the tocopherol content of a balanced daily diet. Various studies have shown that the average α-tocopherol intake is 4–9 mg/d; in the USA the intake of other tocopherols is around 21–30 mg/d[42]. In a Canadian study[44] the ratio of the intakes of tocopherol and polyene acids was 0.52×10^{-3}. It has been suggested that the vitamin E requirement should be based preferably on the polyene acid content of the cells rather than on the polyene acid intake[45]. Newborns, and particularly premature infants, run the risk of an inadequate vitamin E supply[42,46]. An intake exceeding the recommended amount offers no special advantage; toxic effects of overdosage, on the other hand, are practically unknown in man[46].

Vitamin K

This vitamin occurs in plants in the form of phylloquinone and is synthesized as menaquinones by the intestinal bacteria. The requirement of vitamin K appears to be met by a normal diet. Since the adequacy of intestinal synthesis over long periods is uncertain, however, the Food and Nutrition Board, USA[13], has published estimated adequate ranges of dietary vitamin K intake (see Table 8). In these ranges the lower value is calculated on the assumption that about a half of a requirement of 2 µg/d per 1 kg body mass is contributed by intestinal synthesis, the higher value on the assumption that the requirement is supplied exclusively by the diet. The intake recommended for infants allows for the lack of intestinal synthesis at this age. It has been estimated that the average mixed diet provides 300–500 µg/d of vitamin K[47].

Thiamine

The thiamine requirement is closely related to the carbohydrate intake. In men whose energy requirement is met primarily by carbohydrates, the minimum thiamine requirement appears to be 0.30 mg/1000 kcal[48]. For children and adults the Food and Nutrition Board, USA[13], recommends an intake of 0.5 mg/1000 kcal per day, the FAO/WHO[12] one of 0.40 mg/1000 kcal per day. In infants the desirable intake appears to be met when the breast milk consumed meets the child's energy requirement. Since older persons may utilize thiamine less efficiently, the Food and Nutrition Board, USA[13], recommends that the intake should be maintained at 1 mg/d even when the energy value of the diet is less than 2000 kcal/d.

Riboflavin

The riboflavin requirement is related either to the energy intake or the body mass. Like the FAO/WHO[12], the Food and Nutrition Board, USA[13], recommends a daily intake of 0.6 mg/1000 kcal riboflavin for persons of all ages except the elderly and those whose energy intake is less than 2000 kcal/d, for whom a minimum of 1.2 mg/d is recommended. In infants the desirable intake

appears to be met when the breast milk consumed meets the child's energy requirement.

Niacin

The requirement of niacin (nicotinic acid and/or nicotinamide) can be met in part by tryptophan. For nutritional purposes, 60 mg tryptophan can be considered as equivalent to 1 mg niacin, although this relationship does not seem to hold under all circumstances[49]. Like the FAO/WHO[12], the Food and Nutrition Board, USA[13], recommends a daily intake of 6.6 mg/1000 kcal niacin equivalent. In infants the desirable intake to be met when the breast milk consumed meets the child's energy requirement. A niacin intake exceeding 3 g/d has a variety of pharmacological effects[50].

Vitamin B₆

The requirement of vitamin B_6 (pyridoxine, pyridoxal, pyridoxamine) depends on the protein intake. On a low-protein diet the optimum vitamin B_6 intake appears to be around 1.25–1.75 mg/d, on a high-protein diet around 1.75–2.0 mg/d[13], while at a protein intake of 150 g/d the ingestion of 2.16 mg/d vitamin B_6 was barely sufficient to meet the requirement[51]. From these studies it has been concluded that the vitamin B_6 allowance should be calculated on the basis of 0.02 mg of the vitamin per 1 g of dietary protein[13]. An allowance of 2.2 mg vitamin B_6 is therefore adequate for protein intakes up to 110 g/d in men, and one of 2.0 mg for protein intakes up to 100 g/d in women. In infants the requirement seems to be met by calculating 0.015 mg of vitamin B_6 per 1 g protein intake[13]. In pregnancy an intake of 2.6 mg/d is recommended, though there are indications that this may be inadequate to meet the increased requirement[52,53]. In western countries the usual dietary intake of vitamin B_6, estimated to range from 0.5 mg/d to 2.9 mg/d[53], may be insufficient[54].

Folic acid

The diet contains so-called folacin, namely folic-acid compounds that have nutritional properties and can be assayed with *Lactobacillus casei,* together with polyglutamates which must be hydrolyzed with conjugase before the assay. The bulk of the evidence suggests that 25–50% of the dietary folic acid is nutritionally available[13]. Hematological criteria indicate that the minimum folic-acid requirement of adults is about 50 µg/d; an intake of 100–200 µg/d ensures an adequately high serum folic-acid level[13,55]. On the basis of these findings, the FAO/WHO recommends a free-folic-acid intake of 200 µg/d[9,12], while the food and Nutrition Board, USA, takes into account the lower nutritional availability of the polyglutamates and recommends a total folic-acid intake of 400 µg/d[13]. The folic-acid requirement of the infant seems to be met from the breast milk provided the child is adequately breast-fed. In children the requirement lies between those of infants and adults. In one published study[56], in which the daily intake was based on the body mass, a daily allowance of 4.3–5.0 µg/kg proved adequate to meet the requirements of children. In pregnancy the folic-acid requirement is greatly increased, so that the allowances should be doubled.

Vitamin B₁₂

In adults the vitamin B_{12} requirement is quite definitely met by a parenteral intake of 0.5–1.0 µg/d[13,55]. Assuming that on a diet containing up to 3 µg vitamin B_{12} at least 50% is utilized, the Food and Nutrition Board, USA, recommends an intake of 3 µg/d for adolescents and adults. The FAO/WHO recommends 2.0 µg/d[9,12]. The vitamin B_{12} requirement of the infant seems to be met from the breast milk provided the child is adequately breast-fed. Recommendations of intakes for children are fitted to their energy allowances.

Pantothenic acid

This vitamin is widely distributed in foods and there is no clinical evidence of any dietary deficiency. Usual diets in the USA furnish pantothenic acid in amounts ranging from 5 mg/d to 20 mg/d, the average being 7 mg/d[13]. The Food and Nutrition Board, USA[13], recommends a pantothenic-acid intake for adults of 4–7 mg/d, but this may need to be increased in pregnancy and lactation.

Biotin

The dietary requirement of biotin is uncertain since synthesis by intestinal bacteria makes a significant contribution to the available body pool of the vitamin. The usual Western European diets provide 50–100 µg/d, mixed American diets 100–300 µg/d[13,57]; the latter amount is sufficient to meet the needs of practically all healthy adults[13]. In breast-fed infants the biotin requirement appears to be met by the amount present in breast milk.

Ascorbic acid

In adults an ascorbic-acid intake of 10 mg/d is sufficient to cure scurvy. With an average ascorbate-catabolism rate of 2.9% and an average ascorbate-absorption efficiency of 85%, a daily ascorbic-acid intake of 60 mg will maintain an ascorbate body pool of 1500 mg[58], sufficient to prevent overt signs of scurvy in adult males for 30–45 days[59]. These data form the basis of the recommendations of the Food and Nutrition Board, USA[13]. In relation to body mass, the ascorbic-acid requirements of children appear to be higher than those of adults[13]. The ascorbic-acid requirement of the infant seems to be met from the breast milk, provided the child is adequately breast-fed. Intakes of ascorbic acid greatly exceeding physiological requirements (1 g/d or more[60]) may have some pharmacological effects unrelated to the function of the vitamin[13].

Water

Under the most favorable conditions, namely no bodily activity, no visible sweating, low loading of the excretory function of the kidneys, the water intake of the adult subject should be at least 1.5 L/d, including the water contained in foods and that arising from biological oxidations[61]. The water requirement is enormously increased in persons living or working in a hot, dry environment. Under normal conditions a reasonable water allowance is 1 mL/kcal for adults and 1.5 mL/kcal for infants[13]. Water loss due to sweating should be replaced by the frequent drinking of small amounts. A water loss amounting to more than 10–20% of the total body water, i.e., 4–8 L approximately, is potentially fatal[62].

Potassium, sodium, chloride

The normal American diet provides 50–100 mmol/d potassium (2–3.9 g/d)[63], but healthy adults can maintain potassium balance on an intake close to the infant's minimum requirement of about 2.3 mmol/d[13]. The estimates of safe potassium intakes (Table 9) made by the Food and Nutrition Board, USA[13], are based on the sodium intakes since it is important to maintain molar equivalence between the two elements. Breast-feeding provides the infant with about 12 mmol/d (0.45 g/d), an amount sufficient to meet its needs.

The sodium content of the body is regulated by homeostatic mechanisms in such a way that health remains unimpaired over a wide range of sodium intakes. Thus a sodium-chloride intake of 750 mg/d (13 mmol/d) or less, the amount contained in a mainly vegetable diet, is sufficient to maintain a stable sodium balance[64]. It is therefore assumed that a sodium-chloride intake of 0.6–3.5 g/d (10–60 mmol/d) is adequate[63]. But the average sodium-chloride intake in the USA is 10–12 g/d (170–200 mmol/d)[65], in northern Japan over 24 g/d (400 mmol/d)[66].

The lower level of safe sodium intakes, given by the Food and Nutrition Board, USA[13], and shown in Table 9, is based on the intake of a breast-fed infant by extrapolation of the body-surface area. In individuals with no genetic tendency to develop essential hypertension, a sodium-chloride intake of up to 12 g/d (200 mmol/d) does not raise the blood pressure, whereas in susceptible individuals a reduction of the intake to less than 3.5 g/d (60 mmol/d) would be necessary to prevent hypertension[67]. According to a Committee on Nutrition[68] the sodium-chloride intake by infants should not exceed 2.3 g/d (40 mmol/d). The quantity of sodium that adults lose by heavy sweating may reach levels of 350 mmol/d; depending on the severity of losses, a sodium-chloride intake of 2–7 g (34–120 mmol) per 1 L of extra water loss is recommended[13].

The chloride requirement parallels the sodium requirement. Severe vomiting calls for an increased chloride intake. Dietary chloride consists almost exclusively of NaCl, though this is not true of the breast-fed infant, who receives chloride in excess of that equivalent to the sodium. The estimated safe chloride intakes of the Food and Nutrition Board, USA[13], are based on the corresponding sodium intakes.

Calcium

Data on the calcium requirement are characterized by considerable uncertainty[69,70]. In the literature, the calcium intake necessary to ensure a stable calcium balance ranges from less than 200 mg/d to over 1000 mg/d[71]. The desirable calcium intake recommended by the FAO/WHO[7] lies close to the minimum requirement. On account mainly of the high levels of protein and phosphate in the American diet, which increase the calcium loss, the Food and Nutrition Board, USA, recommends an intake of 800 mg/d for adults[13] while at the same time recognizing that persons consuming less protein and phosphate will remain in calcium balance on intakes considerably below this level. In infants the calcium requirement is met when they are breast-fed. Of the calcium in breast milk (300 mg/L), about two-thirds is retained, compared with only about a quarter of that in cow's-milk preparations[13]. In relation to body mass, growing children require 2–4 times as much calcium as adults[13]. The calcium requirement is also greatly increased during pregnancy and lactation. It is very difficult to supply premature infants with enough calcium to maintain skeletal mineralization[72].

Phosphorus

Only a few studies have been made on the phosphorus requirement[70]; in adults it is probably higher – mass for mass – than the calcium requirement, and in fact in western countries the average phosphorus intake (800–1500 mg/d)[73] slightly exceeds the average calcium intake (400–1300 mg/d). The recommendations of the Food and Nutrition Board, USA, are based on a mass Ca/P ratio of 1. Studies of the Ca/P ratio in breast milk provide evidence in support of the recommendation[13] that the Ca/P ratio in the infant diet should be 1.5 and that this should be reduced to 1 at the age of 12 months. In very premature infants the phosphorus requirement (fetal phosphorus requirement) is 60–75 mg/d per 1 kg body mass[74], so that breast milk alone may furnish insufficient phosphorus to maintain skeletal mineralization[75].

Magnesium

Values given in the literature for the magnesium requirement range from 200 mg/d to 700 mg/d[11,13]. The recommended desirable magnesium intake levels are based mainly on the observation that persons on the normal American diet show no signs of magnesium deficiency. This diet has a magnesium content of 110–140 mg/1000 kcal[13,76]. The WHO[11] recommends the following magnesium intakes: children up to 12 months at least 40–70 mg/d; 1–2 year-olds 100 mg/d; 2–3 year-olds 150 mg/d; 3–6 year-olds 200 mg/d. In 6–10-year-old children 250 mg/d and in adults 120 mg/1000 kcal should suffice to meet the requirements[11]. The breast milk appears to provide enough magnesium for healthy infants even when their body mass at birth was low[77]. There is no special knowledge of the magnesium need during pregnancy. A number of investigations made in the USA revealed that none of the pregnant women studied reached the recommended intake of 450 mg/d[53,78].

Iron

In men and in menopausal women, iron losses via the gastrointestinal tract, skin and kidneys amount to 0.012–0.013 mg/d per 1 kg body mass[79,80]. Menstruating women suffer an additional iron loss of 0.4 mg/d[80,81]. In children, the extra iron required for growth must be supplied. In pregnancy, the iron requirement is increased mainly as a result of the increase in the total red-cell volume (Table 10).

The iron content of the diet should be related to the energy intake[82]. In the majority of Swedish diets the iron content is about 5–6 mg/1000 kcal[82], in Finnish diets about 6 mg/1000 kcal[83]. In

Table 9 Estimated safe and adequate daily dietary intakes of potassium, sodium and chloride (Food and Nutrition Board, USA)[13]

Age category	Potassium	Sodium	Chloride
	mg		
Infants			
0–6 months	350–925	115–350	275–700
6–12 months	425–1275	250–750	400–1200
Children and adolescents			
1–3 years..............	550–1650	325–975	500–1500
4–6 years..............	775–2325	450–1350	700–2100
7–10 years	1000–3000	600–1800	925–2775
≥ 11 years	1525–4575	900–2700	1400–4200
Adults.................	1875–5625	1100–3300	1700–5100

Table 10   *Iron balance*[80]

	Body mass	External loss		Preg-nancy 'cost'	Growth require-ment	Total iron require-ment	Food intake require-ment*
		Gastro-intesti-nal tract, skin, kidneys	Menses				
	kg	mg/d					
Infants..	...	...	...	...	...	0.5–1.5	5–15
Children......................................	...	...	...	...	...	0.4–1.0	4–10
Adolescent boys.............................	50–100	0.65–1.3	–	–	0.35–0.7	1–2	10–20
Adolescent girls.............................	45–70	0.6–0.9	0.1–1.4	–	0.3–0.45	1–2.7	10–27
Men	50–100	0.65–1.3	–	–	–	0.65–1.3	6.5–13
Menstruating women	45–70	0.6–0.9	0.1–1.4	–	–	0.7–2.3	7–23
Non-menstruating women	45–70	0.6–0.9	–	–	–	0.6–0.9	6–9
Pregnancy	50–80	0.65–1.0	–	1.0–2.5	–	1.65–3.5	16.5–35

* Assuming 10% absorption.

the USA the daily iron intake of children is about 5–6 mg/ 1000 kcal[2,74], that of women about 5.5–7 mg/1000 kcal[2,74,76], and that of men about 7–8.5 mg/1000 kcal[2,84]. Men with a body iron store of 1000 mg absorb 5.5–7% of their dietary iron[79,81,84]. In women with a body iron store of 300 mg the corresponding figure is 12–13%[79,81]. Excepting those whose energy intake is unusually high, many women do not consume enough iron with food to meet their iron requirement, and this may also apply in pregnancy. For this reason a WHO Expert Group recommends iron supplements of 30–60 mg/d for pregnant women with iron stores and of 120–240 mg/d for pregnant women without iron stores[85]. Newborn infants who exhaust their iron stores run a high risk of iron deficiency; this applies particularly to underweight premature infants at the age of about 2 months and to infants of normal body mass at term when aged 4–6 months[86]. Iron supplements in infancy should be kept flexible on account of the varying need[86]. The iron content of breast milk is low but of high bio-availability. When breast feeding continues for more than 6 months, the iron ingested via the milk may not suffice to meet the child's requirement[87], so that iron supplements for breast-fed infants have been suggested[88].

Zinc

The zinc requirement is not known with certainty[89]. In the light of balance studies, and allowing for 40% absorption of the dietary zinc, the Food and Nutrition Board, USA[13], recommends an intake of 15 mg/d for adults, with supplements of 5 mg/d during pregnancy and 10 mg/d during lactation. These recommendations apply to individuals on a 'balanced' diet. A WHO Expert Committee has also made provisional recommendations, based on three different degrees of bio-availability of the dietary zinc (Table 11). Those for infants are based on the zinc content of breast milk,

Table 11   *Desirable daily zinc allowances (WHO)*[11]

Sex	Age, week of pregnancy	Bio-availability of dietary zinc		
		10%	20%	40%
		mg		
Infants	0–4 months..........	12.5	6.3	3.1
	5–12 months	11.0	5.5	2.8
Males	1–10 years...........	16.0	8.0	4.0
	11–17 years	28.0	14.0	7.0
	≥ 18 years	22.0	11.0	5.5
Females	1–9 years...........	15.5	7.8	3.9
	10–13 years	26.5	13.3	6.6
	≥ 14 years	22.0	11.0	5.5
Pregnancy	0–20 weeks.........	25.5	12.8	6.4
	20–30 weeks.........	29.0	14.5	7.3
	30–40 weeks.........	30.0	15.0	7.5
Lactation	....	54.5	27.3	13.7

which appears to be superior to all other foods as regards the bio-availability of zinc (see page 241). Several studies[53,90–92] have shown that the average US diet does not contain the 15 mg/d recommended by the Food and Nutrition Board, USA[13], and certainly not the 20 mg/d recommended for pregnant women. Particularly a low-protein is likely to run parallel with an inadequate zinc intake[93].

Copper

Estimates of the copper requirement are based on balance studies. Women[94] and preadolescent girls[95] with an intake of 1.6–2.1 mg/d, as well as men[96] with an intake of 1.3 mg/d, were in equilibrium or had a slightly positive balance, though a more recent study[97] has shown that women with an intake of 2 mg/d failed to be in positive balance. In children a positive balance has been observed with intakes as low as 0.035 mg/d per 1 kg body mass[98]. When body-surface losses are taken into account, the adult copper requirement is estimated to be 1.55 mg/d[96]. To allow a safety margin, the Food and Nutrition Board, USA[13], recommends the following copper intakes per 1 kg body mass: adults 2–3 mg/d, infants and children 0.08 mg/d. A WHO Expert Committee[11] has laid down the following guidelines for a desirable copper intake per 1 kg body mass: men 30 μg/d, older children 40 μg/d, young children and infants 80 μg/d.

Copper is widely distributed in foods, but the older analytical data indicating a daily intake of 2–5 mg[99] are now being questioned. A number of dietary surveys have shown that the diet often supplies less than 1 mg/d of copper[91,92,100–102]. Copper deficiency may develop in premature infants nourished on formulas not supplemented with copper, since they have low hepatic copper stores[103].

Manganese

It is assumed that a dietary manganese intake of 2–3 mg/d is sufficient to meet the adult requirement[11]. A lower intake, however, is possibly adequate, since studies made on young women have shown that none of them ingested more than 1.5 mg/d[102]. But in a relevant study a positive balance was not achieved by men at an intake of 2.1 mg/d[101].

In infants an intake of 60 μg/d per 1 kg body mass appears to be adequate[98]. The recommendations by the Food and Nutrition Board, USA[13], take account of the rather low toxicity of the element (see Table 12).

Chromium

Parenteral nutrition studies have shown that a chromium intake of 20–46 μg/d is sufficient to maintain chromium balance[104]. The chromium intake furnished by the typical western diet is estimated to be 50–100 μg/d[13,105]. In a Canadian study the mean intake was 144 μg/d[106]. In infants a chromium intake of 2.4 μg/d per 1 kg body mass appears adequate to maintain a positive chromium balance[98]. For adults the Food and Nutrition Board, USA[13], tentatively recommends a chromium intake of 50–200 μg/d (Table 12). Chromium deficiency could be conceivable in the following circumstances[107]: in women after repeated pregnancies, in diabetics on insulin (as a result of the increased urinary chromium loss), in children with protein-calorie malnutrition, and in old age.

Table 12 *Estimated safe and adequate daily dietary intakes of selected trace elements* (Food and Nutrition Board, USA)[13]*

Age category	Cop-per	Man-ganese	Chro-mium	Molyb-denum	Sele-nium	Fluo-ride
	mg					
Infants						
0–6 months	0.5–0.7	0.5–0.7	0.01–0.04	0.03–0.06	0.01–0.04	0.1–0.5
6–12 months	0.7–1.0	0.7–1.0	0.02–0.06	0.04–0.08	0.02–0.06	0.2–1.0
Children and adolescents						
1–3 years	1.0–1.5	1.0–1.5	0.02–0.08	0.05–0.1	0.02–0.08	0.5–1.5
4–6 years	1.5–2.0	1.5–2.0	0.03–0.12	0.06–0.15	0.03–0.12	1.0–2.5
7–10 years	2.0–2.5	2.0–3.0	0.05–0.2	0.10–0.3	0.05–0.2	1.5–2.5
≥ 11 years	2.0–3.0	2.5–5.0	0.05–0.2	0.15–0.5	0.05–0.2	1.5–2.5
Adults	2.0–3.0	2.5–5.0	0.05–0.2	0.15–0.5	0.05–0.2	1.5–4.0

* Since the toxic levels for many trace elements may be only several times usual intakes, the upper levels for the trace elements given in this table should not be habitually exceeded.

Molybdenum

The molybdenum content of foods varies considerably, depending on the environment in which the food is grown. The molybdenum intake may reach a high value when foods originating from soils rich in molybdenum are consumed[11]. The average molybdenum intake in the USA has been estimated to range from 120 µg/d to 240 µg/d as a result of the interplay of several factors[108]. Adults[99] maintain a slight positive molybdenum balance at an intake of 100–200 µg/d, equivalent to 2 µg/d per 1 kg body mass, infants[98] at an intake of 3.0 µg/d per 1 kg body mass. The safe molybdenum intakes recommended by the Food and Nutrition Board, USA[13], are based on the above data (see Table 12).

Cobalt

Cobalt is a component of vitamin B_{12} and is not required for any other known purpose by the human body. Dietary cobalt intakes range from 0.05 mg/d to 1.8 mg/d[11, 106, 109]. Intakes of 20–30 mg/d or more have a definitely toxic effect[11, 109]. When alcohol is consumed at the same time, however, even lower cobalt intakes can be toxic (on account for instance of the cobalt salts added to beer as stabilizers)[11, 109].

Vanadium, nickel, silicon, tin

Vanadium[11, 110–112], nickel[11, 110, 113] and silicon[110, 111, 114] are essential trace elements for some animal species, but the human requirement is unknown. Tin is probably essential (at least for the rat)[11, 110, 111]. In the USA it has been shown[115] that the dietary intake of vanadium ranges from 12 µg/d to 28 µg/d, that of nickel from 107 µg/d to 176 µg/d. In a Canadian study[106] the mean nickel intake was found to be 460 µg/d. Infants maintain a positive nickel balance at a mean nickel intake of 8.7 µg/d per 1 kg body mass[98]. In a study on silicon[116] the intake of this element on a low-fiber diet was 21 mg/d, on a high-fiber diet 46 mg/d.

Selenium

Selenium must be regarded as an essential element since it is a component of the enzyme glutathione peroxidase[117]. The typical US diet contains about 150 µg/d of the element[118], but elsewhere the content may be much lower (Italy: 13 µg/d) or much higher (Venezuela: 326 µg/d)[119]. Breast-fed infants (according to the data on page 214) receive 10–20 µg/d of this element, those on commercial formulas only 3.5 µg/d[120]. The selenium content of drinking water varies considerably from place to place: where the soil is poor in selenium it is less than 1 µg/L, where the soil is rich in the element between 50 µg/L and 300 µg/L[11]. Studies on selenium metabolism suggest that a selenium intake of 20–30 µg/d may be adequate for health[121]. The Food and Nutrition Board, USA, recommends that a safe and adequate intake for adults is 50–200 µg/d[13]. Fruit and vegetables contain little selenium, so that a vegetarian diet will not meet the selenium requirement[119]. Toxic effects may appear when the selenium intake is maintained at 2400–3000 µg/d or more over long periods[118].

Iodine

The minimum adult iodine requirement is estimated at 50–75 µg/d, or 1 µg/d per 1 kg body mass[13]. To provide an extra safety margin, the Food and Nutrition Board, USA[13], recommends an allowance of 150 µg/d for adolescents and adults. For the latter, a safe intake can be considered to lie between 50 µg/d and 1000 µg/d. The WHO *Handbook on Human Nutritional Requirements*[12] gives optimum intakes of 140 µg/d for men and 100 µg/d for women.

The iodine contained in foods is almost completely absorbed[122]; 15–45% is taken up by the thyroid, the remainder excreted in the urine[123]. If the requirement is not met by the diet, the deficit can be made up by the consumption of iodized table salt. In the USA the iodine content of such salt is 76 µg/g[13], while in Western Germany the upper permissible limit is 5 µg/g[14].

Two studies made in the USA revealed an iodine intake of 240–840 µg/d[124], a study on Belgian children an intake of 11–60 µg/d[125]. In one and the same person the iodine intake may vary widely from day to day[126]. Breast-fed infants (according to the data on page 214) receive 40–80 µg/d.

In predisposed persons, excessive consumption of iodine may result in hyperthyroidism[123], though for this to occur the intake must be considerably in excess of 1000 µg/d over a long period[127].

Fluorine

The main target organs of fluoride in man are the bones and the dental enamel. The protective action of fluoride on the teeth is exerted mainly during the pre-eruptive phase[13, 128, 129]. Animal experiments have demonstrated a favorable effect of fluoride on growth, so that it can be regarded as an essential nutrient[110, 111]. Recent calculations of the fluoride intake in the USA gave low values that depended on the location and the fluoride content of the drinking water. The total fluoride intake of 6-month infants ranged from 0.21 mg/d to 0.54 mg/d, that of young men from 0.91 mg/d to 1.72 mg/d[130]. On the basis of an estimated fluoride intake of 1 mg/d in low-fluoride areas and 4 mg/d in areas with a fluoridated water supply, the Food and Nutrition Board, USA[13], tentatively recommends a total intake of 1.5–4 mg/d as safe and adequate for adults; for younger age groups a maximum intake of 2.5 mg/d is recommended in order to avoid the danger of mottling of the teeth. The optimum fluoride concentration in the drinking water is considered to be 0.7–1.2 mg/L, depending on the climate[131]. The American Academy of Pediatrics[132] takes the view that children up to 3 years should have a fluoride intake of 0.5 mg/d, children over 3 years one of 1.0 mg/d. Infants may have difficulty in reaching the desirable fluoride intake of 0.5 mg/d on account of the low fluoride content of milk and the little water they consume[133].

A fluoride intake of 8–20 mg/d or more maintained for several decades may result in signs of toxicity[131]. Fluorosis is endemic in some parts of India and southern Africa[128]; in one such area in India the fluoride content of the drinking water was 3.5–8.4 mg/L[134].

Sulfur

Sulfur is required mainly in the form of the essential amino acids cystine and methionine. The small amounts of inorganic and organic sulfate in the diet are probably of little significance as far as the sulfate intake is concerned[135].

References

[1] HEGSTED, D. M., *Nutr. Rev.*, **36**, 33 (1978).

[2] HEGSTED, D. M., *J. Amer. diet. Ass.*, **66**, 13 (1975).

[3] MAŠEK, J., *Wld Rev. Nutr. Diet.*, **25**, 1 (1976).

[4] YOUNG, E. G., in BEATON and McHENRY (Eds.), *Nutrition*, volume 2, Academic Press, New York, 1964, page 299.

[5] GOODHART, R.S., in GOODHART and SHILS (Eds.), *Modern Nutrition in Health and Disease*, 5th ed., Lea & Febiger, Philadelphia, 1973, page 403.

[6] PATWARDHAN, V. N., *J. Amer. diet. Ass.*, **56**, 191 (1970); CAMPBELL, J. A., *J. Amer. diet. Ass.*, **64**, 175 (1974).

[7] FAO/WHO Expert Group on Calcium Requirements, *Wld Hlth Org. techn. Rep. Ser.*, No. 230 (1962).

[8] Joint FAO/WHO Expert Group on Requirements of Vitamin A, Thiamine, Riboflavine and Niacin, *Wld Hlth Org. techn. Rep. Ser.*, No. 362 (1967).

[9] Joint FAO/WHO Expert Group on Requirements of Ascorbic Acid, Vitamin D, Vitamin B_{12}, Folate and Iron, *Wld Hlth Org. techn. Rep. Ser.*, No. 452 (1970).

[10] Joint FAO/WHO ad hoc Expert Committee on Energy and Protein Requirements, *Wld Hlth Org. techn. Rep. Ser.*, No. 522 (1973).

[11] WHO Expert Committee on Trace Elements in Human Nutrition, *Wld Hlth Org. techn. Rep. Ser.*, No. 532 (1973).

[12] PASSMORE et al., *Handbook on Human Nutritional Requirements*, World Health Organization, Geneva, 1974.

[13] Food and Nutrition Board, *Recommended Dietary Allowances*, 9th ed., National Academy of Sciences, Washington, D.C., 1980.

[14] *Recommended Daily Amounts of Food Energy and Nutrients for Groups of People in the United Kingdom*, Report on Health and Social Subjects, No. 15, HMSO, London, 1979.

[15] GLATZEL, H., *Ernährung, Ernährungskrankheiten, Appetitlosigkeit*, Urban & Schwarzenberg, Munich, 1976.

[16] RICKARD and GRESHAM, *J. Amer. diet. Ass.*, **66**, 592 (1975).

[17] FOMON and ZIEGLER, *J. Pediat.*, **90**, 504 (1977); GAULL et al., *J. Pediat.*, **90**, 507 (1977).

[18] GARZA et al., *J. Nutr.*, **29**, 280 (1976); GARZA et al., *J. Nutr.*, **107**, 335 (1977); BODWELL et al., *Amer. J. clin. Nutr.*, **32**, 2450 (1979).

[19] *Nutr. Rev.*, **33**, 200 (1975); KOPPLE and SWENDSEID, *J. clin. Invest.*, **55**, 881 (1975).

[20] STURMAN et al., *Pediat. Res.*, **10**, 415 (1976); GAULL et al., *J. Pediat.*, **90**, 348 (1977); BÖHLES, H. J., *Klin. Pädiat.*, **189**, 116 (1977).

[21] IRWIN and HEGSTED, *J. Nutr.*, **101**, 539 (1971).

[22] EL LOZY and HEGSTED, *Amer. J. clin. Nutr.*, **28**, 1052 (1975).

[23] *Nutr. Rev.*, **35**, 122 (1977).

[24] Committee on Nutrition, *Pediatrics*, **49**, 305 (1972).

[25] *Nutr. Rev.*, **33**, 329 (1975); WENE et al., *J. clin. Invest.*, **56**, 127 (1975).

[26] RICHARDSON and SGOUTAS, *Amer. J. clin. Nutr.*, **28**, 258 (1975); FLEMING et al., *Amer. J. clin. Nutr.*, **29**, 976 (1976).

[27] RIZEK et al., *J. Amer. Oil Chem. Soc.*, **51**, 244 (1974).

[28] *Nutr. Rev.*, **37**, 296 (1979).

[29] SPILLER et al., *Amer. J. clin. Nutr.*, **30**, 659 (1977).

[30] BURKITT et al., *Amer. J. med. Ass.*, **229**, 1068 (1974); MENDELOFF, A. I., *Nutr. Rev.*, **33**, 321 (1975); TROWELL, H., *Amer. J. clin. Nutr.*, **29**, 417 (1976); Editorial, *Lancet*, **2**, 337 (1977).

[31] CUMMINGS, J. H., *Gut*, **14**, 69 (1973).

[32] DORFMAN et al., *Amer. J. clin. Nutr.*, **29**, 87 (1976); NICHOLS et al., *Amer. J. clin. Nutr.*, **29**, 1384 (1976).

[33] BINGHAM et al., *Amer. J. clin. Nutr.*, **32**, 1313 (1979).

[34] International Agency for Research on Cancer Intestinal Microecology Group, *Lancet*, **2**, 207 (1977).

[35] SAUERLICH et al., *Vitam. and Horm.*, **32**, 251 (1974).

[36] RODRIGUEZ and IRWIN, *J. Nutr.*, **102**, 909 (1972).

[37] Joint WHO/USAID Meeting on Vitamin A Deficiency and Xerophthalmia, *Wld Hlth Org. techn. Rep. Ser.*, No. 590 (1976).

[38] KÖRNER and VÖLLM, *Int. J. Vitam. Nutr. Res.*, **45**, 363 (1975).

[39] DeLUCA, H. F., *Vitamin D. Metabolism and Function*, Springer, Berlin, 1979; DeLUCA, H. F., *Amer. J. clin. Nutr.*, **29**, 1258 (1976).

[40] *Nutr. Rev.*, **33**, 61 (1975); ARNAUD et al., *Amer. J. clin. Nutr.*, **28**, 512 (1975).

[41] HORWITT, M. K., *Amer. J. clin. Nutr.*, **29**, 569 (1976).

[42] BIERI, J. G., *Nutr. Rev.*, **33**, 161 (1975); BIERI and FARRELL, *Vitam. and Horm.*, **34**, 31 (1976).

[43] HORWITT, M. K., *Amer. J. clin. Nutr.*, **27**, 1182 (1974).

[44] THOMPSON et al., *Amer. J. clin. Nutr.*, **26**, 1349 (1973).

[45] WITTING and LEE, *Amer. J. clin. Nutr.*, **28**, 571 and 577 (1975).

[46] *Nutr. Rev.*, **35**, 57 (1977).

[47] OLSON, R. E., in GOODHART and SHILS (Eds.), *Modern Nutrition in Health and Disease*, 6th ed., Lea & Febiger, Philadelphia, 1980, page 170.

[48] SAUERLICH et al., *Amer. J. clin. Nutr.*, **32**, 2237 (1979).

[49] *Nutr. Rev.*, **32**, 76 (1974); DARBY et al., *Nutr. Rev.*, **33**, 289 (1975).

[50] *J. Amer. med. Ass.*, **231**, 360 (1975).

[51] LINKSWILER, H. M., in *Human Vitamin B_6 Requirements*, National Academy of Sciences, Washington, D.C., 1978, page 279.

[52] *Nutr. Rev.*, **34**, 15 (1976); LUMENG et al., *Amer. J. clin. Nutr.*, **29**, 1376 (1976).

[53] ROEPKE and KIRKSEY, *Amer. J. clin. Nutr.*, **32**, 2249 (1979).

[54] HEGSTED, D. M., *J. Amer. diet. Ass.*, **71**, 9 (1977).

[55] HERBERT, V., *Amer. J. clin. Nutr.*, **21**, 743 (1968).

[56] ASFOUR et al., *Amer. J. clin. Nutr.*, **30**, 1098 (1977).

[57] BONJOUR, J. P., *Int. J. Vitam. Nutr. Res.*, **47**, 107 (1977).

[58] KALLNER et al., *Amer. J. clin. Nutr.*, **32**, 530 (1979).

[59] HODGES et al., *Amer. J. clin. Nutr.*, **24**, 432 (1971).

[60] PAULING, L., *Proc. nat. Acad. Sci. (Wash.)*, **67**, 1643 (1970), and *Amer. J. clin. Nutr.*, **24**, 1294 (1971); CAMERON and PAULING, *Oncology*, **27**, 181 (1973).

[61] MOHLMAN et al., *Aerospace Med.*, **39**, 396 (1968).

[62] *Nutr. Rev.*, **32**, 314 (1974).

[63] MENEELY and BATTARBEE, *Nutr. Rev.*, **34**, 225 (1976).

[64] DAHL, L. K., *Amer. J. clin. Nutr.*, **25**, 231 (1972).

[65] Report, quoted by *Med. Letter*, **22**, 15 (1980).

[66] TOBIAN, L., *Amer. J. clin. Nutr.*, **32**, 2659 (1979).

[67] TOBIAN, L., *Amer. J. clin. Nutr.*, **32**, 2739 (1979).

[68] Committee on Nutrition, *Pediatrics*, **53**, 115 (1974).

[69] WALKER, A. R., *Amer. J. clin. Nutr.*, **25**, 518 (1972); PATERSON, C. R., *Postgrad. med. J.*, **54**, 244 (1978).

[70] HEGSTED, D. M., in GOODHART and SHILS (Eds.), *Modern Nutrition in Health and Disease*, 5th ed., Lea & Febiger, Philadelphia, 1973, page 268.

[71] IRWIN and KIENHOLZ, *J. Nutr.*, **103**, 1019 (1973).

[72] Committee on Nutrition, *Pediatrics*, **62**, 826 (1978).

[73] AVIOLI, L. V., in GOODHART and SHILS (Eds.), *Modern Nutrition in Health and Disease*, 6th ed., Lea & Febiger, Philadelphia, 1980, page 294.

[74] ZIEGLER et al., *Growth*, **40**, 329 (1976).

[75] ROWE et al., *New Engl. J. Med.*, **300**, 293 (1979); SAGY et al., *J. Pediat.*, **96**, 683 (1980).

[76] OHLSON and HARPER, *J. Amer. diet. Ass.*, **69**, 626 (1976).

[77] Committee on Nutrition, *Pediatrics*, **60**, 519 (1977).

[78] PHILIPPS and JOHNSON, *Amer. J. clin. Nutr.*, **30**, 215 (1977); ASHE et al., *Amer. J. clin. Nutr.*, **32**, 286 (1979).

[79] FINCH and MONSEN, *J. Amer. med. Ass.*, **219**, 1462 (1972).

[80] MOORE, C. V., in GOODHART and SHILS (Eds.), *Modern Nutrition in Health and Disease*, 5th ed., Lea & Febiger, Philadelphia, 1973, page 297.

[81] MUNRO, H. N., *Fed. Proc.*, **36**, 2015 (1977).

[82] WRETLIND, A., in HALLBERG et al. (Eds.), *Iron Deficiency*, Academic Press, London, 1970, page 39.

[83] TAKKUNEN and SEPPÄNEN, *Amer. J. clin. Nutr.*, **28**, 1141 (1975).

[84] BJÖRN-RASMUSSEN et al., *J. clin. Invest.*, **53**, 247 (1974).

[85] WHO Group of Experts on Nutritional Anaemias, *Wld Hlth Org. techn. Rep. Ser.*, No. 503 (1972).

[86] Committee on Nutrition, *Pediatrics*, **58**, 765 (1976).

[87] SAARINEN, U. M., *J. Pediat.*, **93**, 177 (1978).

[88] FOMON et al., *Pediatrics*, **63**, 52 (1979).

[89] HALSTED et al., *Amer. J. clin. Nutr.*, **104**, 345 (1974).

[90] SANDSTEAD, H. H., *Amer. J. clin. Nutr.*, **26**, 1251 (1973); WHITE, H. S., *J. Amer. diet. Ass.*, **68**, 243 (1976); HAMBIDGE et al., *Amer. J. clin. Nutr.*, **32**, 2532 (1979).

[91] KLEVAY et al., *J. Amer. med. Ass.*, **241**, 1916 (1979).

[92] KELSAY et al., *Amer. J. clin. Nutr.*, **32**, 2307 (1979).

[93] OSIS et al., *Amer. J. clin. Nutr.*, **25**, 582 (1972); BROWN et al., *J. Amer. diet. Ass.*, **69**, 632 (1976); HUNT et al., *Amer. J. clin. Nutr.*, **32**, 1511 (1979).

[94] ROBINSON et al., *Brit. J. Nutr.*, **30**, 195 (1973).

[95] PRICE et al., *Amer. J. clin. Nutr.*, **23**, 258 (1970).

[96] KLEVAY et al., *Amer. J. clin. Nutr.*, **33**, 45 (1980).

[97] TAPER et al., *Amer. J. clin. Nutr.*, **33**, 1077 (1980).

[98] ALEXANDER et al., *Quart. J. Med.*, NS **43**, 89 (1974).

[99] SEELIG, M. S., *Amer. J. clin. Nutr.*, **25**, 1022 (1972).

[100] WOLF et al., *Fed. Proc.*, **36**, 1175 (1977).

[101] SPENCER et al., *Amer. J. clin. Nutr.*, **32**, 1867 (1979).

[102] WHITE, H. S., *Amer. J. clin. Nutr.*, **55**, 38 (1969).

[103] DELVES, H. T., *Ciba Found. Symp.*, NS **79**, 5 (1980).

[104] JEEJEEBHOY et al., *Amer. J. clin. Nutr.*, **30**, 531 (1977); JACOBSON and WESTER, *Brit. J. Nutr.*, **37**, 107 (1977).

[105] MERTZ, W., *Nutr. Rev.*, **33**, 129 (1975).

[106] SOMERS, E., *J. Food Sci.*, **39**, 215 (1974).

[107] HAMBIDGE, K. M., *Amer. J. clin. Nutr.*, **27**, 505 (1974).

[108] TSONGAS et al., *Amer. J. clin. Nutr.*, **33**, 1103 (1980).

[109] UNDERWOOD, E. J., *Nutr. Rev.*, **33**, 65 (1975).

[110] NIELSEN and SANDSTEAD, *Amer. J. clin. Nutr.*, **27**, 515 (1974).

[111] SCHWARZ, K., *Fed. Proc.*, **33**, 1748 (1974).

[112] HOPKINS and MOHR, *Fed. Proc.*, **33**, 1773 (1974).

[113] NIELSEN and OLLERICH, *Fed. Proc.*, **33**, 1767 (1974).

[114] CARLISLE, E. M., *Fed. Proc.*, **33**, 1758 (1974), and *Nutr. Rev.*, **33**, 257 (1975).

[115] MYRON et al., *Amer. J. clin. Nutr.*, **31**, 527 (1978).

[116] KELSAY et al., *Amer. J. clin. Nutr.*, **32**, 1876 (1979).

[117] SUNDE and HOEKSTRA, *Nutr. Rev.*, **38**, 265 (1980).

[118] *Nutr. Rev.*, **34**, 347 (1976).

[119] THOMSON and ROBINSON, *Amer. J. clin. Nutr.*, **33**, 303 (1980).

[120] LOMBECK et al., *Europ. J. Pediat.*, **125**, 81 (1977).

[121] STEWART et al., *Brit. J. Nutr.*, **40**, 45 (1978).

[122] PITTMAN et al., *New Engl. J. Med.*, **280**, 1431 (1969).

[123] CAVALIERI, R. R., in GOODHART and SHILS (Eds.), *Modern Nutrition in Health and Disease*, 5th ed., Lea & Febiger, Philadelphia, 1973, page 362; STEWART and VIDOR, *Brit. med. J.*, **1**, 372 (1976).

[124] ODDIE et al., *J. clin. Endocr.*, **30**, 659 (1970).

[125] MALVAUX et al., *J. clin. Endocr.*, **29**, 79 (1969).

[126] MALAMOS et al., *J. clin. Endocr.*, **27**, 1372 (1967).

[127] WOLFF, J., *Amer. J. Med.*, **47**, 101 (1969).

[128] McCLURE, F. J., *Water Fluoridation*, National Institutes of Health, Bethesda (Md.), 1970.

[129] SHAW and SWEENEY, in GOODHART and SHILS (Eds.), *Modern Nutrition in Health and Disease*, 5th ed., Lea & Febiger, Philadelphia, 1973, page 733; JENKINS, G. N., *Brit. med. Bull.*, **31**, 142 (1975); WALSH, D.C., *New Engl. J. Med.*, **296**, 1118 (1977).

[130] OPHAUG et al., *Amer. J. clin. Nutr.*, **33**, 324 (1980); SINGER et al., *Amer. J. clin. Nutr.*, **33**, 328 (1980).

[131] FLETCHER, D. C., *J. Amer. med. Ass.*, **231**, 1167 (1975).

[132] Committee on Nutrition, *Pediatrics*, **49**, 456 (1972).

[133] SCHWAB and SCHWARTZ, *J. Pediat.*, **86**, 735 (1975).

[134] KRISHNAMACHARI and KRISHNASWAMY, *Lancet*, **2**, 877 (1973); KRISHNAMACHARI and LAXMAIAH, *Amer. J. clin. Nutr.*, **28**, 1234 (1975).

[135] SIMMONS, W. K., *Amer. J. clin. Nutr.*, **26**, 72 (1973).

Contents of principal nutrients, vitamins and elements in foods

The contents of the various nutrients in the foods listed in the table on pages 243–260 are those considered to constitute the most reliable and representative data in the literature. The following sources have been made use of: food tables of the Food and Agriculture Organization (FAO)[1], of the Agriculture Handbook No.8 (USA)[2], of the Ministry of Agriculture, Fisheries and Food and the Medical Research Council (UK)[3], and of the Ministry of Food, Agriculture and Forestry (GFR)[4]; bibliographies on individual nutrients (cholesterol[5], vitamin B_6[6], folic acid[7,8], vitamin E[9], magnesium[10], copper[10,11], zinc[10,12]). Detailed compilations of the nutrient content of foods are also to be found in the tables of BOWES and CHURCH[13], RANDOIN et al.[14] and the Netherlands Commission on Foods[15], as also in various monographs such as those of ALTMAN and DITTMER[16], PROUDFIT and ROBINSON[17] and TURNER[18]. There are special publications on the subject applicable to South America and the Far East[19,20].

The composition of a particular food is subject to fluctuation, often to a considerable extent, so that users of the tables must bear in mind that the actual content of a particular constituent can differ from the value given, especially in the case of preserved foods, bread, chocolate and sausages. Where meat is concerned, the degree to which the animal has been fattened plays an important role, as do variety, climate, soil composition and stage of ripening in the composition of vegetable foods. The way foods are stored has a marked effect on the maintenance of their water and vitamin contents. Water loss has a concentrating effect on all nutrients.

Nutrients can be lost during the cooking of foods: some vitamins are broken down by heat and oxidation, or vitamins and minerals can dissolve in the water used for boiling and be discarded with it.

The values given are contents per 100 g edible portion of the raw, uncooked food unless otherwise stated. With the exception of the energy content, all data given represent the total content of the component concerned in the food and not simply that part absorbed by the body.

The *water content* is usually determined from the loss in mass at a high temperature, so that the value given may include the content of other readily volatile substances.

The *protein content* is calculated from the nitrogen content using the following multiplication factors: 6.25 for meat and eggs, 6.38 for milk, 5.18–6.25 for vegetables, cereals and nuts (see page 261).

The values for *fats* are the amounts extractable by fat solvents such as ether. Those for polyene fatty acids either the total content of linoleic and arachidonic acids or the difference between the total unsaturated fatty-acid content and the oleic-acid content. The contents of various fatty acids in foods are listed in the table on page 264. The cholesterol content is roughly equal to the unsaponifiable part of the total fats. Cholesterol is practically confined to animal products, though traces have been detected in vegetable oils[21].

The *carbohydrate* content is usually calculated by subtracting the water, protein, fat and ash contents from the total mass. A list of the glucose, fructose and sucrose contents of vegetable foods is to be found on page 263; for the lactose content of milk see page 214.

Fiber. This column gives the content of so-called 'crude fiber', i.e., that part of the food insoluble in water, ethanol, ether, sulfuric acid and sodium hydroxide[22]. The crude fiber content is less than the content of substances not digestible by the endogenous secretions of the gastrointestinal tract, the so-called 'indigestible residue', 'dietary fiber', or 'plantix'[22] (cellulose, hemicellulose, lignins, pectin, plant gums). Values for this constituent in selected foods are given in Table 1. From the nutritional standpoint (cf. page 235), data on the content of indigestible residues are more useful than crude fiber values.

The *energy content* (heat of combustion) has been calculated from the contents of fat, carbohydrate and protein (and ethanol, if present) with the aid of specific factors that take into account the differing extent to which the individual foods are digested (for details see FAO[24]). The values given are therefore those for utilizable energy.

Vitamins. 1 IU vitamin A corresponds to 0.3 μg vitamin A_1 or 0.6 μg β-carotene; 1 IU vitamin D corresponds to 0.025 μg vitamin D_3. Vitamin A contents should as far as possible be expressed in retinol equivalents: 1 retinol equivalent corresponds to 1 μg retinol, 6 μg β-carotene or 12 μg other carotenes convertible into vitamin A.

The values for folic acid are those for the free acid, namely that part of the total folic acid determined by *Lactobacillus casei* in the absence of conjugase. Contents of free and total folic acid in vari-

Table 1
Crude fibre and indigestible residue of foods[23]

100 g dry matter contain	Crude fibre	Indigestible residue
	g	
Endives	13.0	21.7
Carrots	9.0	9.9
Potatoes	2.8	9.9
Cabbage, white	17.5	21.5
Kale, curled	9.0	30.2
Onions	10.0	10.5
Kidney beans	2.8	15.0
Peas, canned	2.3	13.2
Peanuts, roasted	2.6	8.0
Soybeans	2.4	5.1
Oats, rolled	1.7	8.5
Rice, polished	0.7	1.6
Rye bread	1.6	21.0
Whole wheat bread	2.0	15.5
White bread	0.8	4.0
Wheat bran	10.4	56.0

Table 2 *Free and total folic-acid contents of food groups*[7,8]

100 g raw food contain	Free	Total
	μg	
Meats	1–9	2–11
Liver	60–400	60–637
Luncheon meats	1–8	2–9
Fish	3–34	9–44
Eggs	8–19	16–36
Egg yolk	40–142	29–224
Egg white	1–10	3–33
Vegetables	4–176	6–204
Fruits	1–31	2–36
Orange juice	25	53
Grapefruit juice	10	21
Nuts	8–48	24–106
Cereals and cereal products	1–36	8–78
Cow's milk	5–10	9–32

ous foods are given in Table 2. The folic acid in the normal diet is made up of about 25% of the free acid and 75% in the form of polyglutamates[26]. The polyglutamate form is poorly absorbed, though part of it is probably broken down in the intestinal wall to the free acid; free folic acid is absorbed to the extent of 80%[26]. Of all the vitamins, folic acid is the least stable (Table 3), and in finely divided foods 95% or more may be decomposed by prolonged boiling in water.

The values for vitamin E are those for α-tocopherol, because it is this latter compound which primarily determines the vitamin activity in foods. In certain oils, however, including maize oil and soybean oil in particular, the tocopherol content is predominantly accounted for by γ-tocopherol[28].

Elements. Only part of the trace elements in food is absorbed. Little is known of the extent to which copper and manganese are taken up from the diet[29]. 20–40% of dietary zinc[29,30] and 59% of that in breast milk[37] are absorbed. Iron is absorbed to a different extent from different foods (Table 4). The amount of iron absorbed from a meal depends primarily on the composition of the latter (when the meal is rich in meat, for example, the iron in the vegetables is better absorbed) and on the size of the body's iron stores (considerably more is absorbed when these are depleted than when they are at a normal level [Table 4])[34,35]. Thus persons

Table 3 *Vitamin losses during cooking*[8, 27]

	Thiamin	Riboflavin	Niacin	Free folic acid	Ascorbic acid
			%		
Meats	35	20	25	0	–
Meats plus drippings	25	5	10	0	–
Liver	–	–	–	0	–
Cereals	10	0	10	40–80	–
Legumes	20	0	0	–	–
Vegetables (leafy, green and yellow)	40	25	25	89–98	60
Tomatoes	5	5	5	–	15
Vegetables, other	25	15	25	0–80	60
Potatoes	40	25	25	40–90	60

Table 4
Food iron absorption (mean value and extreme range)[31, 32]

		Normal iron-stores	Depleted iron-stores
		% of intake	
Rice	Adults	0.9	–
Maize	Adults	(3.2–4.2)	–
Wheat	Adults	5.1 (2.6–10.1)	–
Soybeans	Adults	6.9 (3–11)	–
Black beans	Adults	(2.0–2.6)	–
Spinach	Adults	1.3	–
Lettuce	Adults	4	–
Chard, Swiss	Adults	(2–6)	–
Beet greens	Adults	(3–6)	–
Cow's milk	Children	11	–
	Adults	2.8	–
Human milk	Infants	49[33]	–
Eggs	Children	11	–
	Adults	3	8
Hemoglobin	Adults	8.2 (5.5–11)	18 (13–34)
Liver	Adults	6.3 (1.5–15)	24 (11–39)
Pork	Adults	28 (14–53)	43 (15–73)

in western countries on a mixed diet absorb about 10% of the dietary iron when their iron stores are normal and about 20% when the stores are depleted[34, 36]. The absorption of calcium, magnesium, iron and zinc is impaired by phosphate, oxalate and phytate (see page 265).

Signs and symbols. Zero values are indicated throughout by a zero (0). A dash (–) in the place of a value means either that no value could be found by the compilers or that the data in the literature are excessively at variance.

References

[1] CHATFIELD, C., *Food Composition Tables for International Use,* FAO Nutritional Studies, No. 3, Food and Agricultural Organization of the United Nations, Washington, 1949; CHATFIELD, C., *Food Composition Tables – Minerals and Vitamins – for International Use,* FAO Nutritional Studies, No. 11, Food and Agricultural Organization of the United Nations, Rome, 1954.

[2] WATT and MERRILL, *Composition of Foods – Raw, Processed, Prepared,* United States Department of Agriculture, Agriculture Handbook, No. 8, Washington (DC), 1963.

[3] PAUL and SOUTHGATE, *McCance and Widdowson's The Composition of Foods,* 4th ed., HMSO, London, 1978.

[4] SOUCI et al., *Die Zusammensetzung der Lebensmittel,* 2 volumes, Wissenschaftliche Verlagsgesellschaft, Stuttgart, 1962–1969.

[5] FEELEY et al., *J. Amer. diet. Ass., 61,* 139 (1972); SWEENEY and WEIHRAUCH, *Crit. Rev. Food Sci. Nutr., 8,* 31 (1977).

[6] KELLER et al., *Voeding, 29,* 24 (1968).

[7] HOPPNER et al., *Canad. Inst. Food Technol. J., 5,* 60 (1972), and *J. Amer. diet. Ass., 63,* 536 (1973).

[8] HURDLE et al., *Amer. J. clin. Nutr., 21,* 1202 (1968); HUSKISSON and RETIEF, *S. Afr. med. J., 44,* 362 (1970).

[9] HERTING and DRURY, *J. Nutr., 81,* 335 (1963); BOOTH and BRADFORD, *Brit. J. Nutr., 17,* 575 (1963); BUNNELL et al., *Amer. J. clin. Nutr., 17,* 1 (1965); THOMPSON et al., *Amer. J. clin. Nutr., 26,* 1349 (1973).

[10] SCHLETTWEIN and MOMMSEN (Eds.), *Spurenelemente in Lebensmitteln,* Internationale Zeitschrift für Vitaminforschung, fascicle No. 13, Huber, Berne, 1973.

[11] PENNINGTON and CALLOWAY, *J. Amer. diet. Ass., 63,* 143 (1973).

[12] MURPHY et al., *J. Amer. diet. Ass., 66,* 345 (1975); FREELAND and COUSINS, *J. Amer. diet. Ass., 68,* 526 (1976); HAEFLEIN and RASMUSSEN, *J. Amer. diet. Ass., 70,* 610 (1977).

[13] CHURCH and CHURCH, *Food Values of Portions Commonly Used,* 12th ed., Lippincott, Philadelphia, 1975.

[14] RANDOIN et al., *Tables de composition des aliments,* 3rd ed., Lanore, Paris, 1961.

[15] *Nederlandse Voedingsmiddelentabel,* Voorlichtingsbureau voor de Voeding, The Hague, 1973.

[16] ALTMAN and DITTMER (Eds.), *Metabolism,* Federation of American Societies for Experimental Biology, Bethesda (Md.), 1968.

[17] ROBINSON, C. H., *Proudfit-Robinson's Normal and Therapeutic Nutrition,* 13th ed., Macmillan, New York, 1967.

[18] TURNER, D. F., *Handbook of Diet Therapy,* 4th ed., University of Chicago Press, Chicago, 1965.

[19] LEUNG and FLORES, *Food Composition Table for Use in Latin America,* National Institutes of Health, Bethesda (Md.), 1961.

[20] LEUNG et al., *Food Composition Table for Use in East Asia,* National Institutes of Health, Bethesda (Md.), 1972.

[21] WEIHRAUCH and GARDNER, *J. Amer. diet. Ass., 73,* 39 (1978).

[22] TROWELL, H., *Lancet, 1,* 503 (1974); SPILLER et al., *Amer. J. clin. Nutr., 29,* 934 (1976); SOUTHGATE, D. A., *Amer. J. clin. Nutr., 31,* S 107 (1978).

[23] HELLENDOORN, E. W., *J. Amer. diet. Ass., 69,* 248 (1976).

[24] *Energy Yielding Components of Food and Computation of Caloric Values,* Food and Agriculture Organization, Nutrition Division, Washington (DC), 1947.

[25] Food and Nutrition Board, *Recommended Dietary Allowances,* 8th ed., National Academy of Sciences, Washington (DC), 1974.

[26] Joint FAO/WHO Expert Group on Vitamin and Mineral Requirements, *Wld Hlth Org. techn. Rep. Ser.,* No. 452 (1970).

[27] Interdepartmental Committee on Nutrition, *Publ. Hlth Rep., (Wash.), 75,* 687 (1960).

[28] SLOVER et al., *J. Amer. Oil Chem. Soc., 46,* 417 (1969).

[29] WHO Expert Committee on Trace Elements in Human Nutrition, *Wld Hlth Org. techn. Rep. Ser.,* No. 532 (1973).

[30] SANDSTEAD, H. H., *Amer. J. clin. Nutr., 26,* 1251 (1973).

[31] LAYRISSE and MARTINEZ-TORRES, *Progr. Hemat., 7,* 137 (1971).

[32] HEINRICH et al., *Klin. Wschr., 55,* 595 (1977).

[33] SAARINEN et al., *J. Pediat., 91,* 36 (1977).

[34] MOORE, C. V., in HALLBERG et al. (Eds.), *Iron Deficiency,* Colloquia Geigy, Academic Press, London, 1970, page 625.

[35] LAYRISSE et al., *Amer. J. clin. Nutr., 27,* 152 (1974).

[36] COOK and MONSEN, *Amer. J. clin. Nutr., 28,* 1289 (1975).

[37] EVANS and JOHNSON, *Amer. J. clin. Nutr., 30,* 873 (1977).

Fruits, Fruit Juices

100 g edible portion (unless otherwise stated) contains	Water g	Proteins g	Fats Total g	Fats Polyunsaturated g	Carbohydrates Total g	Carbohydrates Fibre g	Energy kcal	Energy MJ	A + β-carotene IU	Thiamine mg	Riboflavin mg	B_6 mg	Niacin mg	Free folic acid µg	Pantothenic acid mg	Ascorbic acid mg	α-Tocopherol mg	Others	A Excess acid, B Excess base	Sodium mg	Potassium mg	Calcium mg	Magnesium mg	Iron mg	Copper mg	Zinc mg	Phosphorus mg	Sulfur mg	Chloride mg
Apples (sweet) (*Pirus malus*)	84.0	0.3	0.6	–	15.0	0.9	58	0.24	90	0.04	0.02	0.03	0.1	3	0.1	5[1]	0.3	biotin 1 µg	B	1	116	7	5	0.3	0.08	0.10	10	30	1
– per kg as purchased (refuse 18%)	*688*	*2.5*	*4.9*	*–*	*123*	*7.4*	*476*	*1.99*	*738*	*0.33*	*0.17*	*0.25*	*0.8*	*24*	*0.8*	*41*	*2.5*	*biotin 8 µg*	*B*	*8*	*951*	*57*	*41*	*2.5*	*0.66*	*0.82*	*82*	*246*	*8*
– dried	20.4	3	0.7	–	73.6	4.0	281	1.18	–	0.05	0.08	0.16	0.5	–	–	10[1]	–	–	B	5	557	31	29	1.6	0.24	0.48	52	19	–
Apple juice, fresh	86.9	0.1	trace	–	13	–	47	0.20	–	0.01	0.02	0.03	0.5	2	0.02	1	0.04	biotin 0.5 µg	B	2	100	6	5	0.6	0.35	0.04	9	–	–
Apple sauce, sweetened	75.7	0.2	0.1	–	23.8	0.5	91	0.38	60	0.01	0.01	–	0.1	2	0.07	1	0.09	biotin 0.2 µg	B	0.3	55	4	5	0.5	0.35	0.1	5	5	4
Apricots (*Prunus armeniaca*)	85.3	0.9	0.2	–	12.8	0.6	51	0.21	2700	0.03	0.05	0.07	0.7	7	0.3	7	–	–	B	0.6	440	17	17	0.5	0.12	0.04	23	6	trace
– per kg as purchased (refuse 6%)	*802*	*8.5*	*1.9*	*–*	*120.3*	*5.6*	*479*	*2.00*	*25380*	*0.28*	*0.47*	*0.66*	*6.6*	*66*	*2.8*	*66*	*–*	*–*	*B*	*5.6*	*4136*	*160*	*85*	*4.7*	*1.13*	*0.38*	*216*	*56*	*–*
– canned, sweetened	76.9	0.6	0.1	–	22.0	0.4	86	0.36	1740	0.02	0.02	0.05	0.3	4	0.1	4	–	–	B	2	260	11	7	0.5	0.05	–	15	–	2
– dried	25.0	5.0	0.1	–	66.5	3.0	260	1.09	10990	0.01	0.16	0.25	3.3	10	0.7	12	–	–	B	26	980	67	65	5.5	0.4	0.22	119	160	35
Avocados (*Persea gratissima*)	73.6	2.2	17.0	2	6.0	1.5	171	0.72	290	0.11	0.20	0.61	1.6	31	0.9	14	3.2	–	B	3	340	10	30	0.6	0.4	–	42	19	6
Bananas (*Musa sapientum*)	75.7	1.1	0.2	–	22.2	0.6	85	0.36	190	0.05	0.06	0.32	0.6	12	0.2	10	0.2	biotin 4 µg	B	1	370	8	33	0.7	0.2	0.15	28	12	79
– per kg as purchased (refuse 32%)	*515*	*7.5*	*1.4*	*–*	*151.0*	*4.1*	*578*	*2.42*	*1292*	*0.34*	*0.41*	*2.18*	*4.1*	*82*	*1.4*	*68*	*1.4*	*biotin 27 µg*	*B*	*7*	*2516*	*54*	*224*	*4.8*	*1.36*	*1.0*	*190*	*82*	*537*
Blackberries (*Rubus fruticosus*)	84.5	1.2	0.9	–	12.9	4.1	58	0.24	200	0.03	0.04	0.05	0.4	–	0.25	21	0.35	biotin 0.4 µg	B	4	181	32	24	1.0	0.12	–	19	17	22
– frozen, sweetened	74.3	0.8	0.3	–	24.4	1.8	96	0.40	140	0.02	0.10	–	0.6	2	–	8	–	–	B	1	105	17	12	0.6	–	–	17	11	–
Blueberries (*Vaccinium* sp.)	83.2	0.7	0.5	–	15.3	1.5	62	0.26	100	0.03	0.06	0.091	0.5	–	0.12	14	–	–	B	1	89	15	6	1.0	0.11	–	13	11	–
– frozen, sweetened	72.3	0.6	0.3	–	26.5	0.9	105	0.44	30	0.05	0.05	–	0.4	–	–	–	–	–	B	1	66	6	4	1.0	–	–	11	–	–
Cantaloups (*Cucumis melo*)	91.2	0.7	0.1	–	7.5	0.5	30	0.13	3400[2]	0.04	0.03	0.036	0.4	30	0.26	33	0.1	biotin 3 µg	B	12	230	14	17	0.4	0.04	0.14	16	12	44
– per kg as purchased (refuse 50%)	*456*	*3.5*	*0.5*	*–*	*37.5*	*2.0*	*150*	*0.63*	*17000*	*0.20*	*0.15*	*0.18*	*3.0*	*150*	*1.30*	*165*	*0.5*	*biotin 15 µg*	*B*	*60*	*1150*	*70*	*85*	*2.0*	*0.20*	*0.70*	*80*	*59*	*220*
Cherries (*Prunus avium*)	83.4	1.2	0.4	–	14.6	0.5	60	0.25	1000	0.05	0.06	0.05	0.3	6	0.26	10	0.13	biotin 0.4 µg	B	2	260	19	14	0.5	0.07	0.15	19	8	trace
– per kg as purchased (refuse 10%)	*751*	*10.8*	*3.6*	*–*	*131.4*	*4.5*	*540*	*2.26*	*9000*	*0.45*	*0.54*	*0.45*	*2.7*	*54*	*2.34*	*90*	*1.17*	*biotin 3.6 µg*	*B*	*18*	*2340*	*179*	*132*	*4.7*	*0.66*	*1.4*	*171*	*72*	*–*
Cranberries (*Vaccinium macrocarpon*)	87.9	0.4	0.7	–	10.8	1.4	46	0.19	40	0.03	0.02	0.06	0.1	1	–	12	0.11	–	B	1	65	14	8	0.5	0.09	–	11	7	trace
Cranberry sauce, canned, sweetened	62.1	0.1	0.2	–	37.5	0.2	146	0.61	20	0.01	0.01	–	trace	0.3	–	2	–	–	B	–	17	6	2	0.2	–	–	4	–	–
Currants																													
– red and white (*Ribes rubrum*)	85.7	1.4	0.2	–	12.1	3.4	50	0.21	120	0.04	0.02	0.05	0.3	–	0.06	41	0.1	biotin 2.6 µg	B	2	275	36	15	1.0	0.12	0.2	23	29	13
– black (*Ribes nigrum*)	82	1.0	0.1	–	16.1	5.7	62	0.26	220	0.05	0.03	0.08	0.3	–	0.40	136	1.0	biotin 2.4 µg	B	3	336	17	10	0.9	0.12	0.2	28	33	15
Dates (*Phoenix dactylifera*), dried	22.5	2.2	0.5	–	72.9	2.3	274	1.15	50	0.09	0.10	0.15	2.2	14	0.8	0	–	–	B	1	790	59	58	3.0	0.28	0.30	63	65	290
Elderberries, black (*Sambucus nigra*)	80.9	2.5	0.5	–	15.9	6.8	42	0.18	600	0.07	0.08	0.25	1.5	18	0.18	18	–	biotin 2 µg	B	0.5	305	35	–	1.6	–	–	57	–	–
Figs (*Ficus carica*)	81.7	1.2	0.4	–	16.1	1.4	65	0.27	75	0.09	0.08	0.11	0.4	4	0.30	2	–	–	B	2	190	35	21	0.8	0.06	0.25	22	12	18
– dried	23.0	4.3	1.3	–	69.1	5.6	274	1.15	80	0.10	0.10	0.32	1.7	3	0.44	0	–	–	B	34	780	126	82	4.0	0.35	0.86	77	69	170
Fruit cocktail, canned	79.6	0.4	0.1	–	19.7	0.4	76	0.32	140	0.02	0.01	0.01	0.4	1	0.04	2	–	biotin 0.1 µg	B	5	160	9	8	0.4	0.03	–	12	2	3
Gooseberries (*Ribes grossularia*)	88.9	0.8	0.2	–	9.7	1.9	39	0.16	290	0.15	0.03	0.02	0.3	–	0.15	25	0.4	biotin 0.5 µg	B	1	210	28	9	0.5	0.08	0.09	31	15	11

[1] Wide variations between different varieties. [2] Highly colored variety.

100 g edible portion (unless otherwise stated) contains	Water g	Proteins g	Fats Total g	Fats Polyunsaturated g	Carbohydrates Total g	Carbohydrates Fibre g	Energy kcal	Energy MJ	A + β-carotene IU	Thiamine mg	Riboflavin mg	B6 mg	Niacin mg	Free folic acid µg	Pantothenic acid mg	Ascorbic acid mg	α-Tocopherol	Others	A Excess acid, B Excess base	Sodium mg	Potassium mg	Calcium mg	Magnesium mg	Iron mg	Copper mg	Zinc mg	Phosphorus mg	Sulfur mg	Chloride mg
Grapes (*Vitis vinifera*)	81.4	0.6	0.3	–	17.3	0.5	67	0.28	100	0.05	0.02	0.1	0.3	4	0.08	4	0.7	biotin 2 µg	B	2	250	12	7	0.4	0.1	0.1	20	9	trace
Grape juice	82.9	0.2	trace	–	16.6	trace	66	0.28	–	0.04	0.02	0.021	0.2	2	0.04	2	–	biotin 0.3 µg	B	1	120	11	8	0.3	0.02	0.04	12	–	–
Grapefruit (*Citrus decumana*)	88.4	0.6	0.1	–	9.8	0.5	39	0.16	80	0.04	0.02	0.03	0.2	7	0.25	40	0.25	biotin 3 µg	B	2	198	17	10	0.3	0.02	0.10	16	5	1
- per kg as purchased (refuse 51%)	*433*	*2.9*	*0.5*	–	*48*	*2.6*	*191*	*0.80*	*392*	*0.20*	*0.10*	*0.15*	*1.0*	*35*	*1.23*	*196*	*1.23*	*biotin 15 µg*	*B*	*10*	*970*	*83*	*49*	*1.5*	*0.10*	*0.49*	*78*	*25*	*5*
- canned, sweetened	81.1	0.6	0.1	–	17.8	0.2	70	0.29	10	0.03	0.02	0.02	0.2	11	0.12	30	–	biotin 1.0 µg	B	2	135	13	11	0.3	0.01	0.04	14	–	5
Grapefruit juice, fresh	89.2	0.4	0.1	–	9.8	0.1	41	0.17	10	0.03	0.02	0.014	0.2	10	0.16	45	0.04	biotin 0.7 µg	B	2	150	8	12	0.4	0.01	0.03	14	5	–
Kiwi (*Actinidia chinensis*)	83.9	1.02	–	–	10.2	1.1	36	0.15	–	–	–	–	–	–	–	57	–	–	B	–	–	–	–	–	–	–	–	–	–
Lemons (*Citrus medica*)	90.1	1.1	0.3	–	8.2	0.4	27	0.11	20	0.04	0.02	0.11	0.1	7	0.23	80	–	biotin 0.5 µg	B	6	148	26	9	0.6	0.26	0.17	16	12	5
Lemon juice	91.0	0.5	0.2	–	8.0	–	25	0.10	20	0.03	0.01	0.039	0.1	7	0.1	50	–	–	B	–	140	14	7	0.2	0.13	0.1	11	2	3
Lime juice (*Citrus aurantifolia*)	90.3	0.3	–	–	9.0	–	26	0.11	10	0.02	0.01	0.05	0.1	–	–	32	–	–	B	1	100	9	5	0.2	0.01	–	11	–	4
Loganberries (*Rubus ursinus* var. *loganobaccus*)	83	1.0	0.6	–	14.9	3.0	62	0.26	200	0.03	0.04	–	0.4	–	–	24	–	–	B	1	170	35	25	1.2	0.14	–	17	18	16
Lychees (*Litchi chinensis*)	82.0	0.9	0.3	–	16.5	0.5	64	0.27	–	0.04	0.04	–	0.3	–	–	40	–	–	B	3	170	8	10	0.5	–	–	35	19	3
- canned	79.3	0.4	trace	–	18.1	0.4	68	0.29	–	–	–	–	–	–	–	8	–	–	B	2	75	4	6	0.7	0.11	0.2	12	13	5
Mango (*Mangifera indica*)	81.7	0.7	0.4	–	16.8	0.9	66	0.28	4800	0.05	0.05	–	1.1	–	0.16	35	1	–	B	7	189	10	9	0.4	0.12	–	13	–	–
Nectarines (*Prunus persica* var. *nectarina*)	81.8	0.6	trace	–	17.1	0.4	64	0.27	1650	–	–	–	–	5	–	13	–	–	B	6	294	4	13	0.5	0.06	0.1	24	10	5
Olives (*Olea europaea*) - green, in brine	78.2	1.4	12.7	1	1.3	1.3	116	0.49	300	0.03	0.08	0.02	0.5	–	–	0	–	–	B	2400	55	61	22	1.6	0.23	–	17	32	3750
Oranges (*Citrus sinensis*)	86.0	1.0	0.2	–	12.2	0.5	49	0.21	200	0.10	0.03	0.06	0.2	13	0.2	50	0.23	biotin 1 µg	B	1	170	41	10	0.4	0.07	0.17	23	8	3
- per kg as purchased (refuse 27%)	*628*	*7.3*	*1.5*	–	*89.1*	*3.7*	*358*	*1.50*	*1460*	*0.73*	*0.22*	*0.44*	*1.5*	*95*	*1.5*	*365*	*1.68*	*biotin 7 µg*	*B*	*7*	*1240*	*299*	*73*	*2.9*	*0.51*	*1.2*	*168*	*58*	*22*
Orange juice, fresh	88.7	0.7	0.2	–	10.4	0.1	45	0.19	200	0.09	0.03	0.04	0.2	13-53	0.14	50[1]	0.04	biotin 0.8 µg	B	1	200	11	11	0.3	0.05	0.07	17	5	1
Passion fruit (*Passiflora edulis*)	75.1	2.2	0.7	–	21.2	–	90	0.38	700	trace	0.10	–	1.5	–	–	20	0.1	–	B	28	350	16	39	1.1	0.12	–	54	19	37
Peaches (*Prunus persica*)	86.6	0.6	0.1	–	11.8	0.6	46	0.19	1330	0.02	0.05	0.02	1.0	2	0.12	7	0.87	biotin 2 µg	B	1	160	9	10	0.5	0.05	0.02	19	7	trace
- per kg as purchased (refuse 13%)	*753*	*5.2*	*0.9*	–	*102.7*	*5.2*	*400*	*1.67*	*11570*	*0.17*	*0.44*	*0.17*	*8.7*	*17*	*1.05*	*61*	–	*biotin 18 µg*	*B*	*9*	*1390*	*78*	*87*	*4.4*	*0.45*	*0.17*	*165*	*61*	–
- canned, sweetened	79.1	0.4	0.1	–	20.1	0.4	78	0.33	430	0.01	0.02	0.02	0.6	2	0.05	4	–	biotin 0.2 µg	B	2	107	4	6	0.3	0.06	0.05	12	1	4
- dried	25.0	3.0	0.7	–	68.3	3.1	262	1.10	3900	0.01	0.2	0.15	5.3	10	0.30	18	–	–	B	6	1100	48	48	6.0	0.6	0.05	117	240	11
Pears (*Pirus communis*)	83.2	0.4	0.4	–	15.5	1.5	61	0.26	20	0.01	0.04	0.02	0.1	4	0.07	4	0.5	biotin 0.2 µg	B	2	130	8	9	0.3	0.13	0.16	11	27	trace
- per kg as purchased (refuse 9%)	*757*	*4.6*	*3.6*	–	*141*	*13.7*	*555*	*2.32*	*182*	*0.18*	*0.36*	*0.18*	*0.9*	*36*	*0.64*	*36*	*4.5*	*biotin 1.8 µg*	*B*	*18*	*1183*	*73*	*82*	*2.7*	*1.18*	*1.5*	*100*	*243*	–
- canned, sweetened	79.8	0.2	0.2	–	19.6	0.6	76	0.32	trace	0.01	0.02	0.01	0.1	7	0.02	1	–	–	B	2	52	5	6	0.2	0.04	0.06	7	1	3
Persimmons, Japanese (kaki) (*Diospyros kaki*)	78.8	0.7	0.4	–	19.7	1.6	77	0.32	2710	0.03	0.02	–	0.1	–	–	11	–	–	B	6	174	6	8	0.3	–	–	26	–	–

[1] In canned juice 12.

100 g edible portion (unless otherwise stated) contains	Water g	Proteins g	Fats Total g	Fats Polyunsaturated g	Carbohydrates Total g	Carbohydrates Fibre g	Energy kcal	Energy MJ	A + β-carotene IU	Thiamine	Riboflavin	B6 mg	Niacin	Free folic acid µg	Pantothenic acid	Ascorbic acid	α-Tocopherol	Others	A Excess acid, B Excess base	Sodium mg	Potassium mg	Calcium mg	Magnesium mg	Iron mg	Copper µg	Zinc µg	Phosphorus mg	Sulfur mg	Chloride mg
Pineapple (Ananas sativus)	86.7	0.4	0.2	–	12.2	0.5	47	0.20	70	0.08	0.03	0.08	0.2	9	0.16	17	–	–	B	2	250	17	17	0.5	0.07	0.25	8	3	29
– canned, sweetened	79.9	0.3	0.1	–	19.4	0.3	74	0.31	50	0.08	0.02	0.07	0.2	2	–	7	0.1	–	B	1	94	11	8	0.3	0.05	0.09	5	3	4
Pineapple juice, canned.	85.6	0.4	0.1	–	13.5	0.1	55	0.23	50	0.05	0.02	0.1	0.2	–	0.1	7	–	–	B	1	140	15	15	0.5	–	0.07	9	3	38
Plums (Prunus domestica)	85.7	0.7	0.1	–	12.3	0.7	50	0.21	250	0.07	0.04	0.05	0.5	1	0.13	6	0.7	–	B	2	167	13	13	0.4	0.1	0.05	23	5	trace
– per kg as purchased (refuse 6%)	*806*	*6.6*	*0.9*	*–*	*115.6*	*6.6*	*470*	*1.97*	*2350*	*0.66*	*0.38*	*0.47*	*4.7*	*9*	*1.22*	*56*	*6.65*	*–*	*B*	*19*	*1560*	*122*	*122*	*3.8*	*0.94*	*0.47*	*216*	*47*	*–*
– canned, sweetened	77.4	0.4	0.1	–	21.6	0.3	83	0.35	230	0.02	0.02	0.027	0.4	2	0.08	2	–	–	B	8	142	9	5	0.9	0.16	–	10	–	–
Prunes (Prunus domestica), dried	28.0	2.1	0.6	–	67.4	1.6	255	1.07	1600	0.1	0.17	0.24	1.6	0.7	0.46	3	–	–	B	8	700	51	40	3.9	0.5	–	79	28	3
Quinces (Cydonia oblonga, Cydonia vulgaris)	84	0.3	0.3	–	14.9	2.4	57	0.24	30	0.03	0.02	–	0.2	–	–	15	–	–	B	3	200	14	6	0.3	0.13	–	19	5	2
Raisins (Vitis vinifera), dried.	18.0	2.5	0.2	–	77.4	0.9	289	1.21	20	0.11	0.08	0.3	0.5	4	0.09	1	–	biotin 5 µg	B	31	725	62	35	3.5	0.2	0.1	101	23	9
Raspberries (Rubus idaeus)	84.2	1.2	0.5	–	13.6	3.0	57	0.24	130	0.03	0.09	0.06	0.9	–	0.2	25	0.3	biotin 1.9 µg	B	3	170	41	22	1.0	0.13	–	22	18	22
– frozen, sweetened	74.3	0.7	0.2	–	24.6	2.2	98	0.41	70	0.02	0.02	–	0.6	–	–	21	–	–	B	1	100	13	11	0.6	–	0.15	17	7	–
Raspberry juice, fresh	88	0.2	0	–	11	trace	40	0.17	120	0.02	–	–	–	–	–	20	–	–	B	7	141	29	18	1.0	–	–	14	7	–
Strawberries (Fragaria sp.)	89.9	0.7	0.5	–	8.4	1.3	37	0.15	60	0.03	0.07	0.06	0.6	15	0.34	60	0.22	biotin 1.1 µg	B	1	160	21	12	1.0	0.13	0.09	21	12	18
– frozen, sweetened	75.7	0.4	0.2	–	23.5	0.6	92	0.39	30	0.02	0.06	–	0.5	–	–	53	0.19	–	B	1	104	13	9	0.4	–	–	16	10	2
Tangerines (Citrus nobilis)	87	0.8	0.2	–	11.6	0.5	46	0.19	420	0.07	0.02	0.07	0.2	17	0.20	31	–	–	B	2	126	40	11	0.4	0.1	0.15	18	10	2
– per kg as purchased (refuse 26%)	*644*	*5.9*	*1.5*	*–*	*85.8*	*3.7*	*341*	*1.43*	*3108*	*0.52*	*0.15*	*0.52*	*1.5*	*126*	*1.5*	*229*	*–*	*–*	*B*	*15*	*932*	*296*	*81*	*3.0*	*0.7*	*1.1*	*133*	*74*	*15*
Watermelon (Citrullus vulgaris var. colocynthoides)	92.6	0.5	0.2	–	6.4	0.3	26	0.11	590	0.03	0.03	0.033	0.2	2	0.3	7	–	biotin 4 µg	B	2	100	7	8	0.5	0.07	0.09	10	9	–
Whortleberries, red (Vaccinium vitis idaea)	87.4	0.3	0.5	–	11.6	1.7	42	0.18	30	0.014	0.02	0.012	0.2	–	0.1	12	–	–	B	2	72	14	6	0.5	0.26	0.1	10	–	4
Vegetables																													
Artichokes (Cynara scolymus)	85.5	2.7	0.2	–	10.6	2.4	49	0.20	160	0.08	0.05	–	1.0	–	0.4	12	0.15	–	B	43	430	51	26	1.3	0.2	0.06	94	21	22
Asparagus (Asparagus officinalis)	92.9	2.1	0.2	–	4.1	0.8	21	0.09	900	0.18	0.20	0.14	1.5	58	0.62	33	2.5	–	B	2	278	22	20	1.0	0.14	0.32	62	46	53
– per kg as purchased (refuse 44%)	*520*	*11.8*	*1.1*	*–*	*23*	*4.5*	*118*	*0.49*	*5040*	*1.01*	*1.12*	*0.78*	*8.4*	*325*	*3.47*	*185*	*14*	*–*	*B*	*11*	*1557*	*123*	*112*	*5.6*	*0.78*	*1.8*	*347*	*257*	*297*
– canned, drained solids	92.5	2.4	0.4	–	3.4	0.8	21	0.09	800	0.06	0.10	0.04	0.8	5	0.15	15	–	biotin 2 µg	B	236[1]	166	19	15	1.9	0.01	0.01	53	47	–
Beans																													
– broad (Vicia faba), mature, dry seeds	12.6	24.0	2.2	–	58.2	5.9	339	1.42	30	0.53	0.30	–	2.5	–	0.98	6	–	–	B	1	1210	77	159	6.3	1.2	0.01	374	237	35
– kidney (Phaseolus vulgaris), dry seeds	11.6	21.3	1.6	–	61.6	4.0	338	1.41	0	0.65	0.22	0.28	2.1	25	1.3	2	4	biotin 10 µg	B	2	1310	106	132	6.1	0.84	2.8	429	46	25
– Lima (Phaseolus lunatus)	67.5	8.4	0.5	–	22.1	1.8	123	0.51	290	0.24	0.12	0.55	1.4	–	0.11	29	–	–	B	2	650	52	67	2.8	0.18	0.77	142	60	9
– – canned, drained solids	74.7	5.4	0.3	–	18.3	1.8	96	0.40	190	0.03	0.05	0.08	0.5	–	–	6	–	–	B	236[2]	210	28	26	2.4	–	0.13	70	30	33
– – string (Phaseolus vulgaris)	90.1	1.9	0.2	–	7.1	1.0	32	0.13	600	0.07	0.11	0.14	0.5	39	0.2	19	trace	K 0.29 mg	B	1.7	256	56	26	0.8	0.07	–	44	30	33
– – per kg as purchased (refuse 12%)	*793*	*16.7*	*1.7*	*–*	*62.5*	*8.8*	*272*	*1.14*	*5280*	*0.62*	*0.97*	*1.23*	*4.4*	*343*	*1.8*	*167*	*–*	*K 2.55 mg*	*B*	*15*	*2250*	*493*	*229*	*7.0*	*0.62*	*1.1*	*387*	*264*	*290*
– – canned, drained solids	91.9	1.4	0.1	–	5.2	1.0	24	0.10	470	0.03	0.05	0.043	0.3	–	0.07	4	–	biotin 1 µg	B	236[2]	95	45	13	1.5	0.23	0.01	25	–	300

[1] Unsalted 3.   [2] Unsalted 2.

100 g edible portion (unless otherwise stated) contains	Water g	Proteins g	Fats Total g	Fats Polyunsat. g	Carboh. Total g	Carboh. Fibre g	Energy kcal	Energy MJ	A + β-carotene IU	Thiamine mg	Riboflavin mg	B6 mg	Niacin mg	Free folic acid µg	Pantothenic acid mg	Ascorbic acid mg	α-Tocopherol mg	Others	A Excess acid / B Excess base	Sodium mg	Potassium mg	Calcium mg	Magnesium mg	Iron mg	Copper mg	Zinc mg	Phosphorus mg	Sulfur mg	Chloride mg
Beets (beetroots) (Beta vulgaris)																													
– peeled roots	87.3	1.6	0.1	–	9.9	0.8	43	0.18	20	0.03	0.04	0.05	0.4	69	0.12	10	–	–	B	84	300	25	23	0.7	0.19	0.59	33	15	59
– tops	90.9	2.2	0.3	–	4.6	1.3	24	0.10	6100	0.05	0.17	0.1	0.3	–	0.26	30	–	–	B	130	570	119	71	3.3	0.09	–	40	35	40
Broccoli (Brassica oleracea var. botrytis)	89.1	3.6	0.3	–	5.9	1.5	32	0.13	2500	0.1	0.23	0.17	0.9	47	1.3	113	2	biotin 3 µg	B	15	380	103	24	1.1	0.03	0.27	78	137	55
Brussels sprouts (Brassica oleracea var. gemmifera)	84.8	4.7	0.4	–	8.7	1.2	47	0.20	550	0.10	0.16	0.16	0.9	45	0.72	90	1.0	biotin 0.4 µg; K 0.8–3 mg	B	12	450	32	19	1.5	0.1	0.87	80	147	28
– per kg as purchased (refuse 26%)	*628*	*34.8*	*3.0*	*–*	*64.4*	*8.9*	*348*	*1.48*	*4070*	*0.74*	*1.18*	*1.18*	*6.7*	*333*	*5.33*	*660*	*7.4*	*biotin 3.0 µg; K 5.9–22 mg*	*B*	*89*	*3330*	*237*	*141*	*14.1*	*0.74*	*6.4*	*592*	*691*	*207*
Cabbage																													
– red (Brassica oleracea var. capitata rubra)	91.8	1.5	0.2	–	5.9	1.1	26	0.11	50	0.07	0.05	0.15	0.4	23	0.32	50	0.2	biotin 2 µg	B	4	266	35	18	0.5	0.06	0.3	30	62	45
– savoy (var. sabauda)	90.0	3.0	0.4	–	5.6	1.2	31	0.13	200	0.05	0.06	0.2	0.33	60	0.21	45	0.2	biotin 0.1 µg	B	9	282	47	12	0.9	0.07	0.3	56	68	22
– white (var. capitata alba)	92.1	1.4	0.2	–	5.7	1.5	25	0.10	70	0.05	0.04	0.11	0.32	25	0.26	46	0.7	biotin 0.1 µg	B	13	227	46	23	0.5	0.06	0.18	28	59	23
Carrots (Daucus carota)	88.6	1.1	0.2	–	9.1	1.0	40	0.17	11000[1]	0.06	0.06	0.12	0.6	15	0.27	2–10	0.45	biotin 3 µg	B	50	311	37	21	0.7	0.08	0.52	36	21	69
– per kg as purchased (refuse 18%)	*727*	*9.0*	*1.6*	*–*	*74.6*	*8.2*	*328*	*1.37*	*90200*	*0.49*	*0.49*	*0.98*	*4.9*	*123*	*2.21*	*16–82*	*3.69*	*biotin 25 µg*	*B*	*410*	*2550*	*303*	*172*	*5.7*	*0.66*	*2.7*	*295*	*172*	*566*
– canned, drained solids	91.2	0.8	0.3	–	6.7	0.8	30	0.13	15000	0.03	0.02	0.04	0.3	1	0.11	3	0.5	biotin 2 µg	B	236[2]	110	26	5	0.7	0.04	0.3	22	–	450
Cauliflower (Brassica oleracea var. botrytis)	91.0	2.7	0.2	–	5.2	1.0	27	0.11	60	0.11	0.10	0.20	0.6	32	1.0	78	0.15	–	B	16	350	25	23	1.1	0.14	0.46	56	89	31
Celery (Apium graveolens)																													
– leaves and stalks	94.1	0.9	0.1	–	3.9	0.6	17	0.07	240	0.05	0.03	0.13	0.4	–	–	9	0.7	–	B	96	290	39	25	0.5	0.01	–	40	22	137
– root	88.4	1.8	0.3	–	8.5	1.3	40	0.17	16	0.03	0.03	0.13	0.7	6	–	8	0.2	–	B	100	300	60	12	0.9	0.15	0.31	60	68	50
Chard, Swiss (Beta vulgaris var. cicla)	90.8	1.6	0.4	–	5.6	1.0	27	0.11	6500	0.03	0.09	0.09	0.4	–	0.17	34	1.5	biotin 17 µg; K 3.6 mg	B	147	550	110	65	2.7	0.11	–	29	89	–
Chickpeas (Cicer arietinum), dry seeds	10.7	20.5	4.8	2	61.0	5	360	1.51	50	0.31	0.15	–	2.0	30	–	3	–	–	A	26	797	150	160	6.9	1.5	–	331	180	60
Chicory (Cichorium intybus)	96.2	0.8	0.1	–	3.7	0.6	16	0.07	–	0.07	0.12	0.05	0.40	33	–	10	–	–	B	10	182	18	13	0.69	0.14	0.19	21	18	25
Chives (Allium schoenoprasum)	91.3	1.8	0.3	–	5.8	1.1	28	0.12	5800	0.04	0.11	–	0.3	–	–	22	–	–	B	3	250	76	32	0.9	0.11	–	26	59	43
Corn (sweet), see Maize																													
Cress, garden (Lepidium sativum ssp. sativum)	89.4	2.6	0.7	–	5.5	1.1	32	0.13	9300	0.08	0.26	–	1.0	–	0.30	69	0.7	–	B	14	606	81	27	1.3	0.12	–	76	170	89
Cucumbers (Cucumis sativus)	95.6	0.8	0.1	–	3.0	0.6	13	0.05	300	0.04	0.05	0.04	0.2	10	–	8	0.1	biotin 1 µg	B	5	140	25	9	1.1	0.06	0.12	27	12	25
Dandelion greens (Taraxacum officinale)	85.6	2.7	0.7	–	9.2	1.6	45	0.19	14000	0.19	0.26	–	–	–	–	35	2.5	–	B	76	430	187	36	3.1	0.15	–	66	17	100

[1] Dark varieties; in light varieties 2000.   [2] Unsalted 39.

100 g edible portion (unless otherwise stated) contains	Water g	Proteins g	Fats Total g	Fats Polyunsaturated g	Carbohydrates Total g	Carbohydrates Fibre g	Energy kcal	Energy MJ	A + β-carotene IU	Thiamine mg	Riboflavin mg	B₆ mg	Niacin mg	Free folic acid µg	Pantothenic acid mg	Ascorbic acid mg	α-Tocopherol mg	Others	A Excess acid, B Excess base	Sodium mg	Potassium mg	Calcium mg	Magnesium mg	Iron mg	Copper mg	Zinc mg	Phosphorus mg	Sulfur mg	Chloride mg
Eggplants (aubergines) (*Solanum melongena*)	92.4	1.2	0.2	–	5.6	0.9	25	0.10	10	0.05	0.05	0.07	0.6	8	0.23	5	–	–	B	3	240	12	10	0.4	0.08	0.28	26	9	61
Endives (*Cichorium endivia*)	93.1	1.7	0.1	–	4.1	0.9	20	0.08	3300	0.07	0.14	0.05	0.5	62	–	10	–	–	B	10	380	44	10	1.7	0.09	0.34	67	26	71
Fennel (*Foeniculum vulgare*)	90	1.5	0.1	–	6.4	0.5	27	0.11	3500	0.23	0.11	0.10	0.2	–	–	31	–	biotin 3 µg	B	331	784	35	11	2.7	–	–	51	–	–
Garlic (*Allium sativum*), bulbs	63.8	5.3	0.2	–	29.3	1.1	129	0.54	trace	0.21	0.08	–	0.6	–	0.25	9	–	–	B	32	515	38	36	1.4	0.26	0.59	134	–	30
Horse-radish (*Armoracia lapathifolia*)	76.6	2.8	0.3	–	18.1	2.8	80	0.33	30	0.05	0.11	0.18	0.6	–	–	120	–	–	B	9	554	105	33	2.0	0.14	–	70	210	19
Jerusalem artichokes (*Helianthus tuberosus*)	79.8	2.3	0.1	–	16.7	0.8	75	0.31	20	0.2	0.06	–	1.3	–	–	4	–	–	B	–	300	14	11	3.4	0.15	0.06	78	22	–
Kale (*Brassica oleracea* var. *acephala*)	87.5	4.2	0.8	–	6.0	1.3	38	0.16	8900	0.16	0.26	0.19	2.1	–	0.1–1.4	125	8	biotin 0.5 µg	B	75	410	179	37	2.2	0.09	–	73	115	60
Kohlrabi (*Brassica oleracea* var. *gongylodes*), tubers	90.3	2.0	0.1	–	6.6	1.0	29	0.12	20	0.06	0.04	0.12	0.3	–	0.1	53	–	–	B	10	392	41	48	0.5	0.14	0.23	51	50	57
Leeks (*Allium porrum*), leaves	87.8	2.0	0.3	–	9.4	1.2	44	0.18	50	0.06	0.04	0.25	0.5	–	0.12	18	1.0	biotin 1.4 µg	B	5	300	60	18	1.0	0.3	0.23	50	72	43
Lentils (*Lens esculenta*), dried	11.1	24.7	1.1	–	60.1	3.9	340	1.42	60	0.50	0.25	0.49	2.0	25	1.5	–	–	biotin 13 µg	B	36	810	79	77	8.6	0.7	2–9	377	122	64
Lettuce (*Lactuca sativa*), headed	95.1	1.3	0.2	–	2.5	0.5	14	0.06	970	0.06	0.07	0.07	0.3	24	0.20	8	0.6	biotin 3 µg	B	12	140	35	11	2.0	0.07	0.16	26	12	53
Maize (*Zea mays*)	72.7	3.5	1.0	–	22.1	0.7	96	0.40	400[1]	0.15	0.12	0.22	1.7	27	0.89	12	0.1	biotin 6 µg	B	1	300	3	48	0.7	0.06	–	111	32	11
– canned, drained solids	75.9	2.6	0.8	–	19.8	0.8	84	0.35	350[1]	0.03	0.05	0.27	0.9	–	0.28	4	–	biotin 3 µg	B	236[2]	97	5	19	0.5	0.01	0.6	49	–	460
Mushrooms (champignons) (*Psalliota campestris*)	90.8	2.8[3]	0.24	–	3.7	0.9	22	0.09	0	0.1	0.44	0.05	6.2	20	2.1	5	–	–	B	5	520	9	13	0.8	1.8	0.09	116	34	85
Okra (*Hibiscus esculentus*)	88.9	2.4	0.3	–	7.6	1.0	36	0.15	520	0.17	0.21	0.08	1.0	25	0.26	31	–	–	B	7	190	70	60	1.0	0.19	–	60	30	41
Onions (*Allium cepa*), ripe	89.1	1.5	0.1	–	8.7	0.6	38	0.16	40	0.03	0.04	0.10	0.2	15	0.17	10	0.26	biotin 4 µg	A	10	130	27	8	0.5	0.13	0.09	36	51	20
– dried	4	8.7	1.3	–	82.1	4.4	350	1.46	200	0.25	0.18	–	1.4	–	–	35	–	–	A	88	1380	166	106	3.1	–	–	273	–	–
Parsley (*Petroselinum crispum*)	85.1	3.6	0.6	–	8.5	1.5	44	0.18	8500	0.12	0.26	0.2	1.2	57	0.30	172	1.8	biotin 0.4 µg	B	28	880	203	52	6.2	0.21	0.92	63	190	160
Parsnips (*Pastinaca sativa*)	79.1	1.7	0.5	–	17.5	2.0	76	0.32	30	0.08	0.09	0.1	0.2	–	0.5	16	1.0	biotin 0.1 µg	B	17	340	50	32	0.7	0.10	0.08	77	26	41
Peas (*Pisum sativum*)																													
– edible-podded	86.2	2.6	0.1	–	10.5	1.5	53	0.22	55	0.06	0.10	0.09	0.8	–	0.82	30	–	biotin 9 µg; K 0.3 mg	B	–	–	44	–	1.4	0.23	1.6	54	–	–
– green, unripe	75.0	6.3	0.4	–	17.0	2.0	84	0.35	640	0.32	0.15	0.18	2.5	–	–	27	0.6	–	B	2	370	26	30	2.0	–	–	116	50	38
– green, canned	82.3	3.4	0.4	–	12.7	1.3	67	0.28	450	0.11	0.06	0.05	0.9	9	0.17	9	0.02	biotin 2 µg	B	260[4]	201	25	25	1.6	0.21	1.3	73	44	350
– green, frozen	80.7	5.4	0.3	–	12.8	1.9	73	0.31	680	0.32	0.10	0.09	2.0	21	0.75	19	0.22	–	B	129	150	20	24	2.0	0.22	0.9	90	–	20
– split, dried	9.3	24.2	1.0	–	62.7	1.2	348	1.46	120	0.74	0.29	0.13	3.0	–	2.0	–	–	biotin 2 µg	B	38	910	33	130	5.4	0.58	4.0	270	170	56
Peppers (*Capsicum annuum*)																													
– green chillies	92.8	1.2	0.2	–	5.3	1.4	24	0.10	420	0.08	0.08	0.22	0.5	8	0.23	128	–	–	B	4.2	210	9	12	0.4	0.11	0.03	25	19	18

¹ Based on yellow maize; white contains only a trace.   ² Unsalted.²   ³ ⅗ N × 6.25.   ⁴ Unsalted.³

100 g edible portion (unless otherwise stated) contains	Water g	Proteins g	Fats Total g	Fats Polyunsaturated g	Carbohydrates Total g	Carbohydrates Fibre g	Energy kcal	Energy MJ	A + β-carotene IU	Thiamine mg	Riboflavin mg	B₆ mg	Niacin mg	Free folic acid µg	Pantothenic acid mg	Ascorbic acid mg	α-Tocopherol mg	Others	A Excess acid, B Excess base	Sodium mg	Potassium mg	Calcium mg	Magnesium mg	Iron mg	Copper mg	Zinc mg	Phosphorus mg	Sulfur mg	Chloride mg
Potato chips	1.8	5.3	39.8	8	50.0	1.6	568	2.38	trace	0.21	0.07	0.89	4.8	4	–	16	6.4	–	B	550	1190	40	56	1.8	0.22	0.8	139	–	890
Potatoes (*Solanum tuberosum*)	79.8	2.1	0.1	–	17.7	0.5	76	0.32	trace	0.11	0.04	0.25	1.2	9	0.3	20	0.06	biotin 0.1 µg; K 0.08 mg	B	3	410	8	24	0.8	0.16	0.87	53	35	79
– per kg as purchased (refuse 19%)	646	17.0	0.8	–	143.4	4.1	616	2.58	trace	0.89	0.32	2.03	9.7	75	2.4	162	0.49	biotin 0.8 µg; K 0.65 mg	B	24	3320	65	194	6.5	1.30	7.1	429	284	640
– dried	7.1	8.3	0.6	–	80.4	1.4	352	1.47	trace	0.25	0.10	–	4.8	10	–	26	–	–	B	84	1600	44	–	2.4	0.37	1.1	203	–	–
Pumpkins (*Cucurbita sp.*)	95.0	0.8	0.1	–	3.5	0.6	15	0.06	1600	0.05	0.11	0.06	0.6	8	0.40	9	–	–	B	1	340	21	12	0.8	0.08	0.20	44	10	37
Purslane (*Portulaca oleracea* var. *sativa*)	92.5	1.7	0.4	–	3.8	0.9	21	0.09	2500	0.03	0.10	0.06	0.5	–	0.18	25	–	–	B	2	754	103	151	3.5	–	–	39	–	–
Radishes (*Raphanus sativus*)	93.7	1.1	0.1	–	3.6	0.7	18	0.08	10	0.04	0.04	0.1	0.3	18	–	26	0.2	–	B	15	260	30	15	1.0	0.13	0.16	31	37	19
Rhubarb (*Rheum undulatum*)	94.9	0.5	0.1	–	3.8	0.7	16	0.07	100	0.03	0.03	0.03	0.3	9	0.08	9	–	–	B	3.5	286	96	14	0.8	0.05	–	18	8	87
Rutabagas (*Brassica napus* var. *napobrassica*)	87.0	1.1	0.1	–	11.0	1.1	46	0.19	580	0.07	0.07	0.1	1.1	23	0.11	43	–	–	B	5	239	66	15	0.4	0.08	0.23	39	39	–
Salsify (*Scorzonera hispanica*)	79	3.2	0.6	–	16.4	1.8	77	0.32	10	0.04	0.04	0.18	0.2	–	–	12	–	biotin 0.1 µg	B	5	320	40	23	1.5	–	–	76	–	31
Sauerkraut	92.8	1.0	0.2	–	4.0	0.7	18	0.08	50	0.03	0.04	0.2	0.2	–	0.08	14	–	–	B	650	140	36	7	0.5	0.1	–	18	–	–
Soybeans (*Glycine hispida*), dried	10.0	34.1	17.7	10.7	33.5	4.9	403	1.69	80	1.10	0.31	0.64	2.1	–	1.68	trace	6–11	biotin 60 µg	B	4	1900	226	235	8.4	1.17	3	554	27	7
Spinach (*Spinacia oleracea*)	90.7	3.2	0.3	–	4.3	0.6	26	0.11	8100	0.10	0.20	0.20	0.6	176	0.31	51	2.5	biotin 7 µg; K 0.04–3 mg	B	62	662	106	62	3.1	0.20	0.22	51	–	76
– per kg as purchased (refuse 8%)	834	29.4	2.8	–	39.6	5.5	239	1.00	74520	0.92	1.84	1.84	5.5	1620	2.85	469	23	biotin 65 µg; K 0.37–28 mg	B	570	6090	975	570	28.5	1.84	2.09	469	248	699
– canned	93.0	2.0	0.4	–	3.0	0.7	19	0.08	5500	0.02	0.06	0.095	0.3	29	0.06	14	–	biotin 2 µg	B	320[1]	260	85	63	2.1	–	0.13	26	–	–
– frozen, leaves	91.3	3.0	0.3	–	4.2	0.8	25	0.10	8100	0.1	0.16	–	0.5	–	–	35	–	–	B	53	385	105	65	2.5	–	–	45	–	–
Squash, summer (zucchini) (*Cucurbita pepo* var. *medullosa*)	94.6	1.2	0.1	–	3.6	0.6	17	0.07	320[2]	0.05	0.09	0.09	1.0	23	–	19	–	–	B	1	202	28	10	0.4	0.07	0.2	29	10	18
Sweet potatoes (*Ipomoea batatas*)	70.6	1.7	0.4	–	26.3	0.7	114	0.48	8800	0.10	0.06	0.32	0.6	35	0.93	21	4	biotin 4 µg	B	5	530	32	31	0.7	0.15	0.16	47	15	31
– canned	70.7	1.0	0.2	–	27.5	0.6	114	0.48	5000	0.03	0.03	–	0.6	–	–	8	–	–	B	48	120	13	–	0.7	–	0.06	29	11	51
Tomatoes (*Lycopersicon esculentum*)	93.5	1.1	0.2	–	4.7	0.5	22	0.09	900	0.06	0.04	0.11	0.7	4	0.31	23	0.27	biotin 4 µg	B	3	268	13	11	0.6	0.10	0.01	27	–	78
– canned	93.7	1.0	0.2	–	4.3	0.4	21	0.09	900	0.06	0.03	0.07	0.7	11	0.2	17	0.22	biotin 1.5 µg	B	130[3]	217	6	12	0.5	0.09	0.07	19	5	370
Tomato juice, canned	93.6	0.9	0.1	–	4.3	0.2	19	0.08	800	0.05	0.03	0.19	0.7	4	0.30	16	0.22	–	B	230[3]	230	7	7	0.9	0.05	–	18	–	1810
Tomato ketchup	68.6	2.0	0.4	–	25.4	0.5	106	0.44	1400	0.09	0.07	–	1.6	–	–	15	0.3	–	B	1042	363	22	21	0.8	–	–	50	–	–
Tomato purée	86.0	2.3	0.5	–	9.5	0.5	44	0.18	1200	0.09	0.06	0.18	1.5	–	–	9	–	–	B	590	1160	60	20	1.0	–	–	34	–	–
Turnips (*Brassica rapa*)																													
– root	91.5	1.0	0.2	–	6.6	0.9	30	0.13	trace	0.04	0.07	0.11	0.6	17	0.20	36	0.02	biotin 0.1 µg	B	37	230	39	7	0.5	0.07	0.12	30	22	70
– greens	90.3	3.0	0.3	–	5.0	0.8	28	0.12	7600	0.21	0.39	0.98	0.8	–	0.38	139	2.3	–	B	10	440	260	19	1.8	0.09	–	58	54	–

[1] Unsalted 34.   [2] Including skin.   [3] Unsalted 3.

100 g edible portion (unless otherwise stated) contains	Water g	Proteins g	Fats Total g	Fats Polyunsaturated g	Carbohydrates Total g	Fibre g	Energy kcal	Energy MJ	A + β-carotene IU	Thiamine mg	Riboflavin mg	B₆ mg	Niacin mg	Free folic acid µg	Pantothenic acid mg	Ascorbic acid mg	α-Tocopherol mg	Others	A Excess acid, B Excess base	Sodium mg	Potassium mg	Calcium mg	Magnesium mg	Iron mg	Copper mg	Zinc mg	Phosphorus mg	Sulfur mg	Chloride mg
Watercress (*Nasturtium officinale*)	93.3	2.2	0.3	–	3.0	0.7	19	0.08	4000	0.1	0.27	0.13	0.9	200	0.1	75	1.0	–	B	60	310	151	17	2.0	0.04	0.15	46	130	160
Yeast (*Saccharomyces cerevisiae*) – baker's, compressed	71.0	12.1	0.4	–	11.0	–	86	0.36	trace	0.71	1.65	1.2	11.2	–	5.3	trace	–	biotin 400 µg	A	16	610	13	59	4.9	1.6	2.6	394	–	–
– brewer's, dried	5.0	38.8	1.0	–	38.4	1.7	283	1.18	trace	15.6	4.28	4.2	37.9	175	9.5	trace	–	biotin 80 µg	A	121	1700	210	231	17.3	3.32	8.4	1750	–	36
Yeast, torula (*Torulopsis utilis*), dried	6.0	38.6[1]	1.0	–	37.0	3.3	277	1.16	trace	15.0	5.0	3.5	50.0	–	10.0	–	–	biotin 100 µg	A	15	2050	424	165	20	–	–	1710	–	–
Condiments																													
Basil (*Ocimum basilicum*), powder	–	–	–	–	–	–	–	–	–	–	–	–	–	–	–	–	–	–	–	43	3700	2070	410	43	1.3	5.8	470	–	497
Bay leaves (*Laurus nobilis*)	–	–	–	–	–	–	–	–	–	–	–	–	–	–	–	–	–	–	–	20	2540	970	120	53	0.42	3.7	110	–	36
Cinnamon (*Cinnamomum zeylanicum*), powder	–	–	–	–	–	–	–	–	–	–	–	–	–	–	–	–	–	–	–	13	420	1600	53	4	0.23	1.8	50	–	34
Clove (*Eugenia caryophyllata*), powder	–	–	–	–	–	–	–	–	–	–	–	–	–	–	–	–	–	–	–	250	1170	740	270	12	0.38	7.5	110	–	–
Cumin (*Carum carvi*)	–	–	–	–	–	–	–	–	–	–	–	–	–	–	–	–	–	–	–	160	2070	953	390	48	0.9	4.8	450	–	–
Curry powder	–	10	10	–	25	–	200	0.84	–	–	–	–	–	–	–	–	–	–	–	450	1850	650	284	75	1.04	–	250	86	470
Dill weed (*Anethum graveolens*)	–	–	–	–	–	–	–	–	–	–	–	–	–	–	–	–	–	–	–	110	4850	1170	335	14	0.5	3.3	380	–	–
Ginger (*Zingiber officinale*), powder	–	–	–	–	–	–	–	–	–	–	–	–	–	–	–	–	–	–	–	32	1400	94	180	11	0.32	4.5	150	150	40
Marjoram (*Majorana hortensis*), powder	–	–	–	–	–	–	–	–	–	–	–	–	–	–	–	–	–	–	–	91	1400	2500	330	73	1.10	4.1	230	–	206
Mustard, brown	78.1	5.9	6.3	–	5.3	–	91	0.38	–	–	–	–	–	–	–	–	–	–	A	1310	130	124	48	1.8	–	–	134	–	–
Nutmeg (*Myristica fragrans*)	–	–	–	–	–	–	–	–	–	–	–	–	–	–	–	–	–	–	–	14	410	200	180	2	1.03	1.8	200	–	64
Paprika (*Capsicum annuum*)	–	–	–	–	–	–	–	–	–	–	–	–	–	–	–	–	–	–	–	17	2400	157	160	23	0.61	5	270	–	250
Pepper (*Piper nigrum*) – black	–	–	–	–	–	–	–	–	–	–	–	–	–	–	–	–	–	–	–	11	1220	390	148	17	1.13	1	165	–	110–390
– white	–	–	–	–	–	–	–	–	–	–	–	–	–	–	–	–	–	–	–	9	95	200	65	7	0.8	0.9	153	–	11–49
Rosemary (*Rosmarinus officinalis*), powder	–	–	–	–	–	–	–	–	–	–	–	–	–	–	–	–	–	–	–	44	980	1470	220	33	0.55	3.2	70	–	117
Sage (*Salvia officinalis*), powder	–	–	–	–	–	–	–	–	–	–	–	–	–	–	–	–	–	–	–	10	980	1770	430	27	0.7	5.5	90	–	–
Tarragon (*Artemisia dracunculus*), powder	–	–	–	–	–	–	–	–	–	–	–	–	–	–	–	–	–	–	–	70	3200	1300	350	24	0.9	3.9	320	–	745
Thyme (*Thymus vulgaris*), powder	–	–	–	–	–	–	–	–	–	–	–	–	–	–	–	–	–	–	–	80	950	2070	270	135	0.9	6.4	200	–	85

[1] % N × 6.25.

100 g edible portion (unless otherwise stated) contains	Water g	Proteins g	Fats Total g	Fats Polyunsaturated g	Carbohydrates Total g	Carbohydrates Fibre g	Energy kcal	Energy MJ	A + β-carotene IU	Thiamine mg	Riboflavin mg	B_6 mg	Niacin mg	Free folic acid µg	Pantothenic acid mg	Ascorbic acid mg	α-Tocopherol mg	Others	A Excess acid, B Excess base	Sodium mg	Potassium mg	Calcium mg	Magnesium mg	Iron mg	Copper mg	Zinc mg	Phosphorus mg	Sulfur mg	Chloride mg
Nuts																													
Almonds (*Amygdalus communis*)	4.7	18.6	54.2	10.8	19.5	2.6	598	2.50	75	0.25	0.92	0.10	3.5	33	0.58	trace	15	biotin 20 µg	B	4	773	234	270	4.7	0.14	3.1	504	150	2
Brazil nuts (*Bertholletia excelsa*)	4.6	14.3	66.9	18.4	10.9	3.1	654	2.74	10	1.0	0.12	0.11	7.7	–	0.23	2	6.5	–	A	2	715	180	225	2.8	1.1	4.2	600	198	61
Cashew nuts (*Anacardium occidentale*)	5.2	17.2	45.7	3	29.3	1.4	561	2.35	100	0.43	0.25	–	1.8	8	–	–	–	–	–	15	464	38	267	3.8	–	–	373	–	15
Chestnuts (*Castanea sativa*)	48	3.4	1.9	–	45.6	1.3	213	0.89	0	0.23	0.22	0.29	0.5	–	0.47	6	0.5	biotin 1.3 µg	B	2	410	46	42	1.4	0.43	0.35	74	29	19
– dried	9.0	6.7	4.1	–	78.8	2.5	378	1.58	0	0.34	0.39	–	0.8	–	–	0	–	–	B	4	875	57	74	3.3	0.65	1.0	170	126	–
Coconuts (*Cocos nucifera*)	48	4.2	34	0.6	12.8	3.3	351	1.47	0	0.06	0.03	0.06	0.6	9	0.33	2	0.7	–	B	17	363	13	46	1.7	0.32	1.8	95	44	110
– dried	3.5	7.2	64.9	0.6	23.0	3.9	662	2.77	0	0.06	0.04	–	0.6	–	–	0	–	–	B	28	588	26	90	3.3	0.55	–	187	76	200
Coconut water	94.2	0.3	0.2	–	4.7	trace	22	0.09	0	trace	trace	0.03	0.1	–	0.05	trace	–	–	–	25	147	20	28	0.3	0.4	–	13	24	180
Hazelnuts (*Corylus avellana*)	6.0	12.7	60.9	23	18	3.5	627	2.62	100	0.47	0.55	0.54	1.6	23	1.15	7.5	21	biotin 34 µg	B	3	618	250	150	4.5	1.35	2.4	320	198	10
Peanuts (*Arachis hypogaea*), roasted	1.8	26.2	48.7	14.0	20.6	2.7	582	2.44	360	0.32	0.13	0.3	17.1	28	2.14	0	6.5	biotin 40 µg	A	3	740	74	181	2.2	0.27	3.2	407	380	7
Peanut butter	1.8	27.8	49.4	11.9	17.2	1.9	581	2.43	–	0.13	0.13	0.30	15.7	20	2.5	0	6.0	–	A	350	670	63	178	2.0	0.57	2.9	407	225	500
Pecans (*Carya illinoinensis*)	3.4	9.2	71.2	14	14.6	2.3	687	2.88	130	0.86	0.13	0.19	0.9	13	–	2	1.5	–	–	trace	603	73	142	2.4	1.1	4.5	289	–	–
Pine nuts (*Pinus pinea*)	3.1	13.0	60.5	–	20.5	1.1	635	2.66	0	1.28	0.23	–	4.5	10	–	–	–	–	–	–	–	12	268	5.2	1.4	14	604	–	–
Pistachio nuts (*Pistacia vera*)	5.3	19.3	53.7	10	19.0	1.9	594	2.49	230	0.67	0.2	–	1.4	–	–	7	–	–	–	–	972	131	158	7.3	1.17	4.3	500	–	–
Sunflower seeds (*Helianthus annuus*)	4.8	24	47.3	30	19.9	3.8	560	2.34	50	1.96	0.23	–	5.4	–	–	–	44	–	–	30	920	120	38	7.1	–	–	837	–	–
Walnuts (*Juglans regia*)	3.5	14.8	64.0	47.5	15.8	2.1	651	2.72	30	0.3	0.13	0.73	1.0	48	0.90	2	1.5	biotin 37 µg	A	4	450	99	134	3.1	0.31	3	380	100	23
Grains, flours, pasta[1]																													
Barley (*Hordeum* sp.), pearled	12.0	9.0	1.4	0.8	76.5	0.8	346	1.45	0	0.12	0.05	0.25	3.1	9	0.5	0	0.4	–	A	3	160	16	37	2.0	0.4	2.7	189	110	110
Buckwheat (*Fagopyrum esculentum*), whole meal	14.1	11.7	2.7	–	70	2.6	327	1.37	0	0.58	0.15	0.25	2.9	–	1.5	–	–	–	A	1	680	33	48	2.2	0.7	–	263	–	–
Maize (*Zea mays*)																													
Cornflakes	3.8	7.9	0.4	–	85.3	0.7	385	1.61	0	0.43[3]	0.1	0.06	2.1	14	0.19	0	0.12	biotin 6 µg	A	1160	120	3	14	1.4	0.17	7.7	45	–	1780
Corn flour	12.0	7.8	2.6	1	76.8	0.7	368	1.54	340[3]	0.20	0.06	0.05	1.4	17	0.55	0	0.64	–	A	1	120	6	106	1.8	0.20	2.5	164	–	–
Corn grits	11.0	8.8	1.1	–	78.0	–	365	1.53	440[3]	0.15	0.05	–	0.5	–	–	–	0.31	–	A	1	80	4	20	1.0	0.15	–	73	–	–
Cornstarch (Maizena)	12.0	0.3	trace	–	87.9	0.1	362	1.52	–	trace	0.08	0.005	0.03	–	–	–	–	–	A	4	4	trace	2	0.5	0.05	–	30	–	6
Popcorn	4.0	12.7	5.0	2.0	76.7	2.2	386	1.62	0	0.39	0.12	0.23	2.2	–	–	0	–	–	A	3	240	11	–	2.7	0.31	–	281	–	–
Millet (*Panicum milliaceum*), pealed	11.8	9.9	2.9	–	72.9	3.2	327	1.37	0	0.73	0.38	–	2.8	–	–	0	0.05	–	–	3	430	20	162	6.8	–	4.3	311	–	15
Oatflakes (*Avena sativa*)	10.3	13.8	6.6	2.7	67.6	1.4	387	1.62	–	0.60	0.14	0.75	1.1	–	0.92	0	0.25	–	A	2	340	53	145	3.6	0.74	14	407	199	120

[1] Unenriched products.   [2] Enriched.   [3] Based on yellow maize.

100 g edible portion (unless otherwise stated) contains	Water g	Proteins g	Fats Total g	Fats Polyunsat. g	Carb. Total g	Carb. Fibre g	Energy kcal	Energy MJ	A + β-carotene IU	Thiamine mg	Riboflavin mg	B₆ mg	Niacin mg	Free folic acid µg	Pantothenic acid mg	Ascorbic acid mg	α-Tocopherol mg	Others	A Excess acid / B Excess base	Sodium mg	Potassium mg	Calcium mg	Magnesium mg	Iron mg	Copper mg	Zinc mg	Phosphorus mg	Sulfur mg	Chloride mg
Pasta																													
Macaroni	10.4	12.5	1.2	-	75.2	0.3	369	1.54	0	0.14	0.06	0.06	2.0	4	-	0	-	-	A	26	220	26	57	1.4	0.07	-	150	95	31
Noodles	10.1	13.0	2.9	-	73	0.4	376	1.57	100	0.2	0.08	-	2.1	-	-	-	-	-	A	7	157	20	35	2.1	0.17	2.2	196	-	-
Spaghetti	10.4	12.5	1.2	-	75.2	0.3	369	1.54	0	0.09	0.06	0.06	2.0	4	-	-	0.2	-	A	5	160	23	35	1.2	0.17	1.7	165	97	63
Rice (Oryza sativa)																													
– polished, raw	12.0	6.7	0.4	-	80.4	0.3	362	1.52	0	0.07	0.03	0.15	1.6	15	0.63	0	0.35	biotin 3 µg	A	6	110	24	28	0.8	0.06–0.19	1.3	94	79	27
– polished, cooked	72.6	2.0	0.1	-	24.2	0.1	109	0.46	0	0.02	0.01	0.03	0.4	3	-	0	0.18	-	A	2[1]	38	10	8	0.2	-	0.4	28	27	9
– whole, raw	12.0	7.5	1.9	-	77.4	0.9	360	1.51	0	0.29	0.05	-	4.7	-	-	0	1.2	-	A	9	150	32	119	1.6	0.36	1.4	221	121	23
Rye (Secale cereale)																													
– flour, dark	14.3	10.8	1.5	-	71.8	1.7	310	1.30	0	0.30	0.14	0.35	2.9	31	1.0	0	0.8	biotin 6 µg	A	2	439	23	83	2.6	0.42	1.6	362	134	55
– flour, light	14.6	7.4	1.14	-	76.0	0.4	336	1.41	0	0.19	0.11	-	0.8	-	-	-	-	-	A	1	240	31	73	1.1	-	0.8	185	-	-
Soybean (Glycine hispida)																													
– flour, full-fat	8.0	36.7	20.3	11	30.4	2.4	347	1.45	110	0.85	0.31	0.57	2.1	-	1.68	0	-	biotin 70 µg	B	2	1660	199	240	8.4	-	0.9	558	-	-
– flour, medium fat	8.0	43.4	6.7	3	36.6	2.5	264	1.10	80	0.83	0.36	0.68	2.6	-	2.1	0	-	-	B	1	2030	240	290	9.1	-	-	634	-	-
Tapioca (Manihot utilissima), dried	12.6	0.6	0.2	-	86.4	0.1	360	1.51	0	0	0.1	-	0	2	-	0	0.07	-	0	4	20	12	3	1.0	0.07	-	12	4	13
Wheat (Triticum sp.)																													
– flour, whole	12.6	12.1	2.1	-	71.5	2.1	331	1.39	400	0.55	0.12	0.50	4.3	25	0.8	0	1.0	biotin 7 µg	A	2	290	41	113	3.3	0.40	5.5	372	124	38
– flour, light	12.0	10.5	1.0	-	76.1	0.3	363	1.52	0	0.06	0.05	0.15	0.9	14	0.3	0	0.37	biotin 1 µg	A	2	150	16	25	0.8	0.17	1.7	87	-	45
– semolina	13.1	10.3	0.8	-	76	-	362	1.52	0	0.12	0.04	0.085	1.3	-	-	0	-	-	A	1	112	17	32	1.0	0.15	-	87	92	71
Wheat germs	11.5	26.6	10.9	5	46.7	2.5	363	1.52	650	2.0	0.68	0.92	4.2	257	2.2	0	14.5	-	A	3	827	72	336	9.4	1.2	13	1118	-	80
Bread, rolls, pastry																													
Bread																													
– corn, Northern style	37.9	8.7	5.2	-	45.5	0.3	267	1.12	340	0.20	0.30	-	1.5	-	-	1	-	-	A	690	188	111	-	1.8	-	0.85	155	-	-
– French[2]	30.6	9.1	3.0	-	55.4	0.2	290	1.21	trace	0.08	0.08	-	0.8	-	-	trace	-	-	A	580	90	43	22	0.7	0.12	1.6	85	100	700
– rye, American	35.5	9.1	1.1	-	52.1	0.4	243	1.02	0	0.18	0.07	-	1.4	-	-	0	-	-	A	557	145	75	42	1.6	0.17	0.8	147	-	-
– white	39.0	7.8	1.7	-	49.7	0.2	251	1.05	0	0.18	0.03	0.04	1.4	6	0.3	0	trace	-	A	540	100	100	26	1.7	0.15	0.8	97	79	890
– toasted	24.0	9.6	1.7	-	64.9	0.2	320	1.34	0	0.17	0.04	-	1.8	-	-	0	trace	biotin 6 µg	A	640	130	110	28	2.2	0.16	2.0	100	95	1040
– whole meal	36.4	9.1	2.6	-	49.3	1.5	241	1.01	0	0.30	0.10	0.14	2.8	22	0.6	0	-	-	A	540	220	23	93	2.5	0.27	-	230	81	860
Crackers																													
– graham[2]	6.4	8.0	9.4	1	73.3	1.1	384	1.61	0	0.04	0.21	-	1.5	-	-	0	-	-	A	670	384	40	51	1.9	0.21	1.1	149	-	-
– soda[2]	4.0	9.2	13.1	-	70.6	0.2	438	1.83	0	0.01	0.05	-	1.0	-	-	0	-	-	A	1100	120	22	29	1.5	-	0.7	89	-	-

[1] Unsalted. [2] Prepared with unenriched flour.

100 g edible portion (unless otherwise stated) contains	Water g	Proteins g	Fats Total g	Fats Polyunsaturated g	Carbohydrates Total g	Carbohydrates Fibre g	Energy kcal	Energy MJ	A + β-carotene IU	Thiamine mg	Riboflavin mg	B₆ mg	Niacin mg	Free folic acid µg	Pantothenic acid mg	Ascorbic acid mg	α-Tocopherol mg	Others	A Excess acid, B Excess base	Sodium mg	Potassium mg	Calcium mg	Magnesium mg	Iron mg	Copper mg	Zinc mg	Phosphorus mg	Sulfur mg	Chloride mg
Doughnuts																													
– cake-type	23.7	4.6	18.6	1	51.4	0.1	391	1.64	80	0.16	0.16	–	1.2	–	–	trace	–	–	–	501	90	40	23	1.4	0.11	0.5	190	–	–
– yeast-leavened	28.3	6.3	26.7	2	37.7	0.2	414	1.73	60	0.16	0.16	–	1.3	–	–	0	–	–	–	234	80	38	20	1.5	–	–	76	–	–
Muffins	38.0	7.8	10.1	–	42.3	0.1	294	1.23	100	0.17	0.23	–	1.4	–	–	trace	–	–	A	441	125	104	28	1.6	–	0.4	151	–	–
Pie crust, plain, unbaked¹	20.9	5.7	31.0	2	40.7	0.1	464	1.94	0	0.03	0.03	0.09	0.5	–	0.2	0	1.2	biotin 1 µg	A	410	85	92	15	0.4	0.11	–	69	–	660
Pretzels¹	4.5	9.8	4.5	–	75.9	0.3	390	1.63	0	0.02	0.03	–	0.7	–	–	0	–	–	A	1680	130	22	71	1.5	0.15	1.08	131	130	–
Pumpernickel	34.0	9.1	1.2	1	53.1	1.1	246	1.03	0	0.23	0.14	–	1.2	–	–	0	–	–	–	569	454	84	28	2.4	–	1.14	229	–	–
Rolls, plain, white¹	31.4	8.2	5.6	–	53.0	0.2	298	1.25	0	0.06	0.09	0.06	0.8	7	0.3	trace	0.1	–	A	506	95	74	19	0.7	0.16	0.6	85	–	–
Scones¹	21.5	7.5	14.6	–	55.9	–	391	1.64	500	trace	0.08	0.08	1.2	5	0.2	trace	1.3	biotin 2 µg	–	800	140	620	16	1.5	0.12	0.6	470	130	450
Zwieback¹	5.0	10.7	8.8	–	74.3	0.3	423	1.77	40	0.05	0.07	0.09	0.9	–	–	0	–	–	A	250	150	13	–	0.6	0.5	–	69	–	480
Confectionery, Sugar																													
Candy bars																													
– Bounty bar	7.6	4.8	26.1	–	58.3	–	461	1.93	–	–	–	–	–	–	–	0	–	–	–	180	320	110	43	1.3	0.47	–	140	–	400
– Mars bar	6.9	5.3	18.9	–	66.5	–	446	1.87	–	–	–	–	–	–	–	0	–	–	–	150	250	160	35	1.1	0.31	0.41	150	–	300
Caramel²	7.6	4.0	10.2	–	76.6	0.2	399	1.67	10	0.03	0.17	–	0.2	–	–	trace	–	–	B	226	192	148	–	1.4	–	–	122	–	–
Chocolate																													
– milk, sweetened	0.9	7.7	32.3	–	56.9	0.4	520	2.18	270	0.06	0.34	0.04	0.3	21	–	0	1.1	–	A	120	420	220	55	1.1	1.1	0.2	231	67	270
– plain, sweetened	0.9	4.4	35.1	1.2	57.9	0.5	528	2.21	10	0.02	0.14	0.03	0.3	–	–	trace	0.5	–	A/B	19	397	63	107	1.4	1.1	–	142	32	100
Cocoa, dry powder	5.6	19.8	24.5	0.4	43.6	5.7	299	1.25	10	0.09	0.11	0.05	1.9	31	–	0	0.4	–	A/B	60	900–3200	114	420	12.5	3.9	2–5	709	203	51
Dextrose, anhydrous	trace	0	0	–	99.5	–	385	1.61	0	0	0	–	0	–	0.06	0	–	–	0	1	0.4	–	–	–	–	–	–	–	–
Honey	17.2	0.3	0	–	82.3	–	304	1.27	0	trace	0.04	0.01	0.3	–	–	1	–	–	0	7	51	5	3	0.5	0.05	0.1	6	1	18
Jams	29	0.6	0.1	–	70.0	1.0	272	1.14	10	0.01	0.03	–	0.2	5	–	2	0.1	–	B	16	110	12	10	1.0	0.23	0.04	9	7	9
Maple syrup	33	–	–	–	65	–	252	1.05	–	–	–	–	–	–	–	0	–	–	B	10	176	104	–	1.2	0.45	–	8	–	–
Marshmallow	17.3	2.0	trace	–	80.4	0	319	1.34	0	0	trace	–	–	–	–	0	–	–	–	39	6	18	–	1.6	0.18	0.03	6	–	–
Marzipan	8.8	8.0	18	–	64	–	428	1.79	35	0.12	0.45	0.06	0.9	17	0.35	2	9.1	biotin 2 µg	B	13	400	120	120	2.0	0.08	1.5	220	81	13
Molasses	24	–	–	–	60	–	232	0.97	–	0–0.08	0–0.16	0.27	2.8	7	0.5	0	–	biotin 9 µg	B	40	1500	273	81	6.7	1.9	0.6	69	–	–
Ovaltine, dry powder	2.0	15.2	5.0	–	73.5	–	397	1.66	5000	2.0	3.0	2.3	19.0	80	9.0	15	–	D 450 IU	–	350	1200	360	144	23	0.9	2.0	600	–	–

¹ Prepared with unenriched flour.   ² Full-cream products.

100 g edible portion (unless otherwise stated) contains	Water g	Proteins g	Fats Total g	Polyunsaturated g / Ethyl-alcohol[2] g	Carbohydrates Total g	Fibre g	Energy kcal	Energy MJ	A + β-carotene IU	Thiamine mg	Riboflavin mg	B6 mg	Niacin mg	Free folic acid µg	Pantothenic acid mg	Ascorbic acid mg	α-Tocopherol mg	Others	A Excess acid, B Excess base	Sodium mg	Potassium mg	Calcium mg	Magnesium mg	Iron mg	Copper mg	Zinc mg	Phosphorus mg	Sulfur mg	Chloride mg
Sugar, beet or cane																													
– brown	2.1	0	0	–	96.4	–	373	1.56	0	0.01	0.03	–	0.2	–	–	0	–	–	B	24	230	85	15	3.4	0.35	0.03	19	14	35
– white	trace	0	0	–	99.5	–	385	1.61	0	0	0	–	0	–	–	0	–	–	0	–	3	0	–	trace	0.02	0.02	0	0	trace
Beverages, nonalcoholic																													
Carbonated soft drinks	88	–	–	–	12	0	46	0.19	–	–	–	–	–	–	–	0	–	–	0	1–15[1]	1[1]	–	–	–	–	–	–	–	–
Coffee (unsweetened)	98.5	0.3	–	–	0.8	–	5	0.02	0	0.01	0.01	–	0.9	–	–	0	–	–	B	1–6	80	5	9	0.2	0.02	0.03	5	–	10
Cola drinks	88	–	0.1	–	11	0	43	0.18	–	–	–	–	–	–	–	–	–	–	B	6	–	–	–	–	0.04	–	15	–	–
Tea (unsweetened)	99	0.1	0	–	0.4	–	2	0.01	0	0	0.04	–	0.1	–	–	1	–	–	0	0–2	16	0.3–5	1–13	0.2	0.03	0.02	1–4	–	–
Beverages, alcoholic																													
Beer																													
– ale, brown	–	0.3	–	2.2	3.0	0	29	0.12	–	trace	0.02	0.01	0.26	2.3	0.10	0	–	–	B	16	33	7	6	0.03	0.07	–	11	–	37
– ale, pale	–	0.3	–	3.3	2.0	0	32	0.13	–	trace	0.02	0.01	0.35	3.5	0.10	0	–	–	B	10	49	9	10	0.02	0.04	–	15	–	31
– canned, USA	92.1	0.3	–	3.6	3.8	0	42	0.18	–	trace	0.03	0.01	0.6	–	–	–	–	–	B	7	25	5	–	trace	0.07	0.03	30	–	–
– draught, bitter	–	0.3	–	3.1	2.3	0	32	0.13	–	trace	0.04	0.02	0.47	4.1	0.10	0	–	–	B	12	38	11	9	0.01	0.08	–	13	–	32
– lager	–	0.2	–	3.2	1.5	0	29	0.12	–	trace	0.02	0.02	0.33	4.3	0.10	0	–	–	B	4	34	4	6	trace	trace	–	12	–	19
– stout	–	0.3	–	2.9	4.2	0	38	0.16	–	trace	0.03	0.01	0.26	3.8	0.10	–	–	–	B	23	45	8	8	0.05	0.08	–	17	–	48
Brandy	–	–	–	35–40	–	–	245–280	1.03–1.17	–	–	–	–	–	–	–	0	–	–	0	3	4	–	3	0.5	0.13	–	–	–	–
Fruit wine (cider)	–	–	–	5.2	1.0	–	40	0.17	–	trace	0.01	0.01	–	–	0.03	0	0	biotin 0.6 µg	B	7	72	8	10	0.3	0.09	–	3	–	6
Port wine	–	0.2	–	15.0	14.0	0	161	0.67	–	–	–	–	–	–	–	–	0	–	B	4	75	5	–	–	–	–	11	–	8
Rum	–	–	–	35.1	0	0	246	1.03	–	–	–	–	–	–	–	0	–	–	0	2	3	–	–	–	–	0.04	–	–	–
Sherry																													
– dry	–	0.2	–	15.7	1.4	0	116	0.49	–	trace	0.01	0.01	0.10	0.1	–	0	0	–	B	10	57	7	13	0.39	0.03	–	11	–	12
– medium	–	0.1	–	14.8	3.6	0	118	0.49	–	trace	0.01	0.01	0.08	0.1	–	0	0	–	B	6	89	9	8	0.53	0.10	–	7	–	7
Vermouth																													
– dry	–	0.1	–	13.9	5.5	0	120	0.50	–	trace	trace	0.01	0.04	–	–	0	0	–	B	17	40	7	5	0.34	0.06	0.27	7	–	9
– sweet	–	trace	–	13.0	15.9	0	155	0.65	–	trace	trace	trace	0.04	–	–	0	0	–	B	28	30	6	4	0.35	0.04	0.04	6	–	16
Whisky (Scotch)	–	–	–	35	0	0	245	1.03	–	trace	trace	–	–	–	–	0	0	–	0	1	1	–	–	–	0.05	0.01	–	–	–
Wine[3]	–	0	–	8.8–12.5	0.2–8.0	0	60–120	0.25–0.50	–	0.001–0.005	0.01	0.09	0.05	14	0.04	–	–	–	B	4–7	20–120	3–14	7–16	0.3–5	0.05–0.25	0.2	10	15	7–18

[1] Not true mineral water.   [2] Ethylalcohol has an energy value of 0.0293 MJ/g (7 kcal/g).   [3] Average values.

100 g edible portion (unless otherwise stated) contains	Water g	Proteins g	Fats			Carbohydrates g	Energy		Vitamins										A Excess acid, B Excess base	Elements									
			Total g	Polyunsaturated g	Cholesterol g		kcal	MJ	A + β-carotene IU	Thiamine mg	Riboflavin mg	B$_6$ mg	Niacin mg	Free folic acid µg	Pantothenic acid mg	Ascorbic acid mg	α-Tocopherol mg	Others		Sodium mg	Potassium mg	Calcium mg	Magnesium mg	Iron mg	Copper mg	Zinc mg	Phosphorus mg	Sulfur mg	Chloride mg
Fats, Oils																													
Butter	17.4	0.6	81.0	4	0.25	0.7	716	3.00	3300	trace	0.01	trace	0.1	0	trace	trace	2.4	D 30 IU	A	7†	23	16	1	0.2	0.03	0.2	16	9	10†
Coconut oil	0.1	0.8	99.0	1.4	0.002	0.01	878	3.67	–	–	–	–	–	–	–	–	3.6	–	0	0–4	0–4	0–3	–	–	0.68	0.04	–	–	–
Cod-liver oil	0	0	99.9	–	0.50	0	901	3.77	85000	–	–	–	0	–	–	–	20	D 8500 IU; K 0.05 mg	0	0.1	–	–	–	–	0.05	–	–	–	trace
Corn oil	trace	0	99.9	56	0.001	0	883	3.70	–	–	0	–	–	–	–	–	19	–	0	–	–	–	–	–	0.13	–	–	–	–
Cottonseed oil	trace	0	99.9	50	0.001	0	883	3.70	–	–	–	–	–	–	–	–	30	–	0	–	–	–	–	–	–	–	–	–	–
Lard	1.0	trace	99.0	10	0.1	0	893	3.74	trace	trace	–	trace	trace	–	trace	0	2	–	A	2	1	1	1	0.1	0.02	0.2	3	25	4
Margarine, salted	19.7	0.5	78.4	18	–	0.4	698	2.92	3000	–	–	–	trace	3	–	–	12	D 320 IU	–	800	7	13	5	0.05	0.05	0.16	15	12	1200
Mayonnaise	15.1	1.1	78.9²	32²	–	3.0	718	3.00	280	0.02	0.04	0.10	trace	14	1.0	0	6–24	biotin 12 µg; D 40 IU	A	702	53	18	2	0.5	0.03	0.4	28	21	–
Olive oil	trace	0	99.9	8	–	0	883	3.70	0	0	0	–	0	–	–	0	3	–	0	–	trace	0.5	–	0.08	0.07	0.28	–	–	–
Palm oil	trace	0	99.9	9	0.003	0	883	3.70	–	–	–	–	–	–	–	–	30	–	0	–	–	–	–	–	–	–	–	–	–
Peanut oil	trace	0	99.9	29	0.001	0	883	3.70	–	–	–	–	–	–	–	–	13	–	0	–	–	–	1	0.06	0.08	–	–	–	–
Safflower oil	trace	0	99.9	72	–	0	883	3.70	–	–	–	–	–	–	–	–	31	–	0	–	–	–	–	–	–	–	–	–	–
Soybean oil	trace	0	99.9	60	0.001	0	883	3.70	–	–	–	–	–	–	–	–	18	K 0.5 mg	0	–	–	–	–	0.03	trace	–	–	–	–
Sunflower-seed oil	0.2	0	99.8	63	trace	0	882	3.69	trace	–	0	–	–	–	–	–	49	–	0	–	–	–	–	–	–	–	–	–	–
Eggs																													
Hen's egg																													
– whole, raw	74.0	12.8	11.5	2.3	0.50	0.7	162	0.68	1180	0.12	0.34	0.11	0.1	25	1.6	0	1.6	biotin 20 µg; B$_{12}$ 2 µg; D 200 IU³	A	140	140	54	13	2.3	0.10	1.4	205	197	160
– 1 egg, medium (48 g)	*35.5*	*6.1*	*5.5*	*1.1*	*0.24*	*0.4*	*77*	*0.32*	*580*	*0.06*	*0.16*	*0.05*	*0.04*	*12*	*0.8*	*0*	*0.8*	*³*	*A*	*67*	*67*	*26*	*6*	*1.3*	*0.05*	*0.65*	*98*	*95*	*77*
– egg white, raw	87.6	10.9	0.2	0	0	0.8	51	0.21	0	0.02	0.23	0.22	0.1	2	0.14	0	0	biotin 7 µg	A	190	150	9	11	0.2	0.05	0.03	21	208	170
– 1 egg white, medium (31 g)	*27.0*	*3.3*	*0.1*	*–*	*0*	*0.3*	*16*	*0.07*	*0*	*0.01*	*0.07*	*0.07*	*0.03*	*–*	*0.04*	*0*	*0*	*³*	*A*	*59*	*47*	*3*	*3*	*0.06*	*0.02*	*0.01*	*7*	*64*	*29*
– egg yolk, raw	50.0	16.1	31.9	6.7	1.48	0.6	360	1.51	3400	0.32	0.52	0.30	0.02	47	4.2	0	4.6	biotin 50 µg; B$_{12}$ 5 µg; D 350 IU	A	50	120	141	16	7.2	0.02	3.6	569	194	140
– 1 egg yolk, medium (17 g)	*8.5*	*2.8*	*5.4*	*1.1*	*0.24*	*0.1*	*61*	*0.26*	*580*	*0.05*	*0.09*	*0.05*	*trace*	*8*	*0.7*	*0*	*0.8*	*³*	*A*	*9*	*20*	*23*	*3*	*1.2*	*0.01*	*0.60*	*93*	*32*	*24*
– whole, dried	4.1	47.0	41.2	–	1.9	4.1	592	2.48	4460	0.35	1.23	0.08	0.2	–	7.4	0	–	D 240 IU	A	520	480	190	41	8.7	0.18	5.0	800	630	590
Duck's egg																													
– whole, raw	70.6	13.2	14.2	–	–	0.7	188	0.79	1540	0.16	0.40	–	0.2	–	–	0	–	–	A	191	258	64	–	3.6	–	–	220	–	–

† Unsalted.   ² Prepared with corn oil.   ³ Can be calculated from 100 g values.

100 g edible portion (unless otherwise stated) contains	Water g	Proteins g	Total g	Polyunsaturated g	Cholesterol g	Carbohydrates g	Energy kcal	Energy MJ	A + β-carotene IU	Thiamine mg	Riboflavin mg	B₆ mg	Niacin mg	Free folic acid µg	Pantothenic acid mg	Ascorbic acid mg	α-Tocopherol mg	Others	A Excess acid, B Excess base	Sodium mg	Potassium mg	Calcium mg	Magnesium mg	Iron mg	Copper mg	Zinc mg	Phosphorus mg	Sulfur mg	Chloride mg
Milk																													
Camel's milk	87.1	3.7	4.2	–	–	4.1	69	0.29	120	0.05	0.11	–	0.30	–	–	6	–	–	B	19	114	143	21	0.1	–	–	98	–	105
Cow's milk																													
– pasteurized, whole[1]	88.5	3.2	3.7	0.1	0.013	4.6	64	0.27	140	0.04	0.15	0.05	0.07	5	0.33	1	0.06	biotin 2 µg; B₁₂ 0.2 µg; D 0.5–4 IU; K 5 mg	B	55	139	116	13	0.04	0.01	0.38	89	29	100
– buttermilk	91.2	3.5	0.5	–	0.004	4.0	35	0.15	35	0.04	0.18	0.04	0.1	–	0.36	1	–	biotin 2 µg	B	57	147	109	14	0.1	0.02	0.37	95	30	100
– condensed milk																													
– – sweetened	27.1	8.1	8.7	0.2	0.03	54.3	321	1.34	360	0.08	0.38	0.02	0.2	4	0.85	1	0.3	biotin 3 µg; D 3.5 IU	B	112	314	262	25	0.1	0.04	1.0	206	81	260
– – unsweetened	73.8	7.0	7.9	0.2	0.03	9.7	138	0.58	350	0.06	0.36	0.03	0.2	4	0.85	1	0.6	biotin 3 µg; B₁₂ 0.04 µg; D 3.5 IU	B	118	303	252	25	0.1	0.02	1.1	205	84	350
– dried, whole	2.0	26.4	27.5	0.7	0.11	38.2	502	2.10	1200	0.33	1.1	0.23	0.7	32	2.7	10	0.6	biotin 10 µg; B₁₂ 2 µg	B	410	1330	909	98	0.5	0.16	3.5	708	240	810
– dried, nonfat	3.0	35.9	1.0	–	0.02	52.0	362	1.52	30	0.35	1.80	0.25	0.9	14	3.5	10	–	biotin 16 µg; B₁₂ 3 µg	B	525	1745	1300	143	0.6	0.20	4.4	1016	320	1100
– skimmed	90.9	3.5	0.07	–	0.002	4.8	34	0.14	7	0.038	0.17	0.05	0.1	4	0.28	2	trace	biotin 2 µg	B	53	150	123	14	0.1	0.003	0.4	97	31	100
– Goat's milk	86.6	3.6	4.2	–	–	4.8	71	0.30	120	0.05	0.12	0.027	0.2	0.7	0.35	2	–	biotin 2 µg; B₁₂ 0.03 µg; D 2 IU	B	34	180	129	13	0.1	0.04	0.30	103	16	130
– Human milk[1]	87.7	1.03	4.4	0.3	0.01–0.02	6.9	70	0.29	330	0.01	0.04	0.02	0.18	1.3	0.24	5	0.2	biotin 1 µg; B₁₂ 0.03 µg; D 0.4–9.7 IU	B	17	50	33	3	0.05	0.05	0.28	14	14	42
– Mare's milk	91.1	2.1	1.25	–	–	6.3	44	0.18	45	0.03	0.02	0.03	0.05	–	0.30	10	–	–	B	–	70	100	10	–	–	–	60	–	20
– Sheep's milk	81.6	5.6	7.5	–	–	4.4	107	0.46	200	0.07	0.50	–	0.50	–	0.35	3	–	biotin 9 µg	B	30	190	190	12	0.1	0.04	–	150	–	140
Dairy products																													
Cheese																													
– Camembert	51.3	18.7	22.8	–	0.07	1.8	287	1.20	1010	0.05	0.45	0.25	1.45	–	0.1–0.9	0	–	biotin 5 µg	A	1150[2]	109	382	18	0.5	0.08	3.0	184	–	–
– Cheddar	37	35.0	32.2	1	0.10	2.1	398	1.67	1310	0.03	0.46	0.07	0.1	6	0.40	0	0.8	biotin 1.7 µg; B₁₂ 1.5 µg	A	700[2]	82	750	45	1.0	0.05	–	480	230	–
– cottage, creamed	70	14	14	–	0.014	4	198	0.83	280	0.02	0.24	–	0.1	2	–	–	–	–	A	–	–	82	6	0.3	–	0.47	140	–	–
– – uncreamed	79.4	17.2	0.6	–	0.007	1.8	86	0.36	35	0.04	0.31	0.01	0.1	–	0.1	1	0.1	biotin 2 µg	A	36	95	90	9	0.4	0.58	–	189	–	–
– cream cheese	50.5	14.6	30.5	–	0.11	1.9	338	1.41	1540	0.04	0.28	–	0.1	–	–	0	–	–	A	606[2]	74	62	–	0.2	0.4	–	189	–	150

[1] See also pages 213–216 for more details. [2] Variable, depends on salt content.

100 g edible portion (unless otherwise stated) contains	Water g	Proteins g	Fats Total g	Fats Polyunsaturated g	Fats Cholesterol g	Carbohydrates g	Energy kcal	Energy MJ	A + β-carotene IU	Thiamine mg	Riboflavin mg	B6 mg	Niacin mg	Free folic acid µg	Pantothenic acid mg	Ascorbic acid mg	α-Tocopherol mg	Others	A Excess acid, B Excess base	Sodium mg	Potassium mg	Calcium mg	Magnesium mg	Iron mg	Copper mg	Zinc mg	Phosphorus mg	Sulfur mg	Chloride mg
Cheese (continued)																													
– Edam	43.4	26.1	23.6	–	0.09	3.5	232	1.10	600	0.06	0.35	0.06	0.07	–	0.30	0	1.0	D 84 IU	A	737†	76	765	59	0.7	1.7	1–10	455	–	1180†
– Parmesan	30.0	36.0	26.0	–	0.07	2.9	393	1.64	1060	0.02	0.73	0.10	0.2	–	0.30	0	1.0	B_{12} 1.5 µg	A	760†	150	1140	50	0.4	0.36	3	781	250	1110†
– processed (45% fat²)	51.3	14.4	23.6	–	0.09	6.1	293	1.23	1800	0.034	0.38	0.07	0.22	1	0.52	–	–	B_{12} 0.8 µg; biotin 3 µg	A	1260†	65	547	28	1.0	0.46	1–4	944	–	1020†
– Roquefort	40.0	21.0	32.0	–	0.08	1.8	378	1.58	800	0.06	0.3–0.7	0.15	0.4–0.9	–	0.5–0.7	0	–	B_{12} 1.2 µg	A	1420†	190	700	30–50	1	–	–	430	–	2390†
– Swiss (Emmentaler)	34.9	27.4	30.5	–	0.09	3.4	398	1.67	1140	0.05	0.33	0.09	0.1	2	–	0.5	1.0	D 30 IU	A	620†	100	1180	55	0.9	0.13	4.6	860	–	1210†
Cream, whipping (30%)	64.1	2.2	30.4	0.8	–	2.9	288	1.20	1100³	0.025	0.17	0.035	0.07	trace	0.35	1	–	D 100 IU	B	38	78	75	9	0.1	–	–	63	–	–
Ice cream	62.1	4.0	12.5	–	0.04	20.6	207	0.87	520	0.04	0.19	0.4	0.1	–	0.32	1	0.4	B_{12} 0.4 µg	B	80	112	123	14	0.1	–	0.4	99	–	58
– Whey	93.3	0.9	0.3	–	–	4.7	25	0.10	8–16	0.04	0.08	0.02	0.07	–	–	1.5	–	biotin 2 µg	B	45	129	50	1	–	–	0.05	53	–	140
– Yoghurt⁴	86.1	4.8	3.8	–	–	4.5	71	0.30	145	0.045	0.02	0.05	0.18	–	0.52	2	–	B_{12} 0.2 µg	B	62	190	150	14	0.2	–	–	135	–	67
Meat, Poultry																													
Bacon, medium fat	20.0	9.1	65.0	6.5	0.09	trace	625	2.62	0	0.36	0.11	0.35	1.8	–	–	0	0.4		A	1770	225	13	15	1.2	0.19	1.4	108	–	–
Beef																													
– loin, lean	69.7	21.1	8.2	–	0.07	0	164	0.69	20	0.09	0.19	0.44	5.1	9	0.32	–	–		A	65	355	12	24	3.2	–	5.7	196	190	59
– rib, lean	66.8	20.7	11.6	–	0.07	0	193	0.81	20	0.09	0.18	–	5.0	–	–	–	0.5		A	65	355	12	24	3.1	–	–	208	190	59
– round, total edible	69.0	19.5	12.5	0.3	0.12	–	196	0.82	–	0.08	0.17	0.50	4.7	4	0.52	–	–	biotin 3 µg; B_{12} 2 µg	A	68	400	11	22	2.9	0.08	4.2	180	252	–
– rump, total edible	56.5	17.4	25.3	1	–	0	303	1.27	50	0.08	0.16	–	4.2	–	–	1	–		A	–	–	10	21	2.6	–	2.5	160	–	–
– sirloin, lean	71.8	21.5	5.7	0.4	0.12	0	143	0.60	10	0.09	0.19	–	5.2	6	0.33	0	0.6	B_{12} 1.7 µg	A	65	355	12	24	3.2	–	2.5	200	–	–
– canned, corned	59.3	25.3	12.0	–	–	0	216	0.90	0	0.02	0.23	0.06	3.4	1	0.4	0	0.8		A	950	140	14	15	4.3	0.24	5.6	106	240	1430
– dried, salted	47.7	34.3	6.3	–	0.23	0	203	0.85	–	0.11	0.32	–	3.7	–	–	0	–		A	4300	200	20	–	5.1	–	–	404	–	–
– brain	79.4	10.4	8.0	–	2.36	0.8	120	0.50	580	0.15	0.23	0.16	4.0	1	1.8	14	–	biotin 7 µg; B_{12} 5 µg	A	104	191	11	12	1.6	0.2	–	265	–	–
– heart	75.5	16.8	6.0	0.2	0.15	0.6	128	0.54	20	0.53	0.88	0.29	6.8	1	2.0	6	0.5	biotin 7 µg; B_{12} 10 µg	A	85	286	5	17	4.0	0.3	2.0	195	204	95
– kidney	75.9	15.4	6.7	–	0.38	0.9	130	0.54	1000	0.25	2.1	0.39	6.4	63	4	11	0.2	biotin 24 µg; B_{12} 40 µg	A	180	230	11	11	5.5	0.35	2.0	219	170	200
– liver	69.9	19.7	3.8	0.7	0.32	5.9	136	0.57	44000	0.30	2.9	0.83	13.6	220	7.3	31	1	biotin 100 µg; B_{12} 110 µg	A	81	320	7	15	6.5	2.1	3.9	352	240	90
– lung	80.1	16.9	2.0	–	0.35	trace	90	0.38	–	0.09	0.32	–	4.0	–	1.4	0	–	biotin 6 µg; B_{12} 3 µg	A	–	–	12	–	6.6	–	–	196	173	–
– pancreas	70.6	14.6	12.3	–	–	trace	173	0.72	17	0.10	0.40	–	4.2	–	3.5	58	–	biotin 14 µg; B_{12} 14 µg	A	62	249	9	15	1.0	0.06	–	335	–	–
– spleen	77	18.1	3.4	–	–	trace	108	0.45	–	0.13	0.28	0.12	4.2	–	1.2	6	–	biotin 6 µg; B_{12} 5 µg	A	99	379	7	–	8.9	0.14	–	236	216	–

† Variable, depends on salt content.   ² Fat content in dry matter.   ³ In summer (in winter 500).   ⁴ Citric acid 232 mg.

100 g edible portion (unless otherwise stated) contains	Water g	Proteins g	Fats			Carbohydrates g	Energy		A + β-carotene IU	Vitamins									A Excess acid, B Excess base	Elements									
			Total g	Polyunsaturated g	Cholesterol g		kcal	MJ		Thiamine mg	Riboflavin mg	B6 mg	Niacin mg	Free folic acid µg	Pantothenic acid mg	Ascorbic acid mg	α-Tocopherol mg	Others		Sodium mg	Potassium mg	Calcium mg	Magnesium mg	Iron mg	Copper mg	Zinc mg	Phosphorus mg	Sulfur mg	Chloride mg
Beef (continued)																													
– tongue	68.0	16.4	15.0	–	0.08	0.4	207	0.87	0	0.14	0.27	0.13	5.0	–	2.0	0	–	biotin 3 µg; B12 3 µg	A	80	260	8	10	3.0	0.07	–	182	–	–
– tripe	78	19.0	2.0	–	0.15	0	99	0.41	0	0.01	0.09	–	3.0	–	–	0	0.1	–	A	46	19	69	8	0.9	0.09	1.5	132	80	8
Calf (see also Veal)																													
– brain	79.4	10.2	8.3	–	2.2	0.8	122	0.51	–	0.20	0.20	0.16	3.7	2	2.5	18	1.2	biotin 2 µg; B12 9 µg	A	140	265	9	14	2.6	0.14	1.7	353	130	150
– heart	78.3	12.2	7.6	0.5	–	0.8	124	0.52	30	0.6	1.05	–	6.3	–	2.8	5	–	biotin 15 µg; B12 10 µg	A	120	230	16	18	2.2	0.34	–	350	–	–
– kidney	75.0	16.7	6.4	0.18	0.38	0.8	132	0.55	70	0.37	2.5	0.5	6.5	–	4.0	13	–	biotin 75 µg; B12 25 µg	A	200	290	10	–	3.4	0.51	–	171	–	–
– liver	70.7	19.2	4.7	–	0.30	4.1	140	0.59	22500	0.28	2.72	1.2	17	190	9.7	32	0.2	B12 100 µg; D 50 IU	A	84	295	8	15	5.4	4.4	7.8	311	240	89
– sweetbread (thymus)	75	19.6	3.0	–	0.25	0	111	0.46	–	0.08	0.17	–	2.6	–	–	–	–	–	A	73	519	5	22	0.9	0.08	3	530	–	–
– tongue	74.3	18.5	5.3	–	–	0.9	130	0.54	–	–	–	–	–	–	–	–	–	–	A	84	200	9	10	3.0	–	–	190	–	–
Chicken																													
– fryers, flesh and skin	72.7	20.6	5.6[1]	1.2	0.09	–	138	0.58	30	0.1	0.2	0.50	6.8	[2]	0.80	2.5	0.21	biotin 11 µg	A	83	359	12	37	1.8	0.3	3	200	220	85
– roasters, flesh and skin	66.9	19.5	12.6	0.4	–	0	197	0.82	410	0.08	0.12	–	7.4	–	–	–	–	–	A	–	–	11	–	1.5	–	–	191	–	–
– hens and cocks, flesh and skin	61.3	19.0	18.8	4	–	0	251	1.05	610	0.06	0.13	–	9.2	–	–	–	–	–	A	–	–	11	–	1.3	–	–	182	–	–
– gizzard	78.4	18.3	0.4	–	0.15	0.7	84	0.35	–	0.09	0.25	–	4.8	–	–	–	–	–	A	64	253	8	13	2.7	0.08	3.4	113	–	100
– liver	72.2	19.7	3.7	1.0	0.56	2.9	141	0.59	12100	0.4	2.5	0.80	10.8	290	4.1	35	0.25	biotin 210 µg; B12 56 µg; D 50 IU	A	85	179	12	13	7.9	0.32	–	236	220	–
Duck, medium fat	54.0	16	28.6[4]	6.9	0.07	0	326	1.36	–	0.10	0.24	–	5.6	–	–	8	–	–	A	85	285	15	–	1.8	0.4	2.7	188	–	85
Goat	70	18.7	9.4	0.4	–	0	165	0.69	0	0.17	0.32	–	5.6	–	–	0	–	–	A	–	–	11	–	2.2	–	–	–	–	–
Goose, medium fat	51.0	16.4	31.5[4]	2.5	0.49	0	354	1.48	–	0.10	0.24	0.6	5.6	–	0.6	–	–	–	A	85	420	15	–	1.8	0.3	–	188	–	120
– liver	66	17	10	–	–	5.5	184	0.77	–	0.02	–	0.9	4	–	–	–	–	–	A	140	230	10	–	–	4.9	–	180	–	–
Ham																													
– raw	53.0	15.2	31.0	–	0.07–0.1	0	345	1.44	0	0.74	0.18	0.44	4.0	–	0.64	0	0.28	biotin 5 µg; B12 1 µg	A	59	310	9	18	2.3	0.12	1.7	168	–	59
– boiled	57.0	19.5	20.6	2.0	0.07	0	269	1.13	0	0.54	0.26	0.40	4.2	1	0.53	0	–	B12 0.3 µg	A	876	348	10	17	2.5	–	–	150	–	–
– smoked, raw	42.0	16.9	35.0	–	0.11	0.3	389	1.63	0	0.7	0.19	0.22	4.0	–	0.6	0	–	–	A	2530	248	10	20	2.5	–	–	207	180	2060
– canned, spiced	65.0	18.3	12.3	–	0.07	0.9	193	0.81	0	0.53	0.19	0.22	3.8	–	–	0	–	–	A	1250	280	11	20	2.7	0.22	2.3	156	180	1670
Hare	73	22.3	0.9[4]	–	0.08	0.2	103	0.43	0	0.09	0.19	–	5.0	–	–	–	–	–	A	50	400	12	–	3.2	0.24	–	157	–	–
Horse flesh, lean	74.3	21.7	2.6	–	0.06	0.9	120	0.50	–	0.07	0.12	0.25	4.3	–	0.50	1	–	B12 3 µg	A	44	332	10	23	2.7	0.6	6	150	–	–

[1] Light meat 0.9, dark meat 3.1. [2] Light meat 8, dark meat 12. [3] Light meat 1.1, dark meat 2.8. [4] Variable.

100 g edible portion (unless otherwise stated) contains	Water g	Proteins g	Fats Total g	Fats Polyunsaturated g	Fats Cholesterol g	Carbohydrates g	Energy kcal	Energy MJ	A + β-carotene IU	Thiamine mg	Riboflavin mg	B6 mg	Niacin mg	Free folic acid µg	Pantothenic acid mg	Ascorbic acid mg	α-Tocopherol mg	Others	A Excess acid, B Excess base	Sodium mg	Potassium mg	Calcium mg	Magnesium mg	Iron mg	Copper mg	Zinc mg	Phosphorus mg	Sulfur mg	Chloride mg
Lamb																													
– chops, medium fat	52.0	14.9	32.0	0.7	0.07	0	352	1.48	–	0.13	0.18	0.33	4.3	1	0.59	0	0.18	–	A	61	345	9	14	2.2	0.7	2.4	138	–	60
– leg, medium fat	64.0	18.0	18.0	0.5	0.07	0	239	1.00	–	0.16	0.22	0.32	5.2	1	0.62	0	0.14	–	A	78	380	10	16	2.7	–	3.2	213	–	–
– kidney	77.7	16.8	3.3	–	0.38	0.9	105	0.44	690	0.51	2.42	0.30	7.4	20	4.3	15	0.45	biotin 6 µg; B12 3 µg	A	220	270	13	13	7.5	0.3	1.9	218	180	270
– liver	70.8	21.0	3.9	–	0.30	2.9	136	0.57	50500	0.4	3.28	0.37	16.9	150	7.1	33	0.46	biotin 37 µg; B12 63 µg; biotin 41 µg; D 20 IU	A	76	290	13	14	10.9	6.3	3.9	349	230	83
Pork (see also Bacon and Ham)																													
– cutlets	53.9	15.2	30.6	2.8	0.07	0	341	1.43	0	0.8	0.19	0.48	4.3	4	0.40	0	–	biotin 5 µg; B12 1 µg	A	56	290	9	19	2.3	0.13	1.9	170	–	54
– loin, lean	71.2	18.6	9.9	1.6	0.06	–	168	0.70	–	1.1	0.31	–	6.5	–	0.65	2	–	–	A	70	285	12	22	3.0	–	–	234	–	–
– spare ribs, total edible	51.8	14.5	33.2	–	0.10	0	361	1.51	–	0.70	0.17	–	3.8	–	2.8	18	0.6	B12 1 µg	A	70	285	8	17	2.2	–	–	160	–	–
– brain	78.0	10.6	9.0	–	>2.0	trace	126	0.53	–	0.16	0.28	–	4.3	1	2.5	3	–	B12 3 µg	A	153	312	10	15	3.6	0.3	–	300	–	110
– heart	76.8	16.9	4.8	0.27	–	0.4	117	0.49	30	0.43	1.24	0.43	6.6	–	–	–	0.4	biotin 20 µg; B12 3 µg	A	80	257	6	15	3.3	0.3	–	132	–	180
– kidney	77.8	16.3	5.2	0.29	0.38	0.8	120	0.50	130	0.34	1.8	0.55	9.8	5	3.1	12	0.2	biotin 32 µg; B12 15 µg	A	173	242	11	16	6.7	0.38	3.5	218	213	95
– liver	71.6	20.6	4.8	–	0.30	2.6	131	0.55	10900	0.43	2.7	0.85	16.4	59	7.0	27	–	biotin 27 µg; B12 25 µg	A	77	350	10	18	19	0.85	3.6	316	230	–
– tongue	66.1	16.8	15.6	–	–	0.5	215	0.90	–	0.17	0.29	0.35	5.0	–	0.8	–	0.1	–	A	93	234	9	–	1.4	–	–	186	–	–
Rabbit	70.4	20.4	8.0	1.5	0.07	0	159	0.67	trace	0.04	0.18	0.6	12.8	4	0.75	0	–	B12 10 µg	A	67	360	18	29	2.4	0.24	1.4	210	200	74
Turkey	64.2	20.1	14.7[2]	3.0	0.07	0.4	218	0.91	–	0.13	0.14	–	7.9	2	–	0	–	–	A	66	315	8	19	1.5	0.2	2.2	212	230	100
Veal (see also Calf)																													
– fillet	74.9	21.1	2.7	–	–	0	109	0.46	–	0.10	0.25	0.30	7.0	trace	0.6	0	0.6	B12 1 µg	A	110	360	8	25	1.2	–	–	260	220	68
– rib, cutlets	70.0	19.5	9.0	0.6	–	0	164	0.69	–	0.14	0.26	0.43	6.5	–	0.50	0	–	biotin 2 µg; B12 0.7 µg	A	90	301	11	16	2.9	0.25	3.5	200	–	–
– round with rump	68.0	19.1	12.0	0.8	0.07	0	190	0.80	–	0.18	0.27	0.20	6.3	–	0.91	0	–	B12 0.7 µg	A	90	330	11	15	2.9	0.25	–	206	203	77
Venison	73.0	21.4	3.6	0.3	–	0	124	0.52	–	0.37	0.28	–	7.4	–	–	0	–	–	A	70	336	19	29	5.0	–	–	183	211	41
Whale meat	71	20.6	4.0	–	–	1	125	0.52	1860	0.03	0.1	–	4.4	–	–	8	–	–	A	78	–	12	–	2.4	–	–	144	–	–
Meat products																													
Gelatin, dried	13.0	85.6	0.1	–	–	0	335	1.40	0	0	0	0	0	–	–	0	–	–	0	–	–	10	33	–	0.4	0.32	–	–	–
Pâté de foie gras	53.9	14.2	28.6	–	>0.15	5	340	1.42	3170	0.03	0.60	–	3.3	–	1.2	2	–	B12 3.2 µg	A	740	173	10	15	6.4	0.4	–	191	–	720

¹ Lean meat 6.6.   ² Light meat 7, dark meat 17.

100 g edible portion (unless otherwise stated) contains	Water g	Proteins g	Total g	Polyunsaturated g	Cholesterol g	Carbohydrates g	kcal	MJ	A + β-carotene IU	Thiamine mg	Riboflavin mg	B_6 mg	Niacin mg	Free folic acid µg	Pantothenic acid mg	Ascorbic acid mg	α-Tocopherol mg	Others	A Excess acid, B Excess base	Sodium mg	Potassium mg	Calcium mg	Magnesium mg	Iron mg	Copper mg	Zinc mg	Phosphorus mg	Sulfur mg	Chloride mg
Sausages																													
– beef	50.3	9.6	24.1	–	0.04	11.7	305	1.28	–	0.03	0.13	0.06	5.0	2	0.5	0	0.4	biotin 2 µg	A	810	150	48	13	1.4	0.23	1.2	150	120	1100
– Bologna	56.2	12.1	27.5	–	–	1.1	304	1.27	–	0.16	0.22	–	2.6	2	–	0	–	–	A	1300	230	7	11	1.8	–	1.4	128	120	1280
– frankfurter, cervelat	55.6	12.5	27.6	–	0.07	1.8	256	1.07	0	0.16	0.20	0.03	2.7	2	0.4	0	0.3	biotin 2 µg	A	1100	230	7	11	1.9	0.24	–	133	90	1100
– canned	65.7	13.0	19.6	–	–	–	232	0.97	–	0.03	0.08	–	3.1	–	–	–	0.16	–	A	711	207	10	–	2.7	–	–	185	–	–
– mortadella	52.3	12.4	32.8	–	–	trace	349	1.46	0	0.10	0.15	–	3.1	–	–	0	–	–	A	668	140	12	–	1.4	–	–	238	–	920
– pork, American	38.1	9.4	50.8	–	–	–	498	2.08	–	0.43	0.17	–	2.3	2	0.6	0	–	biotin 3 µg	A	740	–	5	11	–	–	–	92	–	–
– English	45.4	10.6	32.1	–	0.05	9.5	372	1.56	–	0.04	0.12	0.07	3.4	–	0.6	0	0.2	biotin 3 µg	A	760	160	41	10	1.1	0.27	1.2	160	120	1030
– salami	27.7	17.8	49.7	–	0.08	–	524	2.19	–	0.18	0.20	0.15	2.6	2	0.8	0	0.11	–	A	1850	160	10	–	1.0	0.24	1.7	160	190	2460
Fish, Sea foods																													
Carp (*Cyprinus carpio*)	72.4	18.9	7.1	–	–	0	145	0.61	300	0.08	0.04	–	1.5	–	–	1	–	–	A	51	285	34	15	1	–	–	220	–	62
Caviar (*Acipenser sp.; Huso huso*)	46.0	26.9	15.0	–	0.3	3.3	262	1.10	–	0	–	–	–	–	–	–	–	–	A	2200	180	276	–	11.8	–	–	355	–	1800
Clams (*Mya arenaria*)	83.1	10.5	1.3	–	0.05	3.1	70	0.29	–	0.1	0.19	0.08	1.5	–	0.6	2	–	biotin 2 µg	A	121	235	12	63	0.6	–	–	208	–	92
Cod (*Gadus callarias*)	81.2	17.6	0.3	–	0.05	0	78	0.33	0	0.06	0.07	0.20	2.2	6	0.12	trace	0.4	biotin 3 µg; B_{12} 2 µg	A	86	339	11	28	0.5	0.06	0.4	190	–	110
Crab (*Cancer pagurus*), canned or cooked, meat only	77.2	17.4	2.5	–	0.1	1.1	101	0.42	–	0.08	0.08	0.35	2.5	3	0.5	1.8	–	biotin 5 µg	A	550	110	45	48	0.8	1.3	2	182	–	–
Eel (*Anguilla anguilla*)	60.7	12.7	25.6	–	0.05	0	285	1.19	2000	0.15	0.31	0.28	2.2	–	–	–	–	D 5000 IU	A	78	247	18	18	0.7	0.05	0.5	166	–	830
– smoked	50.3	18.6	27.8	–	–	0.8	333	1.39	2500	0.14	0.35	0.15	3.8	–	–	–	–	B_{12} 6 µg; D 6400 IU	A	798	239	95	50	0.7	–	0.7	211	–	69
Flounder (*Platichthys flesus, Pleuronectes flesus*)	81.3	16.7	0.8	–	0.06	0	79	0.33	30	0.22	0.21	0.25	3.8	5	–	–	–	B_{12} 1.6 µg	A	92	332	12	31	0.8	0.18	–	195	200	–
Frog legs (*Rana sp.*)	81.9	16.4	0.3	–	0.04	0	73	0.30	–	0.14	0.25	–	1.2	–	–	5	–	biotin 5 µg; B_{12} 1 µg	A	55	308	18	23	1.5	–	1.4	147	163	130
Haddock (*Melanogrammus aeglefinus*)	80.5	18.3	0.1	–	0.06	0	79	0.33	60	0.06	0.17	0.20	3.0	5	0.14	0	0.6	biotin 5 µg	A	120	300	18	24	0.7	0.23	0.3	197	220	40
– smoked	72.6	23.2	0.4	–	–	0	103	0.43	–	0.06	0.10	–	2.5	–	–	0	–	biotin 10 µg; B_{12} 10 µg; D 900 IU[1]	A	557	300	20	25	1.0	–	–	262	–	160
Halibut (*Hippoglossus hippoglossus*)	75.2	18.6	5.2	–	0.06	0	126	0.53	440	0.09	0.18	0.42	6	7	0.30	0	0.9	B_{12} 10 µg	A	56	340	13	24	0.7	0.23	0.5	211	200	–
Herring (*Clupea harengus*)	62.8	17.3	18.8	–	0.09	0	243	1.02	130	0.06	0.24	0.45	4.3	3	1.0	–	–	biotin 5 µg	A	67	317	57	26	1.1	0.12	–	240	190	88
– pickled	60.2	18.3	14	–	–	–	204	0.85	150	–	0.08	0.15	3.3	–	–	–	–	–	A	1000	–	30	9	–	–	–	150	–	76
– smoked	61.0	22.2	12.9	–	–	0	211	0.88	40	0.04	0.28	0.35	3.3	–	–	5	–	–	A	720	285	66	50	1.4	–	–	254	–	1600
Lobster (*Homarus vulgaris*)	78.5	16.9	1.9	–	0.17	0.5	91	0.38	–	0.15	0.13	–	1.5	–	1.3	–	–	–	A	300	260	29	22	0.6	2.2	2.7	200	170	230
Mackerel (*Scomber scombrus*)	67.2	19.0	12.2	–	0.08	0	191	0.80	450	0.15	0.35	0.70	7.7	–	0.46	0	–	–	A	144	358	5	33	1.0	0.16	–	239	197	500
– smoked	59.4	23.8	13.0	–	–	0	219	0.92	–	0.14	0.35	–	10	–	–	–	–	biotin 2 µg; B_{12} 10 µg; D 700 IU	A	261	275	5	–	1.2	–	–	240	–	170

[1] Without gonads.

100 g edible portion (unless otherwise stated) contains	Water g	Proteins g	Fats Total g	Fats Polyunsaturated g	Fats Cholesterol g	Carbohydrates g	Energy kcal	Energy MJ	A + β-carotene IU	Thiamine mg	Riboflavin mg	B₆ mg	Niacin mg	Free folic acid µg	Pantothenic acid mg	Ascorbic acid mg	α-Tocopherol mg	Others	A Excess acid, B Excess base	Sodium mg	Potassium mg	Calcium mg	Magnesium mg	Iron mg	Copper mg	Zinc mg	Phosphorus mg	Sulfur mg	Chloride mg
Mussels (Mytilus edulis)	82.5	12	1.7	-	0.15	2.2	76	0.32	180	0.16	0.22	-	1.6	-	-	-	0.9	-	A	290	315	88	23	5.8	3.2	2	250	370	460
Ocean perch, Atlantic (Sebastes marinus)	77.9	18.9	3.0	-	-	0	108	0.45	30	0.09	0.08	0.41	2.5	5	-	3	-	B₁₂ 0.46 µg	A	94	345	46	-	1.0	-	-	212	-	-
Octopus (Octopus bimaculatus)	82.2	15.3	0.8	-	0.17	0	73	0.31	-	0.02	0.06	-	1.8	-	-	-	-	-	A	-	-	29	-	0.2	0.44	-	173	-	-
Oysters (Ostrea sp.)	83.0	9.0	1.2	-	0.11–0.33	4.8	68	0.28	310	0.18	0.23	0.11	2.5	10	0.50	trace	0.85	biotin 10 µg; B₁₂ 15 µg; D 5 IU	A	73–505	110–285	94	42	5.5	1.2–3.7	6–100	143	180	-
Perch (Perca fluviatilis)	79.5	18.4	0.8	-	0.07	0	86	0.36	30	0.075	0.12	-	1.7	-	-	-	-	-	A	67	238	20	27	1	-	2.5	198	230	85
Pike (Esox lucius)	80.2	18.2	1.2	-	-	0	89	0.37	-	0.15	0.07	-	1.7	34	-	-	0.2	biotin 2 µg; B₁₂ 1 µg	A	70	300	20	30	0.7	0.25	-	210	200	100
Salmon – Atlantic (Salmo salar)	65.5	19.9	13.6	-	0.04	0	208	0.87	220	0.17	0.17	0.98	7.5	4	0.8	1	-	biotin 5 µg; B₁₂ 3 µg; D 650 IU	A	48	391	29	29	0.8	0.2	0.8	266	170	59
-- canned, solids and liquid	64.2	21.7	12.2	-	-	0	203	0.85	60	0.03	0.18	0.45	6.5	4	0.50	trace	1.5	biotin 15 µg; D 500 IU	A	570	300	93	30	1.4	0.09	0.9	240	220	880
-- smoked	58.9	21.6	9.3	-	-	0	176	0.74	-	0.16	0.17	-	8.8	-	-	-	-	-	A	1880	420	19	32	0.6	0.09	0.4	245	-	2850
chinook, king (Oncorhynchus tshawytscha)	64.2	19.1	15.6	-	-	0	222	0.93	310	0.10	0.23	-	-	-	-	trace	-	-	A	45	399	-	29	-	-	-	301	-	-
-- canned, solids and liquid	64.4	19.6	14.0	-	-	0	210	0.88	230	0.03	0.14	-	7.3	-	-	-	-	-	A	-	366	154	27	0.9	-	-	289	-	-
Sardines (Sardina pilchardus sardina)	70.7	19.2	8.6	-	-	0	160	0.67	180	0.01	0.35	-	9.7	-	-	-	-	-	A	-	560	85	24	2.5	0.17	-	258	-	-
-- canned in oil; solids and liquid	50.6	20.6	24.4	-	0.12	0.6	311	1.30	220	0.02	0.16	0.40	4.4	6	0.5	0	1.1	biotin 4 µg; B₁₂ 23 µg; D 250 IU	A	510	-	354	43	3.5	0.17	-	434	-	-
-- drained solids	61.8	24.0	11.1	-	0.14	1.2	214	0.90	0	0.03	0.20	0.48	5.4	-	0.6	0	0.3	biotin 5 µg; B₁₂ 28 µg; D 300 IU	A	650	590	437	52	2.9	0.04	2.9	499	260	830
Scallops (Pecten sp.)	79.8	15.3	0.2	-	0.04	3.3	79	0.33	10	0.04	0.06	-	1.3	-	-	-	-	biotin 0.3 µg	A	150	420	26	-	1.8	0.12	3.0	208	310	1000
Shrimps (Crangon sp.)	78.2	18.7	2.2	-	0.14	-	97	0.41	60	0.07	0.05	0.13	1.25	-	0.14	2	-	B₁₂ 1 µg	A	140	258	63	42	2.0	0.43	1.9	300	342	-
-- canned, drained solids	70.4	24.2	1.1	-	0.15	0.7	116	0.49	-	0.01	0.03	0.11	1.5	8	0.21	0	-	B₁₂ 2 µg; D 105 IU	A	980	122	115	49	3.1	0.18	1.5	263	-	1510
Snails (Helix)	82	15	0.8	-	-	2	75	0.31	-	-	-	-	-	-	-	-	-	-	A	-	-	170	250	3.5	0.4	2.5	-	140	-
Sole (Solea solea), see values for Flounder																													
Trout (Salmo trutta)	77.6	19.2	2.1	-	0.06	0	101	0.42	150	0.09	0.25	-	3.5	7	0.2	-	6.3	biotin 3 µg; B₁₂ 4.6 µg; D 230 IU	A	39	470	19	25	1.0	0.33	2.5	220	208	-
Tunny (Thunnus thynnus)																			A										
-- canned, solids and liquid	52.5	23.8	20.9	-	0.06	0	290	1.21	90	0.05	0.06	0.25	10.8	-	-	0	-	-	A	420	343	7	33	1.2	0.12	1.7	294	-	690

Iodine content of foods

There is considerable variation in the iodine content of individual foods[1] (see the following table). In sea foods the iodine level is high and fairly constant[2,3] (see the table below). The iodine content of milk, eggs and meat depends on the animal's iodine intake; in plants it varies with the chemical composition of the soil and fertilizers used.

In general, foods contain less iodine in areas where goiter is endemic than where it is a rarity[3,4] (see the table below).

Iodine content of composites of food groups (Maryland, USA)[1]

Samples	100 g edible portion contains	Mean	$s_{\bar{x}}$	Median
		μg iodine		
7	Sea foods	66	18	54
13	Vegetables	32	10	28
12	Meat products	26	7	17.5
11	Eggs	26	8	14.5
18	Dairy products	13	1	13.9
18	Bread, cereals	10	2	10.5
18	Fruits	4	2	1.8

Iodine content of sea foods

100 g edible portion contains	Mean	Range	Reference
	μg iodine		
Cod, dried	100	75–139	3
Haddock	139	122–169	2
Plaice	51	9–107	2
Shrimps	36	29–43	3
Crayfish	44	38–49	3
Octopus	20	15–30	3
Oysters	140	100–200	3
Cod-liver oil	700	510–870	3

Iodine content of foods in areas with and without iodine-deficiency goiter

100 g edible portion contains	Endemic goiter areas		Goiter-free areas	
	Mean	Range	Mean	Range
	μg iodine			
Greece[4]				
Drinking water	0.24	0–1.0	0.47	0.35–0.77
Cow's milk	2.5	0–9.0	4.2	2.6–7.5
Eggs	4.0	1.0–12.5	27.9	3.8–102
Greek soft cheese	8.5	3.6–17.5	15.1	6.7–33.0
Bread	0.5	0–3.7	1.6	0–14.5
Portugal[3]				
Human milk	0.9	trace–1.3	12	8–14
Cheese	4.7	2.6–13.0	30	12–45
Pork, lean meat	4.4	2.1–6.5	30	27–34
Eggs	3.4	2.7–5.2	22	20–23
Olive oil	1.1	0.6–1.5	0.9	trace–1.9
Corn flour	2.7	1.7–4.8	3.4	2.8–3.9
Beans, dry seeds	2.5	1.4–4.9	9.0	8.5–9.5
Potatoes	2.3	0.9–3.1	5.0	3.4–6.6
Onions	1.6	1.0–2.6	4.8	4.6–5.1
Beans, green	3.6	1.8–6.0	4.0	3.1–5.0
Chestnuts	2.8	1.6–4.0	6.1	5.4–7.6
Apples	1.6	0.8–2.5	3.9	3.8–4.2
Wine	0.8	trace–1.2	3.0	2.8–3.2

It is difficult to be sure of the iodine content of bread and other bakery products. In some bakeries, iodate is added to the dough as stabilizer; bread so produced contains up to 900 μg iodine/100 g[5].

Refined salt from underground deposits, as well as recrystallized rock salt, is poor in iodine (< 1 μg/100 g)[3]. Iodinated salt contains potassium iodide in the proportion of 1 : 10000 to 1 : 100000, corresponding to an iodine content of 76–7.6 μg/g NaCl.

Fruit preserves, jams and pharmaceutical products may contain erythrosine as coloring agent containing iodine[6]. Soybean preparations are usually enriched with iodine to counter their goitrogenic tendency[7].

Amino acids in foods

The data given on next page have been taken from lists compiled by the Ministry of Agriculture, Fisheries and Food and the Medical Research Council (UK)[8] and the FAO[9] and are values per 16 g nitrogen. When the conversion factor 6.25 is used (see the note below the table), 16 g nitrogen is equivalent to 100 g protein.

Detailed compilations of the amino-acid content of foods are to be found in the publications of BLOCK and WEISS[10], ORR and WATT[11], and HARVEY[12]. The 1957 FAO Reference Pattern[13] is based on the minimum requirement of essential amino acids. The 1973 FAO Scoring Pattern[14] furnishes a measure of the 'chemical quality' of a protein. A US Committee on Nutrition[15] has listed the amino-acid contents of preparations for the treatment of hereditary metabolic disorders.

More complete data on the phenylalanine and leucine contents of foods – as required for devising a diet low in these amino acids – have been published by BICKEL and BREMER[16] and by NOEL et al.[17].

The proteins of meat and fish, like those of cereal and dairy products, have much the same composition, so that detailed lists for these foods are superfluous. Vegetable proteins on the other hand vary widely in amino-acid composition, but in view of the insignificant amounts of these substances in the normal diet these differences are nutritionally unimportant.

The values given on next page are for the raw foods. The proteins of foods low in carbohydrate are practically unchanged by heating. In bakery products the proteins in the crust are of reduced utilizability. Vegetables are known to lose nitrogeneous constituents on cooking, but this has no nutritional significance.

Free sugars in foods

Data on the content of glucose, fructose and sucrose are given on page 263. Data on the myoinositol content have been compiled by CLEMENTS and DARNELL[40]. The largest amounts of myoinositol were found in fruits, beans, grains and nuts. Fresh vegetables and fruits contain more myoinositol than frozen or canned products.

Conversion factors for calculating protein values from nitrogen content of foods[9,14]

Food	Factor	Food	Factor
Fruits	6.25	Pecans	5.30
Vegetables		Sunflower seeds	5.30
Leafy vegetables	6.25	Walnuts	5.30
Bulbs and roots	6.25	*Grains*	
Legumes		Barley	5.83
Beans, green	6.25	Maize	6.25
– dry seeds	6.25	Millet	5.83
– Lima	6.25	Oats	5.83
Lentils	6.25	Rice	5.95
Peas	6.25	Rye	5.83
Soybeans	5.71	Wheat	
Yeast	6.25	– whole kernel	5.83
		– bran	6.31
Nuts		– embryo	5.80
Almonds	5.18	– endosperm	5.70
Brazil nuts	5.46	*Eggs*	6.25
Cashew nuts	5.30	*Milk*	6.38
Chestnuts	5.30	*Meat*	6.25
Coconuts	5.30	*Fish*	6.25
Hazelnuts	5.30	*Gelatin*	5.55
Peanuts	5.46		

Amino-acid contents of foods

Food	Arginine	Cystine	Histidine	Isoleucine	Leucine	Lysine	Methionine	Phenylalanine	Threonine	Tryptophan	Tyrosine	Valine	Alanine	Aspartic acid	Glutamic acid	Glycine	Proline	Serine
									g amino acid per 16 g nitrogen									
Fruits																		
Apples	2.7	1.3	1.9	3.5	6.2	5.9	0.8	2.6	3.7	1.0	1.4	4.0	4.5	20.8	11.2	3.8	3.2	4.3
Apricots	1.3	–	1.6	1.8	2.9	2.9	0.5	1.6	2.1	0.8	1.3	2.4	3.5	23.5	5.9	1.8	2.7	2.9
Avocados	3.4	–	1.8	3.4	5.4	5.0	1.6	3.5	2.9	1.1	2.2	4.6	6.1	22.6	12.3	4.0	3.8	4.2
Bananas	5.8	2.7	6.1	4.0	5.1	4.3	1.3	4.2	3.0	1.1	2.6	4.2	4.5	10.6	9.3	4.2	4.2	3.8
Dates	3.4	2.1	1.4	2.2	4.3	2.7	1.3	2.9	2.7	2.7	1.4	3.2	4.6	5.9	10.4	4.5	5.8	3.4
Figs	2.2	1.6	1.4	3.0	4.3	4.0	0.8	2.4	3.2	0.8	4.3	3.8	6.1	24.0	9.6	3.4	6.6	5.0
Grapes	7.4	1.6	3.7	0.8	2.1	2.2	3.4	2.1	2.7	0.5	1.8	2.7	4.2	12.2	20.8	3.0	3.4	4.8
Oranges	6.4	1.3	1.4	2.9	2.7	5.3	1.4	3.7	1.4	0.6	2.1	3.8	6.2	14.1	12.2	10.2	5.6	2.9
Peaches	2.1	1.1	2.1	1.6	3.5	3.7	3.8	2.2	3.4	0.5	2.6	5.0	5.0	11.4	17.6	1.9	3.4	4.2
Strawberries	4.3	0.8	1.9	2.2	5.1	4.0	0.2	2.9	3.0	1.1	3.4	2.9	5.1	22.4	14.7	4.0	3.2	3.8
Vegetables																		
Beans																		
– broad	9.0	0.8	2.4	4.0	7.0	6.4	0.6	4.3	3.4	1.0	3.2	4.5	4.2	11.2	15.0	4.2	4.0	4.5
– red kidney	5.8	0.8	2.9	4.2	7.7	7.2	1.1	5.3	4.0	1.0	2.6	4.6	4.2	12.0	14.7	3.8	3.5	5.6
– young, in pod	4.3	1.1	2.4	3.7	6.9	5.4	1.3	4.3	3.8	1.4	3.4	5.0	4.5	12.0	10.7	3.8	3.8	5.3
Beets, root	6.6	1.1	1.3	2.4	4.5	5.3	1.9	3.5	3.4	1.0	3.5	2.4	2.2	18.1	15.2	2.1	2.6	3.5
Broccoli	5.8	1.1	1.8	3.8	5.3	5.1	1.4	3.7	3.7	1.1	–	5.0	–	–	–	–	–	–
Brussels sprouts	6.2	0.6	2.2	4.2	5.4	5.4	1.0	3.7	4.3	1.1	–	4.8	–	–	–	–	–	–
Cabbage	8.3	1.1	2.6	3.0	5.3	3.0	1.0	3.0	3.7	1.0	1.9	4.2	5.1	6.6	8.6	4.8	3.7	4.2
Carrots	4.5	1.1	1.4	3.0	4.5	3.8	1.0	2.7	2.9	0.8	2.2	4.5	4.8	11.7	19.4	2.9	2.9	3.2
Cauliflower	4.5	–	1.9	4.3	6.7	5.6	1.9	3.4	4.2	1.4	1.4	5.8	8.0	8.3	7.7	6.9	–	–
Chickpeas	9.4	1.4	2.7	4.5	7.5	6.9	1.3	5.8	3.8	0.8	2.9	4.5	4.3	11.7	15.8	4.0	4.2	5.1
Lentils	8.6	1.0	2.7	4.3	7.7	7.2	0.8	5.3	4.0	1.0	3.2	5.0	4.3	11.5	16.6	4.2	4.3	5.3
Mushrooms	5.9	0.8	1.3	2.2	3.7	4.5	1.4	2.1	2.7	1.0	1.9	2.6	4.6	4.5	7.0	2.6	5.1	2.7
Peas	9.4	1.1	2.2	4.3	6.9	7.5	1.0	4.6	4.0	1.0	2.7	4.6	4.2	11.0	16.1	4.0	3.8	4.3
Potatoes	5.0	1.3	1.9	4.2	6.1	5.4	1.6	4.3	3.8	1.4	3.0	5.1	3.7	18.4	12.8	3.4	3.8	4.2
Spinach	6.4	1.6	2.6	4.8	9.4	7.2	1.8	6.1	5.3	1.6	5.0	6.1	6.4	9.9	11.7	5.1	4.8	4.8
Sweet potatoes	5.0	1.1	1.3	3.7	5.4	3.4	0.8	3.8	3.8	1.8	2.4	4.5	4.8	13.3	8.6	3.7	3.5	4.2
Yeast																		
Brewer's	5.0	0.9	2.5	5.8	8.0	9.0	1.6	4.8	5.5	–	4.1	7.3	6.8	10.8	10.7	4.8	3.9	5.8
Torula	5.9	0.4	2.3	6.2	4.6	8.8	2.5	3.9	5.3	0.4	3.0	5.3	–	–	–	–	–	–
Nuts																		
Almonds	9.8	1.4	2.2	3.5	6.2	2.2	1.3	4.8	2.4	0.8	2.9	5.1	3.8	9.4	21.9	5.3	4.8	3.5
Brazil nuts	13.3	2.1	2.2	2.9	6.9	2.7	5.8	3.8	2.6	1.1	2.7	4.3	3.5	7.4	18.6	4.5	4.5	4.3
Coconuts	13.1	1.6	2.1	3.8	6.7	3.5	1.8	4.5	3.4	1.1	2.7	5.4	4.5	8.8	18.7	4.5	3.7	4.8
Hazelnuts	14.6	1.1	1.9	5.8	6.2	2.9	1.0	3.7	2.9	1.4	3.7	6.2	–	7.0	20.5	9.4	5.6	9.6
Peanuts	11.2	1.3	2.4	3.4	6.4	3.5	1.1	5.0	2.6	1.1	3.8	4.2	3.8	11.4	18.2	5.6	4.3	4.8
Pecans	10.9	2.1	2.6	5.0	7.4	4.5	1.4	5.1	3.6	1.2	2.7	4.4	–	–	–	–	–	–
Pistachio nuts	8.3	1.7	2.1	4.0	6.8	4.8	1.6	4.9	2.8	–	3.0	6.0	4.2	8.7	19.9	4.5	4.0	5.5
Sunflower seeds	8.0	1.5	2.3	4.3	6.4	3.6	1.9	4.4	3.7	1.4	1.9	5.1	4.2	9.3	21.8	5.4	4.5	4.3
Walnuts	12.6	1.8	2.1	4.0	7.2	1.9	1.4	4.3	3.0	1.0	3.4	4.8	–	–	–	–	–	–
Cereals																		
Barley, pearled	4.8	2.2	2.1	3.5	6.7	2.6	1.6	5.1	3.4	1.6	3.0	5.0	4.2	5.6	23.5	3.8	10.9	4.0
Buckwheat, dark flour	9.8	2.4	2.1	3.4	5.9	3.8	1.5	3.8	3.6	–	2.4	6.7	4.7	8.9	17.3	6.4	4.3	5.0
Corn flour	4.2	1.6	2.7	3.7	12.5	2.7	1.9	5.0	3.7	0.6	3.8	4.8	7.5	6.2	18.9	3.7	9.0	5.0
Millet, pealed	4.7	–	1.9	6.5	12.1	3.0	2.6	4.9	2.4	0.8	–	6.5	–	–	–	–	–	–
Oatmeal	6.2	2.7	2.1	3.8	7.2	3.7	1.8	5.0	3.4	1.3	3.4	5.1	4.5	7.7	21.0	4.6	5.1	4.6
Rice																		
– polished	7.5	1.6	2.4	3.8	8.2	3.7	2.1	4.8	3.4	1.3	4.0	5.8	5.8	9.6	19.2	4.3	4.6	4.6
– whole	8.3	1.4	2.5	3.8	8.2	3.8	2.3	5.2	3.9	–	3.5	5.5	6.0	10.3	20.6	5.0	4.7	5.4
Rye, whole meal	4.6	1.9	2.2	3.5	6.2	3.4	1.4	4.5	3.4	1.1	1.9	4.8	4.3	7.2	24.1	4.3	9.4	3.8
Soybean flour	7.2	1.6	2.6	4.5	7.8	6.4	1.3	5.0	3.8	1.3	3.2	4.8	4.3	11.7	18.2	4.2	5.4	5.1
Wheat																		
– flour, light	3.5	2.6	2.1	3.8	7.0	1.9	1.6	4.8	2.7	1.1	2.6	4.3	3.0	4.3	33.0	3.2	12.6	5.6
– flour, whole	4.6	2.6	2.1	3.4	6.7	2.4	1.6	4.5	2.7	1.1	3.0	4.5	3.7	5.0	27.4	4.0	10.6	5.3
Wheat germs	8.2	2.1	2.9	3.6	6.9	6.5	2.0	4.1	4.2	–	3.1	5.0	6.6	9.2	17.6	6.3	5.5	4.8
Eggs, Milk																		
Eggs, whole	6.1	1.8	2.4	5.6	8.3	6.2	3.2	5.1	5.1	1.8	4.0	7.5	5.4	10.7	12.0	3.0	3.8	7.8
Egg white	5.4	1.8	2.2	5.6	8.2	5.8	3.5	5.8	4.8	1.8	4.0	7.8	5.8	10.9	12.2	3.2	4.0	7.4
Egg yolk	7.2	1.6	2.6	5.8	8.5	7.2	2.6	4.0	5.6	1.8	4.0	6.9	5.0	10.6	10.9	2.7	3.5	8.6
Cow's milk	4.0	1.0	3.0	5.6	10.2	8.2	2.9	5.4	5.0	1.4	4.5	7.4	3.8	8.5	23.0	2.2	9.4	5.9
Human milk	3.7	1.9	2.4	5.1	9.3	6.9	1.4	3.7	4.3	2.2	2.9	6.6	4.0	8.6	17.1	2.4	9.3	4.2
Yoghurt	2.9	0.8	3.4	6.2	11.5	6.9	2.1	5.9	4.5	1.3	5.0	6.9	3.8	6.9	18.4	2.6	7.7	5.8
Meat, Fish, Sea foods																		
Beef	6.7	1.3	3.7	5.1	8.0	9.1	2.7	4.5	4.6	1.3	3.8	5.3	6.4	9.6	17.3	5.6	5.1	4.5
Chicken	6.2	1.3	3.0	4.6	7.5	9.0	2.4	4.5	4.2	1.1	3.5	4.8	5.8	9.1	16.5	5.0	4.2	4.0
Pork	5.9	1.3	4.3	4.5	7.0	9.6	2.7	3.8	4.3	1.1	3.7	4.8	5.4	9.0	16.0	5.3	4.8	4.2
Liver (beef, calf, chicken, pork)	5.3	1.4	3.7	4.3	7.8	8.5	2.4	5.0	4.3	1.3	3.0	5.8	5.3	8.6	12.2	5.0	5.3	4.6
Fish	6.4	1.1	2.9	5.3	8.5	9.8	2.9	4.2	4.8	1.1	3.5	5.8	6.9	10.4	15.2	4.6	4.2	5.0
Crustacean	8.3	1.3	1.9	4.6	8.6	7.8	2.9	4.0	4.6	1.1	3.7	4.8	6.7	10.9	15.7	6.6	4.3	5.1
Molluscs	7.5	1.6	2.4	4.8	7.7	8.0	2.7	4.2	4.6	1.3	4.2	6.2	5.6	11.2	14.1	5.1	4.2	5.1
Gelatin	7.8	trace	0.6	1.4	2.9	4.0	0.8	2.1	1.9	0	0.3	2.2	9.8	5.9	10.1	24.2	13.8[1]	3.7
1957 FAO reference pattern	–	–	–	4.3	4.9	4.3	4.3[2]	5.8[3]	2.8	1.4	–	4.3	–	–	–	–	–	–
1973 FAO scoring pattern	–	–	–	4.0	7.0	5.4	3.5	6.1	4.0	1.0	–	5.0	–	–	–	–	–	–

[1] Also contains 11.7 g hydroxyproline.   [2] Methionine + cystine.   [3] Phenylalanine + tyrosine.

(References page 266)

Free sugars in fruits and vegetables

100 g edible portion contains	Total free sugars*		Glucose		Fructose		Sucrose		Method
	Mean	Range or s	Mean	Range or s	Mean	Range or s	Mean	Range or s	
					g				
Fruits									
Apples	9.86	6.03–15.3	1.82	1.08–2.84	5.93	3.66–7.59	2.11	0.53–5.47	E
Apricots	7.35	3.35–10.4	1.10	0.46–1.97	0.46	0.30–0.84	5.79	2.46–8.49	E
Bananas	14.0		2.67	–	2.67		7.00	–	PC
Blackberries	5.51	4.78–7.38	2.46	2.08–3.34	2.74	2.12–3.64	0.47	0.18–0.65	E
Blueberries	5.84	4.74–6.84	2.32	1.96–2.98	3.28	2.62–3.86	0.24	0.10–0.43	E
Cantaloups (honeydew)	11.1	–	2.56	–	2.65		5.86	–	PC
Cherries, sweet	11.9	9.51–16.06	6.14	5.07–8.67	5.35	4.24–7.19	0.20	0.20–0.40	E
Currants	7.96	–	3.33		3.68	–	0.95	–	PC
Dates, dried	66.0	–	17.7	–	14.1	–	34.0	–	PC
Gooseberries	8.40	–	3.29		3.90	–	1.21	–	PC
Grapes	13.6	8.75–17.3	6.56	3.32–8.64	6.53	4.88–7.80	0.52	0.10–0.88	E
Grapefruit	6.81	5.99–7.96	2.14	1.88–2.40	2.26	1.88–2.84	2.44	1.72–3.83	E
Lemon juice	1.60	–	0.75	–	0.55	–	0.30	–	PC
Oranges	8.23	7.12–9.66	2.44	1.78–2.98	2.56	1.89–3.05	3.23	2.93–3.76	E
Peaches	6.71	4.65–8.58	0.98	0.72–1.42	1.12	0.64–1.60	4.61	3.00–6.06	E
Pears	7.95	5.77–9.74	1.25	0.52–1.80	5.60	4.15–6.59	1.10	0.70–1.71	E
Plums	8.61	6.33–10.83	2.21	1.37–3.62	1.20	0.63–2.21	5.20	3.63–7.24	E
Raspberries	5.38	3.66–9.30	1.80	1.43–2.78	2.04	1.54–3.20	1.51	0.68–3.32	E
Strawberries	5.24	3.96–5.96	2.00	1.45–2.44	2.13	1.08–2.83	1.11	0.31–2.46	E
Tangerines	7.47	5.45–8.28	1.11	0.89–1.30	1.27	1.00–1.45	5.09	3.13–6.06	E
Vegetables									
Artichokes	–	–	0.50	–	1.50	–	0.60	–	PC
Asparagus	2.75		1.50	–	1.13	–	0.12	–	PC
Beans	2.73	s 0.56	1.00	s 0.31	1.34	s 0.22	0.43	s 0.21	E
Beets, root	8.68	s 1.70	0.28	s 0.28	0.25	s 0.25	8.14	s 1.43	E
Broccoli	1.78	s 0.75	0.75	s 0.32	0.75	s 0.32	0.30	s 0.20	E
Brussels sprouts	2.79	s 0.44	0.88	s 0.21	0.79	s 0.18	1.10	s 0.52	E
Cabbage									
– red	3.48	s 0.56	1.70	s 0.33	1.26	s 0.22	0.52	s 0.40	E
– white	4.26	s 1.19	2.11	s 0.53	1.81	s 0.51	0.34	s 0.28	E
Carrots	4.68	s 0.75	1.66	s 0.38	1.47	s 0.29	1.55	s 0.71	E
Cauliflower	2.44	s 0.55	1.18	s 0.25	1.04	s 0.28	0.22	s 0.10	E
Celery, root	2.60	s 0.83	0.09	s 0.10	0.14	s 0.13	2.37	s 0.82	E
Chard, Swiss	1.50	s 0.86	0.93	s 0.56	0.41	s 0.23	0.16	s 0.14	E
Chicory									
– red	1.56	s 0.45	0.71	s 0.26	0.62	s 0.16	0.21	s 0.12	E
– white	3.14	s 0.64	2.01	s 2.01	0.90	s 0.24	0.24	s 0.24	E
Cucumbers	1.85	s 0.38	0.87	s 0.19	0.92	s 0.19	0.06	s 0.06	E
Dandelion greens	1.20	–	0.75	–	0.45	–	trace	–	PC
Eggplants	3.29	–	1.51	–	1.53	–	0.25	–	PC
Fennel	2.64	s 0.60	1.26	s 0.30	1.04	s 0.29	0.34	s 0.15	E
Jerusalem artichokes	2.35	–	0.10	–	trace	–	2.25	–	PC
Kohlrabi	3.93	s 1.16	1.40	s 0.45	1.23	s 0.39	1.29	s 1.15	E
Leeks	3.43	s 0.68	1.30	s 0.33	1.48	s 0.39	0.66	s 0.35	E
Lettuce	1.13	s 0.41	0.44	s 0.18	0.55	s 0.20	0.13	s 0.10	E
Maize (sweet corn)	3.68	–	0.34	–	0.31	–	3.03	–	PC
Okra	2.85	–	1.03	–	1.06	–	0.75	–	PC
Onions	5.61	s 1.04	1.85	s 0.71	1.59	s 0.53	2.14	s 1.03	E
Peas, green	4.55	–	0.05	–	trace	–	4.50	–	PC
– – canned	0.69	s 0.30	0.01	s 0.005	0.01	s 0.006	0.67	s 0.29	E
Peppers, green	2.81	s 0.52	1.42	s 0.25	1.26	s 0.26	0.14	s 0.10	E
Potatoes									
– new	0.38	–	0.15	–	0.09	–	0.14	–	PC
– stored	3.88	–	1.04	–	1.15	–	1.69	–	PC
Pumpkins	4.42	–	1.69	–	1.43	–	1.30	–	PC
Radishes	2.17	s 0.59	1.33	s 0.36	0.72	s 0.23	0.11	s 0.07	E
Rhubarb	0.90	–	0.42	–	0.39	–	0.09	–	PC
Salsify	1.42	–	0.24	–	0.48	–	0.72	–	PC
Spinach	0.52	s 0.34	0.15	s 0.10	0.14	s 0.07	0.23	s 0.19	E
Squash, summer	2.15	s 0.47	0.94	s 0.25	1.05	s 0.19	0.16	s 0.11	E
Sweet potatoes	4.00	–	0.33	–	0.30	–	3.37	–	PC
Tomatoes	2.85	s 0.54	1.21	s 0.26	1.50	s 0.25	0.14	s 0.10	E

* Total free sugars = glucose + fructose + sucrose.

E Enzymatic method[18].
PC Paper chromatography[19, 20].

Composition of Foods — Fatty Acids

(References page 266)

Fatty acid composition of food fats (g fatty acid per 100 g total fatty acids)

Food	C8:0 Caprylic	C10:0 Capric	C12:0 Lauric	C14:0 Myristic	C15:0 Pentadecylic	C16:0 Palmitic	C16:1 Palmitoleic	C16:2 Hexadecadienoic	C17:0 Margaric	C18:0 Stearic	C18:1 Oleic	C18:2 Linoleic	C18:3 Linolenic*	C18:4 Stearidonic	C20:0 Arachidic	C20:1 Eicosenoic	C20:2 Eicosadienoic	C20:4 Arachidonic	C20:5 Timnodonic	C22:0 Behenic	C22:1 Erucic°/Cetoleic°	C22:4 Docosatetraenoic	C22:5 Docosapentaenoic	C22:6 Clupanodonic	C24:0 Lignoceric	C24:1 Selacholeic	Ref.
Plant lipids																											
Almond oil	0	0	0	trace	—	7.0	0.6	—	0.1	1.2	67.3	23.7	0.2	—	0	—	0	—	—	0	0	—	—	—	0	—	27
Cocoa butter	—	0	trace	0.1	—	27.6	0.4	—	trace	33.9	34.0	3.1	trace	—	0.9	—	0	—	—	0	0	—	—	—	0	—	27
Coconut oil	10.1	6.6	45.8	18.4	—	8.0	trace	—	—	2.4	6.0	1.7	0	—	0.6	—	0	—	—	—	—	—	—	—	—	—	27
Corn oil	0	trace	0.1	trace	—	11.5	0.1	—	trace	2.0	28.3	56.3	1.0	—	0.5	—	—	—	—	0.2	0	—	—	—	—	—	27
Cottonseed oil	0	0	trace	0.6	—	22.6	0.5	—	trace	2.6	18.1	52.3	1.7	—	0.5	—	—	—	—	0	0.7	—	—	—	—	—	27
Grape-seed oil	—	0	trace	0.04	—	6.7	0.1	—	—	3.1	12.1	77.3	0.7	—	trace	—	—	—	—	trace	—	—	—	—	—	—	27
Linseed oil	—	0	trace	trace	—	6.0	0.1	—	—	5.1	21.1	14.9	53.0	—	trace	—	0	—	—	—	0	—	—	—	—	—	22
Margarine**	2.2–5.0	1.9–3.7	14.2–29.3	6.1–11.4	—	9.4–22.1	—	—	trace	3.3–8.0	14.3–38.1	10.3–29.3	0–2.5	—	0.7	—	—	—	—	0.4	—	—	—	—	0.3	—	21
Mustard-seed oil	0	0	trace	0.05	—	2.9	0.2	—	trace	1.0	19.4	9.7	21.4	—	—	7.5	0.4	—	—	—	44.4	—	—	—	0.3	2.7	24
Olive oil, European§	—	0	0	trace	—	11.8	0.9	—	trace	2.8	74.5	8.7	1.0	—	0.5	—	0	—	—	trace	—	—	—	—	—	—	24
—, Tunisian	—	0	0	0	—	16.8	1.9	—	trace	2.5	58.9	18.8	0.9	—	1.8	—	0	—	—	0.2	0	—	—	—	—	—	24
Palm-kernel oil	4.9	3.9	48.7	16.0	—	7.6	0	—	trace	1.9	14.2	2.6	0	—	0.8	—	0	—	—	trace	0.2	—	—	—	—	—	27
Palm oil	—	—	trace	1.5	—	45.1	trace	—	0.1	4.8	36.8	10.2	0.5	—	0.5	—	—	—	—	trace	0.1	—	—	—	1.6	—	27
Peanut oil	—	—	trace	trace	—	10.6	0.1	—	trace	3.5	49.5	28.8	1.3	—	1.8	—	0	—	—	3.1	—	—	—	—	—	—	27
Rapeseed oil	0	0	0	0.05	—	3.6	0.2	—	trace	1.4	15.5	13.9	19.0	—	0.8	7.5	0.2	—	—	0.5	45.5†	—	—	—	0.5	—	27
Safflower oil	0	0	trace	0.1	—	7.5	0.1	—	trace	2.6	12.7	75.5	0.8	—	0.7	—	0.5	—	—	0.2	0.1	—	—	—	—	—	27
Sesame oil	0	0	0	trace	—	8.9	0.3	—	0.1	6.0	40.7	41.7	1.7	—	0.8	—	—	—	—	0.4	0	—	—	—	—	—	27
Soybean oil	0	0	trace	0.1	—	10.7	0.1	—	0.1	3.8	23.0	52.4	8.9	—	0.6	—	0	—	—	0.7	trace	—	—	—	—	—	27
Sunflower-seed oil	0	0	0	0.1	—	6.6	0.1	—	trace	4.3	22.4	65.2	0.3	—	0.4	—	—	—	—	0.4	0	—	—	—	—	—	27
Walnut oil	—	—	0	0.02	—	7.0	0.1	—	trace	2.1	18.7	59.8	13.3	—	trace	—	0	—	—	0.7	0	—	—	—	0	—	27
Animal lipids																											
Cow's milk	1.0	2.5	2.9	10.1	—	24.7	3.3	—	—	9.5	22.5	4.0	2.8	—	trace	—	—	—	—	—	—	—	—	—	—	—	28
Eggs	—	—	—	0.6	—	25.5	4.5	—	—	9.9	45.4	13.0	1.7	—	0.9	—	0.5	1.0	—	—	—	0.3	1.3	14.3	—	—	23
Fish																											
Cod	—	—	—	1.8	0.5	33.4	2.4	2.4	0.9	4.0	11.8	1.2	0.8	1.2	trace	1.6	—	3.2	12.4	—	0.7	—	0.6	21.9	—	0.5	25
Cod-liver oil	—	—	0.1	2.8	0.4	10.7	6.9	6.9	1.2	3.7	23.9	1.5	0.9	2.6	—	8.8	0.2	1.0	8.0	trace	5.3	0.3	1.3	14.3	trace	1.0	25
Eel	—	—	1.6	3.7	0.2	12.8	11.8	11.8	0.9	3.2	25.7	1.0	0.4	1.6	—	6.7	—	0.2	12.7	trace	3.8	0.2	1.5	6.9	—	—	26
Herring	—	—	—	5.9	0.6	14.0	12.4	12.4	0.5	1.4	16.9	1.1	trace	—	trace	28.3	—	0.5	0.8	trace	11.6	trace	0.7	0.5	trace	0.9	24
Mackerel	—	—	—	7.6	0.4	18.3	8.3	8.3	0.7	2.2	27.8	1.6	0.6	2.8	—	9.4	—	0.4	8.6	0.2	2.8	trace	1.3	7.6	trace	0.8	25
Salmon	—	—	—	4.9	0.5	28.2	5.3	5.3	0.5	3.9	19.3	0.9	1.3	3.4	—	3.1	—	3.9	7.1	0.5	10.5	trace	1.2	10.8	trace	0.8	25
Trout	—	—	—	15.1	trace	15.3	5.6	5.6	1.5	3.8	27.2	5.2	0.9	—	trace	8.0	0.6	0.5	3.4	0.2	1.3	0.6	2.6	2.5	trace	—	25
Tunny	—	—	—	2.1	0.8	11.9	8.2	8.2	1.5	4.1	19.8	2.1	1.3	1.5	trace	3.0	—	2.2	5.0	0.4	—	—	1.5	19.6	—	0.7	24
Chicken	—	—	—	4.5	0.6	22.1	2.8	2.8	1.2	6.1	39.8	13.5	0.7	0.5	—	2.0	—	3.0	13.2	0.7	—	—	—	17.3	—	—	27
Beef	—	—	4.5	3.2	0.6	26.9	6.3	—	trace	13.0	42.0	2.1	0.6	—	trace	0.6	0.6	1.0	trace	trace	trace	trace	trace	—	—	—	8
Duck	—	—	3.2	1.3	trace	22.8	7.2	—	trace	7.1	39.8	12.1	0.7	—	trace	trace	—	0.7	trace	trace	—	—	trace	1.0	trace	0.9	8
Lamb	—	—	5.4	5.4	0.6	24.2	4.4	—	1.0	20.9	52.8	2.5	2.5	—	—	trace	—	0	trace	trace	—	—	trace	—	—	0.8	8
Pork	—	—	1.6	1.6	trace	27.1	3.4	—	trace	13.8	43.8	7.4	0.9	—	0.7	0.7	—	trace	trace	0.4	trace	—	2.0	—	—	trace	8
Turkey	—	—	0.5	—	trace	25.0	5.0	—	0.5	10.0	21.5	20.0	1.0	—	trace	0.4	—	5.0	1.5	—	—	—	—	5.0	—	—	8

* In plant lipids $C_{18:3}$ + $C_{20:1}$. ° Erucic acid in plant lipids, cetoleic acid in fish. † New strains contain less erucic acid. § Spain, France, Italy. ** Values based on 9 Swiss samples; for American brands, see WEIHRAUCH et al.[29]

Oxalate and phytate in foods

Data on the oxalate content of foods vary widely[30]. In plants the content depends on age as well as on the season, climate and soil composition. The oxalate content of the diet is important in that these salts impair absorption of calcium and magnesium; in addition, when they are absorbed (normally at the most to the extent of 5% of the available oxalate[30]), they may lead to the formation of oxalate stones in the urinary tract.

Phytate interferes with the absorption of calcium[31], iron[32,33] and zinc[32,34] in the gut by forming insoluble compounds with these constituents of the diet.

	Oxalic acid		Phytic acid phosphorus[8] (as part of total phosphorus)
	Hodgkinson[35]	Herrmann[36]	
	mg per 100 g edible portion	mg per 100 g edible portion	%
Fruits, Fruit juices			
Apples	1.5	0	0
Apricots	–	6.8	–
– canned, sweetened	2.8	–	–
Bananas	0.7	–	0
Blackberries	–	12.4	16
Blueberries	–	0	–
Cantaloups	2.7	0	–
Cherries	–	7.2	–
Currants			
– black	4.3	–	–
– red	–	9.9	–
Gooseberries	–	19.3	–
– stewed	2.6	–	–
Grapes	–	7.9	–
Grapefruit	3.3	–	–
Lemon juice	1.5	–	–
Oranges	6.2	–	–
Orange juice	1.2	–	–
Peaches	–	0	–
– canned, sweetened	2.5	–	–
Pears	–	6.2	–
– canned, sweetened	1.5	–	–
Pineapple			
– canned, sweetened	1.5	–	–
Plums	–	11.9	–
– stewed	2.2	–	–
Prunes, dried	–	–	0
Raspberries	2.2	16.4	–
Strawberries	6.7	15.8	–
Whortleberries, red	–	0	–
Vegetables			
Artichokes	–	8.8	–
Asparagus	–	0	–
– boiled	1.7	–	–
Beans			
– broad, boiled	–	–	5
– young, in pod	–	43.7	84
– – boiled	29.7	–	–
Beets, root	–	72.2	–
– boiled	109	–	–
Brussels sprouts	–	6.1	–
– boiled	2.8	–	–
Cabbage			
– red	–	7.4	–
savoy	–	4.9	–
– white	–	0	–
– – boiled	1.2	–	–

	Oxalic acid		Phytic acid phosphorus[8] (as part of total phosphorus)
	Hodgkinson[35]	Herrmann[36]	
	mg per 100 g edible portion	mg per 100 g edible portion	%
Carrots	–	6.1	16
– boiled	14.5	–	–
Cauliflower	–	6.6	–
– boiled	1.1	–	0
Celery	15.2	6.8	0
Chives	1.1	0	–
Cucumbers	–	0	–
Eggplants	–	9.5	–
Endives	–	2.5	–
Fennel	–	5	–
Garlic	–	5	–
Jerusalem artichokes	–	–	25
Kale	–	7.2	–
Kohlrabi	–	2.8	–
Leeks	–	0	–
Lentils	–	–	51
Lettuce	2.2	0	–
Onions	3.0	5.5	0
Parsley	166	5.7	–
Parsnips	–	–	31
Peas, green	–	0	11
– – boiled	1.1	–	–
– dried	–	–	80
Peppers, green	–	0	–
Potatoes	–	0	–
– boiled	5.2	–	21
Pumpkins	0.5	0	–
Radishes	0.3	0	–
Rhubarb	–	537	–
– stewed	447	–	–
Rutabagas	–	0	0
Salsify	–	0	–
Spinach, boiled	571	–	0
Tomatoes	3.9	0	–
Nuts			
Almonds	–	–	82
Brazil nuts	–	–	86
Chestnuts	–	–	18
Coconuts	–	–	81
Peanuts	–	–	57
Walnuts	–	–	42
Cereals			
Barley, pearled	–	–	66
Cornflakes	5	–	25
Oatmeal	–	–	70
Rice, polished	–	–	61
Rye, flour, dark	–	–	72

	Oxalic acid		Phytic acid phosphorus[8] (as part of total phosphorus)
	Hodgkinson[35]	Herrmann[36]	
	mg per 100 g edible portion	mg per 100 g edible portion	%
Rye, flour, light	–	–	31
Sago	–	–	trace
Soybean, flour, full fat	–	–	31
Wheat			
– flour, dark	–	–	70
– flour, light	–	–	30
– shredded	–	–	80
Bread			
Brown	20.9	–	55
White	6.9	–	15
Confectionery			
Cocoa, powder	623	–	15
Marmalade	5.7	–	–
Ovaltine, powder	45.9	–	–
Beverages			
Beer	1.7	–	–
Coffee			
– infusion	1.0	–	–
– instant powder	143	–	–
Tea, infusion	12.5	–	–
Wine (Beaujolais)	3.1	–	–
Eggs			
Hen's egg, boiled	0.45	–	–
Milk, Dairy products			
Cow's milk	0.7	–	–
Butter	0	–	–
Meat			
Beef			
– roasted	1.6	–	–
– canned, corned	0.2	–	–
Chicken, roasted	1.1	–	–
Ham, steamed	1.0	–	–
Kidney, braised	3.2	–	–
Lamb, roasted	1.6	–	–
Liver, braised	4.3	–	–
Pork, roasted	1.7	–	–
Fish			
Flounder, boiled	0.3	–	–
Haddock, boiled	0.2	–	–
Sardines, canned	1.6	–	–

Purine content of foods[37, 38]

When it is necessary that the diet should be low in purines, only about half the usual 400 mg of purines per day should be ingested; this means that the foods listed in group 3 in the following table should be avoided. The individual dietary constituents containing purines differ metabolically however: thus the rise in the serum-uric-acid level caused by a dose of RNA is twice as high as that due to a similar dose of DNA.

Group 1: 0–50 mg purine/100 g	Group 2: 50–150 mg purine/100 g	Group 3: 150–1000 mg purine/100 g
Fruits	Peas, green	Organ meats (brain, kidney, liver, sweetbread)
Fruit juices	Legumes, dried	
Vegetables (except those under group 2)	Cauliflower	Wild game
	Asparagus	Meat extracts
Nuts	Spinach	Anchovies
	Mushrooms	
Cereals, breads (except whole grain products)	Whole grain products	Herrings
		Sardines
Sweets	Poultry (chicken, duck, turkey)	Mackerels
Beverages (coffee, tea, carbonated)		Scallops
	Meats (beef, lamb, pork, veal)	
Fats	Fish (except those under group 3)	
Eggs		
Cow's milk	Oysters	
Dairy products	Shellfish	

Acid content and pH of beverages[39]

	Acid mmol/L	pH
Vinegar (cider)	620	3.2
Grapefruit juice	150	3.5
Pineapple juice	130	3.5
Orange juice	120	3.7
Grape juice	80	3.3
Wine	39–90	2.8–3.8
Cranberry juice	80	2.7
Apricot nectar	59	3.8
Apple juice	55	3.6
Tomato juice	54	4.3
7-Up	51	3.1
Coca-Cola	50	2.8
Ginger ale	49	2.8
Club soda	46	3.7
Peach nectar	38	3.6
Prune juice	33	4.2
Pear nectar	22	3.7
Beer	–	4.4
Cow's milk		
– – skimmed	8	6.6
– – whole	6	6.7
Human milk	–	7.0
Sheep's milk	–	6.5
Coffee		
– infusion	4	5.0
– instant	4	5.2
Cocoa, instant	2	6.8
Tea, instant	1	6.9

References

[1] Vought and London, Amer. J. clin. Nutr., 14, 186 (1964).
[2] Harrison et al., Amer. J. clin. Nutr., 17, 73 (1965).
[3] Gonçalves Ferreira, F. A., Münch. med. Wschr., 109, 2357 (1967).
[4] Koutras et al., Amer. J. clin. Nutr., 23, 870 (1970).
[5] Pittman et al., New Engl. J. Med., 280, 1431 (1969).
[6] Vought et al., J. clin. Endocr., 34, 747 (1972).
[7] Landau et al., Israel J. med. Sci., 8, 1749 (1972).
[8] Paul and Southgate, McCance and Widdowson's The Composition of Foods, 4th ed., HMSO, London, 1978.
[9] Amino-acid Content of Foods and Biological Data on Proteins, FAO Nutritional Studies, No. 24, Food and Agriculture Organization of the United Nations, Rome, 1970.
[10] Block and Weiss, Amino Acid Handbook, Thomas, Springfield, 1956.
[11] Orr and Watt, Amino Acid Content of Foods, United States Department of Agriculture, Home Economics Research Report, No. 4, Washington, 1957.
[12] Harvey, D., Tables of the Amino Acids in Foods and Feedingstuffs, Commonwealth Agricultural Bureaux, Technical Communication, No. 19, Farnham Royal, 2nd ed., 1970.
[13] Joint FAO/WHO Expert Group on Protein Requirements, Wld Hlth Org. techn. Rep. Ser., No. 301 (1965).
[14] Joint FAO/WHO ad hoc Expert Committee on Energy and Protein Requirements, Wld Hlth techn. Rep. Ser., No. 522 (1973).
[15] Committee on Nutrition, Pediatrics, 57, 783 (1976).
[16] Bickel and Bremer, Dtsch. med. Wschr., 92, 700 (1967).
[17] Noel et al., J. Amer. diet. Ass., 69, 62 (1976).
[18] Dako et al., Schweiz. med. Wschr., 100, 897 (1970); Somogyi and Trautner, Schweiz. med. Wschr., 104, 177 (1974); Trautner and Somogyi, Mitt. Lebensmitt. Hyg., 63, 240 (1972).
[19] Göthe and Linneweh, Klin. Wschr., 46, 468 (1968); Salem and Hegazi, J. Sci. Food Agric., 22, 632 (1971).
[20] Shallenberger, R. S., in Sipple and McNutt (Eds.), Sugars in Nutrition, Academic Press, New York, 1974, p. 67.
[21] Hadorn and Zürcher, Mitt. Lebensmitt. Hyg., 58, 351 (1967).
[22] Hadorn and Zürcher, Mitt. Lebensmitt. Hyg., 59, 228 (1968).
[23] Hadorn and Zürcher, Mitt. Lebensmitt. Hyg., 61, 170 (1970).
[24] Reichwald and Meizies, Z. Ernährungsw., 12, 86 (1973).
[25] Gruger et al., J. Amer. Oil Chem. Soc., 41, 662 (1964).
[26] Iverson, J. L., J. Assoc. off. anal. Chem., 53, 1074 (1970).
[27] Roubal, W. T., J. Amer. Oil Chem. Soc., 40, 215 (1963).
[28] Hadorn and Zürcher, Dtsch. Lebensmitt.-Rdsch., 66, 249 (1970).
[29] Weihrauch et al., Food Technol., 31, 80 (1977).
[30] Hagler and Herman, Amer. J. clin. Nutr., 26, 882 (1973).
[31] Reinhold et al., Lancet, 1, 283 (1973).
[32] Haghshenass et al., Amer. J. clin. Nutr., 25, 1143 (1972).
[33] de Meester, C., Lebensm.-Wiss. u. Technol., 5, 155 (1972).
[34] Prasad and Oberleas, Lancet, 1, 1520 (1973).
[35] Hodgkinson, A., Medical Research Council, Mineral Metabolism Unit, Leeds, personal communication.
[36] Herrmann, K., Z. Lebensmitt.-Untersuch., 148, 206 (1972).
[37] Hench, P. S., J. Amer. med. Ass., 116, 453 (1941).
[38] Wolfram, G., Med. Welt, 24, 1969 (1973).
[39] Flick, A. L., Amer. J. dig. Dis., 15, 317 (1970), with additions.
[40] Clements and Darnell, Amer. J. clin. Nutr., 33, 1954 (1980).

G

Notes